THE WORLD'S
GREATEST BOOKS

TWENTIETH CENTURY SERIES

THE PRESIDENT SPEAKS

THE WORLD'S GREATEST BOOKS

TWENTIETH CENTURY SERIES

*BEING ONE PUBLISHER'S SELECTION OF WHAT MIGHT BE
CONSIDERED THE MOST POPULAR LITERATURE PUBLISHED
DURING THE TWENTIETH CENTURY*

WM. H. WISE & CO.
NEW YORK
1944

*The publishers are wholeheartedly cooperating in
the effort to conserve vital materials and manpower
by manufacturing this book in full conformity with
War Production Board Ruling L-245, curtailing the
use of paper by book publishers, and all other United
States Government regulations.*

*This has been accomplished without abbreviating
the book in any way. It is absolutely complete and
unabridged. Not a word, not a paragraph, not a
comma has been omitted.*

TABLE OF CONTENTS

LIST OF PLATES

INTRODUCTION

This volume is an attempt to bring together within the covers of a single book the best of the writings of the twentieth century. As in any anthology of this type, we can only hope that the reader will agree with the choice and the method of presentation.

It would, of course, be impossible to present one hundred complete books in a volume of this size. Such a book would approximate an unabridged dictionary in unwieldiness. But most of us rarely read a book all the way through, word for word. We skip the long descriptions, the duller passages, and hasten on to see what happened in the end. And that is the style followed in this collection. Here are one hundred and two books presented in a condensed version averaging ten pages each, each in the author's own words and style.

To explain more carefully just how these stories are presented, let us suppose that you were unable to read a certain book and asked a friend who had read it to tell you the story, keeping some of the author's individuality of style. Then suppose that friend undertook to pick passages from the book which, when tied together, gave a complete, connected story. It would not be a re-telling of the story in your friend's own words, nor merely a synopsis of the plot, but the story as the author wrote it, in his own words, with all the non-essentials left out.

There may be some who will say that this is not the proper way to read books, that only the intellectually lazy will be content with condensations. To these people we may say, have you read these books, or as many others, all the way through, word for word, as the author wrote them? Few of us do. We struggle to keep up with contemporary books so that we may be familiar with those "everybody is reading," and often it is not until months later that we realize that a certain book has been cited for a Pulitzer Prize, or equal distinction, which was not "being read" at the time it was published. We make a mental resolution to read it at the earliest possible moment—but somehow we never get around to it. Time passes, and we finally forget all about it. Books, even the best of them, go out of print, and all too soon a title becomes simply something that everyone knows by hearsay, as "Oh, yes, that was written back in 19—. Didn't it win some kind of prize?"

These are the books which are collected together in WORLD'S GREATEST BOOKS, 20TH CENTURY SERIES. Here are the books which have won Pulitzer Prizes for the best novels, books which reviewers have picked as the outstanding titles of their year, books which, published in the last forty years, are already a byword in the literary language of America.

The selection was not confined to American writings, nor to fiction. Although the greatest proportion falls within these two groups, there are works by eminent Englishmen, translations from the French and Italian, Scandinavian, and other languages. The best of our fiction is here, as well as the outstanding contributions to the scientific and philosophical literature of our century.

We could only hope to make the selection representative rather than all-inclusive. No doubt every one of us can think of some title which we should have liked to see included, but which the requirements of space forced out. Some, perhaps, may quibble with the inclusion of other titles, but to these we must say that because one must set up some criterion for a work of this nature, we have included the books which are most widely accepted as being great.

What makes a book great? That is one of the most difficult questions to answer. We cannot say a book is great simply because everybody is reading it, and it heads the list of best-sellers. It is easy enough after a book has survived for five or ten centuries to say that it must be great else it would not have lasted. But some other criterion is necessary if one is to select the books of our own century which shall be labelled "great." We are too close to them to be entirely objective, yet it is very possible to pick those which are unworthy. Likewise, every now and then a book comes along which is immediately recognized as truly great, because the author has handled his theme with a sympathy and understanding which is communicated to the reader in language which is not merely adequate, but an excellent example of what our language ought to be—and all too seldom is. The theme may have social implications which make the book important at the moment, but unless it has something more than timeliness, something of the spark of genius which the reader is able to feel, whether or not he can define what it is that impresses him, that book is not great. And this again is a defense of the style of condensation which we have used. Insofar as possible, in keeping the language of the author, we have kept that quality which raises this particular work above the rank and file of the thousands of books which are published every year.

Not that this collection is an attempt to be pedantic about twentieth century literature—far from it. This volume is not for those who assemble great libraries of first editions, nor is it intended to be a lecture on "Literature of the Twentieth Century." Rather is it a volume for the ordinary reader, who enjoys a good story, who likes something a little deeper once in a while, who is not interested in trash, but who may not always read new books as they come out. Then, too, there are already some who are too young to have read the titles which were current during the first fifteen years of our century. It is a book to be comfortable with—even its size was gauged with that quality in mind. It is even right for reading in bed, each title being just about long enough to finish before one becomes too drowsy.

We give you WORLD'S GREATEST BOOKS, 20TH CENTURY SERIES with the hope that we have succeeded in making just such a book as we have described.

THE PUBLISHERS.

H. G. Wells

THE TIME MACHINE

I—Through Time at High Velocity

Any real body must have extension in four directions; it must have length, breadth, thickness and duration. There are really four dimensions, three which we call the three planes of space, and a fourth, time. There is no difference between time and any of the three dimensions of space, except that our consciousness moves along it.

It was at ten o'clock to-day (the Time Traveller said) that the first of all time machines began its career. I gave it a last tap, tried all the screws again, put one more drop of oil on the quartz rod, and sat myself in the saddle. I suppose a suicide who holds a pistol to his skull feels much the same wonder at what will come next as I felt then. I took the starting lever in one hand and the stopping one in the other, pressed the first, and almost immediately the second. I seemed to reel; I felt a nightmare sensation of falling; and looking round, I saw the laboratory exactly as before. Then I noted the clock. A moment before, as it seemed, it had stood at a minute or so past ten; now it was nearly half-past three!

I drew a long breath, set my teeth, gripped the starting lever with both hands, and went off with a thud. Mrs. Watchett came in, and walked, apparently without seeing me, towards the garden door. I suppose it took her a minute or so to traverse the place, but to me she seemed to shoot across the room like a rocket. I pressed the lever over to its extreme position. The night came like the turning out of a lamp, and in another moment came to-morrow. The laboratory grew faint and hazy, then fainter and ever fainter. To-morrow night came black, then day again, night again, day again—faster and faster still. A strange dumb confusedness descended on my mind.

I am afraid I cannot convey the peculiar sensations of time travelling. They are excessively unpleasant. There is a feeling exactly like that one has upon a switchback—of a helpless, headlong motion! I felt the same horrible anticipation, too, of an imminent smash. As I put on pace, night followed day like the flapping of a black wing. The dim suggestion of the laboratory seemed presently to fall away from me, and I saw the sun hopping swiftly across the sky, leaping it every minute, and every minute marking a day, I had a dim impression of scaffolding, but I was already going too fast to be conscious of any moving things. The slowest snail that ever crawled dashed by too fast for me. The twinkling succession of darkness and light was excessively painful to the eye. Then, in the intermittent darknesses, I saw the moon spinning swiftly through her quarters from new to full and had a faint glimpse of the circling stars.

Presently, as I went on, still gaining velocity, the palpitation of night and day merged into one continuous greyness; the sky took on a wonderful deepness of blue, a splendid luminous colour like that of early twilight; the jerking sun became a streak of fire, a brilliant arch in space, the moon a fainter, fluctuating band; and I could see nothing of the stars, save now and then a brighter circle flickering in the blue.

The landscape was misty and vague. I was still on the hillside upon which this house now stands, and the shoulder rose above me grey and dim. I saw trees growing and changing like puffs of vapour, now brown, now green; they grew, spread, shivered and passed away. I saw huge buildings rise up faint and fair, and pass like dreams. The whole surface of the earth seemed changing—melting and flowing under my eyes. The little hands upon the dials that registered my speed raced round faster and faster. Presently I noted that the sun-belt swayed up and down, from solstice to solstice, in a minute or less, and that, consequently, my pace was over a year a minute; and minute by minute the white snow flashed across the world, and vanished, and was followed by the brief green of spring.

The unpleasant sensations of the start were less poignant now. They merged at last into a kind of hysterical exhilaration. I remarked a swaying of the machine, for which I was unable to account. But my mind was too confused to attend to it, so with a kind of madness, I flung myself into futurity.

At first I scarce thought of stopping, scarce thought of anything but these new sensations. But presently a fresh series of impressions grew up in my mind—a certain curiosity, and therewith a certain dread—until at last they took complete possession of me.

What strange developments of humanity, what wonderful advances upon our rudimentary civilization, I thought, might not appear when I came to look nearly into the dim, elusive world that raced and fluctuated before my eyes? I saw great and splendid architecture rising about me, more massive than any buildings of our own time, and yet, as it seemed, built of glimmer and mist. I saw a richer green flow up the hillside, and remain there without any wintry intermission. Even through the veil of my confusion the earth seemed very fair. And so my mind came round to the business of stopping.

The peculiar risk lay in the possibility of my finding some substance in the space which I, or the machine, occupied. So long as I travelled at a high velocity through time, this scarcely mattered: I was, so to speak, attenuated—was slipping like a vapour through the interstices of intervening substances! But to come to a stop involved the jamming of myself, molecule by molecule, into whatever lay in my way; meant bringing my atoms into such intimate contact with those of the obstacle that a profound chemical reaction—possibly a far-reaching explosion—would result, and blow myself and my apparatus out of all possible dimensions—into the Unknown. This possibility had occurred to me again and again while I was making the machine; but then I had cheerfully accepted it as an unavoidable risk.

Now the risk was inevitable I no longer saw it in the same cheerful light. The fact is that, insensibly, the absolute strangeness of everything, the sickly jarring and swaying of the machine, above all, the feeling of prolonged falling, had absolutely upset my nerve. I told myself that I could never stop, and with a gust of petulance I resolved to stop forthwith. Like an impatient fool, I lugged over the lever, and incontinently the thing went reeling over, and I was flung headlong through the air.

A BOOK is a friend whose face is constantly changing. If you read it when you are recovering from an illness, and return to it years after, it is changed surely, with the change in yourself.—*Andrew Lang.*

II—*Strange Little People of the Remote Future*

I LOOKED curiously about me at this world of the remote future. At first things were very confusing. Everything was so entirely different from the world I had known—even the flowers. I resolved to mount to the summit of a crest, perhaps a mile and a half away, from which I could get a wider view of our planet in the year eight hundred and two thousand seven hundred and one A.D.—for that, I should explain, was the date the little dials of my machine recorded.

As a walked I was watchful for every impression that could possibly help to explain the condition of ruinous splendour in which I found the world—for ruinous it was. A little way up the hill, for instance, was a great heap of granite, bound together by masses of aluminium, a vast labyrinth of precipitous walls and crumbled heaps, amidst which were thick heaps of very beautiful pagoda-like plants—nettle possibly—but wonderfully tinted with brown about the leaves, and incapable of stinging. It was evidently the derelict remains of some vast structure. It was here that I was destined, at a later date, to have a very strange experience—the first intimation of a still stranger discovery—but of that I will speak in its proper place.

Looking round, with a sudden thought, from a terrace on which I rested for a while, I realized that there were no small houses to be seen. Apparently the single house, and possibly even the household, had vanished. Here and there among the greenery were palace-like buildings, but the house and the cottage, which form such characteristic features of our own English landscape, had disappeared. There were no hedges, no signs of proprietary rights, no evidences of agriculture. The whole earth had become a garden.

"Communism," said I to myself.

IT was then that I first heard voices, and a moment later a man appeared on the terrace in front of me. He was a slight creature—perhaps four feet high —clad in a purple tunic, girdled at the waist with a leather belt. Sandals or buskins—I could not clearly distinguish which—were on his feet; his legs were bare to the knees, and his head was bare. Noticing that, I noticed for the first time how warm the air was.

He struck me as being a very beautiful and graceful creature, but indescribably frail. His flushed face reminded me of a beautiful consumptive—that hectic beauty of which we used to hear so much.

In another moment we were standing face to face, I and this fragile thing out of futurity. He came straight up to me and laughed into my eyes. The absence from his bearing of any sign of fear struck me at once. Then he turned to two others following him, and spoke to them in a strange and very sweet and liquid tongue.

There were others coming, and presently a little group of perhaps eight or ten of these exquisite creatures were about me. It came into my head, oddly enough, that my voice was too harsh and deep for them. So I shook my head and, pointing to my ears, shook it again.

I pointed to the time machine and to myself. Then, hesitating for a moment to express time, I pointed to the sun. At once a quaintly pretty little figure in chequered purple and white followed my gesture, and then astounded me by imitating the sound of thunder.

For a moment I was staggered, though the import of his gesture was plain enough. The question had come into my mind abruptiy, were these creatures fools? You may hardly understand how it took me. You see, I had always anticipated that the people of the year eight hundred and two thousand odd would be incredibly in front of us in knowledge, art—everything. Then one of them suddenly asked me a question that showed him to be on the intellectual level of one of our five-year-old children —asked me, in fact, if I had come from the sun in a thunderstorm! It let loose the judgment I had suspended upon their clothes, their frail limbs and fragile features. A flood of disappointment rushed across my mind. For a moment I felt that I had built the time machine in vain.

A queer thing I soon discovered, and that was their lack of interest. They would come to me with eager cries of astonishment like children, but, like children, they would soon stop examining me, and wander away after some other toy. It is odd, too, how speedily I came to disregard these little people. I was continually meeting more of these men of the future, who would follow me, chatter and laugh about me, and, having smiled and gesticulated in a friendly way, leave me again to my own devices.

WHEN I looked more attentively at their little figures, I perceived that all had the same form of costume, the same soft, hairless visage, and the same girlish rotunity of limb. In dress, and in all the difference of texture and bearing that now mark off the sexes, these people of the future were alike.

It seemed to me that I had happened upon humanity upon the wane. The ruddy sunset set me thinking of the sunset of mankind. For the first time I began to realize an odd result of the social effort in which we are now engaged. And yet, come to think of it, it is a logical consequence enough. Strength is the outcome of need; security sets a premium on feebleness. The work of ameliorating the conditions of life—the true civilizing process that makes life

more and more secure—had gone steadily on to a climax. One triumph of a united humanity over nature had followed another. And the harvest was what I saw!

I thought of the physical slightness of the people, their lack of intelligence, and those big, abundant ruins, and it strengthened my belief in a perfect conquest of nature. For after the battle comes quiet. Humanity had been strong, energetic and intelligent, and had used all its abundant vitality to alter the conditions under which it lived. And now came the reaction of the altered conditions.

For countless years I judged there had been no danger of war or solitary violence, no danger from wild beasts, no wasting disease to require strength of constitution, no need of toil. For such a life, what we should call the weak are as well equipped as the strong, are indeed no longer weak. Better equipped, indeed, they are, for the strong would be fretted by an energy for which there was no outlet.

No doubt, the exquisite beauty of the buildings I saw was the outcome of the last surgings of the now purposeless energy of mankind before it settled down into perfect harmony with the conditions under which it lived—the flourish of that triumph which began the last great peace. This has ever been the fate of energy in security; it takes to art and to eroticism and then come languor and decay.

Even this artistic impetus would at last die away—had almost died in the time I saw. To adorn themselves with flowers, to dance, to sing in the sunlight; so much was left of the artistic spirit, and no more. Even that would fade in the end into a contented inactivity. We are kept keen on the grindstone of pain and necessity, and it seemed to me that here was that hateful grindstone broken at last!

III—In a World Where Fear Still Reigned

So far as I could see, all the world displayed the same exuberant richness as the Thames Valley. From every hill I climbed I saw the same abundance of splendid buildings, endlessly varied in material and style; the same clustering thickets of evergreens, the same blossom-laden trees and tree ferns. Here and there water shone like silver, and, beyond, the land rose into blue, undulating hills.

I must confess that my satisfaction with my first theories of an automatic civilization and a decadent humanity did not long endure. Yet I could think of no other. Let me put my difficulties. The several big palaces I had explored were mere living places, great dining-halls and sleeping apartments. I could find no machinery, no appliance of any kind. Yet these people were clothed in pleasant fabrics that must need renewal, and their sandals were of complex metalwork.

Somehow such things must be made. And the little people displayed no vestige of a creative tendency. There were no shops, no workshops, no sign of importation among them. They spent all their time in playing gently, in bathing in the river, in making love in a half-playful fashion, in eating fruit and sleeping. I could not see how things were kept going.

Then, again, about the time machine. Something—I knew not what—had taken it into the hollow pedestal of the White Sphinx. *Why?* For the life of me I could not imagine.

And I found, too, that fear had not yet left the world. The little people were fearless enough in the daylight. But they dreaded the dark, dreaded shadows, dreaded black things. Darkness to them was the one thing dreadful. It was a singularly passionate emotion, and it set me thinking and observing. I discovered, then, among other things, that these little people gathered into the great houses after dark, and slept in droves. To enter upon them without a light was to put them into a tumult of apprehension. I never found one out of doors, or one sleeping alone within doors, after dark.

One very hot morning—my fourth, I think—as I was seeking shelter from the heat and glare in a colossal ruin near the great house where I slept and fed, there happened this strange thing. Clambering among these heaps of masonry, I found a narrow gallery, whose end and side windows were blocked by fallen masses of stone. By contrast with the brilliancy outside, it seemed at first impenetrably dark to me. I entered it, groping, for the change from light to blackness made spots of colour swim before me. Suddenly I halted spellbound. Two eyes, luminous by reflection against the daylight, were watching me out of the darkness.

The old instinctive dread of wild beasts came upon me. I clenched my hands and steadfastly looked into the glaring eyeballs. I was afraid to turn. Then the thought of the absolute security in which humanity appeared to be living came to my mind. And then I remembered that strange terror of the dark. Overcoming my fear I advanced and spoke. I put out my hand and touched something soft.

At once the eyes darted sideways, and something white ran past me. I turned with my heart in my mouth, and saw a queer little ape-like figure, its head held down in a peculiar manner, running across the sunlit space behind me. It blundered against a block of granite, staggered aside, and in a moment was hidden in a black shadow beneath another pile of masonry.

My impression of it is, of course, imperfect; but I know it was a dull white, and had strange, large, greyish red eyes; also, that there was flaxen hair on its head and down its back. But, as I say, it went too fast for me to see distinctly. I cannot even say whether it ran on all fours, or only with its forearms held very low. After an instant's pause, I followed it into the ruins. I could not find it at first, but after a time, in the profound obscurity, I came upon a round, well-like opening, half-closed by a fallen pillar.

A sudden thought came to me. Could this thing have vanished down the shaft? I lit a match, and, looking down, I saw a small, white, moving creature, with large bright eyes, which regarded me steadfastly as it retreated. It made me shudder. It was so like a human spider! It was clambering down the wall, and now I saw for the first time a number of metal foot and hand rests, forming a kind of ladder down the shaft. Then the light burned my fingers and fell out of my hand, going out as it dropped, and when I had lit another the little monster had disappeared.

I do not know how long I sat peering down that well. It was not for some time that I could succeed in persuading myself that the thing I had seen was human. But gradually the truth dawned on me—that man had not remained one species, but had differentiated into two distinct animals; that my graceful children of the Upper World were not the sole descendants of our generation, but that this bleached, nocturnal thing was also heir to all the ages.

It was two days before I could follow up the new-found clue in what was manifestly the proper way. I felt a peculiar shrinking from those pallid bodies. They were just the half-bleached colour of the worms in a zoological museum. And they were filthily cold to the touch.

But at last I did find courage to clamber down the shaft. Before I got to the bottom I was in an agony of discomfort; my arms ached, my back was cramped, and I was trembling with the prolonged terror of a fall. Besides this, the unbroken darkness had had a distressing effect upon my eyes. The air was full of the throb and hum of machinery pumping air down the shaft.

IV—Among the Morlocks of the Underways

I do not know how long I lay. I was roused by a soft hand touching my face. Starting up in the darkness, I snatched at my matches, and, hastily striking one, I saw three stooping white creatures, similar to the one I had seen above ground in the ruin, hastily retreating before the light.

I have no doubt they could see me in that rayless obscurity, and they did not seem to have any fear of me, apart from the light. But as soon as I struck a match in order to see them, they fled incontinently, vanishing into dark gutters where their eyes glared in the strangest fashion.

I tried to call to them, but the language they had was apparently different from that of the over-world people, so that I was needs left in my own unaided efforts, and the thought of flight before exploration was even then in my mind. But I said to myself, "You are in for it now," and feeling my way along the tunnel, I found the noise of machinery grew louder. Presently the walls fell away from me, and I came to a large open space, and, striking another match, saw that I had entered a vast arched cavern, which stretched into utter darkness beyond the range of my light. The view was all one could see in the burning of a match.

Necessarily, my memory is vague. Great shapes like big machines rose out of the dimness, and cast grotesque black shadows, in which dim, spectral Morlocks sheltered from the glare. The place, by the bye, was very stuffy and oppressive, and the faint halitus of freshly shed blood was in the air. Some way down the central vista was a little table of white metal, laid with what seemed a meal. The Morlocks, at any rate, were carnivorous.

Even at the time, I remember wondering what large animal could have survived to furnish the red joint I saw. It was all very indistinct—the heavy smell, the big, unmeaning shapes, the obscene figures lurking in the shadows, and only waiting for the darkness to come at me again! Then the match burnt down, and stung my fingers, and fell, a wriggling red spot in the blackness.

In a moment I was clutched by several hands, and there was no mistaking that they were trying to haul me back. I struck another light, and waved it in their dazzled faces. You can scarce imagine how nauseatingly inhuman they looked—those pale, chinless faces, and great, lidless, pinkish grey eyes!—as they stared in their blindness and bewilderment. I retreated again, and when my second match had ended I struck my third. It had almost burnt through when I reached the opening into the shaft. That climb seemed interminable to me. The last few yards was a frightful struggle against faintness. At last, however, I got over the well-mouth and staggered out of the ruin into the blinding sunlight.

And now I understood, to some slight degree at least, the reason of the fear of the upper-world people for the dark. I wondered vaguely what foul villainy it might be that the Morlocks did under the new moon. I felt pretty sure now that my second hypothesis was all wrong. The upper-world people might once have been the favoured aristocracy, and the Morlocks their mechanical servants, but that had long since passed away.

The two species that had resulted from the evolution of man were sliding down towards, or had already arrived at, an entirely new relationship. The Eloi, like the Carlovingian kings, had decayed to a mere beautiful futility. They still possessed the earth on sufferance, since the Morlocks, subterranean for innumerable generations, had come at last to find the daylit surface intolerable. And the Morlocks made their garments, I inferred, and maintained them in their habitual needs, perhaps through the survival of an old habit of service.

But clearly the old order was already in part reversed. The Nemesis of the delicate ones was creeping on apace. Ages ago, thousands of generations ago, man had thrust his brother-man out of the ease and the sunshine. And now that brother was coming back—changed! Already the Eloi had begun to learn one old lesson anew, were becoming reacquainted with fear.

And now came a most unexpected thing. As I approached the pedestal of the Sphinx I found the bronze valves were open. At that I stopped short before them, hesitating to enter.

Within was a small apartment, and on a raised place in the corner of this was the time machine. I had the small levers in my pocket.

I stepped through the bronze frame and up to the time machine, and as I stood and examined it, finding pleasure in the mere touch of the contrivance, the bronze panels suddenly slid up and struck the frame with a clang. I was in the dark—trapped! You may imagine how all my calm vanished. The little brutes were close upon me. One touched me. I made a sweeping blow in the dark at them with the levers, and began to scramble into the saddle of the machine.

There came one hand upon me and

then another. Then I had simply to fight against their persistent fingers for my levers, and at the same time feel for the studs over which these fitted. One, indeed, they almost got away from me. As it slipped from my hand, I had to butt in the dark with my head—I could hear the Morlock's skull ring—to recover it.

But at last the lever was fixed and pulled over. The clinging hands slipped from me. The darkness fell from my eyes. I found myself in the same grey light and tumult I have already described.

A NOTE ON H. G. WELLS

BLIND chance would often seem to bring a man to his true vocation. Herbert George Wells, born at Bromley, Kent, September 21, 1866, son of a professional cricketer, began life as a draper's apprentice, became in turn pupil teacher, chemist, and draper again, before settling down to a pedagogic career. Science he had studied under Huxley and others, taking his B.Sc. at London University. At twenty-seven he had to envisage the ruin of his career just when sensible of progress, a hemorrhage from the lungs compelling him to give up his teaching post and to seek his livelihood at writing.

Beyond editing a students' magazine for a session or two, writing fugitive essays on science and compiling a cram book on biology for London University science examinations, young Mr. Wells had done nothing "literary." The picture of journalistic life painted by J. M. Barrie with such deft touches of humour and truth, in "When a Man's Single," led him to think of writing as a vocation.

OF the many brilliant men of the pen who "arrived" in the nineties, if H. G. Wells has not gone farthest, there is none that has outdistanced him; not Kipling, nor Barrie, nor Shaw. He stands in the foremost rank of contemporary English authors. His intellectual vitality is astonishing; his range of interest immensely wider than that of Thomas Hardy or Rudyard Kipling, though his purely literary qualities rival those of neither. He is less a man of letters than an unusually percipient student of life who uses certain popular literary forms to convey his mental reactions to his fellowmen for their instruction. His books are not to him ends in themselves. All his novels, stories, histories, philosophic and miscellaneous writings, are expressions of a mind profoundly curious about life and its meaning.

Only a man of genius could have dared to write so abundantly and so variously. Since he first came forward in 1895 with no fewer than three novels and a collection of short stories, there has been no year in which Mr. Wells has not added from one to three new books to his list, and nothing that he has written can be regarded as insignificant. A full list of the titles of his books would occupy the major part of this page, and a high percentage of these are worthy of the epithet "great."

H. G. WELLS IN 1895

IT is not pretended that "The Time Machine," "The War of the Worlds," "Tono-Bungay" and "A Modern Utopia" (by which he is to be represented in this volume of the WORLD'S GREATEST LITERATURE SERIES) are his masterpieces; but they are typical. As all these were epitomized by the author himself we have a special reason for their retention. "The Time Machine" was the forerunner of that memorable succession of scientific romances which includes "The Island of Dr. Moreau," "The Sleeper Awakes," "The First Men in the Moon," and "The Food of the Gods," while "Tono-Bungay" is a good example of his skill in the novel of character, afterward developed with even more intimacy of analysis in "Ann Veronica" and "The New Machiavelli." "A Modern Utopia" gives a worthy specimen of his philosophical discussions, later so frequently his method of addressing the world.

During the World War no writer of established reputation so considerably extended his influence and usefulness as Mr. Wells: the direct discussion of old and new problems raised by the War taking the place of the fictional appeal, though of all his war-time writings it is a novel that will endure: "Mr. Britling Sees It Through." But in 1920 his brilliant and original work, "The Outline of History," despite some minor blemishes, carried his literary conquests into a new world and enlarged his already splendid services in the cause of human enlightenment.

In the immediately preceding pages we print the author's own condensed version of "The Time Machine." The novel was published in *The New Review,* and it was instantly successful when it appeared in book form in 1895. Though four decades have passed since Mr. Wells wrote it, the original freshness of "The Time Machine" has not staled.

Mr. Wells has described it as a "brief, astonished stare down the vistas of time to come, something between wonder and amazed, incredulous, defeated laughter."

THE STIRRUP-CUP

DEATH, thou'rt a cordial old and rare:
Look how compounded, with what care,
Time got his wrinkles reaping thee
Sweet herbs from all antiquity.

David to thy distillage went,
Keats, and Gotama excellent,
Omar Khayyám, and Chaucer bright,
And Shakespeare for a king-delight.

Then, Time, let not a drop be spilt:
Hand me the cup whene'er thou wilt;
'Tis thy rich stirrup-cup to me;
I'll drink it down right smilingly.
—*Sidney Lanier* (1842-1881).

Adolf Hitler

MEIN KAMPF

(My Battle)

THE Austrian and Czecho-Slovakian crises of last year, culminating for the moment in the pact of Munich, have awakened the American public as never before to the seriousness to the world and to themselves of the Nazi program, and consequently to the possible significance of every page of the book that can justly be regarded as the Nazi bible. Here, then, in a careful condensation of the authentic text, for all thinking Americans to read and to judge for themselves, is the work which has sold in Germany by the millions, and which is probably the best written evidence of the character, the mind, and the spirit of Adolf Hitler and his government. The text used for this article is published by Reynal & Hitchcock, New York, by arrangement with Houghton Mifflin Company, Boston. ÷ © Houghton Mifflin Company, 1939.

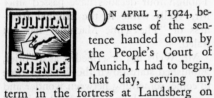

ON APRIL 1, 1924, because of the sentence handed down by the People's Court of Munich, I had to begin, that day, serving my term in the fortress at Landsberg on the Lech.

Thus, after years of uninterrupted work, I was afforded for the first time an opportunity to embark on a task insisted upon by many and felt to be serviceable to the movement by myself. Therefore, I resolved not only to set forth the object of our movement, but also to draw a picture of its development and my development.

Today I consider it my good fortune that Fate designated Braunau on the Inn River as the place of my birth. For this small town is situated on the border between those two German States, the reunion of which seems, at least to us of the younger generation, a task to be furthered with every means our lives long.

German-Austria must return to the great German motherland.[1]

Only when the boundaries of the Reich include even the last German, only when it is no longer possible to assure him

of daily bread inside them, does there arise, out of the distress of the nation, the moral right to acquire foreign soil and territory.

Bavarian by blood and Austrian by nationality, gilded by the light of German martyrdom, there lived, at the end of the eighties of the last century, my parents:[2] the father a faithful civil servant, the mother devoting herself to the cares of the household and looking after her children with eternally the same loving kindness.

A lot of romping around out-of-doors, and the companionship with unusually robust boys made me anything but a stay-at-home. Though I did not brood over my future as a child, I believe that even then my ability for making speeches was trained by stirring discussions with my comrades. I had become a little ringleader and at that time learned easily and did very well in school.

In my father's library I stumbled upon

---

[1] This ambition was fulfilled in March, 1938.

[2] Hitler's family background has been subject for much research and speculation. It is generally assumed that the father, Alois Hitler (1837-1903), was the illegitimate son of Maria Anna Schicklgruber and Johann Hiedler. He bore the name of Alois Schicklgruber until he was forty when, on January 8, 1877, he legally changed his name to Hitler. His third wife, Klara Poelzl (1860-1908), gave birth to Adolf Hitler on April 20, 1889.

a popular edition dealing with the Franco-Prussian War of 1870-71. Before long that great heroic campaign had become my greatest spiritual experience. For the first time the question confronted me: what was the difference between those Germans fighting these battles and the others? Why was it that Austria had not taken part also in this war? Are we not the same as all the other Germans? Do we not all belong together?

WHEN I was twelve years old I decided to become a painter, an artist. My talent for drawing was obvious. My father forbade me to entertain any hope of ever becoming a painter because he wanted me to become a government official, like himself. I declared that under these circumstances I no longer wished to study.

One thing was certain: my apparent failure in school. I learned what, in my opinion, might be necessary to me in my career as a painter. My best efforts were in geography and in history.

When I was thirteen my father died quite suddenly. My mother felt the obligation to continue my education in accordance with my father's wishes. Suddenly an illness came to my aid. Impressed by my illness, my mother agreed to take me out of school and to send me to the Art Academy. But my mother's death put a sudden end to these plans.

Her severe illness had almost exhausted the meager funds left by my father. The orphan's pension which I received was not nearly enough to live on, and so I was faced with the problem of earning my daily bread.

I went to Vienna with a suitcase, containing some clothes and my linen, in my hand and an unshakable determination in my heart. I wanted to become "something"—but in no event an official.

VIENNA, the city that to so many represents the idea of harmless gaiety is to me only the living memory of the most miserable time of my life.

For five years I made a scanty living, first as a worker, then as a painter: it was barely enough to appease even my daily hunger.

And yet, during this time, I learned as I had never learned before. The spare time my work left to me I spent entirely in study. So in a few years I built a foundation of knowledge from which I still draw nourishment.

At the turn of the century Vienna was already a city with unfavorable social conditions. Like a magnet, the Court with all its brilliant splendor attracted the wealth and intelligence from the rest of the State. This wealth was contrasted with a dismal poverty. Thousands of unemployed loitered about in front of the palaces and below in the twilight and mud of the canals, the homeless sought shelter.

There was hardly any other German city where social questions could have been studied better than in Vienna. This study cannot be carried out from above. Those who have never felt the grip of this murderous viper will never know its poisonous fangs. Because I was drawn into the confines of Vienna's suffering, it seemed to invite me not to learn, but rather to use me for experimentation. It was none of its doing that the guinea pig recovered from the operation.

While I was employed as a building worker, my first encounter with Social Democracy took place. After two weeks working on one particular job I realized that no power on earth could induce me to join such an organization.

At noon politics were discussed. I sat somewhere on the side, cautiously studying my new surroundings and heard more than enough. Everything was rejected: the nation was an invention of the capitalistic classes; the country as the instrument of the *bourgeoisie* for the exploitation of the workers; the authority of the law as a means of suppressing the proletariat; the school as an institution for bringing up slaves as well as slave drivers; morality as a sign of sheep-ish patience, and so forth. Nothing remained that was not dragged down into the dirt and the filth of the lowest depths.

Being better informed than my adversaries, I started to argue with them. Finally they applied the one means that wins the easiest victory over reason: terror and force. Some of the leaders gave me the choice of either leaving the job or being thrown from the scaffold. As I was alone and resistance was hopeless, I preferred to leave.

I saw then that the psyche of the great masses is not receptive to half measures or weakness. *If Social Democracy were confronted by a doctrine of greater truthfulness, carried out with the same brutality, then the latter would be victorious, though the struggle might be hard.*

Meanwhile I had learned to understand the connection between this doctrine of destruction and the nature of a race, which hitherto had been unknown to me. *Understanding Jewry alone is the key to the comprehension of the inner, the real, intention of Social Democracy.*

In those years Vienna already had two hundred thousand Jews among its two million inhabitants and so I came upon the Jewish problem. At that time I saw nothing but the religion of the Jew, and for reasons of human tolerance I continued to decline fighting on religious grounds. But my opinions in regard to anti-Semitism began to change in the course of time.

This change caused me most of my severe mental struggles, and only after months of agonizing between reason and feeling, victory began to favor reason. In this struggle the picture that the streets of Vienna showed me rendered me invaluable services. Wherever I went I saw Jews, and the more I saw of them, the sharper I began to distinguish them from other people. In appearance alone they bore no resemblance to the German people.

The scales dropped from my eyes when I found the Jew as the leader of Social Democracy. This put an end to a long internal struggle. It brought me internal happiness to realize definitely that the Jew was no German. Only then I learned to know the seducers of our people.

If, with the help of the Marxian creed, the Jew conquers the nations of this world, his crown will become the funeral wreath of humanity, and once again this planet, empty of mankind, will move through the ether as it did thousands of years ago.

Eternal Nature inexorably revenges the transgressions of her laws.

Therefore, I believe today that I am acting in the sense of the Almighty Creator: *By warding off the Jews I am fighting for the Lord's work.*

I n the spring of 1912 I went to Munich. The reason for this was that my studies directed me towards this metropolis of German art. A *German* town! What a difference as compared with Vienna! It made me sick only to think back to this racial Babylon.

Apart from my professional work, what attracted me most was again the study of current political events, among them especially those of foreign politics.

Germany has an annual increase in population of almost 900,000. The difficulty of feeding this army of new citizens would become greater with every year, and was bound some day to end in a catastrophe, provided ways and means were not found to avert this impending danger of hunger-pauperization in time.

The healthiest way of meeting this difficulty would be to acquire new soil in order annually to send off the superfluous millions, and thus conserve the nation further on the basis of self-sustainment.

For Germany, the only possibility of carrying out a sound territorial policy was to be found in the acquisition of new soil in Europe proper. But Reich leaders knew that the acquisition of new soil was to be attained only in the East and they saw the necessary fight and yet wanted peace at any price; for the watchword of German foreign politics had long ceased to be, preservation of the German nation by all means, but rather, preservation of world peace by all available means. It is well known how this succeeded.

The talk of "peaceful economic conquest" of the world was certainly the greatest folly that was ever made the leading principle of a State policy. Never was a State founded by peaceful economy, but always by the instincts of preserving the species, no matter whether they are found in the field of heroic virtues or sly cunning.

The first powerful lightning flashed upon the earth; the storm broke out, and the thunder of the heavens mingled with the roaring of the batteries of the World War.

As a boy and a young man I had often formed the wish that at least once I might be allowed to prove by deeds that my national enthusiasm was not an empty delusion. So many times had I sung *Deutschland über alles* that I considered it almost a belated favor that I was now allowed to appear as a witness before the tribunal of the Eternal Judge in order to proclaim the truth and sincerity of my convictions.

The enthusiasm gradually cooled down and the exuberant joy was suffocated by the fear of death. The time came when everyone had to fight between the instinct of self-preservation and the admonition of duty. My will finally became master.

At the end of September, 1916, my division joined the Somme battle. This really seemed to resemble hell rather than war. On October 7, 1916, I was wounded.

It was almost on the anniversary of the day of my marching out that I was brought into the hospital at Beelitz near Berlin. What a change! From the mud of the Somme to the white beds.

When I was able to walk again, I was given permission to go to Berlin. I hardly recognized the town. Anger, grumbling, and cursing met me on all sides. But quite apart from this, the general mood was more than bad: shirking of duty was looked upon almost as a sign of higher wisdom.

The offices of the authorities were occupied by Jews. Almost every clerk a Jew and every Jew a clerk. I was amazed by this multitude of fighters of the Chosen People and could not help comparing them with the few representatives they had on the front.[3] In these things I could only see the most ingenious trick of the Jew to divert general attention from himself and draw it to others. While now the Bavarian and the Prussian quarreled, the Jew pulled away their means of existence from under the very nose of each; while abusing the Prussian, the Jew organized the revolution and smashed Prussia as well as Bavaria at the same time.

I could not stand this cursed feud between the German tribes, and I was glad to return to the front.

In the night of October 13, 1918 the English began to throw gas on the southern front of Ypres. Towards midnight a part of us passed out, some of our comrades forever. I stumbled and tottered rearwards with burning eyes, but taking with me my last report of the War. Already a few hours later the eyes had turned into burning coals: it had become dark around me.

As the weeks passed I began to distinguish my surroundings in rough outlines; I could hope to regain my eyesight at least enough that later I would be able to take up some profession. However, I could no longer hope that I would ever again be able to draw; nevertheless, I was on the way to improvement when the monstrous event happened.

[3] Of the 550,000 Jewish citizens of Germany at the time of the War, 100,000 were in uniform. Of these four-fifths saw duty at the front. There were 12,000 casualties, virtually the same ratio as that of the population as a whole. 35,000 Jews were decorated for bravery.

On November 10 the pastor came into the hospital for a short address. He began to tell us that the War was lost and that we had to surrender to the mercy of the victors . . . that the armistice should be accepted with confidence in the generosity of our previous enemies . . . there I could stand no more. I threw myself on my cot and buried my burning head in the covers and pillows.

At the end of November, 1918, I came back to Munich to join the reserve battalion of my regiment. In those days endless plans chased each other in my head. For days I pondered what could be done at all, but the end of all reflections was always the sober conclusion that I, as one without name, did not possess even the least presupposition for any useful activity.

I was given orders to take part in a course which was being held for the members of the army. For the first time in my life I heard a discussion of international exchange and loan capital. As I listened the idea flashed through my mind that now at last I had found the way to one of the most essential principles for the foundation of a new party. In my eyes the character of the stock exchange and loan capital was harmful to economy. Germany's development stood before my eyes too clearly for me not to know that the hardest battle had to be fought, not against hostile nations, but rather against international capital. I sensed a powerful slogan for the coming fight.

But one should remember that even the best idea becomes a danger as soon as it pretends to be an end in itself, but in reality only represents a means to an end. For myself there was only one doctrine: people and country.

What we have to fight for is the security of the existence and the increase of our race and our people, the nourishment of its children and the preservation of the purity of the blood, the freedom and independence of the fatherland in order to enable our people to mature for the fulfillment of the mission which the Creator of the universe has allotted to them.

One day I wanted to speak in the discussion. One of the participants thought it his duty to enter the lists for the Jews, and he began to defend them in lengthy arguments. An overwhelming number of the pupils who were present were of my point of view. The result was that a few days later I was ordered to report to one of the Munich regiments as an instruction officer.

No other task could make me happier than this one, because now I was able to render useful services to that institution which had been infinitely near to my heart, the army.

Also, I could speak with some success. I thus led back many hundreds, probably even thousands, in the course of my lectures to their people and fatherland. Also I became acquainted with a number of comrades with the same convictions who later began to form the basic stock of the new movement.

In the first period of the growth of our movement, nothing made us suffer more than our insignificance. The very fact that our names were not known made our success doubtful. No person in Munich knew that we had started to call ourselves the National Socialist German Workers' Party, except a few adherents and their few friends.

Each Wednesday there took place a so-called committee meeting in one of the Munich cafés. The question under discussion was how to win new followers, but above all to make the name of the movement known at any price.

I still remember how in this first period I myself once carried out about eighty bills announcing our meeting and how in the evening we waited for the masses of people that were to come. After an hour's delay the chairman finally opened the meeting. We were again seven men, the old seven.

Funds were brought together by very

small collections in the circle of us poor devils, so that at last we were able to announce a meeting by an advertisement in the *Münchner Beobachter.* At seven o'clock one hundred and eleven persons were present.

A Munich professor made the principal speech, and I, for the first time in public, was to speak second. I spoke for thirty minutes, and what formerly I had felt in my mind was now proved by reality. After thirty minutes the people were electrified and the enthusiasm found its expression first in the fact that my appeal to the willingness to sacrifice led the audience to donate three hundred marks.

In those days the financial restriction was so great that we did not even have the opportunity of having the leading principles of the movement printed, or leaflets published. Now the foundation was laid for a small fund from which the barest necessities for our urgent needs could be covered.

About October, 1919, the second large meeting took place. Subject: Brest-Litovsk and Versailles. I spoke for almost an hour, and the success was greater than on the occasion of the first demonstration. The number attending had risen to over a hundred and thirty-one. An attempted disturbance was at once nipped in the bud by my comrades. The disturbing individuals were thrown downstairs with their heads knocked about.

The entire winter of 1919-20 was one single fight to strengthen the faith in the victorious power of the young movement and to increase it to that fanaticism which then, in the form of faith, is able to move mountains.

A definite program was established. As regards tactics, a series of demands resulted from this:

(1) In order to win the masses for the national rise, no social sacrifice is too great.

(2) The national education of the great masses can only take place through the detour of a social uplift, since exclusively by this all those general economic presuppositions are created which permit the individual to take part in the cultural goods of the nation.

(3) The nationalization of the great masses can never take place by way of half measures, by a weak emphasis upon a so-called objective viewpoint, but by a ruthless and fanatically one-sided orientation as to the goal to be aimed at.

(4) One can only succeed in winning the souls of a people if, apart from a positive fight of one's own for one's own aims, one also destroys at the same time the supporters of the contrary. In the ruthless attack upon an adversary the people see at all times a proof of their own right. What they want is the victory of the stronger and the annihilation or the unconditional surrender of the weaker.

(5) Peoples who renounce the preservation of their racial purity renounce also the unity of their souls. Without the clearest recognition of the race problem and, with it, of the Jewish question, there will be no rise of the German nation.

(6) The people's community imposes the same obligations on the employer as on the employee. We must tear the German worker away from the delusion of internationalism. We must also attack the conception that is predominate among employers which takes for granted the helpless economic surrender of the employees to them. The bearer of progress can never be the higher class, but the lower one which is fighting for its equal right. A movement which establishes the social and cultural development of the people as its goal will have to draw its followers primarily from the masses.

(7) The goal of a political reform will only be reached by the gaining of political power. Every idea aimed at changing the world has not only the right but also the duty to assure itself

of those means which make possible the carrying-out of its ideas.

(8) The movement is anti-parliamentarian; that means it rejects the principle of a decision by the majority, by which the leader is degraded to the position of the executive of the will of the others. The movement represents the principle of a Germanic democracy: choice of the leader, but absolute authority of the latter.

(9) The future of a movement is conditioned by the fanaticism, even more the intolerance, with which its adherents present it as the only right one and enforce it in the face of other formations of a similar kind.

(10) Party members must not fear the hostility of the adversaries, but they should perceive it as the presumption for the justification of their own existence. They must not shun the hatred of the enemies of our nationality and our view of life, but they should long for it.

At the beginning of 1920 I urged holding the first very great mass meeting. The 24th of February, 1920, was fixed as the date for holding this first great peoples' meeting of the still unknown movement.

When I entered the banquet hall of the Hofbräuhaus in Munich, my heart nearly burst for joy. The enormous room was overfilled by a mass of people numbering almost two thousand. When finally I presented the program to the masses and asked them personally to pronounce judgment upon each point, one after the other was accepted with more and more joy, again and again unanimously. Thus the last thesis found its way to the heart of the mass. Then I was confronted by a hall filled with people united by a new conviction, a new faith, a new will. I knew that now the principles of our movement would never be forgotten.

At the very beginning of our series of great meetings, I commenced the organization of a protective supervision service. Partly they were comrades whom I had known since my military service, others were recently won young party members who, from the very beginning, were instructed and trained to the effect that terror can be broken only by terror. They were saturated with the doctrine that the best weapon of defense is found in the attack and that ours was not a debating club but a fighting community, determined to the utmost.

And how these boys did stand up! Like a swarm of hornets they stormed upon the disturbers of our meetings, without considering their superior force, without considering wounds and bloody sacrifices, filled with the great idea of making a path for the holy mission of our movement.

The organization of our supervising troop cleared a very important question. The movement so far had not possessed any party emblem or flag. The lack of such symbols had not only disadvantages for the moment, but it was unbearable for the future.

After innumerable attempts I worked out the following: a flag with a background of red, with a white circle, and in its center, a black swastika. In the midsummer of 1920 the new flag appeared for the first time.

In the same sense, arm bands were immediately ordered for the supervising detachments: that is, a red band which also showed a white circle with a black swastika.

In the red we had the social idea of the movement, in the white the national idea, in the swastika the mission of the fight for the victory of the Aryan man, and at the same time also the victory of the idea of the creative work which in itself is and will always be anti-Semitic.

The year 1921 had assumed special significance for me and for the movement in an additional direction. After my joining the party I immediately took over the management of the propaganda. I considered this section by far the most important. By the middle of 1921 special events made it appear expedient, after the slow visible success of propaganda, to reorganize the party.

In a general meeting of members I was unanimously given the entire leadership of the movement. At the same time new articles were accepted which entrusted the first chairman with full responsibility. This eliminated decisions of committees and introduced in their stead a system of sharing the work which since that time has proved its value in a most blissful manner.

In December, 1920, we had taken over the *Völkischer Beobachter*. This was now turned into the official organ of the party. First it was published twice weekly. At the beginning of 1923 it became a daily and at the end of August, 1923, it was given its later known great size.

THREE events were infinitely significant for the further shaping of the party.

(1) *The great general demonstration of all patriotic associations in Munich against the* Law for the Protection of the Republic *in the late summer of 1922.*

The arrival of the National Socialists on the large square that was already half filled gave vent to an enormous enthusiasm. I myself had the honor to be allowed to speak as one of the orators before the multitude now counting sixty thousand heads. As a result we were able to redouble our membership of storm troopers.

(2) The *March to Coburg* in October, 1922. Folkish associations intended to hold a so-called German Day at Coburg. I received an invitation to this, with the remark that it would be desirable to bring some people to escort me. As the escort I ordered eight hundred storm troopers who were dispatched by special train from Munich. Similar orders were dispatched to National Socialist storm trooper groups which had been formed in other places. At all places on the way where additional men got in, the transport roused greatest attention. Upon arriving at the station at Co-

burg, we were received by a deputation who brought us the order that we were not allowed to enter the town with flags unfurled and not with music (we had brought a band of forty-two men) and not in closed columns.

I at once flatly rejected such disgraceful conditions and declared that we would immediately march into the town with resounding music and with flags flying. And thus it happened.

Shouting and insulting calls did not disturb the poise of the detachments. The representatives of the true Socialism, of Equality and Fraternity, began to throw stones. With this our patience was at an end, and so for ten minutes blows hailed down destructively from the right and from the left. But after a quarter of an hour nothing red was seen any more in the streets.

The intimidated population summoned courage and by calling and waving dared to greet us. In the evening when we marched away, they broke out in spontaneous jubilation.

The significance of this day was that the storm troopers were strengthened in their self-confidence and in their belief in the correctness of their leadership. The further significance was that now we set out to break systematically the red terror in all places where for many years it had prevented all meetings of people with different opinions, and to restore freedom of assembly.

This logical development lasted up to March, 1923. Then an event occurred which forced me to take the movement from its previous course and to lead it to a change.

(3) The *occupation of the Ruhr district* by the French in the first months of the year 1923 had a great significance for the development of the storm troopers. It led to its re-orientation as a military fighting organization. With such an organization we hoped to break the Reich Government's cowardly policy of evasion.

However, the reshaping of the storm troopers at that time was injurious from the viewpoint of the movement. For the Reich Government would not support us in active resistance against France.

I DO not intend here to portray those events which led to and determined November 8, 1923.[4] I do not want to, because I see therein nothing promising for the future and above all because it is futile to reopen wounds which seem today hardly healed. In addition, it is futile to speak of causes and guilt among men all of whom, perhaps in the depths of their hearts, love their nation equally well, and only missed the common road or failed to understand each other concerning it.

On November 9, 1923, in the fourth year of its existence, the National Socialist German Workers' Party was dissolved

[4] The *putsch* of November 8, 1923 was simple enough. The Ruhr invasion and passive resistance had undermined the last pillars of German economic society. The Hitlerites believed that the Bavarian monarchists were planning a new move to effect a restoration. They resolved to secure the leadership of that movement for themselves and turn the whole venture into a Mussoliniesque march on Berlin. Hitler captured the monarchist manager and the *Reichswehr* (army) commander in Munich and obtained from them a promise of support. Both backed out. But Hitler still had Ludendorff, one of Germany's World War heroes. With him, Hitler undertook the historic march through Munich.
The Bavarian State police fired, a number of Nazis fell dead. The wounded Hitler fled, and found haven in the home of his friend Ernst Hanfstaengl.
This might have meant the disappearance of Hitler's party from German life if the Bavarian party had had certain elements of strength. Hitler's trial was a legal farce. The instigators of attempts like this *putsch* would have been thrown out of Germany if they were not citizens. The judge either ignored this law or Vienna refused to allow Hitler entrance to Austria.
After Hitler's release from prison, the storm troopers were reorganized, not as a military organization, but as a bodyguard to "keep order" at assemblies and to "Keep the streets clear" when demonstrations were being held.
Hitler's villa at Berchtesgaden dates back to this time. Hitler needed a place from which he could, in case of necessity, flee to Austria and thence to Italy. After 1933, the remodeled villa became more famous.

and forbidden throughout the entire territory of the Reich. Today, in November, 1926, it stands again before us, free through the whole Reich, stronger and internally more stable than ever before.

I want to state briefly my position on the question of the extent to which the demand for soil and territory appears to be ethically and morally justified.

Certain pathetic babblers occupy themselves sketching for the German people a rectification of the injustice of 1918 as the goal of its foreign-policy activity, but beyond that find it necessary to assure the entire world of folkish fraternity and sympathy.

The frontiers of the year 1914 signify nothing at all for the future of the German nation. They embodied neither a protection in the past, nor would they embody strength for the future. The distance to England will not be shortened, the size of the Union not achieved; no, France will not even experience a material decrease in her world political importance.

But much as we all today recognize the necessity for a reckoning with France, it will remain largely ineffective if our foreign-policy aim is restricted thereto. It has and will retain significance if it provides the rear cover for an enlargement of our national domain of life in Europe.

We will find this question's solution not in colonial acquisition, but exclusively in the winning of land for settlement which increases the area of the motherland itself.

WE NATIONAL Socialists, however, must go further: *the right to soil and territory can become a duty if decline seems to be in store for a great nation unless it extends its territory.*

With this, we National Socialists consciously draw a line through the foreign-policy trend of our pre-War period. We take up at the halting place of six hundred years ago. We terminate the endless German drive to the south and west of

Europe, and direct our gaze towards the lands in the east.

And if we talk about new soil and territory in Europe today, we think primarily of Russia and its vassal border states.

If the National Socialist movement frees itself from all illusions with respect to our great and important tasks, the catastrophe of 1918 can still become an eternal blessing for the nation's future. Then our nation can emerge from this collapse of our foreign-policy activity. It can then finally get what England has and what even Russia had, and what again and again enables France always to hit on decisions uniformly and basically correct for its interests, that is: a *political testament.*

The political testament of the German nation for its dealing with the outside world, should and must always read substantially:

Never tolerate the establishment of two continental powers in Europe. Germany shall regard as its duty to prevent by armed force any attempt to organize a military power on its frontiers.

We will see that the strength of our nation is founded, not on colonies, but on the European territory of the homeland.

We will never regard the Reich as secure while it is unable to give every national offshoot for centuries his own bit of soil and territory.

We will never forget that the most sacred right in this world is the right to that earth which a man desires to till himself, and the most sacred sacrifice: that blood which a man spills for this earth.

A MAN OF WORDS AND NOT OF DEEDS

A MAN of words and not of deeds
Is like a garden full of weeds;
And when the weeds begin to grow,
It's like a garden full of snow;
And when the snow begins to fall,
It's like a bird upon the wall;
And when the bird away does fly,
It's like an eagle in the sky;
And when the sky begins to roar,
It's like a lion at the door;
And when the door begins to crack,
It's like a stick across your back;
And when your back begins to smart,
It's like a penknife in your heart;
And when your heart begins to bleed,
You're dead, and dead, and dead, indeed.

—*Anon.*

HENRY ADAMS

THE EDUCATION OF HENRY ADAMS

HENRY ADAMS, son of Charles Francis Adams, Minister to England during the Civil War, accomplished one of the major achievements of American historical writing in his "History of the United States during the Administration of Jefferson and Madison" (1889-1891). Later he abandoned American history, and attempted to develop the theory of force or energy as the basic principle of the philosophy of history. "The Education of Henry Adams" was privately printed in 1907, and published in 1918, the year he died.

The Grandson and Greatgrandson of Presidents

UNDER the shadow of Boston State House on the summit of Beacon Hill a child was born on February 16, 1838, and christened later after the tenets of Boston Unitarianism, as Henry Brooks Adams.

Had he been born in Jerusalem under the shadow of the Temple and circumcised in the Synagogue by the high priest under the name of Israel Cohen, he would scarcely have been more distinctly branded, and not much more heavily handicapped, in the races of the coming century.

For two hundred years, every Adams, from father to son, had lived within sight of Boston, and sometimes had lived in it, yet none had ever taken kindly to the town, or been taken kindly by it. Never for a moment did he connect the two ideas of Boston and John Adams; the idea of John Adams went with Quincy.

He knew his grandfather John Quincy Adams as an old man who was always called "the President" but he had no reason to suppose that his Adams grandfather differed in character from his Brooks grandfather of Boston who was equally kind and benevolent. He liked the Adams side best, but for no other reason than that it reminded him of the country, the summer, and the absence of restraint.

Of the influences that warped his mind, none compared with the mere effect of sitting behind a President grandfather in Church and reading over his head the tablet in memory of a President great-grandfather, who had "pledged his life, his fortune, and his sacred honor" to secure the independence of his country and so forth; the boy naturally supposed that other boys had the equivalent of President grandfathers.

The Irish gardener once said to the child: "You'll be thinkin' you'll be President, too!" The casualty of the remark made so strong an impression on his mind that he never forgot it.

He doubted neither about Presidents nor about Churches, and no one suggested at that time a doubt whether a system of society which had lasted since Adam would outlast one Adams more.

HOME influences alone never saved the New England boy from ruin, though sometimes they may have helped to ruin him; and the influences outside of the home were negative. If school helped, it was only by reaction. The dislike of school was so strong as to be a positive gain.

He always reckoned his school days, from ten to sixteen years old, as time thrown away. For success in the life imposed on him he needed, as afterwards appeared, the facile use of only four tools: Mathematics, French, German and Spanish. With these he could master in very short time any special branch of inquiry and feel at home in any society. These four tools necessary to his success in life, he never controlled.

Boston at that time offered few healthy resources for boys or men. The bar-room and billiard-room were more familiar than parents knew. Sport as a pursuit was unknown. Of all pleasures, winter sleighing was still the gayest and most popular.

Books remained as in the eighteenth century, the source of life, and as they came out—Thackeray, Dickens, Tennyson, Macaulay, Carlyle, and the rest—they were devoured. But as far as happiness went, the happiest hours of the boy's education were passed in summer lying on a musty heap of Congressional Documents in the old farmhouse at Quincy, reading "Quentin Durward," "Ivanhoe," and "The Talisman," and raiding the garden at intervals for peaches and pears. On the whole, he learned most then.

A Boy's Thoughts in 1850

FROM time to time my father went to Washington and when I was twelve years old he took me with him. The journey was meant as education, and as education it served the purpose of fixing in his memory the stage of a boy's thought in 1850.

The railway, about the size and character of a modern tramway, rambled through unfenced fields and woods, or through village streets, among a haphazard variety of pigs, cows and negro babies. Slavery struck him in the face; it was a nightmare; a horror; a crime; the sum of all wickedness! Contact made it only more repulsive. He wanted to escape, like the negroes, to free soil.

In Washington he found himself on an earth-road with wheel-tracks meandering from the colonnade of the Treasury hard by, to the white marble columns and fronts of the Post Office and Patent Office which faced each other in the distance, like white Greek temples in the abandoned gravelpits of a deserted Syrian city.

He was taken to see President Taylor. Outside, in a paddock in front, "Old Whitey," the President's charger, was grazing, as they entered; and inside, the President was receiving callers as simply as if he were in the paddock too. The President was friendly, and boy felt no sense of strangeness that he could ever recall.

As for the White House, all the boy's family had lived there, and, barring the eight years of Andrew Jackson's reign, had been more or less at home there ever since it was built. The boy half thought he owned it, and took for granted that he should some day live in it. He felt no sensation whatever before Presidents.

The boy went back to Boston more political than ever. Life was not yet complicated. Every problem had a solution, even the negro.

Little Learned at Harvard

THE next regular step was Harvard College. He was more than glad to go. Generation after generation of his family had gone there, and although none of them ever thought himself the better for it, custom, social ties, convenience, and, above all, economy, kept each generation in the track.

But Harvard College was probably less hurtful than any other university then in existence. It taught little, and that little ill, but it left the mind open, ignorant of facts, but docile. The graduate had few strong prejudices.

The Class of 1858, to which Henry Adams belonged, was a typical collection of young New Englanders, quietly penetrating and aggressively commonplace. Into this unusually dissolvent medium, chance insisted on enlarging Henry Adams's education by tossing a trio of Virginians as little fitted for it as Sioux Indians to a treadmill. The lesson in education was vital to these young men, who, within ten years, killed each other by scores in the act of testing their college conclusions.

Strictly, the Southerner had no mind; he had temperament. He was not a scholar; he had no intellectual training; he could not analyze an idea, and he could not even conceive of admitting two, but in life one could get along very well without ideas, if one had only the social instinct.

Adams liked the Virginians. No one was more obnoxious to them, by name and prejudice; yet their friendship was unbroken and even warm. At a moment when the immediate future posed no problem in education so vital as the relative energy and endurance of North and South, this momentary contact with Southern character was a sort of education for its own sake.

IF THE student got little from his mates, he got little more from his masters. Beyond two or three Greek plays, the student got nothing from the ancient languages. Beyond some incoherent theories of free-trade and protection, he got little from Political Economy. He could not afterwards remember having heard the name of Karl Marx mentioned, though he was most influential on the thought of the time.

The only teaching that appealed to his imagination was a course of lectures by Louis Agassiz on the Glacial Period and Palaeontology, which had more influence on his curiosity than the rest of the college instruction altogether. The entire work of the four years could have been easily put into the work of any four months in after life.

So Henry Adams, well aware that he could not succeed as a scholar, and finding his social position beyond improvement or need of effort, betook himself to the single ambition which otherwise would scarcely have seemed a true outcome of the college. He took to the pen. He wrote.

The college magazine printed his work, and the college societies listened to his addresses. Lavish of praise the readers were not; the audiences, too, listened in silence; but this was all the encouragement any Harvard collegian had a reasonable hope to receive; grave silence was a form of patience that meant possible future acceptance; and Henry Adams went on writing.

Henry Adams and Abraham Lincoln

WHEN, forty years afterwards, Henry Adams looked back over his adventures in search of knowledge, he asked himself whether fortune or fate had ever dealt its cards so wildly to any of his known antecessors as when it led him to begin the study of law and to vote for Abraham Lincoln on the same day.

Not one man in America wanted the Civil War, or expected or intended it. A small minority wanted secession. The vast majority wanted to go on with their occupations in peace. No one, however clever or learned, guessed what happened.

As for Henry Adams, fresh from a post graduate education in Europe, he plunged at once into a lurid atmosphere of politics, quite heedless of any education or forethought. Profoundly ignorant, anxious and curious, the young man packed his modest trunk again, which had not yet time to be unpacked and started for Washington as his father's private secretary.

Ten years had passed since his last visit, but very little had changed. As in 1800 and 1850, so in 1860, the same rude colony was camped in the same forest, with the same unfinished Greek temples for workrooms, and sloughs for roads. The government had an air of social instability and incompleteness that went far to support the right of secession in theory as in fact; but right or wrong, secession was likely to be easy where there was so little to secede from.

He saw Mr. Lincoln but once; at the melancholy function called an Inaugural

Ball. Of course he looked anxiously for a sign of character. He saw a long, awkward figure; a plain, ploughed face; a mind, absent in part, and in part evidently worried by white kid gloves; features that expressed neither self-satisfaction nor any other familiar Americanism; but rather the same painful sense of becoming educated and of needing education that tormented a private secretary, above all a lack of apparent force. Any private secretary would have thought as Adams did, that no man living needed so much education as the new President but that all the education he could get would not be enough.

Hardly a week passed when the newspapers announced that President Lincoln had selected Charles Francis Adams as his Minister to England. Henry packed his trunk again without a word.

On April 13 the storm burst and rolled several hundred thousand young men like Henry Adams into the surf of a wild ocean, all helpless like himself, to be beaten about for four years.

Christian Martyrs in London

THE Adams party landed at Liverpool May 13, 1861, and went instantly up to London: a family of early Christian martyrs about to be flung into an arena of lions, under the glad eyes of Tiberius Palmerston.

Lord Palmerston had already arranged the ceremony. For on May 13 Adams met the official announcement that England recognized the belligerency of the Confederacy. He learned that no one in England—literally no one—doubted that Jefferson Davis had made or would make a nation, and nearly all were glad of it, though not often saying so.

The test was final, for no other shock so violent and sudden could possibly recur. The worst was in full sight. The chances were that the whole family would turn round and go home within a few weeks. For once the private secretary knew his business, which was to imitate his father as closely as possible and hold his tongue.

To him the Legation was social ostracism, terrible beyond anything he had known. Socially, under the best of circumstances, a newcomer in London society needs years to establish a position. Now Henry had no friend, or even enemy, to tell him to be patient.

The private secretary had one source of comfort denied to him—he should not be private secretary long. He kept hoping that the end was near for nearly seven years. To him the Trent Affair [1] was nothing but one of many affairs which he had to copy in a delicate round hand into his books.

The Trent Affair showed where the British government stood and their fixed intention to intervene. The Foreign Secretary's (Lord Russell) replies to Mr. Adams's notes were discourteous in their indifference, and, to an irritable young private secretary of twenty-four, were insolent in their disregard of truth.

Lord Russell's course had been consistent from the first, and had all the look of rigid determination to recognize the Southern Confederacy "with a view" to breaking up the Union. His letter of September 17 hung directly on his encouragement of the Alabama [2] and his protection of the rebel navy; while the whole of his plan had its root in the Proclamation of Belligerency. Henry took for granted the dishonesty of three famous men: Palmerston, the Prime Minister, Russell, the Foreign Secretary and Gladstone, the Chancellor of the Exchequer.

[1] *In October, 1861 a Northern boat intercepted the British mail steamer* Trent *capturing two Confederate diplomats, Mason and Slidell. They were imprisoned in Boston but were released in January, 1862, on the demand of the British government.*

[2] *The* Alabama *was a swift Confederate privateer which was built in England and manned chiefly by British subjects. In its career of plunder it destroyed 57 Northern vessels. When the North won, England agreed to arbitrate. As a result England paid the United States $15,500,000 for losses sustained.*

His Education's Most Mortifying Failure

IN THE heat of the passion at the moment, one drew some harsh moral conclusions. Were they correct? Looking back, forty years afterwards, one asked oneself painfully what sort of a lesson a young man should have drawn.

The dishonesty, as concerned Russell, was denied by Russell himself and disbelieved by most of America's friends in England as well as by Minister Adams. The evidence in Russell's biography, published in 1889, tends to prove that he was not consciously dishonest and that he, in spite of appearances, acted without collusion, agreement, plan, or policy, as far as concerned the rebels. He had stood alone as was his nature.

But Minister Adams always retained his belief that Palmerston could not be trusted. Minister Adams took him to be pugnacious and quarrelsome; but the "Lives" of Russell, Gladstone, and Granville show him to have been good-tempered, conciliatory, avoiding quarrels. He tried to check Russell. He scolded Gladstone. Palmerston told no falsehoods; made no professions; concealed no opinions; was detected in no double dealing whatever.

The most mortifying failure in Henry Adams's long education was that, after forty years of confirmed dislike, distrust, and detraction of Lord Palmerston, he was obliged at last to admit himself in error, and to consent in spirit—for by that time he was nearly as dead as any of them—to beg his pardon.

As for morals, the private secretary could detect no shade of difference between Gladstone and Napoleon except to the advantage of Napoleon. Yet no absurdity that a young man could reach in 1862 would have approached the level that Mr. Gladstone admitted in his confessions of 1896: "I have yet to record an undoubted error—the least excusable of them all. . . . I declared in the heat of the American struggle that Jefferson Davis had made a nation. My offence was indeed only a mistake, but one of incredible grossness, and with such consequences of offence and alarm attached to it, that my failing to perceive them justly exposed me to very severe blame."

Long and patiently did the private secretary forty years afterwards in the twilight of a life of study, reflect upon this confession. His whole theory of conspiracy—of policy—of logic and connection in the affairs of man, resolved into "incredible grossness." He felt no rancor, for he had won the game; he forgave, since he must admit, the "incapacity of viewing subjects all round."

Adams Begins His Own Career

THE campaign of 1864 and the re-election of Mr. Lincoln set the American Minister on so firm a footing that he could safely regard his anxieties as over. His son no longer fretted. The time for going into the army had passed. If he were to be useful at all, it must be as a son, and as a son he was treated with the widest indulgence and trust.

He knew that he was doing himself no good by staying in London. The young Englishmen's custom of pounding up and down Rotten Row every day, in a hack was not to his taste. Evidently he must set to work; he must get a new education; he must begin a career of his own.

Since no other path seemed to offer itself, he decided to join the press and selected Washington as the shortest road to New York, but, in 1868, Washington stood outside the social pale. No Bostonian had ever gone there. One announced one's self as an adventurer and an office-seeker, a person of deplorably bad judgment, and the charges were true. The chances of ending in the gutter were, at best, even.

After seven years' arduous and unsuccessful effort to explore the outskirts of London society, the Washington world offered an easy and delightful repose. When he looked round him on the men he was to work with—or against—he had to admit that nine-tenths of his acquired education was useless and the other tenth, harmful. He must learn to talk to Western Congressmen and to hide his own antecedents. The task was amusing.

He worked, after a fashion; not very hard, but as much as the Government would have required of him for nine hundred dollars a year. He gave three months to an article on the finances of the United States, just then a subject greatly needing treatment and sent it to the *Edinburgh Review*. The editor probably thought it was good, at least he said so; and he printed it. Of course it was reprinted in America, but in England such articles were still anonymous, and the author remained unknown.

The author was not then asking for advertisement. His object was literary. He belonged to the eighteenth century. But the eighteenth century upset all of his plans. For the moment, America was more eighteenth century than himself; it reverted to the stone age.

Grant—the Caveman President

ADAMS had seen a dozen Presidents at the White House, but he found Grant the most curious object of study among them all. A single word with Grant satisfied him that, for his own good, the fewer words he risked the better. The intellect counted for nothing in Grant, only the energy counted. The type was pre-intellectual, archaic, and would have seemed so to the cave dwellers.

That, two thousand years after Alexander the Great and Julius Caesar, a man like Grant should be called the highest product of the most advanced evolution, made evolution ludicrous. One must be as commonplace as Grant's own commonplaces to maintain such an absurdity. The progress of evolution from President Washington to President Grant, was alone evidence enough to upset Darwin.

Grant's administration outraged every rule of ordinary decency, but scores of promising men, whom the country could not well spare, were ruined in saying so. The world cared little for decency. What it wanted, it did not know, probably a system that would work, and the men who could work it; but it found neither. The Administration drove him and thousands of other young men, into active enmity, not only to Grant, but to the system or want of system. No one wanted him; no one wanted any of his friends in reform; the blackmailer alone was the normal product of politics as of business.

All this was excessively amusing. Adams never had been so busy, so interested, so much in the thick of the crowd. He knew Congressmen by scores and newspapermen by the dozen. He wrote for his various organs all sorts of attacks and defences. He enjoyed the life enormously.

But when spring came he took to the woods. Education for education, none ever compared with the delight of the Washington spring. The Potomac and its tributaries squandered beauty. Rock Creek was as wild as the Rocky Mountains. No European spring had shown him the same intermixture of delicate grace and passionate depravity that marked the Maryland May. He could not leave it, but loitered on into July, falling into the Southern ways of the summer village as one whose rights of inheritance could not be questioned. Few Americans were so poor as to question them.

Death—The Sum of Education

ONE fine May afternoon in 1870 Adams drove again up St. James's Street wondering more than ever at the marvels of life.

He had been some weeks in London when he received a telegram from his brother-in-law telling him that his sister had been thrown from a cab and injured, and he had better come on. When he reached Italy tetanus had already set in.

The last lesson—the sum and term of education—began then. He had passed through thirty years of rather varied experience without having once felt the shell of custom broken. He had never seen Nature—only her surface—the sugar-coating that she shows to youth. Flung suddenly in his face, with the harsh brutality of chance, the terror of the blow stayed by him thenceforth for life, until repetition made it more than the will could struggle against; more than he could call on himself to bear.

The usual anondynes of social medicine became evident artifice. Stoicism was perhaps the best; religion was the most human; but the idea that any personal deity could find pleasure or profit in torturing a poor woman, with a fiendish cruelty known to man only in perverted and insane temperaments, could not be held for a moment. For pure blasphemy it made pure atheism a comfort.

He did not know it, and he was twenty years in finding it out; but he had need of all the beauty of the Alps to restore the finite to its accustomed place.

"College is Worth Money to Me!"

HE SAILED home in September to begin again where he had started two years before. He was a free lance and no other career stood in sight or mind.

But no sooner had he reached Washington and made a modest success there than his family set on him to drag him away. He should come to Harvard College. His chief function was not to be that of teacher, but that of editing the *North American Review* which was to be coupled with a professorship in history.

The sum of the matter was that Henry went to Harvard College. What he could gain there he did not know, but in any case it was nothing he sought, nothing he wanted.

The college expected him to pass at least half his time in teaching the boys a few elementary dates and relations, that they might not be a disgrace to the university. This was formal and he could frankly tell the boys that, provided they passed their examinations, they might get their facts where they liked, and use the professor only for questions. His only difficulty on that side was to get them to talk at all. He had to devise schemes to find what they were thinking about, schemes to induce them to risk criticism from their fellows.

He wanted to help the boys to a career, but not one of his many devices to stimulate the intellectual reaction of the student mind satisfied either him or the students. For himself he was clear that the fault lay in the lecture system, which could lead only to inertia.

Such little knowledge of himself as he possessed warranted him in affirming that his mind required conflict, competition, contradiction, even more than that of the student. He would have seated a rival assistant professor whose business should be strictly limited to expressing opposite views. Nothing short of this would ever interest either the professor or the student.

The only part of education that the professor thought a success was the students. He found them excellent company. Their faith in education was so full of pathos that one dared not ask them what they thought they could do with education when they got it. Adams did put the question to one of them and was surprised at the answer: "The degree of Harvard College is worth money to me in Chicago."

So far as it went, the answer was good and settled one's doubts. Adams knew no better, although he had given twenty years to pursuing the same education and was no nearer a result than the young men he lectured.

Twenty Years Later

FIT or unfit, Henry Adams stopped his own education in 1871, and began to apply it for practical uses, like his neighbors. At the end of twenty years he found that he had finished, and could sum up the result. He had no complaint to make against man or woman. Considering the stock complaints against the world, he could not understand why he had nothing to complain of.

Home was Washington. As soon as Grant's administration ended, in 1877, Adams went back there, partly to write history, but chiefly because his seven years of laborious banishment in Boston convinced him that, as far as he had a function in life, it was as stable-companion to statesmen, whether they liked it or not.

Adams had held no office and when his friends asked the reason, he could not go into long explanations, but preferred to answer simply that no President had ever invited him to fill one. The reason was good and was also conveniently true, but left open an awkward doubt of his morals or capacity. Why had no President ever cared to employ him?

Men who neither wrote for newspapers nor made campaign speeches, who rarely subscribed to the campaign fund, and who entered the White House as seldom as possible, placed themselves outside the sphere of usefulness, and did so with entirely adequate knowledge of what they were doing. No one would have been more surprised than Henry Adams had any President asked him to perform so much of a service as to cross the square. Only Texas Congressmen imagined that the President needed their services in some remote consulate after worrying him for months to find one.

During these twenty years he had done as much work, in quantity, as his neighbors wanted; more than they would ever stop to look at, and more than his share. Merely in print, he thought altogether ridiculous the number of volumes he counted on the shelves of public libraries. He had no notion whether they served a useful purpose. He had written them; and they were there.

So, like a horse that wears out, he left the stable and sought pastures as far as possible from the old. Education had ended in 1871; life was complete in 1890; the rest mattered little.

Struck on the Head by Education

IF HE wanted more education he knew no quicker mode than that of being struck on the head by it. As a starting point the shock of finding one's self suspended over the edge of bankruptcy without knowing how one got there, or how to get away, is to be strongly recommended.

Men died like flies under the strain, and Boston grew suddenly old, haggard, and thin. Adams alone waxed fat and was happy, for at last he had got hold of his world and could finish his education interrupted for twenty years. He cared not whether it were worth finishing, if only it amused; but he seemed, for the first time since 1870, to feel that something new and curious was about to happen to the world.

For the first time in several years he saw much of his brother Brooks in Quincy, and was surprised to find him absorbed in the same perplexities. Brooks had discovered or developed a law of history, that civilization followed the stock exchanges. Among other general rules he laid down the paradox that, in the social disequilibrium between capital and labor, the logical outcome was not collectivism, but anarchism; and Henry made note of it for study.

The convulsions of 1893 left its victims in dead-water, and closed much education. While the country braced itself up to an effort such as no one had thought within its powers, the individual crawled as he best could through the wreck.

Virgin to Dynamo

BUT for connecting the nineteenth and twentieth centuries the next few years had no value in the drama of education and might be left out.

In 1900, opened another totally new education, which promised to be by far the most hazardous of all.

When Adams was a boy in Boston, the best chemist in the place had probably never heard of Venus except by way of scandal, or of the Virgin except as idolatry; neither had he heard of dynamos or automobiles or radium; yet his mind was ready to feel the force of all, though the rays were unborn and the women were dead.

They were as different as a magnet is from gravitation, supposing one knew what a magnet was, or gravitation, or love. The force of the Virgin was still felt at Lourdes, and seemed to be as potent as X-rays; but in America neither Venus nor Virgin ever had value as force—at most as sentiment.

The problem in dynamics gravely perplexed an American historian. The Woman had once been supreme; in France she still seemed potent, not merely as a sentiment, but as a force. Why was she unknown in America?

Any one brought up among Puritans knew that sex was sin. In any previous age sex was strength. Neither art nor beauty was needed. Every one, even among Puritans, knew that neither Diana of the Ephesians nor any of the Oriental goddesses was worshipped for her beauty. She was goddess because of her force; she was reproduction—the greatest and most mysterious of all energies.

A mind like that of Adams felt itself helpless. He turned from Virgin to the Dynamo. Before his eyes was the highest energy ever known to man, the creator of four-fifths of his noblest art, exercising vastly more attraction over the human mind than all the steam-engines and dynamos ever dreamed of; and yet this energy was unknown to the American mind.

SYMBOL or energy, the Virgin had acted as the greatest force the Western world ever felt, and had drawn man's activities to herself more strongly than any other power, natural or supernatural, had ever done; the historian's business was to follow the track of the energy. It could scarcely be more complex than radium; it could hardly be deflected, diverted, polarized, absorbed more perplexingly than any other radiant matter. Adams knew nothing about any of them, and he rather inclined to think the Virgin easiest to handle.

The pursuit turned out to be long and tortuous, ending at last in the vast forests of scholastic science. From Zeno to Descartes, hand in hand with Thomas Aquinas, Montaigne, and Pascal, one stumbled as stupidly as though one were still a German student of 1860. Only with the instinct of despair could one force one's self into this old thicket of ignorance after having been repulsed at a score of entrances more promising and more popular.

Thus far, no path had led anywhere, unless perhaps to an exceedingly modest living. Forty-five years of study had proved to be quite futile for the pursuit of power; one controlled no more force in 1900 than in 1850, although the amount of force controlled by society had enormously increased.

To the tired student, the idea that he must give up seemed sheer senility. As long as he could whisper, he would go on as he had begun, bluntly refusing to meet his Creator with the admission that the creation had taught him nothing except that the square of the hypotenuse of a right-angled triangle might for convenience be taken as equal to something else.

Vincent Sheean

PERSONAL HISTORY

O F THE flood of reporters' adventures which have descended upon the American reading public in recent years, "Personal History" is generally conceded to be the best. Since its publication in 1934, Vincent Sheean has devoted himself to writing two comparatively unsuccessful novels and to chasing history around Europe, out of which experiences he has recently written the best selling "Not Peace But A Sword." Mr. Sheean is married to the daughter of an English actor and has a daughter named Linda.

Pseudo-Education

T HE Armistice came when I was eighteen. What it meant to the war generation I can only imagine from the stories they tell; to me it meant that we in the University of Chicago went out of uniform and into civilian clothes.

The world has changed so much that it seems downright indecent to tell the truth: I was sorry when the war ended. We were all patriots then. We knew nothing about the horror and degradation which our elders who had been through the war were to put before us so unremittingly for the next fifteen years. We felt cheated. We had played at being soldiers for a few months with tremendous seriousness, and then the glorious uproar to which we had been preparing our approach suddenly died down. Our part of the war had been a prelude to something that did not take place.

And when demobilization came at last, the prospect of returning to the regular life of the University had become repellent to me. I had nobody to persuade but my mother, who was still too thankful for the Armistice to make many objections. Consequently I went job hunting.

There was a job for me (thanks to a friend) as a reporter on the Chicago *Daily News,* but I must have been phenomenally stupid at it, for I lasted only two or three weeks. When I received my congé, I did, almost without thinking, something that had probably been floating about in the undergrowth of my mind for weeks or months. I walked out of the *Daily News* office and onto a train for New York.

What did I take away from the pseudo-Gothic sanctuary of my pseudo-education? Not much. I had some vague idea of history and philosophy, a bowing acquaintance with English and French literature. I had learned a good deal about snobbery, cruelty, prejudice, injustice and stupidity. I had acquired half a dozen friends—perhaps. I had learned how to dance the fox trot.

Few Hottentots or South Sea Islanders could be less prepared for life in the great world than I was at twenty-one. As I sat in that filthy day coach on the train to New York, I was the least respectable of passengers: my ticket went one way only, and I had no baggage of any kind.

Baptism by Total Immersion

M Y INTRODUCTION to the larger world outside the University was a baptism by total immersion, and in icy water at that. One day I was still thinking (when I thought at all) about books and characters. The next day, I was the familiar friend of murderesses, the apologist of divorcées, a professional observer at the peep-show of misery: a reporter for the New York *Daily News.*

I had an immense amount of innocence to lose, and with the best will in the world I could not lose it quickly enough: the more I found out, the more there seemed to be to find out. Becoming, for the first time, aware of a wide range of possibilities—sexual freedom; self-indulgence in such matters as drink; the pleasures of talk, particularly of political discussion; the pleasures of personal influence or expression, so essential to developing confidence—all hitherto obscured or unknown, I grew, in the less measurable regions, inches every day.

My interest in political discussion outran my information, and when I tried to make up the defects I felt in any such talk with older people than myself, I fell upon the astounding tale of the past few years, the years through which I had lived sealed up behind the walls of the University: the years of the war, of the Russian Revolution, of the Treaty of Versailles.

In talk with people who had actually been present at the Russian Revolution or at the making of the Versailles treaty, these events, once as remote to me as if they had taken place five hundred years before and on another planet, came to have a meaning at least as immediate as that of my latest interview with the newest divorcée or murderess. They were soon to acquire more—much more.

The new curiosities aroused since I had left the University pushed me on towards Europe, and when I came into possession of enough money to be off, I went on my way.

When I reached Paris, I went to the office of the Chicago *Tribune*—drawn there by the notion that anything connected with Chicago must be vaguely all right for me. By what method the editor arrived at his conclusions I never knew; there must have been dozens of stray newspaper men drifting into that office every week, some of them far more experienced than I was. But whatever the reasons, he determined to take me on. Thus, in a click of time, I became what was called a foreign correspondent, a role I was to fill, in the service of that vigorous newspaper, for the next three years.

Under Black Print on White Paper

MY SUITABILITY for the job of foreign correspondent—as distinguished from my specific qualifications, which were dubious—must have been considerable. I was prepared (in interest and self-confidence, at least) to deal with the largest doings of the great, their words and deeds and gestures, as a journalist should—that is, without unduly yielding to their persuasions, believing in their beliefs, or crediting their enthusiasms.

As months and years passed, as I acquired a steadier, more intimate acquaintance with the struggles under the surface of smooth black print on white paper, my political interest deepened into political passion, and I came in time to "take sides" and have opinions, feel them as deeply and express them as violently as any amateur. In so doing I only reversed the familiar procedure by which a good many of my colleagues, having begun with beliefs and enthusiasms, ended in callous indifference towards all human effort.

Older correspondents of my acquaintance had always seemed cynical, unwilling to acknowledge decent motives or behavior in politics; but the more I saw of the materials of history the more I was forced to admit the logic of their scepticism.

It was against the code to say plainly in print any of the things admitted in private conversations: that the Comité des Forges was supporting the Ruhr policy and financing the Rhineland rebellion; that the German financiers were making millions out of the deliberate inflation that ruined their poorer countrymen; that a handful of people were filching fortunes from Spain under Primo de Rivera; that the French general staff was attempting to bring about the annexation of the Palatinate and the Saar; that the press and most of the politicians of continental Europe were on sale to the highest bidder, usually the French.

It amused the older correspondents to see all this, to hint at it sometimes in print; but it never seemed a matter of personal importance to them. They were like a pack of jaded dramatic reviewers: familiar with the technique of the play, but profoundly uninterested in its material.

I STARTED working for the Chicago Tribune towards the end of 1922. Poincaré was then President of the Council in France, bent upon enforcing the letter of the Treaty of Versailles and (in such respects as the Rhineland policy) determined, actually, to go beyond it and cripple Germany forever, if it could be done.

Before I had been many weeks in the service of the newspaper, Poincaré sent French troops into the Ruhr, and for the first two years of my experience the questions of the Ruhr, the Rhineland, and reparations, took precedence over all others in the European political struggle.

The most positive single element in the struggle was the personality of M. Poincaré. He was not only the first politician I ever observed at close range: he was also the least imposing, the least suited to his historic role. From hearing and seeing him repeatedly throughout the momentous two years I reached the conclusion that he hated the Germans as a Jersey farmer hates a rattlesnake.

He came from Lorraine; the war had cost him dear; and he was unable to take a large view of any situation involving the Germans. Deformed, crippled and cramped by patriotic passion, he could not see straight on any question involving the immediate interest of his own country or the most ordinary rights of that eternal enemy, Germany.

If I lived to be a thousand I could never forget the sound of his maniac shriek as he pronounced the word *Allemagne*. The whole curse of Europe was in it; and as I grew familiar with the behavior and ideas of M. Poincaré I could see that the implacability of his hatred, the venom of his curse, was his principal—indeed, almost his only—qualification for his destiny. Few men have filled so great a place in human affairs with so little.

"No German Will Ever Forget . . ."

ONE evening we were told in Paris that a rebellion had broken out at Aix-la-Chapelle [Aachen], directed against the German Reich authorities and not against the Belgian troops in occupation there. It was no more than half an hour after our first news of the trouble that I was sent off at the Gare du Nord.

The hordes of foreign correspondents who descended upon the occupied territories during the trouble lived, generally, at the Breidenbacher Hof in Düsseldorf. It was an excellent hotel with exorbitant prices, a good kitchen, and a head waiter who bore himself like an emperor.

No contrast could possibly have been more striking that that between the well-fed unreality of these foreign correspond-

ents in the Düsseldorf hotel and the starving desperation of the Germans outside. I watched the poor being fed slops and left-overs at the back entrance of our sumptuous Breidenbacher Hof, and it was a spectacle I could have wished to show M. Poincaré.

Conditions in the Palatinate were more disgraceful than elsewhere, because that province had been less subjected to the scrutiny by the Rhineland High Commission and the foreign press. The population was urged by every means at hand to go to night school and learn French, which they were freely told was going to be their language in the future. French signs had been stuck up on the street corners, alongside or above the German names. Rue Foch and Rue Joffre

—what venom those names must have prepared in the feeling of the conquered!

THE French commander-in-chief in the Rheinpfalz was one of the most detestable satraps I was ever obliged to interview: pompous, heartless, stupid, convinced of his right to force a whole German province to do his bidding. The Rheinpfalz was to join its neighbours, Alsace-Lorraine and the Saar, under French rule: that was his plan, and he said it as plainly as he dared.

And yet, in spite of all these curses, the men still went into the woods and cut down evergreen trees to bring home for the most Germanic of festivals, and in the snowy dark night, just at curfew time, the children sang Christmas songs. Why could not the French see that the

vitality of this people could not be conquered, get used to it, live with it, make it as familiar as the face of night and day? Why indeed?

When I went back to the Rhineland a year later for a few days the whole air and manner and feeling of the country had altered. I was surprised at the Germans for forgetting so soon, at the French for reversing everything I had thought of their ambitions and plans.

A French official friend disabused me: "Nobody has forgotten anything," he said. "It's the moment for fine words, that's all." And the assistant manager of the hotel, a Bavarian: "What the French did here won't be forgotten—not even after we've beaten them to death in the next war; no German who was here will ever forget it."

Perhaps they were both right.

Out of the Pesthouse of Europe

EXCEPT for a blessed month at Fiesole, in my first year, I had never had even a week away from attendance upon the pesthouse of Europe. Three years with it left a feeling of disgust. For what I wanted, such politics and such journalism were no good. I had come to want what, I suppose, most maturing people want: to give this unique possession, this one life, somehow, a relation to the world of which it was a tiny segment—to attach it and articulate it, so that comprehension might eventually light up the darkness in which it continued.

There was no hope of this articulation, of this comprehension, in the politics of the time or in the journalism that was its servant. I could never again believe what I read in the newspapers, for example, because I could not believe the politicians, because I had seen them squirming and dodging about, the poor powerless ferrets, trying to find a way out of the system in which they were imprisoned. In this doomed house there was no hope.

If the desired sense of things was to be captured at all, it must be elsewhere.

It was, quite possibly, uncapturable; but the pursuit was one of the primary conditions of life, without which its course, even in youth, would fall into emptiness.

THE events that aroused my fire-horse instinct were not, actually, the ones the newspapers found most interesting. I cared nothing about such events as earthquakes, murders, political elections in the United States, divorces, or transatlantic flights (except Lindbergh's, which captured every imagination).

The events that aroused in me the desire to attend, to witness, were invariably those in which large numbers of men were engaged in some difficult enterprise involving a fundamental idea —an idea of race, class, or even of nation. In what looked like the impending triumph of the Chinese Revolution there was an event of the kind that excited my imagination to the utmost. Without regard to what kind of a job I might do in China, I wanted above all to get there.

In February of 1927 the armies of the Kuomintang captured Shanghai. This event instantly endowed China with all the attributes of suitability.

Modest Profits of 1000%

THE International Settlement and the French Concession, the two foreign *enclaves* that constituted the original city of Shanghai, around which a colossal Chinese city had grown up, gave an instant impression of pompous and rather purse-proud arrogance. The arrogance of the European city was, just now, tempered by a certain amount of apprehension, for the Cantonese armies had occupied the surrounding Chinese city a month before and were held to be "threatening" the existence of the foreign settlement.

Shanghai had nothing—nothing but its money and its ghastly fear of losing it. Cowering angrily behind its barricades, it exhibited human nature without dignity or generosity, denying any fact that might sooner or later threaten its hold over wealth and the sources of wealth.

It never seemed to cross their minds that every penny had been wrung from the Chinese in one way or another, either by the exorbitant profits of the foreign trade—the exploitation of what is called an "undeveloped market," which is to say a market made up of people who do not know when they are being cheated—or by the direct exploitation of Chinese labor.

The second source of wealth was more recent, and its profits had been enormous. The British, Americans and Japanese were able to employ Chinese people of all ages in their factories for any number of hours a day, for wages so small that they barely supported a half-starved and ever-threatened life. The coolie population, which never had enough to eat and often no place to sleep, was easy prey for manufacturers who wished to make the modest profit of a thousand percent.

I never met anybody in Shanghai who revealed the slightest feeling of shame, the slightest consciousness of degradation, in thus taking advantage of human misery in its most appalling forms. On the contrary, the Shanghai foreigners felt virtuous because they gave their coolies a slightly better chance of survival than did the worst of the Chinese employers. Shanghai saw itself as the benefactor of all China, and was horrified at the rising Chinese demand for better conditions of life.

Bourgeois Meets Bolshevik

I BEGAN to approach the fundamental meaning of these vast disturbances that had fascinated me (in part unconsciously) for years. In my first direct meeting with the Bolshevik philosophy in action, I was disturbed by the precision with which it answered the questions I had begun to think unanswerable —the questions of a sensible relationship between one life and many. Whether the Bolshevik solutions were the correct ones was another matter, which might take a long time to determine, but they were at least solutions, and represented the effort of human thought to bring order into the chaos that on every side oppressed and appalled the imagination.

I was, to begin with, a sympathizer. I had the mind and character of an American bourgeois, twenty-seven years old, who had divided his adult years between the subjects to which this book has been chiefly devoted—the living history of the time—and the preoccupations of personal taste.

The mind I directed upon the people and things in China, and upon the whole drama of revolution, had been originally a good one, acquisitive, perceptive, and retentive, but it was softened and discoloured beneath later influences, which constantly suggested that fundamental questions were not worth bothering about. The shock of general reality was what I needed, and I was about to receive it—a seismic disturbance of greater intensity and duration than I would have believed possible a few months before.

Misselwitz of the *New York Times* was staying at the American Consulate in Hankow when I arrived. "One thing you ought to do right away," he said, "is to go and see Mrs. Prohme."

"Who's that?"

"You must have heard something about her. American. Red headed gal, spitfire, mad as a hatter, complete Bolshevik. Works for Borodin. But she's a nice girl, anyway and you'll enjoy talking to her."

"O.K., let's go see her now."

We reached the office just as Mrs. Prohme was coming out. She was slight, not very tall, with short red-gold hair and a frivolous turned-up nose. All in all, she was most unlike my idea of a "wild Bolshevik," and I told her so. She laughed. I had never heard anybody laugh as she did—it was the gayest, most unselfconscious sound in the world. You might have thought that it did not come from a person at all, but from some impulse of gaiety in the air.

She was the kind of girl I had known all my life, but she had, by the direction she had taken, acquired a purpose and point of view that did not seem to me to belong to her. From the first I was conscious of a great puzzle, the puzzle of why she was doing this particular thing at this particular point of the world's compass.

She could see at a glance that I was a typical example of American bourgeois as modified by Paris and London, with a goodish but lazy mind. She could easily, perhaps too easily, consign me to the pigeonhole where many of her own friends and relations belonged.

Her instinctive attack or defence took the form of a quizzical flippancy, as it might with a contemporary (a brother or friend) known years ago in Illinois, who had, since the days of remembered acquaintance, gone off in an opposing direction and acquired a set of ideas that she could not regard as idiosyncratic. Sometimes the flippancy wore thin, but it seldom broke down altogether. The most important conversation in my life—in the true sense, the only conversation I have ever had—began, and for months continued, as a kind of joke.

Economic's Dead Bones Animated

For a few months in 1927, a little more than half a year, Hankow concentrated, symbolized and upheld the hope for a revolution of the world. Delegations came there from all over Europe, Asia and America to see for themselves what constituted Hankow's success, the surprise and delight of a generation of thwarted Communists.

The great expectations of 1917 had come to nothing. Social revolution had failed in Europe and even in Russia it was no longer possible to conceal the life-and-death struggle of opposing elements in the communist party: one that wished to fight for the world revolution and one that wished to advance it by concentration on the existing Soviet State.

Communists everywhere regarded Hankow as not only the most conspicuous success of revolutionary technique since 1917, but as the test case: if its success could be extended and made permanent, the victory of the international (Trotzkyite) tendency was assured; but if Hankow failed, the militant world revolutionists failed as well, and even in Russia the future became obscure.

Between the unrealistic demands of the theoretical Communists and the reactionary demands of foreign capital, Borodin, Moscow's representative in Hankow, was bound to become the scapegoat, not because he attempted to keep a middle course or believed in compromises, but because the situation did not permit a daring experiment in Communism.

Two things that he unquestionably could not do—that Trotzky himself could not have done—were: first, abolish the navies of America, England, Japan and France; and second, make flexible and resolute revolutionary instruments overnight out of the mass of half-awakened Chinese workers and peasants.

I saw Borodin frequently. He was a large, calm man with the natural dignity of a lion or a panther, had the special quality of being in, but above, the battle—the particular quality that seems to me to deserve, in itself and without regard to the judgment of the world, the name of greatness. His slow, resolute way of talking, his refusal to be hurried or to get excited, his insistence upon the fundamental lines of action that determined detailed events, gave a spacious, deliberate character to his conversation, lifting it far above the shallowness of journalism and the hysteria of politics. He seemed to take "the long view" by nature, by an almost physical superiority of vision. Disregarding the economic structure (Marxian economics) with which the Bolshevik mind was preoccupied, it could be seen that the method of thought in itself was "good" —and produced, as in the case of Borodin, a clear, calm view of life.

In Borodin I found an older, better disciplined, better trained and more experienced intelligence than my own: it had already traversed regions that still lay before me. But I do not believe that he shaped any of my opinions; I was too old and too independent to accept other people's ideas about phenomena that I could easily observe for myself.

Sometimes Borodin was able to disentangle a principle from the confusion of external events and show it to me; sometimes he was able to point out a historical direction or a prevailing tendency. He was concerned with the truth and his object in conversation was to extract and demonstrate it. If, therefore, I found every conversation with him illuminating, and approached, in the end, more nearly to his view of the Chinese Revolution than to any other, it was not because of any personal influence he exercised, but because the truth, for me, lay on his side.

Hankow, then—to sum up—was a marvellous revolutionary spectacle, in which the courage and devotion of the Chinese agitators, the skill of the Russians, the high hope and frenzied determination of the workers, and the individual splendour of characters like those of Borodin and Rayna Prohme, combined to give me a glimpse into a new world.

That the dead bones of economics and sociology could be animated with such irresistible life was something I would never have believed six months before in Paris. But although this glimpse into the world of Lenin did supply an electrical thrill, and the characters of the spectacle aroused my sincerest admiration, I still did not surrender to their logic.

Rayna Prohme and I used to spend hours trying to get the fundamental question of revolution into its barest and simplest terms; but during the Hankow period I could not share their conviction that revolution is the best way to a controlled egalitarian economy.

The one indisputable thing was that something was desirable in a world of misrule; something that could bring order out of chaos had to be found if the human race was to justify its pretence of intelligence. But whether or not the desirable something was revolution did not seem to me susceptible of proof, and the revolutionary spectacles that moved me most deeply were still that and nothing more.

Desperation in Hankow

The fall of Hankow was to determine the conduct of the Communist International for years afterwards; it was to turn the mind of the Russian Soviet government away from the militant internationalism of Trotzky to the national socialism of Stalin; it was to drive the genuinely subversive or revolutionary forces in China underground for a desperate struggle that has not yet fully come to the surface; it was to chasten the impatience of Communists all over the world more than any single event since 1917.

In view of these proved results, most of which I could obscurely foresee (with the help of Borodin) before the event had taken place, I was determined to cling to Hankow to the last possible moment, to see the drama played out, to be in at the death.

When the situation in Hankow looked desperate, I urged Rayna Prohme to take refuge in the American Consulate, and asked Mme. Sun Yat-sen if she did not think this wise. Mme. Sun, speaking with sudden gravity, said that she agreed with me; that the capture of Hankow would be a terrible event in which only those under the protection of the foreign guns would be safe; and that Mrs. Prohme had already done enough for the Chinese Revolution without dying for it.

Then, suddenly, the conversation took a gruesome turn. Mme. Sun began it by speaking of the tortures to which the twenty Communists had been subjected in Peking. She explained the difference between garroting and plain strangling, named a number of the more agonizing torments in use among the Chinese reactionaries, and discussed the relative merits of the various forms of execution from the point of view of the executed. Although she seemed a little nervous and was conscious that the dangers she discussed were only a few hours away, I do not believe she was primarily thinking of herself; she was indirectly attempting to persuade Rayna Prohme to go to the American Consulate for the night.

BUT Rayna Prohme dismissed the whole subject with a plain no. Her husband was at home, seriously ill; she had no desire to make a contrite pilgrimage to the consulate; she very nearly agreed with the navy people, who used to say that people who worked for the Chinese Revolution had no right to expect American protection. And that was that.

I made up my mind to a course of action that would force her to be rescued if the city fell. At the first shot, I was going to ask the Prohmes to go to the consulate. If they refused, I intended to demand a naval detachment to remove them to the consulate.

The necessity did not arise, and in a few days I was ashamed of my truculence. But the might-have-been of this incident reveals the strength of sympathy that already attached me to the red-haired revolutionist from Illinois.

On July 15, 1927, Tang Seng-chi, proclaimed the expected counter-revolution; Borodin, Mme. Sun Yat-sen, the Prohmes and the rest scattered in flight, escaping in various disguises and under various names from the vengeance of the war lords. I did not see them again for many weeks, and not the least of my troubles was the constant speculation as to what had become of them.

At Harbin I recorded the feeling in my journal with a sweeping comment "Five months in China and everything I thought worth a damn has gone to pot: depressing experience."

That Moment of Blinding Significance

THE Trans-Siberian journey is at best monotonous and exhausting. It takes the traveller over a country so flat, limitless and dreary that one day seems exactly like another, and by the time we reached Moscow I felt that I had been on the train most of my life. We arrived in Moscow twenty-four hours late. The journey from Harbin had taken nine full days.

I found out where the Chinese were staying and went to the Metropole. There, just as I reached the top of the marble steps and was about to ask the hall porter for information, I saw Rayna Prohme coming towards me.

For six weeks I had imagined her dead, torn to pieces by a mob, broken and sunk in the mud of the Yangtze-kiang or buried obscurely, after days of torture, in some dreary and forgotten Chinese field. These morbid fancies had alternated with others in which I imagined meeting her again, but it had never been wholly credible to me that I might find her, alive and well, by the mere effort of going to Moscow. And yet here she was, coming swiftly across the hall, laughing, hands stretched out, her eyes alight beneath the conflagration of her hair.

HERE I must state, as clearly as possible, the nature of our relationship then and afterwards. It was not a sexual relationship—at least, not as the phrase is currently understood. I shall not attempt to explain the mystery of an all-pervading, all-controlling emotion that had no physical basis, but it existed. If these words fall under the eyes of a reader who cannot believe such a thing possible, he had better stop reading at once, for it will be assumed from here onward that the fact is plain.

Between July 15th and September 18th, when I went up the steps of the Metropole in Moscow, a profound change had taken place in the texture and organization of my mind with respect to all the subjects brought together in this chapter, and, in a wider sense, to the subjects considered in this book.

When I saw her coming towards me the process was already completed, but it needed that moment of blinding significance to become irrevocable. From then on it was impossible to seek the relationships that seemed necessary to life (a relationship of one to many, a place in the chain of cause and effect) without reference to this solar phenomenon, this focus of reality for which the only solid expression was a slip of a girl with red hair. The issues that converged for me upon her fiery head were the most serious any human being has to face, and they converged there, most of all, because she had faced them first.

If this was love it resolved into the largest terms of which such personal emotions are capable, related to the whole life of mankind and the eternal effort of the human spirit to find its own place in the universe.

She came across the hall; I turned and met her, and we both laughed.

"I knew you'd turn up," she said.

Torturing Premonitions

THROUGHOUT that day and for the days that followed I was beset by indefinite and torturing premonitions. They were not correct (what premonitions are?), but they were near enough to what did happen to assume—even at this distance in time—an awful significance. I engaged in a desperate struggle, from that day onward, to keep Rayna from joining the Communist party.

Of all the contradictions of the period, this was perhaps the worst. The center towards which I was magnetized, the focus of the world as I saw it, was Rayna Prohme as revolutionary: it was not revolution alone, and it was not Rayna Prohme alone, but Rayna Prohme integrated and set alight by her conviction.

This was, in fact, my reason for being in Moscow. And yet from the moment I arrived I fought tooth and nail to get her away from her own essential center—to recall her, by whatever means, to the half world in which I wanted to keep on living.

No decision in life could be more final. The vows of a nun, the oaths of matrimony, the resolutions of a soldier giving battle, had not the irrevocable character of this decision. Rayna was not taking it lightly; she had had four years of intimate acquaintance with revolutionary work and she knew what she was doing.

For days the struggle continued with hardly a respite. We neither of us got much sleep, but I was as strong as an ox and did not realize what a terrible strain the whole thing was on her nervous system. No matter how bitterly I may have regretted all this afterwards, it is the fact. When her physical fragility impressed me more than usual, I used it, too, as an argument. She had been having severe headaches for months, and they had lately grown more frequent; aspirin and phenacetin did not help them.

I used to ask her how she proposed to endure the rigours of life as an active revolutionary when her physical resources were so limited. This argument had no effect. She would laugh and say: "In or out of a revolution, I've got to die sometime, and what does it matter?"

O N FRIDAY, November 11th, we argued, almost all night long. It was the last argument. At the end of it, when every element in the problem, personal and general, had been gone over a thousand times, Rayna's resolution was still unshaken. She was to go to the Lenin Institute the following Monday and I was going to leave Moscow as soon as I could do so.

But I wanted one "bourgeois evening" for myself, for the sheer pleasure of it, and to see her once more in a gold dress; but it is possible that I also hoped (madness of course) that silk and flowers, music and white wine from the south, might accomplish what I had failed to do, and bring her back a little way towards the world she had been born into and was now surrendering forever.

We went to the Bolshaya Moskovskaya and had our bourgeois evening. We even danced—twice. Dorothy Thompson came and sat with us, and I told her what was happening. She seemed a little startled and incredulous.

"You understand what it is?" I said. "It's the end of Rayna Prohme. No more Rayna. Finished. Revolutionary Instrument Number 257,849."

The truth of what I was saying was too much to bear quietly just then, and I turned towards Rayna and pounded her thin shoulders.

"The end of Rayna Prohme," I said. "The end of Rayna Prohme."

"The end of Rayna Prohme." That night seemed as final as death itself.

Flame to Ashes

I SLEPT late the next day and walked slowly across to the Metropole in the afternoon to see if Rayna was there. As I came up the steps of the hotel just where I had met Rayna on that evening almost exactly two months before I ran into Anna Louise Strong.

"Mrs. Prohme is very ill," she said in a flat, emotionless voice.

We moved Rayna to a room of her own that day. She refused to have a professional nurse or to go to the Kremlin, and Anna Louise Strong and Sonya Vep agreed to take care of her by turns. The only thing I was good for was sitting in the room, and even this (when Rayna was asleep and the room was quite dark) almost drove me mad.

I was dazed with horror and felt nothing. I came and went; walked in the Red Square; went to the Bolshaya Mos-

kovskaya and drank vodka; returned to the Metropole from time to time to speak to Sonya. One night Rayna woke up and asked Sonya for me, but I was across the square. When I reached the room she was unconscious again.

At seven o'clock the next morning the telephone in my room rang. Anna Louise's voice:

"You'd better come," it said. "Rayna is dead."

R AYNA PROHME died on Monday, November 21, 1927, and was cremated on the following Thursday. I left Moscow the day after the funeral and have not been there since.

An autopsy held on November 22nd by a group of Moscow professors revealed something that did not surprise me: Rayna had died of inflammation of the brain. It must have begun many months before, and all through this time she had been exactly, literally turning to ashes, just as the shell she had discarded was to be burned to ashes at the crematorium. No human being could so irresistibly suggest the quality of flame without being consumed for it.

On the afternoon of the funeral we all marched for hours across Moscow to the new crematorium. The bier, draped in the Red flag and covered with golden flowers, asters, chrysanthemums, all the flowers of Rayna's own colors, a heap of gold and red and brown, was placed on the platform. There were speeches in Chinese, Russian and English—revolutionary speeches. The English sounded just as meaningless as the Chinese as the Russian. Then a signal was given, a switch was turned, and the golden mass of Rayna, her hair and her bright flowers and the Red flag, sank slowly before us into the furnace.

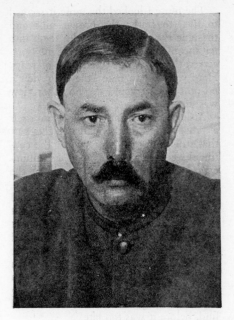

MICHAEL BORODIN
International News Photos

THAT night Borodin came to see me. He had come to say good-bye, he said, and to explain why he had not gone to the funeral. On principle he never went to funerals.

His voice was deeply moved, and he controlled it with difficulty. He did not look at me, but walked from the window to the door and back again.

"I know what this is," he said. "I know exactly. But what is needed is the long view. I have come here to ask you to take the long view—China, Russia . . . A wonderful friend and a wonderful revolutionary instrument have disappeared together. But there is no use in anything unless we take the long view. Remember that. China, Russia . . ."

After a while he shook hands and went away. In the morning I took the train to Berlin.

The Long View

IT is possible to take "the long view," if at all, only by finding a point in time from which events can seem ordered. "The long view" demands more mastery of the materials of an existence, more control of their significance, than I possessed.

At this time I wanted no view at all. I wanted to be submerged again into a life as ordinary as night and day, as familiar as bread and butter, as undramatic as the telephone book. If I never saw beyond the details it could not matter much, I thought. Above all, I did not want to come near the awful alternatives again—the alternatives that seemed to me bound up in the ideas of China and Russia, Revolution, Rayna Prohme.

It was only after two hectic years that I knew Rayna Prohme had conquered. I think I knew it on the Acropolis where I had one moment of extraordinarily sensitized vision. From then on the events of the previous months tended to take their proper shape and proportion. It was the moment in which I saw, for the first time, the entasis of the columns at the corner of the Parthenon.

The more I looked the more it seemed to live, to frame the brown hills and the blue sky, to compose with them into an incomparable perfection of life preserved through cycle upon cycle of years. Here you had to take "the long view"; no other view would do, no other view was possible.

Although duration was not in itself a proof of good, the parts of the past that still expressed most vividly the continuous consciousness of man, communicating in a language understood of the people for century after century, were, like this strange marvel, the best and not the worst parts. And you had to get it in; no view of the world that left it out could be clear or complete; you had to take the age of Pericles with the age of Wall Street, and capitalist imperialism along with Athene and her temple; you had, somehow, to see the whole thing if you could, by whatever light you could find, before it was too late.

It was just as clear now as it had been in the long Moscow argument that I was not a revolutionary, would never be a revolutionary. But how did that affect the long view? I went back in two jumps to my argument with Rayna Prohme, resumed it where it had left off, and was vanquished.

"Of course, you fool! Of course! What else did you expect. You can't go tinkering away with parts of a rotten old machine. You've got to get a new one. The immediate job is to get rid of the present arrangement and contrive a more satisfactory one, without these nation-race-religion tags to help the functioning of capital and empire.

"Who ever told you you had to be a revolutionary? Everybody isn't born with an obligation to act. There are some people who can't act, who go to pieces under action, who can only think straight when they have plenty of time and no noise. But if you see it straight, that's the thing: see what's happening, has happened, will happen—and if you ever manage to do a stroke of work in your life, make it fit in. That's all you have to do."

"That sounds slow and painful. Or else does it mean doing nothing? They also serve who only stand and wait. Is that it?"

"You could do worse. You're no good in journalism or politics or any kind of social action unless you can keep your head above water, see where you're going, where you've been and where everybody else is. Standing and waiting is better, if you are in the right place. Find it and stick to it: a solid place, with a view."

"Easy to say!"

"Well, nothing's easy to do, if you come to that. It won't be easy, but if you don't try you're done for. If you want to relate your own life to its time and space, the particular to the general, the part to the whole, the only way you can do it is by understanding the struggle in its world terms, not in terms of small fanaticisms and minor hatreds.

"The Jewish problem is important, but Zionism isn't. And important as the Jewish problem is, it's only one of the complications in the whole system of organized injustice by which few govern many, hundreds of millions work in darkness to support a few thousands in ease, group imposes on group, one nation oppresses another, and the greater part of the human race has to live in filth and starvation to maintain an artificial system of profit. If you can't fight that— and that's a personal thing—you must at least see it.

"The obligation upon you will be just this: to see things as straight as you can and put them into words that won't falsify them. That's programme enough for one life, and if you can ever do it, you'll have acquired the relationship you want between the one life you've got and the many of which it's a part."

"Harsh words."

"True words. O.K.?"

"O.K."

QUINCY WRIGHT

THE CAUSES OF WAR AND THE CONDITIONS OF PEACE

THIS is a synthesis of thirty studies made by the Departments of Political Science, Economics, History, Sociology, Anthropology, Geography and Psychology at the University of Chicago. Quincy Wright, one of the best known authorities on international law, was chairman of the inquiry, the findings of which he first released in the form of lectures to the Graduate Institute of International Studies at Geneva, Switzerland in 1934. The final report will shortly be published by the University of Chicago Press.

Background of War

CIVILIZATION was invented something over five thousand years ago, perhaps in the Near East, perhaps independently in three places, China and Mexico, as well as the Near East. A written language permitting of the storage of ideas and of communication at a distance was its essence.

From these the possibility of organization larger than the primary group developed. War was certainly a major instrument in the formation of these larger communities, both to impose governors upon the reluctant governed, to expand the area and population under the governors, to defend it from similar attacks by others and to maintain a sense of unity in the community.

As civilization progressed war tended to play an increasing role in society. Its function as a population eliminator probably tended to increase, although until recent times it has never been as important in this connection as pestilence, famine and the practices of religious celibacy and postponed marriage.

The cumulative effect of these tendencies of the great civilizations to expand and of these periodic invasions was to create a realization of the dependence of each community upon a larger world, continually urging a political organization, either by conquest or federation, capable of maintaining order and permitting peaceful intercourse throughout this wider area.

This tendency could be extended to the entire world after the age of discovery less than five centuries ago. The epoch, since this age was initiated by the invention of printing in the west, has witnessed the discovery, exploration and mapping of all parts of the world by Europeans; the rise of experimental science, liberalism and pragmatic philosophy; the development of world trade and geographical division of labor; the invention of steam and electric communication, transportation and power devices and their utilization by peoples in all parts of the world. These changes have brought a rapid increase in the human population, a development of continuous contact between all of its branches and an increasing economic, political and cultural interdependence of widely separated human groups. The human race has, during this period, tended toward greater uniformity and greater unification.

Great improvements in technology and sanitation, the opening of new areas and the development of humanitarian ideologies have greatly reduced the importance of the methods of population elimination. The new check of birth control promises to be the main equilibrating device.

Birth control has already produced population stability in many areas.

War Today Is Different

WAR has continued to occupy a dominant role as a means of preserving the ruling class, the consciousness of national unity, and the balance of power. It has also been an important means of expanding the influence of the principal centers of world civilization over the more backward areas. These functions of war of preserving social solidarity under the existing status quo and of augmenting the influence, power and prestige of the state in the world community have been continuous. They differ little from the function of war among earlier cultures. The significant change has been in the techniques and ideologies of war.

The invention of explosives and later of chemical war, the invention of improved ships and the possibility of general commercial blockade as certain states have become dependent upon overseas trade, the application of steam, electric and gasoline power both in land and in naval military movements, and lastly the invention of aerial and submarine transportation and the greatly increased possibility of bombing civilian centers and destroying merchant commerce—these inventions taken together have made war a more effective instrument of policy when utilized by the industrialized against the non-industrialized states.

But these inventions have made war a less effective instrument of policy between equally industrialized states because their use has made it more likely that a war can only end in losses to both belligerents beyond any possibility of gain to either. In short, a quick decision and a relatively cheap victory is improbable.

The integration of war and preparation for war with business, as war has become more capitalized and as the professional class permanently devoted to it has increased, has assured powerful opposition to its reduction. The changes in its techniques have tended to make its incidence progressively more destructive, both absolutely and relatively to the population, both in military and civil life and in economic disorganization.

Let us consider some of the variations and trends of modern wars in greater detail.

Trends in Modern War

COUNTRIES differ greatly in the frequency with which they have been at war. Since the beginning of the Seventeenth Century there have been about 2300 battles among the European states. In these 2300 battles, France participated in 49 percent; Great Britain and Russia each in 23 percent; Turkey in 15 percent; Spain and The Netherlands each in 11 percent, Sweden in four percent and Denmark in one percent. These percentages are for the whole period of three centuries.

If we tabulate by fifty year periods, it appears that the percentage of participation by France, Austria, Great Britain and Turkey has been constant, that by Prussia and Russia has tended to increase and that by The Netherlands, Sweden and Denmark has decreased to almost nothing in the last century. Clearly the great powers are the great fighters.

We also find that the normal duration of war has been a period of four or five years. Of course, many wars have been shorter because of the defeat of one side. It is also true that wars have sometimes lasted longer than that—we have a Hundred Years War, a Thirty Years War and a Seven Years War,—but if one studies these wars he finds that it is very unusual for a continuous series of campaigns to go on for more than four or five years. These long wars were actually broken by long truces, or vigorous fighting was not carried on at one or both ends of the legal war period.

The typical war, where belligerents are fairly equally balanced, is likely to last for four or five years as did the

American Civil War and the World War. Perhaps four or five years of the strain of war is as much as people organized in the modern state can stand without resting. Signs of break in internal morale are almost certain to appear in one or both of the belligerents after that period.

Let us now consider the general trend in war techniques through the ages. First it seems clear that the size of armies has tended to increase, both absolutely and in proportion to the population.

In the earlier historic periods of each civilization, war had been carried on by a few chieftains with their retainers. Homer's epic of the siege of Troy illustrates this type of army. The oriental empires of Egypt, Babylonia and Assyria beginning with armies of this type, in the course of their history developed large professional armies.

Proceeding through the variations in-

dicated, the Roman army increased in size under the republic reaching a maximum in the early empire of a standing army of approximately 300,000, or about three in each thousand of the population.

Compared to this, armies were small in the Middle Ages, although after the time of Charlemagne, the size of the feudal army increased in all of the countries. At the height of the Middle Ages the proportion of men under arms to the population may have been almost as great as during the Roman Empire, although, of course, this force was distributed among many small states.

Since then there has been a steady rise in the size of armies, absolutely and relatively. In the Eighteenth Century, Marlborough and Frederick the Great had armies of eighty or ninety thousand men. In the Napoleonic period, France had at times as many as two hundred thousand men under arms or ten in each thousand of her population. But during

CONDITIONS IN THE THIRTY YEARS' WAR
Nothing was safe in a country overrun by mercenary troops. Churches were despoiled of their treasures and burnt; cottages were stripped of bedding and clothes and then set on fire; all the livestock was driven off and the least attempt at resistance on the part of the unfortunate villagers was repaid by murder. Pity was an emotion unknown among these hireling troops.
From Callot, "Les misères et les mal-heurs de la guerre," 1633

the World War the belligerents kept the unprecedent proportion of 100 in each thousand or ten percent of their population in the armed forces,—almost ten times as large a proportion as during the Napoleonic period.

Thus, while there have been ups and downs, there has been a trend toward an increase in the absolute and relative size of armies, whether one considers the peace army or the number of persons engaged in battle.

More Peace but More Battles

ANOTHER general trend is the decline in the length of wars and in the proportion of war years to peace years. The data is inadequate to estimate this in early times but there is not much doubt that Greece and Rome were at war a larger proportion of the time than are modern nations. In the Middle Ages Europe was broken up into many fighting groups and small wars were continuous. Important wars occupied a larger proportion of the centuries than during the Roman Empire, but probably less than in Greece or the Roman Republic.

Coming to modern times, we have more accurate statistics. In the Seventeenth Century the great European states were formally at war about 75 percent of the time. In the Eighteenth Century about 50 percent and in the Nineteenth Century about 25 percent of the time. This refers only to legal war.

If we counted the expeditions into America, Asia and Africa against people with inferior war techniques then most of the great powers have been fighting a large proportion of the time, even in the last century. Even the United States

which has perhaps somewhat unjustifiably prided itself on its peacefulness has had only twenty years during its entire history of 158 years when it has not had the army or navy in active operations during some days, somewhere.

ANOTHER trend is an increase in the length of battles, in the number of battles in a war year, and also in the total number of battles during a century. During the Hundred Years War there was only about one battle of importance every ten years. There were, of course, more sieges. In the Seventeenth Century there were about four battles in a war year, in the Eighteenth Century about fifteen, in the Nineteenth Century something like twenty-eight and in the Twentieth Century over fifty.

Although the number of war years has declined, yet the number of battles per war year has increased so much more rapidly, that the total number of battles fought in a century has tended to increase. There have already (1934) been about six hundred battles in the Twentieth Century and it is only a third over. The intensity of war has increased.

More People are Killed

THE cost of war between advanced states both absolutely and relatively to the population has also been greatly increased. This is an exceedingly difficult problem to get data upon. The proportion of persons killed in battle to those engaged has undoubtedly declined. During the Middle Ages, thirty to fifty percent of those engaged in a battle would often be killed. In the Seventeenth Century, forty percent of the defeated side would be killed and about ten percent of the victors. The latter cut down the

defeated enemy as it ran away. Thus at the beginning of the modern period, the average losses in battle were probably about twenty percent of those engaged. In the Eighteenth Century only about ten percent. In the Nineteenth Century the proportion was about the same and in the Twentieth Century about six percent.

The proportion of the population engaged in the armies, however, kept getting bigger and the number of battles also increased. As a result, *the propor-*

tion of the population killed in war has tended to increase. I estimate that of one thousand of the French population who died in the Seventeenth Century, eleven were killed in battle or died of wounds. The corresponding figure for the Eighteenth Century is twenty-seven, for the Nineteenth, thirty, and for the Twentieth Century, sixty-three.

The civilian population used to suffer from the direct ravages of war more than it does now. Air raids are sufficiently serious but during the World War, they did not slaughter as many of the civilian population as in the days when sieges would sometimes result in the slaughter of all of the inhabitants of the fortified place.

War always results in serious losses in the civilian population from decline in the birth rate and this is probably increased because of the increased proportion of the population engaged in war. Death rates reached absolute maxima and birth rates reached absolute minima in most of the belligerent countries during the World War.

In the past, wars have assisted in spreading epidemics. Whether the superior preventive medicine of modern times has decreased these losses is difficult to say. It has been estimated that during the World War in Europe these indirect losses of population were as great as the direct losses. Each was about ten million. Outside of Europe, the indirect losses were much greater because of the ravages of influenza in Asia and America. The world losses during the World War from military action and war-distributed disease have been estimated as over forty million.

War Costs More

WHILE it is difficult to be certain of these generalities in regard to the losses of population, there is little disagreement respecting the increasing economic cost of war, in direct burdens on the government and indirect losses from maldirection of productive forces. War has become so thoroughly capitalized that it is necessary to mobilize the entire resources of the country. Debts of astronomical magnitude are incurred so great that they cannot be paid. The resulting default and the readjustments necessary because of the malapplications of capital during the war bring depressions long after the war. From the standpoint of the loss of human life and the loss of economic wealth, the trend of war has been toward *greater cost, both absolutely and proportionately.*

Two other trends may be mentioned briefly. It appears that the role of strictly military operations in war has tended to decrease. Wars were formerly won through military operations in the field. Now states may fail to win the war even though they win most of the battles. Economic strength and propaganda strength have increased in relative importance. While it is still true that military power is important, it is relatively less important in the winning of war than formerly.

Finally it appears that while the social significance of war has increased, the role of war as an instrument of world politics has tended to decline. Apart from the underlying social function of maintaining the symbols and authority necessary for internal social solidarity, wars have been fought in the past with the immediate object to get booty, to get women, to get land, to control territory. In fact in the history of war, the control of territory has been the main direct objective.

BUT in modern times, the economic object of states is rather to get markets or access to raw materials in territory that remains foreign. Apart from trade in war materials for conducting the war itself, it is difficult to promote trade by hostilities or threats. The fine adjustments of normal international trade and finance are certain to be adversely affected by war. War as an instrument of *rational world politics* has declined.

We are confronted by a paradox. The size of armies, the number of battles, the human and economic expenditures for war are on the increase. The frequency of war, the grand tactical value of military operations and the political role of war are on the decline. As military operations have become more concentrated with longer gaps of peace between, we have cycles of increasing amplitude.

War has become a partially controlled institution, the temporal consequence of which cannot be predicted, but which might be more completely controlled through the application of known political and mechanical techniques. More and more we must consider it from the engineering, constructive and control point of view. Thus the causes of war are less interesting than the conditions of peace.

The Conditions of Peace

THE important conditions of peace certainly include a desire for peace in the human population superior to all hatreds. This involves a renunciation of uncompromising opposition to existing human opinions, to existing material conditions, to the existing state of law and to the existing social institutions, however much these may oppress certain sections of the population. I do not say, however, that it involves a renunciation of a restrained and conciliatory opposition to these things.

Another of the conditions of peace is an organization of the world community adequate to restrain conflicts. We cannot anticipate that human beings or states will renounce opposition to the status quo and plans of reform to such an extent that conflicts will not occur. Consequently controls must be prepared to deal with conflicts so that violence will not accompany them. This involves procedures for moderating extreme opinions, for establishing respect for law, for maintaining a certain balance of material forces and for adapting the organization of the world community itself to new inventions and discoveries.

A THIRD condition of peace is the realization in international relations of a system of law intolerant of violence except as a legally controlled instrument of execution. *While the use of force under authority of the society as a whole to prevent or remedy illegal acts by its members is consistent with a regime of law, the use of violence to change the law is not. Statesmen or jurists who tolerate war as a necessary instrument of legislation in the society of nations, are in fact denying the existence of international law altogether.* A workable system of international law must provide an accurate analysis of the actual interests of the states which use violence and rules which would maximize the satisfaction of those interests. Procedures must be provided to minimize departures from law in particular instances as well as peaceful procedures to assure modification of rules which no longer conform to actual interests.

Finally, the conditions of peace include the continuous application of peaceful techniques for preventing extreme departures from equilibrium among the material forces in the state system.

I have presented these somewhat pedantic propositions to indicate that I regard our problem as approachable from four directions: 1) armaments and the balance of power; 2) international and constitutional law; 3) international organization and procedure; 4) public opinion and propaganda. Before taking these up separately, however, I want to express my conviction that they are all inter-related and that the progress made in one will be barren, perhaps even harmful, for peace, unless progress is made contemporaneously in the others. The maintenance of peace and the prevention of war require us to work on many fronts at the same time.

Sweet are the Uses of Disarmament

WE HAVE usually had disarmament movements after great wars, when countries were nearly bankrupt and wished to save money. After the Napoleonic Wars such a movement was led by Tsar Alexander of Russia. At a later time, when armament rivalry was becoming very intense, toward the end of the nineteenth century, another Tsar of Russia was advised by his Minister of Finance that his exchequer could not stand the strain of maintaining competition with Austria in making big guns and consequently Tsar Nicholas called the first Hague Conference in 1899. Since the World War the same motivation often has been evident, a desire to save money. However, although financial considerations have been important, it has also generally been assumed that important political results might be achieved from disarmament.

It is often said that disarmament can not affect the frequency of war because people will fight—with fists or with clubs if they are denied superior weapons. That undoubtedly is true. Wars may develop between disarmed people, but that, I think, does not prove that they might not be less frequent or less destructive.

Undoubtedly the character of armaments will affect the frequency of war. If armaments are of such character that both countries are pretty sure to destroy each other, they will be less likely to go to war than if they are of a character so that each of them feels it has a chance, with comparatively slight expense, to win a victory.

IT HAS also been said that disarmament arrangements can be of no value because they will be violated. Nations at war, it is assumed, will not pay any attention to bits of paper. There is a certain amount of truth in this. Doubtless if two countries go to war they will start to build armaments as rapidly as they can without attention to the treaty.

But the production lag is a good deal greater than is sometimes supposed. For instance, although the United States had been preparing for war for a year prior to entry into the World War in 1917, and although after that date it stepped up all military production processes to the utmost, yet it was over a year after the United States got into the war before much military equipment other than explosives began to get to the field in France from the United States.

Of course the sanctioning value of a "production lag" depends upon the efficiency of the peace time international inspection. The treaty must provide for such a body to visit periodically all the countries bound, and thus assure that any violation will immediately become known.

I think it is fair to say that successful disarmament treaties have always been accompanied by political arrangements which were believed by the parties to augment their political security or to settle outstanding political problems. Considering the conditions of successful negotiations, I think we must tackle and settle political problems first before we can make much progress on the technical problem of disarmament.

Society's Intellect and Will

I HAVE referred to an adequate system of law and an adequate organization as a condition of peace. Law and organization are clearly related. In a peaceful society law is clear and regularly enforced. Institutions and authorities act smoothly and efficiently to give effect to its policy. We might say that law is

society's intellect and organization is its will.

In the general history of the elimination of violence in private law, whether it is in the relations of individuals within the state or in the violence of the state itself, internally or externally, the process is a very slow one. The extraor-

LEAGUE OF NATIONS PALACE, GENEVA

dinary thing is the number of centuries in which types of violence have persisted after they have seemed to be logically inconsistent with the general theory that the state should monopolize violence. For instance dueling was not abolished in the British army until 1843 and it is still entirely legal in Germany.

IT is only since the World War that there has been an extraordinary effort to develop international law not only in the direction of ameliorating war but abolishing it. We have in two great instruments, the League of Nations Covenant and the Pact of Paris, provisions which so far as the states of the world are concerned do render resort to war in the first instance illegal. The only justification for secondary belligerents, that is for states fighting a state which is already at war, is self-defense and sanction, that is warring against a state which has already gone to war illegally.

As law must be hostile to violence, so organization must restrain internal conflict. Parliaments, administrative and conciliatory bodies, as well as courts, are used in all states so that all conflicts may be settled before they can disrupt the state or degenerate into violence. The same processes can be observed in the community of nations.

It appears that the direction of the development of the state system has been in the direction of more integration during the past three centuries. Certainly there has tended to be a greater amount of international communication—postal communication, telegraph and radio,

news, travel, education—have all of them increased particularly during the past century, and during the past twenty years more than ever.

There has also been a steady progress of international organization. Three centuries ago an unorganized diplomatic service and the consular service were the only regular instruments of international communication. We now have fifty or so public international unions. We have the League of Nations, the World Court, the International Labor Organization and we have a multitude of unofficial or semi-official conferences and organizations meeting continuously.

IT has been well said that a League of Nations cannot be very much more moral than its members. If the states are to become good League members, they must change some of their methods and some of their objectives. It is the function of the League to convince the states that they can accomplish most of their objectives by peaceful means through the League machinery and that other objectives which cannot be accomplished through these methods are not worth accomplishing at all. Whether the League can bring about that reorientation in the concept of sovereignty within the states is doubtless one of the things upon which its future most depends.

Sovereignty must be conceived not as the ultimate source of all rights, powers, duties and liabilities, but only as the source of such rights, powers, duties and liabilities as belong to persons within the sovereign's jurisdiction under the international law. This development of theory must be not merely formal but a consequence of the recognition of the dominant interest of states, and of the population which they represent, in the preservation of peace.

I think we must recognize that the substitution of a means of peaceful change is the only way in which war can permanently be prevented. If sanctions, whether moral, political, economic or military, attempt merely to perpetuate any legal status quo, which will inevitably in time come to be out of harmony with the existing political and economic facts of the world, violence cannot be prevented.

Thus the central problem seems to be a problem greater than that of sanctions: the problem of devising means, whereby change can be effected through peaceful methods. It is to be noticed that universalization of the League would in itself increase the possibilities of peaceful change because in any instance the opinion of states distant from the scene of a particular controversy and less interested in a particular status quo than in the preservation of peace would be an important peaceful influence.

Peace Preserved by Propaganda

WE NOW come to the fourth picture in which the world appears as a population of human individuals, each behaving according to his heredity and experience, as a result of which the population has spread over most of the world.

A modern war must be supported by the masses of the belligerent populations. Weather maps for indicating the changing attitudes of the world's populations might indicate where peace education and propaganda are most needed at a given time. Statesmen are, of course, aware of this and rough estimates of the high and low pressure areas of opinion are the bases upon which they operate.

As wars are made by propaganda, so peace may be preserved by propaganda, but the latter is more difficult because conflict is intrinsically interesting to human beings. On hearing of a conflict situation, we instinctively prick up our ears. In spite of all the peace propagandists' attempts to objectify peace as a particular religion, as international law, as arbitration, as disarmament, as the League of Nations, the public still finds it uninteresting.

ON THE other hand, the speed with which war spreads, especially among the great powers, indicates the interest in war as well as the working of the balance of power. I find that in only three of the fourteen war periods of the last three centuries which have envolved one or more great powers on each side and lasted more than two years, did a single great power avoid being drawn into war. If a great power war breaks out we may expect all the great powers to get in unless the war ends very rapidly.

A belligerent disposition naturally evolves from continuous whetting of the natural war interest. Interest gives familiarity and familiarity gradually brings acceptance. An American population with a tradition of neutrality rapidly became war-minded and eventually a belligerent in both the Napoleonic and the World War periods. The evolution of this belligerency has been traced in detail through studies of the American press during neutrality periods. These studies indicate a gradual shift from objective war stories to stories relating the war to the United States, then as the actual crises involving American interests developed, to an emotional appeal.

The problem of peace propaganda is therefore difficult intrinsically. Some of the methods which have been used are of doubtful expediency. It is, for example, questionable whether emphasis upon the horrors of war creates an attitude favorable to peace. It may instead stimulate an interest in war. A diversion of opinion from the war-like possibilities of pending controversies to other positive interests which would be frustrated by the war may be a more hopeful course for the peace propagandists.

The type of personality ideal prevalent in the community is doubtless of great importance with respect to the development of war attitudes. Quakers and followers of Gandhi have resisted the appeal to violence because of such ideals. But their creeds, obviously, have not been indorsed by the bulk of mankind.

A LARGER proportion of the human race has believed in the rational man guided by enlightened self-interest and subject to passive social regulation. Enlightened self-interest, it is thought, will lead men to abide by contracts and laws if those laws do not go beyond the constitution of the laissez faire state, and self-interest may also if properly construed lead governments to abide by treaties and international law.

Others have believed in the authoritarian state to which the individual is blindly obedient and others in the superman emerging from an unlimited struggle for existence. General acceptance of either of these ideals renders the cause of peace desperate.

Even if the charm, utility and social function of war could be eliminated, war would still recur so long as people devote major attention to preparing for it. If statesmen generally should abandon hope that war may prove a means for

solving their problems, belief in the inevitability of war might be undermined. The expectation of war has been a cause of war.

The attitude conducive to peace is neither that of the ostrich which denies the possibility of war, not that of the cynic which considers war inevitable, but that of the rational man which perceives that war may come, but that its initiation at any time is not inevitable, and that human effort can always, with adequate foresight, do much to prevent its occurrence.

I N CONCLUSION, let me emphasize the value of a central organization with wide powers of communication for education, especially for peace education, which to be effective must be world wide. The maintenance of suitable opinion no less than the maintenance of the balance of power, the development of law and the settlement of controversies in the world community are functions of the League of Nations.

If it has not always been successful in keeping the peace, we may ask whether any state was more successful in keeping the peace over a more limited area during its first twenty years. With a universal membership which the League may some time attain, as time is measured in world history, we may be confident that the League will develop the world trend toward unity and integration before the increasingly destructive periods of war have ruined our civilization.

MAN

Man, proud man,
Dressed in a little brief authority,
Most ignorant of what he's most assured,
His glassy essence, like an angry ape,
Plays such fantastic tricks before high heaven
As make the angels weep; who, with our spleens,
Would all themselves laugh mortal.

—*William Shakespeare* (1564-1616).

OLIVER LA FARGE

LAUGHING BOY

"LAUGHING BOY," presented to you in this form, is a Pulitzer Prize novel. It was written by Oliver La Farge, who was born in New York City in 1901. Mr. La Farge was graduated from Harvard University in 1924. He taught ethnology at Tulane University for three years, after which he made archaeological expeditions to Arizona, Mexico and Guatemala for Tulane, Harvard and Columbia. He is prominent in American Indian affairs and is president of the National Association on Indian Affairs. His whole background would lead him, naturally, to write such a novel as "Laughing Boy," a sympathetic treatment of a Navajo Indian. Of Mr. La Farge, Owen Wister says:

"To choose Navajo Indians as your material, to exclude the white man, save as the merest accidental accessory, to depend wholly on a young Navajo lover and his mate for your plot and your romantic appeal—and to bring it off—is a most uncommon feat. Familiarity with the Navajos, their customs, and their country, would not alone have sufficed to produce 'Laughing Boy,' A born artist, a skillful writer, and that gift of imagination which makes the reader know the characters and believe the events, these were also needed. The tale is haunting and poetic in an extraordinary degree. It's too good a book for the train, with conductors and newsboys breaking in upon the magic of its spell; let the reader take it to a corner in the garden, or a tree or canoe in a quiet place, or to his room when the rest of the house is asleep, and no telephone will disturb him." Mr. La Farge now lives in New York City.

One

A SMALL drum beating rapidy concentrated mixed noises into a staccato unison. Young men gathered about a drummer. They put their arms over each other's shoulders, swaying in time to the one drum that ran like a dull, glowing thread through the singing. A bonfire flared to the left of them. Opposite, and to the right, the older people sat wrapped in their blankets.

Girls in single file stole into the open space, moving quietly and aloof as though the uproar of singing were petrified into a protective wall before it reached them. They prowled back and forth before the line of young men, considering them with predatory judgment.

Laughing Boy at the back of the crowd looked at them with mild interest; he liked to watch their suave movements and the rich display of blankets and jewelry. One caught his attention; he thought she had on more silver, coral, turquoise, and white shell than he had ever seen on any one person. Her blue skirt swung with her short, calculated steps, ankle-length, above the dull red leggins and moccasins with silver buttons. Now she was looking at him.

"Ahalani!" she greeted him.

He stood for a moment in feigned stupidity. He did not want to dance. Suddenly he gave up. She led him around behind the men, not speaking to him. Out in the clear she put her hands on his belt. He pulled his blanket to his chin, masking enjoyment in a pose of contemptuous tolerance, like the other men dancing there.

"You have a fine horse to race, black, with a white star and a white sock." He grunted astonishment. She smiled. "You are a good jeweler, they say. You made that bow-guard. You sold a belt to the American, they say, for sixty-five dollars."

"You are like an old wife, trying to find out about everything a man is doing."

"No, I am not like an old wife."

He stared at the correct impassiveness of her face, at the same time noting delicately chiselled features, set of firm lips, long eyes that even with their lack of expression seemed to speak to him. No, she was not like an old wife. Blood pounded in his ears and his mouth was dry.

When the dance ended he swept his blanket round him with a magnificent gesture and stalked back to the singers.

"Who is that girl," he asked a brave beside him, "the one who has so much hard goods on?"

"She is called Slim Girl, I think," he said. "She is bad. She lives down by the railroad. She is not of the People any more; she is American. She does bad things for the Americans. I do not know how she came to be allowed to dance."

"I do not know what you mean. She is not bad. She is good. She is for me."

HE quit the dance, suddenly very much alone as he left the noise and the light behind him. He followed a sheep trail up a break in a cañon wall. Finally he came to a tiny pool of water surrounded by a square of soft turf with imprints of moccasins. He dabbled his hands, wet his face and drank a little. Then he began to make up a new song.

Now with a god I walk,
Now I step across the summits of mountains,
Now with a god I walk,
Striking across the foothills.
Now on the old age trail, now on the path
    of beauty wandering.
In beauty—*Hozoji, hozoji, hozoji, hozoji-i.*

"*Ahalani!*" The two-toned greeting came from a voice like water.

He returned to himself with a start, stopping his song in embarrassment. Slim Girl stood poised in the luminous darkness by the pool, water-basket in hand. She is a butterfly, he thought, or a hummingbird. I will not go—run away from her.

Slim Girl sat down beside him. They rested thus, without words, looking into the night while contemplation flowed between them like a current. He was restless, no longer on the path of beauty, yet tormented by a new beauty.

"My eldest uncle is here. I am going to speak to him tomorrow," he said.

"You are sure you are going to speak to your uncle?"

"Yes." The second self that is a detached mentor in one's mind recognized that he would never have talked this way with any other woman. Etiquette had been left behind down in the narrowness of Ane'é Tseyi. "But I have nothing to give your parents, only one horse."

"I have no parents; they died when I was in school. I belong to myself. All

OLIVER LA FARGE, native of New York City, makes frequent field trips to Central America, Mexico, and the Southwest. He is an authority on American Indians, and a serious student of "the wide open spaces."

She was brave, brave . . . Something snapped inside of him

Illustration for Oliver LaFarge's
'LAUGHING BOY"

this"—she raised the pieces of jewelry one by one—"is mine and much more. My parents left it for me. Now I do a little work for the missionary's wife at Chiziai; she pays me money, so I grow richer. I shall give you silver to make jewelry, and I shall weave, and you shall have fine horses. We shall be rich together."

The long talking eyes looked into his now, with nothing hidden. He felt her strength, this woman who could talk so straight, who made the direct road seem the only sensible one. It ceased to be strange that they sat and talked about love, while elopement became obvious and commonplace in a scheme of things which was suddenly miraculous.

Two

EARLY in the morning Laughing Boy went off with his horse to find pasture. When he was well away, she put on American clothes and began to trudge to Los Palos.

She did not intend to love any one; had she not learned enough of that? He was necessary to her; he was an axe with which to hew her way back to her people, to the good things of her people. Their children would be Navajo, all Navajo. This was her revenge, that all the efforts of all those very different Americans, to drag her up or to drag her down, in the end would be only tools to serve a Navajo end. But there must be money; the Americans must serve her a little while yet.

It began to be hot when she reached the wretched 'dobes on the outskirts of Los Palos. She stopped by a dome of sticks, old boxes, and bits of canvas. Yellow Singer crawled out into the sun, blinking red eyes.

"Hunh! What is it?"

"I am going to be married this afternoon. I want you to come and sing over us."

"Coyote!" He swore, and then in English, "God damn! What do you want to get married for? What kind of a man have you caught?"

"You talk too much; it may be bad for you some day. You come this afternoon and sing over us. Then you keep your mouth shut."

He read her face, remembering that her grandmother had been an Apache who, in her time, had sat contemplating the antics of men tied on ant-heaps. And he knew this woman pretty well.

"Good, Grandmother," he said respectfully, "we shall come."

She continued down the street until she came to the opposite side of the town where she entered a small, neat, 'dobe house. In a few minutes a man followed her inside, closing the door behind him.

"Well, you're back on time." He leant over to kiss her.

"Don't start dat now. I got to go back soon now. My husban', he makes trouble, dat one. I can' stay away right now. Soon maybe."

He heaved a sigh of exasperation. "I don't think you've got a husband."

"Yes, I have, an' he's a long-hair."

"Well, all right. Tomorrow, then." He kissed her finger-tips. "That's flat, and no two ways about it."

Three

TIME passing and corn growing cannot be seen; one can notice only that the moon has become so much older, the corn so much higher. With a new life, far more thrilling than the old, with a rich supply of silver and choice turquoise, with horses to trade and a cornfield to care for, and all the world made over new, time for Laughing Boy went like a swift, quiet river under cottonwood trees.

He had accepted Slim Girl's difference and unconventionality; he thought he was sure of what she was, but yet admitted that there were things about her that were beyond him. And for some reason, he always resented the idea of her working in the town. He wished she would not go there. Then again, he sympathized entirely with her idea of amassing a fortune.

His silver sold well. His craftsmanship was fine, his invention lively, and his taste in turquoise most exacting. It was strong, pure stuff, real Northern Navajo work, untouched by European influence. Slim Girl got in touch with the Harvey agent, finding him a ready buyer at good prices.

She had learned not to care much for general opinion of herself, and was surprised to find that this tangible evidence of her mythical husband's existence, this visible means of support, made a pleasant difference in the trader's attitude towards her, and eventually in the looks she received from men throughout the town.

To complete her idyll, she wanted to weave and she found it harder than she had expected. Of course, her first blanket was an ambitious one, elaborately designed. When she cut the sorry object from the loom, and looked at it, all crooked, irregular, and full of holes, she could have cried. She wondered why she continued to weave after that. Perhaps it was an offering to her beloved, an unconscious expiation for a guilt she had not admitted.

She worked so steadily that Laughing Boy warned her of the fate of women who wove too much, and forced her to let a day go by. Her muscles were much tougher now, and her fingers had grown clever and hard among the strands.

Despondently, she locked in the selvage, unrolled it on the frame, and sat back on her heels to smoke and look at her latest creation. She saw thin, messy workmanship, irregular lines, blunders, coarsenesses.

Then Laughing Boy came in and began to card the face of the blanket energetically—so roughly that it seemed a gratuitous insult even to her poor work. The scraping tore loose a long wool nap that covered all the errors in weaving. The sharp edges were lost, but the lovely combination she had dreamed of was there, soft and blurred, as though she saw it through tears. She had made a beautiful thing. She looked and looked. "You will be able to put my next blanket under your saddle, and be proud of it. Thank you," she said.

Four

THE corn matured and was harvested. First frost appeared in the night. Laughing Boy began to feel restless.

He spoke to her one night after supper. "There is to be a Night Chant over at Chilbito. My uncle's son wants us to come."

"Let us go, then; I think it will be a good thing. I shall be glad to see your country and your people, and a big dance like that is always good to go to. Your people will not like me, I think, but I do not care, if we are together." This was to be her test that was coming, one more test, and she felt there were enough already.

With entire confidence in his wife's ability to win over these people, Laughing Boy carried himself as though he had not the faintest idea that there might be strained relations between them.

When they arrived, one could see that his family had expected some outlandishness. Now they were puzzled; some disappointed, some pleased to see how normal and Navajo were Laughing Boy and his wife. Her blankets spoke for them with many tongues, and the solid evidences of their prosperity, all Navajo, nothing bizarre or American, but good honest silver, turquoise, coral—"hard goods"—and handsome Indian ponies.

He watched Slim Girl, seeing the shutters closed behind her eyes, correct, sure, in hand, doing just the perfect thing. He was swept by constantly recurring waves of pleasure in her.

Slim Girl watched the ceremonies with interest. She had a sneaking suspicion that the family had gone to the expense of a full Night Chant largely because of the effect they thought it might have on the erring member.

She was interested, excited. These were her people, putting themselves in touch with eternal forces by means of voice, strength, rhythm, colour, design—everything they had to use. They were creating something strong and barbaric and suitable, and still beautiful.

"In beauty it is finished,
In beauty it is finished!"

Five

ANY married couple, no matter how perfect the match, will undergo a critical period of strain, and these two were no exception.

It is too lonely, too strange a life; no one ever comes, thought Laughing Boy. That American town, what is there there? What is this preacher's wife? The look in her face when she returns— I do not know. There is something wrong, always something hidden.

Slim Girl, watching her husband with close attention, felt him change and was troubled. Feeling less sure of herself, she was over-careful, and betrayed more than ever that reserve of something withheld that belonged inevitably to her double life. Each increased the other's uneasiness; it was a circle.

IT HAD come round to the beginning of the Little Snow Moon again, a time of year when horses, seeking feed, are likely to wander. Laughing Boy kept close watch over his herd, and was little surprised one day to find a stallion missing.

Four days passed with no trace of the stallion. On the fifth, acting on the tip of a Hopi mail carrier, he picked up its trail fifteen miles from Los Palos. It had no mind to go back to the herd. At first sight of its master it broke into a trot and thus all morning, matching its pace to his, kept a quarter of a mile between them.

The stallion drew away from him, and he slowed his pace. It cantered past an adobe house standing alone under two cottonwoods at the edge of Los Palos. Laughing Boy advanced cautiously, using the house as cover. As he passed the window, he looked in, and reined his horse so suddenly that it reared, while his heart stopped for a moment and his whole body was a great choking. An agonized, clear voice cried out, inside, "My husband, my husband there!"

And a man said, "My God!"

As he came around the corner, an American, hatless, came out and began to run towards the town. Arrow leaped to bowstring almost of itself. The arrow struck just below the shoulder; the American fell, doubled up, almost turning a somersault, picked himself up, and with a last effort rounded the corner between the outermost houses at the end of the straggling street.

Calmly, he waited before the house. Afterwards there were going to be terrible feelings and thoughts.

Slim Girl stood in the doorway, neat, dressed in American clothes.

"You have killed us both, I think," he said.

Laughing Boy notched another arrow meticulously, drew to the head and released it. The arrow stood, through nearly to the feathers, in her left forearm. He lifted the reins and rode slowly around the corner of the adobe.

Six

THE pony, wandering unguided, brought him within sight of his house. There were Slim Girl's tracks, wind-blurred in the sand. She must have come straight home, arriving before he reached the high place.

She rose with difficulty, steadying herself against the wall as he came in. The arrow had passed through the flesh of the under side of her arm, just missing the artery and the bone. From the barbed iron head to the wound there was blood in the zigzag lightning grooves. He took out his knife.

"What are you going to do?"

"Cut off just by the hole; I can't pull all that through your arm."

"It is a good arrow. Pull it through."

The shaft moved and moved again. Every dart of pain in her arm went doubly through his heart. He jerked it out. She had not moved. She was brave, brave.

Something snapped inside of him. He fell forward, his head close to his knees, and began sobbing. She laid her hand on his shoulder.

"I do not try to say that what I have done is good, but I want to tell you my story, that you do not know; then you can judge rightly."

He hardly had expected her to come so directly to the point. He prepared to sift lies.

"WHEN I was still a little girl, they took me away to the all-year school, as you know. I followed the Jesus trail. I did well, then, at the school. I thought it was very good to work for a preacher.

"Then by and by I fell in love with a man. I was frightened when he wanted me to lie with him, but he made me feel all right because he said we would be married. Then I saw I was going to have a child.

"I went back to the preacher. I was not afraid to tell him, but I was ashamed. The preacher looked angry. He called me bad and ungrateful. I found out that every one said one thing and did another. The Jesus trail seemed to be a lie, too.

"Then the bad women spoke to me. They took me in and fed me; they were kind, those bad women. I learned their trade. In a few months so, with the baby in me, that made me very sick. I suffered much pain, the child was born much too soon, dead. I was glad.

"I hated all Americans, and I made up my mind that an American should pay for what an American had done. I watched for my chance, and by and by I saw it—a man from the East, that one.

"But I wanted my own people. That was why I made friends with a brave named Red Man. He did not care if I was bad, he hoped I might be bad with him. I never was, but I kept him hoping. With him I remembered the ways of The People and wanted to go back to them.

"Then I saw you, and everything changed. I had thought I was dead to men, and now I knew I loved you. With you I could live, without you I was already dead.

"But I kept on going to the American. I thought it right that an American should pay tribute to you and me; I thought it was the perfection of my revenge. I did not tell you. I knew you would not like it. That is all. That is the truth. I have spoken." She sank back, exhausted, with eyes closed.

"You have deceived me, but you have not been untrue to me, I think," he said. "Life without you would be a kind of death. But understand, if we go on together, it is The People's world, and not this world of Americans who have lost their way."

They kissed.

She had unravelled her blanket back

to the beginning, and started again with a design which could not be woven without Laughing Boy, and she knew that there could be no other design.

Seven

WHEN her arm was almost well, Laughing Boy brought three of his best horses to the corral. They prepared to move in beautiful, clear, cold, sunny weather following the first light snow. They set out with fine blankets over their shoulders, their saddles and bridles heavy with silver and brass, leading the pack-horse by a multi-coloured horsehair rope, a splendid couple.

Red Man rode too. He looked up the cañon, saw them, and was swept by an emotion of many factors which time and much mulling over had compounded into one.

I helped that woman, I took care of her. I loved her, in a way. I knew she was bad with Americans, but she would never do it with me. I deserved it from her. And then that fool came out of nowhere and she gave him everything.

He took up his rifle, aimed high for distance and fired. Laughing Boy heard the shots, turned, and ducked as two bullets snapped close to him, before he saw Slim Girl slump forward in the saddle. The bullet had gone clean through her; she was soaked with blood. He lowered her from the saddle and placed her on a couch of blankets.

"This is the end, my husband, my beloved." Her voice was faint, and she paused after every few words. "Do not try to avenge me. Promise me that."

"I promise." He knelt facing her, unmoving, with lines in his face like carving.

Eight

IT was nearly dark when he had laid the last stone on her grave. Now began the four days of waiting. He would make it a vigil, all the four days should be one prayer. This was not an ordinary death.

After some hours he grew calmer, partly because of fatigue. The disaster was accepted as familiar; but nothing could ever make him forget. The remainder of his life would be a monument to her. He felt the thing on his right wrist that was her thin gold circlet and began to chant in a deep voice:

With an empty place in me I wander,
    Nothing will fill it,
    Aya-ah, beautiful.
Forever alone, forever in sorrow I wander,
Forever empty, forever hungry I wander,
With the sorrow of great beauty I wander,
With the emptiness of great beauty I wander
Never alone, never weeping, never empty,
Now on the old age trail, now on the path of
    beauty I wander,
Ahalani, beautiful!

Sleepily he kissed the gold bracelet, saying, "Never alone, never lamenting, never empty. *Ahalani,* beautiful!"

A MIND DISEASED

CANST thou not minister to a mind diseased,
Pluck from the memory a rooted sorrow,
Raze out the written troubles of the brain,
And with some sweet oblivious antidote
Cleanse the stuffed bosom of that perilous stuff
Which weighs upon the heart?
          —*William Shakespeare* (1564-1616).

Richard E. Byrd

ALONE

This is the story of Admiral Byrd's personal experiences alone in the chilly wastes near the South Pole—experiences so personal that he could not bring himself to write about them until four years later. His decision to reveal his sufferings was reached only after his friends convinced him that a confused world had much to learn from his unaided struggle against death. You will find "Alone" radically different from the factual, impersonal accounts of his other great expeditions and flights, as told in "Skyward," "Little America," "Discovery," and "Exploring with Byrd."

The Decision

Bolling advance weather base, which I manned alone during the Antarctic winter night of 1934, was planted in the dark immensity of the Ross Ice Barrier, on a line between Little America and the South Pole. It was the first inland station ever occupied in the world's southernmost continent.

Aside from the meteorological and auroral work, I had no important purposes except a desire to be by myself for a while and to taste peace and quiet and solitude long enough to find out how good they really are.

You might think that a man whose life carried him into remote places would have no special need for quietude. Whoever thinks that has no knowledge of expeditions. Most of the time they move in fearful congestion and uproar, and always under the lash of time. Nor will they ever be different, so long as explorers are not rich men and so long as exploration itself deals with uncertainties.

Now I have been to both poles. In prospect this had promised to be a satisfying achievement. And in a large sense it had been—principally because the poles had been the means of enabling me to enlist public support for the full-scale scientific program which was my real interest.

But for me there was little sense of true achievement. Rather, when I finished stocktaking, I was conscious of a certain aimlessness. This feeling centered on small but increasingly lamentable omissions. For example, books. There was no end to the books that I was forever promising myself to read; but, when it came to reading them, I seemed never to have the time or the patience. This was true of other matters: new ideas, new concepts, and new developments about which I knew little or nothing. It seemed a restricted way to live.

I wanted something more than just privacy in the geographical sense. I wanted to sink roots into some replenishing philosophy. And so it occurred to me, as the situation surrounding Advance Base evolved, that there was the opportunity. Out there on the South Polar barrier, in cold and darkness as complete as that of the Pleistocene, I should have time to catch up, to study and think and listen to the phonograph; and, for maybe seven months, remote from all but the simplest distractions, I should be able to live exactly as I chose, obedient to no necessities but those imposed by wind and night and cold, and to no man's laws but my own.

That risks were involved, all of us knew; but none, so far as we could foresee, that were too great. Otherwise, as leader of a big polar expedition, and subject to all the responsibilities implicit in command, I could not have gone.

That I miscalculated is proved by the fact that I nearly lost my life. I had not counted on discovering how closely a man could come to dying and still not die, or want to die. That experience resolved proportions and relationships for me as nothing else could have done; and it is surprising, approaching the final enlightenment, how little one really has to know or feel sure about.

But Advance Base was no reckless whim. It was the outcome of four years of planning. The original idea came out of my first expedition to the Antarctic, and was an indirect by-product of my interest in polar meteorology.

Of all the different branches of science served by a soundly constituted polar expedition, none to the popular mind has a more practical value than meteorology. The extent to which the poles influence the weather is still a subject for specula-

tion. But some authorities go so far as to say that the region around each pole is the true weather maker.

I was struck by the thought that the most valuable source of meteorological data was still left untouched. No fixed stations had ever been advanced inland; no winter observations had ever been made beyond the coast; and the fragmentary data collected by sledging parties covered only the comparatively mild summer months. Yet, inland, beyond the moderating influence of the seas which surrounded the continent, was the coldest cold on the face of the earth.

It was there that I proposed to plant Advance Base, where weather is manufactured.

Latitude 80° 8′ South

DURING the four and a half months I occupied Advance Base alone, I kept a fairly complete diary. Nearly every night before turning in, I sat down and wrote a thoroughgoing account of the day's doings. Yet, I have been surprised and puzzled, on reading the entries four years later, to find that not more of the emotions and circumstances which I have always associated with the first few days alone were actually committed to paper.

I had stood at the trapdoor and watched the two tractors move away. In the cold air (the temperature was 50° below zero) the exhaust vapor puffed up like a smoke screen. I went below, intending to busy myself with the windspeed records; but the errand was a piece of self-deception which I could not quite bring off.

Obeying an impulse which I had no time to be ashamed of, I rushed up the hatch ladder. Just why, I don't know even now; perhaps for a last look at something alive and moving. Although the cars were by then some distance away, I could still hear the *beep-beep* of the horns and the clatter of the treads, so clearly do sounds carry on that crystal air. I watched until the noise died out; until the receding specks had dropped

for good behind a roll in the Barrier; until only the vanishing exhalations of the vapor remained.

A frozen nose and cheeks sent me below. But, as I slid down the ladder, something gave me a bad turn; and that was that in helping the tractor men stow the sledges I had fallen and wrenched my shoulder. The right one was hurting like the devil.

ALTHOUGH I was up mornings before eight o'clock and rarely went to bed before midnight, the days weren't half long enough for me to accomplish the things I set out to do.

I was not long in discovering one thing: that, if anything was eventually to regularize the rhythm by which I should live at Advance Base, it would not be the weather so much as the weather instruments themselves. I had eight in continuous operation. If I had had any illusions as to being master in my own house, they were soon dispelled. The instruments were masters, not I; and the fact that I knew none too much about them only intensified my humility. There was scarcely an hour in the living day of which a part was not devoted to them or observations connected with them.

APRIL 8

Were it not for my lame shoulder and the difficulties caused by the weather instruments (which were designed for a warmer place), I should be making much better progress in preparing myself for the oncoming darkness. Unpredictable things, small but often annoying, make continuous demands upon my time.

For example, I find that the outlet ventilator fills every three or four days with ice. It's due, I think, to condensation. Anyhow, I've got to watch that. Good ventilation I must have at any cost.

Just to complicate matters, the same trouble is developing in the topside end of the stove-pipe. I'm rather worried about the blockage in the pipe; unless the fumes from the stove escape to the surface, I shall have trouble . . .

Cold

COLD—even April's relatively moderate cold—gave me plenty to think about. At 50° below zero a flashlight dies out in your hand. At 55° kerosene will freeze, and the flame will dry up on the wick. At 60° rubber turns brittle. Below 60°, cold will find the last microscopic touch of oil in an instrument and stop it dead. If there is the slightest breeze, you can hear your breath freeze as it floats away, making a sound like that of Chinese firecrackers. And if you work too hard and breathe too deeply, your lungs will sometimes feel as if they were on fire.

So I had my troubles. At first I had the devil of a time with the weather instruments. The traces become horribly blotched, the pens stuck, and the instruments themselves stopped without rhyme or reason. But, one way or another, I usually managed to contrive a cure. I learned how to thin the ink with glycerine to keep it from freezing, and how to cut the oil in the instruments with gasoline and rub the delicate parts with graphite, which wasn't affected so much by the cold.

Yet, in playing Admirable Crichton to myself, I was far from distinguished. By Naval Academy standards, I should have "bilged out" of Advance Base on cooking alone.

I HAVE only to close my eyes to witness again the succession of culinary disasters. Consider what my diary designated as The Corn Meal Incident. Into a boiler I dumped what seemed a moderate quantity of meal, added a little water, and stood it on the stove to boil. That simple formula gave birth to a Hydra-headed monster. The stuff began to swell and dry up, swell and dry up, with fearful blowing and sucking noises.

All innocently I added water, more water, and still more water. Whereupon the boiler erupted like Vesuvius. All the pots and pans within reach couldn't begin to contain the corn meal that overflowed. It oozed over the stove. It spattered the ceiling. It covered me from head to foot. If I hadn't acted resolutely, I might have been drowned in corn meal.

Seizing the container in my mittened hands, I rushed to the door and hurled it far into the food tunnel. There it continued to give off deadly golden lava until the cold finally stilled the crater.

There were other disasters of the same order. There was the Dried Lima Beans Incident of April 10th. ("It's amazing," the diary reports soberly, "how much water lima beans can absorb, and how long it takes them to cook. At supper time I had enough half-cooked lima beans to feed a ship's company.") My first jelly desert bounced like a rubber ball under my knife; the flapjacks had to be scraped from the pan with a chisel ("And you, the man who sat at a thousand banquets," goes the accusing entry of April 12th).

Thus April moved along. Each night as the last formal act of the day, I crossed off another date on the big calendar on the wall, and each morning consulted the calendar the first thing, to make sure that I hadn't forgotten. Above me the day was dying; the night was rising in its place.

Now with less than a fortnight of

daylight left in this latitude, the sun was just a monstrous ball which could barely hoist itself free from the horizon. It would wheel along for a few hours, obscured by mist, then sink out of sight in the north not long after noon. I found myself watching it as one might watch a departing lover.

Revelations

THE first days of May carried no hint of the calamities that would overtake me at the month's end. On the contrary, they were among the most wonderful days I had ever known. The blizzards departed, the cold moved down from the South Pole, and opposite the moon in a coal-black sky the cast-up light from the departed sun burned like a bonfire. During the first six days the temperature averaged 47.03°; much of the time it was deep in the minus forties and fifties. The winds scarcely blew. And a soundlessness fell over the Barrier. I have never known such utter quiet.

It was a queer business. I felt as though I had been plumped upon another planet or into another geologic horizon of which man had no knowledge or memory. And yet, I thought at the time it was very good for me; I was learning what the philosophers have long been harping on—that a man can live profoundly without masses of things.

For all my realism and skepticism there came over me, too powerfully to be denied, that exalted sense of identification—or oneness—with the outer world which is partly mystical but also certainty. I came to understand what Thoreau meant when he said, "My body is all sentient." There were moments when I felt more *alive* than at any other time in my life. Freed from materialistic distractions, my senses, sharpened in new directions, and the random or commonplace affairs of the sky and the earth and the spirit, which ordinarily I would have ignored if I had noticed them at all, became exciting and portentous.

MAY 6TH

It was one thing to instruct the mind; it was another to make the mind obey. The nature of the distinction was to be a fundamental part of my self-instruction at Advance Base, as is evidenced by a diary entry about this time:

"Something—I don't know what—is getting me down, I've been strangely irritable all day, and since supper have been depressed . . . This would not seem important if I could only put my finger on the trouble, but I can't find any single thing to account for the mood. For the first time, I must admit that the problem of keeping my mind on an even keel is a serious one . . ."

I HAVE a clear recollection of how this entry came to be written. Supper was over, the dishes had been washed, the 8 p.m. "ob" was out of the way, and I had settled down to read. Queerly, my eyes hurt, my head ached a little, though not enough to bother. I couldn't concentrate. My whole being was restive and unaccountably troubled. I got up and paced the room.

I tried to be rational about it. The diary testifies to that. I took my mood apart and studied it as I might have studied the register. Had anything gone wrong during the day? No, it had been a very pleasant day. Though the temperature was in the minus fifties, I had worked hard outside; I had supped well on chicken soup, beans, dehydrated potatoes, spinach, and canned peaches.

Except for the dull ache in my eyes and head, I felt fine; the ache came only at night, anyway, and was gone before I fell asleep. Maybe the fumes from the stove accounted for it. If this was the case, I had better crack the door when the stove was going during the day and spend more time outside.

"The most likely explanation," I concluded that night in the diary, "is that the trouble lies with myself. Manifestly, if I can harmonize the various things within me that may be in conflict and also fit myself more smoothly into this environment, I shall be at peace. It may be that the evenness and the darkness and the absence of life are too much for me to absorb in one chunk. I cannot accept that as a fact, if only because I have been here but forty-three days and many months must be lived out which will be no different from the first . . .

"If I am to survive—at least keep my mental balance—I must control and direct my thoughts. This should not be difficult. Any intelligent man should be able to find means of existence within himself . . ."

Mind Over Matter

EVEN from this distance I maintain that the attitude was a sensible one. The only fault was its glibness. It was true that the only way to keep trouble from intruding was through the censorship and control of the mind. But beyond this was the truth which that night I did not recognize; and this truth was that the whole complex nervous-muscular mechanism which is the body was waiting, as if with bated breath, for the intrusion of familiar stimuli from the outside world, and could not comprehend why they were denied.

A man can isolate himself from habits and conveniences—deliberately, as I have done; or accidentally, as a ship-wrecked sailor might—and force his mind to forget.

But the body is not so easily side-tracked. That is where the conflict arises. I don't think that a man can do without sounds and smells and voices and touch, any more than he can do without phosphorus and calcium.

Nevertheless, I practiced my preachments of a disciplined mind. Or perhaps discipline isn't exactly the right word; for what I did, or tried to do, was to focus my thinking on healthy, constructive images and concepts and thus crowd out the unhealthy ones. I built a wall between myself and the past in an effort to extract every ounce of diversion and creativeness inherent in my immediate surroundings. Every day I experimented

with new schemes for increasing the content of the hours.

My environment was intrinsically treacherous and difficult, but I saw ways to make it agreeable. I tried to cook more rapidly, take weather and auroral observations more expertly, and do routine things systematically. Full mastery of the impinging moment was my goal. I lengthened my walks and did more reading, and kept my thoughts upon an impersonal plane. In other words, I tried resolutely to attend to my business.

Thus in May, as in April, I never really lacked for something to do. For all the hush and evenness and the slow pulse of the night, my existence was anything but static. I was the inspector of snowstorms and the aurora, the night watchman, and father confessor to myself. Something was always happening, for better or worse. For example, the Tuesday radio schedule with Little America was eliminated, to save gasoline; while this left a blank spot in the hours, the remaining two schedules in turn became more animated.

Even in the heart of the Ross Ice Barrier a solitary man had plenty to occupy him. Thus in the diary: " . . . I got Canfield twice tonight—extraordinary! The only games I played, too." . . . "Tonight I sang while washing the dishes. Solitude hasn't mellowed my voice any, but I had great fun. A gala evening, in fact."

Stock Taking

MAY 25

THIS is my sixty-fourth day at Advance Base, and it just so happened that I had some leisure time. I have been taking advantage of this to think back over my stay here and take stock of my situation.

There are three things for which I am par-

ticularly thankful. The first is that my records so far are complete (though blotted and splotched a bit). The second is that my defenses are perfected, and the third is that I have become well adjusted to conditions—especially psychologically. I feel able now to withstand any assaults the beleaguering night may launch.

Indeed, I look forward to the rest of my sojourn with pleasure.

I am finding that life here has become largely a life of the mind. Unhurried reflection is a sort of companion. Yes, solitude is greater than I anticipated. My sense of values is changing, and many things which before were in solution in my mind now seem to be crystallizing. I am better able to tell what in the world is wheat for me and what is chaff. In fact, my definition of success itself is changing. Just lately my views about man and his place in the cosmic scheme have begun to run something like this:

The human race, my intuition tells me, is not outside the cosmic process and is not an accident. It is as much a part of the universe as the trees, the mountains, the aurora, and the stars. My reason approves this; and the findings of science, as I see them, point in the same direction. And, since man is a part of the cosmos and subject to its laws, I see no reason to doubt that these same natural laws operate in the psychological as well as in the physical sphere and that their operation is manifest in the working of the consciousness.

Therefore, it seems to me that convictions of right and wrong, being as they are, products of the consciousness, must also be formed in accordance with these laws. I look upon the conscience as the mechanism which makes us directly aware of them and their significance and serves as a link with the universal intelligence which gives them form and harmoniousness.

I believe further that the age-tested convictions of right and wrong, in which individual aberrations must have been largely canceled out, are as much a manifestation of cosmic law and intelligence as are all other phenomena.

Therefore, the things that mankind has tested and found right make for harmony and progress—or peace; and the things it has found wrong hinder progress and make for discord. The right things lead to rational behavior—such as the substitution of reason for force—and so to freedom. The wrong things lead to brute force and slavery.

But the peace I describe is not passive. It must be won. Real peace comes from struggle that involves such things as effort, discipline, enthusiasm. This is also the way to strength. An inactive peace may lead to sensuality and flabbiness, which are discordant. It is often necessary to fight to lessen discord. This is the paradox.

When a man achieves a fair measure of harmony within himself and his family circle, he achieves peace; and a nation made up of such individuals and groups is a happy nation. As the harmony of a star in its course is expressed by rhythm and grace, so the harmony of a man's life-course is expressed by happiness; this, I believe, is the prime desire of mankind.

"The universe is an almost untouched reservoir of significance and value," and man need not be discouraged because he cannot fathom it. His views of life are no more than a flash in time. The details and distractions are infinite. It is only natural, therefore, that we should never see the picture whole. But the universal goal—the attainment of harmony—is apparent. The very act of perceiving this goal and striving constantly toward it does much in itself to bring us closer and, therefore, becomes an end in itself.

The Blow

SNOW was still falling on Thursday the 31st. The calendar warned, "Radio schedule." I went about the preparations.

We talked back and forth nearly an hour and a half. From my desk in the shack I could hear the engine in the tunnel; for some reason it started skipping. "Wait," I spelled out to them. Unhooking the lantern, I went into the tunnel. The air was thick with exhaust gases. Thinking the mixture was at fault, I bent over the carburator and tinkered with the needle valve. This had little effect. I remember straightening up. And that was the last conscious act of mind that I do remember.

I do not know how long I remained unconscious. It may be that the cold aroused me. Anyhow, after a little while I crawled into the shack. The radio desk emerged from the blur, and then I remembered what I was supposed to do. I fumbled for the key and signed off, thinking how hard it was to spell out what I had to say. If any acknowledgment came, I did not hear it; for I couldn't get the earphones on.

My actions thereafter are uncertain; I don't really know which were nightmares and which were facts. I remember lying on the bunk, fully dressed, and hearing, as if with surprise, the irregular beat of the engine in the tunnel and realizing that I must shut it off to escape asphyxiation. Very probably I dropped to my hands and knees, as I must have appreciated the necessity for keeping my head under the fumes and in the uncontaminated air near the floor. Anyhow, I was on my knees when I reached into the recess and threw the ignition switch.

But the rest of it—the skyrocketing pain in my forehead and eyes, the nausea, the violent beating of my heart, the illusion of being a thin flame drawn between two voids—they could not have been real. Only the cold was real: the numbness in the hands and feet, creeping like a slow paralysis through my body. At least, I could cope with cold. I grasped for the throat of the sleeping bag, and eased in.

Despair

IT is painful to me to dwell on the details of my collapse, particularly as the affairs of Advance Base are now receding into the gentling haze of the past. The subject is one that does not easily bear discussion, if only because a man's hurt, like his love, is most seemly when concealed.

To know I had escaped disaster in one form was only a preliminary step in the process of preparing to avert it in another. The fact was manifest that I was helpless, at least for the time being. I barely had strength to light the candle standing on the tin ledge directly over my head. If so simple a movement could empty me of the little strength that had returned, what chance did I have of bringing in food and fuel, let alone attending to the instruments?

"THE INSTRUMENTS WERE MASTERS, NOT I."

I could live many days without food. I could suck snow to quench thirst. But, ill and weak as I was, I could not live long without heat; and the fuel tank had to be filled every three days. Pondering such difficult matters was too much for me; my mind went blank again. When I awakened and looked at my wrist watch, the time was 7 o'clock. I wasn't quite so weak, and my body craved water.

Waves of dizziness swept from head to foot, but after a little while I was able to reach the chair and push it toward the stove. A little water remained in the bucket on the stove; I dipped it out with a can. The first few swallows my stomach threw up; nevertheless, I persevered until I had at least a cupful down.

The notes which I jotted down a few days afterwards insist this stranger feeling in the dark acted with the utmost deliberation. Perhaps so. Between the pain and the weakness it was hard for more than one thought to find a lodgment.

Even in my stupor I seem to have recognized that the gasoline engine was not solely responsible. The engine dealt the blow which knocked me down, but long before then I had partially perceived a developing weakness. I remembered the headaches and hurt in my eyes earlier in the month.

What reason I could muster indicated the stove as the principal villain. Monoxide poisoning is not necessarily an instantaneous matter. It may be a gradual and cumulative process, brought about by intermittent exposure to the chemistry of the fumes. And the more I thought about the leaky joints in the stove, the more I blamed it.

But all this was shadowy in my mind that last night in May. I wavered between self-recrimination and hopefulness, between pain and an emptiness, devoid of feeling. I knew that I was in a frightful mess, one that would involve my family, the expedition, and God only knew whom else. But it was hard to see what could be done about that. Some-time after three o'clock I drifted off into a dream of horrors.

JUNE 1st was a Friday, a Black Friday for me. The nightmare left me, and about nine o'clock in the morning I awakened with a violent start, as if I had been thrown down a well in my sleep. God, I was thirsty! But I had hardly strength to move. I clung to the sleeping bag, which was the only source of comfort and warmth left to me, and mournfully debated the little that might be done.

Two facts stood clear. One was that my chances of recovering were slim. The other was that in my weakness I was incapable of taking care of myself. These were desperate conclusions, but my mood allowed no others. All that I could reasonably hope for was to prolong my existence for a few days by hoarding my remaining resources; by doing the necessary things *very slowly* and with *great deliberation*. So long as he did that and maintained the right frame of mind, even a very ill man should be able to last a time. So I reasoned, anyway. There was no alternative.

I was able to do a number of small things, in a series of stealthy, deliberate sorties from the bunk. I attended to the inside thermograph and register, changing the sheets, winding the clocks, and inking the pens. After every exertion I rested; the pain in my arms and back and head were almost crucifying.

I filled a thermos jug with warm water, added powdered milk and sugar, and carried the jug into the sleeping bag. My stomach crawled with nauseous sensations; but, by taking a teaspoonful at a time, I finally managed to get a cupful down. After a while the weakness left me, and I felt strong enough to start for the instrument shelter. I reached the hatch and pushed it open, but could go no farther. The night was a gray fog, full of shadows, like my mood. In the shack I lost the milk I had drunk. On the verge of fainting, I made for the bunk.

The Struggle

JUNE 2nd was a Saturday and a prolongation of the melancholy events of the day before. That night, as well as I could estimate, I slept seven or eight hours. Sunday morning brought another anguished struggle to awaken. Sunday meant a radio schedule with Little America and a lie about my condition which every pain-ridden fiber entreated me not to make.

I have often been asked why I did not tell Little America what had happened. My answer is that it was too dangerous for the men to come to me. The intervening darkness, the cold, the rolling vacancies of the Barrier, and the crevasses were all immutable facts. Advance Base was my responsibility. It was unthinkable that willing men at Little America should be made to suffer.

That afternoon I may have been close to going out of my mind; the strain of preparing for the schedule had raised Cain with me. I know that I was in torment, and a notion that I was dying would not leave me. Some time during the evening I came out of the delirium, thirsty and hungry. Along with some milk, I managed to down half a dozen salt crackers, the first solid food since Thursday morning.

Next morning I had much less difficulty waking up, which heartened me. Indeed, matters went somewhat easier. I even managed to empty the slop pail. In the afternoon I had strength enough to crank the phonograph. I played "Adeste Fidelis." It was magnificent to

hear the sound of many voices throbbing in every corner of the shack. *You are on the mend,* an inner voice said; *you really have a chance. One in a hundred, perhaps, but still a chance.*

Little by little I came to my feet and regained a measure of control over my affairs. But the improvement came so gradually and was interrupted by so many attacks that it was perceptible only over a long period; it was most apparent in my somewhat improved ability to control my moods of depression.

The temperature rose to 4°. I was grateful for that. Most of the afternoon the fire was out; and I persuaded myself that the let up from the fumes was helping me to throw off the exhaustion that followed the radio schedule.

JUNE 13

I'VE had the fire out so much of the time that the ice on the walls never melts. I've watched it creep slowly toward the ceiling. It seems to rise at the rate of an inch or so every day. But in spite of everything I seem to be improving.

Still I can't eat properly—have to force food down by chewing it to the point of dissolution. To take my mind off the distress of my stomach, I sometimes play solitaire while I eat. Finished a whole game tonight before I downed three mouthfuls of food.

June was a period of marches and countermarches, of victories and retreats. It went out on a shrinking moon with rising cold. My reviving security was based upon a doubtful equilibrium—one strong blow could break it in two.

Relapse

THE blow did in fact fall on Thursday the 5th of July. That day the gasoline-driven radio generator went out of commission. I had everything in readiness for the schedules, even the engine running. Casually I flipped the switch to test the voltage. Zero, read the dial.

Giving up all intention of meeting the schedule, I fell to on the machine. By supper time I had it apart. The fault

was fatal. The lug on the generator drive shaft had sheared off. No improvisation of mine would do, although I tried everything that my imagination suggested. Bent over with weariness and despair, I concluded finally that my world was falling to pieces.

There remained the emergency handpowered set, but I doubted that I was strong enough to work it as it required the strength of two men, ordinarily. I who did not possess the strength of half a well man, would have to go it alone.

On the appointed hour of our next schedule I had finally succeeded in making the right connections to the hand generator. Rigged up and standing hard by my radio table, the set looked workmanlike and simple. But I had a premonition of what it would do to me.

When I switched to the receiver, I was almost too tired to care whether I got Little America or not.

"Go ahead, KFY. We heard you." It was Little America. How wonderful, how perfectly wonderful, I thought.

I switched to the transmitter, and told them that my engine was "shot" and that I was having a hard time with the emergency set. They replied that they would keep their messages down. Then speaking slowly, Charlie Murphy began: "The possibilities of the journey to Advance Base are being examined; and the preparations are being made with utmost care. If I were you, I wouldn't count overmuch on the possibility of the tractors before the end of July. There is a good chance it may be considerably later."

For an instant I was taken aback. The thought struck me that they knew the trip was dangerous but were still going ahead with it. Had I somehow given myself away? I signed off, cursing my weakness as I sagged over the generator head.

The temperature was 60° below zero, but sweat was pouring down my chest. I turned off the stove and stumbled to the sleeping bag. It was the third serious relapse; and, coming on top of five weeks of depleting illness, it very nearly did me in. If it had not been for the week's supply of fuel, plus the three week's supply of food, which I had stored squirrel-wise near at hand, I doubt whether I could have lived the period out. The pain came back, as did the vomiting and sleeplessness.

False Hopes

JULY 15

THIS has been a day of mixed news. I finally made contact with Little America—which was to the good; but the cranking has left me exhausted—which is to the bad. The most comforting fact is the discovery that the silence has evidently not stirred up Little America. They are still keeping their heads.

Even now, after four years, the whole business sounds fantastic. I was lying about my condition because there was nothing else for me to do. But at Little America they were lying, too. The difference was that *they* were coming to suspect that I was lying and, even as they divined that I was concocting a fiction to mislead them, so *they* in turn concocted their own brand to mislead me.

JULY 16

TODAY, for no reason that I can define, my hopes have risen that the tractor party will actually get through. Poulter is a hard man to stop, and I know the men will be safe in his hands. I really think I feel a little better, perhaps because my hopes now have the facts of the preparations at Little America to feed on.

I hesitate to describe the events that followed. No doomed man pacing a cell in the hope of an eleventh-hour reprieve can possibly have endured more than I endured; for, besides my own skin to think about, I had the lives of five other men on my conscience. All the pre-start excitement drained out of me. I could neither lie quiet nor sit still.

JULY 24

No word. I wish to God I knew where Poulter is.

JULY 25

Nothing—nothing but wind and more snow.

AUGUST 3

Providence has been good to us. Poulter is safe back at Little America, and all my futile tinkering with the radio seems to have borne fruit. The messages really made sense today. Poulter is ready to leave as soon as Haines gives him a good weather report. The growing light is a factor which each day lessens Poulter's hazards; but on my side I have almost ceased to care. A sort of numbness seems to have claimed me.

AUGUST 4

Poulter has started. The fact that he is actually headed south again has pierced my torpor, and hope is once more quickening in my heart.

AUGUST 6

At noon today Poulter was only twenty-one miles south. Yesterday he extricated himself from a crevasse. I shall go to bed now, supported by the hothouse fiction that tomorrow night will find them here. In my heart I know this can't possibly happen.

TUESDAY was heartbreaking. In a matter-of-fact way Murphy informed me that Poulter was once more back in Little America. Twenty-six miles south, or barely half the distance made good on the first attempt, the clutch had given out entirely. Poulter had turned back and was lucky to reach Little America at all.

AUGUST 8

They started again early this morning for the third try. Charlie was cheerful. "Keep the lights going, Dick. This time I really think they're going right through," he said. Well, that remains to be seen. I cannot allow myself to hope again; the drop into failure is too abrupt. The great pity is that I am only half in touch with Little America. I can hear them well enough, but they can't get me. I've already had the transmitter apart once, and I shall have another go at it tonight.

My personal stake in the journey was of dwindling importance. No matter how the trip turned out, whether they reached Advance Base or not, I was convinced that personally I had little to gain; my salvage value was next to zero. Only one thing continued to be important: the expedition's prestige and the safety of the men between me and Little America.

Escape

ABOUT 5 o'clock of August 11th I went up the ladder. The barrier had seldom looked so black and empty. I set off a can of gasoline. No answer came.

At 6 o'clock I was again at the trapdoor. And this time I really saw something. Dead in the north a beam of light lifted itself from the Barrier, swept to the vertical, and fell; then it rose again, touched a star, and went out. This was unmistakably Poulter's searchlight.

This was indeed the world advancing to meet me. In a little while I should see friends and hear voices talking. The escape which for two and a half months had existed only in imagination was now an oncoming reality. It would be hard to describe exactly what that light did to me.

In a little while I could hear on the clear, vibrant air the rumble of the treads, then the *beep-beep-beep* of the horn. Soon I could see the bulking shadow of the tractor. As a greeting I set off the last can of gasoline and the last flare. They were just dying when the cars stopped about a hundred yards

away. Three men jumped out, with Poulter in the center, looming doubly big in furs.

I stood up, but I did not dare to walk forward. I remember shaking hands all around, and Waite insists that I said: "Hello, fellows. Come on below. I have a bowl of hot soup waiting for you."

THE two months that followed the tractor's coming were as pleasant as the others had been miserable. On October 14th Bowlin and Schlossbach arrived from Little America in the *Pilgrim*. I climed the hatch.

Part of me remained forever at Latitude 80° 8′ South: what survived of my youth, my vanity, perhaps, and certainly my skepticism. On the other hand, I did take away something that I had not fully possessed before: appreciation of the sheer beauty and miracle of being alive, and a humble set of values.

All this happened four years ago. Civilization has not altered my ideas. I live more simply now, and with more peace.

JOSEPH C. LINCOLN

MR. PRATT'S PATIENTS

For almost forty years Joseph C. Lincoln (1870—) has been spinning breezy yarns about picturesque Cape Cod characters which have been swallowed with gusto by American readers. They like the salty humor of his lingo, the excitement of his plots and the happy way things turn out in the end. "Mr. Pratt's Patients," published in 1913, has all these pleasant qualities, brim full and running over. You will enjoy the way this broken-down old salt makes good.

Told By Tea Leaves

I was having my fortune told. Sophrony Gott was telling it, with tea leaves. She had drawn off the tea and was shaking the leaves in the bottom of the cup around in circles.

"Well!" says Sophrony, "I'd have scarcely believed it. There's a whole lot here, Mr. Pratt. I can see a lot of things in this cup."

"That's good," says I. "You don't see a fifteen dollar a week job down in the no'th east corner, do you?"

"No," she says. "No-o, not exactly. And yet there's money here, a lot of money. And a letter. I seem to see a letter with good luck in it. There's a journey, too; you're going to take a journey. And what's this? I can see two spirits hovering over your life; one's dark and the other's light. They're going to have consider'ble influence. And here's two men. One of 'em's a sort of thin man with—with kind of thick hair, and the other's a—a—"

"A thick man with kind of thin hair, hey?" I finished for her. "Well, all right; I wouldn't bother any longer if I was you, Mrs. Gott. You've found more in that cup already than the average person could dredge out of a washboiler. If you'll excuse me I cal'late I'll trot along and see if I can locate any of that money."

"But you haven't heard it all. There's lots more. I can see a bottle—that means

sickness. You're going to be mixed up with sickness, Mr. Pratt."

"Going to be! *Have* been, you mean!"

"And here's a dark blot—that means trouble. I'll stir it a little, and—"

"No, you won't. I don't need anybody to stir up any more trouble for me. I'm ever so much obliged to you, Mrs. Gott, but I must be going."

I was on my way to the door when her husband Adoniram got in my way. He was so excited that he actually forgot to be scared of his wife, which is saying something.

"The letter!" he says. "The letter, Sol!"

"It's here," says Sophrony. "It's here, Mr. Pratt. I didn't think of it till—Mr. Pratt, it's the most amazing thing. When I saw that letter for you in the tea leaves I never thought of the mantel-piece."

She gave it to me and the two of 'em stood close alongside when I started to rip open the envelope. I don't patronize Uncle Sam's mails to any great extent, but, generally speaking, a letter for me wasn't such a miracle as all this fuss amounted to.

There was only one sheet of paper in the envelope. This was a bill for eighteen dollars and forty cents for some canvas and a new anchor for the *Dora Bassett* that I'd bought of old man Scudder over at Wapatomac the fall afore I was took sick. I'd paid for it, too; but, like an everlasting idiot, I hadn't took any receipt. A bill for eighteen dollars; and I had less than twelve in my pocket! This was the "luck!"

About an hour later I was setting in the stern of the *Dora Bassett* bound for Wapatomac. Why was I going? I didn't know scarcely; and yet I did, too. I was going to talk Dutch to Nate Scudder. The low-down swindler! What did he think I was; a fool summer chap from the city?

A Familiar Voice

THAT cruise to Wapatomac was a long one. 'Twas pretty fur into the afternoon when I started and I had a little mite of engine trouble to hinder me, besides. It was almost sunset when I made out the Denboro shore, and I had some miles to go then. The more I thought of navigating that channel in the dark the less I liked it. I see a little cove in the shore and decided to anchor the *Dora Bassett* there and go ashore in the skiff and walk the rest of the way.

The place where I beached the skiff was a deserted hole, not even a fish shanty on the beach. Pretty soon I struck into a sort of path that, I cal'lated, might lead to the road I was hunting for. It twisted and turned, and, the first thing I knew, made a sudden bend around a bunch of bayberry scrub and opened out into a big clear space like a lawn. And, back of the lawn, was a big, old-fashioned house, with piazzas stretching in front of it, and all blazing with lights.

Suddenly there was a click and out of the dark about twenty foot to one side of me blazed a stream of light that hit me right plumb in the face and eyes. Then a voice, a female voice, said:

"Now who are you? And what are you doing, sneaking around, interfering with the patients? Well, why don't you answer?"

I tried to answer. I done my best. There was something about that voice that sounded familiar, too. If I could have seen who was talking to me. She took a step toward me and sung out:

"Why! Why! *Mr. Pratt!* What in the wide world fetched you here? I'm awful glad to see you! Don't you know me? I'm Eureka Sparrow."

No wonder I thought the voice was familiar.

Home for Right Livers

"WELL! well, well! Eureka," says I; "this does seem like old times for sartin."

We was inside the kitchen of the big house by this time. I was setting in a chair by the table and Eureka was flying around, busy as a wasp in an empty molasses hogshead, getting supper for me.

She asked me more'n a shipload of questions and I answered 'em best I could, trying hard to get a chance to ask one or two on my own hook. And when I got to Nate Scudder's bill her eyes snapped and she stamped her foot just as I'd seen her do so often in the old days.

"There!" says she, "ain't that just like that Scudder thing! Miss Emeline and me hadn't been in this house more'n two days when round he comes to see if he can't sell us groceries. I guess likely he'd have talked Miss Emeline over, for he saw her first, but I got into the room just in time. You ought to have seen his face when he laid eyes on me. Ho! ho! Miss Emeline was surprised."

"Who's this Miss Emeline you're talking about? And what are you doing here?"

"It's a sanitarium," says Eureka. "The name of it is 'Sea Breeze Bluff.' There you've heard of 'Sea Breeze Bluff Sanitarium for Right Living and Rest,' ain't you?"

"No," says I. "I hate to lower myself in your opinion, Eureka, but I ain't."

"Not of Doctor Lysander P. Wool? His advertisements have been in the papers for ever so long."

Then I begun to get a glimmer of light. "Hold on," I sung out. "You don't mean 'Wool's Willow Wine for the Weak'? Not that feller?"

"Um-hm," says she, nodding emphatic. "That's him. Well, he is running this place. You see, Miss Emeline, she—"

"Belay, Eureka!" I cut in. "If you and me are going to get anywheres on this cruise, I cal'late we'd better go back and start over again at the mark buoy. Suppose you commence by telling me about yourself and how you come here."

So she towed a chair up to the table abreast of me and commenced. And she commenced at Genesis, just as I'd ordered her to.

WHEN Eureka went out at housework, she got a place with a single old maid, name of Miss Emeline Adams, and had been with her ever since. 'Twas her that Eureka called "Miss Emeline."

Well, this Miss Emeline had been poor and every-day and healthy once on a time, but now she was rich and hightoned and ailing. For three years Eureka and Miss Emeline had lived together, winters in Brockton and summers at Wapatomac. They got along fine together.

'Twas after Miss Emeline got her money that she run afoul of "Wool's Willow Wine," and, later on, of Doctor Wool himself. From that time she and the Doctor had been mighty friendly.

"And last winter," goes on Eureka, her good-looking face all lit up like a binnacle lamp, with excitement and enthusiasm; "Doctor Wool came to see us and told us of his great discovery. 'Twas that all his life his theory of curing folks had been wrong. Yes, sir, all wrong! He's discovered that medicines wa'n't what really cured at all. The real cures was those provided by Mother Nature.

" 'Twas Nature that done the curing, and he'd decided to give up his medicine making and start in curing in the right way. He was figgering to open a sanitarium. Well, he'd no sooner said that than Miss Emeline had an inspiration.

Says she, 'I'll help you open one.' And she did. This is it. This is 'Sea Breeze Bluff Sanitarium for Right Living and Rest.' Miss Emeline owns it, and Doctor Wool runs it. There! *now* you understand.

"Oh, he's a wonderful man, Doctor Lysander P. Wool is! You'll say so, too, when you see him, Mr. Pratt. *He* don't bully. He's as gentle and grand and— and noble as a duke or—or a Seneschal in a story book. Talk! You never heard anybody talk the way he can. After he's talked to you for a spell you don't know where you are, scarcely. And you don't care, neither. You're willing to be anywheres so's you can rest back and hear him."

THE praise service broke off there. I cal'late 'twas a mercy, fur's I was concerned. I'd never heard the Wool man talk, so I couldn't judge the effect, but I did know that Eureka's talk had got me whirling. I'd always figgered that my brains was as hard as the average alongshore, but now they was softening up fast.

"Well," says I, "I've dodged the trouble that Sophrony Gott saw in the teacup when she was telling my fortune this afternoon, and I'm going to keep on dodging long's I can. Good-bye, Eureka. I'm awful glad I run across you again and I'm much obliged for the supper."

I was stepping off the porch, but she wouldn't let me go. The mention of that fortune-telling was the kind of bait she liked and she wouldn't let go till she had the whole of it.

"Well!" says she, when I'd finished. "Well, I declare! Ain't that wonderful! Just like a story! And some of it's come true already, ain't it? You did get a letter, even if 'twas only a bill; and you have taken a journey. Maybe it'll all come true. There was two female spirits hovering over you, she said, didn't she? I wonder who they are. Why, perhaps I'm one of 'em."

"And the money!" she says. "There

was a lot of money coming to you from the journey. How do you s'pose that. . . . Oh, my goodness gracious! I do believe. . . . You don't s'pose—"

She stopped. There was a rattle of wheels and the "thump-thump" of horse's hoofs coming along the drive.

"Whoa!" says the feller on the driver's seat. The door of the wagon opened and a big, heavy-built man got out.

"It's the Doctor and Professor Quill, the new patient," says Eureka. "He was coming with the Doctor."

The Professor was long and lanky. He had on a tall hat, and he knocked it off getting out of the carriage. When he stooped to pick it up his hair fell down all around his face. After the two men had gone into the house, Eureka said:

"Promise me that you won't go back to Wellmouth till you've come here again. Come tomorrow morning."

"All right, I'll promise," says I.

"Good-night," says she. "It's wonderful, ain't it? I never knew anything so wonderful. You did see, didn't you? Professor Quill's the thin man with the thick hair, the one Mrs. Gott saw in the teacup. Of course he is! Isn't it wonderful!"

Joined to a Great Work

THE next morning I blew off at Nate Scudder and then sailed back to Eureka. She was waiting for me, all on tiptoe with excitement.

"He expects you," says she. "He's in his office and you're to come right in. I've told him all about you. It's perfectly splendid. Don't you *dare* say anything but yes, Mr. Pratt."

Afore I could ask what I was to say yes to, she was piloting me through two or three big rooms, and knocking on a door.

"Come in," booms the big voice.

And in I marched.

DR. LYSANDER P. WOOL was sitting at the other side of a big table, and the sun, streaming in at the window behind him, lit up the shiny top of his head like a glory.

"Be seated, sir," says he. "Be seated, I beg."

I set down in the chair he pointed out to me. He smiled and thanked me for doing it. I never thought afore that setting down was anything to be proud of 'special, but that smile and the thanks made me feel as if I'd done something wuth while. I told him he was welcome.

"You had something you wanted to say to me, I believe, Doctor Wool," I hove out, by way of suggestion.

He moved his big head up and down slow.

"I did," says he; "I did—er—yes. Eureka, our accomplished young friend in the kitchen, tells me that you are out of employment just now. Is that true?" —ah—

"It's true enough, all right," I said. "More's the pity, it's true enough."

"Yes—er—yes. I see, I see. Well—er— Mr. Pratt, I trust we may be able to change all that, to overcome that difficulty—er—yes. How would you like," he says, "to remain with us; to become one of our little circle?"

"But why? I ain't a Right Liver. There's nothing ails *me*."

"You misunderstand. I mean, how would you like to enter my employ? To become one of the staff of the Sea Breeze Bluff Sanitarium? To join us in our great work for the uplift of humanity?"

"What kind of a job?" says I. "What could I do here?"

"Various things. Superintend the grounds, attend to the livestock, cut the lawns—"

"Well!" says I. "Well! I—I—"

"Say no more," says he. "I see that you accept."

I was on my way to the door, but all at once, through the fog in my head, I begun to sight one reef that I hadn't paid any attention to afore.

"What—what wages do I get?" I asked.

He stood up and laid a hand on my shoulder.

"In a matter like this," he says, "I never permit expense to stand in the way. Salary is a secondary consideration. You will receive thirty dollars a month and your board. Good morning, Mr. Pratt."

At the kitchen door Eureka was waiting for me. She give one look at my face and then she grabbed me by both hands.

"You've said yes," she says. "He's hired you, ain't he?"

"Yes," says I, slow, "he's hired me, I cal'late. I didn't have to say yes; he said it all."

"I knew it!" she sung out. "I knew it! The luck's come! I told you 'twould! And the money, too!"

I leaned up against the door-jamb.

"Money!" I says slow. "Money! . . . Humph! A dollar a day and board is money, I suppose, but I—well, I sha'n't declare no extry dividends right away, I can see that. He said salary was a second consideration. Well, I guess 'tis, Eureka! I guess 'tis."

Love Affair

"EUREKA," says I one morning, "I think I know who Miss Emeline's in love with."

She put down her knife and fork.

"You do, hey?" she says. "Who is it?"

"That Quill man; the Professor one; the thin man with the long hair, that you're so sartin is mixed up in my 'fortune.' "

She acted awful surprised.

"There's something wrong with your sight if you think there's anything more'n friendship between Miss Emeline and the Professor. There ain't, and I know it."

"But, Eureka, look here. They're just made for each other, them two. He's old-familied and quiet and moony and respectable, just the same as she is. And they talk just the same kind of stuff— as if they'd swallowed dictionaries instead of prunes. And, more'n that, they—"

"Nonsense! It ain't so, I tell you. Miss Emeline's love story hasn't got a thing to do with Professor Quill. I tell you, I know it ain't. He ain't the one—no, sir-ee!"

"Then who is?"

"You promise not to tell anybody?" she whispered. "Not a living soul?"

"Not one, living or dead."

"Well, then, I'll tell you. She's been dreaming about Lot Deacon. There!"

"Sho!" says I. "You don't say! That's the most paralyzing notion ever I heard of. There's only one or two p'ints that ain't clear. Who in the name of goodness is Lot Deacon, and where does he live when he's to home?"

"He is her young man," she says. "The one she's engaged to."

"Her young man!" I sung out. "Her young man! And she's engaged to him! Why—why—where?"

"Eighteen years ago, in New Bedford. They was keeping company—engaged, you know. Then they had some foolish squabble or other—something she wanted for the new house they was going to live in when they was married. She thought he ought to buy it, and he said he couldn't afford it. Anyhow, they quarreled and he went off and left her. Next day, she had to go to Boston and stay for a fortni't. When she come back she found he'd skipped aboard a whaler. He'd left her a note saying he was going to make his fortune. *When* he made it he'd come back. He loved her much as ever and if she cared for him she'd wait. And—and she's been waiting ever since."

"Eighteen years?" says I.

"Yes."

"Humph! Well, I must say I admire Miss Emeline's faith, that's all. Sailors are sailors and eighteen years is a long time."

Of course 'twas plain enough why Miss Emeline was possessed with the idea of her Deacon feller's coming back to her, and why she dreamed about him, and all. He was the one real, genuine *big* happening in her precise, prim little life and she just *wouldn't* give him up. Besides, she was a female and, in spite of her primness, had consider'ble of Eureka's hankering for the story book kind of thing, the romantic thing, the tender, sweet, sad, mushy thing. As I say, I laughed when I got by myself, but I didn't mention the subject again. What was the use? If she and Eureka got comfort out of their pet fairy tale, why should I spile their fun?

Opportunities

I USED to take some of the patients cruising in the *Dora Bassett*. In particular Colonel Applegate, a big money man from Providence, R. I., who was hell bent on losing weight. The Colonel was neck deep in his stock doings just at present. There was what he called a "hen on" in Consolidated Brick, and he, being president of the concern, got telegrams and letters by the barrel.

He used to tell about "opportunities" he'd taken advantage of in his day. They had different names and lived in different parts of the country, but he'd took advantage of 'em, all right. If I was an opportunity and owned a ten cent piece I'd bury it when I heard he was anywheres in the neighborhood. And even then I'd sit on the grave.

"I've got an opportunity right now," he says. "One of my little jobs happens to be the presidency of the Consolidated Porcelain Brick Company; the fact is, if you asked me, I should say I was pretty near the whole works. Possibly you've noticed that the papers are giving some space to the company, just now. There's a question of a dividend; perhaps you've noticed that. Some people think we're making money and will declare that dividend. Others think we've been losing money during the past year and will pass it. Whichever way the cat jumps, there's going to be a big difference in the price of the stock. Now I'm the only one that really knows what is going to happen. It's up to me. That's what I call an opportunity."

I should have called it one, myself.

"When is the guileless outsider to be informed as to the cat's jumping?" I asked.

"At the annual meeting in Boston. That's next Friday, four days off. I shall be at that meeting, my boy, and—"

But I interrupted. "You will?" I sung out. "*You* will? Why, Colonel, look a-here! How are you going to get away from the sanitarium? Doctor Wool won't let you off, will he?"

He winked. "There are some things he can't help," he says, "and that's one of 'em. I'll be at that meeting. If I wasn't, there'd be the dickens to pay in the stock market."

THIS was of a Monday. 'Twas Wednesday evening that the big happenings commenced. Colonel Applegate and I were cruising in the *Dora Bassett* when the motor went dead. We drifted and drifted, afore the breeze, which wa'n't directly off shore, but kind of quartering. It carried us up the beach, but further out all the time. 'Twas black night by now, and it got to be nine, and ten, and then eleven o'clock. By and by, off on the port bow, I see a little twinkle of a light. It got brighter and brighter as we drifted nigher to it, and at last I made out that it must be a lamp in the window of some house on a point making out from the main.

I wa'n't used to these latitudes much; most of my cruising had been done further down the Cape a good ways; but I did know that the beach along here was as lonesome as a graveyard, and I'd never heard of anybody's living on it. However, somebody must live there, or else what was the light?

We started screeching; but for a spell it didn't do a mite of good. Then we could see a man's figger, a black shadow against the lamplight.

"Come off and pick us up, won't ye?"

I had to say *that* three times afore the feller in the doorway seemed to sense it. But then he come to life in a hurry. Inside of ten minutes he was alongside in a dory and had us in tow. I found out that this man was Philander Doane. He was what the summer folks label a hermit, meaning somebody that ain't loony, but is next door to it, being odd and queer and independent as a hog on ice. Loony was the only thing he was next door to; for he lived alone in that shanty, fishing and clamming and gunning, and there wa'n't a neighbor nigher than eight miles.

Colonel Applegate insisted that he take us back to the sanitarium immediately. Philander shook his head.

"I wouldn't sail to Wapotomac tonight for no man," he drawled. "It's a long stretch and a dead beat all the way. My catboat's got power in her, but the engine ain't working good; stops every now and then, so I can't use it. No, I'd have to sail, and I don't want to do that. There's too many shoals to risk."

"Colonel Applegate's got to get back, Doane," says I. "It's important."

I might as well have talked to a graven image.

Applegate growled and begged and ordered and swore, but it wa'n't no use.

I thought myself that we'd be picked up pretty soon. I knew my turning up missing wouldn't raise such a dreadful row at the sanitarium, but this would. Not only Cape Cod, but Boston and Providence and the stock market would be anxious to know what had become of *him*. I mentioned it to him once, trying to encourage him, but he only waved his hands and groaned.

"It's that annual meeting, Pratt," he said. "If I'm not at that meeting there'll be the Old Harry to pay. Why—why, they'll think I've skipped out! The papers'll be full of it. Consolidated Brick Common will drop to perdition."

Yes, I was sorry for him, but I couldn't do nothing to help. Walking home was out of the question.

'Twa'n't until two o'clock the following afternoon that we got away from that point and that shanty and that hermit. Then a boat, with an auxiliary, came chugging along. A feller from Wapotomac was running her and Doctor Wool was aboard; so was two young chaps, reporters from Boston papers.

The stock had gone down, down, down. It had "dropped thirty points," so the reporters said. The annual meeting had been postponed until night, and the other directors had given out a statement that, barring the president's absence, everything was fine; but nobody paid any attention to it.

The minute we struck the sanitarium the Colonel sent a half peck of telegrams to Boston. Then he set to work hiring a special train to take him up there. 'Twas arranged for, finally, and he hurried off. Said he'd be back when he could, probably early the following week. Doctor Wool went with him to the station; the Doc was purring directions as to diet and right thinking when they drove out of the yard.

At that meeting the company voted to pay its regular dividend and give out a statement showing that its affairs was in fine shape. Consequently, when the market opened on Saturday, Consolidated Porcelain Brick Common was hitched to a balloon, so to speak, and went up faster than it had gone down. All hands wanted to buy, of course, and such a hurrah you never saw. At twelve o'clock, when the broker works shut down, the price of a share was higher than it had ever been since the company was formed.

COLONEL APPLEGATE only came back to the sanitarium to collect his clothes. I was sorry to say good-by to him. He and I had got on well together. I asked why he'd decided to give up his "treatment."

"I'm tired of being a mark," says he. "I have been one for some time, and now that I know it, I'm going to quit."

"Know? What do you mean?"

"Oh, nothing," says he. "Pratt, how much do you know about the past history of our old friend Wool here?"

"Why, nothing much," says I, trying to guess what he was driving at. "I don't know much of anything. He's had a lot of experience curing folks, that's about all I know. And Miss Adams thinks he's a wonder."

"She does, that's a fact. But I wonder if she. . . . However, that's not my funeral. Only I tell you this, Pratt, for your own good: I wouldn't bank too much on your job here being a permanent one. Good-by."

I wondered what he meant by my job not being permanent. And I wondered, too, what there was about Doctor Wool's "past history." Anyhow, I began to be-lieve that, whatever it was, he'd dropped a flea in the ears of all the other inmates and that the said flea was responsible for their clearing out so sudden.

'Twas plain enough that Wool didn't like the "exodus." He never said noth-ing, of course, and went on his grand, purry, imposing way same as usual. He made proclamations—for Miss Emeline's benefit mainly, I judged—that the de-parting ones was cured and well and he'd told 'em to go. But I didn't believe it and even Eureka was suspicious.

The worst of it was that, though he kept putting advertisements in the papers, no new victims came to take the places of them that had gone. That looked queer to me; seemed almost as if somebody was quietly putting the kibosh on that sanitarium.

The Mysterious Room

IT was lonesome around the place now. Miss Emeline and Professor Quill was the only Right Livers left. I began to notice that Dr. Wool was spending all his time with Professor Quill in a little room on the third floor.

"What do you suppose he does up there, Mr. Pratt?" Eureka asked me.

"I don't know. It's a curious thing, that is. Does Lysander—does Doctor Wool keep you and the cook away from the hall that room opens off of, same as he does me?"

"Yup. He found me there yesterday and he drove me out quick, I tell you. Told me not to come nigh there again. Mr. Pratt, Professor Quill is doing some-thing in that room; he's making some-thing that he and the Doctor don't want anybody else to know about. I'm sure of it. Did you smell anything when you was up in that hall?"

"Like rubber burning, was it?" I asked.

"Yes, that's it exactly," she says.

Well, 'twas a queer business. Lysander the Great started the rumor around that the Professor's being in that room was on account of "special exercising."

Special exercise, hey! Well, it must be a hot old exercise that makes the patient smell like a burnt rubber boot.

And if the idee was to put flesh on poor Quill's bones it wa'n't a success so fur. The poor critter looked thinner and more worried and tired every day. We hardly saw him at all; that is, Eureka and I didn't. And even Miss Emeline saw him only by fits and starts. She was troubled about it, that was plain. One afternoon, down on the beach, when we was alone, she whispered her troubles to me.

"I'm afraid Professor Quill is overtax-ing his brain," she says. "He looks tired; don't you think? I mustn't be selfish. I miss the Professor's society, of course. He and I were very congenial—old friends, you know—and I miss his com-panionship. However, it will be all right soon, I'm sure. It has seemed to me that he has avoided— But there! I am per-mitting myself to become nervous and foolish. Ah! here comes Doctor Wool himself. Now we shall get back into the proper uplifting atmosphere."

We did. That is, I presume likely we did. The Doctor came parading down to us, his big face shining, his smile working overtime, and the whole of him sticking up out of that desolation of sand and pines like a white-washed meeting-house back of a run-down cemetery. He was a wonder to look at, and to hear; and yet I was—well, I was getting hard-ened, I'm afraid. I didn't experience re-ligion *every* time he got into the pulpit. Down in my hold was a doubt, a doubt that kept growing, like a toadstool in a dark cowshed.

Two things I felt fairly sure of: One was that Miss Emeline was right when she started to say that Professor Jonathan Quill avoided her. T'other was a down-right sartinty that he didn't like that avoiding any better'n she did.

The Miracle

A ND now I've worked up to what was the most astonishing happening of all that lit on me while I was at that Rest shop. It's so astonishing, so ever-lasting ridiculous and unbelievable, that I swan to man I hate to tell about it. Eureka and I were alone in the kitchen, and it was just a quarter-past eight. I know, because I looked at the clock when the knock came at the back door.

I answered that knock, wondering who the knocker could be. It turned out to be no man I'd ever seen afore, I was sartin. Men that I knew around Wapa-tomac didn't wear high, shiny plug hats, nor yeller spring overcoats, nor carry canes with ivory heads as big as a cat-boat's anchor, as you might say.

"Good evening," says the feller, brisk and polite. "Does—does a party—a lady, I mean, by the name of Adams live here?"

"Why, yes," says I, doubtful.

Afore I could say any more he pushed past me and walked into the kitchen. Eureka had been standing inside the door, listening, and he pretty nigh bumped into her. He started back and stared at her with all his eyes.

"This—you—this ain't her, is it?" he sung out.

"Ain't who?" says Eureka, about as much surprised as I was to see him act so.

"This is Miss Sparrow," says I. "She's the housekeeper."

Him and Eureka shook hands. She was looking him over from head to foot, yeller overcoat and tall hat and cane and all. I could see her eyes begin to stick out. This feller, whoever he might be, was her idee of the real thing.

"He wants to see Miss Emeline," I put in, by way of explanation.

"Oh," says Eureka, trying not to look disappointed; I do believe she'd been hoping he'd come to see *her*. "Well, Miss Emeline is in her room. I don't know as she has gone to bed—"

The door opened.

"Eureka," said Miss Emeline's voice.

She stopped. She and the stranger looked at each other—looked and looked. And, slow but sure, what little color she had melted away.

"Oh!" she gasped, faint. "Oh! What? Who?"

"Lord A'mighty!" says he. "Emeline!"

"Oh! oh!" pants Miss Emeline. "Lot Deacon!"

And down she went in a heap on the kitchen floor.

Star Boarder

A ND that's the way the miracle hap-pened, just as I've told you. We got Miss Emeline up off that kitchen floor, and set her in a chair and sprinkled water on her; that is, the Deacon man and I did.

Miss Emeline came to after a while, and the first thing she said was: "Does Doctor Wool know?" And when Eureka said that he didn't, being upstairs in the room with Professor Quill, she said not to tell him.

"Don't tell him; don't tell anyone—yet," she stammered. "I—I can't— Oh, Lot, is it really you?"

Eureka tipped me the wink and jerked her head towards the other room. We went out and left 'em together.

Miss Emeline was mighty weak and pale when she opened the door. When we started to speak to her she asked us not to.

Deacon was standing by the table. He looked pretty nigh as shook up as Miss Emeline. He was swabbing at his forehead with the silk handkerchief.

"Hello!" says he, pretty average trembly. "Say, this beats cock-fighting, don't it. I—I guess I'd better be getting back to town and hunt up sleeping quarters. We've fixed it up. She wants me to pretend to be an old friend of hers that has come here for treatment. Then I can stay without all hands knowing—knowing how it is between us. You two have got to promise to keep mum. Will you?"

"Sartin," says I. Eureka looked awful disappointed.

From then on Mr. Lot Deacon, the South American manufacturer, became star boarder, in Colonel Applegate's place, at the Right Livers' Rest. Doctor Lysander fairly poured ile over that ex-whaler. There was nothing too good for him. I judged that the price the new boarder was paying was a big rock in a thirsty land to Lysander the Great just then.

Deacon spent full as much time with Eureka and me as he done with Miss Emeline, though of course he spent a lot with her, too. Eureka heard some of their talk together and she told me every word.

"I can't understand Miss Emeline," she said to me. "She don't act half as glad and radiant and soul-satisfied as she'd ought to, seems to me. Why, I heard 'em talking yesterday. He asked her why she didn't wear the big diamond ring he give her. She kind of shivered like, seemed to me, and she says:

"'I can't, Lot. I can't—not now, if ever.'

"'But why not, Emeline?' he says. 'We're engaged, ain't we? Have been for nineteen year, and Lord knows that's long enough.'

"'Lot,' she says, 'how do you know I want to marry you, after all this long time?'

"'Haven't you been waiting for me all this time?' says he. 'And saying you knew I was coming some day? And dreaming about me? That Sparrow girl says you have.'

"'Did she say that? Has she been talking to you of my affairs? She should know better. If she wasn't such a well-meaning, kind-hearted girl, I should discharge her this moment.'

"You better believe I felt pretty bad when I heard that, Mr. Pratt. But what Mr. Deacon said made me feel so proud I didn't care.

"'Discharge her!' he almost hollered. 'Discharge her! Why, Emeline, how you talk! She's a fine girl! A bully girl! I never saw a better, handsomer, nicer-behaved girl than she is. And I've seen some in my day, all colors and kinds.'

"I tell you I was proud when I heard that, but Miss Emeline only shivered again and asked him please not to speak of the dreadful creatures he'd met in the awful places he'd been in. He went on pleading with her.

"'But, Emeline,' he says, 'how can you talk about marrying me that way? Ain't I been true to you all these years? Didn't I work for nothing but to make you happy some day? What in—I mean what do you think I hunted you up for if it wa'n't for just that? After I found you hadn't married anybody else, of course.'

"She bust out crying. 'Oh, I know it, Lot,' she says. 'I know it. You're a kind, good-hearted man. I know. But are you sure you want to marry—me?'

"'Why—why, Emeline—' he stammered.

"'You must be patient,' she says. 'You must bear with me. And, for my sake, you must learn to speak lower and not use such—such language and slang. Perhaps, if you do that, and never tell Doctor Wool or anyone else a word of this that is between us, I—I—perhaps—'

"I didn't hear any more, Mr. Pratt.

and I wish I hadn't heard that much. What makes her act so? I can't understand. If he wasn't such a splendid man, just like a regular nobleman, I might; but I can't now. Can you?"

I just shook my head. It did seem to me that Eureka's and Miss Emeline's pet romance they'd built so much on wa'n't turning out to be all sugar; there was some vinegar in it.

Baited Hooks

I WAS coming to like the Deacon man first-rate. He and I and Eureka spent more and more time together. He seemed to enjoy being in the kitchen with us full as much as he did confabbing with Wool or Professor Quill. Yes, or even Miss Emeline. And he kept his eyes open; he was as sharp as a razor. There wa'n't much got by him, I tell you.

One day I was out in the barn and he drifted in. I was currying the horse and he sat down on the wheelbarrow and begun to ask questions. Especially about Wool.

"Who is he, anyway? Tell me what you know about him."

I told what I knew, which wa'n't so much. He listened, mighty attentive.

"So Emeline's money—part of it, anyhow—is in that feller's hands. She's backing this Breeze Bluff health factory, is she? I guessed as much. Now tell me something about the schoolmaster, old Long-shanks—Quill, I mean. What is he doing here?"

I said he was a patient, suffering from general breakdown.

"Humph! Does he dance his breakdowns in that room overhead there? He's shut up in that room most of the time, and no one but Wool is allowed to come near him. What is going on in that room?"

I told him about the "exercises." He sniffed.

"Rats!" he says. "Tell that to the marines. You're no marine, Pratt. What do you think is up?"

For a minute I didn't answer. Then I spoke what I'd been thinking for some time.

"I believe," I told him, "that there's something else going on, something that's a dead secret between the Pro-

fessor and the Doctor. Miss Emeline told Eureka once that Professor Quill was, besides being a schoolteacher, a sort of inventor, as you might say. He's invented half a dozen contraptions that have done pretty well for somebody else, though he ain't made much out of 'em. I—"

"Hold on there! Wait a minute. How did Emeline know all this?"

"Why, she and Quill are old friends. They knew each other up to Brockton. Didn't she tell you that?"

"No. No-o. Fact is, she don't seem to want to talk about this Quill feller at all. Hum! . . . Hum! . . ."

"Do you think there's some kind of crooked work going on here?" he asks me.

"There's nothing crooked about Professor Quill. I'll take my oath on that."

"So will I, from what I've seen of him; but it's here, just the same. You know what I'm going to do? I'm going to heave out a line or two baited with the name of Lysander P. I'm in hopes I may get a bite or two that'll lead to information."

When he said that I had an idee. I laid down my currycomb, got a pencil out of my pocket, and wrote a name and address on the back of an old envelope.

"You might heave one of your lines in that direction," says I. "Perhaps you'll get a bite and perhaps you won't."

He read what I'd written. "'Colonel William J. Applegate. Such and such Street, Providence, R. I.,'" says he. "Humph! If I have a business call that takes me away from these latitudes for a week or so pretty soon, don't be surprised. And don't ask too many questions as to where I'm going, either."

Two days later he—Deacon—went off on that "business errand." He told Miss

Emeline he was going to look into a finance affair, that was his excuse to her and to Wool. She seemed resigned to have him go. Their secret had been kept first-rate. Eureka and I were the only outsiders that knew it.

Surprise Party

ONE evening about a week later I went out to the barn to lock up. I was just taking the key out of the door when I felt a hand on my arm. I turned around. There, alongside of me, was Lot Deacon, as large as life—which was large enough, goodness knows.

"Hush!" he whispers. "Don't make any noise. I came on the afternoon train, and I've been hanging around the woods ever since. I don't want anyone to know I'm here. Don't say anything, but come along. I want you to come with me to that room of Quill's."

"But—but he's there, ain't he?"

"No, I think he's gone out. There is no light in the window. And Wool's in his office, so the coast is clear. Come."

That room was a surprise party in its way. The carpet had been pulled off the floor, there was a pine table in the middle, and all around was the most curious mess of truck. Bottles by the dozen and little trays and tools and hammers and measuring things, even a little alcohol lamp and a sort of baby forge which was run by alcohol, too. And rubber—all kinds of rubber. I couldn't make head nor tail of the mess, but Deacon got more interested.

"I—it can't be," he says. "It *can't* be. How could he do it here? Without the equipment or anything? He couldn't! and yet—and yet I believe he has. It's a new process; some new process, with chemicals. If it is—if it is, it is the biggest thing—"

Afore I could ask another question I heard something. So did he. I looked around. There was another room connecting with this one, the Professor's bedroom it was. I grabbed him by the arm and pulled him into it, closing the door easy astern of me.

The knock—a mighty faint, careful knock it was—sounded. Then some one said:

"Professor! Professor Quill, are you there?"

It was Miss Emeline.

NEXT minute there was more footsteps in the hall, heavy, solid footsteps, and I heard Miss Emeline give a little scream.

"Oh!" says she. "Oh, I—"

"Why, Miss Adams!" booms Doctor Wool's voice. "Miss Adams, what are you doing here?"

I expected to hear some sort of excuse or apology. I sartin never expected to hear what I did. When she answered him 'twa'n't to make any excuses.

"Doctor Wool," she says, "why did you tell me that Professor Quill was working on exercises in this room?"

He didn't answer on the jump. I wish I might have seen his face, but he was out of range of the keyhole.

"My dear Miss Adams," he purred. "Really I—I can't understand—"

"Why did you tell me that?"

"I told you because—because you asked me."

"I asked you for the truth and you told me a falsehood. Yes, a deliberate falsehood."

"A falsehood! Miss Adams, I am not accustomed to—"

It didn't make any difference to her what he was accustomed to. The "first family" blood was up; I never heard her speak so sharp and brisk. She flew back at him afore he could get his purr working good.

"You told me a falsehood. Anyone can see that the story is ridiculous and untrue. He has been working at some experiment here, some chemical experiment, I am sure. It is perfectly plain. You knew that I was Professor Quill's friend; that we were old friends. Why have you deceived me in this way?"

He hesitated again. Then I cal'late he

made up his mind to change his course. *That* tack was fetching him further from port every second.

"Emeline," he said, "my dear Emeline, why do you continue to misjudge me? And repulse me? You know that my one ambition in life is to be worthy of you. Why do you repulse me always? Why not yield to my devotion and let me care for you through life? I worship you. I—"

"Don't! don't!" she cried. "I forbid you to touch me. I have told you that I could never marry you. Months ago, when I trusted you absolutely, I told you that. And now, when I— Oh, who is it?"

It came mighty near being Lot Deacon. He was shoving his way past me. But some one else was in that other room ahead of him afore he could open our door.

"What is the matter?" says Professor Quill. "Miss Adams—Doctor Wool, what is it?"

"Nothing is the matter, Professor," he said, soothing. "Calm yourself, my dear sir. Miss Adams and I— Well, we are here, as you see. I feel obliged to disclose your secret to her."

"Of the process? The vulcanizing process? It is new! It is wonderful! It will revolutionize the vulcanizing of rubber, make it as hard and as tough as steel almost and at half the cost of the old, inferior way."

"Hush!" she says again. "Hush, please. I want you to answer me truthfully, Jonathan. I know you will if I ask it. Who is responsible for your being here and at work in this room? Is it that man there?"

"Quill," says Wool, dropping his purr and speaking sharp and quick, "be careful."

"I—I will not lie, Emeline," the Professor said. "Doctor Wool brought me here. He is interested in my invention. I told him of it over a year ago and proved to him that I was on the right track. I owe so much to him. He is back-

ing me with his money. He has kept me here and furnished me with the materials and money to continue experimenting. He— Doctor, I beg your pardon. Forgive me for telling her. She asked me and I couldn't lie—to her."

The Doctor couldn't seem to find words to answer, and yet, if I'd been him, I should have cal'lated I'd better answer then, or never. Afore he made a sound Miss Emeline spoke.

"*He* has backed you—with money?" she said. "*He*—with *his* money? Why, he has no money! I have been supplying him with money to support this sanitarium. And so *much* money! I couldn't understand— Oh!" as if all at once she had begun to understand; "O-oh! is it possible! Doctor Wool, have you been backing Professor Quill's experiment with *my* money? And pretending to me that it was needed to keep this sanitarium from becoming bankrupt. Is *this* where all the thousands I have advanced you have gone? Is it? But why —*why?*"

I was so interested in all this that I'd forgot I was on earth. What reminded me was being pushed pretty nigh off of it. Lot Deacon gave me a shove that sent me reeling, flung the bedroom door open, and walked in.

"I guess I can answer that, Emeline," he said.

"You, Wool, you listen to me. I was onto you the first day I came here. I've had some experience with fakirs and scalawags in my time, and I begun to suspect you as soon as I saw you. Emeline, I'll tell you where your thousands have gone to. That cuss there"—Miss Emeline shivered when he said "cuss," but she looked where he pointed—"is sharp and smart enough; I'll say that for him. Somehow or other he got onto the Professor's vulcanizing process and saw what was in it. It's a wonder, I believe, and properly handled it'll be worth millions to the company that exploits it. Wool knew that. That's why he fetched Quill here and has kept him hid; so no one else would learn of the process.

"And Wool—" he goes on. "Shut up, you! Don't you open your head, or I'll knock it off. This Wool has been forming a stock company with himself at the head of it and holding most of the stock. That's where your thousands have gone, Emeline. Well, what is it, Professor?"

Poor Quill was white as a sheet and wringing both hands.

"Oh, it can't be true!" he said. "It can't be! Your money, Emeline, yours! It is lost, and I am responsible! If And I had hoped—I had hoped that some day I might be rich and could come to you and say—"

Miss Emeline said, "Hush, Jonathan," and stopped him from saying what he'd meant to say. What it was I could guess, and I saw Deacon look at 'em both pretty sharp. As for Doctor Wool, he laughed, laughed scornful and top-lofty.

"This is ridiculous, quite," he said. "My dear Miss Adams, I fear our new patient has been tarrying with the wine cup during his absence. I will explain to you later on, when we are free from interlopers and lunatics, and—er—eavesdroppers."

He started to march out of the room, but Lot stopped him.

"I know why you got out of the patent-medicine game," he says. "I know how near you came to going to state's prison when the Government analyzed your doped 'Willow Wine' and the rest of it. And, by the Almighty, you'll go there yet—for swindling—if you don't clear off these premises inside of twelve hours. I'll give you until noon to-morrow to skip for good. Now get!"

And Dr. Wool got.

I didn't mind—I was having a good time—but poor Miss Emeline shrivelled and shivered.

"Oh, Lot!" says she, and started to go. Professor Quill jumped for'ard and offered her his arm. They left the room together.

"Whew!" says that South American ex-whaler, mopping his forehead. "Whew! Well, I feel some better, anyhow. Come on, Pratt; let's go find Eureka. She's more my type."

"But—but don't you think you'd better go to Miss Emeline?" says I. "Maybe she needs you."

He looked down the hall. Miss Emeline and Quill were just at the top of the stairs, he helping her and she leaning heavy on his arm.

Deacon turned to me.

"Come on, I want to see Eureka," says he.

Fortunes Come True

AH, WELL, that was last September, and now it's April once more. A pile of things have happened.

Lot and Eureka and the Professor and Miss Emeline are married. Eureka and Lot have been pretty much all over creation since, and, judging by Mrs. D.'s letters, he and she have enjoyed the real Paris and the rest of it full as much as they did day-dreaming about 'em.

The Quills are up to Brookline, the vulcanizing invention has been incorporated and there's a whacking big factory being put up in East Cambridge. Neither Jonathan nor his wife will have to worry about finances, I cal'late, even if a dozen wolves in Wool's clothing

turned up to rob 'em. Lot Deacon is president of the new company and Colonel Applegate is on the board of directors.

And I—well, I'm beginning to have a heap more faith in tea-leaf fortune-telling than I did one time. When Sophrony Gott saw that money coming to me in the teacup she sartin had her specs on, or else she's the best guesser in creation.

First thing that made me set up and take notice was a letter from Colonel Applegate. Inside it was a certificate for ten shares of Consolidated Porcelain Brick stock.

"If it hadn't been for you, Pratt, I

should not have made money on that deal. Keep it. If you dare to send it back I'll come down and shut you up in Doane's shanty and feed you on salt mackerel for a month."

But that ain't all. Lot Deacon writes me that I'm to be a shareholder in the vulcanizing business. "You've earned it," says he. "'Twas you that gave me the tip to see Applegate about Wool."

And, to cap the whole thing, Miss Emeline has put me in charge of the whole of her property at Wapatomac, house, land, and all.

She won't take any rent, so you see, from being flat broke, I've come to be a landholder and a stockholder and mercy knows what all. There's only one trouble, and that is that hard cash is middling scurce, even yet. I can't sell my land nor my house nor my stocks, and it costs like fury to live up to 'em.

Eleazir Kendrick, my old partner in the fish-weir business, and me have thought serious of opening up the ex-sanitarium as a summer boarding house for city folks. We may do it; I shouldn't wonder if we did. If we do, I wonder what sort of freaks'll come to stop with us. They can't beat the Right Livers for freakiness, though; nobody could do that.

PROSPICE

FEAR death?—to feel the fog in my throat,
    The mist in my face,
When the snows begin, and the blasts denote
    I am nearing the place,
The power of the night, the press of the storm,
    The post of the foe;
Where he stands, the Arch Fear in a visible form,
    Yet the strong man must go:
For the journey is done and the summit attained,
    And the barriers fall,
Though a battle 's to fight ere the guerdon be gained,
    The reward of it all.
I was ever a fighter, so—one fight more,
    The best and the last!
I would hate that death bandaged my eyes, and forbore,
    And bade me creep past.
No! let me taste the whole of it, fare like my peers
    The heroes of old,
Bear the brunt, in a minute pay glad life's arrears
    Of pain, darkness and cold.
For sudden the worst turns the best to the brave,
    The black minute's at end,
And the elements' rage, the fiend-voices that rave,
    Shall dwindle, shall blend,
Shall change, shall become first a peace, then a joy,
    Then a light, then thy breast,
O thou soul of my soul! I shall clasp thee again,
    And with God be the rest!

                    —R. Browning

MARGARET HALSEY

WITH MALICE TOWARD SOME

MARGARET HALSEY, author of "With Malice Toward Some," was born in Yonkers, New York, in 1910. She attended Yonkers' public schools and Skidmore College, Saratoga, New York. She took an M.A. 1936-1937 at Teachers' College, Columbia University, but she has never taught school. Her book is the result of a trip taken to England with her husband who taught for a year as an exchange professor at Exeter. During this time the author lived in a small English village where she came into contact with the English landed gentry, whom she places in woeful contrast to a class labeled by her with the eloquent coined word "ungentry." Her book has been a consistent best seller ever since its publication.

May 30th

GETTING married was nothing. I had the German measles on my wedding day and a raging temperature, so that I was married under a forced draught, as it were, and afterwards I went back to bed and opened a fresh box of Kleenex.

That seems a long time ago. Now Henry has an exchange professorship for next winter at Exeter, a small college in England, and we are sailing on the *Britannic* tomorrow. I have never traveled, and the suitcases and tissue paper and coat-hangers have wrought me to such a white heat of excitement that I could be put on an anvil and hammered into any shape you want.

June 2nd

WE are having a storm, and the *Britannic* has spent two days trying to conclude a working agreement with the Atlantic Ocean and failing miserably. Henry's stomach and mine are both behaving like perfect little ladies. But it is not everybody's motion and the boat has a horribly front-line-trenches atmosphere about it.

June 7th

THE boat got in today. I am sitting in the waiting room of the Southampton station. My eyes, I am afraid, are going to fall right out of their sockets before the end of the day—I have been looking at everything so strenuously.

Whoever it was that said not Angles but angels, must have been talking about English porters, customs men and railroad attendants. They have been taking care of us with the solicitude you could not hope to receive in the United States unless you were either the President or noticeably pregnant. The porters did not look at their tips, only smiled and raised their caps. I half expected them to say if they had known we were coming, they would have whipped up a cake.

Later

THE English countryside, as we saw it from the train this afternoon, is so intensely rural that it makes the country landscapes at home seem, in retrospect, faintly urban. The thatched houses are low-slung, and have not only the air of having pushed their way up through the ground, but also an air of being quite ready to push their way back down

Here and there the verger stopped and made a speech

Illustration for Margaret Halsey's
"WITH MALICE TOWARD SOME"

again. For the most part, however, the countryside was prospect succeeding prospect of woodland, streams, hills and meadows—all, evidently, custom-tailored by Alfred Lord Tennyson.

But it is so damp! I can almost feel the mould forming on my face and hands.

June 12th

ONCE you get past the English flavor of things, the pattern of Exeter seems to be much like the pattern of American provincial cities—a large, tame population of movie-goers; a handful of upper-crusters, not so tame; a good library; no music to speak off; and a rather distressing preoccupation with entertaining, though the city is a thousand times more interesting than its American counterparts. Just off the main street on one side stands the Cathedral, and just off it on the other side of the hill is a park whose banks of flowers and manicured tidiness make the usual American park look like a bowling alley on Saturday night.

Notes on a Dinner

CANNED GRAPEFRUIT (slightly warmed) —This is unusual and was probably designed as a sop to the Americans.

Soup—Thick and dark and utterly savorless. Tasted as if it had been drained out of the umbrella stand.

Roast beef—It seems a shame to spoil this symmetry of criticism with a word of praise, but I do think English meat much superior to ours, finer textured and with more flavor.

Boiled potatoes and Brussels sprouts— Here is a country where the soil is so fertile that if you plant an acorn in the ground, you have to jump back quickly in order not to have it hit you on the way up. And the English raise Brussels sprouts. Just Brussels sprouts. With sometimes a flyer in cabbage.

Raspberry tart—It is possible to eat English piecrust, whatever you may think at first. The English eat it, and when they stand up and walk away, they hardly bend over at all.

June 13th

I HAVE not only found a house, but I have found a house which qualifies as one of the major satisfactions of life. It is in a village called Yeobridge which dozes primly in the lee of a steep hill, about eight miles from Exeter. A high, moss-encrusted wall, with little ferns growing in the crevices, surrounds the house and only the casement windows of the gables are visible over the top. Inside there is half an acre of English garden with all the habitual picturesqueness of such projects. It is all so attractive, it seems to call for a calendar pasted underneath.

June 18th

HENRY became pro-house as soon as he caught sight of it. The house belongs to a small, elderly widow named Mrs. Emmeline Turney, who has such an eighteenth-century clarity of outline that you would not dare leave a copy of Jane Austen around, for fear she should disappear into it.

English ladies seem to spend half their time gardening and the other half being respected and avoided by English men. I have a theory about their hats. I think they keep them suspended on pulleys from the bedroom ceiling and when they want to put one on, they go and stand directly under it, pull a rope, and it drops down, smack, squarely on top of the head. Then, without touching a finger to it, they march out of the house.

Their universal ineptitude about clothes fills me with a great pity and an overwhelming desire to take them in hand. But I know in advance it would be fruitless. The trouble goes deeper than their having no eye for line and no feeling for color, though they are as dewily unaware of line and color as an orangoutang. The fundamental difficulty is that they are ashamed of having legs and waists and breasts, and so they muffle themselves up as if their bodies were something that had to be smuggled through the customs.

We have taken the house, of course, and we have also taken the maid with it. Her name is Phyllis and she has blue eyes and red, red cheeks and she is so clean she shimmers. When I was piloted into the kitchen to look her over, she blushed like a well-trained sunrise. Mrs. Turney speaks to her kindly, but as from an immeasurable distance. Henry suggests that she probably goes into Exeter twice a week to an American movie and is no doubt waiting hopefully for us to wear silver fox on our night clothes and shoot from the hip.

September 7th

WE have flushed, of all things, an Englishman who does not talk about the weather, and who should it have to be, of course, but the man who is sailing for America at the end of this week to take Henry's place. His name is Mr. Primrose and his most striking quality is that he succeeds in combining a very English repose with a wholly un-English curiosity.

Mr. Primrose charmed us both by laughing. What makes a visiting American feel most helpless and lonely in England is, I think, neither the food nor the climate nor the damp houses nor the relentless subservience of the lower classes nor the spectacle of English gentlemen being conscientiously banal under the impression that it represents a magnificent discipline. What makes an American realize sinkingly that this, by God, is alien corn is the relative scarcity of laughter. You can get a kind of whinnying sound out of the well-bred

English merely by saying that it is raining. But when it comes to humorous language, American similes and metaphors land with a morbid thump in the midst of puzzled silence. The only way to make the English laugh, as laughter is understood in the United States, is to jab them with your elbow and say out of the corner of your mouth, "That's funny." Then they all look nervously around at each other and allow you two decibels of politely acquiescent mirth.

Mr. Primrose charms me by talking to me as if I were a human being and not A Woman. Men who talk well and intelligently to Henry at meetings and committees wag a mischievous finger at me and say archly, "You women! I know you!" (The instinct to reply, "Chrissake, kid, you got me wrong" all but chokes me.) Englishmen, from what I can see, do not talk to women if they can possibly avoid it, and if they must talk to them, they keep the conversation inexorably down to their idea of the level of feminine understanding.

And Englishwomen—even the brainy ones, apparently—meekly concur. Brought up in girls' schools and trained to be as much as possible like perambulating salads, they are incurably afraid of men. Whatever the rest of the world thinks of the English gentleman, the English lady regards him apprehensively as something between God and a goat, and equally formidable on both scores.

September 29th

TOMORROW we move into Yeobridge, and from now on there will be a whole house to spread out in and I shall wear ironed underwear again. Whee!

October 1st

PHYLLIS did most of the unpacking. When we first arrived, she was so frightened of us that I thought she was going to cry, but I sent her around to the post office to buy some stamps and regain her composure, and by the time she returned, her natural instinct for running things had come irresistibly to the surface.

She catechized me delicately on my ideas about housekeeping and appeared surprised and relieved to discover that I am innocent of any. Finally, after a suitable interim, she produced a dinner with magnificent roast beef and an omelet so light that we had to lay our knives across it and even then it struggled. We haled her in and complimented her fervently on the meal, which made her blush and look pleased, but also a little startled, as if she were not used to praise. It looks as if we have a paragon on our hands.

October 2nd

PHYLLIS calls me "Adam." I got Henry to listen too, thinking I might be imagining, but there is no mistaking it. Not a trace of an initial "m." "Madame Bede" and "Adam Bovary" have been going through my head all day.

I have had two callers, a Mrs. Wadhams, who is young, and a Mrs. Pennard, who is not. Mrs. Wadhams came yesterday. She has a stocky, unimaginative body and a face which looks ten years too young for it. Her hair is golden as the traditional guinea and her complexion makes me feel like the beach at low tide. She is, I suppose, that "simple English girl" to whom the British are fond of referring with a tender and rather horticultural pride, as if they grew them on south walls, like apricots.

The Wadhamses live in the house nearest ours, and Captain Wadhams is an officer in the Yeomanry, which seems to be a kind of militia officered by professional army men. They have a year-old son, and Mrs. Wadhams creates a distinct impression that he comes in a bad third in her affections, the pursuits of hunting and gardening easily nosing him out. She uses the word "gentry"

MARGARET HALSEY, the author of "With Malice Toward Some," is the wife of a young Ph.D., who went to England on an exchange professorship. Her book is vitriolic in spots, but she has many good words to say for the English countryside and the English character. The informality of her prose is reflected in this wind-blown photograph.

with entire naturalness, and not as if she hoped I would notice it or as if she noticed it herself, but the expression bounced into me as if it had come from a slingshot.

Mrs. Wadhams had told me that Mrs. Pennard would probably call. "She's the Big Five in Yeobridge," said Mrs. Wadhams in her light, schoolgirlish way.

When I mentioned Mrs. Pennard to Phyllis her round, clean young features fell into an expression which was the best she could get out of them in the way of weary distaste. Mrs. Pennard, it appears, was widowed a good many years ago by a hunting accident and has devoted her time ever since to charity. The list of her good works sounds like freight-car loadings in a banner year and they must cost her considerable amounts in time, trouble and money. From Phyllis's somewhat elliptical account, she regards the manners and morals of servant girls as having been especially committed to her supervision by a Deity who had given them up in despair Himself.

When Mrs. Pennard called today, I was more or less prepared for her—which was a good thing because Mrs. Pennard was not disposed to be cheerful and informal. "A lettuce woman," I thought glibly when she came into the room, for she had grey hair and she wore a beautifully tailored grey tweed coat.

But I gaped with surprise when I heard her voice. It has the teary whine of a slattern trying to put off the rent-collector. Looking with sudden attention at her face, I noticed that every line in it goes downward. It is a face that seriously undermines the repose of the beholder, for it keeps him hearkening for the soft, slow splash that will be Mrs. Pennard's countenance sliding down and landing sadly on Mrs. Pennard's bosom.

October 11th

BOTH Mrs. Wadhams and Mrs. Pennard, when they called, spoke of the college in Exeter with pitying condescension. Mrs. Pennard said tremulously that she understood you did not get a very good class of people there. The Wadhams-Pennard attitude arises, I think, from the fact that most of the students are poor and are trying to pull themselves up a class or two by getting an education.

The English have refined upon our naive American way of judging people by how much money they happen to have at the moment. The subtler English criterion is how much expensive, upper-class education they have been able to afford. Consequently, in England, having had money is just as acceptable as having it, since the upper-class mannerisms persist, even after the bankroll has disappeared. But never having had money is unforgivable, and can only be properly atoned for by never trying to get any.

October 18th

OUR English acquaintances would be utterly incredulous if it were pointed out to them that they are consistently and unendurably insulting to Americans, but it happens to be true. The people we meet as equals have been trained from childhood to patronize Americans as Americans are trained from childhood to clean their teeth, and they do it just as automatically. Generally speaking it is impossible for an American to get through an afternoon or evening in the company of English people without hearing at least half a dozen unmistakable hints that culturally speaking, his compatriots are running neck and neck with the anthropoid apes.

Nobody with any pretensions to good sense objects to fair criticism. It is that the English do not criticize America for critizable things. If they have ever heard of lynching, of municipal corruption, or the violence attendant upon American strikes, no syllable of reference to such shortcomings ever passes their lips. They have just one big blanket indictment of America. It isn't England. What can you do with people like that, except to go home and raise hell in a diary?

November 4th

TODAY was Phyllis's afternoon out and, thinking I was doing her a favor, I washed up the supper dishes. But when she came in and viewed this job lot of benevolence, she swept into the drawing room with so much impetus as to forget her usual delicately respectful pause at the door. "Adam mustn't *do* such things!" she said, in such an agony of shame and embarrassment that she instantly made me ashamed and embarrassed too, from sheer contagion. Henry calmed her down with mild assurances that in the United States perfectly irreproachable ladies sometimes wash the dishes.

WITH MALICE TOWARD SOME

November 12th

MOST of the Yeobridge gentlefolk have visited the paper factory at one time or another, and derived great comfort therefrom. The factory is a small one, planked down in the middle of the English country-side, with trees and hedgerows coming right up to the railroad siding. It is a set-up which pleasantly confirms the gentry in their conviction that the plight of the oppressed classes is greatly exaggerated.

Inside the factory, the country-club-cum-museum note disappears immediately. Mr. Higginson went with us, but the workmen explained the processes. Just as we were leaving, I saw two little boys sweeping an immense, dusty litter down a long corridor. They must have been fourteen, which is the age for leaving school in England, but they were small enough to be taken for nine or ten. They glanced at us apathetically and then went drearily on with their sweeping. Their faces were almost blotted out with fatigue and they moved like sick old men. I touched Mr. Higginson on his pin-striped sleeve and asked him how many boys of that age were employed in the plant, but either he did not hear me over the noise of the machinery or he pretended not to.

There is a curious distinction, incidentally, between English and American conservatives. It lies in their hearing. If an American reactionary has his attention called to subhuman living conditions, he answers with great heat that those people spend all their money on radios and fur coats. The British Tory, on the other hand, smiles radiantly and replies, "We have been having frightful weather, haven't we?"

November 21st

MR. PRIMROSE warned us in his letter that just about the time we are packing up next June to leave England, we will begin to get the hang of Exeter and Yeobridge and to discover which people we would really like to know. I begin to realize how right he is and how mistaken I was to think that living in England for a year would give one an idea of English life. English life is seven-eighths below the surface, like an iceberg, and living in England for a year constitutes an introduction to an introduction to an introduction to it.

January 4th

SERIOUS-MINDED Henry warns fun-loving Peg that she will probably be sorry if she lets her diary trail off. But the fact is, that I am losing the impulse to diarize. The impact of England startled me into making notes, but now —having resolved Yeobridge into the general working proposition that the countryside would melt in your mouth and the gentry will not melt in hell—I slip back into laziness and silence.

January 6th

THE first spring flowers and the lambing season begin this month. Phyllis says Adam will enjoy the English spring. I think I will. Her manner was so primly authoritative that I would not dare not to. While I was out in the garden with her, she said absently, "I think there's going to be a baby there."

"Where?" I asked, looking around.

"Why, Adam," she said, in the tone of one addressing a wilful child, "At the Wadhamses."

Gentlemen, I give you the English Ungentry. The next time we come to this country, I hope Henry will get an exchange with a plumber.

WESTERN WIND

WESTERN wind, when wilt thou blow?
   The small rain down can rain.
Christ, if my Love were in my arms
   And I in my bed again!
                    —*Anonymous.*

How to Develop the Power of Concentration

ERNEST DIMNET

THE ART OF THINKING

"THERE is a tendency to regard the thinker as a specialist instead of as a man worthy of the name," says Abbé Dimnet. So you can see why he would design his own work to help you to think and live at your best, instead of attempting to dazzle you with philosophical jargon. He is one of the few Frenchmen who can write with distinction in English and, despite his 73 years, makes a point of coming every year to America, his self-appointed fountain of youth.

The Exhilaration of Consciousness

THE Art of Thinking is the art of being one's self and this art can only be learned if one is by one's self.

Solitude produces an exhilaration of consciousness, the consciousness of our innermost, whatever that may be. It never fails of this result. [Admiral Byrd's "Alone," Issue No. 19. *Ed.*]

Take strong coffee one morning, to keep yourself awake, lie not in bed but on a couch for two or three hours, and try to simplify and again simplify your problems, that is to say, in most cases, your home-made annoyances. You will soon understand why Descartes made his discoveries lying down in the mornings.

How can we secure solitude when our path is beset with a variety of undesirables? There is no answer to this question if we do not really crave solitude. But if we do, solitude will come, for no magnetism is as strong as a man's wish to be let alone. One day you will notice with satisfaction that you are glad to be kept waiting because this gives you a chance of being left alone; you will know that you really love solitude, and you will not have to seek it or pray for it any more. Solitude will be where you are.

As exterior solitude is the reduction of human beings and even of objects around us to a minimum, concentration or inner solitude is the elimination, one after the other, of all images foreign to a train of thought. The train of thought is often spontaneous: we then call it absorption.

Many people are professionally trained to concentration. Napoleon could pass from one subject to a completely different one, from strategy, for instance, to the Charter of the Comédie-Française, as if he had been another man. He had in his mind what he sometimes called drawers, sometimes atlases, providing him with the matter he required.

Lawyers, or spiritual directors, often surprise us by the undivided attention they can give to one consultant after another, but they limit themselves to kindred cases and are collected rather than concentrated. However they too manage to live in an interior solitude which constant knocking at their door does not succeed in breaking. No doubt, such men are nearer to thought than the ordinary mortal.

No complaint is more frequently heard than "I cannot concentrate" unless it be the other groan, "I have no memory." On cross-examination you find that people who cannot concentrate are conscious either of a heaviness nullifying every intellectual effort, or of a volatility precluding any but a tip-of-the-wing contact with the object of attention. The moment they try to collect and focus their consciousness, it seems as if there arose a whole flight of irrelevant images to mock and confuse them. This accounts for the numerous cases in which people are visibly trying to do anything rather than think.

Can we learn to concentrate? The doubt implied in this question is in itself an inferiority complex responsible for many a failure. As a matter of fact, nine out of ten men or women who possess the capacity of folding their wings round their attention have acquired it by patient practice. Attention is less a gift than a habit, and the knowledge of this ought to encourage those who wish to live inside their own souls.

Interest of any kind produces concentration naturally. Selfish people concentrate on their own immediate profits, idealists on their ideals. We cannot be five minutes with a person without realizing what the nature and elevation of his interest may be: whether it is gain, vanity or pleasure, or whether it is some aspect of our multiform wish for the world's betterment.

The Art of Thinking is largely the finding out what gives our intellect its satisfaction without any effort or any restlessness.

However, we cannot always follow our inclination in thinking as we do in acting. There are dull problems that we have to tackle; we know intellectual duties not any easier to discharge than moral obligations. How can we concentrate on subjects which, not being attractive, naturally produce absent-mindedness?

Let it be understood, to begin with, that concentration is impossible if we are fagged or dull. Too much sleep or too little sleep leaves a vacuum in our brain. So does too much eating or too much fasting. So does too much exercise or too little. Exercise may set all our animal spirits in motion, but tingling arteries generally go along with a spangly rush of disorderly images to the brain. Reading will not help our minds into what we think is the proper path either.

Complete immobility, or a peaceful cigarette, or ten minutes at the open window, or strolling alone under the trees, or, sometimes, a cup of tea, will bring us nearer to the legitimate fountain of our thoughts than anything else.

How to Fill Up Blank Minds

When your heart is calmed by the unusual stillness of your mind, when the moths of distraction have dispersed, you are ready for concentration, but you may still find yourself facing a blank. Many intellectual workers are conscious that their effort to eliminate superfluity seems to have eliminated essentials as well. What do I want to think about? they wonder. What am I interested in? Am I interested in anything?

People endowed with good memories seldom experience this barrenness. On the least provocation they can recall data of all sorts. It is the curse of most people so gifted that their data have long been stereotyped, borrowed as they often are from somebody else and never improved upon.

On the contrary, people conscious of working on living matter, impressions, intuitions or sentiments, pretty well pleased with their minds one day, disgusted the next, are, so to speak, cohabiting with nature, and their intellectual existence is a drama.

Concentration which, at first sight, is obtained by elimination, the elimination of images not harmonious with our trend of thought, can best be obtained by the conjuring of a suitable background. And this background is nothing else than the multiplication of harmonious images.

If I want to concentrate, in order to understand it, on American isolation, for instance, I must, first of all, empty my sensibility of all irritation caused by narrow-minded defenses of this isolation, then I must rapidly people my imagination with such notions as the vastness of America, its lack of obtrusive neighbors, its self-supporting capacity, its tendency to conformity and its surprising realization of the words "foreign," and "foreigner"; if I finally remember that Europe appears to the untraveled Ameri-

ABBÉ ERNEST DIMNET
Courtesy of Simon Schuster, Inc.

can as a many-mouthed hungry monster, my concentration is complete. I can think of nothing but the isolation of America and I understand it so well that, were it not for another set of images near by, I should promptly share it.

Multiply such visions and distraction will not know where to have you.

Tʜɪs is the natural and vital way of thinking. All our notions come from such groups of images and when we wish to restore life to an idea hardening into words we instinctively recall the concrete circumstances from which it was originally evolved. Not otherwise do speakers who hate memorising create in themselves the mood—both intellectual and imaginative—from which real eloquence will flow. The interior cinema unrolling its pictures for their benefit is not, like more abstract trains of thought, at the mercy of distractions; and the hubbub of the dinner-table, or the revolving scenery outside the railway-window, hardly interferes with it.

Another infallible method of concentrating or, so to speak, tempering one's attention, is to take pen in hand and prepare to write down what our mind will dictate. There is in the very gesture something imperative which the most wandering mind seldom resists. A successful writer whom I was asking about her methods of working told me: "I take a blank sheet and a pencil, I sit at a perfectly bare table and pretty quickly a story comes."

But it is especially when we want to be clear and definite, to make up our minds about some issue, that the sheet and pencil process proves helpful.

We Starve Within An Inch of Plenty

Aᴘᴀʀᴛ from the things in which we are vitally interested, the more or less conscious objects on which our egotism concentrates without any outward incentive, teacher, or advice, we spend our lives in vagueness. Even about purely practical issues we are far from being clear. We imagine that other people know definitely their own minds about their children's education, about their own careers, or about the use they should make of their money. The notion helps us to imagine that we ourselves are only separated from decision on these important issues by the lightest curtain of uncertainty.

But it is not so. Other people, like ourselves, live in perpetual vagueness. Like us they foolishly imagine they are thinking of some important subject when they are merely thinking of thinking about it. When this fallacy has been nursed for some time in our subconsciousness we decide that the question admits of no compelling answer and we act according to the pressure of circumstances, or perfunctory advice, or the slogans of the moment. It is surprising how few people's testaments are really their wills. They had never been able to know their own minds, so the lawyer or some relation dictated the document. If we should sit before the blank sheet, and write in two columns the pro and con arguments about an idea that occurs to us, the truth would flash on us. We should either be struck by the evidence of some considerations or, no less startling, should we see the necessity for seeking advice on this or that point. Advice of whom? Do not go back to the illusion of merely thinking of thinking about the possible persons. Take another sheet and write down the pros and cons concerning the advisers. Quite instinctively you will keep those sheets in one envelope. This will be a dossier, in every point similar to those shaping the destinies of empires.

Try this system once; you will never desert it. It is only fair to warn you that the habit is apt to become tyrannical; you will mechanically reach for your pad and pencil, not only when you have to decide about selling your house, but even when you have to pack a trunk.

On the whole, concentration is a natural state which can easily be reproduced by simple methods. It is only supposed to be exceptional because people do not try and, in this, as in so many other things, starve within an inch of plenty. Those who do try have never been disappointed in themselves.

"I find only ordinary thoughts," they complain.

"Yes, but they are your own and it is better to produce ordinary thoughts than nothing."

"I do see glimpses of deep truth or am conscious of brilliant flashes, but they vanish like will o' the wisps."

"Blessed are you. You will not be eloquent, but you will be phosphorescent."

Making Time

HAVE you really no time? No time! The extremity of poverty! Perhaps your idea of having time is not having *some* time to yourself. Examine your conscience and answer: *Very busy people always find time for everything.*

Is there no time you can reclaim, not from your work, not from your exercise, not from your family or friends, but from pleasure that really does not give you much pleasure, from empty talk at the club, from inferior plays, from doubtfully enjoyable weekends or not very profitable trips?

Have you learned how not to give in to idlers? Do you discriminate between kindness and weakness, never refusing to do a good turn, but always refusing to be a dupe? Are you a slave to the telephone?

Do you know how to gather up fragments of time lest they perish? Do you realise the value of minutes? One of the Lamoignons had a wife who always kept him waiting a few minutes before dinner. After a time it occurred to him that eight or ten lines could be written during the interval, and he had paper and ink in a convenient place for that purpose. In time—for years are short but minutes are long—several volumes of spiritual meditations resulted. Mankind might be divided between the multitude who hate to be kept waiting because they get bored and the happy few who rather like it because it gives them time for thought.

What do you do in trains, cars or taxis? If you do nothing in perfect contentment, well and good, but if you feel restless you are to blame. Trollope, who was a commuter, wrote many a chapter on the train.

You cannot be reading or thinking without avoiding company: people no doubt will remark that Vere de Vere keeps very much to himself, but it cannot be helped. If you try to think, you must expect to be a little apart and not a little above.

What time do you get up? Could it not be three quarters of an hour, or half an hour earlier? If you give up reading in bed—a practice condemned by all oculists—you can manage it. Somehow it does the trick. An hour in the morning is worth two later, and the nothingness that must inevitably come in the silly hours afterwards will not submerge you.

Frittering Time Away

Do you often hear yourself saying: "I forgot" or "I didn't think"? These ejaculations mean that you are losing time, have to go over beaten ground several times, through your own fault. We should never forget, at all events so seldom that it will be a surprise.

You will hardly ever forget, you will not be fumbling and recommencing, if you possess two easily acquired habits, foresight and order. To foresee means to imagine in advance. A quarter of an hour can easily be saved in the Pullman if you have visualized what night or morning things ought to be on the top of your suit-case instead of lurking where the fingers will anxiously feel for them when you are in a hurry.

This is an elementary exercise in imaginative foresight. You will do well to visualize more important possibilities such as marriage, old age, illness, death or lunacy, failure in this or incomplete success in that, errors on your part and treason or stupidity on the part of others. Read the future, as your imagination shows you things as they will probably be, only not so bad, jot them down and keep the notes carefully. With surprising rapidity you will find yourself in the possession of notebooks telling you with fullness and clarity all you must do preparatory to moving out or selling out or other important outs and ins.

"What a bore," you exclaim, "what a slavery to things!"—no! what freedom! what independence and security! My note-book is a fortune. So is another fat dossier in which my blunders are recorded for profitable private reading.

Order is the sister of foresight, as you can see. He is unnatural who, visualizing a call on So-and-So, does not put in his greatcoat pocket, or next to his hat, the book long ago borrowed of So-and-So. A bench in the hall strewn with things that have to go out, memos on the rug round your desk, do not mean untidiness but order. Things should be where they will not be forgotten.

Next to lack of order, one of the most fatal ways of wasting time as well as weakening one's life is to hesitate before acting. Some people can dress in forty minutes, because they have learned the automatism which M. Bergson used to recommend so persuasively. Others will take an hour and a half either because they have not adopted the invariable order which, in time, becomes automatism, or because they hesitate before decisions which ought to be mere gestures. You see them looking round and wondering what next, sometimes looking out at the window or smoking a cigarette to brighten up their wits, or endlessly hesitating between two collars or two ties.

Some people simply use up their lives thus beginning and not beginning to begin. In fact, the word "beginning" is terrifying. Nothing can be truer and more encouraging to men equally gifted with a human desire for action and a human indulgence of laziness than the Greek sentence: *The beginning is half the thing*.

Learn to attack things frontally but according to the most scientific methods. Be the Lindbergh of whatever little ocean you have to cross. Our life should consist of a thousand brief dramas, complete in themselves, swift as a game of poker. Some business men have given me a truly artistic pleasure by the infallibility of their dictation. Each letter meant a rapid weighing of pros and cons, a decision, and the thing done at once.

So time can be "made" and the well-worn phrase is not a deception. If you possess lists of things to be done in given circumstances, if your agenda is a clearly-sectioned table showing you at a glance what you have to do, you will be a busy person, but you will have a sense of power over things. And if you know how to concentrate, *i.e.*, how to use the keen edge of your mind, having time and possessing the tool, you will only need good material for thought.

Food for Thought

REMEMBER that our mind is active on a constant succession of more or less connected images. These images characterize our mental quality. Pass from a noble art gallery to the picture department of a store, and you will be conscious of mediocrity coming after distinction. Every man's imagination is a picture gallery. If the pictures were visible, instead of having to be inferred from the talk or general deportment of the individual, we could grade our fellow-beings as we do vases in a shop.

It is useless to stress the general inferiority of the images filling the minds of most human beings. Many of them are hardly superior to those constituting the mentality of the animal, always remembering that animals are not infrequently far above human beings in sensibility or in the capacity for love. The most usual type of human being, of course, is the man or woman imprisoned in his or her paltry existence, and endlessly attentive to each and every one of its shabby details.

Can we think as we like? or is not our thought as fated as our breathing?

Certainly we cannot help thinking any more than we can help breathing, but, just as we can choose to breathe pure air in a pine wood on a high hill, we can place our mind where the images it will work upon will be of a higher nature.

It is impossible to spend an hour in a room with a man approaching greatness without feeling the contagiousness of distinguished thinking. Such men cannot always be found or our chances for meeting them may be limited. But anybody with an average knowledge of the history of nations, literature, philanthropy, or art, not to speak of the great religionists or saints, can people his imagination with groups of superior men in every realm.

Our serious hours cannot be devoted to a more useful occupation than studying the lives or ideas of great men. "Great thoughts arise from the heart," Vauvenargues says; and Joubert: "There is no light in souls in which there is no warmth."

LOVE, whether it be the attraction of Truth, or pure, simple, elemental love, always opens up the intellect and gives it the freedom of genius. Maternity also acts in that way. Animals of course show it wonderfully, and—let it be said without any attempt at cheap paradoxicalness—even artificial women show it too. The transformation lasts as long as the flow of love retains its power.

A missionary of the real kind, a hospital worker of the real kind, the innumerable varieties of social workers, women merely devoted to an ideal of action, are transformed mentally by their work and can write or speak endlessly about it. Intellectual inferiority complexes melt away like thin snow in the proximity of love, and the liberation of the soul is complete.

Stop the stream of your consciousness for an instant, look into your soul, arrest the images forming and dissolving there. What will you see? Petty self-love, of course, but even more frequently, petty irritations. Our nature is neither noble nor generous. We remember slights more easily than kindnesses. We may have lived for days in a home or a foreign country without meeting with anything except courtesy. The moment we feel irritated or offended we forget the happiness and nurse the paltry grievances.

Thoughts worth the name can never arise from a nasty growth. But just as we can prefer decent company to ordinary or worse, or good books to poor ones, we can crush out inferior thoughts, and invite better ones. Good men generally think right. When they do not, it seems unnatural, and the lower parts of our soul, the insurgents in us always ready for an outcry, triumph meanly. Sanctity will be rewarded by a straighter judgment and by a broader sympathy, which is an aspect of intelligence.

Thoughts from Books

READING, to most people, means an ashamed way of killing time disguished under a dignified name. Trifling with print in that manner quickly diminishes the resilience of the intellect. It goes directly against the Art of Thinking.

If you wish to use books as an adjuvant to thought, they must be books that will not merely amuse or put your mind to sleep, but, on the contrary, will keep it wide awake and alert.

What are those books?

What they are *you* know best, and I do not know in the least. A book, like a landscape, is a state of consciousness varying with readers. There exists some book, pamphlet, article in an encyclopaedia, or possibly an old clipping from a newspaper that once set you thinking; there may be many; indeed you may be one of those rare beings with whom a few lines of print are food enough for thought because, as Lamartine says, their thoughts think themselves. The something evocative for you may be poetry, history, philosophy, the sciences, or moral sciences, *i.e.,* the progress of mankind.

No titles, no categories can be given to you by anybody but yourself, and what I am going to say hereafter should not intimidate you into doubting the wisdom of your answer to the entirely personal question: what books help *me* the best to think? What motif has given a chance to some lurking activity deep in you and, during an hour, you have been at your most personal?

The Art of Thinking is merely the art of doing that as easily and as frequently as possible.

And what books should we so read?

THE principle which has never failed to confer superiority on a man's thinking activity is the well worn precept: DO NOT READ GOOD BOOKS —life is too short for that—ONLY READ THE BEST.

This simple recipe is as infallible as good air and good food are in physical hygiene. Yet, it is a fact that nineteen out of twenty . modern people quake away from. "Masterpieces again," they groan, "the 'Aeneid,' the 'Divine Comedy,' 'Paradise Lost,' we have heard that before: rather be ordinary than bored."

The notion that masterpieces are boresome school-books interpreted by dull teachers or examination stuff, is a marvellous product of education. Ignorance is assuredly less deadly, for it can create no such inferiority complex as the school boy's notion of his lack of kinship with the best literature. But this phantasm can easily be exorcised if we modify the above principle to: ONLY READ WHAT GIVES YOU THE GREATEST PLEASURE.

So if you want to be vitalized into the power of thinking real thoughts, and if you want never to know one dull instant while reading, do what has been done by the best specimens of mankind since there have been books: resolutely leave out whatever is not the best. If something in you rebels against this, you are not in the mood for reading this book, you care for no Art of Thinking, or you only want mental lozenges which I cannot produce, and so farewell.

But let it not be till you have drawn up a list of the great books which do possess some attraction for you, and till a few months' experience has shown you which of these gives you unmixed pleasure. Those twenty or thirty volumes will be *your* library, that is to say, your fountain of thought and delight, and when you see people envying you your pleasure in them—they will be your pride.

Does this mean that we should give up contemporary literature, and live entirely in the past? No indeed, for nothing helps thought like questions of the day, and if you do not belong to your own time, what time can you belong to? We should read modern poets and modern novelists and follow art in its most advanced manifestations. But if you try to keep up with the industrialized literary production of today you will be swamped and lost. Is there no way of making a selection?

There are dozens of ways, but here is an easy recipe. Nobody can twit you with an affectation of indifference to the present time if you leave out books which you find are forgotten three months after their publication. Draw up a list of the American writers whose works published several years ago are still on the shelves. Those are the ones it would be unforgiveable to desert, even for far superior reading.

Recipes for Thinking

GREAT books, great men, great problems and great doctrines, great facts and their lessons cannot but result in high thought. The busier we are, the more severe our selection should be. Many men absorbed in business show such a rare quality of culture that we are surprised at it. The reason, invariably, is partly because hard work and even the weariness it leaves carry a nobility with them, but also because there is no room in such lives for inferior mental occupation.

Parents anxious to give their children the best of everything should as resolutely pack away trash of all kinds. It is surprising that intelligent people anxious to do their best should not realize that no book ought to be left in the nursery that is inferior to "Robinson Crusoe," "The Arabian Nights," or Perrault's "Fairy Tales." You will be only too glad if you can teach children to prefer distinction to vulgarity when they see it.

I have been tempted many times to annex Schopenhauer's maxim in his "Paralipomena": "Do not read, think!" or to transform it into: NEVER READ, ALWAYS STUDY. A harsh saying? Not if we realize that we should study nothing that does not interest us, and that studying only applies to the most enjoyable way of extracting from that which will interest us most.

In many cases you will get more from a secretary's, or a friend's analysis, of a book than out of direct reading. For you will be questioning, which is the virile intellectual action, and the other man will be alert.

Busy people who have recourse to this quick way often surprise us by the amount of their knowledge. King Edward VII, who never read anything, was however up-to-date in two or three literatures; shaving, dressing, smoking, he would ask questions of intelligent people or have significant bits read out loud to him, a royal highway to knowledge.

WHATEVER we read we must first comprehend and, when we have comprehended, criticize. Criticizing is only another aspect of the effort to comprehend.

Most people suspend their judgment till somebody else has expressed his own and then they repeat. Such passivity cannot be too early counteracted. If it is done methodically and intelligently it will never produce over-confidence, and the youthful mind will acquire strength during the formative period.

We should be given the habit of critical attention so that our first contact with anything worth the effort will give us as keen an impression as we are capable of. Criticism, when we read, think or feel in that way, is sure to be what it ought always to be, viz., the balance of what we should bow to with what we feel doubtful of. We do not insult great writers or great thinkers by submitting them to this test, but the reverse.

Comprehension is criticism, and criticism or judgment is a mere synonym for THOUGHT.

THOUGHT is within the possibility of innumerable people. Let them keep away from trivialities, and, instead, stock their minds with knowledge worth while; let them range freely through this mass of data, and thought will be actively produced.

Pierre Van Paassen

DAYS OF OUR YEARS

WHY is there war today? That is the question the author sets out to answer. As the representative of the New York *World* he was on hand at the events during the past decade which combined to produce the present gory cataclysm. His startling revelations will do much towards giving you an understanding of what's behind the headlines and something to think about in the nature of a solution to the difficulties which now beset mankind.

The European Kettle Will Explode

FOR thirteen years I have wandered up and down the European continent inquiring and observing, talking with leaders in the social, religious, economic and political spheres in every country. I have lived in France and mixed in all classes of society in Germany, Italy, Rumania, Spain, Belgium, Russia, Morocco, Turkey, Palestine, Austria and Switzerland, but I have yet to meet the man or the woman who longs for war, or who thinks that war would be a benefit to anyone. Yet at best, they only hoped that it would be prevented.

With so much good will in the world, with so general an awareness of the danger, and so universal an opposition to war, why is it that the highways of Europe resound again with the metallic step of heavy-shod legions? Why is the nocturnal sky lurid with the reflection of belching steel ovens? Why are millions of men under arms again?

To solve this puzzle became an anguishing preoccupation with me.

I believe that my Uncle Kees saw the future clearer than many a contemporary statesman. He knew the story of the French Communes' every barricade, and when I was a boy, he patiently explained to me the meaning of the decrees issued by the first Popular Government in Europe. Breathlessly, his eyes aflame, his fists clenched, he would tell me again the story of the last butchery in the cemetery of Père Lachaise.

"On that day," he would burst out, "all the hyenas of Europe, all the crowned and uncrowned wolves thought they had squelched the voice of freedom for all eternity. They set about to re-create the world in their own petty image. What we see around us today is the result: pettiness in art, pettiness in economics, pettiness in love, pettiness in religion. But mark my words, *you* Pierre, *you*, will live to see the day when the whole European kettle is going to explode and the debris will bury this bourgeois world."

"Who will make the kettle explode, Uncle Kees?"

"They will do it themselves, my boy! They live by violence and they will perish by violence!"

Christianity Repudiated

IN 1917, millions of weary hearts thrilled with a new hope. The infinite patience of the martyred peoples had reached the point of exhaustion. The kettle was boiling at last. To prevent an explosion, the governments had closed up all the cracks beforehand and seated themselves on top. Despite these precautionary measures, the pent-up steam was beginning to escape with a snarling hiss. The conviction that the nations had been the victims of a colossal bloody swindle was gaining ground. Here and there the free spirit of human beings who had been imprisoned in the iron-bound cells of nationality during the

98

four years of collective hysteria ventured to look across the borders again. In the suffering eyes of their neighbors they recognized their own features, distorted by the same murderous illusion.

The poilus of France began to debate whether or not to return to their firesides before Clemenceau's "war to the bitter end" should have reached that dismal climax. In the spring of 1918, André Maginot admitted in a secret session of the Chamber that there remained but one single division between Paris and the battle line on which the government could place absolute reliance.

The red flag had been hoisted on the ruined sugar refinery of Souchez. In response, a German regiment had intoned the "Marseillaise" and had walked across no man's land to fraternize. Letters tied to clods of earth were being thrown from one trench to the other. Messages were exchanged. It became necessary to forbid British troops to converse with German prisoners of war. Divisions had to be shifted to break up secret contacts established with the enemy across the line of death.

Strikes were being called in Paris and Lyons. In December, 1917, the metalworkers folded their arms and demonstrated on the boulevards. The sons of the Communards had recognized the futility of the blood bath into which the united front with the ruling class had tricked them.

The repression increased. The bitter disillusion over "millions of lives sacrificed for a resulting zero turned the wrath of those morally responsible for the disaster against the men who had foreseen it." Spy hunts were organized.

The censors redoubled their efforts to prevent the people from learning the extent of the horror.

Crowds were enjoined to silence in public. Shut up—fight! Do not reason—kill!

Free investigation, independence of judgment, human pity—all were put in moth balls and laid in the storage room till after the war. Criticism was abolished, conscience proscribed. Christendom repudiated its name by adopting Mars. The Diety was split into a number of tribal Jehovahs. From a hundred thousand pulpits the voice of Antichrist roared hatred.

Every new retreat of the armies was interpreted as the result of defeatist propaganda; never were the quarreling old generals held responsible. Every diplomatic blunder was attributed to spies; not a single statesman would ever admit that a ghastly error had been made. Civil and military courts were working overtime. The medieval system of *lettres de cachet* was revived in France.

One of the most outspoken pacifists, Almereyda, whose testimony on the witness stand would have revealed the extent of the corruption in high places, was found garroted in his cell. Every morning the meadow behind the castle in Vincennes rang with the salvos of the firing squad.

The prospect of glory and victory had long since receded from view. It now appeared certain that the war, from whatever angle one looked at it, was going to be a bad bargain for everyone concerned. Neither ideals, ambitions, nor national interests were going to be satisfied. Only blood and tears. . .

The Choicest Profits of War

GERMANY had based all her calculations on a swiftly conducted war and an early victory. At the outset she had a supply of stocks which could scarcely have carried her through a year of warfare on two fronts. The Allies, therefore, could have brought the Kaiser to his knees before the end of 1915, by

instituting an economic blockade. But that would have meant giving up the choicest profits of war: the contraband commerce.

Throughout the first three years of the war the Reich received an uninterrupted stream of supplies through Holland, Switzerland, and the Scandinavian countries, especially cotton, without which she could not have continued to fight for a day. This went on until the United States protested that England was crowding her out of the European market.

German capitalism had not neglected its opportunities either; right up to the beginning of 1917, the Krupp works of Essen shipped a quarter of a million tons of steel a month through Switzerland to the Comité des Forges in France. In addition to payment in gold, one of the conditions in this deal was that French aviation was to refrain from bombarding the iron-ore mines, the blast furnaces and the rolling mills of the Longwy district.

Ships loaded with nickel from New Caledonia, destined for Germany, seized by French destroyers in open sea and brought to port at Brest and Cherbourg and there declared prizes of war by the maritime court, were ordered released by the French government and reached Bremen safely.

Representatives of the German chemical trust, of the Swiss copper interests, and of Vickers, Krupp, Schneider-Creusot, and the Comité des Forges met in Vienna at the moment when the armies were locked in a death struggle in the mud of Flanders. Their sole purpose was to devise ways and means of keeping the war going profitably.

"You Die For the Industrialists"

"You think you die for your country; but you die for the industrialists," said Anatole France when he learned the answer of Senator Bérenger as to why the metallurgical district of Thionville was not taken back at the outbreak of the war, when it was undefended by the Germans and the French army was within a stone's throw.

The reason no attempt had been made to recapture Thionville was that it would have brought the war to a premature termination. "For the occupation of Thionville," declared the Senator, "would have reduced Germany to seven million tons of poor steel per year; all production would have been stopped. Seizure of Thionville would have put an end to the war immediately."

Thanks to French ore, made available by the initial order to the French armies to withdraw twenty-two kilometers from the border before a single blow had been struck, Germany was able during four years to inundate the East and West, on land and the high seas, with a torrent of steel. In return for magnetos for airplane motors, shipped by Germany, France gave bauxite, an indispensable ingredient in the manufacture of aluminum for Zeppelins.

The dreadful barbed wire strung out by the British at Ypres and on the Somme, which became a deathtrap for the Prussian Guard, was manufactured by the Germans of Opel and Company, and had found its way through Holland to England. Australia shipped fat to Germany via Norway and Denmark; the Straits Settlements, copra; Ceylon, tea; Wales, coke and coal, tar, ammoniac and glycerine for high explosives, all of it in British ships.

The Allied high command tranquilly figured on finishing the war with fresh forces from America in the fall or winter of 1919. When Lenin repeated his call for peace over and over again, the Entente maintained an obstinate silence. The Allies were more than ever determined to gain the victory without jeopardizing the interests of the ruling classes.

But a new danger loomed on the horizon, and it was growing more and more precise: a further postponement of peace threatened to bring on a social revolution. Only when the upper classes recognized the imminence of what would have been a major disaster to the ruling cliques of bankers and merchants of death was a single high command for all fronts finally instituted, and, upon the urging of America, the economic blockade at last applied in earnest. Germany immediately realized that the end had come. She launched a last desperate offensive and collapsed.

THEN the Armistice was signed! It came not a day too early. Another three months and Soviet France would have been exchanging greetings with the liberated German people. The ruling classes of Europe had recognized the common danger. No tediously prolonged negotiations had been necessary to bring the war to a close.

Europe's bourgeoisie consented in every complicity in order to maintain the established social order. The essential fact of the history of 1919 which does not figure in the official chronicles, consists in the single-mindedness of the ruling classes of every country to arrest the march of humanity towards Socialism. In this way a new problem was added to all the national and international problems of the world: the problem of class. Within a few years that problem dominated all others. It upset all the policies of the preceding century.

Background For Nazi Victory

IT HAS been said that without the occupation of the Ruhr by France, there never would have been a Nazi victory in Germany. I cannot share that view. For, although there is no question that the entire German people smarted under the outrage of their Rhenish fellow citizens being garrisoned by Negro troops, and that a French government really desirous of bringing about a reconciliation between the two peoples would not have been guilty of such a provocation, the decisive hour came much later.

I still see the scene at the Gare du Nord, when Chancellor Bruening arrived in Paris. For the first time, a German statesman was back in the French capital after the humiliation of Versailles. The station was black with people, all eager to catch a glimpse of the German delegation. As Herr Bruening and his colleagues made their way from the platform to the waiting room, they passed a group of railway employees. Suddenly there was a cry, *"Vive l'Allemagne!"* and again, *"Vive la paix! Vive la fraternité humaine!"* (Hail Germany! Hail peace! Hail human brotherhood!)

That demonstration, absolutely spontaneous, by the workers of Paris, augured well for the Chancellor's visit. For days men spoke of nothing else but the reception accorded the representatives of the foe of yesterday. The German Chancellor, completely taken by surprise, had gravely returned the salute. It had been a moment of high emotion. I saw Bruening's eyes fill with tears. Everyone who witnessed the scene had to swallow hard.

But what was the object of Herr Bruening's visit to Paris? Before the imminence of a general catastrophe in the Reich, a financial and economic disaster of the first magnitude, the Chancellor of one of the great European states had come as an humble suppliant to plead the cause of the Reich with Monsieur Pierre Laval. "It was an act of desperation, foolish perhaps, and totally unexpected, but nevertheless an act of courage and greatness," as Jean Richard Bloch said at the time in *Europe*. The people felt similarly, and the instinct of the masses is seldom wrong.

FRANCE alone at that moment could have saved what remained of democracy and republicanism in the Weimar Republic.

Herr Bruening and his collaborators spent the night in conference. They had brought with them irrefutable evidence in figures and facts that Germany was on the verge of the abyss.

At seven in the morning—Bruening went to the Church of Notre Dame de la Victoire. He prayed for an hour and heard Mass. At ten o'clock he was received by M. Laval. The German Chancellor expressed his views, and pleaded with the French Foreign Minister for two hours. When he noticed that he could not soften the heart of the Frenchman, he fell on his knees. He spoke of the misery in his country, the sense of frustration of the German youth, the dull hopelessness of the situation if France would not lift some of the burdens imposed at Versailles. He warned of an economic debacle which might, through its repercussions, drag other countries, France herself, into a chaotic whirlpool. He named "the sinister forces" that were waiting to take over the reins in Germany if he (Bruening) should fail.

Laval shook his head. He would not even place Bruening's request for a loan, or a moratorium, before his colleagues in the cabinet. He refused to hold out the least strand of hope. He led the German Chancellor to the door with a polite expression of adieu.

It was a sunny day in Paris when Pierre Laval signed the death warrant of the German Republic.

Such incidents, which were scarcely noticed in the world at large, had their significance none the less as signposts pointing to the future. They led to the suspicion that while the statesmen were ostensibly as deeply concerned with peace as ever, a vast plot of international ramifications was being woven behind the scenes to bring to nought the ideal of a warless world.

Franco-German Complicity

WHILE the eyes of the world were riveted on Geneva, where the interminable debate went on and on, few were aware that, from 1925 onward, representatives of French and German heavy industry were meeting regularly now in Paris, then in Berlin. Both the German and French metal industry were incurring serious losses as a result of the suspension of armament contracts, and were desperately seeking ways and means to set business in motion again. This could not be done without intimate collaboration.

In May, 1925, Arnold Rechberg, public-relations counsel of the Hugenberg and Thyssen trusts, came to Paris to propose the equipment by France of a German army of 800,000 which was to march into Russia and destroy the Bolshevik regime. Marshal Foch and President Poincaré received the German emissary in the company of Messrs. Robert Pinaud and Charles Laurent, directors of the Comité des Forges, the French steel cartel. They approved the plan which had been worked out by General von Hoffmann.

After days of negotiations, François Coty announced triumphantly in his newspaper Figaro that Poincaré had approved a scheme which would have established a Franco-German condominium over the vast Russian market.

He did not add, however, that this would have obviated the necessity of continuing the talk of general disarmament in Geneva. Foch approved in turn, and Tardieu sent Paul Reynaud to Berlin to arrange the final details.

The plan was wrecked, said Herr Rechberg later, by Lloyd George, who feared a still greater French influence in Europe. But contact between the French and German cannon makers had been established. It was never again broken. The French metal industry agreed to the rearmament of Germany as early as 1925, as being the only condition for the stimulation of the inner French market.

Strange personages were beginning to make their appearance in Geneva to assist the diplomats in clearing the last obstacle off the road towards universal peace and disarmament. Germany sent Constantin von Neurath, director of the Crédit Hongrois, a Hungarian banking institution controlled by Schneider & Cie., the French armament manufacturers. Carl von Schubert took charge of the permanent undersecretaryship for Foreign Affairs and the League of Nations at the Wilhelmstrasse. He was a director of the Krupp metal trust. France, in turn, sent to Berlin as its ambassador François-Poncet, who had but recently been managing director of the Dillinger Huettenwerke, a German armament firm.

They Armed Hitler

PAUL FAURE, deputy for the district of Le Creusot, revealed in the French parliament that Schneider-Creusot, the mammoth French cannon trust, headed by the cousins De Wendel, one of whom was a member of the French Chamber and the other of the German Reichstag, were contributing funds to the infant Nazi party of Adolf Hitler, and that Skoda, the Czechoslovakian armament trust, which is largely controlled by Schneider-Creusot, was supplying Germany with a considerable amount of war material on credit.

Why should Hitler have received French, Czechoslovakian and British money (for Sir Henry Deterding, chairman of Royal Dutch Shell, was also reported amongst the contributors to the Nazi party's funds)?

The answer is simple. One needed but to read the Führer's book, "Mein Kampf." In that document, the upstart party leader, with scarcely ten thousand followers, at the time he wrote the book, announced that his first task upon attaining power would be to rearm the Reich. Did not such a man deserve international sympathy and support? Armament factories all over the Continent were standing idle, dividends were sinking, stock quotations going lower and lower. And not a cloud on the horizon to give the deadly armament industry a little spurt, no danger anywhere to warrant the manufacture of a single gun! Would it not be a godsend if Hitler could come to power and make Germany dangerous once more? Wouldn't that be sufficient excuse to kill all this nonsense in Geneva about world peace and disarmament? Once Germany started to rearm, all could follow suit. For the primary condition of a general armament campaign is the rearmament of only one powerful state. With Germany on the way, "the tragic and ridiculous spectacle" of nations arming because they were afraid, and afraid because they were arming, could start all over again!

Hitler in 1928

ON LOOKING back, it is curious to observe how my first interview with Herr Hitler back in 1928 was considered so unimportant that most newspaper members of the syndicate "buried it inside."

Some prominent Jews in America to whose attention it was called dismissed it as a crude joke, and *Die Welt,* a Jewish newspaper in Vienna, denounced me as a "fantastic sensationalist." Nobody took Hitler seriously ten years ago. I did not myself. The man I saw in the Brown House in Munich impressed me so little that I came away from the interview mentally classifying der Führer as a maniac with an *idée fixe.*

Broek van der Muller, a Hollander in Hitler's entourage in those formative years of the Nazi movement, who wrote the final draft of "Mein Kampf" for him together with Fedor Strasser, had given me hints on the leader's private life.

The company he kept was revealing: Roehm, who openly claimed "the German citizen's inalienable right to be a homosexual," and Goering, who was the admired *pièce de résistance* that staged the weirdest orgies at the house of Hannessen, the millionaire soothsayer. (Goering ordered Hannessen's assassination a week after coming to power.) These men were little calculated to inspire one with respect for the Führer.

It is not true, as Hitler's most intimate associates now proclaim, that they early recognized his almost divine qualities. Otto Strasser, who knew him better than anyone else, spoke to me with snarling contempt of *der Adolf* and of his frequent weeping jags. Goebbels, then only the upstart party's press chief, more than once had his tongue in his cheek when explaining some particularly incoherent passage in one of the Führer's wild tirades.

But he was unquestionably a spell-binder on the platform. Goering only succeeded in stirring up the crowd's amusement with his paunch and his lewd jokes; Goebbels was hated as a shifty and unreliable customer in the party itself. Hitler was the most useful as a propagandist because of his almost

THE PAST AND THE PRESENT
Der Fuehrer and the President of the Reich (1934) von Hindenburg. In the background (l. to r.) Goebbels, Goering and Admiral Raeder.
Acme Photo

demoniacal vehemence, a quality the Germans mistake for sincerity. When he spoke, everything else was forgotten, even the unutterable contempt he expressed for the masses in his book. They hung on his lips, or rather, they seemed hypnotized by the dramatic act he put on, even when he talked nonsense.

"He Does Everything for the German People"

I RECALL one incident in 1932 which revealed not only the hold he had on the people, but also the manner in which it had been established. I had been assigned to follow the Führer's propaganda campaign in the Rhineland. We arrived in Bonn about six-thirty in the evening. The Führer and his party went to the hotel for dinner. After taking some refreshment I drifted over to the hall where he was to make an address that evening. It was packed.

About three quarters of an hour after the meeting was scheduled to begin a Nazi mounted the rostrum and announced that the Führer was being held up by a thunderstorm which had broken over the Rhine. He asked the crowd to be patient for a little while longer, and the band, amid general enthusiasm, struck up *"Die Wacht am Rhein."*

When another half hour had passed and the Führer had not put in an appearance, the same Nazi returned to the speaker's tribune and shouted that although the storm was redoubling in violence, Hitler had just telephoned from a little village up the Rhine that he would be there in less than a half an hour. *"Er kommt,"* bellowed the announcer. *"Durch den Sturm"*—(through the storm). Never will he disappoint us!"

The band struck up "The Good Comrade," and the crowd rose to its feet. When it had finally been worked up to a feverish pitch of expectancy, the Führer, who had been sitting across the street all the time with his friends, walked in, dressed in his brown raincoat. He was splashed with water and mud from head to foot. The crowd was delirious and *sieg-heiled* the unsmiling Führer for five minutes. A middle-aged man, sitting in the front row near the press table, wiped the tears from his eyes and remarked to me, "He does everything for the German people!"

Yes, there lay the secret: not in Hitler, but in the German people. That people sordidly humiliated, without hope, reduced to starvation and poverty, with a youth feeling the frustration and futility of its existence, was ready for anything, any device, no matter how foolish or desperate, to throw off the chains of slavery imposed at Versailles. The German people had lost confidence in the parliamentary game and the methods employed by the diplomats to relieve the burden of Versailles when Hitler came along and behaved, as someone said, "as a man with a cork leg throwing an epileptic fit on a tin roof."

The thing seemed incredible, without watching him perform; and I could easily understand why people, living thousands of miles from the spot, were inclined to dismiss the upstart party leader as a scatter-brained demagogue, a man who would never be taken seriously by soberly analytical Germans.

In the course of that conversation in the Munich Brown House back in 1928, the Führer revealed his intention of rearming the Reich, destroying the Soviet Union "to the applause of the whole civilized world," and reducing the Jews to the status of untouchables.

"I promise," he said, bringing his fist down on the table, "that I will make life impossible for the Jews in Germany, and that I will not rest till I have destroyed the influence of the Jews in the whole of Europe—and in the world. Yes, I swear that the day will come when you in America will see the Jewish plutocrats stand with outstretched hands at doors of the Christian churches begging for alms. They have been Germany's misfortune. They will pay dearly for their crimes!"

To Power on Germany's Empty Stomach

IN SPITE of the German people's poverty and the general sense of frustration and humiliation, Berlin was the most interesting city in Europe in the years immediately preceding Hitler. It was a good deal like Paris under the first year of the Popular Front: popular universities and theaters had made their appearance, houses of culture and youth hostels opened up all over the country, the spirit of experimentation and research in literature, art, science and architecture was evident everywhere.

Cultural and technical exchange with the Soviet Union was ripening into a fruitful collaboration and was one of the most hopeful aspects of the time. Russia and Germany complimented each other in a remarkable way. The Reich had the industries to modernize life in the Soviet Union and to place Socialism in that country on a firm foundation. A close commercial cooperation between the two states could have helped Germany to overcome the colossal handicap of the Versailles Treaty burdens.

It is amazing, in retrospect, how little advantage was taken of that opportunity which might have served to keep Adolf Hitler from marching to power on the empty stomachs of the German people. But even more amazing was the equanimity with which the advent of Hitlerite Fascism was accepted by the leadership of the powerfully organized bodies of the working class.

I was in Berlin in February 1933, when Von Papen was negotiating with Hitler, Goebbels, Roehm and Goering concerning the possibility of including a few Nazi ministers in his cabinet. Everybody in Berlin knew what was up: Von Papen, frightened by General von Schleicher's threat to expose the enormous corruption in connection with the *Ost-Hilfe,* a federal relief scheme for agriculture in East Prussia under which Von Papen's cronies, the landed *Junkers* had been the sole beneficiaries, was trying to form a cabinet without Schleicher.

Nobody expected that Von Papen would have turned to the Nazis, or that he would be successful in drafting Adolf Hitler for the Vice Chancellorship. From Goebbels we learned that the Nazis were holding out for the chief positions in the cabinet, and especially wanted the chancellorship for the Führer.

SCHLEICHER was looking on quietly. He felt that his turn would soon come. He had behind him the Reichswehr command and the great moral authority of President von Hindenburg. Anyway, so he thought. Much later it became known that Meissner, the President's private secretary, with the aid of Oskar von Hindenburg, the President's son, a *Junker* who had shared deeply in the *Ost-Hilfe* graft, kept the doddering old Field Marshal in complete ignorance of the true state of affairs.

In the course of the crisis Hitler called one hundred thousand of his followers to Berlin. The generals were quite willing to drive the brownshirts from the parks and suburbs of Berlin, and finish once and for all with the man whom the President had called an "upstart Bohemian corporal." Had Schleicher and they been able to get Hindenburg's ear that moment, it is not unlikely that Adolf Hitler would have given the world another exhibition of his fleet-footedness. His car stood ready night and day to carry him to safety if things should go wrong.

The organized workers of Berlin were paralyzed at the psychological moment. They took Goering's firing of the Reichstag as a signal that the Nazi repressional machine had gone into action, blasting the last chance of an insurrectionary move. Then, too, the telegrams from Moscow had urged caution. "Let Hitler come. We will follow Hitler!" said Herr Thaelmann, repeating Stalin's diagnosis of the situation.

I went to Munich, little suspecting the experience that was in store for me.

Captured by the German Secret Police

A FEW days after my arrival, I was visited by a German colleague, a subeditor of the *Welt am Abend* in Berlin. He had been my cicerone in the left-wing circles in the capital. He was terribly agitated and asked me to hide him in my room at least for a night. The secret police were on his trail, after shutting up the paper in Berlin and raiding his apartment. He wanted to attempt the crossing of the Swiss frontier, but had no passport, and suggested that I lend him mine. I finally assented.

When I had not heard from him two days after his departure, I took the precaution, as we had agreed, to notify the authorities of the loss of my passport. That turned out to be a serious error. For the passport did arrive with the morning mail the next day, and was received by a desk clerk to whom I had spoken of the missing document.

Three hours later I was trying to explain to the police what could not be explained: the stamp of the German and Swiss border police on my passport testifying that I had crossed into Switzerland, and the absence of another stamp proving that I had returned the same day. I dare say that the brownshirts had a pretty clear idea of what had happened. But they could not charge me with anything definite. After all, the passport was in my possession.

"Are you a Jew?" asked the *Scharführer*.

"No," I said. "I am one hundred per cent Aryan, *so Deutsch wie, ja, wie, Herr Hitler selbst."* (As German as Mr. Hitler himself.)

He looked at me with his fishy-pale Baltic eyes and said not a word, but in the next second he glanced at the leader of the policemen who had taken me in. Without the slightest warning this man struck me across the face with his clenched fist. I staggered and dropped on one knee but quickly recovered my

THE "BROWN HOUSE"
Munich—Center of the National Socialist Party

senses and, without thinking, returned the blow. It was the worst thing I could have done, for in the next instant blows were raining down from all sides and everything turned black.

When I regained consciousness, my clothes were soaking wet. Apparently they had tried to revive me by dousing me with a pail of water. I was sitting in a cell lighted by a lone electric bulb. My head was aching and I could not get my jaws shut. Several teeth were miss-ing. In my mouth was the salty taste of blood.

I was horribly thirsty. The torture of thirst became so great that my head was clearing fast. I stumbled over to the toilet and drank the flushing water. As I bent forward, while sitting on my knees, there was a laugh behind me. A man had pushed open the spyhole in the door and was looking in. It was the Nazi who had struck the first blow.

"Dirty swine," he said.

Concentration Camp

IN DACHAU we were housed in wooden huts. There was no other human habitation in sight on the other side of the triple fence of barbed wire.

My eleven companions in the small barrack were all Germans, except one young fellow, who was an Italian libertarian. He had been employed as a chimney sweep in Munich, and had been taken from his job to the Brown House. Every day he was escorted to the *Kommandantur* of the camp and returned in an unconscious state. He nourished a hope that he would be returned to Italy, although there, too, prison awaited him. But he never did. The notice on the bulletin board said the cause of his death was appendicitis.

Jewish prisoners were housed in a separate hut. During the drill exercises they formed a squad apart. They were forced to bend their knees, or stand on one foot till they collapsed, whereupon they were revived with a pail of water, or left to contract pneumonia in the mud. At the roll call at dawn they had to answer to their names: "Present. I am animal number so much from the Egyptian wilderness!"

For a breach of discipline in their barracks—I think one man's bed had been made up in a nonregulation manner—the Jews were punished collectively one day by having to stand close together on the drill ground in the pouring rain from dawn till sunset. In the evening, after supper, they were commanded to sing the Horst Wessel hymn, the Ger-man national anthem. When only one man's voice was too weakly heard to suit the commander, he ordered a beating for the entire company. Not one Jew had the strength to walk back to the barracks.

I was not maltreated at the camp. On the eleventh day after my arrest, I was driven back to Munich and put on a train to Switzerland, two Nazis accompanying me to the border. Journalistic colleagues, I learned later, who had noticed my absence and made inquiries, had succeeded in speeding my release. At the frontier I was given back my baggage, papers, watch and money, and signed a paper that I had no complaints to make.

Dr. Josef Goebbels, who banned the newspapers for which I was writing, motivated his decision in the following notice. "The correspondent Pierre van Paassen, a Dutch Jew of Lithuanian extraction, whose real name is Pinchas Paskowitz, is an ex-rabbi, who engaged in atrocity-mongering while in Reich territory."

The Munich episode had a curious aftermath in Paris, a few weeks later, when I was asked to say a few words at a mass meeting of protest against the Hitler terror. When I expressed a fear that the outbreak of Nazi barbarism might evoke a nationalistic countercurrent of hatred and military-chauvinism in France and other countries, I was rudely interrupted by someone who shouted in bad French: "This is no time for pacifism! Let Germany be smashed!"

The heckler was the German journalist who had escaped from the house of bondage across the Rhine with the aid of my passport! He had regained his fighting spirit. He subsequently returned to the Reich to engage in underground work, and disappeared in March, 1934, exactly one year after his flight.

Effect Follows Cause

THE process of man's dehumanization occurs in one land after the other. Christianity and the centuries of humanization reveal themselves as but the thinnest veneer imposed on paganism. They come off at the first rub bringing to the surface the old atavistic instincts from the human race's somber infancy. What land is immune today?

Everywhere a single standard of values is being imposed on the peoples. Every statesman speaks in terms of brute strength. True, in one place men still protest passionately that they desire to maintain the old liberties, democracy and the economic status quo but at the same time we see them band themselves together to restrict freedom (with force if needs be), to frustrate the natural evolution of democracy and seek to patch up dilapidated systems of credit and exchange in order that material well-being be confined to their class alone. Over there they loudly condemn the other man's discrimination against the Jew but themselves hang out a sign that reads "Gentiles Only."

All lament the growth of anti-God movements and while professing a religion of brotherly love engage in the blasphemy of keeping millions of brothers in subhuman living conditions while preparing to destroy their neighbors by poison gas, bombing plane and dreadnought.

But what we see in this world today is not proof that the triumph of inhumanity and injustice and lovelessness is final. Long ago it was said: what a man sows that also shall he reap. The apparent triumph of evil in a historical period such as ours is not a mere accidental, unrelated phenomenon. Precisely because there is violence and oppression and hatred, there is a divine order.

Effect follows cause with inexorable accuracy. God's mill, the divine law, operates with relentless precision. When the fundamental law of nature, which is coherence and respect and brotherhood, is trodden underfoot, no other result can be expected but confusion and hatred and war. The whirlwind follows the storm.

The Solution

IN THE reflection of the flames of China and Europe our whole social order stands revealed to its very foundation as being built on colossal greed, mammonism, heartless exploitations, disregard of elementary human rights and violence. A peace based on vengeance, as someone has said, could not produce anything but Hitlers and their ugly entourage.

Europe and the world will in all likelihood have to pass through the phase of Fascism. The old democratic, parliamentary institutions cannot be saved. They have had their time. A new type of man is emerging, the mass-man, "who can no longer be considered in the perspectives of his own individual inner existence."

No doubt a terrible spiritual abasement stands before the door. But Fascism carries in its bosom the seed of its own disintegration. Out of man's dissatisfaction and longing new worlds are born. As the time of the decline of the ancient world, when man was nothing more than a plaything in the hands of the deified autocrat and his destiny riveted to the terrible wheel of fate, the hope in a juster dispensation produced a profound religious inspiration and Christianity was born.

In our time too, before long, the urge will become manifest to bring the rights of the human personality in harmony with the demands of the collectivity. For even if the oppressors and tyrants, be they quasi-almighty superstates or individuals, appear inviolate and intangible as they govern with death and destruction, there will come a time when the peoples will refuse to be treated as minors and semi-idiots, and will demand a return of the freedom of their hands, their intelligence and their conscience. The last word does not belong to the poison-gas philosophers.

The struggle that is coming is a struggle for man. In that struggle Christianity will triumph, "for Christianity alone stands for man and the freedom of the human personality and social justice and the fraternization of the peoples and enlightenment of human existence."

But that triumphant Christianity will not be the Christianity we know. The old Christianity, which identified itself with this world, will perish with that world. It has been weighed and found wanting. It will be a new Christianity that comes up from the depths of the catacombs of suffering and sorrow. Its apostles will be the martyrs and saints of a new religion that will solve the elementary problems of human existence, the conquest of economic slavery and poverty and peace. . . .

IMMORTALITY IN BOOKS

SINCE honour from the honourer proceeds,
How well do they deserve, that memorize
And leave in books for all posterities
The names of worthies and their virtuous deeds;
When all their glory else, like water-weeds
Without their element, presently dies,
And all their greatness quite forgotten lies,
And when and how they flourished no man heeds!
How poor remembrances are statues, tombs
And other monuments that men erect
To princes, which remain in closèd rooms,
Where but a few behold them, in respect
Of books, that to the universal eye
Show how they lived; the other where they lie!

—J. Florio

OF MONEY

GIVE money me; take friendship whoso list!
    For friends are gone, come once adversity;
When money yet remaineth safe in chest,
    That quickly can thee bring from misery.
Fair face show friends, when riches do abound;
    Come time of proof, 'Farewell, they must away!'
Believe me well, they are not to be found,
    If God but send thee once a lowering day.
    Gold never starts aside; but, in distress,
    Finds ways enough to ease thy heaviness.

—B. Googe

Dorothy Canfield

THE BRIMMING CUP

Dorothy Canfield (Fisher) was born in Kansas, received her undergraduate education at Ohio State University, took a Ph.D. at Columbia University, and finally
settled in Arlington, Vermont. Meanwhile, she traveled extensively in Europe, where she
did war work for three years during the World War. Her literary ability has earned her
honorary degrees from Middlebury, Dartmouth, Vermont, Columbia, Ohio State, and
Northwestern. For three years she was secretary of the Horace Mann School in New York,
and is the author of "The Montessori Mother," a significant contribution to modern
elementary education, which has been translated into French, German, and Danish. She
is the author of many novels, among which are "Hillsboro People" (which appears on page
483 of this volume), "The Bent Twig," "Rough Hewn" and "The Deepening Stream." In
1921 she translated Papini's "Life of Christ," another one of the more recent books which is
found in this volume on page 244. Dorothy Canfield is now a whole-hearted Vermonter;
the background of "The Brimming Cup" is the background of her own daily life.

April, 1909

THE ticket-seller of Rocca di Papa looked at them with a bold, intrusive, diagnosing stare: "Lovers!" he told himself conclusively and accepted with vast incuriosity as to reason the coin which the young foreigner put into his hand.

"Of course he hasn't any idea what he's done to deserve it," said the young man to his sweetheart. "Who ever has? You don't suppose for a moment I've any idea what I've done to deserve mine?"

The young foreigners went across the tracks and established themselves on the rocks, just at the brink of the great drop to the Campagna and waited for the last tramway back to Rome. The girl was physically breathless, her lips parted, her eyebrows drawn together:

"Neale, Neale dear, if I could only tell you how I want it to be, how utterly utterly *true* I want us to be. Oh, Neale, it's horribly dangerous, loving anybody. What I'm afraid of, between two people who try to be what we want to be to each other . . . how can I say

it?" She looked at him in an anguish of endeavor, ". . . not to be true to what is deepest and most living in us . . . that would be the betrayal I'm afraid of. No matter what it costs us personally, or what it brings, we must be true to that. We must!"

He took her hand in his silently, and held it close. "That's an undertaking for a life-time's effort, with all the ups and downs and growths of life. And then to try to know what is deepest and most living in another . . . and to try . . . Marise! I will try. I will try with all my might."

"I'll never forget that as long as I live!" she cried out to him.

THE tears stood in his eyes as in hers.
Now they saw the beauty before them, the vast plain, the mountains, the sea: harmonious, serene, ripe with maturity, evocative of all the centuries of conscious life which had unrolled themselves there.

"I don't mind it's being so old that it makes you feel like a midge in the sunshine with only an hour or two of life before you. What if you are, when it's life as we feel it now, such a flood

DOROTHY CANFIELD now writes most of her books in a quiet Vermont village. She seems to have found serenity and peace of mind in the Green Mountain State.

of it, every instant brimming with it. I have wanted, oh so awfully, sometime to be so filled with some emotion, something great and fine, that I would be an urn too full, gushing up in a great flooding rush. Now I have what I prayed for. Now at last I am that, just as I dreamed, the upsurging of the feeling, brimming over, boiling over, brimming over . . . I suppose another way of saying it is 'the fullness of life.' Now I know what that is."

They sank into a reverie, smiling.

"There comes the cable-car, climbing to get us," she said faintly. "And we will go down from this high place of safety into the dark plain, and we will have to cross it, painfully, step by step. Dare you promise me we will not lose our way?" she challenged him, turning toward him.

"I don't promise you anything about it," he answered. "Only I'm not a bit afraid of the plain, nor the way that's before us. Come along with me, and let's see what's there."

March 15, 1920

THE tall, quiet-looking lady with the long dark eyes, who now came in alone, excusing herself for keeping them waiting, must of course be Mrs. Crittenden, Mr. Welles knew. He had had a long experience in judging people quickly by the expression in their faces, and in that short length of time he had decided thankfully that he was really going to like his new neighbor as much as all the rest of it. He gave her a propitiatory smile, hoping she might like him a little, too, and hoping also that she would not mind Vincent. Sometimes people did, especially nice ladies such as evidently Mrs. Crittenden was.

"I'm more than glad to have you both come in to see me, and I am delighted that Mr. Welles is going to settle here. Mr. Marsh didn't need to explain you. It's evident that you don't know Ashley, Vermont, or you'd realize that I've already heard a great deal about you. I know for instance . . ." she laughed and corrected herself, ". . . at least I've been told, how many years you were in the service of your company, and how your pension was voted unanimously by the Directors, and about the silver loving cup your fellow employees gave you when you retired. I believe you are going to find here what . . . what you deserve to find," she said quietly, "I hope we shall be good neighbors to you."

She spoke so kindly, her look on him was so humane, that he felt the water coming to his eyes. Very likely Vincent had seen the silly weak tears so near the surface, for he was changing the subject with a vengeance. He was in a foolishly emotional state.

"Mrs. Crittenden," he was saying, "my curiosity has been touched by that very fine photograph over there. I don't recognize the castle it shows."

"That's in Bayonne," she said. "I lived opposite it long ago when I was a little girl."

MR. WELLES certainly did not see anything in the speech to make Vincent look at her, almost with his jaw dropped. What an awfully nice woman she was, and good-looking, too, with a very nice figure, although not in her very first youth, of course. Between thirty and forty somewhere, but you couldn't tell where. He liked the way she did her black hair, too, smooth and shining and close to her head. It looked as though she'd really combed and brushed it, and most women's hair didn't. She turned to him now, again.

"I mustn't miss the opportunity to cut in ahead of all the other gossips, and give you a great deal of information. In this house, there is first of all my husband. I'm so sorry he is away in Canada just now, on lumbering business. He is Neale Crittenden, a Williams man, who in his youth had thoughts of exploring the world, but has turned out head of the 'Crittenden Manufacturing Company,' which is the high-sounding name of a smallish wood-working business on the other side of the field next to our house.

"Then there is myself. You see me. There is nothing more to that. And there are three children, Paul, Elly, and Mark . . ."

She paused here rather abruptly, and the whimsical accent of good-humored mockery disappeared. He had the queerest fancy that she looked somehow scared,—but of course that was preposterous.

"Your call," she told them both, "happens to fall on a day which marks a turning-point in our family life. This is the very first day in ten years, since Paul's birth, that I have not had at least one of the children beside me. I have felt very queer indeed, all day. It's as though . . . you know, when you have been walking up and up a long flight of stairs, and you go automatically putting one foot up and then the other, and then suddenly . . . your upraised foot falls back with a jar. You've come to the top, and for an instant, you have a gone feeling without your stairs to climb."

It occurred to Mr. Welles that really perhaps the reason why some nice ladies did not like Vincent was just because of his habit of looking at them so hard. He could have no idea how piercing bright his eyes looked when he fixed them on a speaker like that.

"You can't make me believe that by choice you live up here, all the year around," Vincent was saying. "You must nearly perish with homesickness for the big world, you who so evidently belong in it."

"I usually go down once a season to the city for a visit, but last winter I didn't get up the energy to do that. I suppose the real reason why I go less and less to New York, is that it doesn't interest me as it used to. Human significance is what makes interest for me, and when you're used to looking deep into human lives out of a complete knowledge of them as we do up here, the superficial, incoherent glimpses you get in such a smooth, glib-tongued circle as the people I happen to know in New York are boring."

Mr. Marsh remarked speculatively, as though they were speaking of some quite abstract topic, "It may also be possible that you are succumbing to habit and inertia and routine."

SHE was startled and nettled. What a rude thing to say! But the words were no sooner out of his mouth than she had felt a scared wonder if perhaps they were not true. Vincent was changing the subject again.

"Mrs. Crittenden, I've heard from Mr. Welles' house the most tantalizing snatches from your piano. Won't you, now we're close to it, put the final touch to our delightful visit by letting us hear it?"

Marise was annoyed by his *grand seigneur* air of authority. She was shocked to realize that she hadn't felt this little sharp sting of wounded personal vanity since she was a little girl. But it was with all her faculties awakened and keen that she sat down before the piano. What did she know by heart? The Largo in the Chopin Sonata. That would do to come after Beethoven.

She finished the last note of the Largo and sat quiet for a moment. Then she knew that someone had come into the room behind her. The first meeting with the eyes of the man who stood there moved her. So he, too, deeply and greatly loved music! Those piercing eyes were softened and quietly shining. The arrogant lines about the mouth that could look so bitter and skeptical, were as sweet and candid as a child's. He looked exactly what Marise was feeling.

"When are you going back to the city, Mr. Marsh?" asked Marise, as they said good-bye at the door.

"I'll wager that there is one thing your Ashley underground news-service has not told you about us, and that is, that I've come up not only to help Mr. Welles install himself in his new home, but to take a somewhat prolonged rest-cure myself. I've a notion that the air in this lovely spot will do me a world of good."

Mr. Welles' jaw dropped this time, as Vincent suddenly grasped his arm and moved with him down the flag-paved path.

April 20, 1920

MARISE startled herself almost as much as her callers by turning over that leaf in the photograph album quickly and saying with abruptness, "No, never mind that one. It's nothing interesting."

Marise perceived that the children scented something fine and exciting, such as the sensational pictures she was always trying to keep from them. Through the top of Vincent's dark, close-cropped head she could fairly feel the racing, inquiring speculations whirling about. Why, a thousand times why, had she felt this sudden unwillingness to look at the perfectly commonplace photograph in this company?

"There!" she said carelessly, "look at it then."

The little boys bent their eager faces over it. Paul read out the title: "View of the Campagna from the top of the cable-railway at Rocca di Papa. Rome in the distance." Mother certainly *had* spoken to them in that hide-it-away-from-the-children voice, and yet there was nothing there.

As Marsh looked at her, she noted a smouldering glow of carefully repressed exasperation in his eyes. There rose into her consciousness the reason why she had shrunk from looking at the photograph of Rocca di Papa. It was because it was painful for her to remember how she and Neale had felt there, that astounding flood of feeling which had swept them away. What had become of all that? Where now was that high tide?

It must have been ebbing for a long time before she realized it because, hurried, absorbed, surrounded incessantly by small cares as she was, hustled and jostled in her rôle of mother and mistress-of-the-house in servantless America, she had not even had time to know the stupid, tragic thing that was happening to her . . . that she was turning into a slow, vegetating plant instead of maintaining her status as a human being.

And now she understood the meaning of the strange dejection she had felt the day when little Mark went off to school with the others. How curiously jaded and apprehensive she had felt that morning. That was the first time she had *felt* that the tide was ebbing.

June 10, 1920

DISHES clicked, cups were set back with little clinking noises on saucers. All these indoor noises were oddly diminished and unresonant under the open sky, just as the chatting, laughing flow of the voices, even though it rose at times to bursts of mirth which the children's shouts made noisy, never drowned out the sweet, secret talk of the brook to itself.

Marise was aware of all this, richly and happily aware of the complexities of an impression whose total seemed to her, for the moment, felicity itself. How tremendously more *simpático* Marsh had seemed this afternoon than ever before, as though one might really like him and not find him merely exciting and interesting; and Neale, dear Neale, with his calm eyes into which it did everyone good to look.

"Hello," said Neale, looking back toward the house. "Here comes Eugenia. Eugenia is an old friend of my wife's, schoolmates in France together."

After acknowledging the introductions, Eugenia said to Marise casually, "Marisette, here we are the first of June and past, and the roses here are less advanced than they were at Tivoli the last of March. Do you remember the day when we went on the Rocca di Papa expedition? In fact, it was on that very expedition that you got formally engaged, don't you remember?"

Marise heard Eugenia's voice going on, and Neale chiming in with a laugh. Surely everybody must have forgotten. Then she looked at Marsh. He was waiting for her eyes. And when they met his, she felt the lightning flash. He had not forgotten.

July 10, 1920

MARISE and Neale were sitting on the garden bench. "Neale," said Marise, "don't you think that people are saying horrid, distressing things

nowadays? About marriage, I mean, and all relations between men and women and between parents and children. Books are being written to prove that parents' love for their children is only self-love, hypocritically disguised, and sometimes even sexual love camouflaged; and that anybody is better for the children to be with than their mother; and that married people, after the first flare-up of passion is over, hate each other instead of loving?"

"There's a good deal to be said about all that, that's pretty horrid and perfectly true," remarked Neale casually.

Marise started and cried out piercingly, "Neale, how can you say such a thing to *me!*"

Neale was thoroughly astonished, "Why, Marise dear, what are you talking about? You don't have to believe about *yourself* all the generalizing guesses that people are writing down in books, if it contradicts your own experience. Don't you *know* whether you really love Elly and Mark and Paul? Don't you *know* whether we hate each other, you and I? Everybody must decide for himself when a general proposition applies to him, what to believe about his own life and its values. Nobody else can tell him."

Even in her emotion, she had an instant's inward smile at the Neale-like quality of this. She went on, "But don't you think there is such a thing as spoiling beautiful elements in life, for natures that aren't naturally ready to fight for what they want to keep? For instance, when somebody says that children in a marriage are like drift-wood left high on the rocks of a dwindled stream, tokens of a flood-time of passion now gone . . ." She thought by his expression that he knew that Vincent Marsh had said it.

He said heartily, "I should simply call that a nasty-minded remark from somebody who didn't know what he was talking about. And let it go at that." Then after a pause, "Marise, I'm afraid that you *have* to fight for what you want to keep in this world. And I don't believe that anybody else can do your fighting for you."

She cried out to him in a sudden anguish that was beyond her control, *"But suppose you face it and still it springs!"*

He looked at her as though he saw her for the first time that day. And he grew very pale as he looked. Something wordless passed between them. Now he knew at last what she was afraid of.

She felt herself putting to him clearly, piercingly, the question which till then she had not known how to form, *"Neale, what do you want me to do?"*

He said, in a deep, trembling, solemn voice, "Marise, my darling, I want you always to do what is best for *you* to do. What is deepest and most living in you . . . that is what must go on living."

He grasped her hand and held it as though he were taking an oath.

M ARISE sat on the bench where Neale had left her and felt nervous tears stinging in her eyes. When she looked up, she saw Vincent Marsh standing there, extremely pale. He sat down beside her, his eyes on hers. He did not stir from his place, but to her he seemed to tower above her. In his dark, intent face was an exultant look of power and authority which fell on her like a hot wind. With a loud knocking of her heart she knew before he spoke what he would say.

"Come away from the man who is nothing more to you than the house you live in . . . nothing but a habit. You were right, on that evening when you shrank away from the sight of the place in Italy where in your ignorant youth you made the mistake of trying to join your life to his. Make an end!

Make an end! Come away where you will really live and know the fullness of life. Come away from the false notion of duty, which makes you do for the children what you know is not best for them, only because it is the traditional thing to do.

"You are the most living woman who ever wore flesh and blood! And I am a living man! You know when our hands touch, every drop of blood in our two bodies burns! You are a grown woman. You know life as well as I do. You know what this means. You are no longer even a part of his life. You are all of mine. Look at me now."

Vincent looked straight at her, straight and deep and strong into her eyes, and for an instant his burning lips were pressed on hers. The contact was terrible, momentous.

S HE lay down on her bed but could not close her eyes. They remained wide open, looking straight into the blackness and vacancy. She gazed steadily at the wall before her, and called up the life which Vincent Marsh thought the only one that meant richness and abundance for the human spirit.

It hung there, a shimmering mass of lovely colors and exquisite textures and fineness and delicacy and beauty. As she looked at it, it took on the shape of a glorious, uprooted plant, cut off from the very source of life, its glossy surfaces already beginning to wither and dull in the sure approach of corruption and decay. But what beauties were there to pluck, lovely fading beauties, poignant and exquisite sensations, which she was capable of savoring, which she sadly knew she would live and die without, because she had known the unforgettable taste of the other heritage, alive and rooted deep.

Physical excitement, that was what Vincent Marsh could give her which

She finished the last note of the Largo and sat quiet for a
moment. Then she knew that someone had come into the
room behind her.

Illustration for Dorothy Canfield's
"THE BRIMMING CUP"

Neale no longer could. . . . That, and great ease of life, which Neale never would. . . . There was a pause in which she shivered, humiliated. She added lamely to this, a guessed-at possibility for aesthetic sympathy and understanding, perhaps more than Neale could offer. How horrid this searching of herself was! It offended a deep sense of personal dignity and decency!

Somehow she was showing herself that what she wanted was not to get love, but to give all that lay in her to give. She saw in this hour of silence and searching that that was what she wanted. It was something in her which had grown insensibly to life and strength, during all those uncounted hours of humble service to the children. And it was something golden and immortal in her poor, flawed, human heart.

A warm bright wave of feeling swept over her. There in a shadowy, confused procession stood Paul and Elly and little Mark, looking at her out of their clear loving eyes. Their regard was the pure distillation of the innumerable past hours when they had looked at her with love and trust.

At the sight of them, her own children, her heart swelled and opened wide to a conception of something greater and deeper in motherhood than she had had; something so wide and sunflooded that the old selfish, possessive ache, which had called itself love, withered away, its power to hurt her and poison her gone.

She had been trying to span the unfathomable with a mean and grasping desire. Now she knew what she must try to do: give up the lesser and receive the greater.

September 22, 1920

IT was the half hour of pause after lunch. The children played idly with the fox-terrier and lounged on the steps of the side-porch, strong and brown, living cups filled to the brim with life. Neale had pushed his chair back from the table, lighted his pipe, and sat meditating. Presently he put out his hand and laid it on Marise's, who had turned to look down the sun-flooded valley.

It was high-noon, dreamy, entranced, all the world golden with the magnificent weather as a holly-hock is golden with pollen. From the brook came the living voice of the water, with the special note of brave clarity it always had for brilliant noons.

It seemed to Marise that she too was all gold-powdered with the magnificence of life, that in her heart there sang a clear living voice that did not fear high-noons.

TO-MORROW

TO-MORROW, and to-morrow, and to-morrow,
Creeps in this petty pace from day to day,
To the last syllable of recorded time;
And all our yesterdays have lighted fools
The way to dusty death. Out, out, brief candle!
Life's but a walking shadow, a poor player
That struts and frets his hour upon the stage,
And then is heard no more: it is a tale
Told by an idiot, full of sound and fury,
Signifying nothing.

—*William Shakespeare* (1564-1616).

Arnold Bennett

THE OLD WIVES' TALE

As THOMAS HARDY's name is with Wessex, so Arnold Bennett's (1867-1931) name will be inseparably associated with the Five Towns of Hanley, Stoke, Burslem, Longton and Tunstall. In "The Old Wives' Tale" they appear as Handbridge ("the shape of a horse and its rider," the author tells us), Bursley ("of half a donkey"), Knype ("of a pair of trousers"), Longshaw ("of an octopus") and little Turnhill ("of a beetle"). Of Staffordshire, in which county he was born, he says, England can show nothing more beautiful and nothing uglier than the works of nature and the works of man to be seen within its limits. In "The Old Wives' Tale," Mr. Bennett depicts not only the beauty and the ugliness of the works of nature and the works of man, but the beauty and the ugliness, the meanness and the magnanimity, the weakness and the strength, the insignificance and yet the significance of human life and human character. He does this with a power that recalls Charles Dickens.

"THE Old Wives' Tale" is a marvel of meticulous detail. Some novelists show us far things as through a telescope, near things as through a microscope. Not so Arnold Bennett. In the first half of the book he bids us look with him, as it were, through a magnifying glass, which is turned upon one minute spot. The scene is laid in Bursley, but, after a comprehensive glance round, the novelist says, in effect, "You ought to know something of Bursley, but that will do. What matters now is St. Luke's Square."

To St. Luke's Square accordingly we go, appraisingly to cast a look around, again only to be told "That must do for St. Luke's Square. What matters now is one particular house in it," and the focussing glass is turned upon the shop of Mr. Baines, the leading draper [dry-goods dealer] the strangely contrasting characters of whose two daughters, Constance and Sophia, are our main concern.

Someone has said, "You never know what a woman will do—and when you do, she won't do it." That may be true of some, but not of all women. The reader does know what Constance will do—and she does it. Not so Sophia. The creature of impulse but, unlike most creatures of impulse, determined of will and character, she does not know herself

what she will do. But, perhaps, because she, at least, is a character of his own creating, the author knows and lets the reader into the secret. The majority of his characters strike one as taken from life, though possibly each is something of a composite picture, in the sense that the artist has imposed other features or characteristics upon the original. But just as a painted portrait is sometimes truer to life than a photograph, divining the soul within, so Sophia is truer to life, and to feminine nature, than in her portrait had been drawn from a living woman.

One wonders whence came the mercury in her blood. Certainly not from her conventionally-minded, linen-draper parents, for she strikes one as a changeling rather than as a daughter of their house. Her mother is a capable, comfortable, kindly body who, as her husband is now a bed-ridden invalid, is so accustomed to undisputed control of the shop, the house and the children that she has become something of an amiable autocrat, a benignant despot. She flatters herself she can read her two daughters "like a book," and that, like a book, they will be passive in her hands. To her dismay, she discovers that the book of her younger daughter's mind, now that daughter is passing from girlhood into budding womanhood, is written in characters indecipherable to her.

From Mrs. Baines the decree has gone forth that, after leaving school, the two girls shall take their place in the shop. Constance consents, but Sophia, to mother's surprised dismay, announces her intention of staying on at school that she may become a teacher. Most women seek to attain their ends by other than the direct means and arguments used by men. Thus, in a clash of wills, mother and daughter rarely discuss the matter at issue as would a father and son.

Now we must go back for a moment to the days when Sophia was a "gawky girl," and had a glimpse of a young commercial traveller, whose name she did not know, who had called at her father's shop.

Sophia had never forgotten that glimpse. The young man without a name had lived in her mind, brightly glowing, as the very symbol and incarnation of the masculine and the elegant.

During the Bursley Wakes, two years after the opening of the story, an elephant in Wombwell's Menagerie turns "rogue" and has to be shot by members of the local volunteer corps. Even Mrs. Baines cannot resist the temptation to see so rare a sight. She, Constance and Mr. Samuel Povey, who, under Mrs. Baines's proprietary eye, now manages the shop, go off together. When invited to join the party, Sophia, now training to be a teacher, replies disdainfully, "I'm far too busy for elephants!" As her bed-ridden father must never be left unattended, she is deputed to stay with him. From his window, she watches the others depart.

SHE perceived that she had miscalculated the importance of the elephant. It made her regret her scorn of the elephant as an attraction. She was left behind, and the joy of life was calling her. . . She noticed, while she was thus at the bedroom window, a young man descending King Street, followed by a porter trundling a flat barrow of luggage. He passed slowly under the very window. She flushed. She had evidently been startled by the sight of this young man

into no ordinary state of commotion. She glanced at the books on the sofa, and then at her father. Mr. Baines, thin and gaunt and acutely pitiable, still slept. His brain had almost ceased to be active now; he had to be fed and tended like a bearded baby, and he would sleep for hours at a stretch, even in the daytime. Sophia left the room. A moment later, she ran into the shop, an apparition that amazed the young lady assistant.

She finds the commercial traveller, as she had hoped, in the shop, and falls in love with him more passionately than ever; and he is equally attracted and fascinated by her. That he and she may continue to meet thereafter, Sophia promptly abandons her work as a teacher and complies with her mother's wish that she shall go into the shop.

The lovers meet, sometimes casually, sometimes clandestinely, as Mrs. Baines discovers, and to get Sophia out of the way her mother packs the girl off on a visit to her aunt Harriet at Axe. Sophia, of course, is quite aware of what is in the maternal mind.

"You needn't think I don't see why you're sending me away!" exclaimed Sophia, in a hard, furious voice, with glistening eyes. "I'm not so blind as all that!" She kissed her mother—nothing but a contemptuous jerk. Then, as she turned away, she added: "But you let Constance do just as she likes!"

This last fling at her mother means that Mrs. Baines is now—she did not do so at first—acquiescing in a love affair between Constance and Mr. Povey, the manager of the shop. While at her aunt's, Sophia takes money belonging to the latter, and elopes with the young commercial traveller, Gerald Scales by name, who has come into a legacy of £12,000. Later, Sophia writes that she is married to Scales, and that they are going abroad. Then, except for a card at Christmas and the like, Sophia drops out of the story until we reach the second half of the book.

We read of the home-coming to the house in St. Luke's Square after the honeymoon, of Constance and her husband, to whom Mrs. Baines has made over the drapery business. The course of true, but scarcely passionate, love in this case runs smooth. Only a gentle and passing breeze ruffles the otherwise placid surface of Constance's married life. The dilemmas and difficulties, the thoughts and feelings of a young wife, are described with infinite convincing detail.

There is a child of the marriage. Arnold Bennett is a writer of genius; and in a writer, genius is almost invariably associated with extraordinary retentiveness of memory, and with like extraordinary closeness of observation. Whether as a memory of his own childhood (which is scarcely likely in this instance) or as the outcome of his marvellously close observation, the passages describing the infant life of the child of Constance and Povey afford no small insight into the workings of the novelist's mind. Cyril's upbringing, his father's sternness, his mother's indulgent softness, and the result of both upon his character, his first "crime" (theft) and his temperamental oscillations between sullen secretiveness and charm—all these are shown by means of the magic glass which the art of the author places in our hand and focusses as minutely upon Cyril as if he were the central figure in the story. Yet this same Cyril is the only important character about whom the author does not tell us everything. As the book ends we do not know what ultimately became of him.

Then comes the first of the sensational episodes. Samuel Povey has a cousin, Daniel Povey, the leading confectioner, and a member of the local board, as well as a sidesman of St. Luke's. Samuel Povey—upright of character, and chapel-going draper though he be—in his secret heart admires, even envies, his cousin Daniel, for his good looks, his man-of-the-world ways, his sportsmanship, and for his reputation as a story teller, even though some of the stories are Rabelaisian. One night Samuel is accosted by Daniel and taken across to the confectioner's shop.

"You know as my wife drinks?"

He did not know that Mrs. Daniel Povey, at the age of fifty, had definitely taken to drink. There had been rumours that she enjoyed a glass with too much gusto; but "drinks" meant more than that. "She drinks," Daniel Povey continued, "and has done this last two years."

"I'm very sorry to hear it," said Samuel, tremendously shocked by this brutal rending of the cloak of decency.

Then Daniel goes on to tell about the only son of the house. Daniel had come home late that night, having missed the last train, to find Dick sitting on the stairs, nearly naked.

"Sitting on the stairs? Dick?" said Samuel.

"Ay! This is what I come home to!"

"But——"

"Hold on! He's been in bed a couple of days with a feverish cold, caught through lying in damp sheets as his mother had forgot to air. She brings him no supper to night. He calls out. No answer. Then he gets up to go downstairs and see what happened, and he slips on th' stairs and breaks his knee, or puts it out or summat. Sat there hours, seemingly. Couldn't walk either up nor down."

"And was your—wife—was Mrs.——"

"Dead drunk in the parlour, Sam'l."

"But the servant?"

"Servant!" Daniel Povey laughed. "We can't keep our servants. They won't stay, you know that."

Daniel has already carried Dick to bed, but when Samuel asks about Mrs. Daniel Povey, the reply is, "Happen you'd better go and have a look at her. She's in th' parlour." He leads the way thither, and this is what Samuel sees.

In a room as dishevelled and filthy as the bedroom, Mrs. Daniel Povey lay stretched awkwardly on a worn horsehair sofa, her head thrown back, her face discoloured, her eyes bulging, her mouth wet and yawning; a sight horribly offensive. Samuel was frightened; he was struck with fear and with disgust. The singing gas beat down ruthlessly on that dreadful figure. A wife and mother! The lady of a house! The centre of order! The fount of healing! The balm for worry and the refuge of distress! She was vile. Her scanty yellow-grey hair was dirty, her hollowed neck all grime, her hands abominable, her black dress in decay. She was the dishonour of her sex, her situation and her years. . . .

"Ay, Sam'l, lad," said the old man from the door; "I doubt I've killed her! I doubt I killed her. I took and shook her. I got her by the neck, and before I knew where I was, I'd done it. She'll never drink brandy again. This is what it's come to!"

Daniel himself calls in the police, and is arrested.

THENCEFORWARD, Samuel Povey had a mission, religious in its solemn intensity, to defend and save Daniel. He took the enterprise upon himself, spending the whole of himself upon it, to the neglect of his business and the scorn of his health. He lived solely for Daniel's trial, pouring out money in preparation for it. He thought and spoke of nothing else. The affair was his one preoccupation.

But all is to no purpose. Daniel is found guilty, and in spite of a petition for a reprieve, drafted and promoted by Sam and signed by nearly 25,000 of Daniel's fellow townsmen and townswomen, is hanged. Sam himself dies soon afterwards, physically and mentally exhausted by his labours for his unhappy cousin.

The house in St. Luke's Square is put up for sale some time after Sam's death, and Constance, who has been carrying on the business, comes to an arrangement with Mr. Critchlow, the purchaser, whereby he takes over the shop, and Constance remains on, as tenant, in the living rooms overhead, with her son, Cyril. Between these two, as between Mrs. Baines and Sophia, there is a con-

flict of will, and again it is the mother who has to give way. Cyril, against his mother's wish, is set on being an artist. He attends the local school of art, and, to Constance's anguish, for she knows it means his leaving Bursley to live in London, he announces that he has won a national scholarship. The first half of the book closes by showing us Constance as alternately the proud and the broken-hearted mother returning to her lonely home after Cyril has left.

Arnold Bennett now takes up the story of Sophia from the time she left her aunt's house to join Gerald Scales in London. The two are in the bedroom of a hotel, and it is the first moment they have been alone together since Sophia's arrival. "I've got no one but you now," she says. The words chill Scales who is thinking about his responsibilities. He smiles vaguely and proposes a visit to the Doré Gallery. "But what about the wedding?" she asks. "It can't be done here," he replies. "There's been some change in the rules. I only found out for certain late last night. But I have ascertained that it will be as simple as A.B.C. before the English Consul in Paris, and I've got the tickets for us to go over tonight."

She did not suspect that he was using the classic device of the seducer. It was his casualness that staggered her. But Sophia, for all her ignorance and innocence, is shrewd and cautious, and very well able to take care of herself. She refuses to go to Paris or anywhere else until they are married. He does his best to persuade her. "Come now, it will be all right," he says; but she does not stir. When he touches the back of her neck with his lips, she springs to her feet, sobbing and angry. Because she is made for him she hates him furiously. All tenderness has vanished. "I'll thank you not to touch me," she says fiercely. She had given him her lips a few moments ago, but now to put his lips to her neck is an insult. They quarrel. She bids him go, and he goes, leaving her to tell herself that the elopement was "an enormous folly." The strict notions of her elderly relatives were right, after all. It was she who had been wrong, and it would be she who would have to pay.

But Scales comes back. He wanted her. He wanted her with an excessive desire. So he comes back to make his peace, and to say he will marry her. "I shall have her! I shall have her!" he says to himself; but he did not reflect that this fragile slip of the Baines stock, unconsciously drawing on the accumulated strength of generations of honest living, had put a defeat upon him. It was a cardinal moment in the lives of both of them.

DULY married, the two go to Paris, and though Arnold Bennett knows Paris as few know it, and paints picture after picture of power and brilliancy, he does not know Paris as he knows the draper's shop at Bursley. Here he is drawing, not on his childhood's but on his manhood's memory.

In Paris, Sophia, for a day or two, "existed in a rapture of bliss, an ecstasy which could feel no fatigue either of body or spirit." Her husband buys her Paris gowns, at prices which frighten her; takes her to smart restaurants to dine, and helps himself so plenteously to the champagne that, one night, he comments so loudly about a woman accompanying another diner, an Englishman, that the Englishman overhears. The latter is very angry, but "wine affected them in different ways," and he restrains himself, especially as the entrance of a young French journalist, by name Chirac, known personally to both the Englishman and Scales, causes a diversion.

Sophia, fearing trouble, says that she is tired, and proposes returning to the hotel; but Scales refuses, orders brandy, and finally gives the Englishman cause to ask whether Gerald wishes to insult him, because if so . . . they had better settle the matter outside. Gerald replies "At your service," tells Sophia to wait there for him, and the two men leave the room. Sophia, already disillusioned about her husband, is overcome with shame. Though she waits till long past three, Gerald does not return, there is a bill to pay, and she has no money. The chivalrous Chirac, whose admiration of Sophia is evident but reverential, comes to her rescue and offers to escort her to the hotel. Gerald returns at daybreak with blood upon his face. Sophia, who had been furious with him, bathes the wound, and decides that her duty is to treat him "as a wife ought to treat a husband."

In the morning Gerald tells her that he is going, next day, with Chirac, to witness the execution of a murderer, at Auxerre. When he returns to the hotel, supported by Chirac, he is the very image of death.

The appalling spectacle is described with the relentless realism of a Zola; but terrible as is the effect upon Sophia of the details, which, despite all efforts of will, she is, as it were, hypnotised into witnessing, their shock is not so overwhelming as that of the revelation they bring her of an aspect of her husband's character of which she had hitherto had no idea.

The attainment of ambition had utterly destroyed his equilibrium; his curiosity had proved stronger than his stomach. . . . Not long since he had been proudly conversing with impudent women. Now, in swift collapse, he was as flaccid as a sick hound, and as disgusting as an aged drunkard. This was what he had brought her to, then! The horrors of the night, of the dawn and of the morning! Ineffable suffering and humiliation, anguish and torture that could never be forgotten. And after a fatuous vigil of unguessed license, he had tottered back, an offensive beast, to sleep the day away in that filthy chamber. He did not even possess enough spirit to play the rôle of roysterer to the end! And she was bound to him; far, far from any other human aid; cut off irrevocably by her pride from those who would perhaps have protected her from his dangerous folly. . . . Sticking out of the breast-pocket of his soiled coat was the packet which he had received on the previous day. If he had not already lost it, he could only thank his luck.

They had returned to Paris and Sophia, now seriously ill in bed, is told one day that Chirac is enquiring for Monsieur on a matter of importance. Will Madame see him? Sophia does so, to learn that when she had lost sight of Scales on the preceding day, he was in the office of the paper with which Chirac is associated.

"He said he ought to have received 5000 francs, yesterday morning," Chirac tells her, "but he had a telegram saying it would not arrive till to-day. And he had need of 500 francs at once. I had not 500 francs"—he smiles sadly as if to insinuate that he did not handle such sums—"But I borrowed it from the cash box of the journal. It is necessary, absolutely, that I should return it this morning." He spoke with increased seriousness. "Your husband said he would take a cab and bring me the money immediately on the arrival of the post this morning, about nine o'clock." Gerald, she tells herself, had genuinely been at his last franc.

He had not lied when she thought he had lied. The nakedness of his character showed now. Instantly upon the final and definite cessation of the lawful supply of money, he had set his wits to obtain money unlawfully. He had, in fact, simply stolen it from Chirac, with the ornamental addition of endangering Chirac's reputation and situation—as a sort of reward to Chirac for the kindness. And further, no sooner had he got hold of the money than it had intoxicated him, and he had yielded to the first fatuous temptation.

"You did not know that he was coming to me?" asks Chirac.

"No," she tells him, but adds: "it is fortunate that I can pay you." She asks Chirac to accompany her to a *bureau de change*. There she exchanges the English

notes for £200 which she has abstracted from her husband's pocket, returns Chirac his 500 francs, and while he is escorting her back to the hotel in a fiacre, she is taken ill and lapses into unconsciousness.

When consciousness returns she is in bed in a shabby boarding-house flat, the woman-proprietress of which and a younger woman nurse her, with tenderness, back to health. Sophia discovers that both women are visited by men "friends," and is unhappy and uneasy. Chirac, who is in love with her but still holds her in awe, calls, and she learns that Madame the proprietress, a friend of Chirac's, is in money difficulties—she has not paid for the furniture, and an execution is about to be put in. To discharge her own heavy debt to the woman for the kindness with which Sophia was nursed, the latter decides to use part of what is left of the £200 by paying for the furniture, and arranges also to go into partnership with the woman, on the distinct stipulation that the rooms be let only to "respectable" lodgers. As Sophia—consulted by the grocer whose bill she is paying, about a room for a friend of his, by name Niepce—is the means of thus obtaining a respectable boarder, the proprietress is impressed, and agrees to the partnership. Then Chirac also takes a room, and Sophia decides that there are now enough lodgers to make the establishment pay, and that here is the opportunity for her to earn her own living.

The Germans are now besieging Paris, and Sophia turns war-profiteer. She lays in a large stock of provisions while prices are comparatively low, and when prices rise abnormally sells at a huge profit, and so begins to make money.

But Sophia's troubles come. Her beauty brings her the unwelcome attention of her boarders. "I love you, madame," Niepce tells her one day. He admits that he has a wife, but goes on. "You can count on my discretion. I appreciate your scruples. I would come very late to your room." She is very angry, but "he is an old fool" she tells herself. Why not treat him as such? Moreover, he is a very remunerative boarder. By this time she has saved nearly 5,000 francs, and she wishes to make more.

The lovesick Chirac, partly, one suspects, out of bravado, and for once at least to figure as a hero in the beloved one's eyes, partly to secure a "stunt" for his paper, arranges to be one of two men who attempt to leave Paris in a balloon. The ascent, which, by Chirac's entreaty, Sophia witnesses, deeply stirred and with a tightening at her throat, is finely described, but what becomes of Chirac, whom Sophia had come near to loving, we are not told. The Germans enter Paris, and life there becoming more normal, business at Sophia's boarding-house falls off. The street in which it is had a bad name—respectable folk fight shy of it, and to the other sort she shows the door. She hears that an English *pension* in a respectable quarter is for sale, disposes of the boarding-house, buys the English *pension* and turns it into a greater success than ever before, thus making more money.

But Sophia is too beautiful a woman, too commanding a personality, to escape curiosity. To stay in the *pension* comes a Mr. Peel-Swynnerton, the son, the grandson, and several times the nephew of earthenware manufacturers whose name is known and revered in the Five Towns. Being artistic of taste, he happens to be the friend of Constance's son, Cyril, now an artist, from whom Peel-Swynnerton has heard of his aunt. Impressed by Sophia's stately beauty and aloofness, Peel-Swynnerton makes enquiries and, discovering that her name is Scales, suspects that she is his friend's missing aunt. He asks her casually whether anyone of the name of Povey, Cyril Povey, from Bursley, has been staying there.

Sophia is profoundly perturbed. She foresees the upsetting of her existence, the destruction of her calm.

"I've lived alone, and I'll stay as I am. I can't change at my time of life!" she says, and frets herself into a fever. What she fears, happens, Peel-Swynnerton had gone in haste to inform Constance that he has found her long-lost sister. Constance writes rejoicingly to Sophia, begging her to come to Bursley, and pleads so movingly that Sophia's old love for her sister re-awakens. She writes to Constance lovingly, but says she cannot go to Bursley, and invites her sister to Paris. Constance replies that she would come, but is unwell and forbidden to travel. That being so, Sophia's duty is, she feels, to go to her sister. She accepts an offer made for the *pension,* and leaves for her native town.

There is an affecting meeting between the sisters, and Sophia stays a while with Constance at the house where both were born. Sophia's thoughts are all for her sister, whom she hopes never to leave again. But she hates Bursley, and tells herself that to live there would kill her. She sees that Constance is not only growing old, but is growing increasingly, almost unbearably "fussy." "What you want," she tells her sister, "is a change." So she drags the reluctant Constance, who cannot bear to be away from the "house" for more than a few hours at a time, to a fashionable hotel at Buxton.

It soon becomes clear that, their love for each other notwithstanding, Constance and Sophia are, by incompatibility of temperament, and even more by long years of habit, unsuited to end their days in each other's company, as both had hoped. The shadow of approaching end is over both. As to reader and writer life has brought, or will bring, disillusionments, so with Constance and Sophia.

To Sophia, disillusionment came swiftly. The honeymoon was not over before she knew that the lover she had idealised, the husband for whom she had risked everything, was a liar, a cad and a cur. To Constance, disillusionment came more slowly; but now at last she sees that the son, Cyril, whom she loves wholly, is neglectful of, almost indifferent to, his mother's wishes and happiness. Now it seems as if even she and Sophia must each go her own way. It is well that for the one and the other the coming of death is not too long delayed.

Sophia receives, from a relative of the husband she has neither seen nor heard of for thirty-six years, a telegram to say that her husband is at that relative's house, and dangerously ill. She hastens thither, to find that Scales has died.

In her mind she had not pictured Gerald as a very old man. She knew that he was old; she had said to herself that he must be very old, well over seventy. But she had not pictured him. This face on the bed was painfully, pitiably old. A withered face, with the shiny skin all drawn into wrinkles. The stretched skin under the jaw was like the skin of a plucked fowl. The cheek bones stood up, and below them were deep hollows, almost like egg-cups. A short, scraggy white beard covered the lower part of the face. The hair was scanty, irregular and quite white; a little white hair grew in the ears. The shut mouth obviously hid toothless gums, for the lips were sucked in. . . . And on the face was a general expression of final fatigue, of tragic and acute exhaustion. . . . What affected her was that he had once been young, and had grown old.

IT CAME to Sophia herself before many hours had passed. On the return journey she becomes unconscious in the car, is put to bed by Constance, but nothing can be done.

Sophia seemed to be in a kind of coma. The distortion of her handsome face was more marked as time passed. The doctor spoke now and then in a low voice. He said that the attack had ultimately been determined by cold, produced by the rapid motion in the automobile. . . . It was half-past twelve when, after gazing with prolonged intensity at the patient, and after he had tested her mouth and heart, he rose slowly and looked at Constance.

"It is over?" said Constance. And he very slightly moved his head.

Nor does Constance for very long survive Sophia. The Federation of the Five Towns is proposed. To her, in all the world there is only one town, Bursley, and in Bursley, only one house, that in St. Luke's Square. To the damage done to Bursley by the proposed Federation she attributes the fact that Mrs. Critchlow, who is in command of the draper's shop which had first been under the proprietorship of Constance's father, and, after his death, of her husband, had, owing to the falling off of trade, attempted suicide. The shop is closed in consequence. As a draper's shop, it will never open again. This is the end of Baines's. To the proposed Federation she attributes, too, the fact that she is to be turned out of the house she loves, and in which she was born. She receives notice to quit, as the rooms are required by the manager of the new business now opened in the shop below. This is what the threat of Federation has done for her and Bursley. Old as Constance is, she must go to the Town Hall to record her vote against Federation, and she comes back—to die a few days later.

◆

No POSSESSION is gratifying without a companion.—*Seneca.*

A PLEASANT companion on a journey is as good as a carriage.—*Syrus.*

SOME are good, some are middling, the most are bad.—*Martial.*

THE coming years bring many advantages with them: retiring they take away many.—*Horace.*

H. G. WELLS
THE WAR OF THE WORLDS

F IRST published in 1898, The War of the Worlds immediately set Mr. Wells in the very forefront of the writers of scientific romance. It originated in a remark made to him by his brother: "How would it be if some creatures of a vastly superior power suddenly came down upon us and behaved like a drunken man-of-war's crew let loose among some gentle savages?" One day, walking upon Horsell Common he suddenly visualised such invaders just arrived in one of those interplanetary cylinders devised by Jules Verne. He selected Mars as their place of origin as being a planet like the Earth, but older, and so likely to contain creatures more advanced than man, but inhuman, since the chances were vastly against evolutionary processes having worked the same in both planets.

A Falling Star

T HE first star was seen early in the morning rushing over Winchester eastward, high in the atmosphere. Hundreds must have seen it, and taken it for an ordinary falling star. For in those days no one gave a thought to the outer worlds of space as sources of human danger. At most, terrestrial men fancied there might be other men upon Mars, perhaps inferior to themselves and ready to welcome a missionary enterprise. Yet across the gulf of space minds, that are to our minds as ours are to the beasts that perish, regarded this earth with envious eyes, and slowly and surely drew their plans against us.

No one seems to have troubled to look for the fallen thing that night. But early in the morning it was found, almost entirely buried in the sand, among the scattered splinters of a fir-tree on the common between Horsell, Woking and Ottershaw. The uncovered part had the appearance of a huge cylinder, caked over, and its outline softened by a thick, scaly, dun-coloured incrustation. It had a diameter of about thirty yards. A stirring noise within the cylinder was ascribed at first to the unequal cooling of its surface, for at that time it did not occur to anyone that it might be hollow.

When, about sunset, I joined the crowd at the edge of the pit the thing had dug by its impact with the soil, the end of the cylinder was being screwed out from within. Nearly two feet of shining screw projected. Somebody blundered against me, and I narrowly missed being pitched on the top of the screw. As I turned to avoid the fall the lid of the cylinder fell upon the gravel with a ringing concussion. For a moment the cavity seemed perfectly black, for I had the sunset in my eyes.

I think everyone expected to see a man emerge—possibly something a little unlike us terrestrial men, but in all essentials a man. I know I did. But, looking, I presently saw something stirring within the shadow—greyish, billowy movements, one above another, and then two luminous disks like eyes. Then something resembling a little grey snake, about the thickness of a walking-stick, coiled up out of the writhing middle and wriggled in the air towards me, and then another.

A big, greyish, rounded bulk, the size, perhaps, of a bear, was rising slowly and painfully out of the cylinder. As it bulged up and caught the light, it glistened like wet leather. Two large dark-coloured eyes were regarding me steadfastly. It was rounded, and had, one might say, a face. There was a mouth under the eyes, the lipless brim of which quivered and panted and dropped saliva. The body heaved and pulsated convulsively. A lank tentacular appendage gripped the edge of the cylinder, another swayed in the air.

THOSE who have never seen a living Martian can scarcely imagine the strange horror of their appearance. The peculiar V-shaped mouth with its pointed upper lip, the absence of brow ridges, the absence of a chin beneath the wedge-like lower lip, the incessant quivering of this mouth, the Gorgon groups of tentacles, the tumultuous breathing of the lungs in a strange atmosphere, the evident heaviness and painfulness of movement, due to the greater gravitational energy—above all, the extraordinary intensity of the immense eyes—culminated in an effect akin to nausea. There was something fungoid in the oily brown skin, something in the clumsy deliberation of their tedious movements unspeakably terrible. Even at this first encounter, this first glimpse, I was overcome with disgust and dread.

Suddenly the monster vanished. It had toppled over the brim of the cylinder, and fallen into the pit with a thud like the fall of a great mass of leather. I heard it give a peculiar thick cry, and forthwith another of these creatures appeared darkly in the deep shadow of the aperture.

At that my rigour of terror passed away. I turned and, running madly, made for the first group of trees, perhaps a hundred yards away; but I ran, slanting and stumbling, for I could not avert my face from these things. There, among some young pine trees and furze bushes, I stopped, panting, and waited further developments. Once a leash of thin black whips, like the arms of an octopus, flashed across the sunset, and was immediately withdrawn, and afterwards a thin rod rose up, joint by joint, bearing at its apex a circular disk that spun with a wobbling motion.

Suddenly there was a flash of light, and a quantity of luminous greenish smoke came out of the pit in three distinct puffs, which drove up, one after the other, straight into the still air. At

LARGE DARK EYES WERE REGARDING ME STEADFASTLY
From the drawing by Johan Briedé

the same time a faint hissing sound became audible. Beyond the pit stood a little wedge of people, a little knot of small vertical black shapes upon the black ground. As the green smoke rose, their faces flashed out pallid green, and faded again as it vanished.

THEN slowly the hissing passed into humming, into a long, loud droning noise. Slowly a humped shape rose out of the pit, and the ghost of a beam of light seemed to flicker out from it. Forthwith, flashes of actual flame, a bright glare leaping from one to another, sprang from the scattered group of men. It was as if some invisible jet impinged upon them and flashed into white flame. It was as if each man were suddenly and momentarily turned to fire.

Then, by the light of their own destruction, I saw them staggering and falling, their supporters running off.

I stood staring, not as yet realizing that this was death leaping from man to man in that little distant crowd. An almost noiseless and blinding flash of light, and a man fell headlong and lay still, and as the unseen shaft of heat passed over them, pine trees burst into fire, and every dry furze bush became with one dull thud a mass of flames.

It is still a matter of wonder how the Martians are able to slay men so swiftly and so silently. Many think that in some way they are able to generate an intense heat in a chamber of practically absolute non-conductivity. This intense heat they project in a parallel beam against any object they choose by means of a polished parabolic mirror of unknown composition—much as the parabolic mirror of a lighthouse projects a beam of light. But no one has absolutely proved these details. However it is done, it is certain that a beam of heat is the essence of the matter—heat, and invisible, instead of visible light. Whatever is combustible flashes into flame at its touch, lead runs like water, it softens iron, cracks and melts glass, and when it falls upon water incontinently that explodes into steam.

That night nearly forty people lay under the starlight about the pit, charred and distorted beyond recognition, and all night long the common from Horsell to Maybury was deserted, and brightly ablaze.

Fighting Begins

IT was in a storm that I first saw the Martians at large, on the night of the third falling star. A monstrous tripod, higher than many houses, striding over the young pine trees, and smashing them aside in its career; a walking engine of glittering metal, striding now across the heather, articulate ropes of steel dangling from it, and the clattering tumult of its passage mingling with the riot of the thunder. A flash, and it came out vividly, heeling over one way with two feet in the air, to vanish and reappear almost instantly, as it seemed, with the next flash, a hundred yards nearer. Can you imagine a milking stool tilted and bowled violently along the ground? That was the impression those instant flashes gave. But instead of a milking-stool imagine it a great body of machinery on a tripod stand.

Seen nearer, the thing was incredibly strange, for it was no mere insensate machine driving on its way. Machine it was, with a ringing metallic pace, and long flexible glittering tentacles (one of which gripped a young pine tree) swinging and rattling about its strange body. It picked its road as it went striding along, and the brazen hood that surmounted it moved to and fro with the inevitable suggestion of a head looking about it. Behind the main body was a huge thing of white metal like a gigantic fisherman's basket, and puffs of green smoke squirted out from the joints of the limbs as the monster swept by me.

ALL that night the creatures were busy —communicating, I suppose, and maturing their plans. It was not until the next morning that our resistance began. The fighting I saw took place at Shepperton Wey, where a crowd of fugitives were waiting for the ferry.

Suddenly we saw a rush of smoke far away up the river, a puff of smoke that jerked up into the air, and hung; and forthwith the ground heaved under foot, and a heavy explosion shook the air, smashing two or three windows in the houses near, and leaving us astonished.

Quickly, one after the other, one, two, three, four of the armoured Martians appeared, far away over the little trees, across the flat meadows that stretch towards Chertsey, and striding hurriedly towards the river. Little cowled figures they seemed at first, going with a rolling motion and as fast as flying birds.

Then, advancing obliquely towards us, came a fifth. Their armoured bodies glittered in the sun as they swept swiftly forward upon the guns, growing rapidly larger as they drew nearer. One on the extreme left—the remotest, that is—flourished a huge case high in the air, and the ghostly terrible heat-ray I had already seen on Friday night smote towards Chertsey, and struck the town.

"Get under water!" I shouted unheeded. And, as the first Martian towered overhead scarcely a couple of hundred feet away, I flung myself under the surface.

When I raised my head, it was on the bank, and, in a stride, wading halfway across. The knees of its foremost legs bent at the further bank, and in another moment it had raised itself to its full height again, close to the village of Shepperton. Forthwith the six guns, which had been hidden behind the outskirts of that village, fired simultaneously.

The sudden near concussions, the last close upon the first, made my heart jump. The monster was already raising the case generating the heat-ray as the first shell burst six yards above the hood.

Simultaneously two other shells burst in the air near the body as the hood twisted round in time to receive, but not in time to dodge, the fourth shell.

The shell burst clean in the face of the thing. The hood bulged, flashed, was whirled off in a dozen tattered fragments of red flesh and glittering metal.

"Hit!" shouted I, with something between a scream and a cheer.

I heard answering shouts from the people in the water about me. I could have leapt out of the water with that momentary exultation.

The decapitated colossus reeled like a drunken giant, but it did not fall over. It recovered its balance by a miracle, and, no longer heeding its steps, and with the camera that fired the heat-ray now rigidly upheld, it reeled swiftly upon Shepperton. The living intelligence, the Martian within the hood, was slain and splashed to the four winds of heaven, and the thing was now but a mere intricate device of metal whirling to destruction. It drove along in a straight line, incapable of guidance. It struck the tower of Shepperton Church, smashing it down as the impact of a battering-ram might have done, swerved aside, blundered on, and collapsed with a tremendous impact into the river.

A VIOLENT explosion shook the air, and a spout of water, steam, mud and shattered metal shot far up into the sky. As the camera of the heat-ray hit the water, the latter had flashed into steam. In another moment a huge wave, like a muddy tidal bore, but almost scalding hot, came sweeping round the bend upstream. I saw people struggling shorewards, and heard their screaming faintly above the seething and roar of the Martian's collapse.

Then again I ducked, for the other Martians were advancing. When for a moment I raised my head to take breath and throw the hair and water from my eyes, the steam was rising in a whirling white fog that at first hid the Martians altogether. The noise was deafening. Then I saw them dimly, colossal figures of grey, magnified by the mist. They had passed by me, and two were stooping over the ruins of their comrade.

SUDDENLY THERE WAS A FLASH OF LIGHT
From the drawing by Johan Briedé

bridge, its impact was marked by flashes of incandescent white, that gave place at once to smoky lurid flames.

For a moment I stood there, breast-high in the almost boiling water, dumbfounded at my position, hopeless of escape. Through the reek I could see people scrambling out of the water through the reeds, like little frogs hurrying through grass from the advance of a man, or running to and fro in utter dismay on the towing-path.

Then suddenly the white flashes of the heat-ray came leaping towards me. The houses caved in as they dissolved at its touch and darted out flames; the trees changed to fire with a roar. It flickered up and down the towing-path, licking off the people who ran this way and that, and came down to the water's edge not fifty yards from where I stood. It swept across the river to Shepperton, and the water in its track rose in a boiling wheal crested with steam. I turned shoreward.

The third and fourth stood beside him in the water, one perhaps two hundred yards from me, the other towards Lalaham. The generators of the heat-rays waved high, and the hissing beams smote down this way and that.

The air was full of sound, a deafening and confusing conflict of noises, the clangorous din of the Martians, the crash of falling houses, the thud of trees, fences, sheds, flashing into flame, and the crackling and roaring of fire. Dense black smoke was leaping up to mingle with the steam from the river, and as the heat-ray went to and fro over Wey-

In another moment the huge wave, well-nigh at the boiling-point, had rushed upon me. I screamed aloud and, scalded, half-blinded, agonised, I staggered through the leaping, hissing water towards the shore. Had my foot stumbled, it would have been the end. I fell helplessly, in full sight of the Martians, upon the broad, bare gravelly spit that runs down to mark the angle of the Wey and Thames. I expected nothing but death. I have a dim memory of the foot of a Martian coming down within a score of feet of my head, driving straight into the loose gravel, whirling it this way and that, and lifting again; of a long suspense, and then of the four carrying the *débris* of their comrade between them, now clear, and then presently faint, through a veil of smoke, receding interminably, as it seemed to me, across a vast space of river and meadow. By a miracle I had escaped.

But it was not on the heat-ray that the Martians chiefly relied in their march on London. The monsters I saw that evening as I fled were armed with tubes which they discharged like guns. There was no flash, no smoke, simply that loaded detonation. Every minute I expected the fire of some hidden battery to spring upon them, but the evening calm was unbroken. Their figures grew smaller as they receded, and presently the gathering night had swallowed them up. Only towards Sunbury was a dark appearance, as though a conical hill had suddenly come into being there, and remoter across the river, towards Walton, I saw another such summit. They grew lower and broader even as I stared. These, as I knew later, were the black smoke. It was heavy, this vapour, heavier than the densest smoke, so that, after the first tumultuous uprush and outflow of its impact, it sank down through the air and poured over the ground in a manner rather liquid than gaseous, abandoning the hills and streaming into the valleys and ditches and watercourses, even as I have heard the carbonic acid gas that pours from volcanic clefts is wont to do. And the touch of that vapour was death to all that breathes.

One has to imagine the fate of those batteries towards Esher, waiting so tensely in the twilight, as well as one may. Survivors there were none. One may picture the orderly expectation, the officers alert and watchful, the gunners ready, the ammunition piled to hand, the limber gunners with their horses and waggons, the groups of civilian spectators standing as near as they were permitted, the evening stillness, the ambulances and hospital tents, with the burnt and wounded from Weybridge; then the dull resonance of the shots the Martians fired, and the clumsy projectile whirling over the trees and houses, and smashing amidst the neighbouring fields.

One may picture, too, the sudden shifting of the attention, the swiftly spreading coils and bellyings of that blackness advancing headlong, towering heavenward, turning the twilight to a palpable darkness, a strange and horrible antagonist of vapour striding upon its victims, men and horses near it seen dimly running, shrieking, falling headlong, shouts of dismay, the guns suddenly abandoned, men choking and writhing on the ground, and the swift broadening out of the opaque cone of smoke. And then, night and extinction—nothing but a silent mass of impenetrable vapour hiding its dead.

Dead London

So you understand the roaring wave of fear that swept through the greatest city in the world just as Monday was dawning—the stream of flight rising swiftly to a torrent, lashing in a foaming tumult round the railway stations, banked up into a horrible struggle about the shipping in the Thames, and hurrying by every available channel northward and eastward. By ten o'clock the police organization, and by midday even the railway organizations, were losing coherency, losing shape and efficiency, guttering, softening, running at last in that swift liquefaction of the social body.

All the railway lines north of the Thames and the South-Eastern people at Cannon Street had been warned by midnight on Sunday, and trains were being filled, people were fighting savagely for standing-room in the carriages, even at two o'clock. By three, people were being trampled and crushed even in Bishopsgate Street; a couple of hundred yards or more from Liverpool Street station revolvers were fired, people stabbed, and the policemen who had been sent to direct the traffic, exhausted and infuriated, were breaking the heads of the people they were called out to protect.

And as the day advanced the engine-drivers and stokers refused to return to London, the pressure of the flight drove the people in an ever-thickening multitude away from the stations and along the northward running roads. By mid-day a Martian had been seen at Barnes, and a cloud of slowly sinking black vapour drove along the Thames and across the flats of Lambeth, cutting off all escape over the bridges in its advance.

If one could have hung that June morning in a balloon in the blazing blue above London, every northward and eastward road running out of the infinite tangle of streets would have seemed stippled black with the streaming fugitives, each dot a human agony of terror and physical distress.

Directly below him the balloonist would have seen the network of streets far and wide, houses, churches, squares, crescents, gardens—already derelict—spread out like a huge map, and in the southward *blotted*. Over Ealing, Richmond, Wimbledon, it would have seemed as if some monstrous pen had flung ink upon the chart. Steadily, incessantly, each black splash grew and spread, shooting out ramifications this way and that, now banking itself against rising ground, now pouring swiftly over a crest into a new-found valley, exactly as a gout of ink would spread itself upon blotting paper.

And beyond, over the blue hills that rise southward of the river, the glittering Martians went to and fro, calmly and methodically spreading their poison-cloud over this patch of country, and then over that, laying it again with their steam-jets when it had served its purpose, and taking possession of the conquered country. They do not seem to have aimed at extermination so much as at complete demoralisation and the destruction of any opposition. They exploded any stores of powder they came upon, cut every telegraph, and wrecked the railways here and there. They were ham-stringing mankind. They seemed in no hurry to extend the field of operations, and they did not come beyond the central part of London all that day. It is possible that a very considerable number of people in London stuck to their houses through Monday morning.

I have not space to tell you here of my adventures during the days that followed —of how I saw men caught for the Martians' food, of how the third falling star smashed the house where I was resting, and of what I saw while I was hiding there. When I came out into the air again, I found about me the landscape, weird and lurid, of another planet. Everywhere spread a red weed, whose seed the Martians had brought with them. All round were red cactus-shaped plants, knee-high, without a solitary terrestrial growth to dispute their footing. The trees near me were dead and brown, but further a network of red threads scaled the still living stems. I went on my way to Hampstead through scarlet and crimson trees; it was like walking in an avenue of gigantic blood-drops.

How the Martians Were Slain

It was near South Kensington that I first heard the howling. It crept almost imperceptibly upon my senses. It was a sobbing alternation of two notes, "*Ulla, ulla, ulla, ulla,*" keeping on perpetually. I stopped, wondering at this strange, remote wailing. It was as if that mighty desert of houses had found a voice for its fear and solitude. It was not until I emerged from Baker Street that I saw, far away over the trees in the clearness of the sunset, the hood of the Martian giant from which this howling proceeded. I watched him for some time, but he did not move.

I came upon the wrecked handling

machine halfway to St. John's Wood Station. At first I thought a house had fallen across the road. It was only as I clambered among the ruins that I saw, with a start, this mechanical Samson lying, with its tentacles bent and smashed and twisted, among the ruins it had made. It seemed as if it had driven blindly straight at the house, and had been overwhelmed in its overthrow.

A little beyond the ruins about the smashed handling machine I came upon the red weed again, and found Regent's Canal a spongy mass of dark red vegetation.

The dusky houses about me stood faint and tall and dim; the trees towards the park were growing black. All about me the red weed clambered among the ruins, writhing to get above me in the dimness. Far away, I saw a second Martian, motionless as the first, standing in the park towards the Zoological Gardens.

An insane resolve possessed me. I would die and end it. And I would save myself even the trouble of killing myself. I marched on recklessly towards this Titan, and then, as I drew nearer and the light grew, I saw that a multitude of black birds was circling and clustering about the hood. At that my heart gave a bound, and I began running along the road. Great mounds had been heaped about the crest of the hill, making a huge redoubt of it. It was the final and largest place the Martians made.

And from behind these heaps there rose a thin smoke against the sky. Against the skyline an eager dog ran and disappeared. The thought that had flashed into my mind grew real, grew credible. I felt no fear, only a wild, trembling exultation, as I ran up the hill towards the motionless monster. Out of the hood hung lank shreds of brown at which the hungry birds pecked and tore.

I SCRAMBLED up the earthen rampart, and the interior of the redoubt was below me. A mighty space it was, with gigantic machines here and there within it, huge mounds of material and strange shelter places. And, scattered about it, some in their overturned war-machines, and a dozen of them stark and silent and laid in a row, were the Martians— *dead!*—slain by the putrefactive and disease bacteria against which their systems were unprepared; slain as the red weed was being slain; slain, after all man's devices had failed, by the humblest things that God has put upon this earth.

Already when I watched them they were irrevocably doomed, dying and rotting even as they went to and fro. It was inevitable. By the toll of a billion deaths man has bought his birthright of the earth, and it is his against all comers; it would still be his were the Martians ten times as mighty as they are. For neither do men live nor die in vain.

LIFE'S TRAGI-COMEDY

WHAT is our life? A play of passion:
Our mirth? The music of division.
Our mothers' wombs the tiring-houses be,
Where we are dressed for this short comedy.
Heaven the judicious sharp spectator is,
That sits and marks still who do act amiss.
Our graves that hide us from the searching sun,
Are like drawn curtains when the play is done.
Thus march we, playing, to our latest rest;
Only we die in earnest; that's no jest.

—*Sir W. Raleigh*

HENRY F. PRINGLE

THEODORE ROOSEVELT

CAVALRY charge, lion hunt, trust-busting reformer, President of the United States—
flash to mind when T. R. is mentioned. These and other equally interesting facts in
the life of this supremely representative American are fused into an illuminating, convincing and reasonable picture by Henry Pringle, the well known magazine writer and professor in the Columbia School of Journalism whose biography of William Howard Taft
has recently come off the press.

Teedie

A DAY or so after October 27, 1858, a friend of the family called at the Roosevelt home in New York to offer congratulations on the birth of a son. He doubtless hurried away as soon as possible. It was not until the night of June 21, 1905, at a banquet at Williamstown, Massachusetts, that Mr. Morris K. Jesup, now a man of seventy-one, publicly recalled the perfunctory visit of five decades ago.

"You were in your bassinet, making a good deal of a fuss and noise for a youngster of your age," he said, addressing the rugged and exuberant guest of honor. "Your father, however, lifted you out, and asked me to hold you . . ."

Mr. Elihu Root looked up. "Was he hard to hold?" he demanded.

The President must have roared with laughter. But this time, accuracy had been sacrificed to wit. The child born on October 27, 1858, had been all too easy to hold.

Memories lasted through life of nights torn by asthma, when he had scarcely been able to breathe. There remained recollections, "of my father walking up and down the room with me in his arms . . . of sitting up in bed gasping, with father and mother trying to help me."

The urge for physical fitness did not come for some years. He was an owlish, wistful boy; tall for his age at ten or eleven years, with a thin body and pipe-stem legs, with fair hair that was seldom combed, with blue eyes that took in, despite extreme nearsightedness, minute details of an absorbing world. He read constantly, and listened in solemnity to the conversations of his parents while his small brother and sisters played. At seven, he had decided upon the life of a naturalist and about him, until he went to college, clung odors of moribund frogs and worms, and of formaldehyde.

FAR from having an unhappy childhood, however, Theodore had an excellent time on the whole. There was money enough for all necessary comforts of life. In an age before psychoanalysis had been heard of, his parents had the innate wisdom to guide their frail son past the pitfalls of inadequacy. It is important that they were kind and affectionate. It is more important that they were wise.

Getting rid of physical disability was vital; unless this was done, nothing much could be achieved. So he was told by his parents. No evidence exists to show that Teedie, as he was then called, considered periodic illness as anything save a minor inconvenience. But dreary hours with the punching-bag, with dumb-bells and on the horizontal bars began, and gradually Teedie's chest began to expand and muscles to form in his arms.

There are records of victories, as he approached seventeen during the summer of 1875, in the dashes, the broad jump, and the pole vault. He preserved, for a fascinated posterity, data that he had reached a height of five feet eight inches, that he had a chest expansion of 34 inches, and that he weighed 124 pounds.

The bent for natural history continued despite newly discovered joys in sport. The notes in the diary grew more numerous, and also very much more learned. Everything now had its Latin name. Theodore made observations on wolves, "(*canis accidentalis*)" and bears "(*ursus Americanus*)." An aggravating factor was Theodore's interest in taxidermy.

But all normal boys are grubby, the theory being that the grubbier they are, the more normal.

In his autobiography, Roosevelt dwells on the importance of early reading. The naturalist in him was irritated by the "wholly impossible collection of animals" in the "Swiss Family Robinson." He did not care for the first half of "Robinson Crusoe," "although it is unquestionably the best part," but was fascinated by the second part, "containing the adventures . . . with the wolves in the Pyrenees, and out in the Far East."

The preparatory education of Theodore Roosevelt had a single goal, admission to Harvard, and everything was subordinated to that end. In consequence, Arthur H. Cutler, who later founded the Cutler School in New York, was engaged as tutor. Before his death, Cutler left a memorandum testifying to the "alert, vigorous quality of young Roosevelt's mind," adding that he had done exceedingly well in his work. He had particularly enjoyed history and modern languages.

So energetic did Cutler's pupil prove, in fact, that during the final two years he did the equivalent of three years of work. He passed the entrance examinations without difficulty, and in 1876 he made ready to leave for Cambridge.

Fish in a Strange Pond

OUTWARDLY Roosevelt might have been any well-bred young man arriving to begin his college career, certain of his position, aware that he need not mix with the rabble but would make the necessary clubs. Superficially, he conformed admirably to the pattern of the Harvard man of 1876; it was his preferences and tastes, his enthusiasms and squirming curiosity, his talkativeness and his nervousness, which soon made it apparent that he was a fish in a strange pond. Theodore Roosevelt was different from his fellows.

It is not surprising that Theodore was unpopular, and an object of suspicion. Not enthusiasm, but indifference, was Goddess of the Yard. Men had been turned down by the clubs, long before this, because they had been too eager. The languorous Harvard man was typical in 1880; the man who merely observes, who scorns ambition, who despises action; the portrait is the very antithesis of the Roosevelt whom Henry Adams called "pure act."

Another unforgivable sin was a tendency toward too great an interest in what his instructors and professors said, and sometimes he made it worse by taking issue with them in the classroom. This seemed barbaric to young men who considered college mere exposure to thought and who had no serious apprehension of contamination. Roosevelt asked questions, and uttered protests, his eyes gleaming from behind his spectacles. In his chosen field of science this trait was particularly pronounced, and Professor Nathaniel Shaler burst out after one such interruption: "See here, Roosevelt, let me talk. I'm running this course."

Had Theodore not arrived at Harvard with an assured social backing, he might have had a lonely time. As it was, he failed of election as class marshal in his senior year. On the whole, though, he was queer but eligible, and the latter asset was vastly more important than the handicap. In the end he made Porcellian, the loftiest of social honors.

So far as he associated with the other undergraduates at all, he lived among the minority called the club set. At least one classmate, asked for reminiscences in later years, was honest enough to admit that he had barely known Roosevelt.

Alice Lee

"I FIRST saw her on October 18, 1878," he wrote, "and loved her as soon as I saw her sweet, fair young face . . . We spent three years of happiness such as rarely comes to man or woman." So began a memorial to Alice Hathaway Lee of Chestnut Hill, Massachusetts, written by Theodore Roosevelt some time during 1884. She was remembered but rarely mentioned in the thirty-five years that followed.

She walked the stage for so brief a moment, there are so few who can remember and fewer still who will, that Alice Lee remains a fragment. But only partly. To Theodore she was "beautiful in face and form, and lovelier still in spirit," but she was lovely, too, to those who looked with less prejudiced eyes.

It was a turbulent courtship. Mrs. Robert Bacon, then sixteen, long recalled a function at the Pudding [The Hasty Pudding, a Harvard dramatic club] at which Roosevelt had walked up, had pointed across the room to Alice, and had demanded: "See that girl? I am going to marry her. She won't have me, but I am going to have *her!*"

Mrs. Bacon remembered, too, that the gentle Alice was alarmed by the impetuosity of the young man who had suddenly precipitated himself into the circle of more decorous beaus. He did a good deal of talking. He told her about snakes and lizards and other loathsome reptiles that he kept in his room on Winthrop Street.

Alice sometimes discouraged the eager Theodore and then he was plunged into the deepest gloom. He was always to suffer periods of discouragement, when everything seemed black. These were moments of despair. One night, during the first winter of the courtship, a classmate telegraphed to New York in alarm that Roosevelt was somewhere in the woods near Cambridge and refused to come home. A cousin who was particularly close hurried up there, managed somehow to soothe and encourage him.

ROOSEVELT returned to Cambridge for his senior year exuding ardor and determination. That he had already told his family about Alice is demonstrated by an invitation extended to the girl and her mother to spend the Christmas holidays at Oyster Bay. Theodore's mother—his father had died a little less than two years before—seems to have been fond of Alice from the start; nor is this surprising. The young girl and the older woman had much in common. They were gentle and rather quiet. They had charm and grace. Both, for by now Alice's last defenses had been shattered, considered Theodore wholly magnificent.

Even after the engagement was announced, Theodore could find no peace. "Roosevelt," recalled a member of Alice's family, "seemed constantly afraid that some one would run off with her, and threatened duels and everything else. On one occasion he actually sent abroad for a set of French dueling pistols and after great difficulty got them through the Custom House. Theodore's honor was not impugned, however. No blood was shed. No pistols and coffee for two, with frightened young men of Porcellian acting as seconds in the code duello, were served among the quiet New England hills."

His marriage took place at Brookline on October 27, 1880. The day was Theodore's twenty-second birthday, while Alice was nineteen.

HERE, the story of Alice Lee becomes increasingly unsubstantial. It is known that during his first year at Albany, beginning in January, 1882, Alice was with him. Presumably she went to the Assembly Chamber to hear Theodore make his first speeches, and glowed with pride as he rapidly gained public attention by a precocious attempt to impeach a New York judge. Isaac L. Hunt, an assemblyman from the northern part of the State, remembered her as "a very charming woman . . . tall and willowy. I was very much taken with her."

On the whole, Alice must have been decidedly bored; Albany then, as now, was an intellectual Sahara. There must have been periods that dragged interminably until the summer of 1883. Then

she knew that she was to have a baby and Roosevelt, if his subsequent enthusiasm for quantity production of offspring is any indication, was delighted.

Alice went into her ordeal cheerfully. She was not too well, but the doctors were suavely reassuring. Alice enjoyed her new importance. She was playing the only vital part that a woman of the '80's could play—excepting, of course, the preposterous unsexed creatures who were beginning to talk about votes for women.

"A Curse on This House"

As the day of her confinement drew near, Roosevelt's young wife left the house on Forty-fifth Street to stay with her mother-in-law on Fifty-seventh, where an apartment was furnished for her on the third floor. The baby was expected about the middle of February and life at the house on Fifty-seventh Street moved on with this uppermost. Roosevelt was at Albany.

February 13, 1884, was a Wednesday. On the previous Friday Roosevelt's sister and her husband had gone to Baltimore. Just before they took the train home, there was good news. A girl had been born late on Tuesday night, February 12; the doctors said that Alice had survived the ordeal well. So the journey back to New York was made in high spirits.

Seeing a light in the window on the third floor, she gave thanks that the baby had been born and that Alice's suffering was behind her. Then she went up the steps. The door opened. She saw her brother Elliott standing in the doorway, and she knew from his face that something was wrong.

"There is a curse on this house!" he said. "Mother is dying, and Alice is dying too."

It was then about 10:30. An hour later, Roosevelt came in, having been told only that a daughter had been born and having left the Assembly Chamber in the midst of effusive, good-natured congratulations.

He found his wife barely able to recognize him, and all the night, save for one brief moment, he sat at the head of the bed and held her in his arms. Just before 3 o'clock in the morning his mother, who had developed typhoid fever, died, and Theodore, standing by her bed, echoed the words of his brother: "There is a curse on this house." Then he went back upstairs. Dawn dragged into the next day. At 2 o'clock on February 14, 1884, her body weakened by Bright's disease, Alice died.

Somehow, Roosevelt went on with his work; if proof were needed that he had courage and an iron will this fact would serve. On February 20 he was back at Albany to move for the passage of a reform bill. He stayed there until the end of the legislative session.

Assemblyman hunt remembered! "You could not talk to him about it . . . you could see at once that it was a grief too deep . . . He did not want anybody to sympathize with him . . . He hiked away to the wilderness to get away from the world . . . He went out there a broken-hearted man."

Roosevelt saw the relatives of his first wife whenever he was in Boston and the daughter, who was to become Mrs. Nicholas Longworth, frequently visited them. But if Alice Lee, whom he met on that October day in 1878, was ever mentioned, there is no record of it. A door was closed on the three years during which they lived together, a door that was never opened. There is not a word in the autobiography of Theodore Roosevelt to indicate that she had existed.

In time he may have doubted that she had. In December of 1886, he was married again, to Edith Carow whom he had known as a child, and his married life was happy and complete. Five other children came. Four of them married and had children. One, the youngest, fell in an airplane behind the German lines. Honors came to Roosevelt; age came also. Only Alice Lee remains young and does not fade. She is forever fair, like the figure on the Grecian urn.

The Black Trade of Politics

No GREAT reforms burned in Theodore's breast as he began the career that he was to follow with few interruptions until he died. It began, as so many do, partly by accident. In 1880, Roosevelt was not thinking of public office. A fairly typical New Yorker, he had one characteristic that set him apart. He wanted a hand in every thing that was going on. He asked the men whom he knew—bankers and lawyers and teachers—how one took part in civic activities. When they told him that this ambition was quite out of the question, that politics was a black trade which would soil the linen of a gentleman, Roosevelt retorted that he intended to be one of the governing class, "whether the men in control were crude or not." Consequently, although an object of suspicion to those who made their living by belonging to the "governing class," he became actively identified with the Twenty-first District Republican Club.

That he did this shows that Roosevelt, then twenty-two years old, had common sense beyond his age. He did not demand, as other youths fresh from the rarefied atmosphere of Harvard might have done, prompt election to the United States Senate. He started at the bottom, and he was not dismayed by the difficulties.

In September, 1901, when the death of McKinley precipitated Roosevelt into the White House, various claimants came forward as his political discoverer. The weight of the evidence is on the side of one Joe Murray, a lieutenant to the boss of New York's Twenty-first Assembly District. One can only speculate on Murray's motives. His own explanation was that the man the boss proposed to support had not distinguished himself at Albany, that the "Better element" was disgusted with machine methods, and that a stronger candidate had to be found. He asked Roosevelt whether he would run for the legislature. Roosevelt demurred on the ground that he would be open to the accusation of having joined the club for the sake of holding office, but he finally accepted the nomination.

ELECTION DAY was on November 8 that year. Roosevelt was praised by the *New York Times* as a "public spirited citizen, not an office seeker." He was endorsed by the Council of Reform and other civic organizations, but all this goodwill was unimportant. The support that counted was the Republican machine. Roosevelt was sensible enough to place his destiny in the hands of its leaders. Joe Murray became campaign manager. Thus ably advised, Roosevelt swept the district.

It was all quite sudden. Roosevelt had no program of legislative or social reform beyond the vague one of believing that men of intelligence and honor, who did not seek a living from public office, should take an active part in the government.

A more self-confident man than Roosevelt might have known, after the first few months had brought striking success, that public life was his destiny. Roosevelt, however, felt that he was fearfully handicapped by his high ideals. The ephemeral nature of his standing with the people became an obsession, almost from the start. It beats like a refrain in minor key through his letters. In April, 1884, after more than three years of signal accomplishment at Albany, he doubted whether any one realized "the venomous hatred with which I am regarded by the politicians who supported me." After the 1884 campaign he did not "expect to return to politics."

In Roosevelt's final year he did useful work at Albany, but the accomplishments were overshadowed by the unhappiness of his private life. His demands for an investigation of the city government in New York resulted in the appointment of a committee. Roosevelt was made chairman and at the hearings which followed he learned much that was useful in future years. For one thing, he came into contact with police methods and qualified himself for the post on the Police Board that he was to hold a decade later.

Crisis in Police Circles

THE appointment of Theodore Roosevelt in 1895 to the police board of New York, which brought friction and fighting enough to surfeit even his restless spirit, may be traced back to the legislative investigation of 1884 and to one Rev. Charles F. Parkhurst who told his congregation in February, 1892, that New York was "a very hotbed of knavery, debauchery and bestiality."

Police headquarters was still on Mulberry Street in 1895, a gloomy building with subterranean dungeons where rats and vermin assisted the persuasive effectiveness of the third degree. The patrolman of the day was usually abnormally fat and usually abnormally stupid. He could barely read and write. His convenient conscience made strict obedience to the commands of his political sponsor easy. Sometimes he was honest enough. More often, he saw that wealth and a life of ease could be achieved by emulating the accepted methods of grafting upon saloonkeepers, gamblers, and prostitutes.

The arrival at Mulberry Street of any new commissioner was a crisis in police circles. It meant promotions and demotions, and the shifting of favorites from warm inside posts to pounding of cold pavements. The arrival of Roosevelt in May, 1895, was doubly unsettling.

Every one agreed that the new police head had brought a note of action to Mulberry Street. He was noisy, effusive, and picturesque, and his flair for dressing up led him to wear, on hot summer days, a remarkable black silk sash in place of a vest. This, combined with a pink shirt and with its tasseled ends dangling to his knees, was a constant source of astonishment to visitors at headquarters.

In May, 1895, Roosevelt was not quite thirty-seven years old. He was heavier than he had been before, a development that worried him a good deal. But his health was excellent; he was determined to make good, and he saw in the post of police commissioner the opportunity for limitless pleasant excitement.

It was early in the police commissioner days that Roosevelt's teeth, "almost as big as colt's teeth," according to Mr Brisbane, grew famous. It became part of the New York credo that delinquent patrolmen watched uneasily for the approach at night of a dark figure with gleaming molars.

The excursions at night gave Roosevelt the greatest pleasure. There was a fantastic note to the program of dining at some one's home and then, at midnight, sallying forth with a black cloak over his evening clothes and a wide-brimmed hat pulled down over his face. He prowled through dark streets in the hope of finding a patrolman asleep, off his beat, or engaged in diverting conversation with a friendly prostitute. Disguised as he was, the commissioner could often lead some unwary patrolman into insolent defiance when questioned. Then Roosevelt would reduce the wretch to incoherent servility by explaining that he was president of the police board.

The citizens of New York, as they

read of these exploits, glowed with vicarious satisfaction. They had yearned to humble insolent policemen themselves. The approval was entirely unanimous.

The police commissioner years made Roosevelt a national figure; even an international one, inasmuch as the London *Times* carried lengthy accounts of his activities in Mulberry Street. He had earned a just reputation for vigor and for honesty, and this was of value when the lightning struck.

War Mongers

THE fervor of a nation for war is often confused with the fervor of the war party. In time, there was popular enthusiasm enough for the war with Spain, but a debate on April 6, 1897, in the House on the plight of Cuba aroused little interest. In all probability, however, it never would have come had not Joseph Pulitzer and William Randolph Hearst been anxious to increase the circulations of their newspapers. The owner of the New York *World* did his best, but he never equaled Hearst as a maker of war.

In six months a contest with Spain seemed probable. A really proud nation might have scorned war with Spain, a power that was almost bankrupt and had a population of only 18,000,000, however, against 75,000,000 in the United States. All other sentiments, however, were swept aside by the winds of the war fever.

Roosevelt, not McKinley, sensed correctly the temper of the country. He watched with contempt the efforts of McKinley to avoid the struggle. The President, he told his intimates, "has no more backbone than a chocolate éclair."

In summing up his reasons for wanting to declare war on Spain, he said:

I would regard a war with Spain from two viewpoints: First, the advisability on the ground both of humanity and self-interest of interfering on behalf of the Cubans, and of taking one more step toward the complete freeing of America from European domination: second, the benefit done to our people by giving them something to think of which isn't material gain, and especially the benefit done our military forces by trying both the Army and Navy in actual practice. I should be very sorry not to see us make the experiment of trying to land, and therefore to feed and clothe, an expeditionary force, if only for the sake of learning from our blunders. I should hope that the force would have some fighting to do. It would be a great lesson.

The military-spiritual adventure that Roosevelt desired would mean, of course, the loss of many lives, but this was a detail that never bothered him. He was

Cowboy   Historian   Police Commissioner   Naval Secretary   Rough Rider

Courtesy Roosevelt Hous

not, he wrote in 1902, "in the least sensitive about killing any number of men if there is adequate reason."

At any rate, Roosevelt had his war. He had been agitating for it for a long time, and he announced that he would take an active part. He admitted that his family and friends were unanimously opposed to his going to war and insisted that he was not going to do so "in a mere spirit of recklessness or levity." His purpose was to practice what he preached.

Roosevelt was not a coldly calculating person. Nowhere, even in the most confidential of his private letters, is there any sign that he was thinking of political preferment. In due time he accepted the fruits of glory and became governor of New York; to have done otherwise would have been the action of a hypocrite. Not shrewdness but adolescence was behind his desire to become a soldier in the Spanish War. His efforts did not cease until he had been commissioned as lieutenant-colonel of the Rough Riders.

The Rough Riders

NEVER, probably, had so novel a military organization been gathered together. Mingling among the cowboys and momentarily reformed bad men from the West were polo players and steeplechase riders from the Harvard, Yale, and Princeton clubs of New York City. Within a few days, however, they were indistinguishable in their enlisted men's uniforms.

Time was the essence of this war. It was important to defeat the Spaniards. It was vital to get to Cuba ahead of the other brigades so that the Roosevelt contingent might obtain at least their share of the glory. By the afternoon of June 23, 1898, they had landed in Cuba and the advance was under way.

The morning of July 1, the day of

Roosevelt's "crowded hour," dawned. Whether, during the charge that followed, Roosevelt and his men stormed San Juan Hill, became another subject of heated controversy. That Roosevelt was both brave and reckless is beyond question. "The percentage of loss of our regiment," he wrote, "was about seven times . . . that of the other five volunteer regiments."

To those who watched the engagement it seemed remarkable that any of the men survived. To Richard Harding Davis it appeared as though "someone had made an awful and terrible mistake." Roosevelt was a dashing figure, mounted on his horse, shouting encouragement, easily distinguishable because of his blue-polka-dot handkerchief that

Governor of New York   Vice President   President   Peacemaker   Mighty Hunter all the time

he had draped on the brim of his sombrero. But the line of men that followed seemed pathetically thin and a good many dropped from their wounds on the way up the hill.

In retrospect, the battle of July, 1898, assumed in Roosevelt's mind the aspects of a pleasantly dangerous sporting event. On July 5, a friend of the family addressed a letter to Mrs. Roosevelt:

"No hunting trip so far has ever equalled it in Theodore's eyes . . . When I caught up with him the day of the charge . . . (he) was revelling in victory and gore . . . He had just 'doubled up a Spanish officer like a Jack-rabbit' as he retired from a block house—and he encouraged us to 'look at those damned Spanish dead.'"

WHEN Finley Peter Dunne put into the mouth of Mr. Dooley certain observations on the Rooseveltian ego which permeated his book on the war,

he was torn between indignation and amusement. ". . . If I was him," Mr. Dooley had been made to say, "I'd call th' book 'Alone in Cuba.'" Roosevelt, who preferred a club for his own use, could recognize a rapier thrust.

"I regret to state," he wrote Dunne from the Executive Mansion at Albany, "that my family and intimate friends are delighted with your review of my book."

Roosevelt never forgot his Rough Riders, nor indeed, did these heroes forget their colonel. By 1899 he was governor of New York and found himself besieged with petitions for jobs by veterans who "looked upon the governor . . . as their chief and only adviser and friend." It was impossible to take care of all of them, but he did his best as long as he held office. A Rough Rider, to him, was always better qualified for some appointment than any other aspirant.

The Lightning Strikes

THREE paths to the presidential nomination in 1904 opened before Roosevelt while he was governor of New York. One was to seek reelection. The second was to achieve appointment as Secretary of War under McKinley. The third, and the least promising, was the Vice-presidential nomination.

McKinley was unanimously nominated for the Presidency. This was followed immediately by the nomination of Roosevelt for Vice-President. Mrs. Roosevelt, from a box in the balcony, looked down on the proceedings and spectators noticed, or imagined, that she was not too happy.

On September 6, 1901, in Buffalo, New York, McKinley was shot twice by an anarchist. Roosevelt, on September 6, was attending an outing of the Vermont Fish and Game League on Lake Champlain.

However ambitious he may have been, Roosevelt was a warm-hearted and affectionate person. He was also a patriot. The shock of the news must have swept aside consideration of its momentous

meaning to his own career. The single letter that has survived shows that Roosevelt was really grief-stricken. He had forgotten the days when he had referred to McKinley as having a chocolate éclair for a backbone. That he conducted himself with dignity was reflected in all accounts.

An hour and a half after McKinley died the oath of office was administered at the Wilcox home in Buffalo. The house had been dismantled for the summer and in the library, where the small group gathered, the chairs were still shrouded in dust-covers.

Roosevelt's face was nearly expressionless. He spoke in crisp, staccato sentences: "I wish to say that it shall be my aim to continue, absolutely unbroken, the policy of President McKinley for the peace, the prosperity, and the honor of our beloved country."

THE public, intrigued by the novelty of the first colorful President in decades, was more interested in Roosevelt's personality than in his messages

This phase fascinated the Washington correspondents. They sent dispatches pointing to the astonishing fact that he was at his desk by 8:30 in the morning and had visitors for breakfast, luncheon, and dinner. He would, they predicted, collapse unless he took things more easily. They told of his irritation over the constant attendance of secret service men and his attempts to escape on solitary horseback rides or walks. Cartoonists everywhere were elated because no longer would they be lost for ideas—Roosevelt's teeth, his eyeglasses, his fondness for big-game hunting, his exploits as a Rough Rider.

He was one of the few Presidents undimmed by the aura of dignity that normally surrounds the Chief Executive. The people had a fair approximation of what the man was really like. This was, on the whole, fortunate for his career. The newspapers published lengthy accounts of the rapidity with which he disposed of the delegations that flocked to the White House on every conceivable mission. He cut short the oratory of their spokesmen, substituted oratory of his own, and sent them away with pleasant visions of an overwhelming personage who had miraculously combined bluntness and cordiality.

"Trust Buster"

On MARCH 3, 1905, Roosevelt is supposed to have declared:

"Tomorrow I shall come into my office in my own right. Then watch out for me!"

It is really unimportant whether he made such a statement; it represented his viewpoint accurately soon after Election Day. Suspicion had dawned that Roosevelt had no scruples against biting the plump hands which had fed him during the campaign. The end of 1904 had brought signs of a new independence. Roosevelt's public utterances were less cautious. It was rumored that the Bureau of Corporations would start innumerable investigations. Even the tariff might be revised.

"I do not like the social conditions at present," Roosevelt once said to Taft. "The dull, purblind folly of the very rich men; their greed and arrogance . . . and the corruption in business and politics, have tended to produce a very unhealthy condition of excitement and irritation in the popular mind, which shows itself in the great increase in the socialistic propaganda."

Roosevelt was nervously anxious to cure the evils that existed; perhaps Roosevelt's genius lay in the fact that he realized their existence. The assets that gave him power were his fights as a politician and his flair for arousing public interest. The liabilities that held him back were his sparsity of knowledge on economics, which approached ignorance, and his alliance with the Republican party. He had to work through Republican leaders who were conservative, complacent and unafraid. They had no forebodings of the class war which, to Roosevelt, was an immediate possibility.

Always in the back of his mind, also, was the fear that if he went too far or too fast he faced a period of business unrest. A panic might mean the defeat of his party. This was the worst of all possible dangers, for Roosevelt sincerely believed the Democratic party to be far less talented than his own in the science of government. It was permissible to appropriate theories, first conceived by Democrats, although wise to forget that this had been done. To subject the United States to the risk of Democratic rule was close to treason.

Partly because the Government was handicapped by the law and thwarted by clever attorneys employed by the trusts, partly because Roosevelt was so busy on other matters, rather little was accomplished in actual prosecutions or in the dissolution of illegal combinations. Roosevelt's title as "Trust Buster" was, as he would have been the first to insist, an exaggeration. He started only twenty-five proceedings leading to indictments under the Sherman Act, while Taft began forty-five. The significance of Roosevelt's corporation activities lay in what he said rather than what he did. Even the spectacular fine of $29,000,000 assessed against the Standard Oil Company of Indiana came to nothing. The higher courts set aside the penalty and the Standard Oil Company paid nothing.

The fact is that Roosevelt would progress to a certain point in his program to ward off socialism and unrest and then make energetic efforts to appease the right wing. Even the muckrakers, who had brought into the light so many of the evils on which Roosevelt acted, were to learn, in pained surprise, that he endorsed them with distinct reservations.

But one muckraker—the term was original with Roosevelt—inspired the President to one of his brisker fights with Congress. On March 9, 1906, Roosevelt wrote Upton Sinclair whose book on meat packing conditions in Chicago had just been published, that "I shall read it with interest," although Commissioner of Corporations Garfield believed the conclusions regarding the Chicago packing houses "too pessimistic." At the same time he appointed an investigator who would confer with Sinclair and begin an inquiry. Two examiners were appointed and their disclosures moved the President to horrified action.

They told of filth, disease, and gross carelessness in the packing houses. Tuberculosis was prevalent among the workers. Old bits of rope had been discovered in chopped meat about to be placed in cans. The buildings in which the work was done were dark, damp, and badly ventilated.

Then the President let it be known that this was only a "preliminary report," and that additional facts might be published unless the packers told their agents in the House that the bill should be passed. At the same time, because accounts on the reports had been cabled abroad, it appeared probable that the export trade in American meat would suffer. This economic argument, added to Roosevelt's threats of additional exposures, brought passage of the inspection bill on July 1, 1906.

The reform is illustrative of the degree to which the innovations for which Roosevelt received credit were suggested by others.

Roosevelt's passionate interest in the national forests, in reclamation of arid Western lands by irrigation, in conservation of water power and other natural resources, may well be considered as part of his campaign against the malefactors of great wealth. There can be little controversy regarding Roosevelt's contribution to the cause of conservation.

In the opinion of Senator La Follette, who had been one of the allies in the work, conservation would stand as Roosevelt's greatest work. He had, said the Wisconsin Senator, started a world movement "for staying territorial waste and saving for the human race the things . . . on which alone a progressive race life can be founded."

Last Chance For Adventure

On October 27, 1904, the President's birthday, Elihu Root had scribbled a note of congratulation that Roosevelt had reached "The respectable age of forty-six."

"You have made a very good start in life," he said, "and your friends have great hopes for you when you grow up."

This was Roosevelt's tragedy, for he had just turned fifty when the end of the reign arrived. Politics was his true profession; and he had held the most exalted office in the realm of American politics. Wisdom, experience, and precedent—all of them dictated that he lay down the scepter. Roosevelt's intelligence, as distinct from his emotions, made him well aware that only trouble would follow any other course. What however, was he to do? Becoming the ostensible head, the window-dressing for some vast corporation, was quite unthinkable. He did not really enjoy writing. He might have found satisfaction in teaching, but no offer came.

By the summer of 1908, Roosevelt had already decided upon the only possible use of his talents. He told his friend and admirer, Lyman Abbott, that he would write twelve articles a year for the *Outlook,* the weekly journal of opinion which then most closely reflected his political beliefs. For this he was to be paid $12,000 a year. First, however, he would spend a year hunting in Africa, not only for the sake of the sport but because he was anxious to leave Taft unhampered in his arduous task of beginning an administration. This, he said, "is my last chance for . . . a 'great adventure.'"

Those who were closest to Roosevelt and who loved him, however, could not suppress moments of anxiety as they contemplated the journey into Africa. He was not as strong, as his premature death finally proved, as his vitality seemed to indicate. A touch of Cuban fever was still in his blood. He was totally blind in one eye and the sight of the other was imperfect. Although only fifty years old, he was considerably overweight. He was, in fact, in exactly the condition of so many men of middle age—a little soft, and unwilling to admit that the time had come for comparative nonactivity.

But another year of pleasant adolescence began. Roosevelt again faced danger, and jotted down lengthy Latin names of the specimens obtained. It was almost as if time had turned back forty years to the days when he had been a juvenile, but ardent, naturalist. Roosevelt told the story of his hunt, and told it extremely well, in articles written for *Scribner's* and in the subsequent book, "African Game Trails."

No lions did their duty. The party steamed down the White Nile in March, 1910, and the expedition disbanded at Khartum on March 14. Roosevelt had been ill for only five days during the eleven months, and then from the fever contracted at Santiago. The colonel listed 296 specimens shot during the hunt. Included were nine lions, five elephants, thirteen rhinoceroses, and seven hippopotamuses.

"We Shake the World"

Before leaving the White House, President Roosevelt had been invited to give the Romanes Lecture at Oxford. This was followed by invitations to speak in Germany, France and Norway, and his hope, whether sincere or not, that he might retire to private life, was not realized.

Roosevelt was interested, but not dazzled by the monarchs. He was tossed by almost incontrollable glee as he observed the peculiarities of their personalities and life.

In Austria-Hungary, the aging Emperor Joseph was his host at a banquet. He found the Emperor a pleasant although not "a very able man," but at the royal banquet the Emperor and all the Austrian guests had one horrid habit . . . The finger-bowls were brought in, each with a small tumbler of water in the middle; and the Emperor and all the others proceeded to rinse their mouths and then empty them into the finger bowls . . . However, all the guests were delightful.

Then they crossed into Germany, for the most intriguing monarch of all: Kaiser Wilhelm. There Roosevelt was asked to review the troops of Germany with the Kaiser—the first private citizen ever accorded such an honor.

Roosevelt and the Kaiser, astride magnificent chargers, watched the troops file by for five hours. The Kaiser had a photographer on hand to take pictures while the maneuvers were in progress, and he sent a set of prints to Roosevelt's hotel. On the backs of them the Kaiser had scribbled inscriptions.

One of the photographs shows Roosevelt and Wilhelm, on their horses, talking earnestly. On this the Kaiser wrote: "The Colonel of the Rough Riders instructing the German Emperor in field tactics." On another his note was: "When we shake hands we shake the world."

Before Roosevelt left Berlin, a messenger appeared from the German Foreign Office which was anxious to prevent further indiscretion on the Kaiser's part, to ask whether Roosevelt would be so gracious as to return them.

"Oh, no," Roosevelt answered. "His Majesty, the Kaiser, gave the photographs to me and I propose to retain them."

Too Young to Die

THE theory that he was influenced by friendship for the Kaiser is without basis. While he was in the White House, as his Presidential papers definitely prove, Roosevelt preferred Great Britain to Germany, although suspicious, to an extent, of both countries.

In his heart, it is probable, Roosevelt favored the cause of the Allies from the start. Great Britain and France were democracies, Germany an autocracy. The invasion of Belgium filled the newspapers with lengthy descriptions of the horrors of war. All this undoubtedly accelerated Roosevelt's partisanship for the Allies. A second influence was his growing hatred for Woodrow Wilson, the consuming passion of the closing years. No opinion that Roosevelt held, no action which he took, can be considered apart from this hatred.

Roosevelt's great services toward preparedness were marred by his attitude regarding Wilson, who had, after all, the responsibility. He admitted himself, on at least one occasion, that the public was behind Wilson, that the anti-war sentiment was far the stronger. But his letters showed no tolerance, no trust—only hatred. Wilson was "the popular pacifist hero," who had the support of the "professional pacifists, the flubdubs and the mollycoddles."

The announcement by Germany of unrestricted submarine activity meant war. To Wilson, whom House at first believed "too refined, too civilized, too intellectual, too cultivated," for the crushing task which lay ahead, this meant misery and suffering. In Roosevelt it aroused all the slumbering traits of adolescence. To him, war was romantic still. It implied gallantry and chivalry. The cruelest disappointment of a lifetime lay in the fact that he was not permitted to create a division, one similar to the Rough Riders, in 1917.

His four sons fought bravely and well with the American Expeditionary Force. On July 17, 1918, Roosevelt received word that Quentin, the youngest, had been killed in an aerial battle. Hermann Hagedorn, one of Roosevelt's close friends, wrote after seeing Roosevelt at this time that "the old side of him was gone, that old exuberance . . . the boy in him had died." This is the only reference in all the volumes that have been written about Roosevelt that age was creeping on, that the boyishness was gone.

Not much time remained; Roosevelt's own adventure was drawing to its close. At four o'clock in the morning, January 6, 1919, he died. The immediate cause was an embolism in the coronary artery. Few had known that Roosevelt was seriously ill. The darkness came suddenly, and he would, perhaps, have chosen to have it so. He was not forced, as most men are, to watch the creeping shadows. He was spared the chill of twilight. And yet he was too young—only sixty-one—to die.

THE brave and bold persist even against fortune; the timid and cowardly rush to despair through fear alone.—*Tacitus.*

Georgе Santayana

THE LAST PURITAN

Georgе santayana was born in Spain in 1863. He came to the United States in 1874, and attended Harvard University, where, after two years of study in Germany, he became an instructor in the history of philosophy. In 1912, after teaching for 22 years, he resigned as a full professor and went to live in Europe. Santayana is a poet and a philosopher. In 1923 he published his own selections from his poetical words in a book which is significant in the history of modern poetry. His philosophical works include "The Sense of Beauty" (1896), "The Life of Reason or the Phases of Human Progress" (5 vols.) (1905-6), "Scepticism and Animal Faith" (1923), "Realms of Essence" (1927), "Some Turns of Thought in Modern Philosophy" (1933), and many others. "The Last Puritan" is his only novel.

I

The child had been born punctually. This first grave and alarming duty of entering into the world was performed not only unflinchingly but with a flourish: for this thoroughly satisfactory child was a boy. His little organism, long before birth, had put aside the soft and drowsy temptation to be a female.

It was on a first day of October, under the sign, as it were, of autumnal temperance, that Oliver Alden arrived and it was also during this benign interval that his father was accustomed to revisit his family. He came usually for Oliver's birthday, bearing some gift; and he departed after Thanksgiving Day, before there was occasion to retract his thankfulness.

In spite of the coldness and distance between Peter Alden and his wife, with deep distrust on her part and perfect indifference on his, they agreed in many matters of policy, and especially in regard to the education of Oliver. At first, during his early boyhood, he should be brought up at home, like a young prince, though without courtiers. In this way he could be thoroughly well grounded in his studies—something impossible in a modern school—and could acquire the speech and manners of a gentleman. But later on he must be sent to school; not for the sake of his lessons, but for moral and social reasons. The social reason plainly could not be snobbery: there was no older family in America and few richer than the Aldens. On the contrary, social relations were necessary in order to obliterate as far as possible the sense and appearance of this immense superiority.

He was a remarkably good pupil, somewhat calm, as if he had heard all these things before, but evenly absorbent, and evenly retentive. He resented the fact that languages and history had to be remembered at all and found escape in other purer studies such as mathematics and astronomy which at least were free of human taint. For though words and ideas were lacking to express it, his puritan disdain of human weakness and of human genius was at work silently within him.

All his lessons and sports seemed to be taken up as duties, and executed unswervingly, as if to get rid of them as quickly and thoroughly as possible. True, other tasks at once took their place; his life now had absolutely no leisure in it; but at least there was a silent moment of peace as each duty—each enemy—was despatched in turn.

"I CAN'T make out," observed Mrs. Alden to Oliver's governess, "what is the matter with Oliver. He's so strong physically, why should he be so terribly bitter and languid? These two years at school have been so splendid for him, keeping his mind occupied, and giving him plenty of outdoor exercise in their school games: and with always keeping at the head of his class. One would think he ought to be more cheerful and lively, and more like other boys of his age. Oliver is so critical of everything, so dissatisfied and disdainful. One would think he had been crushed by some terrible disappointment."

"Perhaps some great change would set him right," suggested the governess. "What a pity that we can't consult Dr. Alden."

"It wouldn't be impossible to consult him," said Mrs. Alden. "He happens to be in Boston, kept there by delays in getting his yacht ready—brand new, and already in need of expensive repairs. I guess I'll write to him and tell him why we are worried—perhaps foolishly —by Oliver's condition."

The next day Mrs. Alden received a long telegram, suggesting that Oliver should join his father in Boston. A few days' cruise on Massachusetts Bay, while they tried the new engines, might do Oliver good.

So Oliver departed, leaving behind him the narrow world of his boyhood.

II

"NOT bored, I hope," said his father, as Oliver came aft.

"Bored! It's the grandest sight I have ever seen."

"Look out. The sea, when you like it too much, swallows up all your intelligence, before gulping you down in person. Well, it's almost time for lunch, and later Lord Jim—I mean Captain Darnley—will take you in hand and teach you the names of everything you see on board."

"But why do you call him Lord Jim? Did Captain Darnley ever leave his ship to sink with all the passengers, while he slipped away himself in the only boat?"

"Not that: but long ago he got a black mark against him of another sort—was dismissed from the British Navy when he was a midshipman—and he took to a wandering life and sank for a time rather below his station. He is a clergyman's son, like the Lord Jim in the novel, and a first-rate sailor. He lords it over me here; but I confess he does it very well, and to my advantage."

AT THIS moment the Captain appeared at the cabin hatchway, hatless and smiling. Why had this fine looking person been expelled from the Navy? Oliver found out that night when they dined alone together because his father was indisposed.

"Your governor was telling you, was he, that he calls me Lord Jim? Did he explain?"

"He said you had got into some trouble like Lord Jim in the book, only of another sort."

"It's no secret. It filled columns and columns in *The Times*. There was a full-dress court-martial. And what for? Because a few snotties had been overheard calling a spade a spade. Immorality in the British Navy! Three or four years later the mother of one of the lads wouldn't put up with the disgrace and had money enough to appeal for revision. The case was actually recalled and judgment reversed. But I was out of the Navy and in the Yukon, and it was too late for me.

"My poor father was cut to the quick

"My father killed somebody?"
"Yes, of course. Haven't you heard of it?"

Illustration for George Santayana's
"THE LAST PURITAN"

and I hadn't the heart to go home. But I did see my mother privately. If I had been guilty of murder she would have stuck by me all the closer. She had an old grudge of her own against society, and her heart was with her young cub, no matter what he might do."

Having had his say, and being asked no questions, Jim gulped down the rest of his whiskey-and-soda and said he would take a turn below to see how the Doctor was going on. The Doctor's health was precarious, and at any moment this young Oliver might become owner. It would be bad to find oneself without a job or a patron. Better that the old man should hold out a few years longer, until the boy got a thorough liking for the sea.

Oliver had entirely forgotten his father. Absence in this parent seemed as normal as presence was normal in his mother. Oliver's latent feelings began to grow articulate—"Lord Jim's mother stands up for her young cub against the world, while my mother—I never saw it so clearly before—always stands up for the world against her young cub. I don't like lies: and I don't like them in favour of morality, any more than against morality. They make morality false, they make it hypocrisy. It's not the frank fearless people like Lord Jim who are immoral, but the 'moral' people who are cowards and liars. I won't put up with their falsehoods. They shan't scare me any longer. First admit the truth, and then make the best of it. That's a man's work."

Oliver was so absorbed in his ethical meditation that it startled him suddenly to hear a voice at his elbow: "Your father's all right. You know these sleeping draughts of his don't always work and he might be restless without being quite awake or master of his movements. I got the mixture just right. You see, he wasn't a tough chap like

GEORGE SANTAYANA is renowned both as a philosopher and novelist. Born in Spain in 1863, he received his education in the United States and taught philosophy for twenty-two years at Harvard University. The fusing in his mind of the Hispanic and American types of culture results in a philosophical attitude based upon a "belief about nature." His mental outlook enabled him to examine and delineate the New England temperament in his only novel, "The Last Puritan."
Courtesy Charles Scribner's Sons

me, to stand the blow he got when he was a lad. It pretty well staggered him, giving murder such a close shave, and having to quit. No wonder that a modest sensitive man like him should have been scotched for life."

"My father *killed* somebody?"

"Yes, of course. Haven't you heard of it? It was when he was trying to steal the Bible out of the Harvard Chapel for an initiation stunt. A man discovered him in the dark, there was a tustle, and your father laid him low. He had to leave the University and travel abroad with a tutor. That was what kept him so many years wandering in the East, and uncomfortable whenever he came home again."

THE paralysis in Oliver's mind began to yield to a sort of nightmare. But the focus of everything, the red-hot evil to be faced and smothered first, was not the word murder which had been pronounced so airily. It was the other evil thing.

"Did you say," he asked with an effort, "that my father takes drugs? And did you say that he falls into a stupor and is helpless in your hands as if he were dead drunk or hypnotised or worse? And did you laugh at it?"

"Of course. Don't you like that either? He's a medical man. He experiments on himself scientifically, and what are you going to do about it?"

Oliver was angry—angry at having been stunned, angry with Jim for having struck the blow, angry with himself for having lived in a fool's paradise and not having known these things before. No reason for blaming Jim, or blaming himself. Yet how intolerably wrong the whole thing was, the whole corrupt world from which there was no escape, and where such things happened?

JIM took Oliver's hand affectionately in both of his and then he proceeded to pat Oliver on the back, as if the good little boy needed to be comforted. And Oliver did somehow feel comforted. Pride began to seem insufficient and unnecessary. There was something else more genuine, more honest. It was the first time he had found anyone brushing away all laboured scruples and all false shams about the facts of life, and transferring them simply to the plane of human nature. Why pretend that one's relations must be particularly perfect? Why more perfect than other people? Why be obliged to pretend that one was perfect oneself?

The coils of duty in his moral alarm-clock were tightly wound, and the inward bell would ring infallibly. With that unremitting tension of virtue, or of possible sin, always in the background, it was safe to let pleasant visions float across the surface of consciousness when he was going to sleep that night.

How splendid Lord Jim had been all that day, so bold, so easy, so frank, so affectionate, so disinterested, and at bottom so terribly intelligent! He would like to go to England in the summer. It would be nice to stay with Lord Jim in the gabled stone parsonage. He was sure that he would love Jim's metaphysical old Pater and his comfortable old Mater and his lovely fluffy-haired little sister, Rose.

III

THEY were alone in their first-class carriage and Jim had composed himself to sleep on the cushions opposite, while through the neat little frame of the open window the bright English landscape formed for Oliver's dreamy eyes a fugue of green and tender harmonies, full of shifting light and shade, sheep, cows, hedges, ditches and rural silence. When at last they reached the Vicarage, the Darnleys met them.

The Vicar seemed like a raw, bony, rather rude schoolmaster who said only the most conventional things in the most conventional see-saw. There was also a short, square woman in black, loitering near him. Oliver at first supposed her to be some poor parishioner, but she turned out to be Mrs. Darnley. But there, too, was Rose, a tall serene child, who attached herself at once to Jim without question and looked confidently at Oliver, as if she regarded him also as part of her domain.

WHEN they were dressing for dinner Jim explained: "My poor Mater, you have seen what she is. She was a farmer's daughter and when my father was reading for Holy Orders he used to walk a lot alone with a Greek text in his pocket. One day he came upon her by chance, also alone, and somehow, before they knew it, the irreparable had happened. I threatened to turn up at once. The wedding had to be hastened, and poor Pater had to confess everything to his superiors and got a bad name for life, and a wife that other clergymen's ladies wouldn't visit. And that hideous sacrifice of Pater's was wasted after all: because I was disgraced in a much worse way afterwards on my own account."

"Don't worry, Jim," said Oliver. "When my father dies and the yacht is yours, you can sell her and have a little capital to start all over again on."

"Now, by all that's holy, if you don't like me having that yacht, I'll sell her back to you for one dollar as the Doctor sold her to me. For God's sake, Oliver, don't think that I'm plotting to rob you of your money. I have something of my own in the bank, and am still young enough to make my way in the world."

"Why go on like that, Jim? If my father left you half his money, or all of it, I should be delighted. I daresay he'd like to, only he can't—he doesn't dare—on account of Mother and the other people. But he has telegraphed to Boston for that will and has burned it up. The yacht is already yours, and I shall have two-thirds of his fortune when I am of age. Not that I want it: I'm to be a clergyman or professor or something. But he wants me to be independent: and one reason, I'm sure, is because he sees that I—that we are friends; and he knows I would look after you, if you were ever in trouble. And of course I will, no matter what happens."

Suddenly Jim took Oliver in his arms, with a great bear's hug, and positively kissed him. "The Doctor has always been a trump, and you go him one better."

JIM counted on showing Oliver his old school at Radley and so the next afternoon they strolled with Rose through the fields to St. Peter's College. While Jim was visiting old housemasters and matrons, Rose and Oliver had ample leisure to sit on a stile and watch some of the boys playing cricket. He felt an impulse to kiss her, but unfortunately he seldom followed his first impulses. Soon their talk turned to her family.

"Father is really better than Mother, although he can't make a decent cup of tea, and he's really better than Jim, although he can't put on his tie straight, and I have to do it for him."

"So you know how to do things nicely, just as Jim does?"

"Yes."

"And if you tied my tie for me and taught me how to do everything, would you like that?"

"Perhaps."

"Say that you and I were married. How would that do?"

"I don't know."

"Would you like to marry me?"

"Oh yes."

"All right. It's agreed. We're going to be married as soon as I am an old man and you are a young woman. And as we're engaged I think I may kiss you."

"Of course."

"And now let's run and tell Jim we are going to be married. How pleased he will be."

"He won't be pleased. He won't believe it, and Father and Mother won't believe it. You'd better not tell anybody, because you don't believe it yourself."

Oliver laughed and kissed her again. It was much easier to keep the kissing up than to make a beginning. He said this would be a lovely secret, and if it seemed almost too good, and they couldn't quite believe it now, they would prove it some day and be happy ever after.

IV

Peter's impulse was to do the opposite of what his English friends suggested, to be languidly irrational, and to make an attempt to let his son feel the charm of England—of the England that was about to disappear. Schools were still going full tilt. Wasn't Harold Van de Weyer's little boy, Mario, now at Eton? Happy thought. They could go down for the day and Oliver would experience the sensations of having a foreign cousin and peeping into an English public school.

A self-possessed young gentleman, still a little chubby and only just fledged into a tailcoat, was waiting for them, a day or two later, at the station in Windsor. He stood observant but perfectly calm, as if there was infinite time for everything to come round as it chose. If his American relations turned up, well, there they were, and he must do the honors; if they didn't turn up, what of it?

The boy was so exquisitely dressed, so merry, so unconcerned about everything, so innocently sparkling, that to Oliver he hardly seemed human at all. He could not understand how a boy not nearly his own age, in fact almost two years younger, could keep up a flow of conversation with such an elderly relative as his father. The boys he knew never addressed their elders except to ask for something, or mutter a complaint. How dull in comparison, how soggy, tired, sleepy, vague, heavy, ignorant, and uncouth, Oliver felt himself to be!

Mario meantime was mentally taking notes: "Remarkably good-looking. Big, but sensitive. For an American, quite civilised. Silent, probably intelligent. I think he'll do."

The tea-things were set out on a wooden box covered with an irreproachable tablecloth in Mario's quarters. This dingy little room seemed princely to Oliver. Here were feasts, here was freedom, openness, laughter, lordliness, simplicity.

Dr. Alden sat down limply in a chair, his head gently drooping over one shoulder and his eyes closed.

"My father caught a chill this morning," Oliver explained. "He's probably taken some medicine—some sedative—and it's overcome him."

The doctor finally came in to examine him. Nothing serious for the moment. Heart rather erratic, lungs weak, low general condition.

"My father would miss his old slippers and his old razors in the morning," he said to Mario after the doctor had left. "I think I'd better go to London, pay the bill and see to everything myself. The new nurse will watch, and send for the doctor if necessary."

The decision in Oliver's manner and his air of optimism were so evidently forced that Mario ran up to him, caught him by the arm, and said: "I should like awfully to go with you."

"You are very kind," said Oliver. "Would you mind taking my change and paying for everything? I get so mixed up with these shillings and pence."

Mario was only too delighted: not only that he liked having money to spend, even as proxy, but that after all what he had come for was to help Oliver, to smooth things out for him in his trouble. He wondered why only accidental worthless people like himself had a good time in this world, while the great and good like Oliver were unhappy.

In his corner of the empty carriage Oliver felt badly in need of comfort. He could find no peace unless he justified his natural sympathies, theoretically, and turned them into moral maxims.

In one mood one might say: Better be like Jim Darnley, fleshly, since you are living in the flesh, hard enough, coarse enough, loose enough to feel at home in the crowd. In another mood you may say: No: better be like Mario, refined by nature, clear as a crystal, merry without claims, brave without armour. Or yet in another mood, why not think it better to be like himself, burdened but strong, groping but faithful, desolate but proud.

But was he really desolate? Granted that my mother doesn't love me. Nor does Lord Jim, though he likes to be chummy. Nor does Father, really, though he is interested in my future. But Mario really seems to love me. When he takes me by the arm, it's rather as if he said: "I don't care where we go, but I want to go with you."

Besides, Mario is not the only one. There's my governess. I'm her Siegfried. Yes and a lot of other people who hardly know me: Mr. Darnley and Rose. I'm not a cipher for them, or just somebody who is rich. Yet all these people are poor unfortunates. They like me because I treat them kindly and make them feel that somebody likes them.

V

For two years Oliver had not seen the sea or anything beyond it. A sort of ritual rhythm, a sense for distinct moral seasons, had established itself in his mind. The surface of his thoughts had been fully occupied with college life at Williams and he seemed a perfectly conventional young man; yet under this commonplace mask, a secret drama was always being played in his mind, and a suspended allegiance to absent things made his daily routine somewhat perfunctory.

At a certain depth he continued to live always in the light of another world, where only such things moved as had touched his heart.

Now, in the second September after his father's death, accident brought a part of that hidden life to the surface. Mario Van de Weyer, on his way to Harvard College, was landing in New York. And it happened that one day, without being a reporter, Oliver found himself wearing a reporter's badge on his way to meet Mario at the Narrows. Jim Darnley, who was often in New York, had arranged it. The faithful Oliver, when passing through New York, always remembered him. They had dined together the evening before. Jim, though growing a little bald, was more youthful in spirit than ever, and full of projects and utopias for land and sea.

Instead of introducing his foreign cousin to America, Oliver allowed the newcomer to explain America to him, to take him to new places, to show him new people, and to become a link between Oliver himself and many a homely thing disregarded before.

Three years at Williams had proved dull. Oliver decided to go to Harvard for his last year in order to be near Mario and look after him.

As for Mario, the boy couldn't have been more affectionate or more amusing when, at odd moments, they were together; but as for being looked after, you might as well try to look after a comet. First you make him a present of a magnificent auto, such as you would have thought much too fine for yourself. Then you come to Harvard, hoping to moderate his speed in that auto and out of it: and now within three months, before your quiet influence has had time to tell, he upsets himself in the gutter, and requires you to do night work for him which a paid chauffeur would grumble at. And you find that luxurious motor foisted on you against your will, when you had drawn up a severe plan of study from which all motoring was excluded.

"Mario accepts my money, almost without thanks, as if he were doing me a favour and giving me a function in life. And the joke of it is that he is per-

fectly right. Coming to see me, having me to think about, is the happiest part of our day.

"Am I unhappy? Yes, at bottom in a dumb sort of way, as perhaps everybody is. It's a matter of course. I shall be too busy to think of it: and if you never think you are unhappy, are you unhappy at all?"

VI

A JOURNEY round the world taught Oliver little except how inevitably centred and miserably caged he was in himself; not merely psychologically, in his mind and person, but socially and morally in his world. He could never hope to fit in any other.

During those voyages Oliver had read up on the geography and history of the countries they visited; but it had been Mario that had played the cicerone and introduced his cousin to the actual people and places.

More than this, he had prevented Oliver from keeping out of adventures altogether or from taking them too seriously.

Wouldn't it have been really better to live like Mario, not socially labelled, not insured or predestinated, but irresponsibly, even licentiously, within the limits of kindness and honour? Wouldn't it have been better, if only it had been possible?

People like Mario weren't looking for the truth or for the best life: they were merely playing the game. In that sense Mario was more American, more modern, than Oliver himself: or rather he was what men of the world had always been—brilliant slaves of their circumstances.

"I won't be the slave of my circumstances," the proud spirit of Oliver cried in protest. "I will only recognise them, because that is a prerequisite to changing them."

So CONFIRMED in his spiritual self-reliance, Oliver had little confidence in the power of books or professors to give ultimate guidance: yet it was his duty to learn what the authorities might have to teach him: and he bravely settled down in Germany to hard solitary work. After the violence of German theorizing he felt a need to regain his mental balance, to look at things for a while at long range, under the form of eternity. He went to England where the Vicar was always ready to receive him as a pupil.

Jim was there too and he found that his talk had lost its old vividness and variety. The world no longer stimulated his wits or his cynicism: it had become an old story. Everything was a swindle, and he was always the innocent sufferer. Glints of the old Lord Jim would come now and then to the surface, to reopen Oliver's wounds and make it impossible for him to become altogether resigned and indifferent; and it was a melancholy relief when the sailor went off to sea again.

Jim scarcely gone, Rose had come home for the holidays. She was finishing her education (at Oliver's expense) at the Abbey School in High Wycombe. Their childish betrothal was never mentioned and was well understood not to count; yet in Oliver's mind the idea of someday marrying Rose lay in reserve as a possibility that helped to give some shape to the distressing vagueness of his future.

VII

It was with a kind of irritation passing into bewilderment that on the last day of July he received the following telegram:

"*War on. Crossing tonight to join. Mario.*"

Why should these currents of groundless passion, of perversity, of rhetorical nonsense, sweep so devastatingly through the minds of men? Now the newspapers had a new meaning for him. They began to make his moral philosophy seem rather distant, rather empty.

It lasted indefinitely; it became for the callous a sort of normal climate, as war has always been for a great part of mankind; but for the sensitive like Oliver, it seemed like an eternity. His own inaction became intolerable. He must do something, must take part somehow. Accordingly, he resolved to marry Rose Darnley, and to make a will leaving her his whole fortune. Then he could go to the front with a clean conscience.

But it was decreed otherwise. He was speaking to her on the porch the next evening. "I had hoped to say: To my wife, or at least my affianced wife, Rose Darnley, so much. But since you will not be my wife, may I say: To Rose Darnley, whom I have long looked upon as my future wife?"

She bowed her head a little as she passed before him over the cottage threshold, humbled but not shaken by his magnanimity.

A half hour later Oliver left the cottage, his head held high. His earthly person had been rejected, his earthly plan defeated; but by that defeat and rejection his soul had been wonderfully liberated. "I don't need to draw up a new will at all: the old one will do nicely. The Darnleys are provided for in case of my death amply, not extravagantly. So is Mario, so is my governess. I can sleep late tomorrow morning."

With the air of closing a fair bargain, and settling a business matter for good, he drew his marriage license from his pocket, tore it to bits, and let the wind and the rain scatter the fragments in the darkness.

"My people first went to America as exiles into a stark wilderness to lead a life apart, purer and soberer than the carnival life of Christendom. In the world today we are a belated phenomenon, like April snow. Perhaps it is time for us to die.

"If we resist, and try to cling to the fringes, as I have done so far, we are shaken off rudely, or allowed to hang on neglected and disowned. If we attempt to live apart, as my father did, we wither early into respectable ghosts.

"But I can now keep my own thoughts inviolate and not allow the world to override me. I will not accept anything cheaper or cruder than my own conscience. I have dedicated myself to the truth, to living in the presence of the noblest things I can conceive. If I can't live so, I won't live at all."

So thinking, he bundled himself into his corner in the railway carriage whose blinds were pulled down on account of Zeppelins, turned the collar of his coat over his ears, and closed his eyes.

GREATNESS

Honor and shame from no condition rise:
Act well your part, there all the honor lies.
—*Alexander Pope* (1688-1744).

Thousands Have Profited from This

Walter B. Pitkin

LIFE BEGINS AT FORTY

Life after forty. What has it left for us? Professor Pitkin proceeds to demolish the whole mental attitude with a zest and a soundness of argument that makes this book a challenge to middle age. Here are achievements and pleasures of all kinds which are waiting for thousands who can make life begin at forty, as the author did. He has published nineteen books since he hit that milestone and at sixty-one is still going strong as a professor in the Columbia School of Journalism, as a well-known magazine writer and New Jersey farmer.

The Luckiest Generation

You who are crossing forty may not know it, but you are the luckiest generation ever. Every day brings forth some new thing that adds to the joy of life after forty. Work becomes easy and brief. Play grows richer and longer. Leisure lengthens. Best of all, though, is your inner deliverance. A better age has delivered you from the Conviction of Incompetence.

Life begins at forty.

This is the revolutionary outcome of our new Era. This is the supreme reward of the Machine Age, the richest blessing of science. Day before yesterday it wasn't even a dream. Yesterday it was a silly lie. Today it is half a truth. Tomorrow it will be an axiom.

At what did the Minds behind the Machine Age aim? The saving of labor. That's agreed, isn't it? Thereby they sped up production, cut the cost of manufacture, and, quite incidentally, shortened the hours of toil so that men had more leisure.

Thanks to Super-Power and the Machine, housework is becoming a joke; so, as this happens, men and women alike turn from the ancient task of *making a living* to the strange new task

of *living*. And here we arrive at the Revolution.

I said, a moment ago, that at this particular moment in our history it is half a truth that life begins at forty. Money and education and native ability combine variously to make it so. Glance at incomes, and you will see how. Would a worker make something of his life outside of his job? Then he must have a little money over and above the bald necessities. Not much, to be sure. But surely a thin margin. How fares it with us today? Who has this margin? Who lacks it?

Life begins long before forty for some 700,000 Americans born rich enough to do nearly as they please. It begins around forty for some 3,000,000 more whose individual incomes and savings rise through early maturity to something better than $2,000. And it might easily begin at forty for another 12,000,000 or 14,000,000, if these were to organize their affairs to that end.

And so I shall argue that many millions of our citizens can get much more out of their fourth, fifth, and sixth decades of life than out of any of the first three, simply by learning how to live and how to make the most of opportunities within reach.

Assets of the Aging

Nobody knows much about this complex world until he is close to forty. A hundred years ago, a youth might learn his world in a few intense years;

and a man of thirty-five could master it, as far as anybody could. But today that is impossible. Broad and deep perspective is needed to grasp even your

156

neighborhood affairs. Never before has a little knowledge been such a dangerous thing as now. The League of Nations? Trial Marriage? The Business Depression? What chance has any young person of seeing through such webs of fact, blunders, intrigue, and theory.

There was a vogue, some twenty years ago, of promoting young men to posts of high responsibility. It arose, I imagine, from their elders' wish to get out from the heavy strain of swiftly expanding business. But some brilliants took the bit in their teeth and ran away with the show—ending up as most runaways do, in the ditch. Study the inside records of some of the most tragic bankruptcies and ruined fortunes; you will find a startling number of men under forty at the helm of the derelicts.

So the ominous complications of men's larger affairs indicate problems which twenty years of preparation alone can solve.

Many young people believe that as one grows older a uniform decline sets in. Muscles weaken. Eyes grow dim. The hand shakes. Reason totters. By fifty only the shell of a man survives.

Well, things are—thank heaven—hardly so bad. Everything depends upon the skill you have shown in choosing your grandparents and in managing yourself before forty.

After forty, most of us lose interest in changing our work, our play, our domicile, and our friends. While we grow surer of our abilities in advising and leading other people, we do not like such labor nearly as much as when we were younger and less wise. But we manage to enjoy—with only slightly reduced keenness—as wide a variety of things as we did in our twenties. In fact, one of the most striking features of life after forty is the continuity and stability of earlier interests on a plane of somewhat less intense feeling.

After forty no significant failing of dexterity sets in. On the contrary, the more intelligent and the more skilled show pronounced improvement in deftness of hand and fingers throughout middle age.

The brain continues to grow, in curiously irregular spurts, up to forty. As the brain grows only with use, and as the average brain is used up to one-fifth of its capacity, it is probable that few under forty work their minds sufficiently to mature them.

I strongly suspect that this lack of sustained stimulation and effort is one of the causes of the early shrinking of the brain. Certainly the lack of vigorous use leads to prompt decay. And I believe it will some day be rigorously demonstrated that most healthy people who fail to live richly after forty have only their own sloth or stupidity to blame. They will have crippled themselves before forty by indolence, by shirking, and by inane frivolity.

Managing on Mousepower

Now we come to the one serious decline at forty. It is the waning of free energy. To belittle this would be folly; for it changes the entire pattern of life. And rare the man who rearranges his affairs and his outlook in harmony with this profound transformation!

Shall we settle at ten cents on the dollar and go out of business? Not in the least! I maintain that the loss of free energy for strenuous activities need not cramp our style at all. On the contrary, it may be turned to profit by anybody who can keep on using his brain. For his brain can improve with use almost as long as he lives; and it can be used to manage all activities of the body, to the end of more health and happiness. Above all, it is the past master of economy; it makes the least energy deliver the greatest possible results, hence it serves man best of all after forty, when he must watch his horsepower.

So in a fresh sense, life begins at forty. For the brain requires most of the years before forty to perfect the art of managing its body. The better the brain, the earlier it masters all the tricks of economy and accomplishment. But, be it good or bad, it requires much time, especially in these days of baffling complexity. I think it highly probable that the very year which brings the first marked decline in physical energy—namely the thirty-seventh or thirty-eighth—normally lifts our practical intelligence to its final high level. As forty draws near, a man manages himself about as well as he ever can.

Able People Blossom Late

THERE is another side of this strange story of youth and age. Many who distinguish themselves after forty seem to have been stupid, unambitious, or worse in their 'teens and twenties. Many able people, like many geniuses, blossom late. Titian was of no consequence whatsoever until past forty, but he improved up to seventy and worked hard until ninety. Conrad put forth his first successful writing when thirty-nine.

At forty, Al Smith was a faithful Tammany toiler, serving at Albany as speaker of the Assembly. Then, he gave not the slightest sign of maturing into the man he became some ten years later.

At forty, the chief statistician of the American Telephone and Telegraph Company rose to its presidency; and life began for Walter Gifford.

Achievement in many lines begins well before forty; but by far the greater number of highly significant creative and constructive acts will be found on the shady side of that milestone. Thorndike found that the average age at which men of indubitable greatness have produced their masterpieces is 47.4 years. No fewer than 331 eminent men of all kinds were checked up in his inquiry.

Success comes later in our world. Few men are earning up to their full powers until forty or later. Among men destined to cross the $5,000 line of incomes, comparatively few do so until forty.

At forty, in brief, most men have not yet arrived and have not yet found themselves fully. The ablest are just coming into power and self understanding. But even for them the peak of achievement is still more than seven years away. Then and not until then do they know themselves and what they can do. Not until then does the world take their measure and give them their due rank. Not until then, in the complete sense, can they truthfully say they know how to live.

Course of Action

WE RETURN to our central issue. How use our assets after forty? How pay off our liabilities best? What sort of work? What sort of play? Which business suits the man and woman turned forty? What is their wisest use of leisure?

How much free energy have you to spend? Only you, aided perhaps by your family and your physicians, can answer that question. But whatever the answer, fit your choice of work and play after forty to it. And in general, keep in mind that your level of best performance after forty will probably be at least one step below that on which you succeed before forty.

After forty, sensible people lead the Simplified Life. We simplify, we pull in, we concentrate on a few powerful, enduring wishes. So, even though the gross volume of energies may dwindle somewhat, we use them more efficiently. Thus we heighten our chances of success and achievement.

Sooner or later, of course, mere simplifying will not suffice. Around fifty, let us say, one's decline of free energy is almost certain to necessitate stepping down to a lower level. Often this means that new tasks and new recreations must be learned. So we are forced to master anew the Art of Learning.

Lucky the man who, long before

forty, has learned how to think, to write, to speak, to make something with his hands and tools, and to handle people! He has within himself the equipment that enables him to find free outlet for his energies no matter how great or how slight these may be. Hence he can fit his work and play to his age. At forty he does not have to remodel himself. He merely eases up on whatever strains him and lets out a notch or two in other directions. He is the completely adaptable individual.

The man who begins living at forty knows what he wants to do. If he doesn't know that much, he cannot begin to live. For knowing what one desires is much more important than getting the desire. And, not knowing the desire, a man's first business must be to run it down.

Americans nibble at learning. They nibble at discipline. They nibble at thinking. They nibble at everything and engulf nothing. And the result? Well, contemplate American business; or American politics, or American taxes, or American cities, or American anything else you like. Across the baby face of each is written the word Vacant.

Is THERE any remedy? Any escape? Yes, but not an easy one! Such as it is, it is not open to fools. It demands moderate intelligence and the desire to live abundantly after forty. The learner must tackle the fundamentals. He must learn to think, to read, to talk, to write, and to observe. These will not exhaust him; as we have seen, they use up little energy and are therefore appropriate to early middle age.

Nor is this all. Mastery of language and logic—both taken here in their broadest meaning—enormously simplify the labors of managing people. The logical speaker packs into ten minutes what the windbag spills through a wheezy hour. With a given quantum of energy he accomplishes ten times more than the man who commands his speech and thoughts about as well as the average college graduate.

A man has not learned to live until, among other accomplishments, he can say what he wants to say—or, having nothing to say, can keep quiet. How few of us seem to have grown up in this respect! Even the telegraph companies bear witness to this grave charge. Have you ever laughed yourself sore over their stereotyped messages of greeting for Christmas and New Year's Day?

Here we have, in its stark and ugly nakedness the wordless, thoughtless adult. Were his number not legion, the telegraph companies could not continue to exploit these preposterous form messages. So long as the species is absorbed with mere livelihood, it will be content to stumble along with crippled minds. But after forty, when leisure and letdown come, what will such creatures do? So far as I can imagine their inwardness, they must feel like half-blind animals in a trap.

When Utopia comes a child will be taught to use his native language with such skill in both speech and writing that, at forty, he can begin to serve as an adviser rather than as a heavy toiler in his special field. Only through such intensive training will he come to think clearly and express himself convincingly.

New Tricks for Old Dogs

We can teach an old dog new tricks provided the old dog takes an interest in this accomplishment. But usually he will not. And this brings us up against one of the most vexatious of all industrial problems, the hatred and fear of any change which involves a man's deepest behavior patterns.

Ever since the Industrial Revolution began this emotional resistance to change of occupation has retarded progress and caused endless mischief. There is a genuine fear that, if one's old job vanishes, there will be no new one to take its place; and, secondly, an antipathy toward doing something different.

But wherever we can detach good workers and fairly favorable circumstances from the welter of poor workers and irremediable adversities, we find that the competent and the ambitious can transfer their skill to new lines of industry with no grave struggle except the incidental but very real one of tiding themselves over a period of unemployment between the old jobs and the new.

One lesson seems to emerge. Young people ought to be trained to expect and to be prepared for such sudden changes of work. They should be drilled in transferring their skill. And this means that they should learn several jobs simultaneously. The age clamors for versatile workers, for each job tends to fill only part of a man's time and to demand only a small fraction of his abilities.

Even within the professions, the volume of dull routine, simple tasks, and dead-end jobs is amazingly great. Drop in on any of our million school teachers, librarians, pharmacists, and other borderline professionals; the picture is much the same as among the carpenters and masons. Not until you move upward to that thin pure air of the scientist's laboratory, the college professor's lecture room, the operating room of the surgeon, and the magnificent paneled suite of the senior executive, do you find ample outlets for the recognizably superior minds there at work.

So, out of 48,832,589 Americans gainfully employed [1934], you are not going to find more than one or two million who are able to develop themselves in and through their bread-and-butter jobs.

Budget Yourself!

EMANCIPATING yourself so that you are free to master the art of living is largely the reward of character. It is a matter of self-insight, self-planning, and self-control.

Did any mortal ever budget his entire career. I'm sure that nobody has ever known himself well enough to do a decent job in this super-art. Nevertheless, the idea may be roughed in and partly realized, but not until you are well settled—let us say, at a guess, some time in your mid-thirties or early forties. You may start pondering around twenty.

Think of yourself as having fifty more years to go. See the problem as clearly as if it were one in engineering. (It is largely that—a matter of human engineering.) There are precisely 60 minutes in an hour, 24 hours in a day, and you know the rest. Allow 8 hours a night for sleep, 7 hours a day for work, with half of Saturday off. Allow whatever you need for dressing and undressing, for cleaning your teeth, for shaving, for opening your mail and answering routine letters, and for the other unavoidables of modern existence which seldom add joy to life.

What remains? About 2,500 hours a

year for all the good things other than necessities. That's an average, of course. Now let's ask how much the average man and woman can engineer out of those 2,500 hours of yearly freedom.

Lump together in one sticky mass all kinds of pleasures, from chewing a stick of gum up to parachute jumping. Each averages about fifteen minutes of satisfaction. To live at one's best, then, one ought to have some ten thousand distinct experiences of satisfaction annually, over and above the elemental satisfactions of sleeping, eating and working. In half a century, half a million joys!

Which things will fill these periods? That's an engineering problem, I repeat. It's an intricate trick of measuring and weighing energy output, minutes, and relative values. Above all it requires immense skill apportioning time.

Do you doubt this? Then test yourself. It's easy. When you arise some morning start checking up on your day. Years ago, a government clerk in Washington tried to measure the fun he got out of the hours, minute by minute. Probably he failed to enter on the books the best fun of all, which was analyzing himself thus. Do you find it so?

The Enduring Satisfactions

CHEAP and unenduring satisfactions are not for the intelligent forties. They are designed and planned chiefly for our untutored and vulgarized young Americans who spend billions yearly in shoddy activities miscalled amusement and leisure-time entertainment. After forty, we endeavor to find some way of making the worth-while activities of leisure as cheap, as simple, and as easy as possible *without destroying their substance*. This, of course, our schools should long since have undertaken. But as usual, it is the mature and intelligent men and women who must find their own salvation, who do it.

How do it?

Perhaps first, travel. Travel can be one of the noblest forms of busy leisure. Usually it is stupid—a wild rush from place to place, guide book in hand, or else a prolonged joy ride past millions of billboards. To know the world first hand is one of the foundations of culture.

After forty, you may wander footloose again and make a million fresh contacts. Travel grows cheaper and cheaper. You can make it from coast to coast on less than four dollars a day for all expenses, with careful planning. How foolish to sit around like a toad on a stone, when you might as well be getting an eyeful somewhere else. The man who permits himself to be chained to his office desk misses most of the fun of life. So does the housewife who deems it her sacred duty to stick around home just as if she were the paint on the walls.

Next to travel, try reading!

READING is the heart and soul of culture in its highest form. To open the world of good books to the eager leisure-timer, we must make reading much better than it is now. Here older people have the advantage over youth, especially in the understanding of news. Few can read the newspaper until after forty. I mean, of course, that the greater half of this art lies in the swift compre-

hending of backgrounds, and that no young person has had time to acquire these. Only time can paint them on the canvas of memory.

As for general reading, too many of all ages read slowly and inaccurately. As a rule, Americans tend to forsake good books soon after they leave school. The book trade and library figures show this convincingly. To gain the most from the reading of history, philosophy, drama, poetry, criticism, or any other high domain whose medium of expression is language, we must double or treble our reading skill.

Here people over forty can improve their ability as easily as do the youngsters. I know men and women by the dozen, in ages from forty to seventy, all of whom with consistent drill have greatly increased both their speed and their accuracy in reading—and consequently their enjoyment of its pleasures.

TURNING now to conversation, not a man in a million under forty is worth listening to, except for gag lines and clowning. The most brilliant conversationalists I have ever known, indeed, were all over sixty-five. The mastery of the art increases with experience and with the organization and design into which the mature cast their lives.

Were women to take half as much pains in preparing their conversations as in fixing their hair for dinner, life would be merrier—and I'm sure there would be fewer divorces and murders. And if men would only devote one-tenth of the time to cultivating conversation that they now do to cultivating business acquaintances, I suspect that their businesses would improve in the long run. For even a stupid retailer appreciates good talk!

Experimenting and studying just for fun after forty lead to many of the most interesting ways of using leisure and of living especially suited to active Americans after forty. The amateur student and the backyard scientist, ever keen in the pursuit of new discoveries and untried projects, can and do make their lives the envy of the luckless youngsters who must work yet awhile before they glimpse the hospitable threshold of forty. Those who use their leisure to their own real interest and profit are the truly civilized—and happy—in this land of ours.

The Woman's Place

Every Western land is swarming with idle women of middle age whose children have gone off to college or else to work and whose husbands have sunk deeply in the miry ruts of their own business offices. How they dash hither and yon, joining clubs, signing petitions, mixing cocktails, reading best sellers, doing anything to flee from that boredom which is the curse of our industrial barbarism. Their frenzy and flutter reveal their total lack of education. For they live in the midst of unparalleled opportunities that fairly shriek into their deaf ears and dazzle eyes not blind.

To these women I say that ten million careers lie open. In some there is fortune, in others fame, in still others calumny and social ostracism; but in all a chance to use more energy and wit and wisdom than anybody possesses.

During the next thirty years America must be rebuilt from the bottom up—or else go under. Somebody must clean up our filthy cities and their filthier governments. Somebody must plan the designing and erecting of five or ten million new homes to supplant the shacks and firetraps of the profiteering era after the World War. Somebody must exterminate the prevailing high schools, boarding schools and colleges, nearly all preventing the spread of education.

Somebody must work out plans for employing the middle-aged who have lost their jobs during the last years of the Machine Age. Somebody must devote a lifetime or two to speeding the recovery of agriculture—though heaven knows what's to be done. Somebody must educate and organize consumers so that retail prices yield only a fair profit to the middlemen and shippers, under the best possible conditions of distribution. Somebody ought to . . .

Oh, well! There's no end to that list of imperatives.

Now, the planning and the basic research in all these fields of progress must be done by men and women past forty. Why? Simply because the mass of facts involved in each problem cannot be conquered by younger people—barring a few near geniuses. Age has the advantage here. And, in some fields, the woman past forty is best qualified to think and to lead.

Look through the records of eminent women listed in "Who's Who in America." Dozens of them first achieved distinction after forty—and many even later. Authors publishing first books range in age from eighteen to sixty-seven. Those bringing out the last books mentioned were women from thirty-six to eighty-seven years old. More than half the distinguished educational workers were especially active from fifty to seventy-five.

The list is endless. But a small sampling reveals the obvious truth that for a woman, too, life begins at forty.

Look to the elders for leadership. What could be more reasonable?

Before you elders there will be no despair. Behind you no vanity. From childhood to the coming of old age, you will expand serenely, ever learning, ever tasting new joys. At forty you will be wiser and happier than at thirty. At fifty you will be clearer, steadier, and surer than at forty. At sixty you will be planning automobile trips to Mexico, a new sailboat, a fresh study of your village finances.

I say you will. But will you?

If you use your mind, Yes.

Have you a mind?

Let us see!

H. G. WELLS

TONO≈BUNGAY

IN THIS novel Mr. Wells is a realist. Tono-Bungay not only expresses to the full the novelist's capacity for drawing psychological pictures, but also affords him an opportunity, as a social reformer with a keen disgust at the wrongs and muddles of modern life, for an attack, bitter in its implicit sarcasm and aloofness, on the strenuous falsities of the more unscrupulous class of modern commerce. In the patent medicine trade, with its shameless imposition on the credulity of an ignorant public, he dissects what is perhaps its most blatant form. Merciless as is his denunciation of fraudulent methods of accumulating wealth and of the gross materialism of the age, the author's wide human sympathy is revealed in some most charming delineations of character.

I—The Dawn

> ## THE SECRET OF VIGOUR
> ## TONO-BUNGAY

THAT was all. It was simple, and yet in some way arresting. I found myself repeating the word after I had passed; it roused one's attention like the sound of distant guns. "Tono"—what's that? and deep, rich, unhurrying: *"Bun-gay!"*

Then came my uncle's amazing telegram: *"Come to me at once; you are wanted. Three hundred a year certain.—Tono-Bungay."*

"By Jove!" I cried. "Of course! It's something! A patent medicine! I wonder what he wants with me?"

The next day I took an unsanctioned holiday. I discovered my uncle in a wonderfully new silk hat—oh, a splendid hat!—with a rolling brim that went far beyond the common fashion.

"Here we are, George! What did I tell you? Needn't whisper it now, my boy. Shout it—*loud!* Spread it about! Tell everyone! Tono-*Tono*-TONO-BUN-GAY!

"Come right into the sanctum," he said. And whisked me through the door. "Well, here we are, going strong! You see me at it! At it—hard!"

"Hard at what?"

"Read it." And he thrust into my hand a label—that label that has now become one of the most familiar objects on the druggist's shelf, the greenish-blue, rather old-fashioned bordering, the legend, the name in good black type, very clear, and the strong man all set about with lightning flashes above the double column of skilful lies in red—the label of Tono-Bungay. "It's afloat," he said, as I stood puzzling at this. "It's afloat! Here we are at it!"

"It's—What?" said I.

"It's the secret of vigour. Didn't you read the label?"

"Yes; but—"

"And what is it?" I pressed.

"Well," said my uncle, and then leaned forward and spoke softly under the cover of his hand, "it's nothing more or less—"

(But here an unfortunate scruple intervenes. After all, Tono-Bungay is still a marketable commodity and in the hand of purchasers, who bought it from—among other vendors—me. . . . No, I'm afraid I cannot give it away.)

"You see," said my uncle, in a slow confidential whisper, with eyes very wide and a creased forehead, "it's nice because of the"—(here he mentioned a flavouring matter and an aromatic spirit); "it's stimulating because of"—(here he mentioned two very vivid tonics, one with a marked action on the kidneys). "And the"—(here he mentioned two other ingredients)—"make it pretty intoxicating. Cocks their tails. Then there's"—(but I touch on the essential secret). "And there you are. I got it out of an old book of recipes, all except the"—(here he mentioned the more virulent substance, the one that assails the kidneys)—"which is my idea. Modern touch! There you are! I want to let you into this for many reasons."

His voice grew lower and more cunning. He made explanations that my inexperience did not completely explain. I retain an impression of a long credit and a prospective share with some pirate printers, of a third share for a leading magazine and newspaper proprietor.

"I played 'em off one against the other," said my uncle.

I TOOK his point in an instant. He had gone to each of them in turn and said the others had come in.

"I put up four hundred pounds," said my uncle, "myself and my all. And you know"—he assumed a brisk confidence —"I hadn't four hundred pence. At least—"

For a moment he *was* a little embarrassed.

"I *did*," he said, "produce capital. You see, there was that trust affair of yours. I ought, I suppose, in strict legality to have put that straight first. Zzzz—

"It was a bold thing to do," said my uncle, shifting the venue from the region of honour to the region of courage. And then, with a characteristic outburst of piety, "Thank God, it's all come right!"

"Well, George, my boy," he said, after a time, quite happily unconscious of my silent criticism, "what do you think of it all?"

"Well," I said, "in the first place, it's a damned swindle!"

"Tut, tut!" said my uncle. "It's as straight as—it's fair trading."

"So much the worse for trading," I said.

"It's the sort of thing everybody does. After all, there's no harm in the stuff, and it may do good. It might do a lot of good—giving people confidence, for instance, against an epidemic. See? Why not? I don't see where your swindle comes in."

"H'm!" I said. "It's a thing you either see or don't see."

"I'd like to know what sort of trading isn't a swindle in this way. Everybody who does a large advertised trade is selling something common on the strength of saying it's uncommon. Look at Lord Radmore, who did it on lying about the alkali in soap."

"You don't mean to say you think doing this stuff up in bottles and swearing it's the quintessence of strength, and making poor devils buy it as that, is straight?"

"Why not, George? How do we know it mayn't be the quintessence to them so far as they're concerned? There's faith. You put faith in 'em. I grant our labels are a bit emphatic. No good setting people against the medicine. Tell me a solitary trade nowadays that hasn't to be emphatic. It's the modern way. Everybody understands it, everybody allows for it."

"But the world would be no worse, and rather better, if all this stuff of yours was run down a conduit into the Thames."

"Don't see that, George, at all. 'Mong other things, all our people would be out of work. Unemployed! The point is, George—*it makes trade*. And the world lives on trade—commerce! There's a justice in these big things, George. I tell you the world wants trade. It's trade that makes the world go round! Argosies! Venice! Empire!"

My uncle rose suddenly to his feet.

"You think it over, George, you think it over."

Yes; I thought it over thoroughly

enough. Trade rules the world—wealth rather than trade. The thing was true; and true, too, was my uncle's proposition that the quickest way to get wealth is to sell the cheapest thing possible in the dearest bottle. He was right, after all. *Pecunia non olet*—a Roman emperor said that. They knew it then; everyone, except a few young fools, knows it now. It's plain *caveat emptor!*

II—How We Made Tono-Bungay Hum

So I made my peace with my uncle, and we set out upon this bright enterprise of selling slightly injurious rubbish at one-and-three-halfpence and two-and-nine a bottle, including the Government stamp. We made Tono-Bungay hum! It brought us wealth, influence, respect, the confidence of endless people. All that my uncle promised me proved truth and under-statement. Tono-Bungay carried me to freedoms and powers that no life of scientific research, no passionate service of humanity could ever have given me.

It was my uncle's genius that did it. He wrote every advertisement; some of them he even sketched. You must remember his were the days before the *Times* took to enterprise and the vociferous hawking of the "Encyclopedia." That alluring, button-holing, let-me-just-tell-you-quite-soberly-something-you-ought-to-know style of newspaper advertisement, with every now and then a convulsive jump of some attractive phrase into capitals, was then almost a novelty. Very early, too, was that bright little quarter column in the evening papers: "HILARITY—TONO-BUNGAY. Like Mountain Air in the Veins." The penetrating trio of questions: "Are you bored with your business?" "Are you bored with your dinner?" "Are you bored with your wife?", was in our first campaign, when we worked London—south, central and west.

We discussed and worked out distribution together, we really worked infernally hard, and, I recall, we worked with a very decided enthusiasm, not simply on my uncle's part, but on mine. It was a game, an absurd but absurdly interesting game, and the points were scored in cases of bottles. By all modern standards the business was, as my uncle would say, "absolutely bona-fide." We sold our stuff and got the money, and spent the money honestly in lies and clamour to sell more stuff.

Section by section we spread it over the whole of the British Isles; first working the middle-class London suburbs, then the outer suburbs, then the home counties, then going (with new bills and a more pious style of "ad") into Wales, a great field always for a new patent medicine, and then into Lancashire. My uncle had in his inner office a big map of England, and as we took up fresh sections of the local press and our consignments invaded new areas, flags for advertisements and pink underlines for orders showed our progress.

Under the shadow of our great leading line we were presently taking subsidiary specialties into action: "Tono-Bungay Hair Stimulant" was our first supplement. Then came "Concentrated Tono-Bungay" for the eyes, which didn't go.

But we did admirable things with our next subsidiaries, "Tono-Bungay Lozenges" and "Tono-Bungay Chocolate." These we urged upon the public for their extraordinary nutritive and recuperative value in cases of fatigue and strain. I really do believe there was an element of "kick" in the strychnine in these lozenges, especially in those made according to our earlier formula. For we altered all our formulae—invariably weakening them as sales got ahead.

In a little while we were employing travellers and opening up Great Britain at the rate of a hundred square miles a day. My uncle's last addition to the Tono-Bungay group was the Tono-Bungay Mouthwash. The reader has probably read a hundred times that inspiring inquiry of his, "You are Young yet, but are you Sure Nothing has Aged your Gums?" And, after that, we took over the agency for three or four good American lines that worked in with our own, and could be run with it: "Texan Embrocation" and "23—to clear the system" were the chief.

I set down these bare facts. To me they are all linked with the figure of my uncle. I wish I could show you the short, fattening, small-legged man with stiff-cropped hair, disobedient glasses on a perky little nose, and a round stare behind them. I wish you could see him, breathing hard and a little through his nose as his pen scribbled out some absurd inspiration for a poster or a picture page, and make you hear his voice, charged with solemn import like the voice of a squeaky prophet, saying, "George! List'n! I got an idea, George!"

I never really determined whether my uncle regarded Tono-Bungay as a fraud, or whether he didn't come to believe in it in a kind of way by the mere reiteration of his own assertions. I think his average attitude was one of kindly, almost parental, toleration. I remember saying, "But you don't suppose this stuff ever did a human being the slightest good at all?" and how his face assumed a look of protest, as of one reproving harshness and dogmatism.

"You've a hard nature, George," he said. "You're too ready to run things down. How did one *tell?*"

As I look back at them now, those energetic years seem all compacted to a year or so; from the days of our first hazardous beginning with barely a thousand pounds' worth of stuff or credit all told—and that got by something perilously like snatching—to the days when my uncle went to the public on behalf of himself and me (one-tenth share) and our silent partners—the drug wholesalers and the printing people and the owner of that group of magazines and newspapers—to ask with honest confidence for £150,000.

One hundred and fifty thousand—

think of it!—for the goodwill in a string of lies and a trade in bottles of mitigated water!

And the subscriptions came pouring in. My uncle was immensely proud of the flotation. "They've never been given such value," he said, "for a dozen years." The little man plumped up very considerably during the creation of the property, but with the increasing excitements of those magnificent years that followed his passage from trade to finance came dyspepsia and a certain flabbiness and falling away. His abdomen—if the reader will pardon my taking his features in the order of their value—had at first a nice full roundness, but afterwards it lost tone, without, however, losing size. He always went as though he was proud really of it.

There was, I seem to remember, a secular intensification of his features; his nose developed character, became aggressive, stuck out at the world more and more; the obliquity of his mouth, I think, increased. From the face that returns to my memory projects a long cigar that is sometimes cocked jauntily up from the higher corner, and sometimes droops from the lower; it was as eloquent as a dog's tail, and he removed it only for the more emphatic modes of speech. He assumed a broad black ribbon for his glasses, and wore them more and more askew as time went on.

He adopted an urban style of dressing with the onset of Tono-Bungay, and rarely abandoned it; he liked a frock-coat long and full, although that seemed to shorten him.

Of an evening he would wear white waistcoats and plain gold studs. He hated diamonds. "Flashy," he said they were. "Might as well wear an income-tax receipt. All very well for Park Lane. Unsold stock. Not my style. Sober financier, George."

Such was the figure that created and directed the great property of Tono-Bungay, and from the successful reconstruction of that company passed on to a slow crescendo of magnificent creations and promotions until the whole world of investors marvelled. I have already, I think, mentioned how, long before we offered Tono-Bungay to the public, we took over the English agency of certain American specialties. To this were presently added our exploitations of Moggs' Domestic Soap, and so he took up the Domestic Convenience Campaign, that, coupled with his equatorial rotundity and a certain resolute convexity in his bearing, won my uncle his Napoleonic title. It was this that recalled him to one of his dreams of his youth, the Ponderevo Patent Flat. "The thing, George," he said, "wants straightening up. Silly muddle! Things that get in the way. Got to organise it. We got to bring the home up to date! That's my idea, George."

And it was an immense success. The public was, I think, particularly attracted by the homely familiarity of his field of work. You never lost sight of your investment, they felt, with its name on the house-flannel and the shaving-strop—and its allegiance was secured by the Egyptian solidity of his apparent results. Well, I don't intend to write down here the tortuous financial history of Moggs and Sons, of how we prepared the way for a second flotation, Domestic Utilities— "Do Ut," they rendered it in the City. And then came the reconstruction of Tono-Bungay, and then "Household Services" and the boom!

That sort of development is not to be told in detail in a novel. It is, indeed, to be found set out at length, painfully at length, in my uncle's examination and mine in the Bankruptcy Court, and in my own statements after his death.

All sorts of things came and offered themselves to my uncle. So much came to us, that it seemed to me at times as though the whole world of human affairs was ready to prostitute itself to our real and imaginary millions. We did the most extraordinary things; things that it seems absurd to me to leave to any casual man of wealth and enterprise who cares to do them. I had some amazing perceptions of just how modern thought and the supply of fact to the general mind may be controlled by money.

Among other things that my uncle offered for, he tried very hard to buy the *British Medical Journal* and the *Lancet,* and run them on what he called modern lines. That was a very magnificent idea indeed in its way; it would have given a tremendous advantage in the handling of innumerable specialties, and indeed, I scarcely know how far it would not have put the medical profession in our grip. It still amazes me—I shall die amazed—that such a thing should be possible in the modern state. I suppose it is a lingering trace of Plutarch and my ineradicable boyish imagination that, at bottom, our state should be wise, sane and dignified, that makes me think a country which leaves its medical and literary criticism, or, indeed, any such vitally important criticisms, entirely to private enterprise and open to the advances of any purchaser, must be in a frankly hopeless condition.

Well, we boomed, and for four years and a half we lived a life of mingled substance and moonshine. Until our particular unsoundness overtook us, we went about in the most magnificent motor-cars upon tangible high-roads, made ourselves conspicuous and stately in splendid houses, ate sumptuously, and had a perpetual stream of notes and money trickling into our pockets; hundreds and thousands of men and women respected us, saluted us and gave us toil and honour; I asked, and my worksheds rose, my aeroplanes swooped out of nothingness to scare the downland peewits; my uncle waved his hand, and Lady Grove and all its associations of chivalry and ancient peace were his; waved again, and architects were busy planning the great palace he never finished at Crest Hill, and an army of workmen gathered to do his bidding, blue marble came from Canada, and timber from New Zealand; and beneath it all, you know, there was nothing but rainbow gold.

III—The Stick of the Rocket

I was down at Lady Grove on the day of my uncle's examination, winding up affairs at my flying-sheds. And afterwards I wandered up to the downs, and found myself looking down on the huge, abandoned masses of the Crest Hill house. It struck me suddenly as the compactest image and sample of all that passes for progress, of all the advertisement-inflated spending, the aimless building up and pulling down, the enterprise and promise of my age. This was our fruit; this was what we had done, I and my uncle, in the fashion of our time. I was roused from such thoughts by sounds of footsteps behind me. It was my uncle. His face was white.

"It's all up," he said.

He stood swaying, and then came forward with a weak motion of his arm, like a man who cannot see distinctly, and caught at and leaned upon the stile. For a moment we were absolutely still. He made a clumsy gesture towards the great futility below and choked. I discovered that his face was wet with tears, that his wet glasses blinded him. He put up his little fat hand and clawed them off clumsily, felt inefficiently for his pocket handkerchief, and then, to my horror, as he clung to me, he began to weep aloud, this little, old, world-wide swindler. It wasn't just sobbing or shedding tears, it was crying as a child cries. It was—oh, terrible!

"It's cruel!" he blubbered at last. "They asked me questions. They *kep'* asking me questions, George."

He sought for utterance, and spluttered.

"The——bullies!" he shouted. "The ——bullies!"

He ceased to weep. He became suddenly rapid and explanatory.

"It's not a fair game, George. They tire you out. And I'm not well. My stomach's all wrong. And I been and got a cold. I always been li'ble to cold, and this one's on my chest. And then they tell you to speak up. They bait you, and bait you, and bait you. It's torture—the

strain of it. You can't remember what you said. You're bound to contradict yourself. It's like Russia, George. It isn't fair play. I been bellowed at, I been bullied. I been treated like a dog. Dirty cads they are—dirty cads!

"They sprung things on me this morning that I didn't expect. They rushed me! I'd got it all in my hands, and then I was jumped. And there they are in London, doing what they like with me. I don't care!"

"But——" I said, looking down at him perplexed.

"It's abscondin'. They'll have a warrant."

"I don't understand," I said.

"It's all up, George—all up and over." He paused. "Writin' things down—I done something."

His little bloodshot eyes stared at Crest Hill.

"That chap Whitaker Wright," he said, "he had his stuff ready. I haven't. Now you got it, George. That's the sort of hole I'm in."

T
HE incidents of our flight in Lord Roberts' *Beta* do not arrange themselves in any consecutive order. My uncle grew more and more manifestly ill with every stage in our journey. Through most of the long night, when we hung over the Channel, struggling with the east wind, he dozed. Even when we landed in the marshes near Bordeaux, and lost the aeroplane, he only woke and fell asleep again; but he did not finally collapse until I had installed him in an inn at Luxon Gare, a little French frontier town, and organized a sick-room and found a nurse.

I have tried to make you picture my uncle time after time as the adventurer of the early days of Tono-Bungay, as the confident, prosperous plutocrat. And now I have to tell of him strangely changed under the shadow of oncoming death, with his skin lax and yellow and glistening with sweat, his eyes large and glassy, his countenance unfamiliar through the growth of a beard, his nose pinched and thin. Never had he looked so small as now. And he talked to me in a whispering, strained voice—of great issues, of why his life had been, and whither he was going. Poor little man! That last phase is, as it were, disconnected from all the other phases. It was as if he had crawled out of the ruins of his career and looked about him before he died.

H E KNEW he was almost certainly dying. In a way, that took the burden of his cares off his mind.

"It has been a great career, George," he said; "but I shall be glad to rest— glad to rest, glad to rest."

The little Protestant clergyman watched that first night. He had heard of the straits we were in, and he had come to help. In the small hours he raised the house with the alarm that my uncle was dying.

The stuffy little room was crowded when I reached it, and lit by three flickering candles. I felt I was back in the eighteenth century. There lay my poor uncle amidst indescribably tumbled bedclothes, weary of life beyond measure, weary of rambling, and the little clergyman trying to hold his hand and his attention.

Close at hand was the doctor, with one of those cruel and idiotic injection needles modern science puts in the hands of these half-educated young men, keeping my uncle flickeringly alive for no reason whatever. The *religieuse* hovered sleepily in the background with an overdue and neglected dose. In addition, the landlady had not only got up herself, but roused an aged crone of a mother and a partially imbecile husband. There they all were, wearily nocturnal, hastily and carelessly dressed, intent upon the life that flickered and sank, making a public and curious show of its going, queer shapes of human beings lit by three uncertain candles, and every soul of them keenly and avidly resolved to be in at the death.

And my uncle spoilt the climax, and did not die until the next night.

Near the end he suddenly became clearminded and lucid, albeit very weak.

"George," he said.

"I'm here," I said, "close beside you."

"George, you have always been responsible for the *science*. George, you know better than I do. Is—is it proved?"

"What proved?"

"Either way? Death ends all. After so much—such splendid beginnings. Somewhere—something."

I stared at him, amazed. His sunken eyes were very grave.

"It seems to me, George, always, there must be something in me that won't die."

He looked at me as though the decision rested with me.

"I think," he said—"something."

He became silent. For a time he struggled for breath. It seemed such nonsense that he should have to suffer so—poor, silly little man!

"George!" he said, and his weak little hand came out, "perhaps—"

"Yes, I think so," I said stoutly.

"Aren't you sure?"

"Oh, practically sure!" said I. And I think he tried to squeeze my hand.

A ND there I sat, holding his hand tight, and trying to think what seeds of immortality could be found in all his being, what sort of ghost there was in him to wander out into the bleak immensities. Queer fancies came over me. He lay still for a long time, save for a brief struggle or so for breath; and ever and again I wiped his mouth and lips.

I fell into a pit of thought. I did not remark at first the change that was creeping over his face. He lay back on his pillow, made a faint zzzing sound that ceased, and presently, and quite quietly, he died.

I do not know when he died. His hand relaxed insensibly. Suddenly, with a start, with a shock, I found that his mouth had fallen open, and that he was dead.

GERHART HAUPTMANN

ATLANTIS

W ELL as Gerhart Hauptmann's first novel, "Emmanuel Quint," was received, in 1910, it had nothing like the general success of his admirable "Atlantis," which is in reality a fine piece of psychology, quite apart from being a most vivid and engrossing story of life in the New York of modern days, as seen through the eyes of a cultivated German. Very real, too, are the hero's experiences on the doomed liner *Roland;* and very brilliant is the characterisation, even in the exquisite thumbnail sketches in which the author sums up some of his personages, or portrays an episode. This great naturalistic novel is remarkable for the loftiness of its tone, and for the delight of its author in all that is aristocratic in the truest sense of the word.

On Board the Roland

D R. FRIEDRICH VON KAMMACHER caught the North German steamship *Roland,* which left Bremen for New York, on January 23, 1892. To do so he had to get the express from Paris, where he had been staying, to Hâvre, and cross to Southampton, at which port the vessel called.

Although no more than thirty, the young physician already had his full load of care. His wife, Angèle, mother of his three young children, was in a sanatorium in Germany, a hopeless neurasthenic. He himself, bitterly disappointed over the seeming failure of certain bacteriological experiments by which he had hoped to make a worldwide reputation, had thrown up his practice in disgust; and, to make matters worse, he had conceived a sort of passion for a sixteen-year-old Swedish dancer, Ingigerd Hahlström, whose acquaintance he had made in Berlin. To fight this obsession Friedrich von Kammacher had left Berlin for Paris; but now, seeing the names of Miss Hahlström and her father in the passenger list of the *Roland,* he had given way to temptation and hastily decided to cross the Atlantic in the same boat.

It was her gruesome dance, "Mara, or The Spider's Victim," given in the Künstlerhaus, that had fascinated Fried-

rich in the first place. All Berlin was talking next day of the wonderful little dancer, whose instant success was so great that the dancing master, her father, was taking her to the United States to turn it into money.

The voyage began in weather so stormy as to keep many of the passengers below deck for the first day or two. Consequently Friedrich had to contain his impatience until Miss Hahlström should be sufficiently well to make an appearance. Meanwhile he got to know Captain von Kessel, the blond-bearded skipper, and Von Halm, the first officer, both splendid men, calm, assured, imposing; Dr. Wilhelm, the ship's doctor, chatty and *bon enfant,* especially with one of his own profession, was another early and welcome acquaintance. As for the officers and crew generally, the traveller was at once struck by their fine physique and bearing. The sight of them made him proud to be German; and a curious thought flashed through his mind—that surely Providence could never drown so grand a lot of men in mid-ocean, like so many puppies in a pond.

W HEN the wind had dropped, and the sea was smoother, Miss Hahlström at last showed herself. Friedrich found her lying on a deck chair, with her long fair hair flying loose in the

GERHART HAUPTMANN was born at Salzbrunn, Silesia, in 1862, and in his early life studied art at Breslau and Rome. In 1889 he began playwriting and produced "Before Sunrise," "Lonely Lives," "The Fur Coat" and many other dramatic works. With an almost repellant naturalism and realistic depiction of the trivialities of modern life, he struck a new note in contemporary literature. "Emmanuel Quint" and "Atlantis" are his most powerful novels. Hauptmann was awarded the Nobel prize for literature in 1912. His dramatic works have been translated into most European languages.

wind. She was playing with a small doll, and there were several men around her —all quite evidently attracted in a way that was far from pleasing to the young doctor, who, at length, tired of the trivial conversation, moved away, angry with himself for being angry with the others. Presently the girl sent all the men away, with the capriciousness of the spoilt child, and called to Dr. von Kammacher to come and talk to her.

"The very first time I saw you in Berlin," she said, in her archly-innocent way, "I felt there was a bond between us. I knew we should meet again. Are you married?" she inquired indifferently.

Something in her words and her manner repelled Friedrich, who replied coldly that she must not make the mistake of supposing he was one of her ordinary admirers, and that it could not possibly be of any concern to her whether he were married or not. Then he added, more kindly, a word of warning about the men she encouraged. Her reputation, he said, could not be too carefully guarded.

"Reputation!" she exclaimed, with a loud laugh. "I can assure you that has never troubled me for an instant!"

The girl was in a confiding mood, so Friedrich had to listen to a long and shocking story of her past. Young as she was, Ingigerd Hahlström had nothing left to learn. With the most cynical frankness she told him things about herself worse than anything he had met with in all his experience as a doctor.

When Friedrich had taken her back to her cabin, he went to his own, disgusted, disillusioned, sick at heart. "I have set my all on naught!" he exclaimed bitterly. Now that the girl had dishonoured his love for her his conscience pricked him more than ever, and his whole being revolted against the poisonous passion surging within him.

Letters from Friedrich's father and mother, General and Frau von Kammacher, delivered by the French pilot boat, served to steady his mind—good, sensible, affectionate letters which comforted him. Both insisted that he had no cause to reproach himself in respect of his sick wife. Her malady was inherited, and at times, the mother declared, her nervous outbreaks would have driven any man desperate. The old artillery officer strove to cheer his son over his professional set-back, and urged him to have a good holiday, to take things quietly and to come back cured, ready to start afresh, secure in the possession of real talent.

The bad weather returned, after a brief respite, and soon grew worse than ever. Conversation among the first-class passengers was little else than a prolonged grumble on this score, and those who thought about the matter at all pitied the four hundred wretched souls in the steerage, suffering terrible discomfort day and night.

Said one Füllenberg, a gay young spark from Berlin, going out to take up some official position: "Do you know, there are two priests on board? The sailors are furious. They swear something's bound to go wrong. There was fog last night. I hear we only just escaped collision with a derelict!"

THE talk was interrupted by Hahlström, Ingigerd's tall, rather distinguished-looking father, who asked Friedrich to go to his daughter's cabin, as she wished to speak to him. He found her flippant, quite at her ease, as usual, in no way offended by his frankness, nor ashamed at her own confessions of the day before. Despite all that had occurred, Friedrich felt pity, if nothing else, for the child; but remembering Schopenhauer's dictum, "All love is pity," he was careful to keep even his companion in check.

Presently Ingigerd complained of a pain in her chest. "You're a doctor. Will you examine me?" she asked, with a laugh.

"That's Doctor Wilhelm's business," he replied, in his iciest tones.

"So much for your friendship!" retorted the girl, crossly. "I am in pain, and you won't do anything to stop it!"

"If I *were* your doctor I'd order you to live for three years with a German pastor in the country, or with some American farmer. No theatres for you, either on or off the stage. These cursed variety shows have been your ruin!"

When Friedrich returned to the smoking-room someone—he could not tell who—inquired sarcastically "if he had operated on the dancer, to remove the mole?"

Furious and humiliated, he nevertheless ignored the coarse remark; but the sting remained. It showed all too plainly how lightly Ingigerd was held by the men who knew her. Even the stewards, the firemen, the very cabin-boys showed towards her a familiarity which made his blood boil. And yet he remained under her spell!

At length, about the beginning of the third day at sea, the glass rose, the wind and waves abated, and the weather grew so genial that everyone was on deck listening to the band. Champagne flowed at dinner that night. Joy was in the air.

The fine spell was too good to last; next day the weather was worse than ever, and the temperature so low that icicles hung from the rigging. When the storm was at its height, Friedrich, anxious to see how Ingigerd was faring, made his way to her cabin. There he found her, light-hearted as ever, comforting two frightened children. All his ill-will vanished at sight of so much real courage and humour; once again he felt irresistibly drawn towards her.

Then something went wrong with one of the engines. The great vessel stopped, and there was tremendous excitement among the more timorous passengers, especially as the waves now looked even larger and more threatening than before. But Captain von Kessel and his officers sent reassuring messages round, and in a few hours the old, rhythmic beat of the engines was felt once more: the *Roland* was forging full steam ahead! The weather was fitful next day.

Danger

AT DAWN on the morning after, stewards came round to the cabin door and quietly uttered the one word "Danger!" at the same time turning on the electric light.

Friedrich at the time was lying in his birth, dressed. Putting on his heavy overcoat, he went out at once into the gangway, where he met the ship's barber.

"The fires are out," he said. "We've had a collision. Under my shop the water's pouring into the hold."

Everywhere the call-bells were ringing. Seeing that the barber was carrying two life-belts Dr. von Kammacher took one from him and hurried on. "What do you want two for?" he asked.

Captain von Kessel, to all seeming quite undisturbed, was on the bridge with huge Von Halm. The siren was sounding, and from the bows rockets were being fired. The third mate had just received the order:

"Get the boats away! Cut the falls!"

Next came the Captain's brief command: "Women and children starboard!"

Clearly the *Roland* was sinking. Friedrich rushed to Ingigerd's cabin and told her to dress at once. "What's the matter? Are we going down?" she asked, coolly enough, while she got into some clothes. Then she asked anxiously for her father.

"There's no time to think of anybody now," said Friedrich and, picking her up in his arms, he carried her to where a boat was being lowered. It was hard work to get her into it, but at last he succeeded, despite the opposition and a couple of sailors who had lost their heads. With the help of Dr. Wilhelm he contrived to get other women and children in as well.

By now Ingigerd was crying aloud for her father, so Friedrich risked his life going to seek him, all to no purpose. By great good luck he was just in time to find a place in the first boat, which was pulled clear of the doomed liner.

Fog had come on, and at even a little distance the *Roland,* with its load of frantic, screaming humanity, was scarcely visible. And in the water all around the little lifeboat were men and women, struggling to keep afloat, threatening to swamp the frail craft as they strove to clutch it and clamber in. All that could be done was to beat them off without remorse, lest the whole boatload perish as well. At last they got clear away, rowing hard. Then the fog lifted; the *Roland* was gone.

Friedrich von Kammacher and his companions—fifteen in all, they proved, as it turned out, to be the only survivors of the disaster—were picked up late in the afternoon of the same day by the little trading ship *Hamburg,* bound, like themselves, for New York. Captain Butor, the skipper, opined that the *Roland* must have struck a derelict.

"The incredible has actually happened," exclaimed Dr. Wilhelm, shaking hands with Friedrich. "We are saved!"

"Yes," said Friedrich, "we are saved. I wonder what we were saved for?"

The little dancer, subdued and docile, was a pathetic figure as she lay stretched out on a deck chair.

"Was it only chance, I wonder?" she said to Friedrich, "that brought us together on the *Roland* on this voyage?"

"Everything is chance," he said.

Then he told her why he had hurried to catch the boat.

"So it was for my sake," she said softly, "that you so nearly lost your life! And then you saved mine!"

In New York

Great was the excitement when the *Hamburg* landed her rescued travellers on the solid pier of New York, where crowds of hungry reporters were waiting to get sensational stories for their papers.

Friedrich and Ingigerd were hardly ashore before the doctor was greeted by a little man who looked somewhat like a Japanese.

"Hallo, Dr. von Kammacher! How are you? Don't you know me?" and his hand was grasped and warmly shaken.

"What! Willy Snyders! I know you now. What on earth are *you* doing here?"

Some years before, young Snyders had been Friedrich's pupil in Breslau, and had grown into a man since last they met.

"Come on!" he cried, "I'll explain everything later; unless you want to be interviewed by those damned journalists? No? I should think not! There's my cab waiting. Get in, both of you, and I'll take you to my place."

Friedrich introduced Willy Snyders to Ingigerd, and they were about to get into the cab when an elderly man, out of breath and perspiring, came forward apologetically, hat in hand. He represented Webster and Forster, and had brought a carriage, to take Miss Hahlström to the Astor, where rooms had been reserved for her. He hoped she would be able to appear that evening. He would provide her with money and anything else she might need.

When Friedrich told him that Ingigerd could not possibly go on the stage at present; that he, as her physician, absolutely forebade it until she had rested, the agent angrily warned them of the consequences of breaking the contract.

Willy Snyders took them to the house where he lived, an extremely comfortable place leased by a little group of German artists, the most notable of whom was Bonifacius Ritter, a young sculptor of high talent, if not genius. Among his patrons were the Astors, the Goulds and the Vanderbilts, and much of the external carving on the Chicago Exhibition buildings had been entrusted to him. A handsome dandy, he looked like "arriving" very soon. They had as a house-keeper an old Italian woman, Petronilla, whose first thought was to put the little dancer to bed.

Received by Ritter and the rest of the party with the utmost cordiality, Friedrich felt at home immediately, their frank camaraderie being just the kind of tonic he needed. Losing his customary reserve, he told his new friends—the idea having suddenly occurred to him—that he proposed to continue certain studies, begun some years before, with Peter Schmidt, the physician, in Springfield, Massachusetts. Whereupon Willy Snyders told him that Schmidt was now at Meriden, an hour's ride from Springfield.

THAT same evening the music-hall agent made another attempt to induce Ingigerd to dance, on the following night at the latest.

But Friedrich was firm. Miss Hahlström was not fit to dance yet. And at last, losing patience, he declared she should not dance at all. The girl was not yet seventeen. If the agents molested her further he would inform the Society for the Prevention of Cruelty to Children!

An hour later Friedrich, Snyders, Ritter and some of the others were sitting in a box at Webster and Forster's. The great attraction was Arthur Stoss, an armless man who had been saved from the *Roland*. He played the violin, put bullets through the centre of the cards, did all his old tricks in fact, as well as ever. There was frantic applause.

As Friedrich watched him he pictured Captain von Kessel, as he last saw him, calmly giving orders on the bridge of the doomed ship, and he remembered how the captain had once said to him: "My brother has a wife and children. He is a man to be envied.

This hero had perished at his post. The mountebank survived to exploit a disaster costing hundreds of lives!

Next day Peter Schmidt arrived from Meriden. The two friends went on to Ritter's studio, near Central Park. It was very spacious and luxurious, yet very comfortable, and contained artistic treasures of all sorts, among them some wonderful German Madonnas carved in wood, and a real Nuremberg stove, with the authentic Delft tiles of green glaze.

Miss Burns of Birmingham

As THE visitors passed into the studio they noticed a tall, handsome girl of about twenty-five working intently on a clay bust. This was Eva Burns, a pupil from Birmingham, to whom they were presently introduced. When Friedrich had told her how intensely he loved art in general and sculpture in particular—having dabbled in it years ago—she suggested that he should make a fresh start

at once, under Ritter's direction. As he looked into her large, intelligent, meditative eyes the young doctor resolved to take the advice she gave.

Friedrich returned home, after seeing Peter Schmidt off at the station, to find Ingigerd engaged with a young artist named Franck, one of the little group, an eccentric Silesian with gipsy-black hair and eyes.

Ingigerd herself had sent word by Petronilla that she would be free in a quarter of an hour. Without an instant's delay Friedrich went upstairs, knocked loudly at Ingigerd's door, and, receiving no answer, went in. Franck was sitting beside her, sketching rough designs for costumes.

He rose to go as the doctor entered, and the girl, calling him "Rigo," reminded him that he had promised to come again in the morning.

Angry at everything, especially the pet name, Friedrich grew more incensed than ever when Ingigerd told him Franck had said that he was going to paint her portrait.

It was decided that it was hardly right for Ingigerd to stay permanently in a bachelors' club-house, so Snyders found her lodgings with friends on Fifth Avenue.

Before she left, Friedrich had a frank talk with her. He told her of his past life, his unfortunate marriage, everything, and at length asked her plainly could she give up her ambitions and begin a different life afresh with him? Could she—would she—be his comrade for the future?

She was standing by the window, tapping the glass with a pencil.

"Perhaps I might, Dr. von Kammacher," she replied.

"Perhaps?" he echoed angrily.

"Well, I don't know if I am suited to you."

"It is simply a question of love," he said.

"I like you, certainly," was her reply. "But how can I tell if it is love? So far, I have never loved anything but animals."

It was a relief to them both when a Mr. Lilienfeld, manager of the Cosmopolitan Theatre, was announced. He had heard, he said, that Miss Hahlström was resolved not to appear for Webster and Forster; but he hoped she had not decided to retire into private life.

"Oh, no!" replied Ingigerd firmly, before Friedrich could get in a word.

Mr. Lilienfeld offered terms very much larger than those of Webster and Forster, and at once took them both off to a lawyer's office, where the business was promptly arranged.

In the cab on the way back Friedrich begged her not to dance any more, but to go with him and be his all-in-all. He would take her with him the very next day to Meriden, and the music-halls would have a long time to wait for her!

He said this, earnestly, tremulously, as if his very existence hung on her answer. Ingigerd laughed, and Friedrich knew she had no soul, only a body.

Not another word did he say. When they stopped at the club-house he escorted her to the door, pressed her hand and, getting back into the cab, told the driver to go on. He got down at the Hoffman House, where, as he remembered, he had an appointment to meet the men from the *Hamburg*.

There he found them. Their conversation jarred his nerves, and before long he was in the street again.

On Broadway he met Miss Burns, and, as she was going to lunch, he asked if he might take his meal with her. Miss Burns warned him, with her frank laugh, that he would not get anything very epicurean, but he insisted on having the same food as herself, which was baked potatoes, cabbage and fried eggs, washed down with iced water. Friedrich looked in wonder and admiration at her splendid face and figure—the true Titian type.

For the second time that day the young doctor opened his heart, and now it was clear to see he had found a sympathetic listener. Work, manual work for choice, was Miss Burns's prescription.

"Strike out cheerfully into a new path," she said. "Why not return to sculpture?"

He promised to try.

At Ritter's studio next morning Friedrich set about copying the plaster cast of an athlete's arm. He handled the moist clay for several hours, and at the end won the praise not only of Eva Burns, but of Ritter himself, for what he had done. He left the studio in a healthier frame of mind than he had known for years.

Webster and Forster turned the tables on Ingigerd and her friends by themselves calling in the Society for the Prevention of Cruelty to Children, a representative of which, Mr. Garry, stern, unbending, puritanical as any Pilgrim Father who came over in the *Mayflower,* was deputed to be present at a rehearsal in Lilienfeld's theatre.

Friedrich, with Miss Burns, Willy Snyders, Ritter, and others of the artists' group saw Ingigerd go through the "Spider" dance in the presence of stately, silver-haired Mr. Garry, who caused an injunction to be issued preventing the girl from appearing in public.

Appeal was made to the Mayor, and the matter was argued before him at the City Hall. The Mayor was a Tammany man, and Mr. Garry a Republican. Therefore they were deadly enemies. After the representative of "respectability" had roundly abused Lilienfeld, whom, with all his class, he regarded as no better than vermin; after Lilienfeld, in whose eyes Mr. Garry and those like him were simply a crowd of meddlesome, reactionary, prurient-minded humbugs, came the verdict. Mr. Mayor decided in favour of Ingigerd being allowed to do as she chose.

Lilienfeld invited the party, together with the reporters, to celebrate Ingigerd's victory by a luncheon. Friedrich, more and more disgusted at each stage of the sordid business, preferred to take a plainer meal with Miss Burns.

Cleansing Fires

"I HAVE just sent a telegram to Peter Schmidt at Meriden," he said, "telling him I am coming down to-morrow to stay with him. I'm going to turn farmer."

"I'm really sorry you are going away," said Eva Burns, changing colour, but speaking without any apparent trace of sentimentality.

"Oh! but you must come down and see me," he rejoined gaily. "The Mayor's decision settled *my* case too. I don't want to see Ingigerd dance again, still less to follow her round all the music-halls of the world. I am free! At last I am rid of the girl!"

Later in the day Friedrich called at the Lilienfelds', where Ingigerd was now staying. She looked tired, and her greeting was rather off-hand. Presently she asked him if he had packed.

"Why?" he inquired.

"Mr. Lilienfeld," she replied, "has made a contract for me in Boston. You must be ready to go with me the day after to-morrow."

"To the end of the world, dear lady, if you like!" remarked Friedrich, airily, as he took his leave.

Some minutes later Ingigerd, accompanied by a distinguished-looking American, well past his prime, inquired at Peter Schmidt's office for Dr. von Kammacher. The most truthful person in the world, as a rule, Schmidt lied without the slightest hesitation. "Friedrich," he said, "has gone back to Europe. He sailed in a White Star steamer, the *Robert Keats.*" Soon after his arrival at the Schmidts' Friedrich had received letters from her; but she interested him no longer.

Next morning Friedrich left New York for Meriden. Peter Schmidt met him, and shortly had him installed in a comfortable little house overlooking Lake Hanover. Friedrich soon began to assist the Schmidts in their practice, Mrs. Schmidt being a physician, like her husband, working among the people of the district.

Friedrich, who had seen Kocher operate in Berne for a fibroid tumour, and had himself done it successfully on many occasions, was asked by Schmidt to undertake a similar operation as one of his patients, a farmer, and though his nerves were still unstrung he agreed.

As in a dream, but with his hand and brain under perfect control, Friedrich cut into the diseased flesh and removed the growth with the utmost skill.

A cablegram had come for him, but in his preoccupation he had left it in his overcoat pocket, unread. The operation was completely successful, but after the tension of it all the operator himself broke down. Eva Burns came on the following day, to find Friedrich delirious, manifestly very ill. He lay unconscious in his bed, still wearing his fur coat, and on the floor was the cablegram, which read:

"Dear Friedrich, news from Jena. Despite the greatest care Angèle passed away yesterday afternoon. Accept the inevitable calmly, and keep well for the sake of your loving parents."

The Schmidts and Miss Burns, most devoted of nurses, had hard work to save his life. For days he lay on the brink of death; but at the end of a week the fever abated slowly until at last he was out of danger. Friedrich's convalescence was slow, but there was no relapse, and one day Peter Schmidt was able to tell him: "Your body is purged of all poisons and putrid matters." And Dr. von Kammacher himself knew he had passed through cleansing fires.

Eva burns told him, when the spring came, that she had made a decision: that she was going back to England soon, to educate neglected children.

His homesickness grew, as summer came, and he talked so often and so lovingly of Europe that Peter Schmidt caught the infection. His wife had it already. The very thought of going home made a new woman of her. So they all decided to start without delay.

Friedrich, without telling anyone at first, booked a passage in the *Auguste Victoria,* the boat in which Eva Burns was to travel. Willy Snyders and his wife, who divined what was happening, decided to go by a slower, less expensive, steamer. A few days later Eva and Friedrich sailed.

The doctor's parents, with his children, were on the quay at Cuxhaven when the *Auguste Victoria* came in. At first Friedrich saw nothing but the children, but he gathered them all three in his arms. Then Eva came up, and when he looked into her eyes there was no need for Friedrich to tell who and what she was to him.

Presently he bent and laid both hands on the ground. "This is Europe. This is Germany!" he exclaimed. "After this, what else matters?"

FEATHER ON A FINGER

He came to us direct from college—a slight young engineer, with black hair slicked down flat, and white transparent skin which shows pink with just, "Good morning."

It was the girls in the general office who coined his nickname. Bunny.

His ears are neither long nor pointed. His nose half promises, however, to twinkle any minute. And he has bashful eyes and nervous gestures, reminding one of little woodland creatures, scurrying to cover.

He's hard to talk to, but he seems to like his work, and does it all in neat and even tempo.

I wonder, sometimes, whether he knows about his nickname. . . . I wonder, also, whether Life will tame him, build him up, or set its hounds to snapping at his heels.

—*Eunice Pingree.*

SINCLAIR LEWIS

MAIN STREET

SINCLAIR LEWIS, born in Sauk Center, Minn., was graduated from Yale in 1907. Until 1916, he was a reporter and publishers' editor. His first novel, "Our Mr. Wren," appeared in 1914. Four other novels preceded "Main Street," which was published in 1920, becoming an immediate best seller. Other successful novels followed—"Babbitt" (1922), "Arrowsmith" (1925), "Elmer Gantry" (1927), "Dodsworth" (1929), "Ann Vickers" (1933), "It Can't Happen Here" (1935), and "Prodigal Parents" (1938). In 1928, Mr. Lewis married Dorothy Thompson, well-known newspaper columnist and commentator. At present he spends the greater part of the year on his Vermont farm.

I

IT WAS a frail and blue and lonely Carol who trotted to the flat of the Johnson Marburys for Sunday evening supper. The Marburys made a specialty of sandwich-salad-coffee lap suppers, and they regarded Carol as their literary and artistic representative.

The familiar group were trying to be conversational. But there was also a stranger, a thick tall man of thirty-six or -seven, with stolid brown hair, lips used to giving orders, eyes which followed everything good-naturedly, and clothes which you could never quite remember.

Mr. Marbury boomed, "Carol, come over here and meet Dr. Will Kennicott of Gopher Prairie." As she edged toward the stranger and murmured nothing in particular, Carol remembered that Gopher Prairie was a Minnesota wheat-prairie town of something over three thousand people.

"Pleased to meet you," stated Dr. Kennicott. "Marbury tells me you're a high mogul at the public library. I was surprised. Didn't hardly think you were old enough. How do you like your work?"

"It's pleasant, but sometimes I feel shut off from things—the steel stacks, and the everlasting cards smeared all over with red rubber stamps."

"I know but—. Of course I've spent nine years around the Twin Cities—took my B.A. and M.D. over at the U., and had my internship in a hospital in Minneapolis, but still, oh well, you don't get to know folks here, way you do up home. We've got a darn pretty town. Why, we've got seven miles of cement walks already, and building more every day!"

"Is— Do you like your profession? It seems to me that a doctor could transform a whole community, if he wanted to. He's usually the only man in the neighborhood who has any scientific training, isn't he?"

"Yes, that's so, but I guess most of us get rusty. We land in a rut of obstetrics and typhoid and busted legs. What we need is women like you to jump on us. It'd be you that would transform the town."

His kindliness and the firmness of his personality enveloped her and she accepted him as one who had a right to know what she thought and wore and ate and read. She noticed the healthy solidity of his chest. His nose, which had seemed irregular and large, was suddenly virile.

She was jarred out of this serious sweetness when Marbury bounced over to them and with horrible publicity yammered, "Say, what do you two think you're doing? Telling fortunes or making love? Let me warn you that the doc is a frisky bacheldore, Carol."

O F THE love-making of Carol and Will Kennicott there is nothing to be told which may not be heard on every summer evening, on every shadowy block. There was biology and mystery; their speech was slang phrases and flares of poetry; their silences were contentment, or shaky crises when his arm took her shoulder. All the beauty of youth, first discovered when it is passing—and all the commonplaceness of a well-to-do unmarried man encountering a pretty girl at the time when she is slightly weary of her employment and sees no glory ahead nor any man she is glad to serve.

They sat on the bank below the parapet of the old fort, hidden from observation. They were sitting six inches apart, pretending that they had never been nearer.

"You know I'm in love with you, Carol!"

She did not answer. She could not think. Her cheek near his sleeve, she studied a dozen pictures of Gopher Prairie he had brought for her to see. They were streaky; she saw only trees, shrubbery, a porch indistinct in leafy shadows. Then there was a photograph of a clumsy log cabin. In front of it a sagging woman with tight-drawn hair, and a baby, bedraggled, smeary, glorious-eyed.

"Those are the kind of folks I practise among. I operated on this woman on a kitchen table, with my driver giving the anesthetic. Look at the scared baby! Needs some woman with hands like yours. Waiting for you! Just look at that baby's eyes, look how he's begging—"

"Don't! They hurt me. Oh, it would be sweet to help him—so sweet."

As his arms moved toward her she answered all her doubts with "Sweet, so sweet."

II

U NDER the rolling clouds of prairie a moving mass of steel. An irritable clank and rattle beneath a prolonged roar. The sharp scent of oranges cutting the soggy smell of unbathed people and ancient baggage. To each of the passengers his seat was his temporary home, and most of the passengers were slatternly housekeepers. But one seat looked clean and deceptively cool. In it were an obviously prosperous man and a black-haired, fine-skinned girl whose pumps rested on an immaculate horsehide bag.

They were Dr. Will Kennicott and his bride, Carol. They had been married at the end of a year of conversational courtship, and they were on their way to Gopher Prairie after a wedding journey in the Colorado mountains.

She had begun nervously to watch for the entrance to all her future life. A mile from Gopher Prairie she could see the town as a whole. And she saw that only to the eyes of a Kennicott was it exceptional. There was no dignity in it nor any hope of greatness. Only the tall red grain-elevator and a few tinny church-steeples rose from the mass. It was a frontier camp. It was not a place to live in, not possibly, not conceivably.

Kennicott stooped to peer through the windows. He shyly exulted: "Look! Look! There's a bunch come down to welcome us! The whole crowd! I guess they see us now. Yuh, yuh sure, they see us! See 'em waving!"

She was embarrassed by the heartiness of the cheering group. She had the impression that all the men had coarse voices, large damp hands, tooth-brush mustaches, bald spots, and Masonic watch-charms.

Kennicott had told her that he occupied an old house, "but nice and roomy, and well-heated, best furnace I could find on the market." She held his hand tightly and stared ahead as the car swung round a corner and stopped in the street before a prosaic frame house in a small parched lawn.

"You'll find it old-fashioned—what do you call it?—Mid-Victorian. I left it as is, so you could make any changes you felt were necessary." Kennicott sounded doubtful for the first time since he had come back to his own.

In hallway and front parlor she was conscious of dinginess and lugubriousness and airlessless.

"How could people ever live with things like this?" she shuddered. She saw the furniture as a circle of elderly judges, condemning her to death by smothering. She was in this strange still house, among the shadows of dead thoughts and haunting repressions. "I hate it! I hate it! Stop it! They're perfectly comfortable things. Oh, they're horrible! We'll change them, right away."

SINCLAIR LEWIS, first American recipient of the Nobel award in literature, was born in 1885. His satirical novels attacking various facets of the American scene played a definite rôle in the changing of the United States of the past fifteen years. At present, Mr. Lewis is interested in the theatre as a vehicle for his ideas.

III

FROM the Gopher Prairie *Weekly Dauntless:*

> One of the most charming affairs of the season was held Tuesday evening when many of our most prominent citizens gathered to greet the lovely new bride of our popular local physician, Dr. Will Kennicott. All present spoke of the many charms of the bride, formerly Miss Carol Milford of St. Paul. Games and stunts were the order of the day, with merry talk and conversation.

At this affair she had conversed with the intellectual set of Gopher Prairie. They had looked at her in the manner of one who has just beheld a two-headed calf and repeated that he had "never *heard* such funny ideas!" They were staggered to learn that a real tangible person, living in Minnesota could apparently believe that divorce may not always be immoral; that illegitimate children do not bear any special and guaranteed form of curse; that there are ethical authorities outside of the Hebrew Bible; that men have drunk wine, yet not died in the gutter; that the capitalistic system of distribution and the Baptist wedding ceremony were not known in the Garden of Eden; that some persons of apparent intelligence and business ability do not always vote the Republican ticket straight; that some poets do not have long hair.

She knew that if she was ever to effect any of the "reforms" which she had pictured, she must have a starting-place. What confused her during the three or four months after her marriage was not lack of perception that she must be definite, but sheer careless happiness of her first home.

Like a child playing Grandma in a trailing skirt, Carol paraded uptown for her marketing, crying greetings to housewives along the way. Everybody bowed to her, strangers and all, and made her feel that they wanted her, that she belonged here. She never recalled her first

"One of the most charming affairs of the season was held when many of our most prominent citizens gathered to meet the lovely new bride . . ."

Illustration for Sinclair Lewis'
"MAIN STREET"

impression of Main Street; never had precisely the same despair at its ugliness.

But was she becoming an authentic part of the town? She reflected that she did not know whether the people liked her. She had gone to the women at afternoon-coffees, to the merchants in their stores, with so many outpouring comments and whimsies that she hadn't given them a chance to betray their opinions of her. The men smiled—but did they like her? She was lively among the women—but was she one of them? She could not recall many times when she had been admitted to the whispering of scandal which is the secret chamber of Gopher Prairie conversation.

She hazily wanted some one to whom she could say what she thought. On a slow afternoon when she fidgeted over sewing and wished that the telephone would ring, her maid announced Miss Vida Sherwin, one of the teachers at the high school.

"I've been hoping to know the teachers," said Carol. "You see, I was a librarian—"

"Oh, you needn't tell me. I know all about you! Awful how much I know—this gossipy village. We need you so much here. It's a dear loyal town, but it's a rough diamond, and we need you for the polishing, and we're so humble—"

"If I could *help* you in any way—Would I be committing the unpardonable sin if I whispered that I think Gopher Prairie is a tiny bit ugly?"

"Of course it's ugly. Dreadfully! Though I'm probably the only person in town to whom you could safely say that. Except perhaps Guy Pollock, the lawyer—he's simply a darling—intelligence and culture. Have you met him? Oh, you must."

Ensued a fifteen-minute argument about the oldest topic in the world: It's

art, but is it pretty? At the end Carol cried: "I don't care how much we disagree. It's a relief to have somebody talk something besides crops."

When Kennicott came home at five, Carol suggested that Miss Sherwin stay for supper and that Kennicott invite Guy Pollock, the much-praised lawyer.

Carol regretted her impulse. The man would be an opinionated politician, heavily jocular about The Bride. But Guy Pollock offered no humorous remarks and did not ask her if she didn't think Gopher Prairie was "the livest little burg in the state." At supper he hinted his love for Thoreau, Agnes Repplier and Charles Flandrau. Carol wondered why Guy Pollock went on digging at routine law-cases; why he remained in Gopher Prairie. She enjoyed the faint mystery. She felt triumphant and rather literary. She already had a Group. It would be only a while now before she provided the town with fanlights and a knowledge of Galsworthy. She was doing things!

IV

Four days later Vida Sherwin called and casually blew Carol's world to pieces. "May I come in and gossip a while?" she said. "I wonder if you understand that in a secluded community like this every newcomer is on test? People cordial to her but watching her all the time. Of course they have discussed you—"

Carol was working up a small passion of distaste. "It makes me crawly to think of their daring to talk over all I do and say. I resent it. I hate—"

"Will you be impersonal? I'm paying you the compliment that you can be. I want you to be big enough to help me make this town worth while."

"I'll be as impersonal as cold boiled potatoes. What do they say about me? Really. I want to know."

"Of course the illiterate ones resent

your references to anything farther away than Minneapolis. And some think you dress too well. They're suspicious—that's it, suspicious. Every housewife in town is doubtful about your being so chummy with your maid. All right to be kind, but they say you act as though she were your cousin. And I guess I've heard a dozen criticize you because you don't go to church oftener. And I guess some of them feel you are showing off—pretending that your husband is richer than he is."

"Who dared say that? Can't they at least understand me well enough to see that though I might be affected and cul-turine, at least I simply can't commit that other kind of vulgarity." She was huddled on the couch. Shrouded in shame, Carol didn't know when Vida slipped away.

She had tripped into the meadow to teach the lambs a pretty educational dance and found that the lambs were wolves. There was no way out between their pressing gray shoulders. She was surrounded by fangs and sneering eyes. She could not go on enduring their hidden derision. She wanted to flee. She wanted to hide in the generous indif-ference of cities.

Reform the town? All she wanted was to be tolerated!

V

VIDA SHERWIN ran in after school a dozen times after that. But Carol could not yet take her in. She resented this outsider's knowledge of her shame. This morass was not her home, she in-sisted. Her home, and her beautiful town, existed in her mind. They had already been created. What she really had been questing was some one to share them with her. Vida would not; Kennicott could not.

Suddenly she was thinking of Guy Pollock.

She tried to call on one of her hus-band's patients one evening when Ken-nicott was away. They were not at home. Like a child who has no one to play with she loitered through the dark hall. She saw a light under an office door. She knocked. Guy Pollock opened it.

"Why—" she observed, as she reflected that in Gopher Prairie it is not decent to call on a man; as she decided that no, really, she wouldn't go in; and as she went in.

"I didn't know your office was up here."

They made conversation for a little while. Suddenly Carol blurted: "Tell me, Mr. Pollock, what is the matter with Gopher Prairie?"

"Gopher Prairie isn't particularly bad," he replied. "It's like all villages in all countries. Most places that have lost the smell of earth but not yet ac-quired the smell of factory-smoke are just as suspicious and righteous."

She asked impulsively, "You, why do you stay here?"

"I have the Village Virus."

"It sounds dangerous."

"It is. It infects ambitious people who stay too long in the provinces. You'll find it epidemic among lawyers and doctors and ministers—all those people who have had a glimpse of the world that thinks and laughs, but have re-turned to their swamp. I'm a perfect example. When I found that the Village Virus had me, absolute, I didn't want to face new streets and younger men—real competition. It was too easy to go on making out conveyances and arguing ditching cases."

"I know. The Village Virus. Perhaps it will get me. Some day I'm going— oh, no matter. Now I'm sitting at your feet," said Carol.

"THERE's one thing that's the matter with Gopher Prairie, at least with the ruling-class," said Pollock. "The pen-alty we tribal rulers pay is that our subjects watch us every minute. We can't get wholesomely drunk and relax. We have to be so correct about sex morals, and inconspicuous clothes, and doing our commercial trickery only in the traditional ways, that none of us can live up to it, and we become horribly hypocritical."

"Guy! Can't we do something with the town? Really?"

"If I were a sea-gull, and all over silver, think I'd care what a pack of dirty seals thought about my flying?" said Pollock. "Don't be like me—a living dead thing."

With the loneliness of one who has put away a possible love Carol saw that he was a stranger. She saw that he was nothing but a frame on which she had hung shining garments. There was nothing for her to do but go home.

She was marching home. "A Gopher Prairie housewife, married a year, and yearning for a Prince Charming like a *bachfisch* of sixteen! I wouldn't want to fall in love, even if the Prince did come. I wouldn't want to hurt Will. I am fond of Will. I am! He doesn't stir me, not any longer anyway. But I depend on him."

She could—at times—agree with Kennicott that the shaving-and-corsets familiarity of married life was not dreary vulgarity but a wholesome frankness; that artificial reticences might merely be irritating. But she would not listen to his theory that "all this romance stuff is simply moonshine—elegant when you're courting, but no use busting yourself keeping it up all your life."

She realized that she did not definitely look at her husband any more. When he violently chased fragments of fish about his plate with a knife and licked the knife after gobbling them, she was slightly sick. She realized that they found little to say; that, incredibly, they were like the talked-out couples whom she had pitied at restaurants.

VI

THE baby was coming. Each morning she was nauseated, chilly, bedraggled, and certain that she would never again be attractive; each twilight she was afraid. Every matron hinted, "Now that you're going to be a mother, dearie, you'll get over all these ideas of yours and settle down." She felt that willy-nilly she was being initiated into the assembly of housekeepers; with the baby for hostage, she would never escape.

Then the baby was born, without unusual difficulty; a boy with straight back and strong legs. She marveled at the perfection of the miniature hands as noisily as did Kennicott; she was overwhelmed by the trust with which the baby turned to her; passion for him grew with each unpoetic irritating thing she had to do for him. He was named Hugh, for her father.

For two years Carol was a part of the town. Her opinionation seemed dead; she had no apparent desire for escape; her brooding centered in Hugh. She became a part of the town. Its philosophy and its feuds dominated her.

Carol sat on a gritty couch and sank into fear. Could this drabness of life keep up forever? Would she some day so despise herself and her neighbors that she would walk Main Street, an old skinny eccentric woman in a mangy cat's-fur?

SHE was at Sunday morning service at the Baptist Church in a solemn row with her husband and a visiting aunt who had nagged them into going. Across the aisle, two rows back, was a strange young man who shone among the cud-chewing citizens like a visitant from the sun. He suggested an ocean beach, a tennis court, anything but the sun-blistered utility of Main Street.

How could she meet him? She must. She pictured, and ridiculed, herself as walking up to him and remarking, "I am sick with the Village Virus. Will you please tell me what people are saying and playing in New York?"

When she found out who he was, Carol was exceeding sick. This person whom she had pictured in white flannels on a tennis court was Erik Valborg, apprentice tailor! Mending dirty jackets! Respectfully holding a tape-measure about a paunch!

And yet, she insisted, this boy was also himself.

She walked up the railroad track with Hugh, this Sunday afternoon. She saw Erik Valborg coming, tramping sullenly and alone, striking at the rails with a stick. They greeted each other with "Hello."

They sat on a heap of discarded railroad ties. Erik talked of books; flamed like a recent convert to any faith. She was dizzy. He looked at her reverently. She could hear him saying "I've always wanted to know a woman whom I could talk to like this."

But he was really saying, "I'm staying here for a year. Then I'll go East to art-school. I'll learn what I'm good for: designing clothes, stage-settings, illustrating, or selling collars to fat men."

"Can you stand it here in town for a year?"

"With you to look at."

"Please," said Carol helplessly and then to herself, "The Village Virus—the village virtuousness. My hair—just scrambled together. What can Erik see in me—a wedded spinster. He does like me! Because I'm the only woman who's decent to him. How long before he'll wake up to me?"

She assured herself that she wasn't in love with him but merely "fond of him and interested in his success." Yet in him she had discovered both her need of youth and the fact that youth would welcome her. It was not Erik to whom she must escape, but universal and joyous youth, in class-rooms, in offices, in

meetings to protest against Things in General. . . . But universal and joyous youth rather resembled Erik.

Their night came unheralded. Kennicott was on a country call. It was cool, but Carol was huddled on the porch, rocking, meditating, rocking. Suddenly Erik was coming, turning in, swinging open the screen door, touching her hand. "Saw your husband driving out of town. Couldn't stand it."

She did not look at him but she could divine his tremulousness as they stumbled indoors. Her eyes were closed. Her thoughts were formless but many-colored. She felt his kiss, diffident and reverent.

Then she knew that it was impossible . . .

VII

FOR a month which was one suspended moment of doubt she saw Erik only casually. Each morning, each afternoon, each evening was a compartment divided from all other units of time, distinguished by a sudden "Oh! I want to see Erik!" which was as devastating as though she had never said it before.

One afternoon Kennicott sauntered into the living room. His manner of closing the door was in the nature of a command. He looked like a physician about to give sound and undesired advice.

Before he could launch into his heavy discourse she desperately got in, "Please! I want you to know that I was going to tell you everything, tonight."

He leaned forward, thick capable hands on thick sturdy thighs, mature and slow, yet beseeching: "Do you realize what my job is? I go round twenty-four hours a day, in mud and blizzard, trying my damnedest to heal everybody, rich or poor. And I can stand the cold and the bumpy roads and the lonely rides at night. All I need is to have you here at home to welcome me. I don't expect you to be passionate—not any more—I don't—but I do expect you to appreciate my work. I bring babies into the world, and save lives, and make cranky husbands quit being mean to their wives. And then you go and moon over a Swede tailor because he can talk about how to put ruchings on a skirt!"

Kennicott rose quickly, sat on the couch, took both her hands. "Suppose he fails—as he will! Suppose he goes back to tailoring, and you're his wife. Is that going to be this artistic life you've been thinking about? Yes, and you'll have a squalling brat every year, tugging at you while you press clothes, and you won't love 'em like you do Hugh upstairs, all downy and asleep—"

"Please! Not any more!" Her face was on his knee. She snatched up his hand, she kissed it. "This marriage, it weaves people together. It's not easy to break, even when it ought to be broken."

"And do you want to break it?"

"No!"

That evening Kennicott gave her, without comment, an envelope. The letter was signed "E.V."

> I know I can't do anything but make trouble for you. I am going away. I will do as big things as I can. I can't write—I love you too much. God keep you.

SHE tried to be content, which was a contradiction in terms. She fanatically cleaned house all April. She knitted a sweater for Hugh. She was diligent at Red Cross work.

One day Kennicott asked forlornly, "Uh—Carrie, what the devil is the matter with you? What do you want?"

"I don't belong to Gopher Prairie," she railed. "That isn't meant as a condemnation of Gopher Prairie, and it may be a condemnation of me. All right! I don't care! I don't belong here, and I'm going. I'm not asking permission any more. I'm simply going."

He grunted. "Do you mind telling me, if it isn't too much trouble, how long you're going for?"

"I don't know. Perhaps for a year. Perhaps for a lifetime."

"Of course a little thing like Hugh makes no difference!"

"Yes, all the difference. That's why I'm going to take him with me."

"Suppose I refuse?"

"You won't!"

VIII

SHE set out for Washington in October—just before the war ended—and found employment in the Bureau of War Risk Insurance. Washington gave her all the graciousness in which she had had faith: white columns seen across leafy parks, spacious avenues. With a congressman's secretary and a teacher Carol leased a small flat. Here she found home, her own place and her own people. She was encouraged to believe that she had not been abnormal in viewing Gopher Prairie as unduly tedious and slatternly.

The chart which plots Carol's progress is not easy to read, but a few lines are traceable.

The thing she gained by living in Washington was not information about office-systems and labor unions but renewed courage, that amiable contempt called poise. Her glimpse of tasks involving millions of people reduced Main Street from bloated importance to its actual pettiness. She could never again be quite so awed by the power with which she herself had endowed its prominent citizens.

From her work and from her association with women who had organized suffrage associations in hostile cities, or had defended political prisoners, she caught something of an impersonal attitude; saw that she had been as touchily personal as Gopher Prairie's most confirmed gossips.

And why, she began to ask, did she rage at individuals? Not individuals but institutions are the enemies, and they most afflict the disciples who the most generously serve them. They insinuate their tyranny under a hundred guises and pompous names, such as Polite Society, the Family, the Church, Sound Business, the Party, the Superior White Race; and the only defense against them, Carol beheld, is unembittered laughter.

She realized that she had come East not to conquer it, but to conquer herself—and she was doing it.

Though she should return, she said, she would not be utterly defeated. She was glad of her rebellion. The prairie was no longer empty land in the sun-glare; it was the living tawny beast which she had fought and made beautiful by fighting; and in the village streets were shadows of her desires and the sound of her marching.

The Chimney Sweeper

When my mother died I was very young,
And my father sold me while yet my tongue
Could scarcely cry, " 'Weep! 'weep! 'weep! 'weep!"
So your chimneys I sweep, and in soot I sleep.

There's little Tom Dacre, who cried when his head,
That curled like a lamb's back, was shaved: so I said
"Hush, Tom! never mind it, for, when your head's bare
You know that the soot cannot spoil your white hair."

And so he was quiet, and that very night,
As Tom was a-sleeping, he had such a sight!—
That thousands of sweepers, Dick, Joe, Ned and Jack,
Were all of them locked up in coffins of black.

And by came an Angel, who had a bright key,
And he opened the coffins and set them all free;
Then down a green plain leaping, laughing, they run,
And wash in a river, and shine in the sun.

Then naked and white, all their bags left behind,
They rise upon clouds and sport in the wind;
And the Angel told Tom, if he'd be a good boy,
He'd have God for his father, and never want joy.

And so Tom awoke; and we rose in the dark,
And got with our bags and our brushes to work.
Though the morning was cold, Tom was happy and warm;
So if all do their duty, they need not fear harm.

—*William Blake* (1757-1827).

Alexis Carrel

MAN THE UNKNOWN

"MAN THE UNKNOWN" will be eagerly read if only for the reason that it is written by Alexis Carrel. For with his initial successes in suturing blood vessels, in transplanting organs and treating infected wounds, he has made some of the greatest contributions to modern surgery in its fight to save human life. With Colonel Charles A. Lindbergh, he kept various human organs, severed from the body, alive for several days. But unlike most specialists, his painstaking work in the laboratories of the Rockefeller Institute of Medical Research has not caused him to lose sight of Man as a whole—his mind, body and soul. It is in this book that he fuses his vast scientific knowledge with his wide human experience to show how men can have happier and more useful lives and so build up a crumbling civilization.

Scientific Slip-Up

THERE is a strange disparity between the sciences of inert matter and those of life. In learning the secret of the constitution and of the properties of matter, we have gained the mastery of almost everything which exists on the surface of the earth, excepting ourselves.

Man, as known to the specialists, is far from being the concrete man, the real man. He is, at the same time, the corpse dissected by the anatomists, the consciousness observed by the psychologists and the great teachers of the spiritual life, and the personality which introspection shows to everyone as lying in the depth of himself. He is the amazing community of cells and nutrient fluids whose organized laws are studied by the physiologists. He is the compound of tissues and consciousness that hygienists and educators endeavor to lead to its optimum development while it extends into time.

He is the *homo economicus* who must ceaselessly consume manufactured products in order that the machines, of which he is made a slave, may be kept at work. But he is also the poet, the hero, and the saint. He is not only the prodigiously complex being analyzed by our scientific techniques, but also the tendencies, the conjectures, the aspirations of humanity. Our conceptions of him are imbued with metaphysics. They are founded on so much and such imprecise data that the temptation is great to choose among them those which please us. Therefore, our idea of man varies according to our feelings and beliefs.

Although we possess the treasury of the observations accumulated by the scientists, the philosphers, the poets, and the great mystics of all times, we have grasped only certain aspects of ourselves. We do not apprehend man as a whole. We know him as composed of distinct parts. And even these parts are created by our methods. Each one of us is made up of a procession of phantoms, in the midst of which strides an unknowable reality.

The slow progress of the knowledge of the human being, as compared with the splendid ascension of physics, astronomy, chemistry, and mechanics, is due to our ancestors' lack of leisure, to the complexity of the subject, and to the structure of our mind. Those obstacles are fundamental.

The knowledge of ourselves will never attain the elegant simplicity, the abstractness, and the beauty of physics. The factors that have retarded its development are not likely to vanish. We must realize clearly that the science of man is the most difficult of all sciences, and will probably remain so.

SCIENCE develops at random. Its progress depends on fortuitous conditions, such as the birth of men of genius, the form of their mind, the direction taken by their curiosity. It is not at all actuated by a desire to improve the state of human beings. The discoveries responsible for industrial civilization were brought forth at the fancy of the scientists' intuitions and of the more or less casual circumstances of their careers. If Galileo, Newton, or Lavoisier had applied their intellectual powers to the study of body and consciousness, our world probably would be different today.

In general, discoveries are developed without any prevision of their consequences. These consequences, however, have revolutionized the world and made our civilization what it is.

What is the good of increasing the comfort, the luxury, the beauty, the size and the complications of our civilization, if our weakness prevents us from guiding it to our best advantage? It is really not worth while to go on elaborating a way of living that is bringing about the demoralization and the disappearance of the noblest elements of the great race. Is it necessary to increase production unceasingly, so that men may consume larger and larger quantities of useless things? There is not the shadow of a doubt that mechanical, physical, and chemical sciences are incapable of giving us intelligence, moral discipline, health, nervous equilibrium, security, and peace.

Our curiosity must turn aside from its present path, and take another direction. It must leave the physical and physiological in order to follow the mental and the spiritual. So far sciences, concerning themselves with human beings, have confined their activities to certain aspects of their subject. In physiology, hygiene and medicine, as well as in the study of education and of political and social economy, scientists have been chiefly absorbed by the organic, humoral, and intellectual aspects of man. They have not paid any great attention to his affective and moral form, his inner life, his character, his esthetic and religious needs, the common substratum of organic and psychological activities, the intimate relations of the individual and of his mental and spiritual environment.

A radical change is indispensable. This change requires both the work of specialists devoting their efforts to the particular knowledge related to our body and our mind, and of scientists capable of integrating the discoveries of the specialists in the function of man as a whole. The new science must progress, by a double effort of analysis and synthesis, toward a conception of the human individual at once sufficiently complete and sufficiently simple to serve as a basis for our action.

The Crumbling Basis of Civilization

IT is convenient to divide man's mental activities into intellectual, moral, esthetic, and religious, although such classification is nothing but an artifact. Intellectual activity is, at the same time, distinct and indistinct from the flowing mass of our other states of consciousness.

To study this aspect of ourselves, we separate it artificially from an indivisible wholeness. In reality, the man who thinks, observes, and reasons, is, at the same time, happy or unhappy, disturbed or serene, stimulated or depressed by his appetites and aversions.

Everyone knows that love, hate, anger, and fear are capable of bringing confusion even to logic. In order to manifest themselves, these states of consciousness require certain modifications of the chemical exchanges. The more intense the emotional disturbances, the more active become these exchanges. They give to each human being his temperament. Temperament changes from one individual to the other, from one race to the other. It is a mixture of mental, physiological, and structural characteristics. It is man himself.

What factors bring about the weakening of temperament in certain social groups and in certain nations? It seems that the violence of the emotional moods diminishes when wealth increases, when education is generalized, when diet becomes more elaborate. The forms of life, of education, or of food brought by modern civilization perhaps tend to give us the qualities of cattle, or to develop our emotional impulses inharmoniously.

ALEXIS CARREL
Courtesy Harper & Bros.

MORAL activity is equivalent to the aptitude possessed by man to impose upon himself a rule of conduct, to choose between several possible acts those which he considers to be good, to get rid of his own selfishness and maliciousness. It creates in him the feeling of obligation, of duty. This peculiar sense is observed only in a small number of individuals. In most of them it remains virtual. But the fact of its existence cannot be denied. In the course of the history of mankind its importance has been demonstrated to be fundamental. It is related both to intelligence and to esthetic and religious senses. In highly civilized beings, will and intelligence are one and the same function. From will and intelligence come all moral values.

Moral sense, like intellectual activity, apparently depends on certain structural and functional states of the body. These states result from the immanent constitution of our tissues and our minds, and also from factors which have acted upon us during our development. In other terms, human beings possess innate tendencies. Each one, in a certain measure, is born good, mediocre, or bad. But, like intelligence, moral sense can be developed by education, discipline, and will power.

In order to keep his mental and organic balance, man must impose upon himself an inner rule. The state can thrust legality upon people by force. But not morality.

Intelligence, will power, and morality are very closely related. But moral sense is more important than intelligence. When it disappears from a nation the whole social structure crumbles.

Moral sense must be studied in as positive a manner as intelligence. Such a study is certainly difficult. But without any doubt, moral activities are located within the domain of scientific observation.

In modern civilization individuals whose conduct is inspired by a moral ideal are very seldom encountered. However, such individuals still exist. We cannot help noticing their aspect when we meet them. This form of beauty is far more impressive than the beauty of nature and of science. It gives to those who possess its divine gifts, a strange, an inexplicable power. It increases the strength of intellect. It establishes peace among men. Much more than science, art, and religious rites, moral beauty is the basis of civilization.

Neglected Human Essentials

IN MODERN men, we seldom observe the manifestations of mystical activity, or religious sense. The tendency to mysticity, even in its most rudimentary form, is exceptional. Much more exceptional than moral sense. Nevertheless, it remains one of the essential human activities.

Religious activity assumes various aspects, as does moral activity. In its more elementary state it consists of a vague aspiration toward a power transcending the material and mental forms of our world, a kind of unformulated prayer, a quest for more absolute beauty than that of the art of science.

The beauty pursued by the mystic is still richer and more indefinable than the ideal of an artist. It has no form. It cannot be expressed in any language. It hides within the things of the visible world. It manifests itself rarely. It requires an elevation of the mind toward a being who is the source of all things, toward a power, a center of forces, whom the mystic calls God.

Nobody should ask whether mystical experience is true or false, whether it is autosuggestion, hallucination, or a journey of the soul beyond the dimensions of our world and its union with a high reality. One must be content with having an operational concept of such an experience. Mysticism is splendidly generous. It brings to man the fulfillment of his highest desires. Inner strength, spiritual light, divine love, ineffable peace. Religious intuition is as real as esthetic inspiration. Through the contemplation of superhuman beauty, mystics and poets may reach the ultimate truth.

HIGH culture is not necessary to fertilize moral, esthetic and religious senses and to bring forth artists, poets, and mystics, and all those who disinterestedly contemplate the various aspects of beauty. These activities are almost sufficient within themselves. They do not require association with great intelligence to supply man with an aptitude for happiness. They seem to strengthen organic functions. Their development must be the supreme goal of education, because they give equilibrium to the individual. They make him a solid building stone of the social edifice. To those who constitute the multitudes of industrial civilization, moral sense is far more necessary than intelligence.

The distribution of mental activities varies greatly in the different social groups. Most civilized men manifest only an elementary form of consciousness. They are capable of the easy work which, in modern society, insures the survival of the individual. They produce, they consume, they satisfy their psychological appetites. They also take pleasure in watching athletic spectacles in great crowds, in seeing childish and vulgar moving pictures, in being rapidly transported without effort, or in looking at swiftly moving objects. They are soft, sentimental, lascivious, and violent. They have no moral, esthetic, or religious sense.

Despite the immense sums spent on education, we have failed to develop completely the students' intellectual and moral activities. Even in the élite of the population, consciousness often lacks harmony and strength. The elementary functions are dispersed, of poor quality, and of low intensity.

The happiest and most useful men consist of a well integrated whole of intellectual, moral, and organic activities. The quality of these activities, and their equilibrium, gives to such a type its superiority over the others. Their intensity determines the social level of a given individual. The degree of this intensity makes of him a tradesman or a bank president, a little physician or a celebrated professor, a village mayor or a president of the United States. The development of complete human beings must be the aim of our efforts.

Matter Over Mind and Vice Versa

EVERYONE knows how human personality is modified by diseases of the liver, the stomach, and the intestines. Obviously the cells of the organs discharge into the bodily fluids certain substances that react upon our mental and spiritual functions.

In general, great poets, artists, and saints, as well as conquerors, are strongly sexed. The removal of the genital glands, even in adult individuals, produces some modifications of the mental state. After extirpation of the ovaries, women become apathetic and lose part of their intellectual activity or moral sense. The personality of men who have undergone castration is altered in a more or less marked way. It is well known that sexual excesses impede intellectual activity.

In order to reach its full power, intelligence seems to require both the presence of well-developed sexual glands and the temporary repression of the sexual appetite. Freud has rightly emphasized the capital importance of sexual impulses in the activities of consciousness. However, his observations refer chiefly to sick people. His conclusions should not be generalized to include normal individuals, especially those who are endowed with strong nervous systems and mastery over themselves. While the weak, the nervous, and the unbalanced become more abnormal when their sexual appetites are repressed, the strong are rendered still stronger by practicing such a form of asceticism.

The interdependence of mental activities and physiological functions does not agree with the classical conception that places the soul exclusively in the brain. In fact, the entire body appears to be the substratum of mental and spiritual energies. Thought is the offspring of the endocrine glands as well as of the cerebral cortex. The integrity of the organism is indispensable. Man thinks, invents, loves, suffers, admires, and prays with his brain and all his organs.

EACH state of consciousness probably has a corresponding organic expression. Emotions, as is well known, determine the dilatation or the contraction of the small arteries, through the vasomotor nerves. They are, therefore, accompanied by changes in the circulation of the blood in tissues and organs. Pleasure causes the skin of the face to flush. Anger and fear turn it white. In certain individuals, bad news may bring about a spasm of the coronary arteries, anemia of the heart, and sudden death. The affective states act on all the glands by increasing or decreasing their circulation. They stimulate or stop the secretions, or modify their chemical constitution.

Thus, envy, hate, fear, when these sentiments are habitual, are capable of starting organic changes and genuine diseases. Moral suffering profoundly disturbs health.

The instability of modern life, the ceaseless agitation, and the lack of security, create states of consciousness which bring about nervous and organic disorders of the stomach and of the intestines, defective nutrition, and passage of intestinal microbes into the circulatory apparatus. Colitis and the accompanying infections of the kidneys and of the bladder are the remote results of mental and moral unbalance.

Such diseases are almost unknown in social groups where life is simpler and not so agitated, where anxiety is less constant. In a like manner, those who keep the peace of their inner self in the midst of the tumult of the modern city are immune to nervous and organic disorders.

The unification of the desires, the application of the mind to a single purpose, produces a sort of inner peace. Man integrates himself by meditation, just as by action. But he should not be content with contemplating the beauty of nature, the masterpieces of the artists and the poets, the majestic constructions of philosophical thought, the mathematical formulas which express natural laws. He must also be the soul which strives to attain a moral idea, searches for light in the darkness of the world, marches forward along the mystic way, and renounces itself in order to apprehend the invisible substratum of the universe.

Miracles Can Happen

CERTAIN spiritual activities may cause anatomical as well as functional modifications of the tissues and the organs. These organic phenomena are observed in various circumstances, among them being the state of prayer.

The prayer which is followed by organic effects is of a special nature. First, it is entirely disinterested. Man offers himself to God. He stands before Him like the canvas before the painter or the marble before the sculptor. At the same time, he asks for His grace, exposes his needs and those of his brothers in suffering. Generally, the patient who is cured is not praying for himself, but for another. Such a type of prayer demands complete renunciation—that is—a higher form of asceticism. The modest, the ignorant, and the poor are more capable of this self-denial than the rich and the intellectual. When it possesses such characteristic, prayer may set in motion a strange phenomenon, the miracle.

In all countries, at all times, people have believed in the existence of miracles, in the more or less rapid healing of the sick at places of pilgrimage. But after the great impetus of science during the nineteenth century, such beliefs completely disappeared. It was generally admitted, not only that miracles did not exist, but that they could not exist. Such is still the attitude of most physiologists and physicians.

However, in view of the facts observed during the last fifty years this attitude cannot be sustained. The most important cases of miraculous healing have been recorded by the Medical Bureau of Lourdes. Our present conception of the influence of prayer upon pathological lesions is based upon the observation of patients who have been cured almost instantaneously of various affections, such as peritoneal tuberculosis, cold abscesses, suppurating wounds, lupus, cancer, etc.

The process of healing changes little from one individual to another. Often, an acute pain. Then a sudden sensation of being cured. In a few seconds, a few minutes, at the most a few hours, wounds are cicatrized, pathological symptoms disappear, appetite returns. Sometimes functional disorders vanish before the anatomical lesions are repaired.

The only condition indispensable to the occurrence of the phenomenon is prayer. But there is no need for the patient himself to pray, or even to have any religious faith. It is sufficient that some one around him be in a state of prayer. Such facts are of profound significance. They show the reality of certain relations, of a still unknown nature, between psychological and organic processes. They prove the objective importance of the spiritual activities, which hygienists, physicians, educators, and sociologists have almost always neglected to study. They open a new world.

Mind—the Weakest Link

THE mind is not as robust as the body. It is remarkable that mental diseases by themselves are more numerous than all the other diseases put together. Hospitals for the insane are full to overflowing, and unable to receive all those who should be restrained.

In the whole of the United States, the hospitals care for almost eight times more feeble-minded or lunatics than consumptives. Each year, about sixty-eight thousand new cases are admitted to insane asylums and similar institutions. If the admissions continue at such a rate, about one million of the children and young people attending schools and colleges will be confined in asylums.

These figures show how great is the fragility of the consciousness of civilized men, and how important for modern society is the problem of mental health. The diseases of the mind are more dangerous than tuberculosis, cancer, heart and kidney diseases, and even typhus, plague, and cholera. They are to be feared, not only because they increase the number of criminals, but chiefly because they weaken the white races.

Physicians are utterly incapable of protecting consciousness against its unknown enemies. The symptoms of mental diseases and the different types of feeble-mindedness have been well classified. But we are completely ignorant of the nature of these disorders. We have not ascertained whether they are due to structural lesions of the brain or to changes in the composition of blood plasma, or to both these causes.

The extreme complexity of the subject is the main cause of ignorance. There are no techniques permitting the exploration of the unknown world of the nervous cells, of their association and projecting fibers, and of the cerebral and mental processes.

THE discovery of the causes of mental diseases would be more important than that of their nature. Such knowledge could lead to the prevention of these maladies. Feeble-mindedness and insanity are perhaps the price of industrial civilization, and of the resulting changes in our ways of life. However, these affections are often part of the inheritance received from his parents by each individual. They manifest themselves among people whose nervous system is already unbalanced.

Dementia praecox and circular insanity manifest themselves more especially in the social groups where life is restless and disordered, food too elaborate or too poor, and syphilis frequent. And also when the nervous system is hereditarily unstable, when moral discipline has been suppressed, when selfishness, irresponsibility, and dispersion are customary.

There are probably some relations between these factors and the genesis of psychoses. The modern habits of living hide a fundamental defect. In the environment created by technology, our most specific functions develop incompletely. Despite the marvels of scientific civilization, human personality tends to dissolve.

The Fountain of Youth

THE failure of hygiene and medicine is a strange fact. In spite of the progress achieved in the heating, ventilation, and lighting of houses, of dietary hygiene, bathrooms, and sports, of periodical medical examinations, and increasing numbers of medical specialists, not even one day has been added to the span of human life. Are we to believe that hygienists, chemists, and physicians are mistaken in their ruling of the existence of the individual, like politicians, economists, and financiers, in the organization of the life of the nation? The causes of this failure of modern life are not exactly known. Indeed, hygienists and physicians cannot be held responsible for it. The premature wear-

ing out of modern men is probably due to worries, lack of economic security, overwork, absence of moral discipline, and excesses of all sorts.

A better knowledge of the mechanisms of physiological duration could bring a solution of the problem of longevity. But the science of man is still too rudimentary to be useful. We must, then, ascertain, in a purely empirical manner, whether life can be made longer. The presence of a few centenarians in every country demonstrates the extent of our temporal potentialities.

No practical conclusions, however, have resulted so far from the observation of these centenarians. Obviously, longevity is hereditary. But it depends also on the conditions of development. When descendants of families where longevity is usual come to dwell in large cities, they generally lose, in one or two generations, the capacity of living to be old.

But longevity is only desirable if it increases the duration of youth, and not that of old age. The lengthening of the senescent period would be a calamity. The aging individual, when not capable of providing for himself, is an encumbrance to his family and to the community.

If an old man were given the glands of a still-born infant and the blood of a young man, he would possibly be rejuvenated. For true age depends on progressive changes of the tissues and humors. Many technical difficulties remain to be overcome before such an operation can be undertaken. We have no way of selecting organs suitable to a given individual. But the progress of science is swift. With the aid of the methods already existing, and of those which will be discovered, we must pursue the search for the great secret.

Man will never tire of seeking immorality. He will not attain it, because he is bound by certain laws of his organic constitution. He may succeed in retarding, perhaps even in reversing in some measure, the inexorable advance of physiological time. Never will he vanquish death. Death is the price he has to pay for his brain and his personality. But some day, medicine will teach him that old age, free from diseases of the body and the soul, is not to be feared. To illness, and not to senescence, are due most of our woes.

The Cause of Most of Our Woe

ALL organic functions are modified, as soon as microbes or viruses cross the frontiers of the body and invade the tissues. Illness sets in. Its characteristics depend on the mode of adjustment of the tissues to the pathological changes of their medium. For instance, fever is the reply of the body to the presence of bacteria and viruses.

Other adaptive reactions are determined by the production of poisons by the organism itself, the lack of certain substances indispensable to nutrition, and the disturbances in the activities of various glands. The symptoms of Bright's disease, of scurvy, of exophthalmic goiter, express the accommodation of the organism to substances which diseased kidneys are no longer able to eliminate, to the absence of a vitamine, to the secretion of toxic products by the thyroid gland.

The accommodation to pathogenic agents assumes two different aspects. On one side, it opposes their invasion of the body and tends to bring about their destruction. On the other, it repairs the lesions the organism has suffered, and causes the poisons generated by the bacteria or by the tissues themselves to disappear.

Disease is nothing but the development of these processes. It is equivalent to the struggle of the body against a disturbing agent and to its effort to persist in time. But it may be, as in cancer or insanity, the expression of the passive decay of an organ, or of consciousness.

Certain families are observed to be susceptible to tuberculosis, appendicitis, cancer, or mental disorders. Others resist all diseases except the degenerative ones occurring during old age. But natural immunity does not exclusively derive from our ancestral constitution. It may come also from the mode of life and alimentation, as Reid Hunt showed long ago. Some diets were found to increase the susceptibility of mice to experimental typhoid fever. The frequency of pneumonia may also be modified by food.

WE SHOULD ascertain whether natural resistance to infections could be conferred on man by definite conditions of life. Injections of specific vaccine or serum for each disease, repeated medical examinations of the whole population, construction of gigantic hospitals, are expensive and not very effective means of preventing diseases and of developing a nation's health. Good health should be natural. Such innate resistance gives the individual a strength, a boldness, which he does not possess when his survival depends on physicians.

Either alone or with the aid of specific serums of non-specific chemical and physical medications, the patient fights against the invading microbes. But there are pathogenic agents against which the tissues do not react, which do not elicit any response from the adaptive mechanisms. Such is, for instance, the agent of syphilis. Once it has penetrated the body, it never spontaneously leaves its victim. It takes up its abode in the skin, the blood vessels, the brain, or the bones. Neither the cells nor the humors are able to destroy it. Syphilis yields only to prolonged treatment.

Likewise, cancer meets with no opposition from the organism. Tumors, whether benign or malignant, are so much like normal tissues that the body is not aware of their presence. They often develop in individuals who for a long time show no evidence of being affected. The symptoms, when they appear, are not the expression of a reaction of the organism. They are the direct result of the misdoings of the tumor, of its toxic products, of the destruction of an essential organ, or of the compression of a nerve. The progress of cancer is inexorable, because tissues and humors do not react against the invasion of the diseased cells.

In the course of an illness, the body meets with situations never previously encountered. It tends, nevertheless, to adapt itself to these new conditions by eliminating the pathogenic agents and repairing the lesions they have caused. In the absence of such adaptive power, living beings could not endure, because they are ceaselessly exposed to the attacks of viruses or bacteria, and to the structural failure of innumerable elements of the organic systems.

An individual's survival was formerly wholly due to his adaptive capacity. Modern civilization, with the help of hygiene, comfort, good food, soft living, hospitals, physicians, and nurses, has kept alive many human beings of poor quality. These weaklings and their descendants contribute, in a large measure, to the enfeeblement of the white races. We should perhaps renounce this artificial form of health and exclusively pursue natural health, which results from the excellence of the adaptive functions and from the inherent resistance to disease.

How Man Attains His Highest Development

THE exercise of the adaptive functions appears to be indispensable to the optimum development of man. Are we not organized to live under changing and irregular conditions?

Man attains his highest development when he is exposed to the rigors of the seasons, when he sometimes goes without sleep and sometimes sleeps for long hours, when his meals are sometimes abundant and sometimes scanty, when he conquers food and shelter at the price of strenuous efforts. He has also to train his muscles, to tire himself and rest, to fight, suffer, and be happy, to love and to hate. He needs alternately to strain and to relax. He must strive against his fellow men or against himself.

He is made for such an existence, just as the stomach is made for digesting food. When his adaptive processes work most intensely, he develops his virility to the fullest extent. It is a primary datum of observation that hardships make nervous resistance and health. We know how strong physically and morally are those who, since childhood, have been submitted to intelligent discipline, who have endured some privations and adapted themselves to adverse conditions. The effect of the deficiencies of adaptation upon the development of man is not as yet completely known. In the large cities, there are many individuals whose adaptive activities are permanently at rest. Sometimes the consequences of this phenomenon become obvious. They manifest themselves especially in the children of rich families. They are crammed with food, they sleep as much as they like, have no responsibility, never make an intellectual or moral effort, learn only what amuses them, and struggle against nothing.

The result is well known. They generally become pleasant and handsome, often strong, easily tired, extremely selfish, without intellectual acuteness, moral sense, and nervous resistance. These defects are not of ancestral origin. They are observed in the descendants of the men who built up American in-dustries, as well as in those of the newcomers.

As optimum development requires the activity of all organic systems, a decrease in the value of man necessarily follows the decay of the adaptive functions. Modern men need more nervous resistance, intelligence, and moral energy than muscular power. The acquisition of these qualities calls for effort and discipline.

Apparently, there is no adaptation possible to ceaseless agitation, intellectual dispersion, alcoholism, precocious sexual excesses, noise, polluted air, and adulterated foods. If such is the case, we must modify our mode of life and our environment, even at the cost of a destructive revolution. After all, the purpose of civilization is not the progress of science and machines but the progress of man.

Democratic Equality Impossible

MODERN society ignores the individual. It only takes account of human beings. It believes in the reality of the Universals and treats men as abstractions. The confusion of the concepts of the individual and of the human being has led industrial civilization to a fundamental error, the standardization of men.

If we were all identical, we could be reared and made to live and work in great herds, like cattle. But each one has his own personality. He cannot be treated like a symbol. Children should not be placed, at a very early age, in schools where they are educated wholesale. As is well known, most great men have been brought up in comparative solitude, or have refused to enter the mold of the school. In order to reach his full strength, the individual requires the relative isolation and the attention of the restricted social group consisting of the family.

The neglect of individuality by our social institutions is, likewise, responsible for the atrophy of adults. Man does not stand, without damage, the mode of existence and the uniform and stupid work imposed on factory and office workers, on all those who take part in mass production. In the immensity of modern cities he is isolated and as if lost.

On the contrary, the individual remains a man when he belongs to a small group, when he inhabits a village or a small town where his relative importance is greater, when he can hope to become in his turn an influential citizen.

ANOTHER error, due to the confusion of the concepts of human being and individual, is democratic equality. The feeble-minded and the man of genius should not be equal before the law. The stupid, and the unintelligent, those who are incapable of attention, of effort, have no right to a higher education. It is absurd to give them the same electoral power as fully developed individuals. Sexes are not equal. To disregard all these inequalities is very dangerous. The democratic principle has contributed to the collapse of civilization in opposing the development of an élite. It is obvious that, on the contrary, individual inequalities must be respected. In modern society the great, the small, the average, and the mediocre are needed. But we should not attempt to develop the higher types by the same procedures as the lower.

The individual has become narrow, specialized, immoral, unintelligent, incapable of managing himself and his own institutions. But at the same time the biological sciences have revealed to us the most precious of all secrets—the laws of the development of our body and of our consciousness. This knowledge has brought to humanity the means of renovating itself. As long as the hereditary qualities of the race remain, the strength and the audacity of his forefathers can be resurrected in modern man by his own will. But is he still capable of such an effort?

Humanity Is Master of Its Destiny

For the first time in history, humanity, helped by science, has become master of its destiny. But will we be capable of using this knowledge of ourselves to our real advantage?

We will be faced by a single obstacle, our inertia. And not by the incapacity of our race to rise again. We know that intellectual apathy, immorality, and criminality are not, in general, hereditary. We can develop our innately good qualities if we earnestly wish to do so. Modern society has not stifled all the focuses of intellectual culture, moral courage, virtue, and audacity. The flame is still burning.

What we accomplished once we are capable of accomplishing again. Should our civilization collapse, we would build up another one. But is it indispensable to suffer the agony of chaos before reaching order and peace? Can we not rise again, without undergoing the bloody regeneration of total overthrow? Are we capable of renovating ourselves, of avoiding cataclysms, and of continuing our ascension?

Data must be the basis of the construction of man. Our first task is to make them utilizable. Every year we hear of the progress made by eugenists, geneticists, statisticians, behaviorists, physiologists, anatomists, biological chemists, physical chemists, psychologists, physicians, hygienists, endocrinologists, psychiatrists, immunologists, educators, social workers, clergymen, sociologists, economists, etc.

But the practical results of these accomplishments are surprisingly small.

This immense amount of information is disseminated in technical reviews, in treatises, in the brains of men of science. No one has it in his possession. We have now to put together its disparate fragments, and to make this knowledge live within the midst of at least a few individuals. Then, it will become productive.

Is it possible for a single brain to assimilate such a gigantic amount of knowledge? It seems that such an accomplishment is not impossible. In about twenty-five years of uninterrupted study, one could learn these sciences. At the age of fifty, those who have submitted themselves to this discipline could effectively direct the construction of the human being and of a civilization based on his true nature.

A group of such men must live like monks of the great contemplative orders, and not like university professors, and still less like business men. Sacrifice seems to be a necessary condition of progress. There are now, as in former times, men ready for the supreme renunciation. Why should not some individuals sacrifice their lives to acquire the science indispensable to the making of man and of his environment? The sacrifice of oneself is not very difficult for one burning with the passion for a great adventure. And there is no more beautiful and dangerous adventure than the renovation of modern man.

We know that the evolution of humanity is very slow, that the study of its problems demands the lifetime of several generations of scientists. We need, therefore, an institution capable of providing for at least a century of uninterrupted investigation concerning man. Modern society should be given an intellectual focus, an immortal brain, capable of conceiving and planning its future, and of promoting and pushing forward fundamental researches, in spite of the death of individual researchers, or the bankruptcy of the research institutes. Such an organization would be the salvation of the white races in their staggering advance toward civilization.

It would endeavor to discover how modern civilization could mold itself to man without crushing any of his essential qualities. Its silent meditation would protect the inhabitants of the new city from the mechanical inventions which are dangerous for their body or their mind, from the adulteration of thought as well as food, from the whims of the specialists in education, nutrition, morals, sociology, etc., from all the progress inspired, not by the needs of the public, but by the greed or the illusions of the inventors. An institution of this sort would acquire enough knowledge to prevent the organic and mental deterioration of civilized nations.

For the first time in the history of humanity, a crumbling civilization is capable of discerning the causes of its decay. For the first time, it has at its disposal the gigantic strength of science. Will we utilize this knowledge and this power? It is our only hope of escaping the fate common to all great civilizations of the past. Our destiny is in our hands. On the new road, we must now go forward.

———◆———

ON THE DEATH OF DR. BENJAMIN FRANKLIN

Thus, some tall tree that long hath stood
The glory of its native wood,
By storms destroyed, or length of years,
Demands the tribute of our tears.

The pile, that took long time to raise,
To dust returns by slow decays:
But, when its destined years are o'er,
We must regret the loss the more.

So long accustomed to your aid,
The world laments your exit made;
So long befriended by your art,
Philisopher, 'tis hard to part!—

When monarchs tumble to the ground,
Successors easily are found:
But, matchless FRANKLIN! what a few
Can hope to rival such as YOU,
Who seized from kings their sceptred pride,
And turned the lightning's darts aside!
                        —*Philip Freneau* (1752-1832).

Francis Hackett

HENRY THE EIGHTH

This is the story of a man's search for happiness which he never found. It does not particularly concern us that this man was a king, that he upset and rearranged the economic, political and religious structure of England and bloodied the history of his times in the quest. We are more concerned with six women, all of whom failed him in one way or another, and in failure earned for their husband the title of "The Blue-Beard of English History."

"Long Live the King"

Henry VIII had come to the Tower of London. While the old king lay in his coffin amid a blaze of candles, in the hush of death, the young king moved away to the center of excitement.

The White Tower housed him. It was not a festive residence. Though it had been made gracious by eager hands, with fresh straw on the floor and tapestries on the walls, these thick walls knew secrets that no tapestry could hide. Here Henry's boy uncles had been murdered for his grand-uncle, their bodies hidden under the stairs that he trod. Below these windows Warwick had been beheaded by his father. Here his grandfather Edward had ordered Henry VI to be slain.

Its gloom and baseness, stealthy with assassination, laden with treachery, sharp with torture, bearing in its muffled bosom something besides crime, it spoke of emergencies that had been seized white hot and dreadful dangers that had been surmounted; it held the ax of authority in readiness, the weapons of the kingdom, the first and last resorts of monarchy in peril. It was grim, but it was also reassuring. The heady mixture of its horror and glory tingled in Henry as the new and marvelous wine of power.

On his death-bed, Henry VII had urged his son to complete his marriage, and everything depended on the council.

So far as Catherine of Aragon was concerned, the young king knew that she asked nothing better than to marry him, and for himself, feeling instinct to be of minor consequence, he would not postpone the marriage. She was five years older than he and that would not be altered by the running of time. He knew that Catherine had been married to his brother, and he knew that a Spanish alliance was imperative.

For Catherine it was no sacrifice of self. Through it she entered the long promised land. Into every detail of the wedding and coronation Catherine plunged with sparkling eyes and busy hands.

Catherine's sway turned out to be deeply respectable. Even on the days he went hunting, Henry heard three masses, and sometimes five on other days, though these five could be obligingly telescoped. Every evening in the Queen's chamber he heard vespers and complines. She prayed at midnight and at five in the morning; and already the heir she designed for Henry was the temporal object of her devotional life.

But the youth was not always on his knees in devotion. He cared too much for life, for the gorgeous toy of monarchy, not to play with it like the adolescent Gargantua. He took childish pleasure in the more violent forms of dancing, in immense leaps and pirouettes. When he rode before the ladies, he made his mount prance and career, rear and capriole. And he was so insatiable in his desire to impress and to dazzle that he turned from theological disputations and triumphs in the ring, to the composing of hymns and the singing of his own lyrics. His hand was heavy and his invention flat, yet it was another tremendous effort to defy the law of gravity and to rise into the mood of the Renaissance.

Catherine of Aragon

CATHERINE, however, knew him for what he was. As she stood by him, "rather ugly than otherwise," looking steadily out with her prominent, fixed blue eyes, she scanned the jeweled nobles, the silken prelates, the gay-clad ambassadors, the "handsome damsels of sumptuous appearance" for those who would make the best of her husband.

Her own hope, to give him an heir, was destined to a terrible disappointment within a few months. Her first child was still-born.

Their next child was born at the beginning of 1511, and called Henry. But their happiness was daunted in six weeks. The child died.

A year later came a third bitter disappointment of their married life.

"It is said," wrote a Venetian in Rome a few months later, the Vatican having sharp ears in England, "that the King of England means to repudiate his present wife, the daughter of the King of Spain and his brother's widow, because he is unable to have children by her, and intends to marry a daughter of the French Duke of Bourbon."

In the midst of this rancor, a son was born prematurely, due, the Spanish said, to Henry's brutality and Catherine's alarms.

At last on February 18, 1516, she who had suffered so many disappointments successfully launched a child into the world. This was the Princess Mary, who was to be known as Queen Mary Tudor.

The prudent Venetian Ambassador hardly knew whether to leave flowers or a wreath when he learned that the baby was a girl. He visited Henry, and on murmuring to the father that a man must resign himself to the will of God, "who distributes his favors as he pleases," Henry buoyantly declared, "We are both young: if it was a daughter this time, the sons will follow, by the grace of God!"

Henry was unusually good humored and good natured, unusually gay. The glittering pageants of 1517 and 1518 found him happy in his attendance on Catherine. But the thing that helped him most to behave charmingly to his wife was his discovery that he had charms for other women.

Catherine knew too well that her handsome maids in waiting found disturbing favor in his eyes. She sat knitting, counting her stitches, watching him, yet seeing no more than it paid her to see. Her real compensation was Mary, whose welfare and education engrossed her and who was as devoted and dutiful a child as a conscientious mother could wish.

AT THE Alhambra Catherine's fate had first been decided by her parents. She was almost an infant when her bridegroom had been chosen for her, the Spanish ambassadors inspecting the baby Arthur, first dressed, then naked, then asleep. The motto of the transaction had been put in bald words by a bald diplomat: "Princes do not marry for love; they take wives only to beget children." That was the beginning of the century.

Now Catherine's fate was once more being weighed in political scales in the same city of Madrid. Why not annul her marriage? Why not break this bond with the Emperor and Spain? Her face was already heavy and worn. She had had ten years of miscarriages. But she had failed in her mission. "Princes do not marry for love; they takes wives only to beget children."

Any political marriage could be annulled. Henry fed on the prospect.

Less Sober Intimates

Henry found himself thrown less with his queen and her sober intimates, and more with the younger group who were far from sharing the grave, feudal tradition. This junior group centered in the Boleyns.

By making Thomas Boleyn the treasurer of the household and employing his son George as an envoy, it was natural, so far as the gaping world was concerned, to keep the elder daughter, Mary Boleyn near him, and pay many visits to the treasurer at Hever.

When Mary was about to have a child, which caused a smile, it was supposed that Henry would relax his attentions to the Boleyns.

On the contrary, Henry kept on seeking the pleasant seclusion of the castle in Kent, where he could count on the obsequious cordiality of the father and the silent favor of the mother. But the attraction could not be Mary. And the only other attraction was the younger Anne.

In 1522 when the young Mary was deeply his mistress, Anne Boleyn returned to England after her schooling in the French court. No statecraft or solemnity weighed her first appearance. She danced into English history, a laughing girl. She was fifteen.

But Henry did not as yet see this young Boleyn except as a political pawn. He was dallying with Mary. He wanted Anne to marry an Irishman upon whose estates Thomas Boleyn had a claim which the red-headed Lord Ormand violently contested. To marry Anne Boleyn to this fire-brand would unite the two families forever. But she preferred to be a maid to Queen Catherine, a spinster, a nun, to marrying this red-head. She would remain at the English court and enjoy life as it came to her.

It was in 1526 that "Caesar" first really saw her. She was than a girl of nineteen.

The stretching years of marital quiet, of endurance or acquiescence, did not alter the fact that he was an incompletely married man. And now, without willing it, he reached the crisis that so often arrives; he looked out and saw a new and wonderful possibility from which he was debarred. Full blooded and always under the pressure of desire, he supposed at first that this was another pleasant polygamous episode, but as it proffered itself to him it broke in on his heart that he had never been in love before. Henry combated this vision at first, which was natural. But his body had spoken and his heart had spoken in the same language.

And then a surprise greeted him. The atmosphere of Hever, hitherto one of serene complaisance without current or ripple, became keen with the presence of a living will. Anne Boleyn was mistress of her own body. The girl might seem tame, but she was "wild for to hold."

When Anne appeared at nineteen, he was thirty-five, and Catherine was a sick and saddened matron of forty-one. The young girl was of the slender, swaying figure that is like a daffodil on its stalk; Catherine was squat, white and dropsical. Anne Boleyn had a clever pointed face, quick expression, long, fine fingers, and was ready on the instant with a witticism or a peal of laughter; Henry's wife never laughed.

Catherine was not, in any light sense, a person; she was the wife and mother, a link in the long chain of racial continuity, based on the throne, backed by the Church, rooted in the family, a block of institutional granite set in her weak human flesh and her quivering nerves.

Anne came under Henry's loving eyes when she still seemed untied and uncommitted, her very light and slender person declaring she was unattached, and her big black eyes cleaving untracked waters and leaving behind a sea-fire in the heart of the male, king though he was.

She Changed the Course of English History

Anne boleyn's refusal to accept the role of Henry's mistress unconditionally changed the course of English history. In the next six years, step by step, Henry would be forced to deploy every regiment he could muster—to seek victory through the legates, the universities of Europe, the printing press, a proposed church council, and a complete manipulation of his own ecclesiastics and his own parliament. And all this so that he could secure his divorce safely and soundly inside the Catholic Church.

Catherine, on her part, could marshal ambassadors and cardinals and magnates and the emperor to counteract through canon law and public opinion, papal tradition and papal experience, the onslaughts and concussions made by Henry. By the pride and iron of this woman alone, by her embodiment of a passion and a conviction, Henry was to learn that he must either give up the divorce or give up the Church.

As the struggle proceeded, Henry ceased to be adolescent. His respect for law, which had the quality of deference at the start, became an estimate of force. He passed from a youth of barbaric ostentation and pomposity to a closely measured and intricately reasoned middle age. What had begun as a clash of personalities developed as a shock of vested interests, a war of institutions.

Out of his love for Anne grew a divorce, which, to be valid, required an entirely new foreign policy, a new council, a new hierarchy, a new church establishment, a new chancellor, and, strangest of all, a new wife. And with these novelties the man himself evolved, if not a new nature, at least a nature alarmingly new in its assertion.

The divorce issued by legal English authority was a happy moment for Anne Boleyn. In all the handsome pride of youth, she was ready to cross the formal threshold of her ambition.

Queen Anne Boleyn

Sometime in January of 1533, between dawn and breakfast, in a corner of York Place, the wedding took place. The date of January 25th is generally accepted, the more gallant chroniclers, taking note of Anne's condition, set it as far back as November.

Only till September was Henry obliged to wait for the birth of his heir. To his own way of thinking, he was not a superstitious man, but he was reassured that so many people could guarantee him that it would be a boy.

On September seventh Anne was delivered. The sad truth could not be hidden: the heir was a girl. Her name would be Elizabeth, after Henry's mother and Anne's mother. The imperialists, like good Christians, clucked over the disappointment: and not one felt the disgrace of Elizabeth more than the father.

The birth of a daughter undeniably weakened Anne Boleyn's position. Her enemies were encouraged, and believed it was not too soon to detach those who only stood by her because of fair weather.

With her usual directness and the presumptuousness that came from her confidence in Henry's favor, Anne set out to impose her baby Elizabeth on England. Her animosity had been quickened rather than tempered by her disappointment as to the sex of the child, and she demanded forthwith that the stubborn half-sister Mary be declared illegitimate and compelled to act as a maid to the infant.

Henry agreed to the humiliation of Mary. But he sniffed danger in the air. He knew that, so far, the English people had not been won to Anne Boleyn, or given any good reason for preferring a daughter by Anne to the older daughter by Catherine.

This was her one way of carrying all before her, but it ignored the danger of her position. She was the young wife of a divorced man. When she was Henry's mistress, she could point to the harness that galled him and stir his imagination and his self pity to discard the wife whom he did not love. But in marrying him, she became the institutional wife and took the great obligations of publicly satisfying him as the Queen of his subjects and the mother of his children. In stepping into Catherine's shoes, she had really stepped into Catherine's shackles.

Within a year of her coronation, Anne could see how troubled and restive Henry was, but she did not at once believe she had a rival. The news of it was fetched to her by her brother's wife, whose gift for prying was considerable. Who the girl was, how far it had gone, how long it would last—these were all minor details beside the detestable fact that there was a girl, and that she was a member of the anti-Boleyn faction.

CONFRONTED with this little rift in their union, Anne acted drastically. She told him she was again with child. This was the best news he could have. As the mother of an heir, she could give him a great and lasting satisfaction, and with this happy prospect before him he stopped trifling and became the loyal husband for a while.

In September, Anne had to admit to Henry that she was not going to have a child. With elemental simplicity he rebounded into his flirtation. Anne's anger at this renewal of an affair with an enemy made her try to order the girl away from court, but

Henry retorted with a brusque countermand, savagely reminding Anne that she derived her authority from him alone and telling her to remember where she came from.

The wish for a boy was not impossible of fulfillment, but while she could hold Henry long enough to woo him to this end, she had the chagrin, the humiliation, the shame of his contemptuous infidelity. The retiring young woman had been lady-in-waiting to Anne Boleyn as Anne herself had been to Catherine.

JANE SEYMOUR was four years younger than Anne Boleyn, the daughter of a good county family who had a spoonful of royal blood in their veins from the times of Edward III. Jane was the very reverse of her former mistress:

HENRY VIII
From the painting by Holbein at Windsor Castle

where Anne was sparkling, she was still; where Anne was challenging, she was meek. Here in this gentle presence, her pale eyes vibrating uncertainly to Henry, the nerves that Anne had entangled by her sweeping ambitions were one by one relaxed and mellowed in the consciousness of adoration. The music might be simple, the range limited, the instrument rather warbling, but there was something in its loving kindness that dissolved into Henry's veins.

She probably thought that Anne was in truth a concubine. She, unlike Anne, was a well-bred lady. She must have pitied Henry for falling into the clutches of this aggressive woman, and believed him to be sorely misunderstood.

Anne was again pregnant. If she bore him a son, she could count herself safe. But what if her pregnancy did not result in satisfying Henry? If she disappointed him, and he turned against her? Perhaps

he would take Jane Seymour, who was now at court receiving his presents.

This was the prelude of a terrible misfortune. On January 24th Norfolk burst in to Anne to say that Henry had fallen off his horse so heavily that at first they thought he was killed. On January 29th, Anne gave birth to a dead male child.

In the early part of 1535, following her accident, Anne Boleyn was definitely aware of Henry's neglect. Henry had made Jane Seymour's brother a gentleman of his chamber, as once before he had made George Boleyn a gentleman of his chamber. Anne might scintillate among her courtiers, and they might laugh at her pert comment and delight in her black eyes. But Henry cared naught for mockery and waggishness. What he liked best was the unsullied modesty and deference of a pure, good woman.

The Terrors of the Tower

ONE Mark Smeaton had come penniless to court, but by his gift as a music player and his elegance as a dancer had found favor with Anne and Henry, had been amply rewarded, and was apparently a mobile, pleasant, sentimental youth. To be asked by Cromwell, the King's Secretary, to dinner must have seemed a signal honor; we may imagine that he leaped lightly from the boat and arrived merrily at the Secretary's door in the blithe April forenoon.

But the entertainment to which he was bidden was a grim one. The Secretary had delved into many lives. He had examined papists and Lutherans, priors and abbesses, monks, nuns, traitors, debtors, the broken and hounded, the suppliant, the defiant, the alert, the terrified. This child of pleasure that now sat opposite him was as formidable as a paralyzed rabbit.

How did he pay for that ring he was wearing? Who gave it to him? How much did that doublet cost? Where did he get it? What else did he get? When?

How much? What did she say? Come! Have you no answer? A look to the soundless men. A harmless rope on Smeaton's damp ringlets. A rope tightened by a stick. What else? A nod. Tightened again. Sterner and louder questions, with thinning lips and knuckles rapping. Questions shouted and beads of sweat on Smeaton's trembling lips. But had she yielded to him? She had. She had. How often? It must have been— Yes. Yes. Anything. Well, confess . . . Names. Who else? *You are lying.* And so on.

Smeaton was taken upstairs after this experience, flung into a room till further notice, and locked up. Then Cromwell sent a message to Henry.

WHEN Henry received the message, his heavy fat face quivered with insupportable rage at the rôle that had been thrust on him. She had held him at a distance. She had so refused herself to him that he had gone down on his knees to her and offered her the crown of England. And this was the woman who had betrayed him with every gamester in the court, who had laughed at him behind his back, who had lavished his money, spent his honor and boasted of his impotence. A sullen fury, full of a hideous congested righteousness, took complete possession of this maddened soul. He hated every smile she had ever smiled. To cut her neck from her body could alone kill her smile.

They told her that she was to prepare to go by the barge to the Tower. Smeaton, they declared, had confessed to adultery with her.

In the lodging where she found herself, four unfamiliar matrons selected by Cromwell were ready to wait on her. Anne had no comprehension that every word she uttered was being garnered and sent at once to Cromwell. Her excitement, wild and unguarded, mounted as each bit of news came through to her. She was living out the feelings that came to her, or rather she had become the mere aeolian of her feelings.

The charges against Anne could now be framed into indictments. She found herself accused not only of adultery with four men and of incest with her brother, but also accused of treason, plotting the king's death and destruction, and "often saying she would marry one of them as soon as the King died."

The infidelities of which she was accused had been detailed in each indictment—one of them a month after Elizabeth was born and another a month before the disappointment of January 29th. The dates at which Henry's death was plotted were also fixed with equal definiteness and inopportuneness, if ordinary motives were to be considered.

But the trail turned on something besides evidence. Anne had become Queen of England through Henry's obstinate attachment to her and against the social, religious, class and personal feelings of most of her own kind and a great many of the common people. She was indicted not for unchastity but for unpopularity: and Henry and Cromwell both felt that they could risk her conviction by peers who had been her steadfast enemies.

SHE almost won the day. Even after her peers pronounced her guilty she was able to stand firm and appeal only to God. During the evidence, such as it was, she had been "unmoved as a stone, and had carried herself as if she was receiving some great honor." "Her face spoke more than words, and no one who looked on her would have thought her guilty."

True to her court tradition, she had requested that her head should not be cut off by the common headsman who used an ax, but by an executioner who could wield the sword. This had been allowed, and the man had been sent for from Calais.

No foreigners were admitted to the place of execution but the English public crowded in—headed by Cromwell.

Her voice had nearly left her, but in a low monotone, she said that she had not come to preach but to die. She asked everyone to pray for the King, who was so good, remitted her offenses to God and asked forgiveness of all whom she had wronged.

As she finished her few words, she knelt down, while one of the matrons bound her eyes. "O God, have pity on my soul; O God, have pity on my soul? O God, have pity—" The stroke of the sword severed her neck: her little head rolled to the straw. At once the matrons lifted the trunk, her life blood still flowing. They gathered her broken body into a coffin. Thomas Cromwell had seen all.

Jane Seymour

WAS the bride-elect already a mother-elect? Why the violent haste in getting rid of Anne? Why at last a precipitate marriage without any bargaining for a bride with the French or with the Emperor? Why execution rather than divorce?

The new marriage demanded Anne's

death to clear the decks. So it was declared explicitly. And Anne's death would have become doubly necessary if Jane was quick with child. All that Henry needed to urge him into decision was to know that Jane Seymour could indeed become a mother. His mania was to secure a male heir.

And their precipitate marriage, within ten days, without any decent preparation, without a word to the public, without a chance for France or the Empire to treat the new Queen with becoming dignity, without anything more ceremonious on Henry's part than an order to change *A* into *J*, fairly implied that this new wife was not so much a person in herself whom he appreciated or valued but the female envelope of a guaranteed heir.

On October twelfth at two in the morning, Jane labored and brought forth Edward. The baby was puny, but living, and Henry's heart was lifted into heaven. By the simple act of being born this infant changed the center of national gravity: Henry gave place to him; Jane gave place to him; and the whole court grouped itself around him. A morsel of puling ignominy, a shrinking inchworm, he blindly and automatically became the lottery ticket on which a nation staked its fate, the inheritor of a dynasty whose crown alone at this instant would snuff him out like a ha'penny dip.

Baptism, at the moment, was a sacrament in good standing; and as Edward was given his dip in the healing waters, his mother, Jane, was big-eyed with fever. She half saw and half imagined the triumph of her life, while Death, raising and lowering its curtains, obliterated her and allowed her to recover, dipped her in its own waters. She lived nine days longer, till October 24th.

Anne of Cleves

WITH Jane's death, Henry had a glimpse of sorrow and it was a new and bewildering experience for him. She had become his companion and his habit, and he had no other family to lean upon, except his two girls Mary and Elizabeth. But neither could cross the broad moat with which he had himself surrounded.

"The King is in good health," wrote one of the Privy Chamber a week after the funeral, "and merry as a widower may be." Good health is much, especially when appetite attends it, and Henry was gradually passing from sorrow into numbness.

It was beyond doubt a good thing to have Henry eligible. Why could not a French bride be solicited and an Imperialist one at the same time?

The envoy at Brussels could find nothing worthy of Henry. "The Duke of Cleves has a daughter, but there is no great praise either of her personage or her beauty."

But Anne of Cleves was the sister of a potential nuisance. Cromwell saw in her a good match for Henry. The motive was clear cut. But not till Henry saw Holbein's portrait of Anne of Cleves did he allow Cromwell to begin in earnest. Finally the marriage was arranged.

Henry wished his new bride to have the most honorable of receptions. He debated what high personage was worthy to greet her at Calais. He ordered his palaces done over, and had ships newly decorated. Then he held himself ready to start from London to meet his bride and by beholding her to "nourish love."

ANNE, for her part, was equally excited as she set out with a "brave equipage" from the valley of the Rhine. She had reached and passed her thirtieth year without ever dreaming she might become Queen of England. To depart on this palpitating adventure, at the age of thirty-four was to soar into a new world.

This Anne had none of the black-eyed audacities that had brought the other Anne to ruin. The least bit pockmarked, unfortunately, "tall and thin, of medium beauty, and of very assured and resolute countenance," she made up in stauncher virtues for what she lacked in charm.

Henry had decided, with the gallantry of a knight, to waylay her at Rochester, thirty miles or so out of London. He had not forgotten a New Year's present —a set of sable furs—and he tremulously sent an equirry before him to announce his coming. On seeing his future Queen, the equirry was dismayed, the lady was so far unlike what was reported, but he returned with the discreet word that she was awaiting her lord. Then the king went into her chamber.

As he stood on the threshold, his jaw dropped, "marvelously astonished and abashed." Could this be she? He entered to embrace and kiss her, but "a discontentment and disliking of her person" so overwhelmed him that after mumbling twenty words he left her, too upset to offer her his present.

The wedding was postponed, to Anne's alarm. To the last Henry showed himself amazingly peevish. Even as Cromwell came to say that he was ready to fetch the blushing bride, Henry made one final weak man's lamentation. "My lord, if it were not to satisfy the world and my realm, I would not do that I must do this day for no earthly thing." With that he went to the altar, scowling to the last, and Anne "demure and sad."

The public knew nothing. A royal marriage was announced in church, and Anne of Cleves rejoiced every one who favored religious change. The union, in fact, was the crown of Cromwell's policy. For Henry the abbeys had been drained, and that gold stream had turned to the wheel of royal supremacy. The papacy had been demolished. The marriage with Anne of Cleves was a masterly innovation, even if it obliged the King to go somewhat against his nature.

The King Is Restive

BUT Henry was dangerously restive. He had married Anne under compulsion. There was no fun in it. In the spring of the year, he began inviting one of the young ladies of the court, Katheryn Howard by name, to private dinners and suppers.

Norfolk's father had brought eighteen children into the world, and Katheryn was the daughter of one of the poorer and obscurer half-brothers, Edmund Howard. She had doubtless been named for Henry's first wife. The mother dying young, Katheryn had been entrusted to the old Duchess of Norfolk, the grandmother of Anne Boleyn.

This was a venerable lady in whose shambling and disheveled establishment the child had pushed up like a rose in a neglected garden, a glorious young creature of round features, fine coloring, sparkling and bubbling life, endowed with feeling, with romping blood. She had never been bridled in mind or body. She had been born in the year 1523. She was four when Henry divorced Catherine. She was ten when he married Anne Boleyn. She was fully seven years younger than Henry's girl. This was the eternal vivifier, the young wilding, that whips stale blood.

At first, she must have skipped away, her blood curdling. But to drench the repugnant with perfume was an act in which her uncle was not inexpert. And when Katheryn, poor as a broken shoe, looked at night into her mirror, her eyes could see the aura of a crown.

By May Henry had begun to quarrel with Anne of Cleves. The enormous danger of a collapse in this German marriage was all too plain to Cromwell. He had built everything on it, and on Henry's stability in it.

HENRY made his decision and declared Cromwell had been counterworking his aims for the settlement of religion. When the privy council met he was declared a traitor and rowed to the Tower—the place where Smeaton had shrieked, where Anne's throat was cut.

A small committee of select men paid a call on Anne of Cleves shortly after Cromwell's arrest. When these trusty men entered, Anne of Cleves swooned. She thought her hour had come. But they gently brought her to and advised her that if she yielded gracefully she would be treated with distinguished consideration. She would become a pensioner and receive a certificate of honorable discharge, declaring that she was leaving Henry in the same state in which she had arrived. On this level, her position was strong, and Anne went down to it with perfect dignity and good sense.

So serenely did it work, and so happy was Henry to have his own way without friction, that he gave Anne a most admirable settlement. She was to have four thousand pounds a year, two splendid houses with great parks, the most exquisite clothes, jewels, and to be known in the future as the King's sister, having precedence over all ladies in England, after the Queen and the King's children. It was hard on the taxpayers, but otherwise felicitous.

Katheryn Howard

KATHERYN was a juvenile delinquent. In the great establishment over which the wealthy Duchess of Norfolk presided there were enough girls to constitute a boarding school, but it was a boarding school of full-blooded and high-spirited youngsters with no religious training, no lessons, no mental interests, no discipline. When the old lady was safely in bed in the evening, the girls' dormitory was artfully opened and in came "the light young men."

One Francis Derham was a leading spirit in the midnight parties and he and Katheryn soon fell in love. Their affair stretched from her fourteenth or fifteenth to her eighteenth year, a rainbow of delight.

On Henry's suddenly favoring the girl, who seemed charged with mischief and vivacity, young Derham cleared out to Ireland, to try his hand at piracy. But the young pirate's hold, by that time, had been broken.

The man who took his place in Katheryn's affections was Thomas Culpeper, one of Henry's brightest favorites. Henry had heaped him with stewardships and sinecures and tossed him an abbey, which indicates that the young dandy had made himself agreeable. One extremely ugly story was hinted, but Katheryn Howard did not see a ruffian in Culpeper. She saw a man of her own people, her own age, her own inclination. When she was waiting on Anne of Cleves, she had made up her mind, quite frankly, to "try him."

It was a fitful volcano that Katheryn, as queen, had to live with. But while she soothed him with whatever endearments are appropriate to a King her mind was busy with Thomas Culpeper.

She was in love with Culpeper and it began to be possible for the two young people to be together. The young dandy was not instantly persuaded, but he was in love with Katheryn.

Katheryn seemed to think that a love affair was "secret" if it were not deliberately announced at Paul's Cross. At Greenwich, at Lincoln, at Pomfret, at York, her "secret" interviews were discussed. She was still the young girl fooling the old Duchess.

WHEN the news got to Henry he called the Council and in a few days confessions began to pour in. Henry's own pure life, and his own part in the coupling, which every one believed to have antedated the marriage, were not in question. It was not he who had tainted her blood but she who had "tainted the royal blood." It was not he who, by his scruples and his caprices and his political maneuvers, had sapped the foundations of marriage; it was she who was criminal.

When word came to her that both Lords and Commons had passed the act of attainder and that the King would allow her to plead before parliament, she did not ask to defend herself. She submitted entirely to the King's mercy and owned that she deserved death.

When she came to the block on the morning of February 13th, it was set on the spot where her cousin Anne Boleyn had been executed. A large number of people had gathered at the scaffold.

She spoke a few breathless words. A Spaniard heard them and wrote them:

"Brothers, by the journey upon which I am bound, I have not wronged the King. But it is true that long before the King took me, I loved Culpeper. I would rather have had him for a husband than be mistress of the world, but sin blinded me and the greed of grandeur; and since mine is the fault, mine also is the suffering, and my great sorrow is that Culpeper should have had to die through me."

At these words she could go no farther. She turned to the headsman and said, "Pray hasten with thy office."

Falling on her knees she began to pray. Then the headsman severed her bent neck.

Katharine Parr

HENRY's fifth marriage had gone wrong, as his fourth marriage had gone wrong, and his second and his first. Whatever doubts his loyal subjects had secretly expressed in all the earlier cases, they were able to say, "This time we are sorry for him." And they were sorry for him, sorrier than for Katheryn Howard.

Henry looked badly. When he was married to Katheryn, as Holbein showed, he was still plumped with pride and there was a September richness in his body. Suddenly, as with a cruel hand, he was stricken in years. He was only fifty, and that was not old.

The blow that Katheryn had dealt his confidence had sunk into his being and gone deep. He had made her his Queen, rained jewels on her, caressed her, displayed her, and no anger, no death stroke, could cancel the knowledge that he had never won her. His defeat could not be disguised.

In a desolate household, with so many terrible memories and so much to make Henry look baffled and hunted, there began to emerge a new and charming figure, a figure of benignity and life.

Katharine Parr was a lady of the court but one of those who push up by themselves in any society, affluent in their natures, well-molded, rich, gracious, like a crocus under the autumn leaves. She possessed the odd gift that can turn any one not a monster into a human being —the solvency of good will.

At home in the court but not at first observed by his Majesty, Katharine was receiving the approaches of her compeer in age and class, Thomas Seymour, Edward's younger uncle. But Katharine did not succumb to Thomas Seymour in the first days of courtship. She was living in an age when passionate natures wrecked themselves and she was old enough to observe the world she lived in as well as to listen to her heart.

BUT while she was still free, Henry laid on her the weight of his approval. Perhaps he had seen how devoted she was to Mary, how she mothered Edward and won Elizabeth. Perhaps the narrowed field of choice, and her staid widowhood in contrast to the flagrant freshness of Katheryn Howard, caught his skittish mind.

When Henry smiled on her and opened his mind to her in the spring of 1543, she was said to have given a cry of horror.

"It were better to be your mistress than your wife!"

Still it was not in her to think any one evil. A woman with compassion, in whom pity linked with humility and kindness with the obedience of the subject, could hardly help seeing in him the incomplete man who has missed the secret of happiness. She could not give it to him. But she could nurse him. He could never need the core of her being; that was Thomas Seymour's. And she could give him what he needed, and what his tormented country needed, the climate of goodwill. Had she escaped him, she knew his favor would change to a bright animosity that would destroy her young man's career.

Henry's sixth marriage did not seem to portend any change in policy, religious or political. He was wedded on July 12, 1543. It was a pleasant and simple ceremony, with both his daughters there to be glad for their new stepmother, and "none opposing but all applauding the marriage." Henry said "Yea" with beaming goodwill to the questions that the Bishop put to him in English and Katharine clasping hands with him on her promise, plighted herself "to be bonayr and boxome in bed and at board, till death us depart."

The pane through which Henry was looking at the political scene was no longer clear. It was iridescent with his sick and writhing body. At last he made his will. He was to be buried in the still unfinished chapel at Windsor. Jane Seymour, his true and loving wife, was to lie with him. She had borne him a son. Edward and his heirs, Mary and her heirs, Elizabeth and her heirs, and next the children of his sister Mary's two daughters, were bequeathed the crown.

He sent for Katharine. "It is God's will that we should part," he said with his masterful simplicity, "and I order that these gentlemen honor you and treat you as if I were living still." He had just named Thomas Seymour a member of the council.

She could not answer for weeping, and he ordered her to leave him.

His condition grew worse hour by hour, while parliament, like a good dog, watched for a movement or token from the master. Every breath was watched. The councilors who came out of the sick-chamber marked a grave change; he could not last. And so he died.

He was buried at Windsor, though not as he had planned. His council named a Protector, not as he had decided.

Out of the wreck of all his marriages, the female child, Elizabeth, at whose birth he winced, whom he despised and rejected, took the scepter he meant for war-lords and raised it to heights of which the poets sing. The Cromwell whom he beheaded would have a descendant.

On approximately the 101st anniversary of Henry's death, on the site of Whitehall where he died, Oliver Cromwell would behead the King of England. Strong passions breed strong passions.

When Molly Smiles

When Molly smiles beneath her cow,
I feel my heart—I can't tell how;
When Molly is on Sunday dressed,
On Sundays I can take no rest.

What can I do? on worky days
I leave my work on her to gaze.
What shall I say? At sermons, I
Forget the text when Molly's by.

Good master curate, teach me how
To mind your preaching and my plough:
And if for this you'll raise a spell,
A good fat goose shall thank you well.

—*Anonymous*

F. Van Wyck Mason

THREE HARBOURS

F VAN WYCK MASON, widely known author of international mysteries and historical serials, is a native New Englander and a graduate of Harvard. During the World War he joined the French Army at the age of sixteen, later transferring to the American Service. Although he now spends most of his summers on Nantucket Island and his winters in Bermuda, he has traveled extensively in Europe, the Near East, North Africa, Central America, and in the United States. "Three Harbours" is his twentieth published book. It is the adventures of the brothers Robert and David Ashton in and between the three harbors of Norfolk, Boston and Bermuda during the Revolutionary War.

Norfolk—1774

ROB ASHTON and his wife Peggy stood alone at the end of a wharf in Norfolk, Virginia, watching their brigantine put out to sea. *The Assistance* looked terribly shabby and old. Rob hoped it would last to Boston.

Well, out there sailed every penny he and Peggy had. But, by God, they didn't owe a fig to anybody. He felt Peggy give his arm an ecstatic squeeze when a faded Union Jack was hoisted to the òld brigantine's main gaff. Well, for better or worse, there she went.

Off Cape Cod—1774

STEPHEN FARISH, stolidly pacing the poopdeck, vowed that he didn't enjoy cruising in a blind fog near the treacherous shoals of Cape Cod. But every time he thought how smart Mr. Robert Ashton was about this trip, a grin creased his leather brown lips. By Godfreys, he had shipped only what was likely to bring the highest prices. Tobacco, salt and cloth. Yes, sir! Mr. Ashton was the sort of owner a skipper could cotton to.

Below, David Ashton was repacking his sea chest. When he had finished, he started to draw the charges from his pistols. From somewhere beyond the porthole came a resounding boom. David recognized its origin instantly and started for the deck.

"You heard that cannon? Means a man-of-war! What are we going to do, Captain?"

"It will be best to fire a gun," Captain Farish seemed to be thinking aloud. "They may take us for another man-of-war and leave us be. If we ring a bell she'll know for certain we are merchantmen and hold us up on account of that embargo act."

The captain then caught up the gunner's match and jammed it into the signal-gun. An orange flame spurted vertically just as a member of the crew screamed, "Jesus! There's her bowsprit!"

Quick as a swooping hawk, a tall ship materialized out of the smoky atmosphere, rushed straight at the brigantine. Wise members of the crew threw themselves flat.

A grinding, rending crash filled David's ears. A yard thundered down amidships; smashed the long boat.

An enraged voice began bellowing, "They fired on us, sir!"

"Then fire back! Sink the lousy dogs!"

After a few minutes of bedlam, a grim, tough-looking lieutenant of marines clambered over the shattered bulwarks. Coolly he surveyed the damaged brigantine.

F. VAN WYCK MASON, author of "Three Harbours," the background knowledge of which was gained through extensive acquaintance with both New England and Bermuda history and tradition.
Courtesy J. B. Lippincott Co.

"What can you expect if you fire into one of His Majesty's ships?"

Farish wet his lips. "We only fired a signal gun, then you ran us down."

"I believe signal guns are not customarily charged with shot. Your fire smashed our hawse hold," replied the lieutenant arrogantly.

"That hole was caused by the collision. Maybe one of our anchor flukes did it."

The marine only shook his head sharply, motioned David, Farish and his mate to the port rail. The lieutenant then drew from among the broken staves a molasses covered bayonet, then a pike head and a pair of pistols.

The lieutenant's jaw clicked. "Smuggling arms? That alters matters. You are, I perceive, an extra-peaceful merchantman." The marine's sarcasm was deadly. "Sergeant, fetch a rope and secure these honest mariners."

When they had tied him up, Farish turned to David and growled. "I pray the Lord your brother is granted a

chance someday to take this out of your hide! If you had told him what you intended, I'd have only respect for you. But it was the trick of a sneaking dog to ship these arms without telling him. You've smashed your brother's business. Ruined him! And smuggling weapons ain't no slight matter these days, either. We'll likely be shipped to the East Indies as slaves."

Salem—1774

IT was pleasantly warm in the court room. After nearly a month in Salem jail, one forgot there were such things as soap, clean linen and beds.

Farish's dried apple of a face was the picture of discouragement. Only Buff, the giant negro, remained unperturbed. After all, the jail food was some better than he got back in Norfolk and he was used to leg irons.

"Your Honors!" David struggled to his feet. "May I speak?" He stood erect, a grimy unkempt figure outlined against the whitewashed wall. "I beg of you, to dismiss the other prisoners. The fault is principally mine, because I collected the arms and arranged for their transportation. And may I state that my brother, Robert, is a most loyal subject of His Majesty. That, gentlemen, is why I didn't inform him about the arms. He never would have allowed them aboard his vessel."

In Stephen Farish's opinion the deliberation of the judges appeared ominously brief. The bailiff began to read, "Verdict of this Court. *The Assistance* is hereby condemned, together with all her cargo. Prize money for the sale shall be divided among the officers of the vessel which captured it. We do hold the crew of *The Assistance* guiltless of wilfully transporting arms. But as an example to disaffected subjects of the Crown, this Court hereby sentences David Ashton to ten years' penal servitude at a destination later to be decided. Stephen Farish will

"Smuggling arms? That alters matters."

Illustration for F. Van Wyck Mason's
"THREE HARBOURS"

serve one year at hard labor in His Majesty's prison at Boston."

Ten years—if he lived—of chains, loathsome food and dirt. David shivered. What a fool he had been to meddle in politics. It would be 1784 before he was free again.

Norfolk—1775

EVERYBODY, even his worst enemies, admired Robert Ashton for one thing. Not once did he ever reproach his brother. He made no attempt to explain David's astounding duplicity, even to himself. When people offered sympathy or expressed indignation, he only turned aside in silence.

Peggy, who showed pregnancy in more ways than one, staged a tearful scene and uttered bitter, unreasonable reproaches when he told her he must sell their house. Only in that way would he be able to buy a new boat.

He had heard of a little schooner belonging to a patriot trader ruined by the embargo. The schooner, as Robert had fully expected, was small and damp and her sails were very, very old, but she did have a wide stern cabin and there was plenty of room in her holds. With the crying need for powder, which Bermuda could furnish, he had better get there as fast as he could to cash in on the high prices.

What bothered him most was what he should do about Peggy. Should he take her along? He didn't like the idea since the baby was going to arrive in a month or so, but what else was there for him to do?

Boston—June, 1775

BUFF sure didn't like the idea of pitting Hannibal, his fighting cock, with steel gaffs on and he was only doing it because Mr. David told him he must. Mr. David must know best.

David Ashton had hesitated about doing it but Corporal Mahoney had settled all doubts.

"Mr. Ashton," the Corporal had whispered when he brought the food the evening before. "It's ordered to Halifax I am; the transport sails in two days. If I'm to help yez, I've got to finger me money tomorrey night."

Thanks to Hannibal's savage ring craft and the negro's selection of birds calculated to bring real backing to a bout, the bribery fund had grown steadily throughout the late winter and spring. Right now there wasn't a more famous fighting chicken in North America than Hannibal. All in all, the wars of Hannibal had gone well and the bag of bills and silver hidden in the chimney of David's cell was growing.

That night Buff emptied his pockets and counted the coins as high as he could count. He was not sure how much Hannibal had won, but it was fifty pounds easy. Mr. David had only asked for forty.

A small canvas bag of coins, dropped into Corporal Mahoney's hands, wrought the miracle.

DAVID could have laughed from sheer joy when he found himself standing with the others on a meadow eaten hard and flat by sheep. Ringing them in were a dozen roughly dressed men holding flintlocks at varying degrees of readiness.

So these then were samples of the doughty rebels all America was talking about.

David drew himself up. "My name is Ashton and I have come to dedicate my sword to the sacred cause of Liberty. This is Captain Farish and here is an Irishman who is deserting. He helped us escape from Stone Jail."

One of the Provincials closed his fingers over David's ankle and slid them up and down two or three times.

"He ent lying, Cap. The ridges and smooth skin is there all right. Prison stink's on him, too."

Cambridge—1775

THE *Blue Anchor* was so jammed one had literally to fight one's way into the Cambridge taproom in which Lord Percy had, not so long ago, rested on his way to Lexington. Hemmed in by eager listeners, a politician was making a speech from the top of a billiard table.

"Fellow Americans, I declare before God Almighty, we must fight for our very existence—all of us! I tell you the British *must* be kept in Boston! If they march out and beat us, the bloody-backs will ravage and burn all the country, just like Injuns. They will shoot down our people in cold blood. You remember Concord? Lexington?"

A deafening clamor was his answer.

"Well, we licked them there, and with God's help, we can lick them again on Bunker Hill."

David took a swig from a bottle of brandy he'd brought and laughed right out until passersby gaped at him. Gad! he certainly was hanging on a beauty. But when he swayed a bit, he straightened up. Gen'lemen didn't stagger. After another pull David decided on his course. It was very simple. If he saw a light at the brown house next door, he would go up and knock.

A line of light wavered under the door and a woman's voice queried: "Who—who is there?"

"David Trelawney, Ma'am, of Williamsburg, Virginia," he announced. David Trelawney for years had been his *nom d'amour*.

The girl was so very small. She reminded him of Rob's wife, Peggy. She was so demure and genteel looking David was sure he'd made a bad mistake until he noticed just a trace of paint on her lips.

"My name is Madelaine," the young woman told him nervously. "You—have money?"

"Is that enough?" Hurriedly he placed three gold sovereigns on the table.

He could not believe after so many tortured barren hours that an end had come to them. And in such a delightful way. Miracle of miracles! This girl, all warm and soft, was going to be his in a very few moments.

Bunker Hill—1775

WHY in hell didn't Stark give the command? The damned British were right on top of them! *Why didn't he?* Closer! Closer!

Jonathan Stark's husky voice suddenly roared out. "Pick the officers! Aim crossbelts. Ready—Fire!"

Out there the lines of muskets were wavering and bayonets were swaying like steel reeds under a gale of death. Not over sixty feet off lay a long squirming windrow of bodies dressed in scarlet and white. Agonized shrieks from the pile of men in the meadow made an inferno of sound.

David Ashton was gradually recovering from his first sense of horror. He wanted a drink of liquor the worst way.

An officer emitted a startled grunt. "Look alive, boys. Here they come again!" The English were scaling the daisy and mustard flower-dotted slope almost rapidly, as if the bloodied corpses weren't there.

Men began to yell, "Oh God, there isn't any more powder!"

When the other men heard they dropped their useless muskets and commenced throwing stones. David made such an iron windmill of his musket that the British began to give way before him. But a British light infantryman slipped in behind him and jabbed his bayonet deep into the Virginian's right shoulder. A snarl of panting grenadiers closed in and a whole constellation of steel stars hovered above him. Were Madelaine's cool fingertips brushing his forehead?

A hand grabbed his good arm and tugged him over onto his back. A tired voice directed: "Tie a rag over that hole in his shoulder. We must take some prisoners to show for this hellish day's work."

En Route to Bermuda—1775

THE *Desdemona* was proving a better sailer than Rob had been expecting. Seven knots. Not bad speed for such an old relic. He was proud of Peggy. Precious few young women of Norfolk would even dream of going to sea in the family way, and seven months along, too. Suddenly he heard someone calling his name frantically.

When he appeared on deck the watch stood grouped about a brown figure at the foot of the mainmast. It was the steward sprawling, twisting slowly, on the gray canvas topsail. Rob, recognizing a distinctive putrid odor, caught his breath. *Small pox!*

Two nights later Peggy woke up to find her arm red and swollen. "Cut it off!" she moaned. "Please cut it off. I can't stand this any longer!"

Distracted, Rob shook his head. A fool could tell that the arm ought to come off, but for him to attempt such an operation would be tantamount to murder. Peggy was tossing in a wild delirium. Heavily her ungainly figure writhed and twisted on the sheet. By the whale-oil lantern the infected arm looked black and swollen to gigantic proportions all the way to the shoulder. For hours he sat, motionless, watching the purplish features of his wife.

Pearly streaks of light had commenced to erase stars of the lesser magnitudes when Margaret Ashton abruptly abandoned her struggles to draw breath.

THE quartermaster craned his sinewy neck. Was that a light on shore? At the end of five minutes he saw another light wink into existence. He checked his course. "That must be the Bermudas. Couldn't be anything else."

The quartermaster's further words were jolted out of his mouth for, without warning, the *Desdemona* suddenly bucked, her whole hull shuddered and her masts tottered. Then, as she settled back on an even keel, from below arose a dull grinding and rasping.

Searching his soul for curses, Rob dashed aft.

"Look! My God, *look!*" As Rob stared ahead, the quartermaster's eyes became concentric rings of white. "See that? The harbour lights! They're going out!"

"Wreckers—" the quartermaster choked. "The real harbour must lie somewheres to starboard—" He felt better. It wasn't his fault the schooner had broke her back on the coral.

A few minutes later they could distinguish a boat coming towards them. Finally it drew alongside. The minute Rob laid eyes on the foremost caller, he felt an instinctive attraction. "I am deputy customs collector for this parish," the stranger announced. "My name is Ashton—Peter Ashton."

Rob shook his cousin's plump but surprisingly firm hand. "This is a pleasure, Cousin Peter."

"Cousin? Gad's my life! You can't be Robert Ashton?" An instant later Peter's manner changed. He looked acutely unhappy. "How did this happen?"

"A runaway slave brought the disease aboard in Norfolk."

Peter Ashton shook his head. "I don't mean that. How did you come to get piled up like this?"

Rob explained the manner in which his quartermaster had been deceived into taking false lights.

"False lights!" Peter Ashton's fingers snapped loud as a pistol's report. Peter clapped his cousin on the back. "Oh my God! If you only knew how funny this is—"

"If you imagine I'm about to collect insurance money, you're wrong."

"No insurance! Hear that? Why, I

couldn't figure out why Cazelles tied lanterns on his herd cows last night and put them on the beach. Now it's perfectly clear. I think that Cazelles will be glad to settle out of court. Incidently what a mannerless oaf I am! I trust you left the charming Mrs. Ashton well?"

Rob's expression checked the flow of compliments.

"She-she was aboard."

"Good God! How awful!" Giving his cousin a small reassuring hug, he said, "It may be, Cousin Robert, that you have come to the right place to—er—recover from your loss. Bermuda is interesting these days, one might say. My sister's governess is a very charming young lady from London."

Bermuda—1775

Even after she had locked her bedroom door Andrea Grenville continued smiling. It had been a glorious night to be out of doors. Briefly she wondered what devilment Susan Ashton had devised during her absence. To think of sleeping in the same house with David Ashton's own brother. Would Robert resemble him? After fishing between her mattresses a moment, she located her journal. Dutifully she wrote:

Mr. Robert Ashton is sleeping here tonight. Mr. Peter Ashton tells us the blows his American Cousin has suffer'd at the Hand of Fortune have left him cold and reserv'd. It must be monstrous sad to lose a Wife in so cruel a fashion. My heart bleeds for him.

It was so hot that she decided to take a walk in the garden before going to bed.

A few minutes later Rob noticed a moving patch in the moonlight. From behind the summerhouse stepped a young woman. When she saw Rob, she stood quite still and gazed at him so effectively that he felt his face grow scarlet.

"You are Susan's tutor?" he said finally.

Andrea's laugh was surprisingly tremulous. "If I can be dignified with so august a title."

Rob was thinking he had never seen anyone quite like her. The straight way this girl carried herself, the fineness of her features and her poise seemed incongruous in an ordinary governess.

"You are Miss Grenville then?"

"Yes, I believe I met your brother in London."

Andrea was astounded to see his features freeze, take on a wooden expression. It was evident he had no inclination to talk about David. She couldn't help wondering why.

Boston—August, 1775

Life in Boston during the heat of early August was not pleasant. It was desperately hard on body and soul. But of all the population, none fared so badly as the wounded of both sides. Unshaven, unwashed and naked save for filthy bandages, thirteen of the original thirty provincial prisoners had survived by August 14th. They tossed on woolen blankets that were clotted with blood and sticky from pus leaking through their dressings.

How Madelaine had learned of his capture and whereabouts David often wondered, but she would never confess even when he asked.

"Oh, David, your poor shoulder!" He would always remember the way she dropped on her knees beside him. She smelt so wonderfully fresh and sweet; a breath of lavender. To every one of the thirteen haggard wretches she gave a drink. Many of them could only look their unutterable gratitude. Others lay with tears slipping over smudged, bite-marked cheeks.

"If there was only some way to make you understand how much your coming has meant to this awful place," David muttered. "If there was only something I could do to prove my gratitude."

She remained as she was, slowly stroking his fingers. "I am very, very glad you said that. You see—I—well, today I —have missed my time—again."

His head snapped over and he looked at her hard. "You think—?"

Her soft brown head nodded. "I am sure of it or I wouldn't have spoken. Life is so hard—even for children with —with a name."

To his vast surprise, the idea of fathering a child seemed somehow inordinately pleasing. "And when, Ma'am," David asked, "may I have the pleasure of marrying you?"

"Whenever you wish."

"If you will wait only a little while, the Reverend Dr. Eliot will be coming in. I am sure that he will perform the ceremony. It may be our only chance for a long time, and in this instance, it seems a trifle important, doesn't it, Bright Eyes?"

M ADELAINE ASHTON's unremitting efforts soon bore fruit, and General Howe issued special orders that the poisonous conditions in the prison ward be remedied.

Miracle of miracles! Eight clean mattresses were lugged in. Four soldiers lifted him. But one of them hadn't got a good hold. Or else the frail cloth covering of David's old mattress gave way. Anyhow the invalid fell heavily to the floor.

David was relieved. He knew the wound had been pulled; he was sure he had felt a newly joined tissue tear. His shoulder hurt like fury but, lying on his fresh and much softer mattress, he felt there was no use complaining. What could a prisoner expect?

David Ashton never learned that he was dying. He reckoned it was mighty fine to lie still and rest. Loss of blood made him so drowsy he forgot that God-awful pain in his shoulder and drifted peacefully off to sleep—forever.

Bermuda—1775

"T HERE, damn you!" Peter chortled and tossed the sack, but it was so heavy it knocked the breath from Rob's lungs, sent him staggering.

"What's this?"

"Present from Hector Cazalles—rat him! There are your damages settled in full! Scared hell out of him. Listen to this piece of law." In jerky little sentences Peter began to read:

" 'Casting Away A Vessel. Whomsoever with intent—to bring a Vessel into danger—exhibits False lights—guilty of a Felony and shall suffer imprisonment for a term of seven—Years with or without solitary confinement.' "

Peter mopped a streaming forehead. "When I promised Cazalles we'd see he got solitary confinement, he quit his back talk. He judged if ever we got him into jail we would see he didn't own a sixpence when he came out."

Rob stood a moment, hefting the dirty, lumpy canvas bag. When the magnitude of what Peter had accomplished sank in, his eyes filled. *Seven thousand Spanish dollars!* By God, he hadn't dared hope to handle so much in years.

A NDREA was feeling that elation peculiar to a woman conscious that her newest dress is a success. Full skirted, white, and sprigged with tiny blue flowers, it was indeed becoming.

Critically she was appraising Rob who had wandered with her into the summerhouse, to escape a shower. No call for padding on those shoulders. He was wearing a new outfit. She approved his choice of fob and seals. Though unaffected and solid, they lent a new and pleasing air of dash. The lace on his shirt front and cuffs was good, even tasteful.

Rob was thankful that the rain had stopped. Soon they could go walking and perhaps—well, he was damned if he wouldn't kiss her.

"I'm sailing for America—tomorrow."

"You really are serious? I had so hoped you would stay longer. I shall miss—" Suddenly the truth struck breath from her body. "You don't mean you are going on the ship that has come to steal the powder? Oh, Rob! Don't—" Her voice broke. "Suppose anything happens—to you—."

As if they had gone there a thousand times, his arms slipped about her waist. To Andrea the moment became iridescent.

"My dear! My dear!" he whispered. "I had meant to wait. It isn't fair to speak now; it isn't fair."

"Why, darling? Why isn't it fair? Why can't we be married?"

"We shall," whispered Rob, "we shall."

It was something to have things settled, Andrea thought. Settled for both of them. They had each other. They had faith. The years might bring hardships, but there would be no faltering on either part. So much was settled——.

The Tiger

Tiger, tiger, burning bright
In the forests of the night,
What immortal hand or eye
Could frame thy fearful symmetry?

In what distant deeps or skies
Burnt the fire of thine eyes?
On what wings dare he aspire?
What the hand dare seize the fire?

And what shoulder and what art
Could twist the sinews of thy heart?
And, when thy heart began to beat,
What dread hand and what dread feet?

What the hammer? What the chain?
In what furnace was thy brain?
What the anvil? What dread grasp
Dare its deadly terrors clasp?

When the stars threw down their spears,
And watered heaven with their tears,
Did He smile His work to see?
Did He who made the lamb make thee?

Tiger, tiger, burning bright
In the forests of the night,
What immortal hand or eye
Dare frame thy fearful symmetry?
            —*William Blake* (1757-1827).

Herbert Agar

THE PEOPLE'S CHOICE

Dɪᴅ you know that the struggle between "vested interests" and "the people", which has reached its climax with Franklin D. Roosevelt, began in George Washington's administration? We have chosen three great Presidents, typifying three different phases in American government, to show how and why this struggle developed. "The People's Choice" sweeps away many popular misconceptions concerning Washington, Jackson and Wilson and gives the background against which one can follow present events at the White House with greater intelligence. The author who has also published a novel, a book of verse and a play, has lived for several years in London where he has been literary editor of "The English Review" and has handled newspaper contacts for the American Ambassador.

Oligarchy

Rᴀᴅɪᴄᴀʟs accused Washington of betraying his cause when he became head of a government formed to safeguard the rights of property. American democrats called him a "crocodile," "hyena, "traitor." For Washington had no illusions about the virtues, or the abstract rights, of mankind. He believed in discipline and authority. "Mankind," wrote Washington, "when left to themselves, are unfit for their own government." Such remarks came naturally from the first president of what was intended to be an aristocratic republic.

Born into a ruling class, but into a subordinate position within that class, he was made to feel from childhood that much was expected of him. At the same time, it was clear that if he was to justify his birth and become one of the important men of Virginia, he would have to do so by his own efforts. He lived in surroundings where he could acquire an education in men and manners; but his ambition was never lulled by the knowledge that even if he failed to make anything of himself his life would be smooth and comfortable.

At the age of sixteen he began to earn his own living in what was then, in that land-hungry Virginian society, the respectable profession of surveying. His job took him at once out of his accustomed world, into the unknown, exciting West.

There was nothing romantic about Washington's imagination; he responded to the West, and the Red Indian, with the practical interest of an empire-builder. Washington became the first "American," in that he was the first colonial leader to think, and act, nationally; and it is probable that an important reason for this was his early experience with the world across the mountains.

It was too vast and rich a world for its future to be considered in terms of Virginia; and early in his life Washington came to the belief that Providence intended a new and splendid nation to arise among these so novel and so favourable conditions.

Finally, when his ambition had been strengthened and his imagination enlarged, Washington became financially independent, and could give his life to public service when the occasion came.

In 1758, Washington got engaged to marry Martha Custis, one of the richest women in Virginia. For some years past, Washington had been in love with Sally Fairfax, the wife of his friend George Fairfax. After his engagement, Washington wrote to Mrs. Fairfax, indicating, in roundabout and guarded fashion, that he was in love with her, but that he could not, in honour, tell her so.

This is the most important passion of Washington's life, and although he suppressed it except for the one guarded statement, he never forgot Sally Fairfax. In 1798, the year before he died, he wrote to her in England, and after remarking on the many important events in the quarter-century since the Fairfaxes had left America, he added: "None of which events, however, not all of them together, have been able to eradicate from my mind the recollection of those happy moments, the happiest in my life, which I have enjoyed in your company."

This almost complete suppression of his emotions is characteristic of Washington.

The cold and impressive strength that was his in later life was not come by accidentally; it was the result of long control. A portrait painter, after studying Washington's face, said it was the face of a man with tremendous passions. These passions were subdued to Washington's will, with the result that when he set his heart on something, he pursued it with a concentration of purpose that could not be withstood.

With such a temperament, he might have dissipated himself in frothy swashbuckling, or in any other form of easy passion; instead, he trained himself to a disciplined, forbidding strength. The bottled-up, denied passion that such discipline implies may explain why Washington, from young manhood on, gave so many strangers the impression that he was destined for greatness.

Father of His Country

In considering Washington's motives for siding with the patriots against the English, it must be remembered that his Western land schemes not only turned him against the British Empire, but turned him toward the idea of an American nation, since the world across the mountains was too huge for one colony to exploit.

So when Washington made his appearance on the political stage, he made it as the first American—though he did not, in the beginning, see any need to leave the British Empire. As late as October, 1775, after he had become Commander-in-Chief of the rebel army, he was still opposed to independence. But from the moment when he decided to fight England rather than allow her to hamper colonial development he began to think of the thirteen colonies as a unit, with a common destiny. He was opposing the British Empire, not to protect Virginia lawyers from a stamp tax, but to create the Western empire of his dreams. And to do that he had need of a united America.

Washington was forty-three when he became Commander-in-Chief; he had reached full maturity, but had not yet lost any of his physical strength or hardihood. The question of Washington's purely military capacities will probably never be settled, for his was not a strictly military task. He seldom had an army with which he could oppose the enemy in decisive battle, and he never had a united country behind him. His job was to keep any army of some sort in the field, and wait for the English to lose the war. This the English did, in spite of the fact that it often seemed impossible.

After peace was made with England, Washington desired a stronger union between the states than the Articles of Confederation. He did not, however, intend to take part in a political movement for this purpose. He had his own work to do at Mount Vernon, and the only part he foresaw for himself in public affairs was that of an adviser who would use his great personal influence on the side of the right. But when the Federalists were ready to make their attempt at a peaceful revolution, they needed Washington's active support if they were to have any chance to succeed. So Washington was drawn into politics, the activity for which he was temperamentally least fitted.

The work that Washington had to leave unfinished at Mount Vernon was not simply that of a country gentleman administering a large estate. Washington was aiming, by experiment and example, at the reform of American husbandry. He had learned that in the implements used, in the size of crops, and particularly in the size of farm animals, the United States was far behind England. Washington studied the new books, corresponded with men like Arthur Young in England, imported implements, and tried out new methods. This work seemed to him as important as any he could do for the welfare of the agricultural empire that he foresaw in North America; and it was work that he knew himself fitted for by training, taste, and character.

If Washington was still dreaming of a purely agricultural United States, the men who had secured the adoption of the new Constitution, and the man who was to determine the economic policies of Washington's administration, had no such illusions. These men understood the economic forces at work under the surface of American life. They saw that the issue between the friends of a strong central government and the supporters of the old loose confederacy was not one of political theory, but of financial interest.

The creditor, commercial, financial classes wanted a strong government that could compel the payment of debts, that could suppress paper money, that could remove commercial restrictions between the States and make commercial treaties with foreign powers.

THE farmer and mechanic classes, however, wanted none of this. Their **grievance against** England had been that the British Government adopted precisely this policy, and having broken free from England, they now expected cheap money and light taxation.

None of the radical leaders was present at the Philadelphia Convention that made the new Constitution. Jefferson was in Paris, as American Minister; Patrick Henry refused to attend; Samuel Adams was not chosen. The Convention consisted of the friends of property and business—merchants, lawyers, speculators in public lands and public securities. The Constitution that these men drew up had, in their opinion, two great merits: it provided for as strong a central government as the people could be persuaded to accept.

Even after the adoption of this strong, conservative Constitution, the financial interests of the country did not feel themselves safe. Most Americans, after all, were still poor farmers, and these farmers had shown themselves susceptible to radical, inflationist propaganda. There was danger that the new government might be captured by the agrarians. Security could only come, the counter-revolution could only be stabilized, if a large capitalist class were quickly formed and if an economic policy were adopted which would make as many people as possible feel that their interests were identified with those of the capitalist class. It was this which Alexander Hamilton, whom Washington appointed Secretary of the Treasury, set himself to do.

First Republican

SHORTLY after Washington's Administration got under way, Jefferson returned from France, whereupon Washington asked him to become Secretary of State. The agrarian, egalitarian Jefferson, full of the newest French ideas, was opposed to Hamilton in theory and in temperament. They disagreed with increasing bitterness at Cabinet meetings, until Jefferson, finding that Washington supported Hamilton on every important point, resigned his office and set himself to create a party of opposition, a party that would seek to undo the centralizing, authoritarian, capitalistic, oligarchic counter-revolution of the Federalists.

It has been the custom to picture Washington as outside, or above, this

Hamilton-Jefferson quarrel—a quarrel from which arose the two main parties of American political history. But Washington was not outside the quarrel; he was a firm supporter of Hamilton and of all Hamilton's major policies. Even

THOMAS JEFFERSON

if he had understood the full economic consequences of Hamilton's statecraft, even if he had seen that his Secretary of the Treasury was fastening large-scale capitalism upon the country of which he had himself written that "the introduction of anything which will divert our attention from agriculture must be extremely prejudicial if not ruinous to us," Washington would probably have sided with Hamilton notwithstanding. For there was a temperamental affinity between Washington and Hamilton: both men were realistic and logical; both were authoritarian; both distrusted the political capacities of the common people; both had a strong love of property and a strong tendency to acquire more and more of it.

Washington believed that Jefferson, by stirring up the people to agitate for their

"rights," was endangering the life of the country. Of the "Democratic Societies," organized to protest against the conservative tenor of his administration, Washington wrote, "If these self-created societies cannot be discontinued, they will destroy the government of the country." And again, "My opinion is that you could as soon scrub the blackamoor white as to change the principles of a professed Democrat, and that he will leave nothing unattempted to overturn the government of the country."

AFTER four years in office, Washington hoped to return to Mount Vernon; but Hamilton insisted that he accept a second term as President. The repercussions of the French Revolution were beginning to be felt in America by 1792, when the Presidential elections were held.

The Jeffersonian group was becoming more and more extreme in its demands for legislation in the interests of the poor, instead of in the interests of Hamilton's moneyed class. If Washington stepped down now, said Hamilton, the Jeffersonians might come to power and all the good work that had been accomplished might be undone. After another four years, however, capitalism and sound business principles would be safely entrenched. So, reluctantly, Washington stayed on in Philadelphia, where the Government was now seated pending the building of the new capital city on the Potomac.

It was at that time that Washington came in contact with the fickleness and cruelty of the lunatic mob. Naturally, this did not incline him toward the party of democracy. In the last year of life—the year before the elections in which Jefferson came to power—Washington, in a letter to Patrick Henry, described the growth of the Jeffersonian party as a crisis "when everything dear and valuable to us is assailed, when this party hangs upon the wheels of government as a dead weight."

And in the same year he expressed

similar anti-Republican feeling in a letter to his nephew. In the light of such evidence, it is foolish to describe Washington as a non-party man, or as holding the balance evenly between Hamilton and Jefferson. Washington was not so flaccid in the face of a fundamental situation.

Democracy

IN THE frontier States democracy was not an ideal; it was an inescapable condition, like the weather. It had not been striven for; it had been thrust upon these States. It was praised sentimentally, but nothing was done to protect it. Had the Westerners really cherished their democracy, they would have clung to a Jeffersonian simple life, they would have defended themselves against the wealth, the inequalities, that industrial progress offered them. In fact, it was the wealth and inequalities they wanted. So their democracy was not a chosen way, but a transition—made as brief as possible—between an anarchic backwoods life and an anarchic plutocracy. The West was a period; it was never a plan.

The industrial East—growing in wealth and beginning to tap the cheap labour supply of Europe—had what it considered a plan; but this was merely the desire to establish the Hamiltonian economic programme as quickly as possible.

The new Eastern leaders were content to take Hamilton's economics and combine them with the politics of the frontier West. The unpleasantness of the result was long concealed, because so rich and vital a country as young America can survive political anarchy—for a time.

WHEN Andrew Jackson arrived at the White House after his inauguration he held a reception for "the people," who behaved even worse than their most hostile critics could have hoped. Punchbowls were spilled, glasses broken, chairs ruined by muddy boots. Thousands of rough Westerners had made the trip to see "their" President installed in "their" White House, and it is probable that the worse they behaved the better they pleased Jackson, who was proud to dramatize his contempt for the ways of the upper classes.

Jackson was no newspaper-made hero, but a genuine leader of the people. He really possessed the qualities for which his followers loved him, and he did the best for his country that was possible for an honest, ignorant, untrained, undisciplined man. If democracy had been able to find more Andrew Jacksons to lead it, it might not be discredited today. But once it had been proved that with the new democratic West (and with the rapid extension of suffrage in the older States) it was possible to elect a man with no public record, no positive pro-

ANDREW JACKSON

gramme, and no knowledge, the politicians took the hint. In the future it would be the norm for the American Presidents—with the added requirement of no strength of will, so that they would do what they were told.

Jackson was born on the frontier in 1767, just at the dividing line between North and South Carolina. After fighting in the War for Independence, he was able to study law, being admitted to the bar in 1787, the year of the Constitutional Convention at Philadelphia. In 1788 he was appointed prosecuting attorney of the western district of North Carolina, and moved across the mountains to the land that was soon to become the State of Tennessee.

This move was probably the chief determining event of Jackson's life. Had he remained east of the mountains he would have grown into a Southerner and been assimilated, along with his backwoods neighbours, into the new prosperous planting system of that district. Nothing could have altered Jackson's strange, fierce character; but his views, in so far as he had any, were the obvious product of his environment; so it is probable that the decision to cross the mountains had an effect on history.

B Y 1824, as the time for the Presidential elections approached, Jackson was established as the hero of the Western democracy, and, to a great extent, of "the people" everywhere. Violent, brave, successful, honest, and foolish, there was much about him to stir the enthusiasm of simple men. He was a moderately successful farmer and the owner of a few slaves; he had an intuitive feeling that the very rich were knaves; aside from that, his politics consisted of patriotism, a dislike of direct taxes, and a belief that the government should be economical. To the ruling classes of the day, his candidacy seemed absurd, for he was almost totally ignorant, spoke inaccurately, wrote worse, had little experience with government, and none with foreign affairs.

One of the first results of Jackson's election was the formation of two new parties. Under Monroe and J. Q. Adams the country had been changing so rapidly that the politicians and their organizations had not been able to keep pace. But the affection and hatred inspired by Jackson were themselves enough to create parties; the issues came later. The rank and file of Jackson's followers were the farmer-labour group throughout the country—yeomen and petty planters in the South, pioneer farmers in the West, labourers and German and Irish immigrants in the Eastern cities.

Jefferson's old party had been called Democratic-Republican. The Jackson men dropped the word Republican, and became the Democratic Party. In the eighteen-thirties it was a class party, strong only because it had a dynamic leader and crafty organizers, but internally weak because "the people" in the three parts of the country did not have similar economic interests.

"For the People"

T HE bitterest fight of Jackson's life was the "War on the Bank." The Bank of the United States was much disliked by the debtor class. For after the panic of 1819, which resulted from an orgy of speculation following the War of 1812, the National Bank foreclosed many hundreds of mortgages, thus coming to own large parts of many Western cities. The West began to call the Bank "the Monster."

Since most of the Jacksonian democrats were poor, an attack on this rapacious "Monster" was good politics, and Jackson's "kitchen cabinet" (of unofficial advisers) persuaded him that the Bank was nothing but the tool of the people's enemies, of the rich Easterners who sneered at Jackson's motley following.

The people of the United States were delighted with this combat. Jackson had assured them that the "money power" was their enemy, and they accepted the statement as obvious truth; Jackson was destroying the chief symbol of this power, and they thought the act both courageous and statesmanlike. The fact that he had no alternative plan, nothing to put in the place of the one agency that had discouraged "wild-cat" banking and the more insane forms of speculation, did not impress them. Neither did the fact that the "War on the Bank" was immediately followed by the worst financial depression the country has ever known and that "the people" of Jackson's cherishing were the chief sufferers from this disaster. The politicians, observing all this, learned a useful lesson about the new forces of democracy: that if a man seemed bluff and unpretentious, and talked about protecting the people, he could deprive them of every penny they possessed and they would still support him. Jackson had done this by mistake, and had made no profit; but surely a more far-sighted man could do it by intention?

Another vital problem which was becoming sicklied o'er with cant about "the people" was the problem of the public lands. The election of 1828 decided for all time that these lands would not be used wisely; but a further question remained: namely, in whose interest were they to be plundered?

Democracy might have been made workable if the nation had controlled the growth of the West so that the new, ungainly, backwoods states would not outnumber those with a settled civilization, had kept every dollar that could be made from the public domain in the hands of the National Government and used that endowment to promote the health and education of the citizens.

Also, a good thing might have been made of democracy by following Jefferson's ideal—supressing capitalism, discouraging industry, forcing the country to rely upon its boundless farmlands and to become a social as well as a political democracy, a nation of small-scale, independent, landowning farmers. That was a pleasing dream; but it never reached the stature of a plan. Jefferson lacked the political and economic realism to see, in time, what must be done if Hamilton was to be countered. By the time Jefferson had grasped the implications of Hamilton's scheme, it was too late to resist.

But neither of these plans, however, was even attempted, and the planless haphazard government which actually developed was a travesty of the democratic principle.

Plutocracy

OF THE three forms of democracy that have existed in America, the worst triumphed: the democracy of massed city populations, ignorant foreign labour, graft, and "machine politics"—the democracy, in other words that was really plutocracy.

The new masters of America had no vision of an ordered state. They wanted to be let alone, so that they could make a great deal of money. To gain this freedom, they were willing to do what was necessary in the way of corrupting the Government. Beyond that, they had no interest in politics.

The third period, therefore, was one of growing anarchy. The only reason the Government worked at all was that the country had such huge riches it could afford to waste most of them and still be better off than many countries. But the system was hard on posterity.

When the country began to fill up, when, in 1890, the old frontier disappeared and there was little more free land, when the time came that intelligent planning was needed in order to keep the country prosperous, trouble began. By the end of the century, a farmers' revolt and a labourers' revolt had appeared. These revolts found political expression in the Progressive Movement, which, for a few years, improved the moral tone of politics, but which came to nothing because it, too, was without a plan. For the Progressives had no new, thought-out vision of an organized State. So their movement died, and Harding became President.

The Progressive Era in American politics came to its full fruition in Wilson. That the achievements proved vain, that the end of the Progressive Era was Warren Harding and Coolidge Prosperity, is the result, not of the personal failure of Wilson, but of the insufficiency of liberalism before the problems of the twentieth century.

It is an interesting fact that Wilson's rise to power was promoted by the very men whom he thought it his life's work to frustrate. With cynical realism, these men decided that a liberal in the White House might be a nuisance, but would never be really dangerous. He would express, and satisfy, the people's demand for "reform"; he might pass some irritating laws; but then the whole thing would blow over and the rich could return to their traditional work of growing richer. But unless the people were given this mild vent for their discontent, something unpleasant, something effective, might happen.

The choice, to their subsequent sorrow, fell on Wilson, at that time President of Princeton University, a student of history and politics, but with a reputation as a public speaker and as a man of charm and force.

Through his youth it was Wilson's fixed purpose to go in for politics, in defence of liberalism and the simple, virtuous society of his childhood. On leaving college, Wilson studied law presumably because law is the highroad to advancement in American politics. He practised for a time in Atlanta, and then, being very poor and finding

the profession little to his taste, he decided to alter the whole plan of his life to abandon politics and take up college teaching. Instead of dealing with public affairs at first hand, he determined to become an influence through his books and students.

In his academic work, Wilson was never distinguished as a scholar. His books, though interesting in the light of his later career, are unimportant. He made no contributions to knowledge, and his five volume popular history of the United States is commonplace. The slow, exacting world of scholarship did not attract him; and his mind was not notably original or profound, so he could not use the findings of other men as the basis for historical thought which is of value to the adult world.

As a teacher of undergraduates, however, he excelled. He could dramatize and make exciting the issues of politics and law. He could infuse his subject with moral energy—for, in spite of a tendency to dilute reality with abstractions, he passionately felt that a crisis in American politics was approaching and that he knew the one way in which his country could be preserved.

For the same reasons that explain his success as a college teacher, Wilson was in demand on the lecture platform. After he had been for a dozen years at Princeton, there were influential men all over the country who had studied under him, whose minds he had stirred and who had a proper gratitude and respect for him. And there were earnest lecture audiences who thought him a prophet. He had done exactly what he had set out to do—had made himself an indirect influence on the political thought of the country.

Years of Authentic Greatness

Wilson was the second Democratic President to be elected since 1856. The reason for the party's weakness during all these years was the lack of an issue. The Civil War had settled the old issue between the agrarians and the business men. After 1865, anyone who suggested reverting to a policy that might diminish the profits of industry would be a political suicide. The Democrats.

herefore, while pretending still to herish the interest of the farmer, had no important policy to offer which was an alternative to that of the Republicans.

The Democratic Party was not an opposition—it was merely a substitute. It was an amorphous coalition of all who were dissatisfied with the Republicans, but who did not know what they wished to do about it: Western farmers, whenver money became too expensive and heir debts too burdensome; Southern farmers no matter what their financial status, since reconstruction had left the Republican Party an object of hatred in the South; Southern industrialists (when, toward the close of the century, industry began to develop in the South) for the same reason; the new immigrants, who felt that their capitalist rulers were against them and who therefore turned against the party in power; a few rich Easterners, who had risen from among the new immigrants, or whose interests were chiefly commercial so that they disliked the ever-rising Republican tariffs. Such a group had no economic or political unity, had nothing in common but a distaste for the Republicans, and a desire to get them out of office and to get themselves in.

Wilson was temperamentally a Jeffersonian and believed in democracy as a religious dogma. He believed that in crises of the national life the people were divinely inspired, and that their decisions had a supernatural sanction.

One of Wilson's plans for increasing the people's power was to restore the Presidency to its full ancient prestige, making of the President the immediate interpreter of the people's will, in which capacity he should have complete control over Congress. His conception of the office was not very different from that of a Greek tyrant—and the tyrant, as Plato points out, is the usual successor to inchoate democracy. Such was Wilson's solution to the problem of the growing leaderlessness and irresponsibility of American government.

For his first eighteen months in office,

Wilson carried all before him. So long as he had an enthusiastic following to whom he could appeal, he made short work of his opponents. It was when the following began to lose interest, when the first excitement died down, that his inability to meet opposition became clear.

Wilson's first demand on Congress was for an honest lowering of the tariff. At once the old game began. If Congress had been left to itself, there would have been months of dark bargaining followed by a bill in which all the important rates were higher than ever. The tariff lobby had never been defeated. There had been no real reduction since before the Civil War.

WILSON waited until matters looked very bad, then issued a statement to the press: "Washington," he said, "has seldom seen so numerous, so industrious, or so insidious a lobby. There is evidence that money without limit is being used to sustain this lobby and to create an appearance of a pressure of opinion antagonistic to some of the chief items of the tariff bill. Only public opinion can check and destroy it."

Public opinion, through the West and South, responded so violently that Congress was coerced. In the East, Wilson was criticized for demagogy. "Is it possible," asked the New York Times with solemn absurdity, "that the President had mistaken for lobbying the ordinary, usual and perfectly legitimate measures taken by protected interests to present their case to Congress?"

The same use of public opinion to coerce Congress was made by Wilson in support of all his important measures. But when the World War broke out in Europe, American interests began to veer away from Progressive reforms at home; new passions and new alignments began to make themselves felt. Wilson's great days were over. He had become the master that he planned to be; he had passed the laws that he promised. During the first year of his Presidency it must have seemed to him that the whole

Progressive dream was realized. And to what did it all come? With a few years the country had relapsed into a slough more malodorous than that from which the Progressives had lifted it.

Liberalism was clearly not the answer to the American dilemma. It was too tentative, too lacking in the courage to go boldly to the right or to the left. It was a dream, not a plan.

"Moral Dictator of the World"

THE work of presenting the war to the people as a noble moral effort came naturally to Wilson, and he did it supremely well. The people responded with enthusiasm. The issues seemed clear and satisfying and Wilson was convinced that he and his countrymen were destined to teach the whole world how to govern itself. What other motive could the Deity have had in permitting all this carnage? Wilson's zeal and conviction of high purpose were felt by the nation, which entered the war united and with delight.

The Armistice was concluded on the understanding that peace was to be based on Wilson's Fourteen Points—minus Point Two, which provided for the freedom of the seas. A few of these points were specific and clear—such as that on the restoration of Belgium and that on the return of Alsace-Lorraine to France. Others, however, were little more than affirmations of moral purpose.

To Wilson himself, the supremely important point was the Fourteenth, which called for the creation of a League of Nations. He appears to have felt that if only the League were created any injustices in the treaty would soon be rectified, and that if the League were not created the great moral uprising of peoples (which he considered the war to have been) would have taken place in vain. Therefore, he was tempted to bargain for the League by conceding other points.

However, Germany had been promised that peace would be made on the basis of Thirteen Points, and Wilson saw that the moral uprising must not be allowed to end in the breaking of this promise. It was here that the vagueness of the Points did its fatal work. For Wilson, in fact, made concessions on other points in

order to get his League of Nations, and then (to judge by his subsequent speeches in America) deceived himself into believing he had made no concessions, that the promise to Germany had been kept.

THE strain had been too great. Events had conspired, in 1917 and 1918, to make him feel that he was the moral dictator of the world. Then suddenly it turned out that he was nothing of the sort, that his orders were not obeyed, that the world in its invincible ignorance had other plans. He had either to face this fact and admit that he had failed in his new rôle of spiritual conqueror, or else he had to persuade himself that he had really succeeded, that the treaty was all he had said it was going to be, that it was a new world even if it did have shabby edges. He chose the latter course, and thereafter his ruin was swift.

Before he sailed for Paris, he had already ensured an unpleasant reception for whatever treaty he brought home. Before the elections of 1918 he had appealed to the country to return a Democratic Congress, putting his pleas in such a way as to suggest that Republicans could not be trusted to behave themselves in a world crisis. The country, perversely, had returned a Republican Congress.

In addition to this unwise appeal to the country, Wilson had made a further political blunder in the appointment of the Peace Commissioners. He made the Commission into an almost wholly partisan group, containing only one Republican member and that one a man who in no sense represented his party.

These two mistakes of Wilson's were the result of his chief character-defect: his failure to remember that opponents could be honest, decent men. It was wicked to make the world's peace into a party issue. Nevertheless, had Wilson kept his head clear, had he returned home with his treaty and urged it on the country for what it was—a poor thing, but the best that he could get—he could have roused the country, to support him once again, and his treaty, League and all, might have been accepted.

B UT it was a new Wilson who returned from Paris. His enemies had always accused him of hiding the truth among his florid phrases. It had never before been true, for back of his phrases (at least in his domestic politics) there had been clarity of purpose. But now the old taunt appeared to be justified, and, having alienated the partisan Republicans, Wilson proceeded to alienate his natural liberal supporters as well, by declaring that the treaty was a wholly good thing, that it embodied the Thirteen Points, that it was a true foundation for universal peace.

In the summer of 1919, the Senate having refused to accept the treaty without important reservations, Wilson began a tour of the country to win popular support. The strain and the shock of the last six months had been too much for him. In September he collapsed.

Wilson outlived President Harding, who succeeded him. He had lived long enough to see the country relapse into conditions as disgraceful as those of the seventies, and to see that the relapse was unlamented. It is not known whether this affected his views on democracy, or his faith in progress; whether, at the end, he would have subscribed to his statement made in the brave days before he first held public office: "All through the centuries there has been this slow, painful struggle forward, forward, up, up, a little at a time, along the entire incline, the interminable way."

WHEN DAISIES PIED

WHEN daisies pied and violets blue,
    And lady-smocks all silver-white,
And cuckoo-buds of yellow hue
    Do paint the meadows with delight,
The cuckoo then, on every tree,
Mocks married men; for thus sings he,
            Cuckoo;
Cuckoo, cuckoo: O word of fear,
Unpleasing to a married ear!

When shepherds pipe on oaten straws,
    And merry larks are ploughmen's clocks,
When turtles tread, and rooks, and daws,
    And maidens bleach their summer smocks,
The cuckoo then, on every tree,
Mocks married men; for thus sings he,
            Cuckoo;
Cuckoo, cuckoo: O word of fear,
Unpleasing to a married ear!
                —William Shakespeare

Emil Ludwig

NAPOLEON

A LITTLE over a century ago, as today, there was a man in Europe who was a god to some and a monster to others. It is only recently that someone has been able to sift out passion and prejudice and present Napoleon, *the man,* who could be both god and monster.

A Kingdom in a Garden

A TACITURN boy, small, shy, and lonely, sits reading in a corner of the garden. It is his own plot in the school garden at Brienne, and he had made a fence round it. Really, only a third of the enclosure is his own, but he has fenced in the plots of neighbours on either side. They may come in too; but woe to anyone else who disturbs his privacy!

He rushes furiously at the intruder. A little while ago, when the boys had had a fireworks' display, two of his school mates, who had been slightly burned, had run away to his garden for refuge. He had driven them out, flourishing a hoe at them.

No punishment will bring him to reason on this matter. The masters shake their heads and let him go his own way. "The youngster is made of granite," says one of them, "but there is a volcano inside."

No one may touch this little kingdom of his in the garden, though part of it is usurped. He has an ardent feeling for his own independence. Writing to his father, he says: "I would rather be the first among the workmen in a factory than the last among the artists in the Academy."

Did he get the idea out of Plutarch? Certainly he has an enthusiasm for that author, the lives of the great men as sketched by Plutarch, especially the Roman heroes. Of these, he is always

dreaming. No one tells us that he ever saw this boy laugh.

To his schoolfellows he seems half a savage, or at best a queer foreigner. He scarcely knows a word of French, and has little inclination to learn the language of the foe. What a tiny little chap he is, and what a ridiculous name! His coat is too long. No pocket-money, nothing to spend, and yet he claims to be of noble birth! The scions of the French nobility laugh. Who cares about Corsican noblemen?

The young Napoleon writes to his father: "I am tired of explaining my poverty; of having to endure the mockery of these foreign boys whose only superiority is in respect of money, for in nobility of feeling they are far beneath me. Must I really humble myself before these purse-proud fellows?" The answer from the island is: "We have no money. You must stay where you are."

He stays five years; and, just as his revolutionary feeling is intensified by every slight, so does his self-confidence grow proportionally with the growth of his contempt for his fellows. The masters have a good opinion of him, although he does not make much headway except in mathematics, history, and geography—subjects which appeal to a precise mind, seeing eyes, and also to the bitterness of spirit characteristic of one who belongs to a conquered race.

For always his thoughts turn back to his native island. He has a presentiment that some day he will set Corsica free

As yet all the lad of fourteen can do is to pore over books about his homeland, for he who would make history must first study history. He devours, too, all that Voltaire, Rousseau, and the great king of Prussia shortly before his death, have written on behalf of the liberation of Corsica.

Such a boy as this—solitary, suspicious, questing and rebellious, brooding rancorously over vast designs—what is he likely to become?

The Self-Crowned Emperor

ON DECEMBER 2, 1804, in Notre Dame, an abundance of precious stones reflects the light of myriad candles, so that the place looks more like a banqueting hall than a church. Everything has been prepared for weeks beforehand. A skilful museum director has even produced a colourable imitation of Charlemagne's sceptre. Ancient parchments from the days of the Roi Soleil had been consulted, to ensure that the crowning of his revolutionist should vie in every respect with that of the legitimate monarchs of France. Ségur had studied the etiquette of the occasion with the utmost care; Isabey had rehearsed the whole affair with an array of dolls; the old palace, Paris, France were in a fever.

The Emperor is in a pleasant humour. Early in the morning, he makes sure that Josephine's crown is a good fit. The great procession drives to the cathedral. Napoleon, robed in an antique imperial mantle, strides to the high altar leading the empress by the hand. Josephine's charm helps to divest the great moment of a certain sense of embarrassment. Surrounded by attendant Cardinals, the pope is seated, waiting. The organ peals.

Then, when the appointed instant has come, and all are expecting this man who had never bowed the knee to any one, to kneel before the Holy Father, Napoleon, to the amazement of the congregation, seizes the crown, turns his back on the pope and the altar, and, standing upright as always, crowns himself in the sight of France. Then he crowns his kneeling wife.

ALL who describe the occasion agree in saying that the Emperor was pale but handsome. He resembled Emperor Augustus; and from now onwards, as if by some mystical power, his features grew more and more like those of the first emperor of Rome. There on the steps of a temple stands a soldier whom a dozen years before this day no one had ever heard of, who since then has performed no miracles but only done deeds, and has now crowned himself with the golden laurels of these deeds. But his mantle is broidered with golden bees, the emblem of activity.

When he was seated on the throne, crown on head, with the pope in front of him he said in a low aside to his brother: "Joseph, if only Father could see this!" The remark, poignant of such an hour in the mouth of a man who was never wont to speak of his father, is fundamentally natural. The perfect simplicity, the unsophisticated innocence, of his course of action, lead his mind back to his origin. Memories of family feuds on the island, of the pride and ambition of the Corsican clans, direct his thoughts towards the stock from which he has sprung.

Semblance never holds his attention, which always reaches out to the core of reality. Thus he is not bewildered even in this amazing hour. When he wants to whisper something to his uncle, who stands just in front of him during Mass, he gives the cardinal a gentle dig in the back with his sceptre.

As soon as all is over, and, alone with Josephine, he goes in to dinner, he says with a sigh of relief: "Thank God we're through with it! A day on the battle-field would have pleased me better!" At their little dinner he tells her to keep on her crown, as if he and she were poet and actress, for, he says, she is charming, his little Creole woman an empress.

Thus, in the most natural way in the

world, he unmasks the whole masquerade, and we are at ease once more as we see the son of the revolution laughing his own empire to scorn.

The freedom of spirit shown by the foregoing petty details is splendidly illuminated by an admission he made the same evening, when, to a confidant, he summed up the whole matter with sceptical emotion: "No, Decrès, I have come into the world too late. There is nothing great left for me to do. I do not deny that I have had a fine career, but what a difference between me and the heroes of antiquity. Look at Alexander, for instance.

NAPOLEON IN HIS CORONATION ROBES

After he had conquered Asia, he declares himself to be the son of Jupiter, and the whole East believes him, save only his mother and Aristotle and a handful of Athenian pedants. But if I, nowadays, were to declare myself the son of the Father Eternal, every fishwife would laugh in my face. There is nothing great left for me to do."

By nature he is endowed with immense powers, and is overburdened by their incredible weight. Nothing can be adequate to his aspirations, now that he had learned how readily people obey the man who can command obedience by his skill and by his deeds. He is strong in his own strength; what does Voltaire's enlightenment, what does Rousseau,

matter to him. How can he wish to establish democracy, to install popular government, when he knows the weakness of the popular instincts, and all the corruptness of the ideals of the people?

To expand his sway, to spread his name widely and ever more widely, to leave more than a half page record of himself in the book of universal history, to sacrifice life itself to the little golden circlet on his head, to do these things without enjoyment and without leisure and without pause—this is life.

When, during these days, the sketch for an imperial seal is laid before him and he sees a lion couchant, he draws his pen across the picture and writes in the margin: "An eagle volant."

Conquest

THE brilliantly lighted ballroom forms a background where Poland displays her greatest beauty and her most precious jewels. This is the evening of evenings. In the old palace of Poland's kings at Warsaw, the Emperor of the French is to be shown the calibre of the nation that has been suffering so long

Will he admire the national dance, its music and its figures? Will the eyes of the ladies ravish him, those eyes which are pools of Slavic melancholy? Will the flattery of the speeches of the idolising comparisons appearing in the newspapers make his heart as wax? Such, according to the sanguine, are the questions upon which hang the fate of the nation.

He has spoken to many in cheerful vein; now he is standing in a recess, dividing his attention between his interlocutor and the dancers. Suddenly his gaze is focused on a special point, and he forgets to carry on the conversation. Then he approaches a group and draws the lady of his choice out of the circle of her companions.

She is a gentle, fair-haired beauty, dainty and small, has blue eyes, appears to be of a yielding disposition and is eighteen years of age. She is simpler in her dress than any of the others, and her behavior is correspondingly quiet and without display or the lure of coquetry. The Emperor chooses her as partner in contradance, delights in her grace and her lovely voice, finds her broken French bewitching. While she smiles and is covered with confusion, her name is whispered from room to room through the palace: Countess Walewska.

"I had eyes only for you," he writes to the countess next day. "I admired only you, and longed to be with you alone. Send me an answer quickly, in order that the fire which is consuming me may be appeased. N."

But the messenger returns with neither answer nor tiding of any sort. The Emperor is nonplussed. Something quite new. Twelve years ago the brigadier general might have had such a rebuff. But Napoleon, never. The more enchanting, therefore, is this lady who shrinks back so virginally from the unveiled desire of a man.

"Have I displeased you? I hoped the opposite. Or has your first feeling vanished? My passion grows. You rob me of my rest. Vouchsafe a little joy, a little happiness, to the poor heart that would fain worship you! Is it so hard to give me an answer? You now owe me two." This second letter is unsigned.

TERRIBLE the position of the adjutant who for the second time has failed in the carrying out of a movement ordered by his chief. For the missive is again unanswered. The Emperor, controlling his passion, writes again.

"There are moments in life when high position is a heavy burden. That is borne in on me at this moment. . . If only you would! None but you can overcome the obstacles which separate us. Oh, come, come! All your wishes shall be fulfilled! Your country will be even dearer to me, if you have compassion on my heart. N."

The third love-letter is intelligently composed, and therefore achieves its purpose—but it discloses to us the tragical mask of destiny, the destiny of one who wishes to walk along the course he had planned for himself, and who is sacrificing his human happiness to this heroical monomania.

Now having fallen passionately in love, he dismisses his secretaries, will not discuss matters with his generals, refuses to admit deputations, will not go out riding. The whole mechanism he has constructed is stationary. The palace, the army, Paris, Europe—let them wait.

He, more a slave than any other, refuses today to obey the nature of things; a man of thirty-seven whose wife, well past forty, no longer stirs his passion. Profoundly moved by a girl, he must devise lures from his other realms, must tempt her with the freedom of her country, in order that, after nearly a decade of quiescent feeling, he may spread upon the shoulders of a young woman the mantle of his yearning for tranquility.

She, alarmed at the assault of this virile will, sits the same afternoon among her friends and relatives who are urging the sacrifice upon her, for Poland's sake. In this mood, she at length goes to see him. The three evening hours she spends with him are spent in tears. By gentle arts he restores her to calm, and to her astonishment she finds that this dreaded man of iron is a tender wooer.

Not until three days later does she become his. Then she comes to see him every evening. Never has he known another woman who did not expect his magician's hand to shower on her the treasures of the universe: jewels, palaces, crowns, money. This woman wants nothing from him, and gives him everything.

Countess Walewska is the quiet and loving companion whom Napoleon's stormy soul has sought. It will be long before he will be willing to part from her. "She is an angel. It may justly be said that her spirit is as lovely as her features."

Meeting of Minds

IN ERFURT, the Emperor had an hour's talk with Goethe. A fleeting moment in the course of a thousand years; there has been nothing to compare with it since the meeting between Diogenes and Alexander.

Goethe, who learned everything from nature, though in the reality of the world of men he could only find the confirmation of his previous imaginings, felt that this conversation was one of the greatest events in his life, and he described it as such. To the Emperor it was less significant.

For Goethe had followed the Emperor's course for a decade, marvelling all the while; and in his old age he said such profound things about Napoleon that a century after their utterance they have not been excelled. Napoleon, on the other hand, knew almost nothing about Goethe; in especial, he never surmised the poet's personal admiration for himself, since the German had hitherto confided his feelings only to his intimates, and even now kept his own counsel.

But such as Napoleon and Goethe need but look in a man's eyes to know all about him. Napoleon sits breakfasting at a large, round table; on his right is Talleyrand; on his left, Daru. Now he looks up, and seeing the poet framed in the doorway, invites Goethe to approach. The Emperor is silent, amazed. There stands the sexagenarian, the most beautiful, the halest of old men, Goethe in the calm of his age, at the pinnacle of a strenuously wrought harmony of spirit, a harmony he had never possessed before and was so soon to lose. Napoleon is too full of admiration to speak. Then, more to himself, than to his companions, he says:

"Voilà un homme!"

That is the golden shaft which pierces the heart and illuminates the scene: the word of a seer, deeply felt, an impression rather than a judgment. Precisely because the world ruler does not know that a world ruler is now before him, this utterance, the like of which he had never made to or of any one in the past and which he is never to make in the future, shows the godlike kinship of a genius with his brother genius. Then the Emperor assumes the offensive:

"Does it please you here, Herr Goethe?"

Goethe, too, knows how to seize political opportunities, and rejoins: "Very much; and I hope these days will also prove advantageous to our little country."

"Is your people happy?" asks the Emperor, not noticing that he had phrased the question as if he were talking to a sovereign prince. Really, he has no interest now in Saxony, and is thinking: "How can this man of genius be useful to me? What a pity he does not write history. He would certainly do much better than our folk; and, besides, this would have redoubled value coming from a foreigner." He therefore says:

"You would do well to stay here for the whole period of the conference, that you may write your impression of this great drama. What does Herr Goethe think of the suggestion?"

Napoleon ends with the question (so unconsonant with his customary dictatorial manner). Goethe says cautiously:

"I have not the pen of a classical author."

"That's in the political vein," thinks the Emperor. But what he says is:

"Your duke has invited me to Weimar. For a time he was sulky, but now he is in a better humour."

"If he was sulky, Sire, the punishment was certainly rather sharp; but perhaps I ought not express an opinion on these matters. At any rate, we all owe him reverence."

"Splendid!" thinks Napoleon. "He stands in front of his master, but lets me see he knows that the duke is a donkey. I must get this man to write my 'Caesar' for me! The effect in France would be bigger than that of winning a battle!" His spoken words are:

"Tragedy should be the school of kings and peoples; there is no other field in which the poet can win such laurels. Why do you not write 'Caesar's Death,' more worthily, more splendidly than in Voltaire's attempt? This might be the greatest work of your life. The aim of the tragedy would be to show how much happiness Caesar would have conferred on the human race had he been given time to carry out his far-reaching plans. Come to Paris! I urge you to do so! Thence you will get a wider prospect of the world, and there you find the most abundant materials for new imaginative creations."

The poet expresses his thanks for the proposal, and says he would deem himself happy were it possible to accept.

"That is as far as I had better go," thinks the Emperor. Out loud: "I hope you will come to the theatre this evening. You will find a lot of princes there. Do you know the prince-primate?

NAPOLEON IN EXILE

You'll see him in his box, fast asleep, with his head pillowed on the king of Württemberg's shoulder. Do you know the tsar? You ought to dedicate something to him in honour of Erfurt!"

Thus the Emperor gives a third hint. Will Goethe take it? But the poet only smiles civilly and candidly declares:

"I have never done anything of that sort, Sire, and therefore I have never had occasion to repent it."

A touch! A touch! The Emperor of the French cannot but feel it! Marvellous to relate, the son of the revolution tries to strengthen his position:

"In the reign of Louis XIV, our great authors held other views!"

"No doubt they did, Sire; but we do not know whether they may not have repented."

"How true!" is the Emperor's thought when he hears this sceptical answer which is really a skirmisher's attack on the part of the German. Consequently he makes no attempt to detain the poet when the latter, with a deprecatory gesture, himself closes the interview and bids the Emperor farewell—another breach of court traditions, with which Goethe is perfectly familiar.

Thus the amazing upshot of this conversation between the two men of genius is that the Emperor, to whom the dialogue was merely interesting, had vainly solicited a favour of the poet to whom it was the greatest encounter in his life. The explanation is simple: The Emperor wanted to make use of the poet, whereas the poet did not need the Emperor.

"Death to the Tyrant"

IN OCTOBER, Napoleon is holding a great review in Schönbrun. A young man forces his way into the palace. He is arrested. When he is searched, he is found to be carrying a long knife and the picture of a girl. Examined in the guard room, he refuses to give any information, and says he will only explain himself to the Emperor in person. Soon the lad of eighteen, a fair-haired youth, serious of aspect, frank and courageous but courteous, is confronted with Napoleon. His name is Friedrich Staps, and he is the son of a Tyrolese pastor. Napoleon questions him in French.

"Yes, I intended to kill you."

"You must be mad, young man, or ill."

"I am neither mad nor ill, but in full possession of my faculties."

"Then why do you want to kill me?"

"Because you are ruining my country."

"Your country?"

"It is mine, as it is that of all good Germans."

"Who was the instigator?"

"No one. My heart told me that by killing you, I should do good service to Germany and to Europe."

"Have you even seen me before?"

"In Erfurt. Then I believed you would make no more wars, and I was your greatest admirer."

The Emperor sends for his physician in the hope that the young fellow will be declared a lunatic; but the doctor having made his examination, says that Staps is of sound mind.

"I told you so," says Friedrich.

The Emperor is uneasy. He is loath to make an end of so frank and bold a youth.

"You are distraught. You are bringing affliction on your family. Ask my forgiveness, and say you are sorry. Then I will grant you your life!"

Never before has Napoleon spoken thus, at any rate to an assassin. The young man remains steadfast. Has Napoleon lost the power of suggestion. "Well?"

"I do not want your forgiveness, and I am not sorry. My only regret is that I have failed."

The Emperor grows angry.

"The devil! A crime means nothing to you, then?"

"To kill you wouldn't be a crime, but a public service," says Staps, still perfectly respectful.

"Hm. Whose portrait is this."

"The girl I love."

"Will she approve this attempt of ours?"

"She will be sorry it has miscarried.

"What a pretty girl," thinks the Emperor. "Am I really to be baffled by this young fellow? No, I will save him, will pardon him. What does it matter to me if he hates me? If I pardon you, I suppose it will gladden the heart of this girl?"

Friedrich's blue eyes flashed, and he says firmly: "Then I shall be able to kill you after all!"

The Emperor turns away, and leaves the prisoner to his doom. So great is the impression wrought by the youth. We cannot call it alarm. Caution is too mild a word. The trouble is that a shadow has fallen across his soul.

The same morning, the assassin is shot, and the Emperor returns to the topic: "The thing is unprecedented! So young a man, a German, a Protestant, well brought up; and such a crime. How did he meet his end?"

The answer is that Staps, in face of the firing squad, had cried in loud tones: "Liberty for ever! Death to the tyrant!"

Upward to the Stars

MAITLAND stands on the quarter-deck. Napoleon raises his hat, a thing he had not always done to greet princes, and addresses the captain as follows: "I come to place myself under the protection of your king and your laws."

The British naval officers are introduced to him, and he asks about the seafights in which they have been engaged. Then, with the detachment of a man discussing ancient history, he talks about the English navy and the French, says that the English sailors are cleaner and more efficient, and argues with his host about certain punishments customary in the navy after a fight.

No repining! Here stands a gamester who has lost the game.

For the most part, Napoleon stays in his cabin. A few days' patience, and he will be able to go ashore, and live where he pleases. At length, however, feeling the need of fresh air, he comes up the gangway and mounts the poop. There he stands, the great defeated foe, in his old world-famous green coat: defenceless. But the man with the simple, impenetrable countenance must radiate an aura of dignity and suffering, for an extraordinary thing happens. Thousands of heads are bared. As far as Napoleon's gaze can reach, on the boats, the ships, throughout the harbour, not a man remains covered.

Such was the judgment of the British nation, which in this tense moment cleared itself from all the contumely so soon to be heaped upon its name. The waiting lasted three days. On the fourth, British officers entered the Emperor's cabin, and laid before him a paper.

The document was to the effect that it would not be consistent with the government's duties towards England and her allies to allow General Bonaparte any further opportunity of disturbing the peace of Europe, and it would therefore be necessary to restrain his liberty to "whatever extent may be necessary for securing the first and paramount object." St. Helena would be his place of residence, as it was healthy, and would admit of a smaller degree of restraint than might be necessary elsewhere. He could take with him three officers, a physician, and twelve servants.

Napoleon, we are told, "laid the paper on the table, and, after a pause, began to protest in vigorous terms." He said: "I am not a prisoner of war . . . I came on board the *Bellerophon* of my own free will, after previous negotiation with the commander. I threw myself on your protection, and claimed the rights of hospitality. The tricolour was still waving over Rochefort and Bordeaux. I might have gone back to the army; or might for years have lived secretly among the people, who were devoted to me.

"Instead I have fallen into a trap, your government has acted dishonourably and has dishonoured your flag. . . St. Helena will kill me in three months. I am used to riding twenty leagues a day. What can I do on a little rock at the world's end? I will not go! If your government wishes to kill me, that can be done here. . . I gave the prince regent an opportunity of performing the finest action of his life. I have been the greatest of his country's foes, and I paid you the highest compliment in the world by voluntarily entrusting myself to your protection. What you are proposing will be an everlasting disgrace to the whole British nation!"

FROM under the brutal pressure of this fist, the spirit of what he is crushing rises in a tenuous column. He upon whom the doom is enforced has acquired a power over himself, a power which sustains him in his powerlessness—stoicism. After the first outbreak, he bears the injustice with indomitable firmness, enduring for ten days the indignity of his position at Plymouth, and unruffled while England seizes his baggage and his money.

In due course, the Emperor and his companions were transferred to the *Northumberland,* which set sail for St. Helena. It was on an August morning that, for the last time, Napoleon set eyes on the coast of France, looming through the mist. But what did he care about the coast? The centre of his interest lay many miles to the eastward—Paris, which he had wooed more hotly than all the rest of the world, Paris, which had rejected his suit.

By evening, he loses sight of Europe, which he has ruled. Darkling is the sea, which he has never been able to rule. He stands in the bows, not looking backwards, nor forwards either. He looks upwards toward the stars. He is seeking his own star.

———◆———

KING DEATH

KING Death was a rare old fellow,
  He sat where no sun could shine,
And he lifted his hand so yellow,
  And poured out his coal-black wine.
    Hurrah, for the coal-black wine!

There came to him many a maiden
  Whose eyes had forgot to shine,
And widows with grief o'erladen,
  For a draught of his sleepy wine.
    Hurrah, for the coal-black wine!

The scholar left all his learning,
  The poet his fancied woes,
And the beauty her bloom returning
  As the beads of the black wine rose.
    Hurrah, for the coal-black wine!

All came to the royal old fellow,
  Who laughed till his eyes dropped brine,
And he gave them his hand so yellow,
  And pledged them in Death's black wine.
    Hurrah, for the coal-black wine!
        —*Bryan Waller Procter* (1787-1874)

Rudyard Kipling

THE JUNGLE BOOKS

"THE JUNGLE BOOKS" are on the "must" list of every child's library. But "to those who read between the lines," says Frederic Taber Cooper, "the Jungle Books are far more than a childhood classic. They are the life of modern India, told in allegory, and in Kaa, the python, and Gagheera the black panther, and all the rest we have the types of native life, with its stored-up wisdom of old, primeval instincts, its simplicity of outlook upon the present-day world." Kipling's animals are peculiarly convincing. They act and talk—when they do talk,—in accordance with their animal characteristics, and never give the impression that they are humans masking in fur, feathers or scales.

Mowgli of the Wolf Pack

THEODORE ROOSEVELT once took up his parable against the "nature fakers"—all the prolific writers of so-called nature stories who attribute the thoughts and emotions of men and women to wild or domesticated animals, not even excluding the humble inhabitants of a rabbit warren. But he did not extend his condemnation, which was based on a wide knowledge of every conceivable variety of big game, to Rudyard Kipling, whose immortal "Jungle Books" set the literary fashion that has brought into being "Tarzan of the Apes," that wildly improbable romance of the woods which has been one of the most crowd-compelling of entertainments both as a spoken drama and as a moving picture.

The two "Jungle Books" are not only masterpieces of English literature—they are also contributions to natural history, which have prompted many to exchange the rifle for the camera and study the habits and mentality of the living creature after the manner of Henri Fabre, the famous French naturalist (see Issue No. 22), whose loving-careful and life-long observation of insects has upset so many *ex cathedrâ* theories and finally confuted statements of supposed fact which have been repeated by writer after writer.

In his Preface to the first "Jungle Book," the author—"editor" he calls himself—gives a droll list of the "specialists" he claims to have consulted. He offers his thanks in the first place "to the scholarly and accomplished Bahadur Shah, baggage elephant 174 on the Indian Register, who, with his amiable sister Pudmini, most courteously supplied the history of 'Toomai of the Elephants,' and much of the information contained in 'Her Majesty's Servants'." His other informants, most of whom, we are told, desire to preserve the strictest anonymity (it might be assumed that, living as they do in an environment where "eat or be eaten" is the chief rule of existence, they would get into serious trouble if they were known to have given away racial secrets) include "Sahi, a savant of infinite research and industry, a member of the recently disbanded Seeonee Pack, and an artist well known at most of the local fairs of Southern India, where his muzzled dance with his master attracts the youth, beauty and culture of many villages."

In point of fact, the author is indebted for his intimate knowledge of the Indian fauna to his own powers of minute observation and to the help of many other human observers who have listened to the call of the jungle, and with their own eyes studied the manners and customs of its four-footed and footless inhabitants, acquiring a wealth of curious information not to be found in printed books.

Chief of these eye-witnesses was the author's father, J. Lockwood Kipling, C.I.E., who was as remarkable a man in his way as his more famous son; he had the jungle by heart and at heart, and his knowledge of teeming life, and of the animal lore and legends of the native races, has never perhaps been equalled.

The Human Cub

ROMULUS and Remus were brought up by a wolf mother, and there are many other legendary precedents for the adoption of Mowgli by a married member of the Seeonee Pack, led by the great, grey, grim Akela, who was superior to all his four-footed brethren in strength and cunning. It would never have happened but for the insolence of Shere Khan, a tiger lame from birth, who lived by killing the villagers' cattle.

Shere Khan was not popular with the other inhabitants of the jungle, for his depredations caused men to scour its fastnesses and set the grass afire, which was very inconvenient for wolves. Moreover, he was in the habit of changing his quarters without due warning, which is contrary to the Law of the Jungle. Again, this code forbids any beast to eat man, except when he is killing to show his children how to kill, and then he must hunt outside the hunting-grounds of his pack or tribe.

The real reason for this is that man-killing means, sooner or later, the arrival of white men on elephants, with guns, and hundreds of brown men with gongs and rockets and torches. Then everybody in the jungle suffers. The reason the beasts give among themselves is that Man is the weakest and most defenceless of all living things, and it is unsportsmanlike to touch him. They say, too—and it is true—that man-eaters become mangy and lose their teeth.

So when the jackal—Tabaqui the Dishlicker—visits the cave of Father and Mother Wolf, to tell them that Shere Khan intends to hunt in their neighborhood for the next moon, neither the obsequious, yet impudent, messenger nor his message is well received. Soon, too soon, the maneater is heard without at his unholy hunting. The snarling, singsong whine of a tiger who has caught nothing changes to the humming purr which seems to come from everywhere and is intended to bewilder the beast's prey. The purr ends in the full-throated "Aaarh!" of the great cat's charge, but is followed by a howl of pain, for he has foolishly jumped at the woodcutter's fire and has burnt his feet. Then Mother Wolf hears something coming up the hill, and as it enters the family cave Father Wolf stops in the middle of his spring, for he sees before him a naked brown baby, who can just toddle. The soft, dimpled, little man's cub is absolutely fearless; he looks up into Father Wolf's gaunt face and laughs.

MOTHER WOLF is pleased with the baby's boldness, and thinks that mothering a man's cub is a thing never heard of before, a thing to be proud of. So when Shere Khan, who had missed the child's parents, the woodcutter and his wife, sticks his great square head and shoulders into the entrance of the cave—it is far too narrow for his body to follow—and demands his meat, and fills the place with the thunder of his angry roaring, Mother Wolf, her eyes like two green moons, defies the "striped cattle-killer" and refuses to give the child up. Mother Wolf had been known as "The Demon," when she ran with the Pack, and she insults the mangy man-eater. "He shall live," she says, "to run with the Pack and to hunt with the Pack; and in the end, look you, hunter of little naked cubs—frog-eater—fish-killer—he shall hunt thee!"

She repeats her prophecy when Shere Khan has departed and her mate asks if she means to keep the man's cub; "Assuredly I will keep him. Lie still, little frog. O thou Mowgli—for Mowgli the Frog I will call thee—the time will come when thou wilt hunt Shere Khan as he has hunted thee."

The prophecy comes true.

Mowgli's Education

IT IS a law of the Pack that, as soon as a wolf's cubs are old enough to stand on their feet, he must bring them to the Pack Council, which is generally held once a month at full moon, in order that the other wolves may identify them. After that inspection the cubs are free to run where they please, and until they have killed their first buck, no excuse is accepted if a grown wolf of the Pack kills one of them: the punishment being death. So Mowgli, with the cubs of his foster-parents, is in due season presented at the Council, which is held on a hill-top covered with stones and boulders where a hundred wolves could hide. Akela lies on his rock and below him sit forty or more wolves of every size and colour, from badger-coloured veterans who could kill a buck alone to black three-year-olds who think they could.

The looking-over proceeds with little noise and less talk until Mowgli is pushed into the centre, where he sits laughing and playing with some pebbles that glisten in the moonlight. A roar comes from behind the rocks as Shere Khan demands the man's cub, but Akela, the leader of the Pack, goes on with his monotonous cry of "Look—look well, O wolves," merely stopping it to remind his followers that they have nothing to do with the order of any outsider.

A four-year-old wolf repeats the tiger's question: "What have the Free People to do with a man's cub?" So Akela asks who among the Free People speaks for Mowgli, and when he gets no answer, the valiant foster-mother gets ready for her last fierce fight, if it comes to fighting.

In the end Baloo, the brown bear who teaches the wolf cubs the Law of the Jungle, and Bagheera, the black panther, who offers a fat bull that he has just killed not half a mile away, speak for the man's cub, and he is looked over and accepted as a member of the Seeonee wolf-pack.

Baloo is responsible for teaching him the Law of the Jungle in its applications to wolves, and the author of this ever-green romance gives us in verse a few specimens of the simpler rulings, all of which are based on the principle that "the strength of the Pack is the Wolf, and the strength of the Wolf is the Pack." The whole poem is an ingenious effort to translate into men's language the code of instinctive observances which determines the life of the animals who, like Man himself, combine gregarious habits with a large degree of individuality. The wolf is warned not to be a parasite, like the jackal, but to get food of his own, and to hunt only for the livelihood of himself and his family:

Ye may kill for yourselves, and your mates,
  and your cubs as they need, and you can;
But kill not for pleasure of killing, and *seven
  times never kill Man.*

The wolf's home, like the Englishman's, is his castle:

The Lair of the Wolf is his refuge, and where
  he has made him his home,
Not even the Head Wolf may enter, not even
  the Council may come.

Like all very old codes of man's making, rules of health are prescribed—"wash daily from nose-tip to tail-tip; drink deeply, but never too deep," is wholesome advice. Wolves are to keep peace with the Lords of the Jungle—the tiger, panther, bear, the silent elephant and the valiant boar—and there are excellent rules devised to limit fighting among the wolves themselves as far as possible:

When Pack meets with Pack in the Jungle, and
  neither will go from the trail,
Lie down till the leaders have spoken—it may
  be fair words shall prevail.
When ye fight with a wolf of the Pack, ye
  must fight him alone and afar,
Lest others take part in the quarrel, and the
  Pack is diminished by war.

Finally, in all that the code leaves open, the word of the Head Wolf is law. Here, no doubt, the author might be accused of creating wolves mentally in Man's image; indeed one critic has described Akela's followers as "four-footed Kiplings." But we know so little about the *vie intime* of wild, gregarious animals that there may be more truth in this chapter of animal sociology than is generally believed.

Mowgli grows up with the wolf cubs, and Father Wolf teaches him the meaning of the sights and sounds and smells of the Jungle, where, as is the case in all the wilderness, it is the minute, almost imperceptible, things that matter most. Baloo and Bagheera are also his instructors in jungle-craft; the former shows him, for example, where honey is to be found, and the latter trains him so well in tree-climbing that he learns to fling himself almost as boldly through the branches as the grey ape. He is the beloved "Little Brother" of those jungle lords, and he likes to adopt Bagheera's habit of sleeping through the long, drowsy day and hunting at night— "Good Hunting!" is the usual greeting among these friends.

As HE grows older, Mowgli becomes as strong and swift and beautiful as a sylvan deity, and is respected as much for his physical powers as for the spiritual might that shines in his eyes. He finds that the wolves cannot stand his steady gaze, and even the brotherly Bagheera—Bagheera, born in the cages of the King's palace at Oodeypore, who understands the mysterious spirit of Man better than the other four-footed free companions—must drop his eyes when Mowgli looks long into them. A lovely and loyal youth with the might of woodland creatures, and their keen and ineluctable senses to serve a human intellect that is not to be deceived by conventional shams—what more fascinating character has ever been created by novelist or poet?

Ten years after the human cub took refuge in the cave of his foster-parents the trouble with Shere Khan comes to a climax. Mowgli is inclined to despise the danger, thinking the lame tiger to be "all long tail and loud talk—like Mao, the Peacock." But Shere Khan has been plotting successfully with the Pack, flattering the younger wolves and expressing his surprise that they should be content to be "led by a dying wolf and a man's cub." Akela is growing old, and the crisis comes when for the first time while leading the Pack in a night hunt, he misses the kill and is knocked over by the escaping buck. When a Pack leader has missed his kill, he is called the "Dead Wolf" as long as he lives, which is not long, as a rule.

Here the author is psychologically correct, for there can be no doubt that the leadership of a wolf pack is determined as it was with the human race in an early stage of primitive civilization, wherein anthropologists discover:

> The king who slew the slayer,
> And shall himself be slain.

A council is summoned to dispose of Akela—"toothless fool" Shere Khan, who has no right to be there, calls him to his face—and also of Mowgli. But Mowgli is there with a fire-pot, snatched from his village, and with the help of the dreaded "Red Flower" he terrorizes the assembly and puts the cowardly Shere Khan to flight. Then, in sorrow, he decides to go back to men; promising, however, to return and lay out the man-eater's hide upon the council rock.

HE GOES back to the village to the amazement of its inhabitants, and Messua, his mother, takes him to her hut, gives him milk and begins to teach him man's talk. He is quick at learning the ways and customs of men, though he loathes wearing a cloth about him, and cannot understand caste. However, he is soon a man again, so to speak, and is able to herd buffaloes and join the circle of gossips, which meets every evening under a great fig-tree. He scoffs at old Buldeo, the village hunter, who explains that the tiger that had carried off Messua's son (as was still believed) is a ghost-tiger—an incarnation, in fact, of Purun Dass, the dead money lender who limped from a blow he got in a riot when his account books were burnt. Buldeo, annoyed at hearing his tales described as "cobwebs and moonshine," tells the "jungle brat," if he is so wise, to kill the man-eater since the Government offers a reward for his hide.

Mowgli gets news of Shere Khan's whereabouts from his four-footed foster-brothers, and the time comes when, with Akela's help, he takes his revenge by a most ingenious stratagem. He and the wolves divide the herd of buffaloes into two clumps, the cow-buffaloes with their calves, and the bulls, old and young, and taking the latter round in a long, long circle, arrange that Shere Khan, heavy with food and drink in his ravine, should be caught between the detachments and trampled to death. So Shere Khan dies a dog's death, and Mowgli sets to work to skin him. Old Buldeo catches him at the task and, wishing to get the reward for himself, orders him to leave the carcass—whereupon Mowgli tells Akela to look after the old hunter, who finds himself flat on the ground and a gaunt, grey wolf standing over him. He thinks it black sorcery, and expects every minute to see Mowgli himself turn into a tiger. He is allowed to escape and tell his story to the villagers who receive Mowgli as a sorcerer, a jungle-demon, with blowing of conches and the banging of temple bells and a shower of stones and insults.

So he is cast out of the Man pack and returns to the Wolf pack, showing the tiger's striped hide on the Council rock. The wolves, tired of the evil results of past lawlessness, ask him to lead them, but he replies: "Man pack and Wolf pack have cast me out. Now I will hunt alone in the Jungle."

But, as things befall, he has to take vengeance on the village and, later on, when he has reached his full strength and power of mind and will, save the Seeonee Pack from destruction. The villagers barricade Messua and her husband in their hut, insisting they are the parents of a devil-child, and preparing the torture to make them confess they are witch and wizard, after which they would be burnt alive. The pair are rich, and this is a consideration with their persecutors, who intend to share their lands and herds between them and to tell the English they died of snake bite. They are rescued in time, with Bagheera's help, and then Mowgli asks Hathi, the elephant, and his three sons, to let the jungle in on the village. The villagers, though idle, senseless and cruel, are not to be killed or maimed, but their habitations and their tilled lands are to be utterly wrecked and ruined. All the inhabitants of the jungle, beasts and green things, assist in wiping out the village, and here is a stanza, with its mournful, haunting refrain so characteristic of Kipling's verse of Mowgli's declaration of destruction, his "Song against People:"

I will let loose against you the fleet-footed
    vines—
I will call in the Jungle to stamp out your
    lines!
  The roofs shall fade before it,
  The house-beams shall fall.
And the *Karela*, the bitter *Karela*,
  Shall cover it all.

So, his debts duly paid, Mowgli goes back to the Jungle life—back to:

    . . . . the nights of swift running,
Fair ranging, far-seeing, good hunting, sure
    cunning!

EPIGRAM

To JOHN I owed great obligation;
    But John unhappily thought fit
To publish it to all the nation,
    Sure John and I are more than quit.
                    —*M. Prior*

GIOVANNI PAPINI

LIFE OF CHRIST

PAPINI was born in Italy in 1881. He recounts his unhappy childhood in "The Failure" (1912). After a life of religious unbelief, despite his profession of an idealistic philosophy of pragmatism, he embraced Catholicism. Shortly thereafter, in 1921, he published his "Life of Christ," which immediately became a best seller. It was translated in 1923 by Dorothy Canfield. The condensation presented here has been prepared from her text.

The Nativity

JESUS was born in a stable, a real stable, not the bright, airy portico which Christian painters have created for the Son of David, as if ashamed that their God should have laid down in poverty and dirt. And not the modern Christmas-eve "Holy Stable," either, made of plaster of paris, with little candy-like statuettes, the Holy Stable, clean and prettily painted, with a neat, tidy manger, an ecstatic Ass, a contrite Ox, and Angels fluttering their wreaths on the roof—this is not the stable where Jesus was born.

The poor, old stable of Christ's old, poor country is only four rough walls, a dirty pavement, a roof of beams and slate. It is dark and reeking. The filthiest place in the world was the first room of the only Pure Man ever born of woman.

It was not by chance that Christ was born here. What is the world but an immense stable where men produce filth and wallow in it? Upon this earthy pigsty, where no decorations or perfumes can hide the odor of filth, Jesus appeared one night, born of a stainless Virgin armed only with innocence.

Jesus was brought back to his father's house in Nazareth, humble house and shop where the hammer pounded and the rasp scraped until the setting of the sun. Luke, the wise doctor, tells us that the boy grew and was strong; that is, that he was not sickly and overworked. Every year, says Luke, the parents of Jesus went to Jerusalem for the feast of unleavened bread in memory of the escape from Egypt.

Jesus and the Wise Men of the Temple

ON THE twelfth Passover after the group from Nazareth was returned from the Holy City, Mary found that her Son was not with them. For three long days she sought Him. Finally she came to the Temple, looked about in the courts, and saw in the shadow of a portico a group of old men talking. She discovered that her Son was in the midst of those old men. They were asking Him questions and He was answering. They marveled at Him, astonished that a boy should know the words of the Lord so well.

She clutched Him, took Him away, and then the happy mother remembered the despairing mother, "Son, why hast thou thus dealt with us? Behold, thy father and I have sought thee sorrowing." And he answered, saying: "How is it that ye sought me? Wist ye not that I must be about my Father's business?"

Weighty words, especially when said by a twelve-year-old boy to a mother who has sought him for three long days.

And, the Evangelist goes on, "And they understood not the saying which he spake unto them." But after so many

Thus died a God

Illustration for Giovanni Papini's
"LIFE OF CHRIST"

centuries of Christian experience we can understand those words, which seemed at first sight to be hard and proud.

THE hour for really leaving His home had not come for Jesus. With His father and mother He once more went along the road to Nazareth and returned to Joseph's shop to help him in his trade.

It must never be forgotten that Jesus was a working man and the adopted son of a working man: that He was born poor, among people who worked with their hands. Before He gave out His gospel He earned his daily bread with the labor of His hands.

Jesus, the carpenter, lived in His youth in the midst of these things, made with His hands, and for the first time by means of these things manufactured by Him, entered into communion with the daily life of men, with the most intimate and sacred life—home life.

GIOVANNI PAPINI

Jesus Learns from the Carpenter's Trade

HIS trade taught Him that to live means to transform dead and useless things into living and useful things: that just as a child's crib or a wife's bed can be made of a log of olive wood, gnarled, knotty and earthy, so the filthy money-changer and the wretched prostitute can be transformed into true citizens of the Kingdom of Heaven.

Often while the thin, light shavings curled up under the steel of His plane and the sawdust rained down on the ground, Jesus must have thought of the promises of the Father, of the prophecies of old times, of what He was to create, not with boards and rules, but with spirit and truth.

His life to come was already set down day by day in pages written before His earthly birth. He knew that God promised Moses a new prophet: "I will raise them up a prophet from among their brethren, like unto thee, and will put my words in his mouth; and he shall speak unto them all that I shall command him."

And He knew that the prophet Isaiah had announced his coming: "For unto us a child is born, unto us a son is given: and the government shall be upon his shoulders: and his name shall be called Wonderful, Counsellor, the mighty God, and everlasting Father, the Prince of Peace.

"But he is wounded for our transgressions, he is bruised for our iniquities: the chastisement of our peace is upon him: and with his stripes we are healed."

These and other words are remembered by Jesus before His departure. He foresees it all and does not turn away from it. He knows His fate, the hatred of the powerful, the deafness of His friends, the scourgings, insults, piercing of the hands and feet, tortures and death.

He knows that the Jews are not awaiting a poor, gentle, despised Messiah. They are dreaming of a terrestrial Messiah, an armed King who will revenge Himself on the enemies of Israel. He knows that He cannot give them what they seek, that He cannot be the victorious warrior and the proud king towering up among subject kings. He knows that His kingdom is not of this earth and that He will be able to offer them only a little bread, all His blood and all His love.

Jesus Conquers Satan

THE fact that we know nothing of the life of Jesus from His twelfth to His thirtieth year, exactly the years of fallible adolescence, of hot-blooded youth, has given rise to the idea that He was in that period, or at least held Himself to have been, a sinner like other men. But nothing of what we know of those years gives any indication of this supposed existence of sin in Christ's life between the innocence of its beginning and the glory of its ending.

There is not even the appearance of a conversion in Christ's life. His first words have the same accent as the last. The spring from which they run is clear from the first day; there is no muddy sediment of evil. He begins with frank absolute certainty, with the recognizable authority of purity. You can feel that He left nothing turbid back of Him.

Jesus came among the sinners, but He was no sinner. He was, however, no rigorous Puritan. He knew life: He did not refuse life which though not a good in itself is a prerequisite condition of all good things. Eating and drinking are not wrong, nor sending a friendly look to the thief lurking in the shade, nor to the woman who has colored her lips to hide the telltale traces of unasked kisses.

JESUS conquered Satan in Himself and now went out to conquer him among men whom He met.

Jesus taught His Galileans on the thresholds of their shabby little white houses, on the small shady open places of their cities or the shore of the lake, leaning against a beached boat, His feet on the stones, towards evening when the sun sank red in the west.

In the early days we find Him most often at Capernaum. His journeys began there and ended there. Matthew called it "His city." Situated on the caravan route from Damascus to the sea, Capernaum had become, little by little, a commercial center of some importance. But there were still peasants who went out to their fields every day, and fishermen who went forth to their boats.

Among the fishermen of Capernaum, Jesus found His first disciples. Not by chance did Jesus select His first companions from among fishermen. The fisherman who lives a great part of his days in the pure solitude of the water is the man who knows how to wait. He is the patient, unhurried man who lets down his nets and leaves the rest to God. He does not desire sudden riches, and is glad if he can exchange the results of his fishing for a little bread and wine. He washes his hands in water and his spirit in solitude.

Of these fishermen who would have died in the obscurity of Capernaum without any one except their neighbors being aware of them, Jesus made saints whom men even today remember and invoke.

Fate knows no better way to punish the great for their greatness than by sending them such teachers.

Jesus Transforms His Disciples

JESUS knew that his disciples were rough but had integrity, were ignorant but ardent, and that He could in the end mold them according to His desire, bring them up to His level, fashion them like river clay which when molded becomes eternal beauty.

Yet we see them hard of head and of heart, not able to understand the clearest parables of the Master; not always capable of understanding, even after His death, who Jesus had been and what sort of a new Kingdom was proclaimed by Him; often lacking in faith, in love, in brotherly affection; eager for pay; somnolent, doubtful, materialistic, avaricious, cowardly.

One of them denies Him three times; one of them delays giving Him due reverence until He is in the sepulchre; one is not willing to admit His resurrection; one sells Him to his enemies. Others, when they thought Christ's teachings were on a too-lofty-level, "went back and walked no more with Him."

The flame from the Holy Ghost was needed for the transformation; until the day of the Pentecost their imperfect nature had too often the upper hand. To the Twelve much should be pardoned because, after having deserted Him in the Garden of Gethsemane, they never forgot Him and left to all eternity the memory of His word and of His life.

All but John died violently for their faith in Him. Peter died on the cross, nailed head downward. Thomas met a martyr's death in India, Andrew was crucified at Patras, Bartholomew was crucified in Armenia. Simon the Zealot and Matthew, like their Master, ended their lives on the cross.

Love Divine, All Love Excelling

THE world of antiquity did not know love. It knew passion for a woman, friendship for a friend, justice for the citizen, hospitality for the foreigner; but it did not know love.

In the noblest heroic world of antiquity there is no place for that love which destroys hate and takes the place of hate, for love stronger than the strength of hate, more ardent, more implacable, more faithful, for love which is not forgetfulness of wrong, but love of wrong, because wrong is a misfortune for him who commits it rather than for him who suffers. There is no place for love for enemies in the world of antiquity.

Jesus was the first to speak of such love. It is the greatest and most original of Jesus' conceptions. Of all His teachings this was the newest to men; this is still His greatest innovation. It is new even to us, new because it is not understood, not imitated, not obeyed; infinitely eternal like truth.

"Ye have heard that it hath been said, Thou shalt love thy neighbor and hate thine enemy. But I say unto you, Love your enemies, bless them that curse you, do good to them that hate you, and pray for them which despitefully use you and persecute you; That ye may be the children of your Father which is in Heaven."

Jesus had only one aim: to transform men from beasts to saints by means of love. Is it not possible to make another life out of this life, to change this world to a world more divine, at last to bring down Heaven and the laws of Heaven upon earth? This new life, this earthly but celestial world is the Kingdom of Heaven, and to bring about the Kingdom we must transfigure and deify ourselves; become like God, imitate God.

To make over the entire man, to create a new man, the most tenacious center of the old man must be destroyed. From self love come all the misfortunes, massacres and miseries of the world. To tame the old Adam self-love must be torn out of him, and in its place must be put the love most opposed to his present nature, love for his enemies.

The total transformation of mankind is such a sublime paradox that it can be reached only by fantastic means. It is an extraordinary undertaking, wild and unnatural, to be accomplished only with an extraordinary exaltation, opposed to Nature.

To love one's neighbor as one's self is an insufficient formula, a concession to the universal egotism. For he who loves himself cannot perfectly love others, and finds himself perforce in conflict with others. All things which religions, morals, and laws call sins, vices, and crimes begin in self-love, in the hatred for others which springs from that one solitary, disordered love.

Jesus Teaches His Disciples to Pray

THE disciples asked Jesus for a prayer. He had told them to pray briefly and secretly, but they were not satisfied with any prayers recommended by the lukewarm, bookish priests of the Temple. They wanted a prayer of their own which would be like a countersign among the fraternity of Christ.

Jesus on the Mount taught for the first time the Pater-noster, the only prayer which He ever taught:

OUR FATHER *who art in heaven, hallowed by Thy name. Thy Kingdom come. Thy will be done in earth as it is in heaven. Give us this day our daily bread. And forgive us our debts as we forgive our debtors. And lead us not into temptation but deliver us from evil . . .*

This is one of the simplest prayers in the world, the most profound which goes up from human homes to God, a prayer neither literary nor theological— neither bold nor servile—the most beautiful of all prayers. Reading it over word for word today like a new text, which we read for the first time, it loses its ritual banality, and freshens into its first meaning.

JESUS knew that that exalted teaching on the heights would not suffice to spread the good news to all. He knew that men need less abstract words, pic-ture-making words, narrated words words almost as tangible as facts. And He knew that even these would not be enough.

The simple, rustic, coarse, humble people who followed Jesus were men whose lives were based on material things, men who could only understand spiritual things slowly, with great effort through material proofs, signs and material symbols.

They gave miracles a weight and meaning much greater than that which Jesus gave them. Jesus was always reluctant to perform miracles. He did not feel that this divine power of His was of supreme importance. If He yielded it was to reward the faith of the sorrowing man or woman. The Gospel show that for Himself, for His own salvation, He never performed miracles.

Jesus did not believe that pain was necessary to conquer evil. Evil is evil and must be driven away, but pain also is evil. Sorrow of the soul is enough for salvation: why should the body suffer also, needlessly? The old Jews thought of sickness as a punishment: Christian believe it above all as an aid to conversion.

The healings of Jesus are two-fold: they are healings not only of bodies but of souls, and it is soul-sickness which Jesus wished especially to heal, so that the Kingdom of Heaven might be founded on earth.

"Upon this rock I will build my Church"

FEW of us dare to ask ourselves, "Who am I?" and there are still fewer who can answer. Jesus knew with ineffable certainty what His real name was, and what was His superhuman nature. Now that the end was near He felt that His faithful followers might know His real name, at last—even they.

The recognition of His superb human mission, that name which not one of them up to that time had pronounced, that recognition on the part of the Twelve should be free and spontaneous should burst out, an impetuous confession of love, from one of those soul should be pronounced by one of those mouths.

"But whom say ye that I am?" And then there came to Simon Peter the great light that was almost too great for him and made him first to all eternity.

"Thou art the Christ, the Son of the living God."

At last from Peter the Rock there

sprang forth the wellspring which from that day to this has quenched the thirsty of sixty generations of men. Weighty consequences flow from the choice of Peter for this proclamation. It is a reward which calls for other recompense: "Thou art Peter, and upon this rock I will build my church; and the gates of Hell shall not prevail against thee. And I will give unto thee the keys of the kingdom of heaven; and whatsoever thou shalt bind on earth shall be bound in Heaven: and whatsoever thou shalt loose on earth shall be loosed in Heaven."

Weighty words from which have emerged one of the greatest Kingdoms which men have established upon the earth; the only one of the old kingdoms which still lives on in the same city which saw the rise and fall of the proudest and most pompous of earthly kingdoms.

For these words many men suffered, many were tortured, many were killed. To deny or uphold, to interpret or cancel these words, thousands of men have been killed in city squares and battles, kingdoms have been divided, societies have been shaken and rent, nations have waged war, emperors and beggars have given their all.

Jesus Drives the Money Changers from the Temple

JESUS had known that He must soon die a shameful death. He kept His certainty of death in His own heart until His last hours. He did not wish to sadden His disciples who would have shrunk from following a condemned man. They thought of Him as a king on His throne and not as a criminal on the gallows; triumphant, receiving homage and tribute, not spat upon, beaten, and insulted; come to raise the dead and not to be executed like an assassin.

He was to buy immortality for all those who obey Him and the cancelation of all sins committed by men by His imprisonment and death. The price was hard and bitter but without the few days of His Passion and burial He could not have secured centuries of life and freedom for men.

The disciples were troubled at His revelation and unwilling to believe. But now they knew all and He could go on His way towards Jerusalem in order that His words should be fulfilled to the very last.

He went up to the Temple of Jerusalem where all His enemies were assembled. He went to the Temple to destroy the Temple. He knew that this house of God had been turned into a house of Mammon. Here men trafficked in money.

He had in His hand a length of rope, which He knotted together like a whip, and with it He opened a passageway through the astonished people. The benches of the money-changers crashed down at the first shock. Jesus, His whip on high, drove the money-changers toward the door. And He repeated in a loud voice, "My house shall be called the house of prayer; but ye have made it a den of thieves!"

This action of Jesus was a righteous purification of the sanctuary. Business, that modern god, was for Him a form of theft. Christ, Who pitied the rich, but Who hated and detested wealth, the great wall which cuts off men from the vision of the Kingdom of Heaven, broke up the den of thieves. But with that violent action, He antagonized all the commercial middle-class of Jerusalem.

These men of money found ready hearing with the men of Law, already embittered for other reasons, so much the more because Jesus, in disturbing the business of the Temple, had condemned and harmed the priests themselves. These priests who did business in the Temple made a good income from selling turtle-doves for Jewish sacrifices and the money changers paid them thousands of shekels every year for the use of the Temple as a place of business.

Priests and Merchants Plot Against Jesus

IN THEIR eyes Jesus could not possibly be a Divine Redeemer. No spectacular and magic signs had been seen: He had contented Himself with healing the sick, with talking about love, and with loving. They had seen Him dining with publicans and sinners, and worse than everything else, had heard with horror that His disciples did not always wash their hands before sitting down to the table. But the greatest horror, the unendurable scandal, had been His lack of respect for the Sabbath. Jesus had not hesitated to cure the sick, even on the Sabbath, and He held it no crime on that day to do good to His unfortunate brothers. He even shamelessly gloried

in this, claiming blasphemously that the Sabbath was made for man, rather than man for the Sabbath.

As long as He went about in the provinces drawing after Him a few dozen peasants, they had let Him alone, sure that some day or other, the last beggar would leave Him.

It was perhaps that very evening that priests and merchants agreed on the purchase of a betrayer and a cross. The bourgeoisie were to give the small amount of money necessary; the clergy to find the religious pretext; the foreign government, naturally desiring to be on good terms with the clergy and bourgeoisie, would lend its soldiers.

Jesus' Last Supper with His Disciples

JESUS had but one more day of freedom. Before leaving His friends, those who were to abandon Him that night, He wished once more to dip His bread in the same platter with them. Before suffering thirst, nailed upon the cross, He wished to drink a cup of wine with His companions.

Judas had finished his bargain, he had thirty pieces of silver on his person wrapped tightly so that they would not clink. But he knew no peace.

Jesus had always loved them, all of them, even Judas: He was willing to wash and wipe those twenty-four callous and sweaty feet, in order to engrave on those unwilling hearts, still swollen with vanity, the truth which His lips had so long vainly pronounced: "And whosoever shall exalt himself shall be abased; and he that shall humble himself shall be exalted."

This supper which was the viaticum of an ending, was also a wonderful beginning. In the midst of these thirteen Jews the observance of the Jewish Passover was about to be transfigured into something incomparably higher and more universal, into something unequaled and ineffable; into the great Christian mystery. The simple eating

of bread was to become actual communion with God.

Jesus, who saw how insufficiently they understood, took the loaves, blessed them, broke them, and, as He gave them each a piece, set the dreadful truth before their eyes. "Take, eat; This is my body which is given for you: this do in remembrance of me."

I will leave you therefore not merely a memory; I will be present with a mystic but real presence in every particle of bread consecrated to Me and this bread shall be a living necessary food for souls, and My promise to be with you shall be fulfilled till time shall be no more.

As soon as they had eaten the bread, Jesus filled the common cup and gave it to the Apostle nearest Him, "Drink ye all of it; for this is my blood of the new testament, which is shed for many."

The blood which was to be shed the next day, on Golgotha, was real blood, actual, warm blood congealing on the cross in clots which all the tears shed by Christians can never wash away. But the blood of the Last Supper symbolizes a soul which gave itself up to make over into His own likeness, the souls shut up in the bodies of men; which was given to those who asked for it and to those who fled away from it. He was to suffer for the sake of those who had received it and for those who had blasphemed it.

Then the only friend remaining to Judas warned him, "Verily I say unto you, that one of you shall betray me."

The eleven were capable of leaving Him alone in the midst of the guards, but they never could have brought themselves to sell Him for money, and at this they shuddered.

He added no more but repeated the vigorous words of the Psalmist which was like a prophetic funeral oration for Him:

"I shall not die, but live. The Lord hath chastened me sore: but he hath not given me over unto death. Bind the sacrifice with cords, even unto the horns of the altar."

The Victim was ready and the next day the people of Jerusalem were to see a new altar of wood and iron, high on the hill of Golgotha.

They Crucify Jesus

As ancient writers admitted, crucifixion was the cruelest and blackest of punishments. It gave the greatest torture for the longest time. If tetanus set in, a merciful torpor hastened death; but there were men who held out, suffering always more and more, until the second day after crucifixion, and even longer. The thirst of their fever, the congestion of their hearts, the rigidity of their veins, their cramped muscles, the dizziness and terrible pains in the head, the ever-greater agony—all these were not enough to make an end of them. But most men died at the end of twelve hours.

Thus died a God, who had called mean souls to holiness but had fallen into the hands of vilifiers and demons. He had brought life, and in return they gave Him the most ignominious death Roman law allowed.

All this was necessary that men should learn again the road to the earthly Paradise; that they should mount above drunken bestiality and attain the exalta-

tion of saints; that they should be resurrected from their sluggish folly which seems life and is death, to the magnificence of the Kingdom of Heaven.

Although millions of men have since wept when thinking of that day, on that Friday around the cross, all except the women were laughing. Mary, His mother, Mary Magdalene, Mary, the wife of Cleophas, Salome, mother of James and John, were present, terrified witnesses of His death.

Deftly and skillfully they began to wash the body in order that His burial, performed at night and in haste, would not be unworthy of Him for whom they wept. The head was wrapped in a napkin and another white cloth was spread over the face, after they had all kissed Him on the forehead. They placed the white wrapped body in the cave and closed the opening with a great stone. Then they went away silently promising to return there as soon as the feast-day had passed.

"He is not here; He is risen!"

The sun had not yet risen on the day which for us is Sunday, when the women once more drew near the garden. When they came near the rock they stood still, astounded. The opening of the sepulcher showed black against the darkness. The great stone had been removed! At the right of the opening, seated, was a young man clothed in a long white garment, showing in that

darkness like snow. He seemed to be waiting for them.

He said unto them:

"Be not affrighted: he is not here: for he is risen. Go quickly, and tell his disciples that he is risen from the dead."

All four of them, quivering with terror and joy, left the grotto to hasten where they had been sent. But after a few steps, Mary of Magdala stopped, and the others went along the road towards the city without waiting for her.

Suddenly she turned and saw a man near her. He raised his hand and said: "Woman, why weepest thou? Whom seekest thou?"

At this, as if awakened with a start, the despairing woman found her lost Master and fell at His feet in the dewy grass and clasped in her hands those bare feet still showing the two red marks of the nails. She remained there, kneeling on the ground.

But Jesus said to her, "Touch me not, for I am not yet ascended to my Father, but go to my brethren, and say unt them, I ascend unto my Father, an your Father; and to my God, and t your God."

And at once, He withdrew from th kneeling woman, and moved among th flowers, crowned with sunshine.

Mary watched Him until He had di appeared; then she lifted herself up fror the grass, her face convulsed, wild, blin with joy, and ran after her companion

Jesus Ascends into Heaven

HE REMAINED in the midst of men for forty days after the resurrection. Although His body seemed human, His life was transfigured into the ultimate sublimation of humanity. He did not, as before, lead a life in common with the disciples, because He was separated now from the life of living men. But He reappeared to them more than once to reaffirm His great promises, and perhaps to explain to those most capable of receiving them those mysteries which were not written down in any book but were passed on.

The last time they saw Him was on the Mount of Olives. It was one of the last evenings of May and the clouds in that golden hour seemed to rise from the warm earth towards nearby Heaven, like incense from fragrant offering

The Disciples asked Jesus this que tion: "Lord, wilt thou at this time r store the Kingdom of God?"

And Christ answered: "It is not fc you to know the times or the seasor which the Father has put in his ow power. But ye shall receive power, afte that the Holy Ghost is come upon you and ye shall be witnesses unto me bot in Jerusalem, and in all Judea, and i Samaria, and unto the uttermost part of the earth."

And having said this, He lifted u His hands and blessed them. And whil they beheld, He was taken up from th earth and suddenly a shining clou wrapped Him about and hid Him fron their sight.

SLEEP

COME, Sleep; O sleep! the certain knot of peace,
The baiting-place of wit, the balm of woe,
The poor man's wealth, the prisoner's release,
Th' indifferent judge between the high and low;
With shield of proof shield me from out the prease
Of those fierce darts Despair at me doth throw:
O make in me those civil wars to cease;
I will good tribute pay, if thou do so.
Take thou of me smooth pillows, sweetest bed,
A chamber deaf to noise and blind to light,
A rosy garland and a weary head;
And if these things, as being thine by right,
    Move not thy heavy grace, thou shalt in me,
    Livelier than elsewhere, Stella's image see.
          —*Sir Philip Sidney* (1554-86).

Edith Wharton

THE AGE OF INNOCENCE

"Edith wharton is a writer who brings glory on the name of America, and "The Age of Innocence" is her best book. It is one of the best novels of the twentieth century and looks like a permanent addition to literature."—*William Lyon Phelps.*

Sweet Sorrow

It was a crowded night at Wallack's theatre. The play was "The Shaughraun," with Harry Montague and Ada Dyas as the lovers. The actress, who was standing near the mantel-piece and looking down into the fire, wore a gray cashmere dress moulded to her tall figure and flowing in long lines about her feet. Around her neck was a narrow black velvet ribbon with the ends falling down her back.

When her wooer turned from her, she rested her arms against the mantel-shelf and bowed her face in her hands. On the threshold he paused to look at her; then he stole back, lifted one of the ends of velvet ribbon, kissed it and left the room without her hearing him or changing her attitude.

It was always for the sake of that particular scene that Newland Archer went to see "The Shaughraun." On the evening in question the little scene acquired an added poignancy by reminding him—he could not have said why —of his leave-taking from Madame Olenska after their confidential talk a week or ten days earlier.

It would have been difficult to discover any resemblance between the two situations as between the appearance of the persons concerned. Newland Archer could not pretend to anything approaching the young English actor's romantic good looks, and Miss Dyas was a tall red-haired woman of monumental build whose pale and pleasantly ugly face was utterly unlike Ellen Olenska's vivid countenance. Nor were Archer and Madame Olenska two lovers parting in heart-broken silence; they were client and lawyer separating after a talk which had given the lawyer the worst possible impression of the client's case.

Archer had left her with the conviction that Count Olenski's accusation was not unfounded. The mysterious person who figured in his wife's past as "the secretary" had probably not been unrewarded for his share in her escape. The conditions from which she had fled were intolerable, past speaking of, past believing: she was young, she was frightened, she was desperate—what more natural than that she should be grateful to her rescuer?

The pity was that her gratitude put her, in the law's eyes and the world's, on a par with her abominable husband. Archer had made her understand this, as he was bound to do; he had also made her understand that simple-hearted, kindly New York, on whose larger charity she had apparently counted, was precisely the place where she could least hope for indulgence.

To have to make this fact plain to her —and to witness her resigned acceptance of it—had been intolerably painful to him. He felt himself drawn to her by obscure feelings of jealousy and pity, as if her dumbly-confessed error had put her at his mercy, humbling yet endearing her. She had understood the uselessness of the divorce proceeding; and with infinite relief the family had turned their eyes from the "unpleasantness" she had spared them.

These incidents had made the memory

of his last talk with Madame Olenska so vivid to the young man that as the curtain fell on the parting of the two actors his eyes filled with tears, and he stood up to leave the theatre. In so doing, he turned to the side of the house behind him and saw the lady of whom he was thinking seated in a neighboring box. Their eyes met and it was impossible not to go to the box. She turned and spoke in a low voice.

"Do you think," she asked, glancing toward the stage, "he will send her a bunch of yellow roses tomorrow morning?"

Archer reddened, and his heart gave a leap of surprise. He had called only twice on Madame Olenska, and each time he had sent her a box of yellow roses, and each time without a card. She had never before made any allusion to the flowers.

"I was thinking of that too—I was going to leave the theatre in order to take the picture away with me," he said.

To his surprise her color rose, reluctantly and duskily. She looked down and said, after a pause: "What do you do while May is away?"

"I stick to my work," he answered, faintly annoyed by the question.

He was conscious that Madame Olenska was looking at him under lowered lids. Only the day before he had received a letter from May Welland in which, with characteristic candour, she had asked him to "be kind to Ellen" in her absence. His wise May—how he had loved her for that letter! But he had not meant to act on it; he was too busy, to begin with, and he did not care, as an engaged man, to play too conspicuously the part of Madame Olenska's champion.

Yet he never saw her, or exchanged a word with her, without feeling that, after all, May's ingenuousness almost amounted to the gift of divination. Ellen Olenska was lonely and she was unhappy.

Sentimental Journey

THE next morning Archer scoured the town in vain for more yellow roses. In consequence of this search, he arrived late at the office, perceived that his doing so made no difference whatever to any one, and was filled with sudden exasperation at the elaborate futility of his life. Why should he not be, at that moment, on the sands of St. Augustine with May Welland? No one was deceived by his pretense of activity.

He had, to be sure, other tastes and interests; he spent his vacations in European travel, cultivated the "clever people" May spoke of, and generally tried to "keep up," as he had somewhat wistfully put it to Madame Olenska. But once he was married what would become of this narrow margin of life in which his real experiences were lived? He had seen enough of other young men who had dreamed his dream, though perhaps less ardently, and who had gradually sunk into the placid and luxurious routine of their elders.

From the office he sent a note by messenger to Madame Olenska, asking if he might call that afternoon, and begging her to let him find a reply at his club. But it was only on the third morning that he received a line by post from the Countess Olenska. To his surprise it was dated from Skuytercliff, whither she had retreated with the van der Luydens.

"I ran away," the writer began abruptly "the day after I saw you at the play, and these kind friends have taken me in. I wanted to be quiet, and think things over. I feel myself so safe here. I wish that you were here with us." She ended without any allusion to the date of her return.

He felt a distinct disappointment on learning that she was away; and almost immediately remembered that, only the day before, he had refused an invitation to spend the following Sunday with the Reggie Chiverses at their house on the Hudson, a few miles below Skuytercliff. He wrote a hurried telegram, knowing that Mrs. Reggie didn't object to her visitors' suddenly changing their minds, and that there was always a room to spare in her elastic house.

COMING down a foot-path that crossed the highway, he caught sight of a slight figure in a red cloak, with a big dog runnnig ahead. He hurried forward, and Madame Olenska stopped short with a smile of welcome.

"Ah, you've come!" she said, and drew her hand from her muff. The red cloak made her look gay and vivid, like the Ellen Mingott she had been in the old days; and he laughed as he took her hand, and answered: "I came to see what you were running away from."

Her face clouded over, but she answered: "Ah, well—you will see, presently."

They were walking past the house of van der Luyden, the old Patroon, with its squat walls and small square windows compactly grouped about a central chimney. The shutters stood wide, and through one of the newly-washed windows Archer caught the light of a fire.

"Why—the house is open!" he said.

She stood still. "No; only for today, at least. I wanted to see it, and Mr. van der Luyden had the fire lit and the windows opened, so that we might stop there on the way back from church this morning." She ran up the steps and tried the door. "It's still unlocked—what luck!"

Madame Olenska, dropping her cloak, sat down in one of the chairs. Archer leaned against the chimney and looked at her.

"You're laughing now; but when you wrote me you were unhappy," he said.

"Yes." She paused. "But I can't feel unhappy when you're here."

"I sha'n't be here long," he rejoined, his lips stiffening with the effort to say so much and no more.

"No; I know. But I'm improvident: I live in the moment when I'm happy."

The words stole through him like a temptation, and to close his senses to it he moved away from the hearth and stood gazing out at the black tree-boles against the snow.

"Ellen, if I'm really a help to you—if you really wanted me to come—tell me what's wrong, tell me what it is you're running away from," he insisted.

For a long moment she was silent; and in that moment Archer imagined her, almost heard her, stealing up behind him to throw her light arms about his neck. While he waited, soul and body throbbing with the miracle to come, his eyes mechanically received the image of a heavily-coated man with his fur collar turned up who was advancing along the path to the house. The man was Julius Beaufort, one of Madame Olenska's most ardent admirers.

Madame Olenska had sprung up and moved to his side, slipping her hand into his; but after a glance through the window she paled and shrank back.

"I didn't know he was here," Madame Olenska murmured. Her hand still clung to Archer's; but he drew away from her, and walking out into the passage threw open the door of the house.

"Hallo, Beaufort—this way! Madame Olenska was expecting you," he said.

Lighted with Fire

IT WAS only half-past eight when he rang the bell under the wisteria; not as late as he had intended by half an hour—but a singular restlessness had driven him to her door.

She was dressed as if for a ball. Everything about her shimmered and glimmered softly, as if her dress had been woven out of candle-beams; and she car-

ried her head high, like a pretty woman challenging a roomful of rivals.

His heart tightened with the thought that this was the last evening by that fireside, and that in a moment the carriage would come and carry her away.

"You know that your aunt believes you will go back to your husband?"

Madame Olenska raised her head

quickly. A deep blush rose to her face and spread over her neck and shoulders. "Many cruel things have been believed of me," she said.

"Oh, Ellen—forgive me: I'm a fool and a brute!"

She smiled a little. "You are horribly nervous; you have your own troubles. I know you think that May's father and mother are unreasonable about your marriage, and of course I agree with you. In Europe people don't understand our long American engagements."

"Yes," he said abruptly; "I went south to ask May to marry me after Easter. There's no reason why we shouldn't be married then. But May thinks my impatience a bad sign. She thinks that I want to marry her at once to get away from some one that I—care for more."

Madame Olenska examined this curiously. "But if she thinks that—why isn't she in a hurry too?"

"Because she's not like that; she's so much nobler. She insists all the more on a long engagement, to give me time—"

"Time to give her up for the other woman?"

"If I want to."

Madame Olenska leaned toward the fire and gazed into it with fixed eyes. Down the quiet street Archer heard the approaching trot of her horses. She half rose and looked about her with absent eyes. Her fan and gloves lay on the sofa beside her and she picked them up mechanically.

"I suppose I must be going."

A RCHER felt that at any cost he must keep her beside him, must make her give him the rest of her evening. "May guessed the truth," he said. "There is another woman—but not the one she thinks. You are the woman I would have married if it had been possible for either of us."

"Possible for either of us?" She looked at him with unfeigned astonishment. "And you say that—when it's you who've made it impossible?"

He stared at her, groping in a blackness through which a single arrow of light tore its blinding way.

"*I've* made it impossible—?"

"You, you, you!" she cried, her lip trembling like a child's on the verge of tears. "Isn't it you who made me give up divorcing—give it up because you showed me how selfish and wicked it was, how one must sacrifice one's self to preserve the dignity of marriage . . . and to spare one's family the publicity, the scandal? And because my family was going to be your family—for May's sake and for yours—I did what you told me, what you proved to me that I ought to do. Ah," she broke out with a sudden laugh, "I've made no secret of having done it for you!"

He started up and came to her side. "Ellen! What madness! Nothing's done that can't be undone. I'm still free, and you're going to be." He had her in his arms, her face like a wet flower at his lips, and all their vain terrors shriveling up like ghosts at sunrise. The thing that astonished him was that he should have stood for five minutes arguing with her across the width of the room, when just touching her made everything so simple.

She gave him back all his kiss, but after a moment he felt her stiffening in his arms, and she put him aside and stood up.

"Ah, my poor Newland—I suppose this had to be. But it doesn't in the least alter things," she said, looking down at him in her turn from the hearth.

"It alters the whole of life for me."

"No, no—it mustn't, it can't. You're engaged to May Welland; and I'm married."

He stood up too, flushed and resolute. "Nonsense! We won't talk of your marriage; but do you see me marrying May after this?"

"I don't see you," she said at length, "putting that question to May. Do you?"

"May is ready to give me up."

"What! Three days after you've entreated her on your knees to hasten your marriage?"

"She's refused; that gives me the right—"

At that moment the bell sent a long tinkle through the house. A moment later the maid came in carrying a telegram. Her mistress smiled and took the yellow envelope. She tore it open and carried it to the lamp; then, when the door had closed again, she handed the telegram to Archer.

It was dated from St. Augustine, and addressed to the Countess Olenska. In it he read: "Papa and Mamma agree marriage after Easter. Am telegraphing Newland. Am too happy for words and love you dearly. Your grateful May."

The Smouldering Hearth

EVERY detail of the day had been so carefully thought out that the young couple, after the wedding-breakfast, had ample time to put on their travelling-clothes, descend the wide Mingott stairs between laughing bridesmaids and weeping parents, and get into the brougham under the traditional shower of rice and satin slippers; and there was still half an hour left in which to drive to the station, buy the last weeklies at the book-stall with the air of seasoned travellers, and settle themselves in the reserved compartment in which May's maid had already placed her dove-colored travelling cloak and glaringly new dressing bag from London.

The old du Lac aunts at Rhinebeck had put their house at the disposal of the bridal couple, with a readiness inspired by the prospect of spending a week in New York with Mrs. Archer; and Archer, glad to escape the usual "bridal suite" in a Philadelphia or Baltimore hotel, had accepted with an equal alacrity.

Once they were settled in their compartment, and the train, shaking off the endless wooden suburbs, had pushed out into the pale landscape of spring, talk became easier than Archer had expected. May was still, in look and tone, the simple girl of yesterday, eager to compare notes with him as to the incidents of the wedding, and discussing them as impartially as a bridesmaid talking it all over with an usher. At first Archer had fancied that this detachment was the disguise of an inward tremor, but her clear eyes revealed only the most tranquil unawareness. She was alone for the first time with her husband; but her husband was only the charming comrade of yesterday. There was no one whom she liked as much, no one whom she trusted as completely, and the culminating "lark" of the whole delightful adventure of engagement and marriage was to be off with him alone on a journey, like a grown-up person, like a "married woman," in fact.

Perhaps that faculty of unawareness was what gave her eyes their transparency, and her face the look of representing a type rather than a person; as if she might have been chosen to pose for a Civic Virtue or a Greek goddess. The blood that ran so close to her fair skin might have been preserving fluid rather than a ravaging element; yet her look of indestructible youthfulness made her seem neither hard nor dull, but only primitive and pure. In the thick of this meditation Archer suddenly felt himself looking at her with the startled gaze of a stranger.

In the spring twilight the train stopped at the Rhinebeck station, and they walked along the platform to the waiting carriage.

"Ah, how awfully kind of the van der Luydens—they've sent their man over from Skuytercliff to meet us," Archer exclaimed, as a sedate person out of livery approached them and relieved the maid of her bags.

"I'm extremely sorry, sir," said this emissary, "that a little accident has occurred at the Miss' du Lacs: a leak in the water tank. It happened yesterday, and Mr. van der Luyden, who heard of it this morning, sent a house-maid up by the early train to get the Patroon's house ready. It will be quite comfortable, I think you'll find, sir."

And as they drove off, with the maid beside the coachman, and their shining bridal bags on the seat before them she went on excitedly: "Only fancy, I've never been inside it—have you? The van der Luydens show it to so few people. But they opened it for Ellen, it seems and she told me what a darling little place it was; she says it's the only house she's seen in America that she could imagine being perfectly happy in."

I T WAS undoubtedly gratifying to be the husband of one of the handsomest and most popular young married women in New York, especially when she was also one of the sweetest-tempered and most reasonable of wives; and Archer had never been insensible to such advantages. As for the momentary madness which had fallen upon him on the eve of his marriage, he had trained himself to regard it as the last of his discarded experiments. The idea that he could ever, in his senses, have dreamed of marrying the Countess Olenska had become almost unthinkable, and she remained in his memory simply the most plaintive and poignant of a line of ghosts.

He had heard the Countess Olenska's name pronounced often enough during the year and a half since they had last met, and was even familiar with the main incidents of her life in the interval. He knew that she had spent the previous summer at Newport, where she appeared to have gone a great deal into society. But in the autumn she had decided to establish herself in Washington. There, during the winter, he had heard of her (as one always heard of pretty women in Washington) as shining in the "brilliant diplomatic society" that was supposed to make up for the social short-comings of the Administration.

He had listened to these accounts, and to various contradictory reports on her appearance, her conversation, her point of view and her choice of friends, with the detachment with which one listens to reminiscences of some one long since dead, until one day in Boston. . . .

Reunion

H E STARTED to walk across the Common; and on the first bench, under a tree, he saw her sitting. As he approached he was struck by her listless attitude; she sat there as if she had nothing else to do. He came a step or two nearer, and she turned and looked at him.

"Oh"—she said; and for the first time he noticed a startled look on her face; but in another moment it gave way to a slow smile of wonder and contentment.

"What on earth are you doing in this wilderness?" He had really no idea what he was saying: he felt as if he were shouting at her across endless distances, and she might vanish again before he could overtake her.

They did not look at each other, but straight ahead at the people passing along the path. Finally she turned her eyes again to his face and said: "You're not changed."

He felt like answering: "I was, till I saw you again": but instead he stood up abruptly and glanced about him at the untidy sweltering park.

"This is horrible. Why shouldn't we go out a little on the bay? There's a breeze, and it will be cooler. My train doesn't leave till evening: I'm going back to New York. Why shouldn't we? I swear I only want to hear about you, to know what you've been doing. It's a hundred years since we've met—it may be another hundred before we meet again."

She frowned perplexedly, and then smiled her agreement.

T HEY lunched slowly and meditatively, with mute intervals between rushes of talk; for, the spell once broken, they had much to say, and yet moments when saying became the mere accompaniment of long duologues of silence.

Archer kept the talk from his own affairs, not with conscious intention but because he did not want to miss a word of her history; and leaning on the table, her chin resting on her clasped hands, she talked to him of the year and a half since they had met.

"If it's not worth while to have given up, to have missed things, so that others may be saved from disillusionment and misery—then everything, everything that made my other life seem by contrast so bare and so poor because no one there took account of them—all these things are a sham or a dream—"

'What's the use? You gave me my first glimpse of real life, and at the same moment you asked me to go on with a sham one. It's beyond human enduring —that's all."

"Oh, don't say that; when I'm enduring it!" she burst out, her eyes filling.

But after a moment the sense of waste and ruin overcame him. There they were, close together and safe and shut in; yet so chained to their separate destinies that they might as well have been half the world apart.

"What a life for you—" he groaned.

"Oh—as long as it's a part of yours. And mine a part of yours."

At that he sprang up, forgetting everything but the sweetness of her face. She rose too, not as if to meet him or to flee from him, but quietly, as though the worst of the task were done and she had only to wait so quietly that, as he came close, her outstretched hands acted not as a check but as a guide to him. They fell into his, while her arms, extended but not rigid, kept him far enough off to let her surrendered face say the rest.

They may have stood in that way for a long time, or only for a few moments; but it was long enough for her silence to communicate all she had to say, and for him to feel that only one thing mattered. He must do nothing to make this meeting their last; he must leave their future to her care, asking only that she should keep fast hold of it.

Where Is That Country?

Four months had passed since the midsummer day that he and Madame Olenska had spent together; and since then he had not seen her. Since then he had built up within himself a kind of sanctuary in which she was throned among his secret thoughts and longings. Little by little it became the scene of his real life, of his only rational activities; thither he brought the books he read, the ideas and feelings which nourished him, his judgments and his visions.

Outside it, in the scene of his actual life, he moved with a growing sense of unreality and insufficiency, blundering against familiar prejudices and traditional points of view as an absent-minded man goes on bumping into the furniture of his own room. Absent—that was what he was; so absent from everything most densely real and near to those about him that it sometimes startled him to find they still imagined he was there.

Now he was pacing the platform, waiting for the Washington express. The clanging and groaning of the train came nearer, and it staggered slowly into the station like a prey-laden monster into its lair. And then, suddenly, he saw Madame Olenska's pale and surprised face close at hand, and had again the mortified sensation of having forgotten what she looked like. They reached each other, their hands met, and he drew her arm through his. "This way—I have a carriage," he said.

After that it all happened as he had dreamed. He helped her into the brougham with her bags, and had afterward the vague recollection of having properly reassured her about her grandmother.

"If only it doesn't mean—poor Granny!"

Her hand remained in his, and as he bent over, unbuttoned her tight brown glove, and kissed her palm as if he had kissed a relic. She disengaged herself with a faint smile.

"Do you know—I hardly remembered you?"

"Hardly remembered me?"

"I mean: how shall I explain? I—it's always so. *Each time you happen to me all over again."*

"Oh, yes: I know! I know!"

"Does it—do I too: to you?" he insisted.

She nodded, looking out of the window.

'Ellen—Ellen—Ellen!"

She made no answer, and he sat in silence, watching her profile grow indistinct against the snow-streaked dusk beyond the window.

"What a pretty carriage! Is it May's?" she asked, suddenly turning her face from the window.

"Yes."

"It was May who sent you to fetch me, then. How kind of her! But you ought not to have come," she said in an altered voice; and suddenly she turned, flung her arms about him and pressed her lips to his.

As they gained the street Archer began to speak hurriedly. "Don't suppose that I don't understand your reasons for not wanting to let this feeling between us dwindle into an ordinary hole-and-corner love-affair. I couldn't have spoken like this yesterday, because when we've been apart, and I'm looking forward to seeing you come; and you're so much more than I remembered, and what I want of you is so much more than an hour or two every now and then, with wastes of thirsty waiting between, that I can sit perfectly still beside you, like this, with that other vision in my mind, just quietly trusting to it to come true."

For a moment she made no reply; then she asked, hardly above a whisper: "What do you mean by trusting to it to come true?"

"Why—you know it will, don't you?"

"Your vision of you and me to-

gether?" She burst into a sudden hard laugh. "You choose your place well to put it to me."

"Do you mean because we're in my wife's brougham? Shall we get out and walk, then?"

She laughed again, more gently. "No; I shan't get out and walk, because my business is to get to Granny's as quickly as I can." And then after a pause. "Is it your idea, then, that I should live with you as your mistress—since I can't be your wife?" she asked.

Her question pulled him up with a jerk, and he floundered.

"I want—I want somehow to get away with you into a world where words like that—categories like that—won't exist. Where we shall be simply two human beings who love each other, who are the whole of life to each other; and nothing else on earth will matter."

She drew a deep sigh that ended in another laugh. "Oh, my dear—where is that country? Have you ever been there?" she asked; and as he remained sullenly dumb she went on: "I know so many who've tried to find it; and believe me, they all got out by mistake at wayside stations: at places like Boulogne, or Pisa, or Monte Carlo—and it wasn't at all different from the old world they'd left, but only rather smaller and dingier and more promiscuous."

Archer choked with the sense of wasted minutes and vain words.

"Then what, exactly, is your plan for us?" he asked.

"For us? But there's no us in that sense! We're near each other only if we stay far from each other. Then we can be ourselves. Otherwise we're only Newland Archer, the husband of Ellen Olenska's cousin, and Ellen Olenska, the cousin of Newland Archer's wife trying to be happy behind the backs of the people who trust them."

"Ah, I'm beyond that," he groaned.

"No, you're not! You've never been beyond. And I have," she said, in a strange voice, "and I know what it looks like there."

He pressed the bell, and the carriage drew up beside the curbstone.

"Why are we stopping? This is not Granny's," Madame Olenska exclaimed.

"No: I shall get out here," he stammered, opening the door and jumping to the pavement. He closed the door, thrust his hands in his pockets, and walked at a sharp pace down Fifth Avenue to his own house.

Decisions

IT WAS only natural that Madame Olenska should have hastened from Washington in response to her grandmother's summons; but that she should have decided to remain under her roof —especially now that Mrs. Mingott had almost regained her health—was less easy to explain.

Archer was sure that Madame Olenska's decision had not been influenced by the change in her financial situation. He knew the exact figure of the small allowance which her husband had allowed her at their separation. Without the addition of her grandmother's allowance it was hardly enough to live on. Yet Archer was convinced that Madame Olenska had not accepted her grandmother's offer from interested motives.

He did not have far to seek for the reason. He knew that she was fighting her fate as he had fought his, and clinging desperately to her resolve that they should not break faith with the people who trusted them. But during the ten days which had elapsed since her return to New York she had perhaps guessed from his silence, and from the fact of his making no attempt to see her, that he was meditating a decisive step.

At the thought, a sudden fear of her own weakness might have seized her and she might have felt that, after all, it was better to accept the compromise usual in such cases, and follow the line of least resistance.

As far as he was concerned wherever she went, he was going. He meant to have a talk with May that should cut off any other alternative.

"MAY—" he began, standing a few feet from her chair and looking over at her as if the slight distance between them were an unbridgeable abyss.

The sound of his voice echoed uncannily through the homelike hush, and he repeated: "There is something I've got to tell you . . . about myself . . ."

She sat silent, without a movement or a tremor of her lashes. She was extremely pale, but her face had a curious tranquillity of expression that seemed drawn from some secret inner source.

Archer checked the conventional phrases of self-accusal that were crowding to his lips. He was determined to put the case baldly, without vain recrimination or excuse. "Madame Olenska—" he said; but at the name his wife raised her hand as if to silence him. As she did so the gas-light struck on the gold of her wedding ring.

"Oh, why should we talk about Ellen tonight?" she asked, with a slight pout of impatience. "What does it matter, now it's all over?"

"All over—what do you mean?" he asked in an indistinct stammer.

May still looked at him with transparent eyes. "Why—since she's going back to Europe so soon; since Granny approves and understands, and has arranged to make her independent of her husband—"

She broke off, and Archer, grasping the corner of the mantel-piece in one convulsed hand, and steadying himself against it, made a vain effort to extend the same control to his reeling thoughts. He understood that his own eyes must be unbearable, and turning away, rested his elbows on the mantel-shelf and covered his face. Neither spoke for a long time. At length Archer began abruptly: "There's something I must tell you."

She looked at him quickly. "Yes, dear. I've seen it coming on, Newland! You've been so wickedly overworked—"

"Perhaps it's that. Anyhow, I want to make a break to go away on a long trip, ever so far."

"Ever so far?" she asked. "But I'm afraid you can't dear. . . ." she said in an unsteady voice. "Not unless you'll take me with you." And then, as he was silent, she went on, in tones so clear and evenly pitched that each separate syllable tapped like a little hammer on his brain: "That is, if the doctors will let me go . . . but I'm afraid they won't. For you see, Newland, I've been sure since this morning of something I've been so longing and hoping for—"

He looked up at her with a sick stare, and she sank down, all dew and roses, and hid her face against his knee.

"Oh, my dear," he said, holding her to him while his cold hand stroked her hair.

There was a long pause, which the inner devils filled with strident laughter; then May freed herself from his arms and stood up.

"You didn't guess—?"

"Yes—I; no. That is, of course I hoped—"

They looked at each other for an instant and again fell silent; then, turning his eyes from hers, he asked abruptly: "Have you told any one else?"

"Only Ellen."

"Ah—" said Archer, his heart stopping.

He felt that his wife was watching him intently. "Did you *mind* my telling her first, Newland?"

Twenty-six Years After

Archer had pictured often enough, in the first impatient years, the scene of his return to Paris; then the personal vision had faded, and he had simply tried to see the city as the setting of Madame Olenska's life.

Now the spectacle was before him in its glory, and as he looked out on it he felt shy, old-fashioned, inadequate: a mere grey speck of a man compared with the ruthless magnificent fellow he had dreamed of being.

Dallas's hand came down cheerily on his shoulder. "Hullo, father: this is something like, isn't it?" They stood for a while looking out in silence, and then the young man said: "By the way, I've got a message for you: the Countess Olenska expects us both at half-past five."

He said it lightly, carelessly, as he might have imparted any casual item of information, such as the hour at which their train was to leave for Florence.

Archer continued to stare at him. "You told her I was here?"

"Of course—why not?" Dallas's eyebrows went up whimsically.

"I say, father, she was the woman you'd have chucked everything for: only you didn't, wasn't she?"

"I didn't," echoed Archer with a kind of solemnity.

"No; you date, you see, dear old boy. But mother said—"

"Your mother?"

"Yes; the day before she died. It was when she sent for me alone—you remember? She said she knew we were safe with you, and always would be, because once, when she asked you to, you'd given up the thing you wanted most."

Archer received this strange communication in silence. His eyes remained unseeingly fixed on the thronged sunlit square below the window. At length he said in a low voice: "She never asked me."

"No. I forgot. You never did ask each other anything, did you. And you never told each other anything. You just sat and watched each other, and guessed at what was going on underneath. A deaf-and-dumb asylum, in fact! Well, I back your generation for knowing more about each other's private thoughts than we ever have time to find out about our own.—I say, Dad," Dallas broke off, "you're not angry with me? If you are, let's make it up and go to lunch at Henri's."

André Maurois

DISRAELI

"Could a romance writer in after years have a better or more wondrous hero than that of an individual who at twenty years of age wrote "Vivian Grey"; who later went into politics, faced, fought and conquered the great political giant of those days; and who subsequently led thanes and earls to battle, while he caused reluctant squires to carry his lance? What a hero would not that be for some future novelist, and what a magnificent climax for the third volume of his story, when he led him, in his gold coat of office, to kiss the Queen's hand as the Chancellor of the Exchequer!"—*William Makepeace Thackeray.*

Foot in the Stirrup

King william iv died on the evening of the anniversary of Waterloo in 1837. He was succeeded by a girl queen, eighteen years old.

At eleven o'clock the next morning Victoria called her first council. Disraeli went to Kensington Palace with Lord Lyndhurst, who was going to pledge fealty to his Sovereign. On his return, Lyndhurst, deeply moved, described to Disraeli this assembly of all that was most illustrious in England, the sea of white plumes and stars and uniforms, the doors suddenly flung open, a silence deep as that of a forest, and the young girl advancing to her throne in this crowd of prelates, statesmen and generals.

Disraeli was spellbound by the recital. There he saw united all the things he loved: the pomp of ceremony, a glittering gravity, the chivalrous homage to a woman of all the strength of England. How he would have loved, he also, to kneel before his queen, to kiss that youthful hand. But he was nobody and years were passing.

The accession of a new Sovereign brought with it the dissolution of Parliament and a General Election. This time Disraeli, well backed by Lyndhurst, received numerous offers of safe constituencies. Among others Wyndham Lewis, the husband of the flirtatious lit-tle chatterbox he had formerly met at the Bulwer's (Bulwer-Lytton), asked him if he would like to be his fellow member for Maidstone, a constituency with two seats where the Conservatives were bound to win.

It was to Mrs. Wyndham Lewis that he owed the offer. For a long time he regarded her as very tiresome. Once at the Rothschilds', the lady of the house had said to him: "Mr. Disraeli, will you take Mrs. Wyndham Lewis in to dinner?" "Oh, anything rather than that insufferable woman!" he had replied. "However . . . great is Allah!" And sticking his thumbs, as he liked to do, in the armholes of his waistcoat, he had marched off to the torture.

But after a few meetings he changed his mind. She had neither wit nor culture, but she talked about affairs with good sense. Her judgments on politicians were not foolish. More than once he had found her advice sound. And in the end he allowed himself to become quite a frequent guest at dinner at the Wyndham Lewis's large London house overlooking Hyde Park.

It was obvious that Mrs. Wyndham Lewis was interested in him. She admired him and was able to be of service to him, a blend which women savour in friendship, and he paid his court to her, half-serious, half-humourous, which pleased the fancy of this ripe beauty.

During the campaign she played the part of his electoral godmother. Disraeli wrote her affable letters, telling her of his pleasure in seeing their two names side by side on the placards. He had completely forgotten his first antipathy.

IT WAS to the material solicitude of this talkative little woman that he owed his seat. His meeting with Mrs. Wyndham Lewis herself he owed to the friendship of Bulwer. That friendship had sprung from his book "Vivian Grey." "Vivian Grey" would never have been written had it not been for the collapse of Murray's newspaper and the South American speculations in which he had lost heavily. Those speculations had been entered upon by virtue of the time he spent trying to be a solicitor in the chambers at Frederick's Place. To those chambers he had been sent because he had been persecuted at Dr. Cogan's school by the other children because he was Jewish. This had shown his father the impossibility of a University education.

Thus, step by step, running right back into childhood, he traced an unbroken chain of circumstances in which an unlucky event was the cause of fortunate events, and the latter in turn the causes of disasters and reverses. How hard it was, in this perfect but obscure ordering to find a rule or a law! How mysterious it all was! It brought him to the point of regarding existence as a continuous miracle. And yet through all this darkling forest, there ran a gleaming Ariadne's thread—the will of Benjamin Disraeli.

On the methods and results of his acts he might have been deceived; he had almost always been mistaken. But never had he lost either a clear view of the goal or the firm resolve to attain it. Perhaps that sufficed. . . . Certainly that sufficed, as here he was with his foot in the stirrup.

Benjamin Disraeli, M.P. . . . a fine title and a fine adventure. In a few months an assembly prone to admiration would be listening to perfect periods to muscular phrases, to the astounding conjunctions of rare adjectives and vigorous nouns. A few years and the Right Honourable Benjamin Disraeli would be at the head of the Colonial Office or the Exchequer of this great Empire. And after that . . .

Refuge of Lasting Tenderness

ONE morning about six months after his entering Parliament, he had news of the sudden death of his colleague, Wyndham Lewis. He hastened to his widow, whom he found greatly overwhelmed.

From then on he began to visit her faithfully, and to write to her when he could not. The closing formulas of their letters grew more inflamed. From "ever your affectionate friend" he had passed to "Farewell! I am happy if you are."

It was significant that he was beginning to send her openly exultant recitals of his successes. "Every paper in London, Radical, Whig, or Tory, has spoken of my speech in the highest terms of panegyric." Or "The Londonderrys gave the most magnificent banquet at Holdernesse House conceivable. There were only 150 asked, and all sat down. Fanny was faithful, and asked me, and I figure in the Morning Post accordingly." Mrs Wyndham Lewis was beginning to be one of the family.

Was he thinking of marriage? He was not blind to the possible objections. He was thirty-three, she was forty-five. She was far from holding a status in fashionable society as brilliant as his own; the hostesses who quarrelled for Disraeli were not enthusiasts for Mary Anne. A fortune? Wyndham Lewis had left his wife a life-interest in the Grosvenor Gate house, and an income of about £4000. It was enough to live on and to entertain worthily, but there would be no spare capital to allow of Disraeli debts being paid off.

Moreover, Mary Anne was far from being a cultivated woman. Society found her rather ridiculous; it was said that she had never been able to remember which came first, the Greeks or the Romans. After a conversation about Swift, she asked for his address to invite him to dinner. Other women found her stupid and frivolous; she talked a great deal, and with alarming exuberance; her frankness reached the pitch of tactlessness. In matters of furniture or clothes her taste was freakish and detestable. A young writer and a future Minister of the Crown could surely find a more brilliant wife.

But Disraeli judged otherwise. Contrary to fashionable opinion, he did not think her stupid. Her frivolous talk amused and relaxed him. He had had only too many brilliant friends amongst women, and he had no mind to find himself obliged to withstand an assault of wit in his own home. Mary Anne admired him; he felt that she lived only

for him. In his moments of depression, which were frequent, he had need of consolation. He had suffered more severely from his thorny beginnings than his cold manner allowed one to suppose.

There are some men who feel the need of keeping their independence for the sake of romantic adventures; Disraeli had made trial of passionate love, only to find at once that it was in conflict with ambition. To him the refuge of a lasting tenderness was far more tempting.

He had always been impulsive. As soon as he felt persuaded that Mary Anne was a desirable wife, he told her so.

On August 28th, 1839, they were married at St. George's, Hanover Square. In her account book Mary Anne entered a note: "Gloves 2/6. In hand £300. Married. 28. 8. 1839. Dear Dizzy became my husband."

Mephistopheles

FIVE years of campaigning had taught him many lessons. Loyalty and courage, he had learned, do more for a man than dazzling clothes or dazzling speeches; a faked greatness does not last; fidelity to a party, however ungrateful, is a necessary virtue in politics. His work was greater, far greater, than that of the young dandy who had entered Parliament in 1837.

But his position was not stable. All the intellectual elect detested him and vowed never again to join hands with him. At Court, the Queen and Prince Albert, an austere and lofty-minded man, regarded him as a man of unprincipled ambitions. His erudition alarmed everyone. To reassure them he tried to put his wit under a bushel. On leaving an interview with him, one powerful landed proprietor had declared that Mr. Disraeli was not a very intelligent man, but was certainly a very worthy man. A good impression, but all too rare.

Although he was leader of the party in the Commons, he did not feel himself respected. Disraeli was the Mephistopheles to the Conservative party's

Faust. "Strength and youth shall I give you, but on one condition: that I must ever be by your side." Faust put up with Mephisto, but he hardly liked him.

It was admitted that the new leader carried out his duties well. When he was not in the House he was turning over Blue-Books, taking notes, preparing speeches. Only Mary Anne maintained contact with the solid world, and at last Dizzy could show openly that profound contempt for frivolity which the need of making a good impression had long forced him to conceal. Often enough, when with friends, he would pass the whole evening without uttering more than a word or two. So lost in thought did he appear that people hardly ventured to address him.

His aspect reminded one inevitably of the stone figures of ancient Egypt. When he was violently attacked, he affected sleep. If the attack touched him on the quick, he would slightly draw back the point of one foot, or pull slightly at the cuff of his shirt. It was the only sign of life that the most minute observers could detect in him. Even in the lobbies he glided noiselessly along like a ghost, without seeming to notice the presence of external objects. When he spoke, it was without gesture, without calling effects of the voice into play.

Disraeli's great task was "the education of the Party"; he had to extricate it from Protection, to raise it from a caste feeling to a national feeling, to teach it to take heed of popular comfort and of the solidity of the Empire. He put forward a bold program to take the place of Protection, in the shape of an Imperial reform of Parliament: to admit the Colonies to a share in the administration of the Empire, to balance with their vote the democratic vote of the towns, and thus to introduce fresh elements and put an end to the absurd rivalries of Town *versus* Country, Industry *versus* Agriculture. "Romantic imaginings," thought the noble Lord, and returned to his pleasures.

When Disraeli was made Chancellor of the Exchequer he was like a young girl on the day of her first ball. He went to obtain his Chancellor's robe of black silk heavily broidered with gold braid; it descended from the great Pitt.

"You will find it very heavy," said the judge who received him.

"Oh, I find it uncommonly light," he answered.

Gladstone versus Disraeli

The beginnings were none too bad. The Queen herself was amused by the reports which it was the duty of the leader of the House of Commons to address to her every evening: "Mr. Disraeli (alias Dizzy) writes very curious reports, much in the style of his books."

The House was awaiting the election. But when this was over, and it took an unfavourable turn, the unhappy Chancellor knew very well that he would not be allowed a long taste of the duties in which he found so much pleasure. Gladstone in particular had a watching eye on him.

Although neither one nor the other would have desired it, political life was slowly assuming the form of a duel between these two. To all outward appearance they were good friends. Their wives exchanged visits. Sometimes, after a somewhat lively sitting, Gladstone would even come in to say good evening to Mary Anne. But their temperaments clashed and the paths of their careers crossed. Without Disraeli, Gladstone would have been the Conservative Prime Minister.

When the two rivals rose in succession on a very dark day in December 1852, for the budget discussion, it seemed that two supernatural powers were opposing each other. Gladstone with his well-chiseled profile, his onyx eyes, his crest of black hair thrown backward with a powerful gesture, seemed like the Spirit of Ocean. Disraeli with his shining curls, his slightly stooping figure, his long supple hands, seemed rather a Spirit of Fire. As soon as they began to speak it was obvious that Disraeli had more genius, but Gladstone had assumed a tone of moral superiority which was more pleasing to the House.

Never had a Budget been attacked in Parliament as that of Disraeli's was. For a whole week, night after night, it had been mocked at, made game of, scorned. All the brilliant economists in turn had demonstrated its ignorance and folly. All had underlined its abandonment of Protection.

When at last Disraeli spoke, the smothered violence of his sarcasm showed that he had not been unscathed. He forced a calm, sustained tone upon himself, but from time to time there escaped a phrase of such bitter irony as to seem almost agonized. His opening— "I was not born and bred a Chancellor of the Exchequer: I am one of the Parliamentary rabble"—had strange reverberations of Rousseau, very unexpected in the leader of the Conservative Party. A violent storm raged throughout the whole of his lengthy speech. The quick flashes of lightning, the roll of thunder, made a congruous setting for the diabolic figure whom his adversaries believed they were gazing upon.

At four o'clock in the morning the Ministry was overturned by 305 votes to 286. The taste of power had been brief. Nothing can convey the grace of Disraeli's farewells. He showed no trace of sadness, but asked pardon of the House for the unwonted warmth of his speech. And the curtain fell.

That evening Gladstone noted in his journal that God knew how much he regretted having been the instrument chosen to bring about the fall of Disraeli. The man had, in all conscience, great talents. "I would only pray that they might be well used."

"Never Explain, Never Complain"

DISRAELI had become more taciturn than ever, and there were not more than two people in London who could remember having seen him smile. He retained all his relish for high play, but was he ever to hold the winning hand?

A hundred times over he had delivered speeches which were declared to be the finest that Parliament had ever listened to. Many times over had he stormed the opposite benches, but either the chief would back out at the last obstacle, or the Ministry, once formed, would collapse after a few months. And then for a long time the Crimean War had imposed a kind of party truce in Lord Palmerston's favour.

For the prolonged clouding of Conservative fortunes, Disraeli was held responsible by a whole clique of enemies. He knew that he had done his best, that he had acted honourably, that he had given his life to a party. Ambitious? Of course he had been ambitious, and he still believed that only by love or fame are men inspired to great deeds. And cynical? Without a doubt—but what romantic passion lay hidden still beneath that cynicism!

Mary Anne considered him the greatest genius of all time, and treasured up the tiniest scraps of paper on which he jotted a note. Sometimes, and even in public, she took his hand and kissed it with humility. She still continued to drop reprehensible remarks. At Windsor she said to a Princess of the blood: "But perhaps, my dear, you don't know what it is to have an affectionate husband!" One day the cold and daring George Smythe made bold to ask Disraeli whether his wife's conversation did not annoy him just a little.

"Oh, no! I'm never put out by that."— "Well, Diz, you must be a man of most extraordinary qualities."—"Not at all. I only possess one quality in which most men are deficient! Gratitude." And to some one else he said: "She believed in me when men despised me." Every year, on the anniversary of their wedding, he wrote for her a short piece of verse.

Sixty . . . sixty-one . . . Slow and short, the years were passing. The sessions, with their man-made rhythm, rolled on to the diviner rhythm of the seasons. Disraeli was growing old. Doubtless he was never now to be Prime Minister.

It was a pity; he would have loved power. But the spirit must not be allowed to dwell too much on what was denied one: what one actually had was none too bad, bearing in mind the humble beginnings. "To the brave, nothing is difficult," he used to say in his younger days. And for some time now he had adopted another: "Never explain, never complain." Avoid useless words.

The British Lion Roars

IN 1859 *Punch* published a cartoon representing a sleeping lion, which Bright, Disraeli and Russell were trying to rouse by prodding with red-hot iron bars. On each bar was the word "Reform." The image was exact. Ever since the partial reform of 1832, which had enfranchised so limited a class of electors, every party strove in turn to interest the British Lion in a new measure. But the well-fed Lion continued to snore, and the parliamentary Limbo was peopled with the ghosts of still-born reforms.

Suddenly, at the very outset of Derby's tenure of office, the British Lion quite inexplicably woke up in a bad temper, and burst the bars of his cage, as represented by the railings of Hyde Park. For three days on end crowds gathered loudly demanding Reform, and troops had to be brought up. Watching the demonstrators from her window, Mary Anne saw that they had all the appearance of amusing themselves, and conceived a sympathy. And all of a sudden Disraeli saw a magnificent stroke to play.

In his heart of hearts he had always been friendly to the idea of a suffrage extended to the more responsible section of the working-classes. That union of the aristocracy and the people which he had preached in "Sybil" would thus find its expression, and the boldest step would perhaps be also the wisest. "Why not grant a domestic vote," he said to Derby, "one household, one vote, whatever the rental, with appropriate restrictions of time and residence." It was at least a feasible principle, and a conservative principle.

So in a hostile Parliament, Disraeli put through a bill which Whig Governments had vainly sought to pass for thirty years. It was a great parliamentary triumph. Gladstone felt as much and noted in his diary: "A smash perhaps without example."

"I met Gladstone at breakfast," wrote one observer. "He seems quite awed by the diabolic cleverness of Dizzy." Derby was delighted; he recognized that the measure was "a leap in the dark," but he added, rubbing his hands, "don't you see that we have dished the Whigs?"

THE success greatly altered Disraeli's position in Parliament, and a new character was taking shape in the popular imagination; that of the Sphinx *Punch* published a drawing which showed an immense stone Sphinx being dragged towards the temple of Reform by a horde of naked slaves, Gladstone among them, flogged onwards by Lord Derby. It was entitled "D'Israel-i in Triumph."

None who then met him could escape this complex impression of power and wizardry. The face had veritably acquired the immobility of stone, and there was a profound difference between him and the mortal men who surrounded him. "I would as soon have thoughts of sitting down at table with Hamlet or Lear, or the Wandering Jew," wrote a contemporary after meeting him. And he added: "They say, and say truly enough, 'What an actor the man is!'—and yet the ultimate impression is of absolute sincerity and unreserve."

Duff Cooper will have it that he is an alien. "What's England to him, or he to England? That is just where they are wrong. Whig or Radical or Tory don't matter much, perhaps; but this mightier Venice—this Imperial Republic on which the sun never sets—that vision fascinates him, or I am much mistaken. England is the Israel of his imagination, and he will be the Imperial Minister before he dies—if he gets the chance."

On Top of the Greasy Pole

AND this chance, contrary to all expectations, was close at hand. Derby's attacks of gout became so frequent, and so rarely was he able to fulfil the duties of his post, that he felt it his duty in the end to arrange for his retirement.

On the day of the chief's formal resignation, a messenger came to bid Disraeli have audience with Her Majesty at Osborne. Next day Disraeli was received. The Queen seemed radiant, and held out her hand, saying, "You must kiss my hand." He fell on one knee, and very wholeheartedly he kissed that small plump hand. He was profoundly happy. After all, life was worth living.

On the whole his welcome was favourable. "A triumph of industry, courage and patience," even his adversaries admitted. When he entered the House of Commons for the first time as Prime Minister, the lobbies were thronged with men who had gathered to acclaim him. John Stuart Mill was speaking and had to break off for several minutes.

A month later Mary Anne, as the wife of the Prime Minister, gave a great reception at the Foreign Office, where Lord Stanley had been good enough to lend her the necessary rooms for the evening. The weather was wretched; London was swept by a hurricane of wind and rain. Nevertheless, everybody was there, the whole Conservative party, some Liberals too, the Gladstones among them, and many friends.

Dizzy, in all his glory, escorted the Princess of Wales round the rooms; on the Prince's arm was Mrs. Dizzy, looking very old and very ill. For a month now she had a cancer, and knew it, but she refused to tell her husband. This mixture of the glorious and the decrepit added a touch of melancholy.

A wave of sympathy had enveloped this old couple after all their struggles. They had been accepted. In every drawing room in London the wife of the Prime Minister was simply known as "Mary Anne."

Disraeli himself bore in mind the astonishing acrobatics which had brought about his elevation. "Yes," he replied to those who offered their congratulations, "I've climbed to the top of the greasy pole."

The Widow of Windsor

DISRAELI had exasperated more men than one in the course of his life, but women he had found indulgent. It was a woman, Mrs. Austen, who had found a publisher for "Vivian Grey"; it was women, the Sheridan sisters, then Lady Cork and Lady Londonderry, who had launched him into society; it was a woman, Mary Anne, who had given him a seat in Parliament. At every turning of memory's pathway he found one of those ministering faces leaning over his own self-disgust and vexation of soul. He looked with an expert eye on his Sovereign, with her white tulle cap, waiting for him at the top of the state staircase, and he felt delightfully at ease.

Since the death of her dearly loved consort, the Queen had lived in solitary grandeur. She had vowed to respect every wish and every custom of Albert's. Swathed in crèpe, she wandered from castle to castle, from Windsor to Osborne, from Osborne to Balmoral. The public complained of her seclusion, and she suffered from the knowledge of her unpopularity. No one understood her, and no one had understood Albert either, and he had suffered from that, he too. . . . No one except Mr. Disraeli.

Their natures, superficially so different, had subtle affinities of their own. Both would think with simple-hearted pride of the vast Eastern Empire governed, from a hyperborean island, by this stout, self-willed little woman and old, stooping minister. People might think some of the Queen's foibles ridiculous, and many of Disraeli's artificial, but in both of them dwelt courage and greatness.

Through him she could savour more fully the pleasure of being a Sovereign. He set her with such manifest happiness at the head of the splendid procession of life. When he talked to her of her realms, she could feel herself all-powerful. With this Minister who described Cabinet meetings to her as if they were scenes of fiction, for whom politics was a talk of personal adventures, her public business recovered the charm it had held in Albert's day.

Disraeli knew that he was amusing to the Queen, and found pleasure in addressing ironic and perfectly polished epistles to her Majesty. Did she always grasp them? She grasped much more fully than her familiars supposed. She relished the diversion of a successful sleight-of-hand, and then with a sharp sense for reality, she firmly led the magician back towards the desired course.

ONE day Mary Anne received a box of fresh primroses from Windsor, with a letter from the Princess Christian. "Mamma desires me to send you the accompanying flowers in her name for Mr. Disraeli. She heard him say one day that he was so fond of May and of all those lovely spring flowers that she has ventured to send him these, as they will make his rooms look so bright. The flowers come from Windsor."

Mary Anne replied with a sentence which Dizzy had obviously edited for her: "I performed the most pleasing office which I ever had to fulfil in obeying Her Majesty's commands. Mr. Disraeli is passionately fond of flowers, and their lustre and perfume were enhanced by the condescending hand which had showered upon him all the treasures of spring."

The Minister sent all his novels to the Queen. The Queen presented the Minister with her "Journal of Our Life in the Highlands." "We authors, Ma'am . . ." the Premier would often say thereafter, and a smile showed on the masterful little mouth. Every week the primroses from Windsor, the violets from Osborne, would arrive at Grosvenor Gate in their moss-lined boxes. The official correspondence became a curious blend of pastoral poetry and realist politics.

"He Would Reform the Solar System"

GLADSTONE was never the man to sit down among ashes. So ill did he conceal his spite that, contrary to parliamentary usage, he picked a quarrel in the very first week of Disraeli's Government. In carrying out the electoral Reform, Disraeli had certainly stolen a weapon from the Liberal party's armoury, but happily there remained much else to be reformed. The House of Lords could be reformed, and the Church, and the Crown, and the Army, and Education. Gladstone was ready to reform the solar system rather than leave Disraeli peacefully enjoying an unjust fortune. But with a very exact sense of what was actual in politics, he selected the Church and in particular the Irish Church.

The disestablishment of the Irish Church might be a just measure, but Disraeli considered it to be the first step in a dangerous direction, and a reversal of the Constitution. He made ready, therefore, to engage in electoral battle on the ground chosen by Gladstone. There, against a paradoxical assailant, he would stand forth as the paradoxical champion of the Church.

Whilst awaiting the election results in the country, at Hawarden, Gladstone would sometimes cover thirty-three miles on foot in his day, and come home in the evening thirsting for further activity. More frequently he would fell trees. This was his favourite pastime; he flung himself upon these venerable trunks as zealously as if they were old-established wrongs.

On December 1st, 1868, he was in his shirt sleeves, just raising his woodman's axe, when a message reached him by telegram. The queen announced the visit of General Grey. "Very significant," said Mr. Gladstone to his companion, and went on with his task.

AFTER a few minutes the blows of the axe ceased, and he remarked with the deepest gravity, "My mission is to pacify Ireland." And in his journal he noted: "The Almighty seems to sustain and spare me for some purpose of his own, deeply unworthy as I know myself to be. Glory be to his name!" Thus upheld by divine forces, and supported in the Commons by a stout majority, conscious of an athlete's body and a temper of steel, he felt himself invincible.

When Disraeli learned the full result of the elections and his defeat, his first thought had been to withdraw from political life. Custom entitled him to request a peerage and to find an honourable retirement in the House of Lords.

But on reflection he did not like the idea of abandoning a defeated party and a front line post in the Commons. When the Queen showed herself anxious to recognize his services, he asked that Mary Anne should be made a peeress, he himself remaining plain Mr. Disraeli. The Queen graciously approved this plan, and he chose for his wife the title of Beaconsfield, from the Buckinghamshire town.

Disraeli knew that the great Burke, had he lived longer, would have liked to become Lord Beaconsfield. He himself had created a lord of that name in "Vivian Grey." He always found pleasure in transposing his novels into real life. So Mary Anne became Viscountess Beaconsfield, and Dizzy remained Dizzy.

Death of the Heart

MEANWHILE, Mary Anne was very ill. From 1866 she had had a cancer of the stomach; she knew it, but forced herself to hide the truth from Dizzy, whilst he, thinking that she was ignorant of it, affected to speak lightly of the disease. Courageously she continued to live a social life.

In 1872 the young *chargé d'affaires* of the French Embassy saw, in one drawing room, a strange being trapped out like a kind of pagoda, whom he took for some aged rajah. It was Mary Anne, and behind her was Dizzy, painted and sepulchral, his last ringlet dyed jet-black and fixed on his bald brow. On her heart Mary Anne wore, as one wears the badge of an order, a huge medallion which framed a portrait of her husband. She was eighty-one, and he, sixty-eight; a ridiculous and touching pair.

She did not think she could stand a journey, so they spent the summer of 1872 together in London. They drove in the carriage, visiting unknown districts and trying to forget that the park stretching before their windows was called Hyde. Then, as she grew gradually worse, she tried to think that the country would do her good. But she was past curing; her stomach refused all nourishment. Although she died literally of starvation, she still received a few friends with a very good grace, taking the air with them in her little trap drawn by the old pony.

As soon as she had left the room, Disraeli would talk of his wife's sufferings, and for the first time his visitors would see that face, which they had always known as impassive, overwhelmed by emotion. When it was obvious that she was beyond recovery, he wired for Montagu Corry to come, feeling himself unable to bear the catastrophe alone. She died on September 15th, 1872.

While she lived, his Mary Anne had been justly proud of the fact that she spared Dizzy all those vexatious cares which exhaust a man's mind. Since his marriage, house and servants had for him become perfect machines to which he need not give a moment's thought. But once gone, she could no longer protect her great man. Her fortune had only been a life-interest, even the house passed to heirs, and Dizzy had to move out and take refuge in an hotel. Never again would he know the kindliness of a true shelter. The loneliness of the hotel, the worst loneliness of all, alive only with stupid furniture, dreary meals and unknown neighbours—such would be his.

Power

HIS political friends had fears that his bereavement might become the pretext for a complete retirement. The opposite happened. Finding nothing within himself but mournful thoughts, he sought activity, and to escape from thinking, resumed the battle.

The moment happened to be favourable. The tactics of waiting had produced good results. He had given Gladstone plenty of rope; Gladstone had rushed in here, there and everywhere; it only remained to profit by the errors which are inevitably born of all activity.

Tempering the impatience of his followers, he was anxious to avoid taking office until Gladstone's energy had been exhausted by fresh reverses. Experience had shown him only too well the fragility of Cabinets lacking the support of a strong majority. In a speech at Manchester he described the last moments of the Ministry's death agony: "As time advanced it was not difficult to perceive that extravagance was being substituted for energy by the Government." The unnatural stimulus was subsiding. Their paroxysms ended in prostration.

At last Gladstone held the elections. The Conservatives secured a clear majority of fifty seats over all parties together, and of more than a hundred over the Liberals alone. At last it was proved that a popular electorate could, as Disraeli had always maintained, be a conservative electorate.

The Conservatives had not always understood the politics of their Chief, as they henceforward styled Disraeli, but he had led them to the most astounding victory they had ever achieved. The fact must be faced: his spells might not be intelligible, but they were potent.

AT LAST he knew that he would be accepted for what he was. He loosened his grip on himself. His wit was less harsh, less sarcastic. Yes, this time he was indeed at the summit. No longer did he feel within him that restless need of climbing ever higher, of domination. At last he ought to be happy.

But to a friend's congratulations he replied: "For me, it is twenty years too late. Give me your age and your health!" And he was heard to murmur, "Power! It has come to me too late. There were days when, on waking, I felt I could move dynasties and governments; but that has passed away."

He had always been so great an admirer of youth, and his own had been frittered away because his starting point was set so low; he had needed forty years to reach the level from which a Peel or a Gladstone had started off. A misfortune of birth—the hardest maybe of all, because the most unjust. Now it had come "too late."

What could he do with this importunate fame of his? "Perhaps, and probably, I ought to be pleased. I can only tell you the truth . . . I am wearied to extinction and profoundly unhappy . . . I do not think there is really any person much unhappier than I am, and not fantastically so. Fortune, fashion, fame, even power, may increase, and do heighten happiness, but they cannot create it. Happiness can only spring from the affections. I am alone, with nothing to sustain me, but, occasionally, a little sympathy on paper, and that grudgingly. It is a terrible lot, almost intolerable."

Action

HE WAS anxious that the Conservative party's advent to power should be marked by a policy of generosity. Now was the moment to put into action the ideas of "Coningsby" and "Sybil." Law after law was passed: equality of obligations between employers and employed: enlargement of the rights of Trade Unions; reduction of the hours of work to fifty-six in the week; half-holidays on Saturday; and numerous sanitary laws.

Another idea cherished by the Prime Minister from his youth upward and now installed in power with him, with the idea of the Empire, was the idea that England nowadays could not be considered apart from the Colonies.

For the organization of this Empire he had a programme: colonial autonomy accompanied by an Imperial customs tariff, a Crown right over unoccupied territory, a military entente, and lastly the creation of an Imperial Parliament in London.

Just then so new and so bold did this policy seem, that he could not yet apply it, but he seized every opportunity for a striking display of his sentiments, and the importance he attached to Imperial communications.

On November 15th, 1875, Frederick Greenwood, the editor of the *Pall Mall Gazette,* called upon Lord Derby at the Foreign Office. He had dined on the previous evening with a financier well versed in Egyptian affairs, and had learned that the Khedive, being short of money, was desirous of selling his 177,000 shares in the Suez Canal.

Greenwood considered that it was in England's interest to acquire the Khedive's holding, as the Canal was the highway to India. Derby showed no great enthusiasm; he had a horror of large projects. But Disraeli's imagination was fired. He found that the Khedive was glad enough to deal with England, but he required money at once.

Parliament was not in session, and four millions was not a sum which could be taken on the Budget without a vote of credit.

"Scarcely breathing time! But the thing must be done," wrote Disraeli to the Queen.

On the day of the Cabinet's deliberation, Montagu Corry was posted in the anteroom. The Chief put his head round the half-opened door, and said one word: "Yes." Ten minutes later Corry was in New Court at Rothschild's, whom he found at table. He told him that Disraeli needed four millions on the following day. Rothschild was eating grapes. He took one, spat out the skin, and said: "What is your security?"

"The British Government."

"You shall have it."

"The Days of the Giants Are Over"

THUS the political vessel, tossed on the waves of fortune and climate, of the favour of the House and the humour of the Sovereign, rode the seas pretty well. But the skipper was very ill. So poor did his health become that more than once he told the Queen that he wanted to leave political life. This was a prospect which she would not have at any price, and she suggested that it would be easy to elevate the Prime Minister to the House of Lords "where the fatigue would be *far* less and where he would be able to *direct* everything."

This time he accepted. He took the name which he had had bestowed on Mary Anne, that of Beaconsfield, but whereas she had been only a Viscountess, he became the Earl of Beaconsfield and Viscount Hughenden of Hughenden.

When members learned the news they gathered in groups, deeply moved. Voices were lowered on the benches, as if there was a coffin in the chamber. A supporter, Sir William Hart Dyke, said: "All the real chivalry and delight of party politics seem to have departed: nothing remains but routine."

And that was the feeling of the whole House. The interest taken by this old man in the game of life had in the end communicated itself to all those about him. With him one never knew what the morrow might not bring, but one could be certain that at least it would be nothing dull.

Sir William Harcourt, an opponent, quoted the words of Metternich at the death of Napoleon: "You will perhaps think that when I heard of his death I felt a satisfaction at the great adversary of my country and my policy. It was just the reverse. I experienced only a sense of regret at the thought that I should never again have converse with that great intelligence."

"Alas! alas!" wrote another, "we shall never see your like again. The days of the giants are over. Ichabod! Ichabod!"

When shortly afterwards the Queen opened the session of Parliament, a strange, motionless figure was seen standing by her side, draped in scarlet and ermine. It was the new Lord Beaconsfield. With perfect composure he came forward and bowed, shook hands, raised his hat, as the ritual demanded, and then, having become Leader of the House of Lords on the very day of his entering it, he began to speak:

"I am dead, dead, but in the Elysian Fields."

Eugene O'Neill

STRANGE INTERLUDE

EUGENE O'NEILL, born in 1888, is today perhaps the leading dramatist of America. He has won the Pulitzer drama prize three times: with "Beyond the Horizon" in 1920, "Anna Christie" in 1922, and "Strange Interlude" in 1928. Other notable plays from his pen include: "Emperor Jones" (1921), "The Hairy Ape" (1922), "Desire Under the Elms" (1924), "Marco Millions" (1924), "The Great God Brown" (1925), "Dynamo" (1928), "Ah! Wilderness" (1933), and "Days Without End" (1934). "Strange Interlude" employs the dramatic device of the "aside," or spoken thought, indicated in this condensation by the speeches set in small type. The expression of the subconscious mind in this play is part of the technique of psychoanalysis.

Act One

THERE are three men in NINA's life. Her dead fiancé, GORDON SHAW, who was shot down in the war and whose memory is always with her, and the career-minded DR. NED DARRELL who prescribes marriage to the third, SAM EVANS.

NINA has been Mrs. Evans for several months when the scene opens on the cheerless dining room of the Evans homestead in northern New York. NINA is writing a letter to NED, the doctor. There is an air of inner calm about her —quite different from her strained, nerve-wracked expression in the interval between GORDON's death and her marriage.

NINA (*looking up from the letter, thinking embarrassedly*):

Should I have told him? . . . no . . . not even Sam . . . I want to keep it just my baby as long as I can . . . how delighted Ned will be when he hears! . . . he always said it would be the best thing for me . . . well, I do feel happy when I think . . . and I love Sam now . . . in a way . . . it will be his baby too . . .

(*Then with a happy sigh, turns back to the letter and reads part of what she has written over to herself*):

You really must meet his mother sometime— a strange woman from the bit I saw of her last night. She has been writing Sam regularly

once a week ever since we were married, the most urgent invitations to visit her. They were really more like commands, or prayers. Sam's feeling toward her puzzles and shocks me. It was just as though he'd forgotten he had a mother. And yet as soon as he saw her he was sweet enough.

EVANS *and his mother enter the dining room. Sam looks timorously happy, as if he could not quite believe in his good fortune and had constantly to re-assure himself about it. He radiates love and devotion and boyish adoration.*

His mother is a tiny woman with a frail figure. She is only about forty-five but she looks at least sixty. Her big dark eyes are grim with the prisoner-pain of a walled-in soul. Yet a sweet loving kindness, the ghost of an old faith and trust in life's goodness, hovers girlishly, fleetingly, about the corners of her mouth.

EVANS (*as they come in—rattling on in a cocksure, boastful way of a boy showing off his prowess before his mother, confident of thrilled adulation*): I'm making good, all right, all right—since I got married. Why, to show you, Cole—he's the manager— called me into his office and told me he'd had his eye on me, that my stuff was exactly what they wanted, and he thought I had the makings of a real find. How's that? That's certainly fair enough, isn't it?

MRS. EVANS (*vaguely—she has evidently not heard much of what he said*): That's fine, Sammy.

(*Thinking apprehensively*):

I do hope I'm wrong! . . . but that old shiver of dread took me the minute she stepped in the door . . . I don't think she's told Sammy but I got to make sure . . .

(*Sam goes out through the kitchen door, leaving the two women alone.*)

NINA: Good morning—Mother. (*She comes over and kisses her—slips down and sits on the floor beside her*): Would you like . . . to talk to me?

MRS. EVANS (*dully*): Yes. You love my boy, don't you?

NINA (*startled—forcing a smile, quickly*): Why, of course!

(*Reassuring herself*):

No, it isn't a lie . . . I do love him . . . the father of my baby . . .

MRS. EVANS (*blurts out*): Are you going to have a baby, Nina?

NINA (*simply*): Yes, Mother.

MRS. EVANS (*hopelessly*): But you can't! You've got to make up your mind you can't!

(*Thinking fiercely—even with satisfaction*):

Tell her! . . . make her suffer what I was made to suffer! . . .

NINA (*thinking with terrified foreboding*):

I knew it! . . . Out of a blue sky . . . black! . . .

(*Bewilderedly*):

What do you mean? How can you say a thing like that?

MRS. EVANS (*with a flat relentless tone-*

EUGENE O'NEILL

lessness): It's the curse on the Evanses. My husband's mother—she was an only child—died in an asylum and her father before her. I didn't know about the Evanses until after I married my husband. He asked me to forgive him, he said he loved me so much he'd have gone mad without me. So I forgave him. I loved him an awful lot. We'd swore we'd never have children, we never forgot to be careful for two whole years. Then one night we'd both gone to a dance, we both had a little punch—just enough to forget—driving home in the moonlight! such little things at the back of big things!

NINA (*in a dull moan*): I don't believe you! I won't believe you!

MRS. EVANS (*drones on*): My husband, Sammy's father, in spite of all he and I fought against it, he finally gave in to it when Sammy was only eight; he couldn't keep up any more living in fear for Sammy, thinking any minute the curse might get him. Living like that with that fear is awful torment! I know that! I went through it by his side! It nearly drove me crazy, too—but I didn't have it in my blood! And that's why I'm telling you! You got to see you can't, Nina!

NINA (*suddenly breaking out—frenziedly*): I don't believe you! I don't believe Sam would ever have married me if he knew—!

MRS. EVANS (*sharply*): Who said Sammy knew? He don't know a single thing about it! That's been the work of my life, keeping him from knowing. When his father gave up and went off into it I sent Sammy right off to boarding school. I kept him away at school in winter and camp in summers and I went to see him. I never let him come home.

NINA (*with wild mockery*): And I thought Sam was so normal—so healthy and sane—not like me! I thought he'd give me such healthy, happy children and I'd forget myself in them. I hate you. Why didn't you tell him he must never marry!

MRS. EVANS: What reason could I give, without telling him everything? And I never heard about you till after you were married. Then I wanted to write to you but I was scared he might read it. I just kept hoping you wouldn't want children right away—until I'd seen you and told you everything. And I thought you'd love him like I did his father, and be satisfied with him alone.

NINA (*lifting her head—wildly*): No! I don't! I won't! I'll leave him!

MRS. EVANS (*shaking her, fiercely*): You can't! He'd go crazy sure then! You'd be a devil! Don't you see how he loves you?

(*Very sadly and bitterly*):

I can't tell you not to leave him, not if you don't love him. But you oughtn't to have married him when you didn't love him. And it'll be your fault, what'll happens.

NINA (*torturedly*): What will happen? —what do you mean?—Sam will be all right—just as he was before—and it's not my fault anyway!

(*Then thinking conscience-strickenly*):

Poor Sam . . . she's right . . . it's not his fault . . . it's mine . . . I wanted to use him to save myself . . . I acted the coward.

MRS. EVANS (*breaking into intense pleading*): Oh, I'd get down on my knees to you, don't make my boy run that risk! You got to give one Evans, the last one, a chance to live in this world! And you'll learn to love him, if you give up enough for him. Then you can feel proud of having lived fair to him who gave you love and trusted in you!

NINA (*struck—confusedly*): Yes—that's true, isn't it?

(*Thinking strangely*):

Lived fair . . . pride . . . trust . . . play the game! . . . who is speaking to me? . . . Gordon! . . . oh, Gordon, do you mean I must give Sam the life I didn't give you?

(*Speaking mechanically in a dull voice*):

All right, Mother. I'll stay with Sam.

MRS. EVANS (*thinking miserably*):

She's giving her life to save my Sammy . . . I got to save her! . . .

(*Stammeringly*):

Maybe, Nina—I can see how much Sam wants you to have a baby. Sammy's got to feel sure you love him—to be happy. Whatever you can do to make him happy is good—is good, Nina! I don't care what! You've got to have a healthy baby—sometime —so's you can both be happy! It's your rightful duty!

NINA (*sobbing pitifully*): Don't! Please Mother!

MRS. EVANS (*with sudden tenderness—gathering Nina up in her arms, brokenly*): You poor child! You're like the daughter of my sorrow! You're closer to me now than Sammy could be! I want you to be happy!

"I swore I'd never again meddle with human lives, Nina!"

Illustration for Eugene O'Neill's
"STRANGE INTERLUDE"

Act Two

SCENE: *An evening in the study of* NINA's *childhood home about seven months later. There is a noise of steps from the hall and Doctor* NED DARRELL *enters. There is a quality about him, provoking and disturbing to women, of intense passion which he has rigidly trained himself to control and set free only for the objective satisfaction of studying his own and their reactions; and so he has come to consider himself immune to love through his scientific understanding of its real sexual nature.*

NINA *enters silently behind him.* DARRELL *immediately senses her presence, turns and greets her with a smile of affectionate admiration.*

NINA (*uneasy under his glance*):

I hate that professional look in his eyes . . . watching symptoms—without seeing me.

(*With resentful mockery*):

Well, what do you suspect is wrong with the patient now, Doctor?

DARRELL (*quickly averting his eyes— sits down—jokingly*): Same old unjust accusation! You were always reading diagnosis into me, when what I was really thinking was what a becoming gown, or—

NINA (*teasingly*): By the way, aren't you getting yourself engaged to some fair lady or other?

DARRELL (*emphatically*): Not on your life!

NINA (*sarcastically*): Then you don't believe in taking your own medicine? Why Doctor! If you had a nice girl to love—whose character you could shape, in whose unselfish devotion you could find peace, think how much good it would do you.

DARRELL (*after a quick, keen glance*): I recognize my arguments. Was I really wrong on every point, Nina?

NINA (*harshly*): On every single point, Doctor! I must say you proceeded very unscientifically, Doctor!

(*Then in a dull monotonous tone*):

When we went to visit Sam's mother I'd known for two months that I was going to have a baby. I loved it so it seemed at times that Gordon must be its real father, that Gordon must have come to me in a dream while I was lying asleep beside Sam! I almost loved Sam then.

DARRELL (*thinking with scornful jealousy*):

Ha! . . . the hero again! . . . comes to her bed! . . . becomes the father of his child! . . . I'll be damned if hers isn't the most idiotic obsession I ever . . .

NINA: And then Sam's mother told me I couldn't have my baby. You see, Doctor, Sam's father had lost his mind for years before he died. So of course I had to agree it would be wrong—and I had an operation.

DARRELL (*profoundly shocked and stunned*): Good God! Are you crazy, Nina? Poor Sam of all people!

NINA (*with monotonous insistence*): I've promised Sam's mother I'd make him happy! He's unhappy now because he thinks he isn't able to give me a child. So I must have another baby—somehow—don't you think, Doctor?—to make us both happy?

(*She looks up at him pleadingly. For a moment they stare into each other's eyes—then both turn away in guilty confusion.*)

DARRELL (*as if listening to himself*):

Sam is my friend . . . well, and isn't she your friend? . . . her two hands are so warm! I must not even hint at my desire!

(*Judicially calm*):

The man should like and admire he should be her good friend want to help her, but he shou' love her—although he might, harm to anyone, desire her.

NINA: Ned does not love her—but he used to like her and, I think, desire her. Does he now, Doctor?

DARRELL (*thinking*):

I desire her! . . . I desire happiness!

(*Tremblingly now—gently*):

But, Madame, I must confess the Ned you are speaking of is I, and I am Ned.

NINA (*gently*): And I am Nina, who wants her baby. I should be so grateful, Ned.

DARRELL (*taking her hand in both of his and kissing it humbly—with a sob*): Yes—yes, Nina—yes—for your happiness—in that spirit.

(*Thinking, fiercely triumphant*):

I shall be happy for a while! . . .

Act Three

SCENE: *The sitting room of a small house* EVANS *has rented near New York. It is several months later.* NINA *is sitting in a chair near the center. A great change is noticeable in her face and bearing. She is again the pregnant woman, but this time there is a triumphant strength about her expression, a ruthless self-confidence in her eyes.*

(*As if listening for something within her—joyfully*):

There! . . . that can't be my imagination . . . I felt it plainly . . . life . . . my baby . . . my only baby . . . the other never really lived . . . this is the child of my love! and I love Ned! . . . I've loved him ever since that first afternoon . . . when I went to him . . . so scientifically! . . .

(EVANS *enters from the hallway in rear. He is dressed carefully but his clothes are old ones and he has forgotten to shave. His eyes look pitiably harried, his manner has become a distressingly obvious attempt to cover up a chronic state of nervousness. He is arguing with himself.*)

Tell her! . . . go on! . . . she's acted like a good sport . . . but she's beginning to hate you . . . and you can't blame her . . . she wanted children . . . and you haven't been able . . .

(*Stammering*):

Ned is coming. His car has just stopped outside.

(NED DARRELL *comes in from the rear. His face looks older. There is an expression of defensive bitterness and self-resentment about his mouth and eyes. This vanishes into one of desire and joy as he sees* NINA. *He starts toward her impulsively.*)

Nina!

(*Then stops short as he sees* EVANS.)

NINA (*forgetting* EVANS, *gets to her feet as if to receive* DARRELL *in her arms—with love*): Ned!

EVANS (*affectionately and gratefully*): Hello, Ned!

(*He holds out his hand which Darrell takes mechanically.*)

NINA (*watching* EVANS *with contempt—then in a tone of curt dismissal*): You'd better go and shave, hadn't you, if you're going to town?

EVANS: Yes, of course. Excuse me, will you?

DARRELL (*thinking bitterly*):

Sometimes I almost hate her! . . . if it wasn't for her I'd have kept my peace of mind . . . it's idiotic to feel guilty . . . if Sam only didn't trust me!

(*Suddenly taking her in his arms and kissing her frantically*):

Nina! Beautiful!

NINA (*triumphantly—between kisses*):

You love me, don't you? Say you do, Ned!

DARRELL (*passionately*): Yes! Yes!

(*A noise from the hall and* EVANS *comes in from the rear. He sees them together but mistakes the meaning.*)

EVANS (*genially*): Well, Doc, how's the patient? I think she's much better, don't you?

DARRELL: Yes; much better.

NINA (*matter-of-factly*): I must see how lunch is coming on. You'll stay, of course, Ned? We want to have a long talk with you after lunch, Sam—don't we, Ned?
(*She goes out.*)

EVANS: What did Nina mean, you want a long talk with me? Or is it a secret?

DARRELL (*controlling an impulse toward hysterical laughter*): A secret? Yes, you bet it's a secret!

(*He suddenly turns to* EVANS *who has been staring at him, puzzledly—in a whisper*):

Look here, Sam. I can't stay to lunch. I'm sailing for Europe in a few days and I have a million things to do. I haven't told anyone. I came out today to say good-bye. And now for your secret! It ought to make you very happy, Sam. You're going to be a father, old scout, that's the secret! And now I've got to run. Good-bye.

EVANS (*stares after him dumbly*): Thank you—Ned.

Act Four

SCENE: *Nearly twelve years later. The sitting room of the Evans' apartment on Park Avenue, New York City.* NINA *and* DARRELL *and their son,* GORDON, *are in the room.* NINA *is in the full bloom of her womanhood.* GORDON *is eleven—a fine boy with the figure of an athlete.* DARRELL *has aged greatly. He has the look of a man with no definite aim or ambition which he can relate to living.*

(*Thinking disjointedly*):

Why did I doubt myself? . . . now she loves me . . . she's loved me right along . . .

(NINA *comes in from the kitchen.*)

NINA: Sam! What's come over you, Sam?

EVANS (*tenderly*): Ned told me—the secret—and I'm so happy, dear!

NINA (*stammering*): Ned told you—what?

EVANS (*tenderly*): That we're going to have a child, dear.

NINA: He told you we—we—you, the father—?

(*Then suddenly—wildly*):

Ned! Where is Ned?

EVANS: Didn't he tell you he was sailing for Europe? If it's something important, perhaps I can locate—

NINA: No, nothing—nothing important—nothing is important—ha—!

(*She stifles an hysterical laugh—then on the verge of fainting*):

Sam! Help me—

EVANS (*rushing to support her*): Poor darling.

(*Thinking jubilantly*):

Her condition . . . this *kness comes from her condition.*

resentfully):

GORDON (*thin* *out of here! . . . why* *I wish Darre* *one of his old trips again* *don't he go* *was gone more'n a year* *. . . last t* *died!*
was hop *ing him—with loving*

NIN

hy baby . . . my little m *him has been happiness*

handsome he is! . . . not at all like Ned . . . when I was carrying him I was fighting to forget Ned . . . hoping he would be like Gordon . . . and he is . . . poor Ned, I've made him suffer a great deal . . . No, I can't blame myself . . . no woman can make a man happy who has no purpose in life! . . . It was I who shamed him into taking up biology and starting the station in the West Indies . . . if I hadn't he'd simply have hung around me year after year, doing nothing . . . Why doesn't he go back to the West Indies? . . . I always get a terrible feeling after he's been back a while that he's waiting for Sam to die! . . . or go insane!

NINA: When are you going back to the West Indies, Ned? I don't see how you can afford to leave your work for such long periods. Don't you grow rusty?

DARRELL: My work was finished twelve years ago. As I believe you know, I ended it with an experiment which resulted so successfully that any further meddling with human lives would have been superfluous!

NINA (*pityingly*): Ned!

DARRELL: But you meant my present dabbling about. You know better than to call that work. It's merely my hobby. My backing Sam has made me so wealthy that I'm forced to take up a hobby. The good Samuel is an A one success. He has a charming wife and a darling boy, and a Park Avenue apartment and a membership in an expensive golf club. And, above all, he rests so complacently on the proud assurance that he is self-made! Would he be grateful if he knew how much I'd really done for him!

NINA (*sternly*): Ned!

GORDON (*his fists clenched, trembling with rage*): You—shut up—making fun of my father! I hate you!

NINA: Gordon! How dare you talk like that to your Uncle Ned!

GORDON (*rebelliously*): He's not my uncle! He's not my anything! I won't 'pologize—never!

(*He goes out, rear.*)

DARRELL (*his expression changing to one of pity—goes to her and puts his hand on her head—tenderly*): I'm sorry.

(*With remorseful tenderness*):

Dreadful, what you've done, Nina. Why, you've given me the only happiness I've known! And no matter what I may say or do in bitterness, I'm proud—and grateful, Nina!

NINA: Dearest, it's wonderful of you to say that! Can't we be brave enough—for you to go away—now, on this note——sure of our love?

DARRELL: Yes! I'll go—this minute if you wish.

NINA: But you'll surely come back to me!

DARRELL: Surely.

(*She kisses him. GORDON appears in the doorway and stands for a moment in a passion of jealousy and rage and grief, watching them. Then he vanishes as silently as he had come.*)

Act Five

SCENE: *Late afternoon in late June, ten years later, cruising afterdeck of the Evans motor cruiser anchored near the finish line at Poughkeepsie. NINA whose hair has turned nearly white is sitting by a table aft. DARRELL, who again has the air of a detached scientist is at her left developed by the logically by continued success, is leaning of continued success, is leaning of the rail with MADELINE ARNOLD, the girl of*

about nineteen who looks as if she generally gets what she wants.

EVANS: Soon be time for the start. Gosh, I'll bet Gordon's some keyed-up right at this moment.

MADELINE: Poor kid! I'll bet he is!

NINA (*thinking with intense bitterness*):

That tone in her voice! . . . her love already possesses him! . . . my son . . . But she won't . . . as long as I live.

(*Flatly*):

Yes, he must be nervous.

MADELINE: But you can bank on Gordon never losing his nerve.

NINA: I'm quite aware my son isn't a weakling—

EVANS:

What a nasty crack! I'm not going to let Nina come between Gordon and Madeline. By God, I'm going to see to it their marriage goes through on schedule, no matter how much Nina kicks up!

MADELINE (*suddenly*): They're off! Navy and Washington are leading— Gordon's third!

(*Madeline and Evans go off to watch the race.*)

DARRELL: There's a young lady who seems to care a lot whether Gordon comes in last or not.

NINA (*trying to be appealing*): Yes. Gordon is hers now, Ned. That is, they're engaged. But, of course, that doesn't necessarily mean— Why for Gordon to take her seriously is too idiotic for words!

DARRELL (*thinking cynically*):

She must have no real claim to dispute your ownership, eh? . . . you'd like to make her the same sort of convenient slave for him in a physical sense that I was for you!

(*Resentfully*):

I can't agree with you. I find her quite charming. It seems to me if I were in Gordon's shoes I'd do exactly what he has done.

(*In confusion—thinking bitterly*):

In Gordon's shoes! . . . I always was in Gordon Shaw's shoes! . . . and why am I taking this young Gordon's part? What has he for me, for God's sake?

NINA: You'll have to give Gordon a good talking to, Ned.

DARRELL: I swore I'd never again med-

dle with human lives, Nina! We've meddled enough. Besides, I'm quite sure Gordon isn't my son. I was only a body to you. Your first Gordon used to come back to life. I was never more to you than a substitute for your dead lover! Gordon is really Gordon's son!

(*Thinking exultantly*):

I'm free! . . . I've beaten her at last!

(EVANS *and* MADELINE *enter, rushing to the rail of the afterdeck and training their glasses up the river.*)

NINA (*with a smile of cruel triumph— thinking*):

I can pretend I'm forced to tell her . . . as Sam's mother did with me. It can't help succeeding . . . my Gordon will come back.

Madeline!

MADELINE: Yes, Mrs. Evans. They're getting closer. Why don't you come and watch?

NINA: There's something I must tell you. You've probably wondered why I objected to your engagement. It's because the marriage is impossible. I speak as your friend! You must break your engagement with him at once!

MADELINE: But why—why?

NINA: Why? Because—

DARRELL: No, Nina!

(*He draws Madeline aside*):

Miss Arnold, as a doctor I feel it my duty to tell you that Mrs. Evans isn't herself. She's just passed through a crucial period in a woman's life and she's morbidly jealous of you and subject to queer delusions. So get back to the race! And God bless you!

(*Steps quickly to Nina's side*):

I'm sorry, Nina, but I not to meddle.

EVANS (*leaning far ov*

One spurt more will do it! Stroke! Stroke! Now! Over the line, boy! That's done it! He's won! He's won!

MADELINE: Gordon! Gordon! He's won!

EVANS (*embracing* NINA *frantically*): Aren't you happy, Nina? Our Gordon! The greatest ever!

NINA (*trying to force out a last despairing protest*): No!—not yours!—mine! and Gordon's! Gordon is Gordon's!—he was my Gordon!—his Gordon is mine!

EVANS (*humoring her*): Of course he's yours, dear—and a dead ringer for Gordon Shaw, too! Gordon's body! Gordon's spirit! Your body and spirit, too, Nina! He's not like me, lucky for him! I'm a poor boob! I never could row worth a damn!

(*He suddenly staggers as if he were very drunk—then gives a gasp and collapses inertly on the deck.*)

NINA: My husband. Sam! Oh, Ned, did all our old secret hopes do this at last?

DARRELL (*professionally, staring at her coldly*): Bosh, Mrs. Evans! We're not in the Congo that we can believe in evil charms!

(*His voice suddenly breaking with sincere human grief*):

Sam, old boy! I'm so damned sorry! I would give my life to save you!

NINA (*in dull anguish*): Save—again? Dear husband, you have tried to make me happy, I will give you my happiness again! I will give you Gordon to give to Madeline!

MADELINE (*still standing on the rail, staring after Gordon's shell*): Gordon! . . . dear lover. How tired . . . but you'll soon rest in my arms . . . soon! . . .

THE MEANS TO ATTAIN HAPPY LIFE

MARTIAL, the things that do attain
    The happy life be these, I find:—
The richesse left, not got with pain;
    The fruitful ground, the quiet mind;

The equal friend; no grudge, no strife;
    No charge of rule, nor governance;
Without disease, the healthful life;
    The household of continuance;

The mean diet, no delicate fare;
    True wisdom join'd with simpleness;
The night dischargèd of all care,
    Where wine the wit may not oppress.

The faithful wife, without debate;
    Such sleeps as may beguile the night:
Contented with thine own estate
    Ne wish for death, ne fear his might.
    —Henry Howard, Earl of Surrey (1516-47).

EDWARD STREETER

MONKEY BUSINESS

EDWARD STREETER gained national prominence through the publication in 1918 of his book, "Dere Mable," love letters of a rookie. Streeter himself was an officer in the 27th (N. Y.) Division. He now lives on Long Island and commutes to New York, where he is a banker. His latest literary success is a hilarious dissertation on commuting, published under the title, "Daily Except Sunday."

THE breeze, what there was of it, was abeam. Like a luminous white cloud in the darkness the yawl trickled lazily down the Sound. Dinner had been ample. The crew sprawled about the cockpit and the cabin roof listening to the Doctor.

Braced against the cabin bulkhead the latter was off on his favorite topic—psychiatry. He told of his student days in Vienna. Of his work under Freud and Jung. Neuroses, libidos, ids, Oedipus complexes, repressions, danced crazily through his talk. To us it sounded more like the Wizard of Oz than a discussion of human behavior.

McNulty sat astride the wheel box, a light finger on the king spoke, sucking his pipe and listening. McNulty was a New York harbor pilot. Half his life was spent in a little flat in Brooklyn, the other half guiding sleek liners and rusty tramps through the Narrows or tossing idly in a pilot boat off Ambrose Channel Lightship waiting for business.

Now he was taking a busman's holiday, running down the Sound by moonlight to the Vineyard. He loved boats the way other men love women. His devotion assured him a welcome in every yacht club from Larchmont to New London.

The Doctor stopped to light his pipe. There was no sound but the ripple of the water along the strakes. Mac broke the silence.

"Docthors do a lot of good in this worrld, an' I'd be th' last one t' blame thim f'r makin' things hard. That's just what y' might call self persavation. If people only knew how aisy it was t' take an ol' toob of a boat out o' Noo York harber where 'ud th' pilots be? An' likewise if themometers was made so's a man could read his own timpachoor who'd be callin' on th' docthor t' do it, I'm askin'?

"But bein' as this ain't no perfessional gatherin' I'd like t' say t' y' Doc that all th' stuff ye've been tellin' us sounds like th' ravin's of Kilkinney cats t' me."

He paused, as if waiting for an argument, but the Doctor remained silent.

"Now I've knocked around in me time. I've lived with all kinds. An' sometimes I've lived with mesif which is even harder. I guess I learned somethin' from both. At laste I got this far without bein' fished out from under a dock with a boat hook or concked on th' head with a lead pipe. But I'm tellin' ye if I believed in all thim complexes an' new roses y' been tellin' about I'd a gone nuts years ago.

"Ivry man's got to ixplain things to himself different, I suppose. An' if y'r gittin paid f'r th' explanation y' got t' give y'r patients their money's worth. But t' me it's a lot simpler than it seems t' be t' you.

"In case y'r interested, which y' probably ain't, I'd ixplain it more like this. In the upper part of what people insist on callin' me bodily timple theys a fellow sittin' on a stool like th' lookout on a freight train caboose. He's dressed in ᵃ white duck suit like one of these ᵃ ological guys. On his head he's

283

of thim round porter's caps with a black vizer. An' on th' front of it it says KEEPER in nate gold letters.

"That's me. At laste that's th' me y' see sittin' here talkin' t' y' out th' window o' th' caboose. An' a finer, better-mainin', more upright Dimmycrat y'll niver want t' see.

"But down below this guy, where fortunately the observation ain't so good, they's another party. An' whin y'r eyes gits used t' th' darkness y'll see what looks like a queer lookin' little ape sittin' in th' corner sulkin'.

"That's me too. Only they got that part o' me stowed in th' hold cause if y' could see it I wouldn't be sittin' here now. I'd be in jail—if they could find room there.

"Now it's th' keeper's job t' manage this ooorang ootang an' they's nothin' about it he's proud of. Hiven knows how old th' crature is—maybe a million, maybe more—but he ain't got no môre sinse than th' day he was born. They's no tachin' him ittykit or th' dacent ways of livin'. He niver heard of Imily Post an it ain't troublin' him none ayther.

"The only thing he knows is what he wants. An' what he wants ain't always in th' best interests of civil-ization. An' if he ain't wantin' somethin' he can't have, he's seein' somethin' that ain't there an' scarin' hisself to death. There's no tryin' t' guess what he's goin' t' do next. One minit he'll be layin' in th' corner, quiet as a mouse, an' thin, all of a sudden, he'll get it in his nut a flock o' banshees is chasin' him an' he'll start runnin' around, screamin' an' gibberin', 'til th' whole place is bedlim.

"Thim is th' times whin th' Keeper has t' crawl down an' hold him in his lap an' pat him 'til he gets quiet. If th' Keeper knows his job he'll tell him ivry-thin' is hunky dory, an' how ivrybody says he's th' best ape iver swung in a tree, an' t' go t' sleep an' whin he wakes up he'll git a bunch o' banannas.

"In some ways it's lucky he's got as little sinse as he has. If he couldn't be kidded a bit there'd be no livin' with him.

Mac paused to relight his pipe. "Go on," said the Doctor, "I'm interested."

"Well, Doc, you remember that guy Cooey ivrybody was talkin' about a few years ago? He knew all about this stuff. All that feller done, when y' come right down to it, was t' run a school f'r Keepers. He's th' one ye'll ricollect that taught thim t' sit in their cabooses an' holler down 'Ivry day in ivry way y'r becomin' a better an' better munk—ye cross-eyed little baboon ye.' Only o' course they didn't let 'em hear th' last part.

"An' after a while th' little feller'd begin t' believe it. He'd kind of look dreamy-eyed an' suck his thumbs an' go off t' sleep in a corner, which 'ud give th' Keeper a chance t' catch up on his newspaper.

"An' on days whin th' chimp was holdin' onto his stummick an' complainin' about his misery, this feller Cooey taught th' Keepers t' stick their heads down an' say 'They aint nothin' th' matter with you, dopey. You feel fine.' An' if they said it loud enough an' long enough th' munk begun t' believe that too. An' pretty soon he fergot his stummick an' was lyin' on his back, chortlin' to himself, happy as a clam.

"The trouble is you can kid him into shuttin' up f'r a while but y' can't train him so's you can depend on him. He's the only livin' cratchure I iver come up against, ixcept a Raypublican, that wont learn.

"Oh, he'll fool you. Th' Keeper'll think he's got him broke o' some bad habit. He'll play round th' cage like a little gentleman f'r months—I've seen him behave f'r years. Thin, whin ivry-thin's under control an' y'r dozin' off thinkin' what a nice comfortable worrld it is, all hell breaks loose down below—an' he's at it again.

"As I think back on it thim is th' times he's apt t' be worst. It's as if he suddenly got wise t' th' fact th' Keeper'd been foolin' him all this time. It gets him so hoppin' mad he tries t' make up f'r it by breakin' ivrythin' in sight."

The Doctor sat up and knocked his

pipe against the rail. "If he can work that out what makes you think this charming little creature you've been describing has no sense, Mac?"

"'Cause he aint. I ought t' know. I been tryin' t' knock some into him f'r orty-five years."

"Did you ever really get the better of him?"

"No. That's what I'm tellin' y'. Ivry time y' think y' got th' critter down he'll come up behind y' an pull th' chair out from under y' if he has t' wait half a life time f'r th' chance."

"The way you tell it, Mac, he doesn't sound as dumb to me as the Keeper."

"Listen, Doc, I wouldn't want t' be gittin' into any argymints with a feller that knows all ye do. An what's more I'll go as far as this with yez. Maybe both is crazy. But after all which one is th' Keeper? It seems to me that's th' whole point in th' thing. Will one of yez lads pull in th' main sheet a bit."

My Lady Greensleeves

Alas! my love, you do me wrong
    To cast me off discourteously;
And I have lovèd you so long,
    Delighting in your company.

    Greensleeves was all my joy!
    Greensleeves was my delight!
    Greensleeves was my heart of gold!
        And who but Lady Greensleeves!

I bought thee petticoats of the best,
    The cloth so fine as fine as might be;
I gave thee jewels for thy chest,
    And all this cost I spent on thee.
        Greensleeves, &c.

Thy gown was of the grassy green,
    The sleeves of satin hanging by;
Which made thee be our harvest queen:
    And yet thou wouldest not love me!
        Greensleeves, &c.

Greensleeves now farewell! adieu!
    God I pray to prosper thee!
For I am still thy lover true:
    Come once again and love me!

    Greensleeves was all my joy!
    Greensleeves was my delight!
    Greensleeves was my heart of gold!
        And who but Lady Greensleeves!
          —Anonymous

Michael Pupin

FROM IMMIGRANT TO INVENTOR

Today, more than ever before, we are conscious of the problem of assimilating the homeless refugees who are escaping to us from a Europe torn by war and prejudice. Somehow they will be absorbed; and many, like Michael Pupin (1858-1935), will add lustre to the name of their foster country. His story about the Serbian peasant boy who became a great American scientist won the Pulitzer Prize for autobiography in 1923.

Penniless Immigrant

When I landed at Castle Garden, forty-eight years ago, I had only five cents in my pocket. Had I brought five hundred dollars, instead of five cents from Serbia, my immediate career in the new, and to me a perfectly strange, land would have been the same. A young immigrant, such as I was then, does not begin his career until he has spent all the money which he has brought with him.

It is no handicap to a boy immigrant to land here penniless; it is not a handicap to any boy to be penniless when he strikes out for an independent career, provided that he has the stamina to stand the hardships that may be in store for him.

He who has never crossed the stormy Atlantic during the month of March in the crowded steerage of an immigrant ship does not know what hardships are. Many a night I spent on the deck of that immigrant ship hugging the warm smoke-stack and adjusting my position so as to avoid the force of the gale and the sharpness of its icy chilliness. All I had was the light suit of clothes which I carried on my back. Everything else I had converted into money with which to pay my transportation expenses. I could not rest during the cold nights of March without much shivering and unbearable discomfort. If it had not been for the warm smoke-stack I should have died of cold.

A blast of the everlasting gales had car-

ried away my hat, and a Turkish fez such as the Serbs of Bosnia wear was the only head-gear I had. It was providential that I had not succeeded in selling it at Prague. Most of my fellow emigrants thought that I was a Turk and cared little about my discomforts. But, nevertheless, I felt quite brave and strong in the daytime: at night, however, when, standing alone alongside of the smoke-stack, I beheld through the howling darkness the white rims of the mountain-high waves speeding on like maddened dragons toward the tumbling ship, my heart sank low. It was my implicit trust in God and in his regard for my mother's prayers which enabled me to overcome my fear and bravely face the horrors of the angry seas.

On the fourteenth day, early in the morning, the flat coast-line of Long Island hove in sight. Nobody in the motley crowd of excited immigrants was more happy to see the promised land than I was. It was a clear, mild, and sunny March morning, and as we approached New York Harbor the warm sun-rays seemed to thaw out the chilliness which I had accumulated in my body by continuous exposure to the wintry blasts of the North Atlantic.

The immigrant ship, *Westphalia*, landed at Hoboken and a tug took us to Castle Garden. We were carefully examined and cross-examined, and when my turn came the examining officials shook their heads and seemed to find me wanting. I confessed that I had only five cents in my pocket and had no relatives here, and that I knew nobody in their country except Franklin, Lincoln, and Harriet Beecher Stowe, whose "Uncle Tom's Cabin" I had read in translation.

One of the officials who had one leg only, and walked with a crutch, seemed much impressed by this remark, and looking very kindly into my eyes, said in German: "You showed good taste when you picked your American acquaintances."

I confessed also to the examining officials that I had no training in the arts and crafts, but that I was anxious to learn, and that this desire had brought me to America. In answer to the question why I had not stayed at home or in Prague to learn instead of wandering across the sea with so little on my back and nothing in my pocket, I said that the Hungarian and Austrian authorities had formed a strong prejudice against me on account of my sympathies with the people of my province which had been recently ceded to Hungary. We objected to being cheated out of our ancient rights and privileges which the Austrian emperor had guaranteed to us for services rendered loyally to the Empire. I spoke with feeling, and I felt that I made an impression upon the examiners.

The Swiss veteran who walked on crutches was particularly attentive while I was being cross-examined, and nodded approvingly whenever I scored a point with my answers. He whispered something to the other officials, and they finally informed me that I could pass on. He looked me up a little later and informed me that the examiners had made an exception in my favor and admitted me, and that I must look sharp and find a job as soon as possible.

The First Opportunity

A SWISS foreman on a Delaware farm offered me a job, which was to drive a team of mules and help in the work of hauling things to the field preparatory for spring planting. I accepted gladly, feeling confident that I knew all about driving animals, although I had never even seen a mule in all my experiences in Serbia.

The first impression of an American farm was dismal. In the messroom, however, where supper was served, everything was neat and lovely, and the supper looked to me like a holiday feast. I became more reconciled to the American farm.

Presently I saw a young girl, somewhat younger than myself. She pretended to be helping the women, but I soon discovered that she had another mission. Her appearance reminded me of a young Vila, a Serbian fairy, who in the old Serbian ballads plays a most wonderful part. Her luminous blue eyes, her finely chiselled features, and her graceful movements made a strange impression upon me. I imagined that she could hear the faintest sound, that she could see in the darkest night, and that, like a real Vila, she could feel not only the faintest breezes but even the thoughts of people near her.

She certainly felt my thoughts. Pointing to a table in a corner of the dining room, she directed my attention to writing paper and ink. I spent the evening writing a letter to my mother. This was my wish, and the Vila must have read it in my face.

ONE evening when I was sitting alone near the warm stove in the messroom, she came in and said: "Good evening!" I answered by repeating her greeting, but pronounced it badly. She corrected me, and, when I repeated her greeting the second time, I did much better, and she applauded my genuine effort.

Then she proceeded to teach me English words for everything in the dining room and before that first lesson was over I knew some twenty English words and pronounced them to her satisfaction. The next day I repeated these words aloud over and over again during my

MICHAEL PUPIN
Underwood and Underwood

trips to the fields, until I thought that even the mules knew them by heart. At the second lesson on the following evening I scored a high mark from my teacher and added twenty more words to my English vocabulary. As time went on, my vocabulary increased at a rapid rate, and my young teacher was most enthusiastic.

At the end of the first month on the Delaware farm my confidence in the use of the English language had grown strong. During the second month I grew

bold enough to join in lengthy conversations. During these conversations the Vila sat still and seemed to be all attention. She was all eyes and ears, and I knew that she was making mental notes of every mistake in my grammar and pronunciation. At the next lesson she would correct every one of these mistakes, and then she watched at the next family gathering to see whether I should repeat them. But I did not; my highest ambition was to show myself worthy of the title "smart" which she had given me.

One evening, Vila's mother asked me about my mother and her hopes for my future. I gave her a glowing account of my mother, and wound up by saying that she did not expect me to become an American farmer, and that I came to America to learn what I could not learn in a peasant country like Serbia. She was much touched, and then in simple and solemn language she revealed to me a new truth I never forgot and which I found confirmed by all my experiences in this great land: that this is a country of opportunities which are open equally to all; that each individual must see these opportunities and must be prepared to make good use of them when he finds them. She commended me warmly for making good use of all the opportunities which I had found on the farm, and advised me strongly to go in search of new opportunities. Vila agreed with her, and I prepared to leave the hospitable shores of Delaware.

From Princeton to the Bowery

THE next day I was up long before sunrise and bade good-by to the farm. After many hours of wandering, I crossed a bridge over a canal and entered a town which appeared to me like so many beautiful convents.

The tramp of many miles through woods and meadows without any breakfast had made me ravenously hungry and somewhat tired. I bought a shining loaf of bread and selected a seat under an elm near a building like the residence of the Archbishop of Prague.

Many boys, looking like students, passed by on their way to the ecclesiastical looking buildings; one of them watched my appetite as if he envied it, and inquired whether I should like some Italian cheese with my bread. I answered that Serbian cheese would suit me better. He laughed and said that Serbia and Serbian cheese were unknown at Princeton. I answered that some day perhaps Princeton might hear from Serbia.

(It is a curious fact, that in 1914, I was the first man who was invited to

Princeton to give an address on the subject of the Austrian ultimatum to Serbia.)

Later as I was walking slowly and thoughtfully toward the railroad-station, a student met me and engaged me in conversation. He knew a great deal about Serbia, and even about the Serbs of Austria-Hungary, and when I told him that I had come to America in search of knowledge, he expressed the hope that he might some day see me enrolled as a student in Princeton.

A student at Princeton! With fellow students and friends like this divinely handsome and gentle youth who accompanied me to the station! Impossible! thought I, as I looked through the car-window and saw the academic halls of Princeton gradually disappear in the distance, and realized at the same time that the train was taking me back to the Bowery.

In less than a week I found a job in a famous cracker factory on Cortlandt Street in New York. A place was given me in a squad of boys and girls who punched the firm's name upon a particular kind of biscuit. The job was easy from the point of view of physical strength, but it required much manual dexterity. In spite of my ambition to advance to a high place in the squad I progressed very slowly. The great opportunities which, according to my good friends on the Delaware farm awaited me in this country were certainly not in the direction of arts requiring great manual dexterity. I was convinced of that every time I made a comparison between myself and the other boys who were doing the same manual work in the factory that I did. They were my superiors.

In one thing, however, I thought I was their superior. They did not know much about the latest things described in the *Scientific American,* nor in the scientific supplements of the Sunday *Sun,* which I read assiduously with the aid of a pocket dictionary.

The educational opportunities in the factory also escaped them. Jim, the boiler-room engineer and fireman of the factory, became interested in my scientific reading and encouraged me by paying several compliments to my interest in these things. He once suggested that some day, perhaps, I might become his scientific assistant in the boiler-room, if I did not mind shovelling coal and attending to the busy fires.

He was joking, but I took him seriously. Every morning before the factory started I was with Jim, who was getting the steam up and preparing to blow the whistle and start the wheels going. I volunteered to assist him and after a time I understood the manipulations in the boiler-room quite well, according to Jim. He was my first professor in engineering.

Jim was a humble fireman and boiler-room engineer; his early education was scanty, so that he was not much on books; but he was awed by them. Referring to my habit of carrying a pocket dictionary in my hip pocket and looking up in it the meaning and the pronunciation of every word which was new to me, he would exclaim jokingly, "Look in the book," whenever some obscure points arose in our boiler-room discussions.

His admiration for books was much increased when I related to him the story of James Watt and his experiments with the steam-engine, a story which I had dug out of an old encyclopaedia in the Cooper Union Library. When I told him that James Watt had perfected his steam-engine and thus started the development of the modern steam-engine several years before the Declaration of Independence, he dropped a remark which I never forgot. He said: "The English made us write the Declaration of Independence, and they also gave us the steam-engine with which we made our independence good." Jim was not much on learning but he was brimful of native practical philosophy.

A Mr. Paul, the youngest and most active member of the New England Cracker Factory in Cortlandt Street, paid frequent visits to the boiler-room. One morning he made a very early visit before the steam-whistle had blown and the steam-engine had started on its daily routine, and he found me in the boiler room, a busy volunteer fireman. Jim introduced me to him in a jocular way as a student who found his way from Princeton to Cortlandt Street, where in the daytime I was rapidly learning every trick of the biscuit industry while in

the evening I was absorbing all the wisdom of Cooper Union.

A few days later Mr. Paul informed me that my fame as a student in mechanical drawing in the evening classes of Cooper Union, had reached the board of directors of the New England Cracker Factory, and that they had resolved to offer me a job of assistant to the shipping clerk. It meant not only more pay but also social advancement. I felt as people in England probably feel when peerage is conferred upon them.

"Prep" School

THE factory in Cortlandt Street was in many respects a college in which Jim was the chaplain; and it had a professor who should be mentioned here. His name was Bilharz. He knew nothing, nor did he care for the concrete or practical things of life, but always lived in dreams about things which happened centuries ago. He knew Latin and Greek and all kinds of literatures, but never made any attempt to make use of his knowledge. He informed me once by an accidental slip of the tongue that he had studied theology at the University of Freiburg, in southern Germany, and would have become a priest if an unfortunate love-affair had not put an end to his ecclesiastical aspirations. Although a German he spoke English well, was a finished scholar who had lived in America for a number of years, and had a memory for sound which impressed me as most remarkable.

When he discovered that I sincerely admired his learning and was interested in his puzzling personality he became quite communicative, sometimes almost human. His English accent was excellent. I asked his opinion about my accent and he assured me that it was rotten, but that it could be fixed up if I submitted to a course of training prescribed for me by my Vila on the Delaware farm. We finally made the start in what he called my preparation for Nassau Hall. In the course of less than a month I finished reciting to Bilharz the Declaration

of Independence, the American Constitution, and Lincoln's speech at Gettysburg, submitting to many corrections and making many efforts to give each word its proper pronunciation. Finally he accepted my performance as satisfactory.

By that time I knew these documents by heart. So did Bilharz, and he, in spite of himself, liked them so well that he accused me of conspiring to make an American out of him. "You are sinking rapidly, my boy, in the whirlpool of American democracy, and you are dragging me down with you," said Bilharz one evening, when I objected to some of the amendments which he offered in order to harmonize the American theory of freedom with the principles of German socialism.

ONE day in Broome Street near the Bowery I saw a store with a sign bearing the name of Lukanitch. The man of that name must be a Serb, thought I, and I walked in, longing to hear the language which I had not heard for over three years.

When I disclosed my name to Lukanitch he asked me my father's name, and when I told him his eyes looked like two scintillating stars. After relating to me that my father had befriended him nearly thirty years prior to that time and that he had often stayed as guest at my father's house whenever his annual tours through Serbia took him through Idvor he begged me to come to his house on the following Sunday and dine.

Lukanitch and his family became my devoted friends, and they were just as interested in my plans and aspirations as if I had been a member of their family. The son assured me that my knowledge of English, mathematics, and science would easily take me into college. He even prophesied a most successful college career, pointing at my big chest and broad shoulders and feeling my hard biceps. "You will make a splendid college oarsman," said he, "and they will do anything for you at Columbia if you are a good oarsman."

He did his best to turn my eyes from Nassau Hall to Columbia. He succeeded, but not so much on account of my prospects in rowing as on account of other things. I was impressed by the official name of that institution: "Columbia College in the City of New York."

The fact that the college was located in the city of New York carried much weight because New York appealed to my imagination more than any other place in the world. The impression which it made upon my mind as the immigrant ship moved into New York Harbor on that clear and sunny March day when I first passed through Castle Garden, the Gate of America, never faded.

Civilizing the Balkan Barbarian

MY PROGRESS in Greek and Latin grammar under the guidance of Bilharz was rapid even before I had decided to steer for Columbia. It was a question of memory and of analysis. My memory had had a stiff linguistic training during the several years preceding that date, in trying to master the English language with all its vagaries in spelling and pronunciation. These vagaries I did not find in the grammars of the classical languages, which appeared to be as definite and as exact as the geometrical theorems in Euclid. Mathematics was always my strong point, and a good memory is a characteristic virtue of the Serb race; I, therefore, had an easy road in my classical studies with Bilharz.

As time went on I saw that entrance to Columbia College was within easy reach so far as my studies were concerned. But here again the old question of "social unpreparedness" stared me in the face. The college of Hamilton and Jay expected certain other things which I did not have and could not get from books. A jump from the Cortlandt Street factory to Columbia College, from Jim and Bilharz to patriarchal President Barnard and the famous professors at Columbia, appeared to me like a jump over Columbia's great and venerable traditions. My subsequent experience showed me that my anxiety was justifiable.

I have already mentioned that a short time before I ran away from Prague and headed for the United States I had read a translation of Harriet Beecher Stowe's "Uncle Tom's Cabin." When I heard that Henry Ward Beecher, a brother of the author, was preaching in Plymouth Church I determined to hear him.

Beecher was preaching to all humanity and not to a particular creed. I saw in him a living example of that type of American who, like Hamilton and Jay and the other great men of whom I had heard, was the spiritual and intellectual giants of the Revolutionary period. Beecher was the sunrise which dispelled much of that mist which prevented my eyes, just as it prevents all foreign eyes, from seeing the clear outline of American civilization.

Beecher's congregation seemed to me like a beehive full of honey-hearted beings. One of those honey-hearted disciples was a Doctor Charles Shepard. When I disclosed my plans to the good doctor he offered to help me carry them out. He needed a clerical assistant in his office and offered me the job, and then spoke of getting a friend of his to help me prepare for entrance to Columbia.

His friend was Professor Webster who taught Greek and Latin at Adelphi Academy in Brooklyn. I jumped at Doctor Shepard's offer.

After a few private lessons he invited me to join his classes in Greek and Latin, where I was received with many signs of cordiality from both the boys and girls. Like myself, they were preparing for college. I attended these classes three times a week. After a while I entertained some of them with Serbian poetry and also with Serbian *kolo* dancing. I made every effort to make them forget that I was a Balkan barbarian; but everybody, as if reading my thoughts, assured me that I was contributing more to Adelphi Academy than I was getting in return. I knew better. I felt that the association with those splendid boys and girls and with Professor Webster contributed much more to my preparation for Columbia than all the book work which I had ever done anywhere.

During the last week of September of 1879 I presented myself at Columbia for entrance examinations. They were oral, and were conducted by the professors themselves. The first two books of the Iliad, excepting the catalogue of ships, and the four orations of Cicero, I knew by heart. The professors were greatly surprised and asked me why I had taken so much trouble. I told them that it was no trouble, because Serbs delight in memorizing beautiful lines. Besides, I assured the professors, I wanted to do in Greek and Latin as well as I possibly could, so as to gain free tuition.

The other examinations gave me no trouble, thanks to my training with Bilharz and with the lecturers in the evening classes at Cooper Union. A note from the Registrar's office informed me a few days later that I was enrolled as a student in Columbia College with freedom from all tuition fees. There was no person happier than I!

Scholastic Success

At the end of the freshman year I gained two prizes of one hundred dollars each, one in Greek and the other in mathematics. They were won in stiff competitive examinations and meant a considerable scholastic success.

At the beginning of my sophomore year eight of my classmates formed a class, the Octagon, and invited me to coach them in Greek and in mathematics, twice a week. My success with the Octagon class established my reputation as a doctor for "lame ducks." Coaching lame ducks was very remunerative and also left me with plenty of leisure time for tennis, horseback riding, or swimming and diving.

My coaching experience was remunerative not only from the material but also from the cultural side; it brought me in touch with some of the best exponents of New York's social life, where I found a hearty welcome, a friendly sympathy, and many lessons which I considered as among the most valuable acquisitions in my college life.

Lewis Morris Rutherfurd, a trustee of Columbia College, was at that time the head of the famous Rutherfurd family. His sons, Lewis and Winthrop, were my fellow students at Columbia. Lewis just squeezed his way through college, but Winthrop, owing to circumstances beyond his control, threatened to drop by the academic roadside; the load of some seven conditions was too heavy and too discouraging.

His father suggested that Winthrop and I go to his country place, where we could rule supreme and spend the summer preparing for Winthrop's autumn examination. Winthrop consented, in order to please his family, and he agreed to a definite programme of work which I prescribed.

"Winthrop is very fond of you," said Rutherfurd senior, "and if you fail to pull him through, that will be the end of his college career. Your job is a difficult one, almost hopeless, but if you should succeed you would place me under a very great obligation."

In the autumn Winthrop got rid of most of his conditions, proceeded with his class, and eventually graduated from Columbia in 1884.

ONE day toward the end of my senior year I told my mentor, Rutherfurd, of a lectureroom experiment performed by a professor of physics at Columbia College. This experiment was the first announcement to me that Faraday was one of the great discoverers in electrical science. When I finished my description of the experiment and assured Rutherfurd that it was the most thrilling physical phenomenon that I had ever seen, and that I had remained awake almost all night after seeing it, he looked pleased, and informed me that this very phenomenon was the basis of Maxwell's new Electrical Theory.

This was the experiment which helped me to decide a very weighty question. I had been informed that in recognition of my high standing in science as well as in letters I could choose either of two graduate fellowships, one in letters or one in science, each worth five hundred dollars a year. Either would have meant the opportunity of an additional three years of study.

The magic experiment which had told me the first story of Faraday's great discoveries, had aroused my dormant enthusiasm for physics and caused me to turn to science, my first love. Nevertheless, I did not accept the fellowship in science and stay three years longer at Columbia; I preferred to take up the study of Faraday and of Maxwell in the British Isles, where these two great physicists were born and where they had made their great discoveries.

There was the added excitement at this time of getting my citizenship papers. I received them on the day before I was graduated. Two ceremonies which are recorded in my life as two red-letter days took place on two successive days. One ceremony made me only a Bachelor of Arts. The other made me a citizen of the United States.

What Is Light?

I HAD come to Cambridge to study physics and find out how Maxwell answered the question "What is Light?" But my advisers felt that I was not prepared to attend advanced courses in physics and much less to read Maxwell's famous mathematical treatise on his new electrical theory without intensive training in mathematics.

The students majoring in mathematics did not know as much of Greek and Latin, of history and economics, or literature and physical sciences, as I did, but their training in mathematics was far superior to mine. I had been warned that stiff work was before me for a good part of a whole academic year, if I was to keep up with the young mathematical athletes, which was correct. Problems over which I puzzled in vain for many hours, they would solve in several seconds. I experienced many moments of despair, and I needed all the tonic which the King's College chapel could give me.

Long before the end of the academic year, I became quite skilled in solving dynamical problems and was able to keep pace with the class. My advisers were pleased. I did not think that I had found there what I had expected to find. In the course of time I discovered that I was not alone in my opinion. Many Cambridge men failed to find in mathematical drills the stimulation of the scientific spirit which leads to original research.

Some of the greatest living Cambridge physicists of those days felt that this system had its defects and called for remedies. It was claimed that this method, having no direct connection with the nascent problems of scientific research, was artificial and unproductive. Maxwell, undoubtedly inspired by Thomson, was one of the earliest leaders of the Cambridge movement which favored more the spirit of research and less the art of solving cleverly formulated mathematical problems.

The Cavendish Physics Laboratory, organized by Maxwell and first opened in 1874, was a concrete expression of this movement. A similar movement was taking place in the United States in those days. The organization of the physics laboratory at Johns Hopkins in 1876 marked a new and most fruitful era of scientific research in the United States.

WHEN the Easter term approached its end in May I began to think of my summer vacation. I finally decided to visit some little place in France and learn French. The names of Laplace, La Grange, and Ampère were mentioned so often and with so much veneration by Maxwell, that I felt ashamed of my ignorance of the language of France, and off I went with no other books in my bag beside Campbell's "Life of Maxwell" and a French grammar.

While visiting the great Sorbonne and the Collège de France in the Quartier Latin, I found a great treasure in a second-hand bookshop: La Grange's great treatise "Méchanique Analytique," first published under the auspices of the French Academy in 1788. La Grange, the Newton of France! There was no student of dynamics who had not heard of his name and of his great treatise. My two months' stay in France had enabled me to appreciate fully the beauty of the language and of this great work, and my mathematical training at Cambridge had eliminated many difficulties of the technique.

I had promised my mother to visit her during that summer. On my journey to Idvor I wasted no time looking to right or left of my speeding train; La Grange was talking to me, and I had neither eyes nor ears for anybody or for anything else.

By the end of that heavenly vacation I had mastered a good part of La Grange's classical treatise, and in addition I had re-read carefully Campbell's "Life of Maxwell," and I understood many things which I had seen in Cambridge and had not understood before.

I told my mother that Maxwell and La Grange were two great saints in the world of science, and she regarded my reading during that summer as a study of the lives of saints. When I related to her the many traditions of the old university, and informed her that one learned there, not only from the teachers living there at that time, but also from great teachers who had long departed, a luminous expression in her eyes told me that she was about to reveal to me an original thought.

"I go to church, my son," she said "not so much because I expect the priest to reveal to me some new divine truth but because I wish to look at the icons of saints. That reminds me of their saintly work, and through the contemplation of their work I communicate with God. Cambridge is a great temple consecrated to the *eternal truth;* it is filled with icons of the great saints of science. The contemplation of their saintly work will enable you to communicate with the spirit of *eternal truth.*"

With this thought in her mind my mother was most happy when I bade her goodby and repeated her own words.

My work in Cambridge, guided principally by Maxwell and La Grange, reminded me continually of the fathers of the sciences which I was studying and of the material things to which their labors gave a meaning. These thoughts gave me a satisfactory interpretation of my mother's words which were dominated by a spirit of piety and reverence. This spirit, I always thought, is needed in science.

The Fullness of Life

WHEN I finished my work at Cambridge I went to Berlin to study experimental physics with Hermann von Helmholtz, the famous professor of physics at the University of Berlin, the formulator of the principle of conservation of energy, and the first interpreter of the meaning of color both in vision and in music and speech. Next to Bismarck and the old Emperor he was at that time the most illustrious man in the German Empire.

When I told him that I had never had an opportunity to work in a physical laboratory and had paid exclusive attention to mathematical physics, he smiled and suggested that I should make up this deficiency as soon as possible. "A few experiments successfully carried out usually lead to results more important than all mathematical theories," he assured me.

During my first year's study in Berlin I attended Helmholtz's lectures on experimental physics. He threw the searchlight of his giant intellect upon the meaning of the experiments, and they blazed up like the brilliant colors of a flower garden when a beam of sunlight breaks through the clouds and tears up the dark shadows which cover the landscape on a cloudy summer day. Toward the end of that semester I felt certain that I understood Helmholtz's interpretation of Faraday, and of Maxwell's answer to the question: "What is light?"

But the Faraday-Maxwell electromagnetic theory, my research in physical chemistry, and the learned essays of Helmholtz and of all the other fathers of physical chemistry disappeared from my mind as if they had never been there when I met the sister of my Columbia classmate, A. V. Williams Jackson. The only problem that could find a place in my mind was the question: Will she accept me? She finally did, and I made

a bee-line for New York in order to find out how soon I could get a job there.

The Columbia authorities were organizing at that time a new department in the School of Mines, the Department of Electrical Engineering, and they were glad to see me and consult me about it. It was to start a year from that time, that is, the end of September, 1889. I was offered a position in it as "Teacher of Mathematical Physics in the department of Electrical Engineering." I accepted gladly and hurried back to Europe, proud as a peacock. My fiancée and her family met me in London and I was married in the Greek church, according to the rites of the Orthodox faith and the faith of my mother and of all my ancestors.

"Marriage gives that fullness of life which nothing else can give," said Helmholtz when I saw him again in Berlin and informed him that I was married and that I had been promised an academic position at Columbia College. He approved my dropping the experimental research and substituting in its place a research in physical chemistry.

This research was finished in the early spring and I sent it to Helmholtz who was then in Baden-Baden. He telegraphed: "Your successful effort approved and accepted." Never before, nor since have I received a telegram which made me more happy. The examinations gave me no serious trouble, and in the late spring of that year I had my doctor's degree and became a citizen in the world of science.

In the Cowshed

A SMALL brick shed, a temporary structure, had been built at Columbia College to accommodate the new department of Electrical Engineering. The students called it the "cowshed," and the boy who invented the name did not indulge in any stretching the imagination. It certainly looked like a cowshed.

I was given to understand that any

additional equipment during the first year would have to be bought from contributions outside of the university. We raised some money by giving a course of twelve popular lectures for which we charged ten dollars per person. We raised in this manner three hundred dollars and bought additional equipment.

The experience, however, was worth

many times that amount. Our audience consisted of business men and lawyers, who were either interested in the electrical industries, or expected to become interested. They had hardly any previous scientific training.

When I told them that electrical science was one of the most exact of all physical sciences, some shook their heads and exhibited considerable scepticism. One of them asked me: "Doctor, do you know what electricity is?" "No," said I, and he added another question: "Then how can you have an exact science of electricity when you do not even know what electricity is?"

To this I retorted: "Do you know what matter is? Of course you do not, nor does anybody else know it, and yet who will deny that there are exact sciences relating to material things? Do you deny that astronomy is an exact science?" It is a difficult thing to make unscientific people understand that science studies first and foremost the *activities of things and not their ultimate nature.*

In that first course of public lectures I found it necessary to devote much of my exposition to the correction of erroneous notions lodged in the minds of my audience. When I told that audience that no electrical generator generates electricity, because electricity was made by God, and, according to Faraday, its quantity in the universe is constant, and that for every positive charge there is an equal negative one; most members of my audience were inclined to think that I was talking metaphysics.

"Then what does it generate?" asked one of my hearers. I answered: "It generates the motion of electricity, and by that motion it furnishes us with means of doing useful work like telegraphy, telephony, and electrical lighting." Then I added: "The electrical science studies the forces which make electricity move against the reactions of the bodies through which it moves; in the overcoming of these reactions the moving electricity does useful work." Illustrations

from dynamics of material bodies did not help very much, because my audience had hardly any knowledge of even the underlying principles of Newton's great work.

A famous lawyer, a trustee of a great educational institution, looked surprised when I told him that one cannot teach science without laboratories both for the elementary and the advanced instruction. He actually believed that graduate schools in science needed only a lot of blackboards, chalk, and sponges, and a lecturer who could prepare his lectures by reading books.

THESE instrumentalities are cheaper than laboratories, and that appeals to many university trustees. The teacher who can lecture from books and not from his experience in the laboratory is also much cheaper. But heaven help the country which trusts its destiny to cheap men operating with cheap instrumentalities.

Most of the energy of the teachers of physical sciences was consumed in the lecture room; they were pedagogues, "pouring information into passive recipients," as Barnard described it. My own case was a typical one. How could I do any research as long as I had at my disposal only a dynamo, a motor, an alternator, and a few crude measuring instruments, all intended to be used every day for the instruction of electrical engineering students?

When the professor of engineering died, in the summer of 1891, a part of his work, theory of heat and hydraulics, was assigned to me. The professor of dynamics died a little later, and his work also was transferred to me. I was to carry the additional load of lecture-room work temporarily, but was relieved from it, in part only, after several years. As a reward my title was advanced to adjunct professor, with an advance of salary to two thousand five hundred dollars per annum. Not until after this pedagogic load was taken off my back could any scientific research be seriously thought of.

I Save $100,000,000

WHEN I was able to look around for a problem of research which I could manage with my meagre laboratory facilities, I found distortions in an alternating current when the current was magnetizing iron in electrical power apparatus. This distortion consisted of the addition of higher harmonics to the normal harmonic changes in the current. This reminded me of harmonics in musical instruments and in the human voice.

Helmholtz was the first to analyze the vowels in the human voice by studying the harmonics which they contained. He detected different harmonics by the employment of acoustical resonators; it was an epoch-making research. I proceeded to search for a similar procedure for the analysis of distorted alternating currents, and found it. I constructed electrical resonators based upon dynamical principles similar to those in the acoustical resonators employed by Helmholtz.

These electrical resonators play a most important part in the radio art of today. In fact people turning a knob on their radio-receiving sets in order to find the correct wave length for a certain broadcasting station are employing the principle which I discovered then.

My most important invention was the inductance-coil. This coil is now known all over the world as the Pupin coil, and many people think that the coil itself is the invention.

When it became known that I had studied at the Universities of Cambridge and of Berlin, my English and German friends claimed the credit for the invention because of the scientific training which I had received at their universities. I think that the French had a better claim, because it was La Grange who helped me more than any mathematical reading.

As a matter of fact, the engineers of the American Telephone and Telegraph Company, and the herdsmen of Idvor, deserve most of the credit. The first formulated the problem, the solution of which led to the invention; and the second taught me the art of signalling through the ground, which guided me to the physical principle that underlies the invention.

A vice-president of the American Telephone and Telegraph Company, who is a very high authority in telephony, informed me recently that one way to describe, roughly, the value of the invention is as follows: "If during the past twenty-two years his company had been compelled to extend its network of conductors so as to give, without employing my invention, the same service which it is giving today, it would have had to spend at least one hundred million dollars more.

But after quoting him I wish to call attention to the fact which the public overlooks. I ask, where are those one hundred million dollars which the invention saved? I know that not even a microscopic part of them is in the pockets of the inventor. I have figured out also, with the same accuracy with which I once figured out the invention, that those hundred million dollars are not in the pockets of the telephone company. They must be, therefore, in the pockets of the American public. The invention made it possible to give telephone service, which is now being given, at a lower rate than would have been possible if one hundred million dollars more had been spent.

Occidental vs. Oriental Trading

ONE morning a man stepped suddenly into my office at Columbia, and introduced himself as Mr. Green, organizer and promoter of the Marconi Company of America.

"Are your wireless inventions for sale?" asked Mr. Green, without preliminary talk.

"They are," I answered.

"How much?" asked Mr. Green.

I gave him the first figure that came into my head, and he, not a bit daunted, asked whether I would take one-half in cash and one-half in stock. I asked him for twenty-four hours to decide. "All right," said he, and promised to call again the next day at the same hour. The next day the deal was closed, he making a certain cash payment immediately and I agreeing to furnish certain documents.

I was fairly well acquainted with trading transactions in my native land: my father often took me to market-places where he bought and sold cattle and horses. I remember well the never-ending bartering which very often ended in a fizzle. Mr. Green had none of that Orientalism, and his utter indifference to the figures involved in the deal astonished me. He also took it for granted that I could and would perform all the fine things which I promised to perform; that was very flattering to me, but I was too much of an Oriental to accept, without some apprehension, his apparently implicit trust in me.

That reminds me of an incident which happened eight years ago. The Serbian Government cabled me to make a contract for five thousand tons of lard: I was its only diplomatic and consular representative in America during the war. I called up the representatives of Swift and of Armour and told them over the telephone what was wanted, requesting them to file their bids.

Two days later I met them in my office and some Serbian war commissioners happened to be present. The contract was closed in less than thirty minutes, and when I told the commissioners that it involved one million dollars they crossed themselves in utter amazement. In Belgrade, they assured me, the closing of such a contract would have required at least a month.

A few months after my deal with Green I was in Berlin, by invitation, for the purpose of negotiating, for my telephone invention, a business agreement with a famous electrical firm. After the completion of my negotiations in Berlin I visited my relatives in Idvor.

On a Sunday in August during that visit I was dining in their garden. Presently somebody knocked on the garden gate and my brother-in-law opened it. There stood a rider, holding with one hand his horse, which was covered with foam; in the other hand he held a telegram which he had brought in haste from the telegraph station in another village, about five miles away from Idvor. My native village had neither a telegraph nor a telephone line, although I, its son, aspired to connect telephonically every person in the United States to every other.

The telegram in the rider's hand was for me, sent by my attorney, telling me that, on the day before, my final papers had been delivered to the Marconi Company and that the check for the final payments was in his hands.

"Good news," I said to myself, and gave the rider a tip of ten florins to reward him for his haste.

Some people had gathered outside when they saw the ten-florin note in the rider's hand and heard him brag that he had delivered to me a telegram from America. The older peasants who had gone to school with me in my boyhood days asked me if the telegram really had come from America. When I said yes, and that it had been sent on that very morning, they looked at each other and winked, as if signalling to be on guard lest I fool them with an American yarn.

Then the oldest among them addressed me as follows: "Did you not tell us that between here and America there are four empires, each bigger than Austria, and then a great ocean, which one cannot cross in less than a week even in the fastest ships?"

"I certainly did say that, and I repeat it now," said I.

"How can a telegram cross all that distance in less than a day."

"It could do it in less than a minute if man's clumsiness did not delay it. I could travel from here to Vienna in less than a second," said I, and carefully watched his expression.

The old man seemed undecided; he did not know whether to take offense at my attempt to work off a silly yarn on him, or to proceed with his cross-examination, and finally decided in favor of the latter course.

"Who invented all that?" asked he impatiently.

"An American did it," said I boastfully.

"These Americans must be very clever people," said he and waited eagerly for my reply.

"Yes, indeed, they are very clever people," said I.

"Much more clever than anybody in this village?" was his next question, and when I assured him that the Americans were much more clever than anybody in Idvor, he fired at me the following parting shot:

"Then how in the name of St. Michael do you manage to make a living there?"

To-Day

So here hath been dawning
    Another blue Day:
Think, wilt thou let it
    Slip useless away?

Out of Eternity
    This new Day is born;
Into Eternity,
    At night, will return.

Behold it aforetime
    No eye ever did:
So soon it for ever
    From all eyes is hid.

Here hath been dawning
    Another blue Day:
Think, wilt thou let it
    Slip useless away?
          —T. Carlyle

The Soldier

Thy voice is heard through rolling drums,
    That beat to battle where he stands;
Thy face across his fancy comes,
    And gives the battle to his hands:

A moment, while the trumpets blow,
    He sees his brood about thy knee;
The next, like fire he meets the foe,
    And strikes him dead for thine and thee.
          —Alfred Tennyson

Robert Edwin Peary
THE NORTH POLE

Polar exploration began in the days of Henry VIII. In 1588 John Davis discovered the strait which bears his name and achieved for Britain what was then the Farthest North, 72° 12′, a point 1,128 miles from the Geographical North Pole. Scores of hardy navigators, British, French, Dutch, German, Scandinavian and Russian, followed; but not till April 6, 1909, in the expedition so graphically described in this book was the goal reached by Robert Peary, of the U. S. Navy. Some of Peary's claims have been questioned, but a committee of inquiry in 1909 held his claims to be fully justified, and on May 9, 1926, Lieutenant-Commander R. E. Byrd and Mr. Floyd Bennett, in a Fokker aeroplane, flew over the North Pole and completely verified Peary's observations.

From New York to Cape Sheridan

Peary likened the attainment of the North Pole to the winning of a game of chess in which all the moves were planned in advance. He had played the game with varying fortune for 23 years. Each defeat brought fresh knowledge of the game, but the lure of the North always came back until at last his dream of years came true.

The *Roosevelt,* in which the expedition left New York on July 6, 1908, was built of American timber in an American shipyard, engined by an American firm with American metal, and constructed on American designs. Even the smallest of the supplies were American. Captain Bartlett and the crew were Newfoundlanders; but one of Peary's assistants was a negro, Matthew Henson, who had been with him since 1887. All told, the personnel numbered 22. The route was by Sydney (Cape Breton), the Strait of Belle Isle, Davis Strait, Baffin Bay and Smith Sound.

At Cape York, where is the southernmost of the Eskimo villages which stretch along the western coast of Greenland from Cape York to Etah, and at other points, Peary enlisted his Eskimo helpers. Since 1891 he had been living and working with these interesting people and he had their absolute confidence. He believed with Sir Clements Markham

in their descent from an ancient Siberian tribe driven out on the Arctic Ocean by Tartar invaders in the Middle Ages. The explorer devotes many pages to their habits, customs and beliefs.

They are, he says, in many ways quite different from the Eskimos of Danish Greenland or those of any other Arctic territory. They are savages, but they are not savage; they are without government, but they are not lawless; they are utterly uneducated according to our standard, yet they exhibit a remarkable degree of intelligence. In temperament like children, with all a child's delight in little things, they are nevertheless enduring as the most mature of civilized men and women, and the best of them are faithful unto death. Without religion and having no idea of God, they will share their last meal with anyone who is hungry, while the aged and the helpless among them are taken care of as a matter of course. They are healthy and pure-blooded; they have no vices, no intoxicants, and no bad habits—not even gambling. Altogether, they are a people unique on the face of the earth.

In recruiting work and expeditions between Cape York and Etah Peary had the services of another vessel, the *Erik.* When the two ships parted, the *Roosevelt's* company had been supplemented by 49 Eskimos (22 men, 17 women and 10 children) and accommodation found for 246 dogs. The dogs were fed chiefly on walrus. The Eskimo men like to have their families with them when they go on long trips. Between Etah and Cape Sheridan, the winter quarters, stretched the Kennedy and Robeson Channels, packed with almost solid ice. At Cape Beechey the Shores of Greenland on the east and Ellesmere Land and Grant Land on the west are no more than 11 miles apart. The floating ice is composed of huge sheets broken off from the glacial fringe of north Grant Land and often between 80 and 100 feet thick. As seven-eighths of these heavy floes are under water one does not realize how thick they are until one sees where a huge mass has been driven upon the shore, and stands there high and dry.

Near Cape Frazer the tides meet from Baffin Bay on the south and Lincoln Sea on the north, and in the narrows the variation between high and low tide is sometimes as much as 14 feet.

As a rule, looking across the channel, there seems to be no water—nothing but uneven and tortured ice. When the tide is at the ebb the ship follows the narrow crack of water between the shore and the moving pack of the centre, driving ahead with all her force; then, when the flood tide begins to rush violently southward, the ship must hurry to shelter in some niche of the shore ice, or behind some point of rock, to save herself from destruction or being driven south.

Only Peary's detailed knowledge of the coasts and Bartlett's energy and ice experience enabled the *Roosevelt* to pass successfully to and fro between this Arctic Scylla and Charybdis. To the perils of the ice, fog added another dangerous factor. Every person on board had to be ready with a little bundle to get over the side at a moment's notice after lowering the boats and throwing on to the ice the essential supplies kept stowed near to the ship's rail. Meanwhile the Eskimos were kept busy making sledges and dog harness, while their womenfolk were put to work making and mending winter garments. One or two trips were made

ROBERT EDWIN PEARY

ashore, when caches of supplies were landed. On occasion dynamite was used for blasting the ice. For 13 days before winter quarters at Cape Sheridan were reached neither the leader nor the ship's captain had their clothes off. But at last the prolonged struggle was over and Cape Sheridan reached on September 5.

The first to be got ashore were the dogs. Then followed the stores. Then the ship was cleaned up and so lightened that it might float with the high tide to a safe position inside the ice barrier. The adjacent shore for a quarter of a mile was lined with boxes. The heavier cases had been made to specified dimensions and were utilised in the construction of houses, the tops being placed inside and the covers removed so that the contents could be taken out as needed as from a shelf. Each house was thus like a large grocery store. The roofs were made of sails, and walls and roofs were banked in solidly with snow. It was regarded as of good augury that, when the *Roosevelt* was got inshore, her nose pointed almost true north. The winter was passing in hunting, fishing, making sledging equipment, in various side journeys, and in moving stores along the northern shore of Grant Land to Cape Columbia, which was chosen as the point of departure for the crucial journey over the frozen sea to the Pole.

A Midnight Alarm

Four months of darkness had to be endured. Only for some eight or ten days in each month of winter is there moonlight. It was then that the hunting was done. During the utter blackness most of the party were on board ship. But their minds were kept so occupied that the traditional and maddening melancholy of the Arctic winter was avoided. It is at this period that the Eskimos are subject to a curious form of hysteria called *piblokto,* a name also given to madness among the Eskimo dogs. By November 25 only 160 dogs were left; had an epidemic deprived the party of these dogs success would never have been achieved.

Once at midnight a sudden movement of the ice put the *Roosevelt* in peril. All fires were hastily put out, lest live coals spilled from a stove might start that horror of an Arctic winter night—the "ship on fire." Happily, the danger passed, but the vessel did not regain an even keel until the spring. To give variety to the work the men who remained with the ship during one moon went into the field the next; and mental as well as physical stimulus was not lacking, for Peary had with him a first-class library of Arctic and Antarctic literature; there were games; one of the party had an accordion, another a banjo; and there was a gramophone. Both Thanksgiving Day and Christmas Day were suitably observed. So passed the long winter night.

Between Cape Sheridan and Cape Columbia lay 90 miles along the ice-foot and across the land; from Cape Columbia the ice track to the Pole was 413 miles, with no smooth and very little level ice, and the way is scarred by "leads" or lanes of open water, varying from mere cracks to rivers two miles wide, and running east and west farther than the eye can see. These leads may open unexpectedly. For this reason Peary never used a sleeping-bag, preferring to have his legs and arms free for emergency. Among the other difficulties were the terrific wind and the intense cold. It was so cold much of the time that the brandy was frozen solid, the petroleum was white and viscid, and the dogs could hardly be seen for the steam of their breath.

The sledge divisions, or pioneer and supporting parties, left the *Roosevelt* between February 15 and 22, Captain Bartlett leading the first, and rendezvoused at Cape Columbia. When Peary left on February 22 there were in the field for the northern work seven members of the expedition, 19 Eskimos, 140 dogs and 28 sledges. The trail to Cape Columbia had been kept open by hunting parties and supply-trains. At Cape Columbia where all met on the last day of February, two Eskimos were disabled, one by a frosted heel and the other by a swollen knee, and the explorer's plans were further disarranged by a throat distemper which caused the death of six dogs. Bartlett and George Borup departed on February 28. On the following day one by one the other divisions drew out along the trail left by the pioneers, Peary bringing up the rear. All was silence, for the freezing east wind carried all sounds away, and men and dogs were almost immediately swallowed up in wind, haze and drifting snow.

By a system of relay parties a more or less effective trail was kept open and supplies and igloos were prepared for the main party, which was to make the final drive to the Pole. On the second day open water was encountered. The lateral movement of the lead had carried Bartlett's trail with it. The trail, however, was soon picked up by an Eskimo. On the third day they "could almost see the sun again." Then came an agonising delay of six days beside an impassable lead, waiting for the ice to close over the black water. One of the relay parties not arriving as expected Peary began to figure out how the sledges could be used as fuel for the cookers. More of mental wear and tear, he says, was crowded into those days than into all the rest of the 15 months they were absent from civilization. Some of the Eskimos began to lose their nerve. At length all were on the move again, and on March 18 crossed the 84th parallel.

Gradually, as supplies diminished, the supporting parties returned to Cape Columbia. At 84° 29′ Dr. Goodsell, the surgeon, the moral effect of whose presence on the ship was desirable, and David MacMillan, who had a frosted heel, went back. At 85° 23′ George Borup, a young Yale athlete, and at 86° 38′ Professor Ross Marvin, of Cornell, also faced south. Marvin was full of plans for the future. Peary's last words to him were "Be careful of the leads, my boy!"

Soon after Marvin left, the sun was obscured and a dull, lead-coloured haze spread over all the sky. It was a shadowless light and one in which it was impossible to see for any considerable distance. That shadowless light is not unusual on the ice-fields of the Polar sea; but this was the first occasion on which we had encountered it since leaving the land. A more ghastly atmosphere could not have been imagined even by Dante himself—sky and ice seemed utterly wan and unreal.

The 87th parallel was passed on a day of dazzling sunshine, which made the smoked goggles absolutely essential. The temperature dropped from − 30° to − 40° and there was a biting northeasterly breeze. In this remote wilderness the tracks of two foxes were seen. The explorers were now in the region of perpetual light. Three years before, at 87° 6′, the explorer had been forced to turn back. Back now, he dared not build too surely on success. Between him and his goal were still 180 nautical miles of treacherous ice; and on the very day when 87° 6′ was passed and the men were asleep in their igloos a sudden crack in the ice set all afloat. Only by

prompt and strenuous work was the peril averted. New igloos had to be built, and though on the day following all were tired enough to rest, the prospect of enforced inaction by an open lead whose further shore could not be seen in the smoke-like haze was not a happy one.

As far as the evidence of the senses went the party might be encamped on the edge of that open Polar sea which myth-makers have imagined as for ever barring the way of man to the northern end of the earth's axis. It was heartbreaking, but there was nothing to do but wait. After breakfast they overhauled the sledges and made a few repairs, dried out some garments over the little oil lamp which was carried for that purpose, and Bartlett made a sounding of 1,260 fathoms but found no bottom. When their watches told them it was bedtime— for they were now in the period of perpetual sunlight—they again turned into the igloos which had been hurriedly built the night before. A low murmur as of distant surf was issuing from the blackness ahead, and steadily growing in volume. To the inexperienced it might have seemed an ominous sound, but to them it was a cheering thing because they knew it meant the narrowing and perhaps the closing of the stretch of open water that barred our way.

Their hopes were realized the next morning, and they rushed forward in haste lest the ice should open again. At the next camp preparations were made for the final stages of the journey. The supporting parties had been worked to the limit and the men Peary expected to form the main party at the last had things made as easy as possible for them.

Bartlett, upon whom circumstances had thrust the brunt of the pioneering, returned at 87° 46′ 49″. Why, the question may be asked, did not Peary choose Bartlett instead of Henson as his chief fellow traveller over the 133 nautical miles between this point and the Pole? In his previous attempts to reach the Pole, Henson had been with him to his farthest north. Henson was almost as skilful as the Eskimos in ice technique and in handling sledges and dogs. But he had not the daring and initiative of Bartlett or Marvin, or MacMillan, or Borup; and had he been sent back with one of the supporting parties and had encountered conditions similar to those Peary had to face in 1906 he and his party would never have reached the land at all.

At the Summit of the World

So it was that, a little after midnight on the morning of April 2, with food and fuel supplies ample for 40 days, Peary and Henson and four Eskimos (Egingwah, Seegloo, Ootah and Ooqueah) started on the final stage of the great adventure. They had five sledges and 40 dogs, the pick of the 140 with which they had left the ship.

This was the time for which Peary had reserved all his energies, the time for which he had worked for 22 years, for which he had lived the simple life and trained himself as for a race. In spite of his years he felt fit for the demands of the coming days and was eager to be on the trail. The party, equipment and supplies were beyond his most sanguine dreams of earlier years. All these men had a blind confidence that Peary would somehow get them back to land. But he recognized fully that all the impetus of the party centred in him. Whatever pace he set, the others would make good; but if he played out, they would stop like a car with a punctured tire. He had no fault to find with the conditions, and faced them with confidence.

The temperature was — 25°, the going the best since leaving land, when Peary, for the first time, himself took the lead. For ten hours they travelled without stopping, well over the 88th parallel. As they went on they saw the full moon circle round the heavens opposite the sun, a disk of silver opposite a disk of gold. The next day they hustled along for another ten hours till they were half-way to the 89th parallel. All day they heard the ice grinding and groaning, but no motion was visible. On the 4th the going was even better. Hours of sleep were curtailed. The air, keen as frozen steel, burned their faces so that they cracked, causing excruciating pain. At 89° 25', only 35 miles from the Pole, all were pretty well played out; but after a little rest a new start was made before midnight on the 5th.

The weather was overcast and there was the same grey and shadowless light as on the march after Marvin had turned

ROUTE FROM CAPE YORK TO THE POLE

back. The sky was a colourless pall gradually deepening to almost black at the horizon, and the ice was a ghastly and chalky white. How different it seemed from the glittering fields, canopied with blue and lit by the sun and the full moon, over which they had been travelling for the last four days.

But 30 miles were covered in 12 hours actual travelling; and when, at 10 a.m. on April 6, at the end of the fifth march after Bartlett's departure, 89° 57' was reached Peary said he was too exhausted to realize at the moment that his life's purpose had been achieved. After a few hours' sleep, and accompanied by two Eskimos, he pushed on another ten miles thus passing from the western to the eastern hemisphere, at the summit of the world, travelling south though going in precisely the same direction.

Where they were one day and one night constituted a year, a hundred such days and nights constituted a century. Had they stood in that spot during the six months of the Arctic winter night they should have seen every star of the northern hemisphere circling the sky at the same distance from the horizon with the North Star practically in the zenith.

The temperature varied from — 11° to — 30°, and conditions on the whole were favourable to observations, the making of which, together with the planting of the U. S. ensign and other flags, and the leaving of a written record in a glass bottle, kept the explorer active during the 30 hours which were spent at the Pole. He turned south about 4 p.m. on April 7, not, however, without warning memories of the perils encountered when returning in 1906. "We had found the Pole. Should we return to tell the story?" As the land had to be reached before the next spring tides, double marches were made, and beyond having to use an occasional "ice-cake ferry" over a lead, they had little difficulty till they reached the baleful area of the Big Lead which had held them in check so many days on the northward journey and had nearly caused overwhelming disaster in 1906. They found that Bartlett had here lost the main trail and they were forced, themselves, for the rest of the journey, to follow the new trail made by the captain. Repeatedly fresh tracks of bear and hare and fox were passed and Cape Columbia was safely reached at 6 a.m. on April 23. So far, except for general loss of weight and an attack of quinsy suffered by the leader, all were in good health.

When the last sledge came to the almost vertical edge of the glacial fringe of Grant Land Peary thought his Eskimos had gone crazy. They yelled and called and danced until they fell from utter exhaustion. As Ootah sank down he remarked: "The devil is asleep or having trouble with his wife, or we should never have come back so easily."

The return from the Pole was accomplished in 16 marches, and the entire journey from land to Pole and back again occupied 53 days, or 43 marches. All "slept gloriously" for practically two days, the brief waking intervals being occupied with eating and drying their clothes. They reached Cape Hecla in one march of 45 miles and the *Roosevelt* in another of equal length. Peary's heart thrilled as he caught sight of the little black ship lying in its icy berth; but the first news he heard from Bartlett was tragic.

He told him that Marvin had been drowned at the Big Lead. The news staggered Peary, killing all the joy he felt at the sight of the ship and her captain. Marvin was the only white man in the party of which he was in command. As was customary on breaking camp he had gone out ahead of the Eskimos, leaving the natives to break camp, harness the dogs, and follow. When he came to the Big Lead, the recent ice of which was safe and secure at the edges, it is probable that, hurrying on, he did not notice the gradual thinning toward the centre until it was too late and he was in the water. The Eskimos were too far in the rear to hear his calls for help and in that ice-cold water the end must have come very quickly. It was, of course, impossible for them to rescue the body since there was no way of their getting near it. They knew what had happened to Marvin when they came up; but with the childish superstition peculiar to their race, they camped there for a while on the possibility that he might come back.

There was much to do before Peary could leave Cape Sheridan. But all went well. Memorial cairns were erected on those northern shores, one to Ross Marvin and another recording Peary's several Polar journeys. Then, on July 18, with only the memory of Marvin's tragic fate to lessen their high spirits, the *Roosevelt* pulled slowly out from Cape Sheridan. The Eskimos, suitably rewarded, were distributed to their homes, Cape York was cleared on August 26, and the travellers reached home in the following September.

No Coward Soul Is Mine

No coward soul is mine,
No trembler in the world's storm-troubled sphere:
　　I see Heaven's glories shine,
And faith shines equal, arming me from fear.

　　O God within my breast,
Almighty, ever-present Deity!
　　Life—that in me has rest,
As I—undying life—have power in Thee!

　　Vain are the thousand creeds
That move men's hearts: unutterably vain;
　　Worthless as withered weeds,
Or idlest froth amid the boundless main,

　　To waken doubt in one
Holding so fast by thine infinity;
　　So surely anchored on
The steadfast rock of immortality.

　　With wide-embracing love
Thy spirit animates eternal years,
　　Pervades and broods above,
Changes, sustains, dissolves, creates, and rears.

　　Though earth and man were gone,
And suns and universes ceased to be,
　　And Thou wert left alone,
Every existence would exist in thee.

　　There is not room for Death
Nor atom that his might could render void:
　　Thou—THOU art Being and Breath,
And what THOU art may never be destroyed.
　　　　　　　　　　　　　　　—*E. Brontë*

Edith Wharton

ETHAN FROME

EDITH WHARTON was born in New York in 1862. After her marriage in 1885, she spent much time abroad. She was a close friend of the novelist, Henry James (1843-1916), who admired her work and influenced her style. She was awarded a Litt.D. by Yale University. Her best known novels are "The House of Mirth" (1905), "Ethan Frome" (1911), "The Age of Innocence" (1920). Out of the World War came "Fighting France" (1915), "The Marne" (1918), "A Son at the Front" (1923). Her autobiography, "A Backward Glance," appeared in 1934. Mrs. Wharton died in 1937.

Snowbound

IF YOU know Starkfield, Massachusetts, you know the post-office. If you know the post-office you must have seen Ethan Frome drive up to it, drop the reins on his hollow-backed bay and drag himself across the brick pavement to the white colonnade: and you must have asked who he was.

It was there that, several years ago, I saw him for the first time; and the sight pulled me up sharp. Even then he was the most striking figure in Starkfield, though he was the ruin of a man. It was the careless powerful look he had, in spite of a lameness checking each step like the jerk of a chain, that marked him. There was something black and unapproachable in his face, and he was so stiffened and grizzled that I took him for an old man and was surprised to hear that he was not more than fifty-two.

"He's looked that way ever since he had his smash-up; and that's twenty-four years ago come next February," I was told.

All the dwellers in Starkfield had troubles enough of their own to make them comparatively indifferent to others'. But although all conceded that Ethan Frome's had been beyond the common measure, no one gave me an explanation of the look in his face which, as I persisted in thinking, neither poverty nor physical suffering could have put there. Nevertheless, I might have contented myself with not knowing his story if it had not been for the accident of personal contact with the man.

I had been sent up by my employers on a job connected with the big power-house at Corbury Junction. Thus I found myself anchored in Starkfield—the nearest habitable spot—for the best part of the winter. I made an agreement with the proprietor of the Starkfield livery stable to take me daily to Corbury Flats, where I could pick up my train for the Junction.

BUT about the middle of the winter an epidemic spread through the Starkfield stables with the result that I was hard put to it to find a horse that could take me to the Flats. Then it was suggested that Ethan Frome's bay was still on his legs and that his owner might be glad to drive me over. The arrangements were made without difficulty.

For a week he drove me over every morning to Corbury Flats and on my return in the afternoon met me again and carried me back through the icy night to Starkfield. He would drive in silence, never turning his face toward mine, nor answering, except in monosyllables, the questions I put, or such slight pleasantries as I ventured. He seemed a part of the mute melancholy landscape, an incarnation of its frozen woe, with all that was warm and sentient in him fast bound below the surface. But there was nothing unfriendly in his silence. I simply felt that he lived in a depth of moral isolation too remote for casual access.

Frome met me at the Junction one bleak winter's afternoon as usual. Before we had gone very far the clouds gathered, bringing an early night, and the snow began to fall straight and steady in a soft universal diffusion.

The small ray of Frome's lantern was soon lost in this smothering medium, in which even his sense of direction, and the bay's homing instinct, finally ceased to serve us. Two or three times some ghostly landmark sprang up to warn us that we were astray, and then was sucked back into the mist; and when we finally regained our road the old horse began to show exhaustion.

We struggled on for another mile or two, and at last reached a point where Frome, peering into what seemed to me formless night, said: "That's my gate down yonder."

"Look here, Frome," I began, "there's no earthly use in your going any farther—" but he interrupted me: "Nor you neither. There's been about enough of this for anybody."

I understood that he was offering me a night's shelter at the farm. Staggering along in Frome's wake I floundered toward a square of light which trembled through the screen of snow. He lifted his lantern, found the latch, and led the way into the house. On our right a line of light marked the door of the room which had sent its ray across the night; and behind the door I heard a woman's voice droning querulously. Then he opened the door.

"Come in," he said; and as he spoke the droning voice grew still . . .

It was that night that I found the clue to Ethan Frome, and began to put together this vision of his story . . .

Young Ethan Frome

Young Ethan Frome walked at a quick pace along the deserted street. The hush of midnight lay on the village as all its waking life was gathered behind the church windows, from which strains of dance-music flowed with the broad bands of yellow light.

To keep out of range of the revealing rays from within, he made a circuit through the untrodden snow and gradually approached the farther angle of the basement wall and edged his way cautiously forward to the nearest window, holding back his straight spare body and craning his neck till he got a glimpse of the room.

The floor was thronged with girls and young men. Frome's heart was beating fast. He had been straining for a glimpse of a dark head under a cherry-colored scarf.

Then she passed down the line, her light figure swinging from hand to hand in circles of increasing swiftness. Frome, at each turn, caught sight of her laughing, panting lips, the cloud of dark hair about her forehead, and the dark eyes which seemed the only fixed points in a maze of flying colors.

Frome was in the habit of walking into Starkfield to fetch home his wife's cousin, Mattie Silver, on the rare evenings when some chance of amusement drew her to the village. When his wife first proposed that they should give Mattie an occasional evening out he had inwardly demurred at having to do the extra two miles to the village and back after his hard day on the farm; but not long afterward he had reached the point of wishing that Starkfield might give all its nights to revelry.

Mattie Silver had lived under his roof for a year, and from early morning till they met at supper he had frequent chances of seeing her; but no moments in her company were comparable to those when, her arm in his, and her

Suddenly the door opened and he saw his wife

Illustration for Edith Wharton's
"ETHAN FROME"

light step flying to keep time with his long stride, they walked back through the night to the farm.

Her hopeful young life was like the lighting of a fire on a cold hearth. She had an eye to see and an ear to hear: he could show her things and tell her things, and taste the bliss of feeling that all he imparted left long reverberations and echoes he could wake at will.

She was almost the last to leave the hall. He slipped an arm through hers and fancied it was faintly pressed against her side. He longed to stoop his cheek and rub it against her scarf. He would have liked to stand there with her all night in the blackness.

THEY walked for a while in silence. When they came to the dip of the Corbury road they paused. Its icy slope, scored by innumerable sled runners, looked like a mirror scratched by travellers at an inn.

"Would you like to come and coast here some night?" he asked.

"Oh, would you, Ethan? It would be lovely!"

She lingered, pressing closer to his side. "Ned Hale and Ruth Varnum came just as near running into the big elm at the bottom. We were all sure they were going to be killed." Her shiver ran down his arm. "Wouldn't it have been too awful? They're so happy!"

The inflection with which she had said of the engaged couple "They're so happy!" made the words sound as if she had been thinking of herself and him.

"The elm is dangerous, though. It ought to be cut down," she insisted.

They walked on in silence through the blackness. Half-way up the slope Mattie stumbled against some unseen obstruction and clutched his sleeve to steady herself. For the first time he stole his arm about her, and she did not resist. They walked on as if they were floating on a summer stream.

Zeena always went to bed as soon as she had her supper, and the shutterless windows of the house were dark. A dead cucumber-vine dangled from the porch like the crape streamer tied to the door for a death, and the thought flashed through Ethan's brain: "If it was there for Zeena—" Then he had a distinct sight of his wife lying in their bedroom asleep, her mouth slightly open, her false teeth in a tumbler by the bed . . .

It was Zeena's habit, when they came back late from the village, to leave the key under the mat. Ethan stood before the door, his head heavy with dreams, his arm still about Mattie. "Matt—" he began, not knowing what he meant to say. She slipped out of his hold without speaking, and he stooped down and felt for the key.

Below the lower panel of the door, he caught a faint ray of light. Suddenly the door opened and he saw his wife.

AGAINST the dark background of the kitchen she stood up tall and angular, one hand drawing a quilted counterpane to her flat breast, while the other held a lamp. The light, on a level with her chin, drew out of the darkness her puckered throat and the projecting wrist of the hand that clutched the quilt, and deepened fantastically the hollows and prominences of her high-boned face. To Ethan this sight of her came with the intense precision of the last dream before waking. He felt as if he had never before known what his wife looked like.

"Pretty late for you to be up, Zeena," Ethan joked, stamping the snow from his boots.

"I felt so mean I couldn't sleep."

Mattie came forward, unwinding her wraps, "I'm so sorry, Zeena! Isn't there anything I can do?"

"No, there's nothing." Zeena turned away from her. "You might 'a' shook off the snow outside," she said to her husband.

She walked out of the kitchen ahead of them and pausing in the hall raised the lamp at arm's-length, as if to light them up the stairs.

Ethan went up in his wife's wake,

and followed her across the threshold of their room.

WHEN Ethan came downstairs the next morning he found Zeena already seated at the table. Her husband stopped short at the sight of her. Instead of her usual calico wrapper and knitted shawl she wore her best dress of brown merino. On the floor beside her stood his old valise and a bandbox.

"Why, where are you going, Zeena?" he exclaimed.

"I've got my shooting pains so bad that I'm going to Bettsbridge and see that new doctor," she answered in a matter-of-fact tone.

In spite of her sedentary habits, such abrupt decisions were not without precedent in Zeena's history. Twice or thrice before she had suddenly packed off to seek the advice of some new doctor and her husband had grown to dread these expeditions because of their cost. Her abrupt resolve to seek medical advice showed that, as usual, she was wholly absorbed in her health. A rapid calculation showed Ethan that Zeena could not be back at the farm before the following evening . . .

Ethan tried to say something befitting the occasion, but there was only one thought in his mind: the fact that, for the first time since Mattie had come to live with them, Zeena was to be away for a night . . .

Frustration

WHEN he had put his wife on the train he began to think of his return to Mattie. By nature grave and inarticulate, he admired recklessness and gaiety in others and was warmed to the marrow by friendly human intercourse.

When he had been to school in Worcester he had not been much of a hand at a good time, but he had secretly gloried in being clapped on the back and hailed as "Old Ethe." The cessation of such familiarities had increased the chill of his return to Starkfield.

Left alone after his father's accident, to carry the burden of farm and mill, he had had no time for convivial loiterings in the village; and when his mother fell ill the loneliness of the house grew more oppressive than that of the fields. Sometimes, in the long winter evenings, when in desperation her son asked her why she didn't "say something," she would lift a finger and answer: "Because I'm listening. They're talking so out there that I can't hear you."

It was only when she drew toward her last illness, and his cousin Zenobia Pierce came over from the next valley to help him nurse her, that human speech was heard again in the house. Zeena laughed at him for not knowing the simplest sick-bed duties and told him to "go right along out" and leave her to see to things.

The mere fact of obeying her orders, of feeling free to go about his business again, restored his shaken balance and magnified his sense of what he owed her.

After the funeral when he saw her preparing to go away, he was seized with an unreasoning dread of being left alone on the farm; and before he knew what he was doing he had asked her to stay there with him. He had often thought since that it would not have happened if his mother had died in the spring instead of winter . . .

When they married it was agreed that they would sell the farm and saw-mill and try their luck in a large town. He had always wanted to be an engineer, and to live in towns, where there were lectures and big libraries, and "fellows doing things."

But purchasers were slow in coming, and while he waited for them Ethan learned the impossibility of transplanting her. Within a year of their marriage she had developed the "sickliness" which had since made her notable even in a community rich in pathological instances. Then she fell silent. He recalled his mother's growing taciturnity and wondered if Zeena were also turning "queer."

As he drew near the farm he saw a light twinkling in the house above him. "She's up in her room" he said to himself, "fixing herself up for supper"; and he remembered Zeena's sarcastic stare when Mattie, on the evening of her arrival, had come down to supper with smoothed hair and a ribbon at her neck.

She met him at the door standing just as Zeena had stood, a lifted lamp in her hand, against the black background of the kitchen. She held the lamp at the same level, and it drew out with the same distinctness her slim young throat and the brown wrist no bigger than a child's. Then striking upward, it threw a lustrous fleck on her lips, edged her eyes with velvet shade, and laid a milky whiteness above the black curve of her brows.

Through her hair she had run a streak of crimson ribbon. This tribute to the unusual transformed and glorified her. She seemed to Ethan taller, fuller, more womanly in shape and motion.

She set the lamp on the table, and he saw that it was carefully laid for supper, with fresh doughnuts, stewed blueberries and his favourite pickles in a dish of gay red glass.

Ethan was suffocated with the sense of well-being. They drew their chairs up to the table. Except when he was steering a big log down the mountain to his mill he had never known such a thrilling sense of mastery.

After she had cleared the table and washed the dishes she sat down, her hands clasped on her work, and it seemed to him that a warm current flowed toward him along the strip of stuff that lay unrolled between them. Cautiously he slid his hand palm-downward along the table till his finger-tips touched the end of the stuff.

Her glance fell on his hand, which now completely covered the end of her work and grasped it as if it were a part of herself. He saw a scarcely perceptible tremor cross her face, and without knowing what he did he stooped his head and kissed the bit of stuff in his hold.

But just as his lips rested on it he felt it glide slowly from beneath them, and saw that Mattie had risen and was silently rolling up her work.

"Good night, Matt," he said as she put her foot on the first step of the stairs.

She turned and looked at him a moment. "Good night, Ethan," she answered and went up.

When the door of her room had closed on her he remembered that he had not even touched her hand.

Zeena Enjoys Bad Health

The next evening when Ethan returned from the village, Mattie met him at the door.

"Oh, Ethan—Zeena's come," she said in a whisper, clutching his sleeve.

They stood and stared at each other, pale as culprits.

"How is she?" he asked, dropping his voice to Mattie's whisper.

She looked away from him uncertainly. "I don't know. She went right up to her room."

He listened for Zeena's step and, not hearing it, called her name up the stairs.

She did not answer, and after a moment's hesitation he went up and opened her door.

"Well, Zeena," he ventured from the threshold. "Supper's ready. Ain't you coming?"

She replied: "I don't feel as if I could touch a morsel. Fact is, I'm sicker than you think. I've got complications."

Almost everybody in the neighbourhood had "troubles," frankly localized and specified; but only the chosen had "complications." Ethan's heart was jerking to and fro between two extremities of feeling, but for a moment compassion prevailed.

"Is that what the new doctor told you?" he asked, instinctively lowering his voice. "What does he want you should do?"

"He wants I should have a hired girl. He says I oughtn't to have to do a single thing around the house. Aunt Martha found me a girl right off. She'll be over tomorrow afternoon."

Wrath and dismay contended in Ethan. He had foreseen an immediate demand for money, but not a permanent drain on his scant resources. He no longer believed what Zeena had told him of the supposed seriousness of her state.

"Did the doctor tell you how I was to pay her wages?"

Her voice rose furiously with his. "No, he didn't. For I'd 'a' been ashamed to tell him that you grudged me the money to get back my health, when I lost it nursing your own mother!"

"You lost your health nursing mother?"

"Yes: and my folks all told me at the time you couldn't do no less than marry me after—"

"Zeena!"

Through the obscurity which hid their faces their thoughts seemed to dart at each other like serpents shooting venom. It was the first scene of open anger between the couple in their sad seven years together.

"You know I haven't got the money to pay for a girl, Zeena. You'll have to send her back: I can't do it."

Zeena, while he spoke, seemed to be following out some elaborate mental calculation. She emerged from it to say: "There'll be Mattie's board less, anyhow—"

He stopped short, not grasping what he heard. "Mattie's board less—?" he began.

Zeena laughed. It was an odd unfamiliar sound—he did not remember ever having heard her laugh before.

"You didn't suppose I was going to keep two girls, did you? No wonder you were scared at the expense!"

"I don't know what you mean," he said. "Mattie Silver's not a hired girl. She's your relation."

"She's a pauper that's hung onto us after her father'd done his best to ruin us. I've kep' her here a whole year: it's somebody else's turn now."

As the shrill words shot out Ethan heard a tap on the door.

"Ethan — Zeena!" Mattie's voice sounded gaily from the landing, "do you know what time it is? Supper's been ready half an hour."

Ethan roused himself with an effort and opened the door. "Go along, Matt. Zeena's just a little tired. I'm coming."

"You ain't going to do it, Zeena? You can't put her out of the house like a thief—a poor girl without friends or money. If you do a thing like that what do you suppose folks'll say of you?"

She replied in the same smooth voice: "I know well enough what they say of my having kep' her here so long as I have."

His wife's retort was like a knife-cut across the sinews and he felt suddenly weak and powerless. Zeena's words revealed the peril of more pleading.

Ethan looked at her with loathing. She was no longer the listless creature who had lived at his side in a state of sullen self-absorption, but a mysterious alien presence, an evil energy secreted from the long years of silent brooding. He took a wild step forward and then stopped.

"You're—you're not coming down?" he said in a bewildered voice.

"No. I guess I'll lay down on the bed a little while," she answered mildly; and he turned and walked out of the room.

In the kitchen Mattie was sitting by the stove. She sprang to her feet as Ethan entered.

"Ethan, there's something wrong! I knew there was!"

She seemed to melt against him in

her terror, and he caught her in his arms, held her fast there, felt her lashes beat his cheek like netted butterflies.

He cried out as if he saw her drowning in a dream: "You can't go, Matt! I'll never let you!"

"Go—go?" she stammered. "Must I go? Ethan, what has happened? Is Zeena mad with me?"

The cry steadied him, though it deepened his wrath and pity. "No, no," he assured her. "This new doctor told her she won't get well unless she lays up and don't do a thing about the house—not for months—"

She lifted her head and looked straight at him. "And she wants somebody handier in my place? Is that it?"

"Oh, God—oh, God," he groaned. The glow of passion he had felt for her had melted to an aching tenderness. "Oh, Matt—Matt—where'll you go to?"

"You're letting your supper get cold," she admonished him with a pale gleam of gaiety.

He dropped down into a chair and hid his face in his hands.

L ATE that night when the house was quiet, Ethan crept downstairs. He found his tobacco pouch and pipe on the kitchen table and under them was a scrap of paper on which three words were written: "Don't trouble, Ethan."

Confused emotions of rebellion stormed in him. He was too young, too strong, too full of the sap of living, to submit so easily to the destruction of his hopes. He rummaged around for a sheet of paper and began to write:

"Zeena: I've done all I could for you, and I don't see as it's been any use. I

don't blame you, nor I don't blame myself. Maybe both of us will do better separate. I'm going to try my luck West, and you can sell the farm and mill, and keep the money—"

His pen paused on the word, which brought home to him the relentless conditions of his lot. If he gave the farm and mill to Zeena, what would be left him to start his own life with? Once in the West he was sure of picking up work—he would not have feared to try his chance alone. But with Mattie depending on him the case was different.

And what of Zeena's fate? Farm and mill were mortgaged to the limit of their value, and even if she found a purchaser it was doubtful if she could clear a thousand dollars on the sale. Even if she were in better health than she imagined, she could never carry on the burden alone.

A moment ago he had wondered what he and Mattie were to live on when they reached the West; now he saw that he had not even the money to take her there. Borrowing was out of the question: six months before he had given his only security to raise funds for necessary repairs on the mill, and he knew that without security no one at Starkfield would lend him ten dollars.

The inexorable facts closed in on him like prison-warders hand-cuffing a convict. There was no way out—none. He was a prisoner for life, and now his one ray of light was to be extinguished.

He crept back heavily to the sofa, stretching himself out with limbs so leaden that he felt as if they would never move again. Tears rose in his throat and slowly burned their way to his lids.

Suicide in the Snow

M ATTIE's bag and shawl lay ready by the door. Mattie in her hat and jacket was standing in the kitchen with her back to Ethan.

"Where's Zeena?" he asked.

"She went upstairs right after dinner. She said she had those shooting pains again, and didn't want to be disturbed."

"Didn't she say good-bye to you?"

"No, that was all she said."

"Come on," he said almost gaily. "We got lots of time for a good ride, before your train leaves."

They drove for a while in silence. Suddenly he turned to her. "Matt, what do you mean to do?"

She did not answer at once, but at length she said: "I'll try to get a place in a store."

"You know you can't do it. The bad air and the standing all day nearly killed you before. And now you're going to throw away all the good Starkfield has done you."

There seemed to be no answer to this, and again they drove on for a while without speaking. With every yard of the way some spot where they had stood, and laughed together or been silent, clutched at Ethan and dragged him back.

"Isn't there any of your father's folks could help you?"

"There isn't any of 'em I'd ask."

He lowered his voice to say: "You know there's nothing I wouldn't do for you if I could."

"I know there isn't."

"I suppose you'll marry!"

"Oh, Ethan!" she cried.

"I'd a'most rather have you dead than that!"

"Oh, I wish I was, I wish I was!" she sobbed.

As they drew near the end of the village the cries of children reached them, and they saw a knot of boys, with sleds behind them, scattering in the open space before the brow of the hill.

Some erratic impulse prompted Ethan to say: "How'd you like me to take you coasting now?"

She forced a laugh. "Why, there isn't time!"

"There's all the time we want. Come along!" His one desire now was to postpone the moment of turning the sorrel toward the Flats.

"But there isn't a sled round anywhere."

"Yes, there is! Right over there under the spruces." He caught Mattie's hand and drew her after him toward the sled.

She seated herself obediently and he took his place behind her, so close that her hair brushed his face. They sat there, straining their eyes down the long hill. She pressed a sudden drenched cheek against his face. "Ethan! Ethan! I want

you to take me down so 't we'll never come up any more."

"Matt! What on earth do you mean?"

She put her lips close to his ear to say: "Right into the big elm. You said you could. So we'd never have to leave each other any more."

He saw the road to the Flats under the night and heard the whistle of the train up the line. The spruces swathed them in blackness and silence. They might have been in their coffins underground. He said to himself: "Perhaps it'll feel like this . . . ?" and then again: "After this I shan't feel anything . . ."

"Come," Mattie whispered, tugging at his hand. Her sombre violence constrained him: she seemed the embodied instrument of fate.

He strained his eyes through the dimness, and they seemed less keen, less capable than usual. He leaned back and drew her mouth to his . . .

Just as they started he heard the sorrel's whinny. Half-way down there was a sudden drop, then a rise, and after that another long delirious descent. Then the big elm shot up ahead, lying in wait for them at the bend of the road, and he said between his teeth: "We can fetch it: I know we can fetch it—"

The big tree loomed bigger and closer, and as they bore down on it he thought: "It's waiting for us: it seems to know." But suddenly his wife's face, with twisted monstrous lineaments, thrust itself between him and his goal, and he made an instinctive movement to brush it aside. The sled swerved in response, but he righted it again, kept it straight, and drove down on the black projecting mass. There was a last instant when the air shot past him like millions of fiery wires, and then the elm—

The querulous drone ceased as I entered Frome's kitchen, and of the two women sitting there I could not tell which had been the speaker.

One of them, on my appearing, raised her tall bony figure from her seat. A slatternly calico wrapper hung from her shoulders and the wisps of her thin gray hair were drawn away from a high forehead and fastened at the back by a broken comb. She had pale opaque eyes which revealed nothing and reflected nothing, and her narrow lips were the same sallow colour as her face.

The other woman was much smaller and slighter. She sat huddled in an arm-chair near the stove, and when I came in she turned her head quickly toward me, without the least corresponding movement of her body. Her hair was as gray as her companion's, her face as bloodless and shrivelled, but amber-tinted, with swarthy shadows sharpening the nose and hollowing the temples. Under her shapeless dress her body kept its limp immobility, and her dark eyes had the bright witch-like stare that disease of the spine sometimes gives.

Frome stood hesitatingly before them as he advanced; then he looked at me and said: "This is my wife, Mis' Frome." After another interval he added, turning toward the figure in the arm-chair, "And this is Miss Mattie Silver . . ."

A Wet Sheet and a Flowing Sea

A wet sheet and a flowing sea,
   A wind that follows fast,
And fills the white and rustling sail,
   And bends the gallant mast—
And bends the gallant mast, my boys,
   While, like the eagle free,
Away the good ship flies, and leaves
   Old England on the lee.

"O for a soft and gentle mind!"
   I heard a fair one cry;
But give to me the snoring breeze
   And white waves heaving high—
And white waves heaving high, my boys,
   The good ship tight and free;
The world of waters is our home,
   And merry men are we.

There's tempest in yon hornèd moon,
   And lightning in yon cloud;
And hark the music, mariners!
   The wind is piping loud—
The wind is piping loud, my boys,
   The lightning flashing free;
While the hollow oak our palace is,
   Our heritage the sea.
       —*Allan Cunningham* (1784-1842).

Helen Keller

THE STORY OF MY LIFE

MARK TWAIN has said that the two most interesting characters in the Nineteenth Century are Napoleon and Helen Keller. She is also one of the bright spots in the Twentieth Century, for although she has lived all but the first two years of her life in total darkness, she has brought the light of knowledge to herself and to thousands of deaf-blind for whom her achievements have been an unrivaled inspiration.

Plunged Into Darkness

I WAS born on June 27, 1880, in Tuscumbia, a little town in northern Alabama.

The family on my father's side is descended from Caspar Keller, a native of Switzerland, who settled in Maryland. One of my Swiss ancestors was the first teacher of the deaf in Zurich and wrote a book on the subject of their education —rather a singular coincidence.

My Grandmother Keller was a daughter of one of Lafayette's aides, Alexander Moore, and grand-daughter of Alexander Spotswood, an early Colonial Governor of Virginia. She was also second cousin of Robert E. Lee.

My father, Arthur H. Keller, was a captain in the Confederate Army, and my mother, Kate Adams, was his second wife and many years younger. Her brother, Charles, married Lucy Helen Everett, who belonged to the same family of Everetts as Edward Everett and Dr. Edward Everett Hale.

The beginning of my life was simple and much like every other little life. I came, I saw, and I conquered, as the first baby in the family always does.

I am told that while I was still in long dresses I showed many signs of an eager, self-asserting disposition. Everything that I saw other people do I insisted upon imitating. At six months I could pipe out "How d'ye," and one day I attracted everyone's attention by saying "Tea, tea, tea" quite plainly. Even after my illness I remembered one of the words I had learned in these early months. It was the word "water," and I continued to make some sound for that word after all other speech was lost. I ceased making the sound "wah-wah" only when I learned to spell the word.

They tell me I walked the day I was a year old. My mother had just taken me out of the bath-tub and was holding me in her lap, when I was suddenly attracted by the flickering shadows of leaves that danced in the sunlight on the smooth floor. I slipped from my mother's lap and almost ran toward them. The impulse gone, I fell down and cried for her to take me up in her arms.

THESE happy days did not last long. One brief spring, musical with the song of the robin and mocking bird, one summer rich in fruit and roses, one autumn of gold and crimson sped by and left their gifts at the feet of an eager, delighted child. Then in the dreary month of February, came the illness which closed my eyes and ears and plunged me into the unconsciousness of a new-born baby.

They called it acute congestion of the stomach and brain. The doctor thought I could not live. Early one morning, however, the fever left me as suddenly and mysteriously as it had come. There was great rejoicing in the family that morning, but no one, not even the doctor, knew that I should never see or hear again.

I fancy I still have confused recollections of that illness. I especially remember the tenderness with which my mother tried to soothe me in my waking hours of fret and pain, and the agony and bewilderment with which I awoke. Gradually I got used to the silence and darkness that surrounded me.

I cannot recall what happened during the first months after my illness. I only know that I sat in my mother's lap or clung to her dress as she went about her household duties. My hands felt every object and observed every motion, and in this way I learned to know many things. Soon I felt the need of some communication with others and began to make crude signs. A shake of the head meant "no" and a nod, "Yes," a pull meant "Come" and a push, "Go." My mother, moreover, succeeded in making me understand a good deal. I always knew when she wished me to bring her something.

I understood a good deal of what was going on about me. At five I learned to fold and put away the clean clothes when they were brought in from the laundry, and I distinguished my own from the rest. I knew by the way my mother and aunt dressed when they were going out, and I invariably begged to go with them. I was always sent for when there was company, and when the guests took their leave, I waved my hand to them, I think with a vague remembrance of the meaning of the gesture.

I do not remember when I first realized that I was different from other people; but I knew it before my teacher came to me. I had noticed that my mother and my friends did not use signs as I did when they wanted anything done, but talked with their mouths. Sometimes I stood between two persons who were conversing and touched their lips. I could not understand, and was vexed. I moved my lips and gesticulated frantically without result. This made me so angry at times that I kicked and screamed until I was exhausted.

Many incidents of those early years are fixed in my memory, isolated, but clear and distinct, making the sense of that silent, aimless, dayless life all the more intense. One day I happened to spill water on my apron, and I spread it out to dry before the fire which was flickering on the sitting-room hearth. The apron did not dry quickly enough to suit me, so I drew nearer and threw it right over the hot ashes. The fire leaped into life; the flames encircled me so that in a moment my clothes were blazing. I made a terrified noise that brought my old nurse to the rescue. Throwing a blanket over me, she almost suffocated me, but she put out the fire. Except my hands and hair I was not badly burned.

About this time I found out the use of a key. One morning I locked my mother up in the pantry, where she was obliged to remain three hours, as the servants were in a detached part of the house. She kept pounding on the door, while I sat outside on the porch steps and laughed with glee as I felt the jar of the pounding. This most naughty prank of mine convinced my parents that I must be taught as soon as possible!

A Spirit Set Free

The most important day I remember in all my life is the one on which my teacher, Anne Mansfield Sullivan, came to me. I am filled with wonder when I consider the immeasurable contrasts between the two lives which that day connects. It was the third of March, 1887, three months before I was seven years old.

On the afternoon of that eventful day, I stood on the porch,—dumb, expectant. I guessed vaguely from my mother's signs and from the hurrying to and fro in the house that something unusual was about to happen, so I went to the door and waited on the steps.

I felt approaching footsteps. I stretched out my hand, as I supposed, to my mother. Some one took it, and I was caught up and held close in the arms of her who had come to reveal all things to me, and, more than all things else, to love me.

The morning after my teacher came she led me into her room and gave me a doll. The little blind children at the Perkins Institution had sent it; but I did not know this until afterward. When I had played with it a little while, Miss Sullivan slowly spelled into my hand the word "d-o-l-l." I was at once interested in this finger play and tried to imitate. When I finally succeeded in making the letters correctly I was flushed with childish pleasure and pride. Running downstairs to my mother I held up my hand and made the letters for doll.

I did not know that I was spelling or even that words existed; I was simply making my fingers go in monkey-like imitation. In the days that followed I learned to spell in this uncomprehending way a great many words, among them pin, hat, cup and a few verbs like sit, stand and walk. But my teacher had been with me several weeks before I understood that everything has a name.

One day, while I was playing with my new doll, Miss Sullivan put my big rag doll into my lap also, spelled "d-o-l-l" and tried to make me understand that "d-o-l-l" applied to both.

Earlier in the day we had a tussle over the words "m-u-g" and "w-a-t-e-r." Miss Sullivan had tried to impress it upon me that "m-u-g" is mug and that "w-a-t-e-r" is water, but I persisted in confounding the two. In despair she had dropped the subject for the time, only to renew it at the first opportunity.

We were walking down the path to the well-house. Some one was drawing water and my teacher placed my hand under the spout. As the cool stream gushed over one hand she spelled into the other the word "water," first slowly, then rapidly. I stood still, my whole attention fixed upon the motions of her fingers. Suddenly I felt a misty consciousness as of something forgotten—a thrill of returning thought; and somehow the mystery of language was revealed to me. I knew then that "w-a-t-e-r" meant the wonderful cool something that was flowing over my hand. That living word awakened my soul, gave it light, hope, joy, set it free!

I left the well-house eager to learn. Everything had a name, and each name gave birth to a new thought. As we returned to the house every object which I touched seemed to quiver with life. That was because I saw everything with the strange, new sight that had come to me.

Miss Sullivan's Story

ANNE MANSFIELD SULLIVAN was the daughter of poor Irish immigrant parents who died when she was a child. She was put in an almshouse and when it became apparent that she was becoming blind she was sent, at the age of fourteen, to the Perkins Institution for the Blind in Boston.

She was forced to begin her education at the lowest and most elementary point; but she showed from the very start that she had in herself the force and capacity which insure success. She finally graduated from Perkins Institution in 1886 with her sight practically restored by an operation.

When Captain Keller applied to the director for a teacher for his daughter Helen, Anne Sullivan was recommended. The only time she had to prepare herself for the work with her pupil was from August 1886, to February 1887. It must be remembered that Miss Sullivan had to solve her problems unaided by previous teaching experience or the assistance of any other teacher.

Here follow passages from some of Miss Sullivan's letters and reports. The first letter is dated March 6, 1887, three days after her arrival in Tuscumbia.

"It was 6.30 when I reached Tuscumbia. I found Mrs. Keller waiting for me at the station. My first question was, 'Where is Helen?' I tried with all my night to control the eagerness that made me tremble so that I could hardly walk. As we approached the house I saw a child standing in the doorway and Captain Keller said, 'There she is. She has known all day that some one was expected, and she has been wild ever since her mother went to the station for you.' I had scarcely put my foot on the steps, when she rushed toward me with force that would have thrown me backward if Captain Keller had not been behind me.

"There's nothing pale and delicate about Helen. She is large, strong, and ruddy, and as unrestrained in her movements as a young colt. She has none of those nervous habits that are so noticeable and so distressing in blind children. Her body is well formed and vigorous, and Mrs. Keller says she had not been ill a day since the illness that deprived her of her sight and hearing.

"Her face is hard to describe. It is intelligent, but lacks mobility, or soul, or something. Her mouth is large and finely shaped. You see at a glance that she is blind.

"She is very quick-tempered and wilful, and nobody, except her halfbrother James, has attempted to control her. The greatest problem I shall have to solve is how to discipline and control her without breaking her spirit. I shall go rather slowly at first and try to win her love."

MONDAY P.M.

"I HAD a battle royal with Helen this morning. Although I try very hard not to force issues, I find it very difficult to avoid them.

"Helen's table manners are appalling. She puts her hands in our plates and helps herself, and when the dishes are passed, she grabs them and takes out whatever she wants. This morning I would not let her put her hand in my plate. She persisted and a contest of wills followed. Naturally the family was much disturbed, and left the room.

"I locked the dining-room door, and proceeded to eat my breakfast, though the food almost choked me. Helen was lying on the floor, kicking and screaming and trying to pull my chair from under me. She kept this up for half an hour, then she got up to see what I was doing. I let her see that I was eating, but did not let her put her hand in the plate. She pinched me, and I slapped her every time she did it.

"Then she went all round the table to see who was there, and finding no one but me, she screamed bewildered. After a few minutes she came back to her place and began to eat her breakfast with her fingers. I gave her a spoon which she threw on the floor. I forced her out of the chair and made her pick it up. Finally I succeeded in getting her back in her chair again, and held the spoon in her hand, compelling her to take up the food with it and put it in her mouth. In a few minutes she yielded and finished her breakfast peaceably.

"Then we had another tussle over folding her napkin. When she had finished, she threw it on the floor and ran toward the door. Finding it locked she began to kick and scream all over again. It was another hour before I succeeded in getting her napkin folded. Then I let her out into the warm sunshine and went up to my room and threw myself on the bed exhausted. I had a good cry and felt better."

MARCH 20, 1887

"MY HEART is singing for joy this morning. A miracle has happened! The light of understanding has shone upon my little pupil's mind, and behold, all things are changed!

"The wild little creature of two weeks ago has been transformed into a gentle child. She is sitting by me as I write, her face serene and happy, crocheting a long red chain of Scotch wool. She learned the stitch this week, and is very proud of the achievement. When she succeeded in making a chain that would reach across the room, she patted herself on the arm and put the first work of her hands lovingly against her cheek.

"The great step—the step that counts—has been taken. The little savage has learned her first lesson in obedience, and finds the yoke easy. It now remains my pleasant task to direct and mould the beautiful intelligence that is beginning to stir. Already people notice the change in Helen."

An Inquiring Mind

I HAD now the key to all language, and I was eager to learn to use it. At first when my teacher told me about a new thing I asked very few questions. My ideas were vague, and my vocabulary was inadequate; but as my knowledge of things grew, and I learned more and more words, my field of inquiry broadened, and I would return again to the same subject, eager for further information.

I remember the morning that I first asked the meaning of the word, "love." Miss Sullivan put her arm gently round me and spelled into my hand, "I love Helen."

"What is love?" I asked.

She drew me closer to her and said, "It is here," pointing to my heart, whose beats I was conscious of for the first time. Her words puzzled me very much because I did not then understand anything unless I touched it.

A day or two afterward I was stringing beads of different sizes in symmetrical groups. Finally I noticed a very obvious error in the sequence and for an instant I concentrated my attention on the lesson and tried to think how I should have arranged the beads. Miss Sullivan touched my forehead and spelled with decided emphasis, "Think."

In a flash I knew that the word was the name of the process that was going on in my head. This was my first conscious perception of an abstract idea.

For a long time I was still trying to find a meaning for "love" in the light of this new idea. The sun had been under a cloud all day, and there had been brief showers; but suddenly the sun broke forth in all its southern splendour.

Again I asked my teacher, "Is this not love?"

"Love is something like the clouds that were in the sky before the sun came out," she replied. Then in simpler words than these, which at the time I could not have understood, she explained: "You cannot touch the clouds, you know; but you feel the rain and know how glad the flowers and the thirsty earth are to have it after a hot day. You cannot touch love either; but you feel the sweetness that it pours into everything. Without love you would not be happy or want to play."

The beautiful truth burst upon my mind—I felt that there were invisible lines stretched between my spirit and the spirits of others.

FROM the beginning of my education Miss Sullivan made it a practice to speak to me as she would speak to any hearing child; the only difference was that she spelled the sentences into my hand instead of speaking them. If I did not know the words and idioms necessary to express my thoughts she supplied them, even suggesting conversation when I was unable to keep up my end of the dialogue.

This process was continued for several years; for the deaf child does not learn in a month, or even in two or three years, the numberless idioms and expressions used in the simplest daily intercourse. The little hearing-child learns these from constant repetition and imitation. The conversations she hears in her home stimulates her mind and suggests topics and calls forth the spontaneous expression of her own thoughts. This natural exchange of ideas is denied to the deaf child.

My teacher, realizing this, determined to supply the kinds of stimulus I lacked. This she did by repeating to me as far as possible, verbatim, what she heard, and by showing me how I could take part in the conversation. But it was a long time before I ventured to take the initiative, and still longer before I could find something appropriate to say at the right time.

THE next important step in my education was learning to read.

As soon as I could spell a few words my teacher gave me slips of cardboard on which were printed words in raised letters. I quickly learned that each printed word stood for an object, an act, or a quality. I had a frame in which I could arrange the words in little sentences; but before I ever put sentences in the frame I used to make them in objects. I found the slips of paper which represented, for example, "doll," "is," "on," "bed" and placed each name on its object; then I put my doll on the bed with the words is, on, bed arranged beside the doll, thus making a sentence of the words, and at the same time carrying out the idea of the sentence.

From the printed slip it was but a step to the printed book. I took my "Reader for Beginners" and hunted for the words I knew; when I found them my joy was like that of a game of hide-and-seek.

For a long time I had no regular lessons. Even when I studied most earnestly it seemed more like play than work. Everything Miss Sullivan taught me she illustrated by a beautiful story or a poem. Whenever anything delighted or interested me she talked it over with me just as if she were a little girl herself. What many children think of with dread as painful plodding through grammar, hard sums and harder definitions, is today one of my most precious memories.

It was my teacher's genius, her quick sympathy, her loving tact which made the first years of my education so beautiful. It was because she seized the right moment to impart knowledge that made it so pleasant and acceptable to me.

The Dumb Can Speak

IT WAS in the spring of 1890 that I learned to speak. The impulse to utter audible sounds had always been strong within me. I used to make noises, keeping one hand on my throat while the other hand felt the movements of my lips. I was pleased with anything that made a noise and liked to feel the cat purr and the dog bark. I also liked to keep my hand on a singer's throat, or on a piano when it was being played.

My friends say that I laughed and cried naturally, and for awhile I made many sounds and word-elements, not because they were a means of communication, but because the need of exercising my vocal organs was imperative.

I had known for a long time that the people about me used a method of communication different from mine; and even before I knew that a deaf child could be taught to speak, I was conscious of dissatisfaction with the means of communication I already possessed. I persisted in using my lips and voice. Friends tried to discourage this tendency fearing lest it would lead to disappointment. But I persisted, and an event soon occurred which resulted in the breaking down of this great barrier —I discovered that a deaf and blind girl in Norway had learned to speak.

I resolved that I, too, would learn to speak. I would not rest satisfied until my teacher took me, for advice and assistance, to Miss Sarah Fuller, principal of the Horace Mann School. This lovely, sweet-natured lady offered to teach me herself, and we began on the twenty-sixth of March, 1890.

Miss Fuller's method was this: she passed my hand lightly over her face, and let me feel the position of her tongue and lips when she made a sound. I was eager to imitate every motion and in an hour had learned six elements of speech: M, P, A, S, T, I.

Miss Fuller gave me eleven lessons in all. I shall never forget the surprise and delight I felt when I uttered my first connected sentence, "It is warm." True, they were broken and stammering syllables; but they were human speech. My soul, conscious of new strength, came out of bondage, and was reaching through those broken symbols of speech to all knowledge and all faith.

But it must not be supposed that I could really talk in this short time. I had learned only the elements of speech. Miss Fuller and Miss Sullivan could understand me, but most people would not have understood one word in a hundred.

Nor is it true that, after I had learned these elements, I did the rest myself.

In the first place, I laboured night and day before I could be understood even by my most intimate friends; in the second place, I needed Miss Sullivan's assistance constantly in my efforts to articulate each sound clearly and to combine all sounds in a thousand ways. She still reminds me of mispronounced words.

Listening to Miss Keller

[MISS FULLER, who gave her the first lessons, has written authoritatively about Miss Keller's speech. The following is an excerpt from her account: "Let me try to give some impression of Miss Keller's speech.

"Her voice is low and pleasant to listen to. Her speech lacks variety and modulation; it runs in a sing-song when she is reading aloud; and when she speaks with fair degree of loudness, it hovers about two or three middle tones. Her voice has an aspirate quality; there seems always to be too much breath for the amount of tone. Some of her notes are musical and charming. When she is telling a child's story, or one with pathos in it, her voice runs into pretty slurs from one tone to another. This is like the effect of the slow dwelling on long words, not quite well managed, that one notices in a child who is telling a story.

"The principal thing that is lacking is sentence accent and variety in the inflection of phrases. Miss Keller pronounces each word as a foreigner does when he is still labouring with the elements of a sentence, or as children sometimes read in school when they have to pick out each word.

"It is hard to say whether or not Miss Keller's speech is easy to understand. Some understand her readily; others do not. Her friends grow accustomed to her speech and forget that it is different from that of any one else. Children seldom have any difficulty in understanding her; which suggests that her deliberate, measured speech is like theirs, before they come to the adult trick of running all the words of a phrase into one movement of the breath. I am told that Miss Keller speaks better than most other deaf people."]

Preparing for College

IN the summer of 1894, I attended the meeting at Chautauqua of the American Association to Promote the Teaching of Speech to the Deaf. There it was arranged that I should go to the Wright-Humason School for the Deaf in New York City. I went there in October, 1894, accompanied by Miss Sullivan. This school was chosen especially for the purpose of obtaining the highest advantages in vocal culture and training in lip-reading. In addition to my work in these subjects, I studied, during the two years I was in the school, arithmetic, physical geography, French and German.

Miss Reamy, my German teacher, could use the manual alphabet, and after I had acquired a small vocabulary, we talked together in German whenever we had a chance, and in a few months I could understand almost everything she said. Before the end of the first year I read "Wilhelm Tell" with the greatest delight. Indeed, I think I made more progress in German than in any of my other studies.

My progress in lip-reading and speech was not what my teachers and I had hoped and expected it would be. It was my ambition to speak like other people, and my teachers believed that this could be accomplished; but, although we worked hard and faithfully, yet we did not quite reach our goal. I suppose we aimed too high, and disappointment was therefore inevitable.

I regarded arithmetic as a system of pitfalls. I hung about the dangerous frontier of "guess," avoiding with infinite trouble to myself and others the broad valley of reason. When I was not guessing, I was jumping at conclusions, and this fault, in addition to my dullness, aggravated my difficulties more than was right or necessary.

But although these disappointments caused me great depression at times, I pursued my other studies with unflagging interest, especially physical geography. It was a joy to learn the secrets of nature: how—in the picturesque language of the Old Testament—the winds are made to blow from the four corners of the heavens, how the vapours ascend from the ends of the earth, how rivers are cut out among the rocks, and mountains are overturned by the roots, and in what ways man may overcome many forces mightier than himself. The two years in New York were happy ones, and I look back to them with genuine pleasure.

In october, 1896, I entered the Cambridge School for Young Ladies, to be prepared for Radcliffe.

When I was a little girl, I visited Wellesley and surprised my friends by the announcement, "Some day I shall go to college—but I shall go to Harvard!" When asked why I would not go to Wellesley, I replied that there were only girls there.

The thought of going to college took root in my heart and became an earnest desire, which impelled me to enter into competition for a degree with seeing-and-hearing-girls, in the face of the strong opposition of many true and wise friends. When I left New York the idea had become a fixed purpose; and it was decided that I should go to Cambridge.

This was the nearest approach I could get to Harvard and to the fulfillment of my childish declaration.

Of course my instructors had had no experience in teaching any but normal pupils, and my only means of conversing with them was reading their lips. My studies for the first year were English history, English literature, German, Latin, arithmetic, Latin composition and occasional themes. Until then I had never taken a course of study with the idea of preparing for college; but I had been well drilled in English by Miss Sullivan, and it soon became evident to my teachers that I needed no special instruction in this subject beyond a critical study of the books prescribed by the college. I had had, moreover, a good start in French, and received six months' instruction in Latin; but German was the subject with which I was most familiar.

In spite, however, of these advantages, there were serious drawbacks to my progress. Miss Sullivan could not spell out in my hand all that the books required, and it was very difficult to have text books embossed in time to be of use to me, although my friends in London and Philadelphia were willing to hasten the work. For a while, indeed, I had to copy my Latin in braille, so that I could recite with the other girls. My instructors soon became sufficiently familiar with my imperfect speech to answer my questions readily and correct mistakes. I could not make notes in class or write exercises; but I wrote all my compositions and translations at home on my typewriter.

Each day Miss Sullivan went to the classes with me and spelled into my hand with infinite patience all the teachers said. In study hours she had to look up new words for me and read and reread notes and books I did not have in raised print. The tedium of that work is hard to conceive.

I took my preliminary examinations for Radcliffe from the 29th of June to the 3rd of July in 1897. The subjects I offered were Elementary and Advanced German, French, Latin, English, and Greek and Roman history, making nine hours in all. I passed in everything, and received "honours" in German and English.

On the 29th and 30th of June, 1899, I passed my final examinations for Radcliffe College. The first day I had Elementary Greek and Advanced Latin, and, the second day Geometry, Algebra and Advanced Greek.

The struggle for admission to college was ended, and I could now enter Radcliffe whenever I pleased. Before I entered college, however, it was thought best that I should study another year. It was not, therefore, until the fall of 1900 that my dream of going to college was realized.

Higher Education

I AM frequently asked how I overcame the peculiar conditions under which I worked in college. In the classroom I was of course practically alone. The professor was as remote as if he were speaking through a telephone. The lectures were spelled into my hand as rapidly as possible, and much of the individuality of the lecturer was lost to me in the effort to keep in the race. The words rushed through my hand like hounds in pursuit of a hare which they often missed.

I could not make notes during the lectures, because my hands were busy listening. Usually I jotted down what I could remember of them when I got home. I wrote the exercises, daily themes, criticisms and hour-tests, and the mid-year and final examinations, on my typewriter, so that the professors had no difficulty in finding out how little I knew.

Very few of the books required in the various courses were printed for the blind, and I was obliged to have them spelled into my hand. Consequently I needed more time to prepare my lessons than other girls. The manual part took longer, and I had perplexities which they had not. There were days when the close attention I had to give to details chafed my spirit, and the thought that I must spend hours reading a few chapters, while in the world without other girls were laughing and singing and dancing, made me rebellious; but I soon recovered my buoyancy and laughed the discontent out of my heart.

While my days at Radcliffe were still in the future, they were encircled with a halo of romance, which they have lost; but in the transition from the romantic to the actual, I learned many things I should never have known had I not tried the experiment. One of them is the precious science of patience, which teaches us that we should take our education as we would take a walk in the country, leisurely, our minds hospitably open to impressions of every sort. Such knowledge floods the soul unseen with a soundless tidal wave of deepening thought. "Knowledge is power."

Rather, knowledge is happiness, because to have knowledge—broad, deep knowledge—is to know true ends from false, and lofty things from low. To know the thoughts and deeds that have marked man's progress is to feel the great heart-throbs of humanity through the centuries; and if one does not feel in these pulsations a heavenward striving, one must indeed be deaf to the harmonies of life.

Pleasures and Amusements

I TRUST that my readers have not concluded that my studies are my only preoccupation; my pleasures and amusements are many and varied.

More than once in the course of my story I have referred to my love of the country. When I was quite a little girl, I learned to row and swim, and during the summer, when I am at Wrentham, Massachusetts, I almost lived in my boat. Nothing gives me greater pleasure than to take my friends out rowing when they visit me. Of course, I cannot guide the boat very well. Some one usually sits in the stern and manages the rudder while I row.

I also enjoy canoeing, and I suppose you will smile when I say that I especially like it on moonlight nights. I cannot, it is true, see the moon climb up the sky behind the pines and steal softly across the heavens, making a shining path for us to follow; but I know she is there, and as I lie back among the pillows and put my hand in the water, I fancy that I feel the shimmer of her garments as she passes.

My favourite amusement is sailing. In the summer of 1901 I visited Nova Scotia, and had opportunities such as I had not enjoyed before to make the acquaintance of the ocean. After spending a few days in Evangeline's country, about which Longfellow's beautiful poem has woven a spell of enchantment, Miss Sullivan and I went to Halifax, where we remained the greater part of the summer.

People who think that all sensations reach us through the eye and the ear have expressed surprise that I should notice any difference, except possibly the absence of pavements, between walking in city streets and in country roads. They forget that my whole body is alive to conditions about me. The rumble and roar of the city smites the nerves of my face, and I feel the ceaseless tramp of an unseen multitude, and the dissonant tumult frets my spirit. The grinding of heavy wagons on hard pavements and the monotonous clangor of machinery are all the more torturing to the nerves if one's attention is not diverted by the panorama that is always present in the noisy streets to people who can see.

IN THE country one sees only Nature's fair works, and one's soul is not saddened by the cruel struggle for mere existence that goes on in the crowded city. Several times I have visited the narrow, dirty streets where the poor live, and I grow hot and indignant to think that good people should be content to live in fine houses and become strong and beautiful, while others are condemned to live in hideous, sunless tenements and grow ugly, withered and cringing. The children who crowd these grimy alleys, half-clad and underfed, shrink away from your outstretched hand as if from a blow. Dear little creatures, they crouch in my heart and haunt me with a constant sense of pain. It is impossible not to think of all this when I return to the country after a year of work in town.

What a joy it is to feel the soft, springy earth under my feet once more, to follow grassy roads that lead to ferny brooks where I can bathe my fingers in a cataract of rippling notes, or to clamber over a stone wall into green fields that tumble and roll and climb in riotous gladness!

Next to a leisurely walk I enjoy a "spin" on my bicycle. It is splendid to feel the wind blowing in my face and the springy motion of my iron steed. The rapid rush through the air gives me a delicious sense of strength and buoyancy.

Whenever it is possible, my dog accompanies me on a walk or ride or sail. I have had many dog friends—huge mastiffs, soft-eyed spaniels, a woodwise setter and honest, homely bull terriers. They seem to understand my limitations, and always keep close beside me when I am alone. I love their affectionate ways and the eloquent wag of their tails.

When a rainy day keeps me indoors, I amuse myself after the manner of other women. I like to knit and crochet; I read in the happy-go-lucky way I love, here and there a line; or perhaps I play a game or two of checkers or chess with a friend. I have a special board on which I play these games. The squares are cut out, so that the men stand in them firmly. The black checkers are flat and the white ones curved on top. Each checker has a hole in the middle in which a brass knob can be placed to distinguish the king from the commons.

Mᵁˢᵉᵁᵐˢ and art stores are also sources of pleasure and inspiration. Doubtless it will seem strange to many that the hand unaided by sight can feel action, sentiment, beauty in the cold marble; and yet it is true that I derive genuine pleasure from touching great works of art. As my fingertips trace line and curve, they discover the thought and emotion which the artist has portrayed. I can feel in the faces of gods and heroes hate, courage and love, just as I can detect them in living faces I am permitted to touch. I feel in Diana's posture the grace and freedom of the forest and the spirit that tames the mountain lion and subdues the fiercest passions. My soul delights in the repose and gracious curves of the Venus; and in Barré's bronzes the secrets of the jungle are revealed to me.

Is it not true, then, that my life with all its limitations touches at many points the life of the World Beautiful? Everything has its wonders, even darkness and silence, and I learn, whatever state I may be in, therein to be content.

Sometimes, it is true, a sense of isolation enfolds me like a cold mist as I sit alone and wait at life's shut gate. Beyond there is light, and music, and sweet companionship; but I may not enter. Fate, silent, pitiless, bars the way. Fain would I question his imperious decree; but my heart is still undisciplined and passionate; but my tongue will not utter the bitter, futile words that rise to my lips, and they fall back into my heart like unshed tears.

Silence sits immense upon my soul. Then comes hope with a smile and whispers, "There is joy in self-forgetfulness." So I try to make the light in others' eyes my sun, the music in others' ears my symphony, the smile on others' lips my happiness.

[Aғᴛᴇʀ Helen Keller graduated from Radcliffe in 1904 she and her teacher bought a large house in Wrentham, Massachusetts, near Boston. This purchase was made possible by the success of "The Story of My Life," which was published during her junior year in college and which, by its continued sale in this and other countries, brought her a sizable income.

Her book and achievements brought an invitation to appear at the St. Louis Exposition of 1904 in order to awaken a world-wide interest in the education of the deaf-blind. A young author and editor, Mr. John Macy, travelled with her and Miss Sullivan, thereby stirring up the rumor that Helen Keller was going to marry him. But it was Miss Sullivan who finally became his wife in 1905. However, Mrs. Macy continued to be the eyes and ears for Helen and Mr. Macy became her best literary critic, pruning her style of its wordiness and curbing her tendency toward dogmatic preaching.

The Keller-Macy household at Wrentham soon became a clearing house for information regarding the blind. Up to that time certain strides had been made in their education but little had been done toward the prevention of blindness. Miss Keller wrote many articles which had far-reaching results in this important field. One, in particular, which was printed in the Ladies' Home Journal in 1907, created a furor. It was a discussion of blindness in new-born children which ventured into the field of venereal disease where no womanly woman of that day had ever dared to venture.

As the years passed Miss Keller discovered that she could not continue to make a living at writing because she was limited to two subjects—herself and the blind. It was suggested in 1910 that she might be able to develop her speaking capacities so that she could go into the lecture business. She, therefore, began to take singing lessons in order to enlarge her vocal cords to a point where she could be heard in an auditorium. By 1913 she was able to undertake a series of lecture tours which proved to be financially successful.

Meanwhile her interests had gone far beyond herself and the blind. She was a natural crusader and the Macys' interest in socialism served to bring their cause home to her. She took an active part in a strike of Lawrence, Massachusetts, mill workers in 1912. Curiously enough, not she but the mill-workers were blamed for using her to advertise their cause. In the same way the suffragettes were criticised for letting her, a "helpless woman", march in their parades, although she was strong for woman suffrage.

WHEN during the World War she lifted her voice for peace she was called a "supermegaphone for undesirable citizens." At the same time she was severely criticised for giving the proceeds from the German translations of her books to the German soldiers blinded in the war. People overlooked the fact that her money went to the French and British war-blind as well. All through the war she worked tirelessly for the blind soldiers, wrote them letters of encouragement, visited them, and raised money for them.

Several years later, during the "noble experiment" she said that she did not think that prohibition had worked or could work. Then she was tearfully accused throughout the country of betraying all that was beautiful and fine.

She was an arch-priestess when she stood with the majority, an ignorant woman who did not know what she was talking about when she was against it. Editorial writers even went so far as to say that because she was deaf, dumb and blind she could have no competent knowledge of anything.

In 1918 she tried her hand in still another field—the movies. She and Mrs. Macy appeared in a picture called "Deliverance" which was the story of their life together. Unfortunately it was a financial failure.

In 1920 she was much more successful in vaudeville. Like Madame Schumann-Heink who did the same thing ten years later, she was severely criticised but she felt that it was honest work and was glad to have it. Two years on the road was a severe strain. As Mrs. Macy's eyesight was beginning to fail they decided to retire and write again. "Midstream," an autobiography which covered the period after 1902, appeared in 1929.

On October 20, 1936, one of the closest and most beautiful friendships of all time was ended in the death of Anne Sullivan Macy. Many people consider her as remarkable as Helen Keller herself. Albert Einstein said to her once: "Your work, Mrs. Macy, has interested me more than any other achievement in modern education. Not only did you impart language to Helen Keller, you unfolded her personality, and such work has in it an element of the super-human."

The period after Mrs. Macy's death has been one of profound spiritual readjustment for Helen Keller. The extent to which she has had to readjust her life and thinking has been described in her "Journal" which was published in 1938. Luckily Miss Polly Thomson, who has been her secretary since 1914, has been able to help her to the extent that she still finds interest in travelling and is able to lecture and carry on her work for the blind.]

"THAT was excellently observed," say I when I read a passage in another where his opinion agrees with mine. When we differ, then I pronounce him to be mistaken.—*Swift.*

OPPORTUNITY has hair on her forehead, but is bald behind. If you meet her seize her, for once let slip, Jove himself cannot catch her again.—*Phaedrus.*

THERE is no such thing as a dumb poet or a handless painter. The essence of an artist is that he should be articulate.—*Swinburne.*

THE Present is the living sum-total of the whole Past.—*Carlyle.*

HUGH WALPOLE

THE CATHEDRAL

HUGH WALPOLE was born in New Zealand in 1884, and was educated at Cambridge. He wrote two novels at the age of twenty. Since then he has written many more. "The Wooden Horse," in 1909, was the first of his novels to be published. "The Cathedral," an excellent example of his art and deservedly popular, was published in 1922. This study has been especially prepared for this volume.

Seeds of Trouble

READER, have you ever lived in the moral and intellectual atmosphere of a cathedral town? Have you ever experienced the strange sensations arising from the living presence of events dead and gone; of shadows of history that haunt the lives of the men and women of to-day; of long-vanished rituals and ceremonies that revisit the glimpses of the moon; the conventions of a community which play with mysteries and moralities sacred and profane; the autocracy of a building that has weathered the centuries, outlived creeds, survived reformations, convocations; a Work of Man and a Work of Art that is honourable and venerable and beautiful; which enshrines God in the past, the present, the future "as He was in the beginning, is now, and ever shall be . . ." A cathedral with its trim precincts, cloisters, green lawns; prim Georgian houses with neat white steps, polished knockers and drawn curtains; the sanctuaries and strongholds of the ecclesiastical proprieties—and of men, women, children; some ghosts of to-day and yesterday and the day to come. . . . And do you think . . . Are there any secrets and heart-burnings and tragedies behind those polite barricades of theological austerity? Listen . . .

IT is difficult to realize to-day how apart from the world Polchester was in the latter years of the reign of Queen Victoria—in 1897. It might have been, al-most, a walled-up fortress of the Middle Ages; self-contained, self-satisfied, the very inhabitants made it a point of honour that its spirit of rigid and moral autocracy should be maintained at all costs. The higher social grades of Polchester society were, of course, extremely moral, what small tittle-tattling scandal might from time to time pass from mouth to mouth was kept jealously guarded—and made the most of. The little city breathed propriety, its streets were neat and clean; shops were, of course, a necessity, men must eat and drink—or at least imbibe—for no one "drank" in Polchester. Of course, there was a circulating library—that "evergreen tree of diabolical knowledge"—with the latest works of fiction in gaudy bindings; Miss Milton was librarian (chosen, perhaps, on the strength of certain literary associations of an ecclesiastical nature connected with her name), and, of course, there was a High Street and a castle. And the cathedral; castle and cathedral dominated the town from their eminence, especially the cathedral.

The River Pol ran through the town to the sea. On a stretch of the Pol below the town was the suburb of Seatown. It was not handsome. It might have been romantic in the old days when strange ships came gliding up the tideway; in these latter days it was chiefly remarkable for bad drainage, bad drinking, bad living, and bad dying.

It was in 1887 that Adam Brandon had come to the town; one-time curate at Portsmouth, then chaplain to the bishop of Worcester; in 1875 he had accepted a living at Pompret, in Wiltshire. At Polchester he was, first of all, canon and afterwards archdeacon. By personal influence and strength of character he came to be alluded to as "the king of Polchester." He was a magnificent—not too strong a word—a magnificent specimen of manhood. Fifty-eight years of age now, six feet two or three in height, athletic, hair curly and fair and thick; young-looking, energetic. The Polchester ladies said he was "like a Greek god," and their evidence had never been refuted. Archdeacon Brandon was not unduly elated by this feminine worship. God had seen fit—in a fit of boredom, perhaps, at having to make so many inferior men—to present the world with this fine type of man; fine in body, fine in soul, fine in intellect. Brandon was safe, however, from the feminine world of Polchester. In 1875 he had married Amy Broughton, then a girl of twenty. They had a boy, Falcon, now twenty-one, and a girl, Joan, just eighteen. Mrs. Brandon was (society thought) a very insignificant sort of woman; rather dull, decidedly insignificant. She bore her husband's occasional outbursts of temper very meekly; she acquiesced in his opinion that God had put him into this world to rule. Of course, he ruled to the glory of God, and he ruled—it was occasionally a stern necessity—to the glory of himself. On the whole he was satisfied with himself and his family. And, above all, he was satisfied with Polchester; he was contented to live there, spend the remainder of his days there, die and be buried there—when the time came—with, of course, the appropriate ceremonies.

Evensong at the cathedral. A small but select congregation; Mrs. Combermere, Miss Dobell, Mrs. Cole, Mr. Drake, Mr. Thompson; mere shadows the archdeacon glances at. He also glances at the magnificent tomb of the Black Bishop; black marble, effigy in robes and mitre, at the feet a pair of gauntlets; angels support the Black Bishop's head; four armed knights; the motto, "God giveth Strength." A martyr to the Church; murdered in this very nave by villains who feared neither God nor man. "He died bravely defending this great house of prayer, and is now in eternal happiness . . ." All as it should be. The archdeacon feels very proud, very satisfied. He reads the Lesson—all about the money-changers; old Cobbett, the verger, who has acquired the fine art of sleeping with his eyes open during Lessons and Sermons, wakes up with a start; the archdeacon's splendid voice is unusually vibrant, exulting.

"Ronder comes to-day, doesn't he?"

"Ronder?" Brandon repeated, coming abruptly out of his secret exultation.

"Yes—Hart-Smith's successor."

"Oh, yes—I believe he does."

The great gates close with a clang. Brandon walks slowly home. Any news? Any letter from his son "Falk," who is at Oxford? No. Strange; there has been no news from Falk for three weeks. And Joan's reading those trashy novels again? And mother (Mrs. Brandon is now forty-two) can't get the trashy novel *she* wants, because Miss Milton sits on the new ones, and keeps them for that Mrs. Sampson—hey? What trifles.

The door opens suddenly; it is Falk, good-looking, fair, frank, slim, fearless. The archdeacon is amazed. . . .

"What's the matter?" he said at last.

"I've been sent down," said Falk.

"Sent down!"

"Yes, for ragging. They wanted to do it last term."

"Sent down!" The archdeacon shot to his feet, his voice suddenly lifted to a cry.

"And you have the impertinence to come and tell me! You walk in as though nothing had happened! You walk in——"

"Of course you're angry—I knew you would be. Anyway, Oxford's a rotten place; you won't have to pay my bills any more, anyway."

Falk turned and went.

THE same train that had brought Falk brought the new canon, Ronder, and his aunt, Miss Alice Ronder. The new canon is a modernist; he is also rather fat and rubicund, good tempered, jocular and very tactful. Miss Stiles, a talkative old friend of Aunt Ronder, soon lets light into the new canon's keen intelligence. He will have to fight Brandon, or knuckle under. Brandon is the proudest man in England. Ronder loves a fight; without undue presumption, it always seemed to Ronder that as soon as he thought "so and so," then God also thought "so and so,"—a wonderful partnership; everyone else just became pawns in a Divine game of chess.

And now Brandon is troubled; troubled in spirit. After all that he has done for Polchester—and for the cathedral—this Falk business seems most unjust; a blow to his dignity. Other seeds of trouble are springing into young and thorny shoots. Joan—a charming girl, devoted to her father and mother, but snubbed for all her amiable qualities, forms an attachment for young Lord St. Leath—Johnny to his familiars, and soon "Johnny" to Joan. They meet at Miss Milton's Library; and Miss Milton gets into serious trouble for showing favouritism in the matter of the trashy novels. As a matter of fact, she loses her post. But though, like her great namesake, "fallen on evil times and evil tongues," she nurses a shrewd spirit of revenge. After this library incident we see Joan at the St. James' vicarage, and meet the rector, Mr. Morris—a quiet, kindly man. Joan's mother thinks highly—very highly —of him; and perhaps (but she never says so, she is so reserved) Mrs. Brandon is not quite happy at home; perhaps she doesn't think so highly of the archdeacon as that handsome autocrat thinks of himself; indeed, she is secretly miserable beyond endurance. Mr. Morris shows Joan the fine view of the cathedral from his upper windows——

"I don't like it," said Joan, turning away. "It doesn't care what happens to us."

"Why should it?" he answered. "Think of all it's seen—the battles and the fights and the plunder—and it doesn't care! We can do what we like and it will remain the same."

"People could come and knock it down," Joan said.

"I believe it would still be there if they did. The rock would be there and the spirit of the cathedral. . . What do people matter beside a thing like that? Why, we're ants. . . ! I think I know what you mean about fearing it. . . . Well, good-bye," he said smiling. "Come again."

"I like him," thought Joan as she walked away.

Brandon quickly surmounts the shock of Falk's unexpected return. But misfortunes do not as a rule come singly. His next annoyance is strangely humorous—for so dignified a man. His top-hat is seized by an elephant's trunk during the progress of a circus procession through the town. This is a tremendous indignity. There is much talk about this unfortunate incident; not a little quiet laughter. However, important matters push this unpleasant episode into the background. There is Ronder, for instance; he is becoming unduly popular; Brandon feels that here is a man who will test his mettle. The first battle is waged over a trifle, shall the Chapter provide a roller for the school cricketground? Brandon is against it; Ronder is for it—in fact, he has gone into the financial aspects of this important question. The voting is even; the dean is afraid that it falls to him to give a casting vote; he thinks that Canon Ronder has made out his case—the first time for many years that Brandon has met with defeat; he gathers his papers, and looking neither to the right nor the left he strides from the room. Ronder tactfully tries to make this victory a peaceful—at least a friendly—one. "Really there is nothing to discuss, Canon," says Brandon. "Talking things over won't help us."

WHAT is Falk doing during this time? He is not at home much; he has rather despised his sister; is rather indifferent to his quiet, homely mother; quite indifferent to his father, contemptuous of the cathedral and all its works, past, present and to come. Seatown attracts him; not its bad drainage, or bad living, or bad dying. Nor is the "Dog and Pilchard," kept by that jovial but rather queer man Hogg, the attraction. But Hogg's rather handsome daughter is. He cannot resist that spell. She does not encourage him; but there is a shadow of cruelty hanging over the jolly-looking "Dog and Pilchard,"—father Hogg is not so kind as he looks. Annie is for London—and freedom. If—if Falk will take her, well and good; but if not, never mind, she will go alone and fight her own battle. She is straight, and knows there are distinctions—but she loves him. He is far better than she had supposed—he is tender, warm-hearted, to be trusted. He had realized her unhappiness:

"No one else in this place seemed to notice it. I believe God meant us to be friends, meant me to bring you happiness."

"Happiness?" she shivered. "Isn't it cold tonight? Do you see that strange green cloud? Ah, now it is gone. All the light is going. . . . Do you believe in God?"

He came closer to her. His hand touched her arm. "Yes," he answered, fiercely. "And He means me to care for you." She did not move. . . . He bent forward and kissed her neck, her mouth, her eyes.

Jubilee

A.D. 1897 was the great Jubilee year of the Great Little Queen. Polchester was, of course, excessively loyal. The programme had long been arranged; the great Service in the Cathedral, the Ball in the Assembly Rooms, the Flower Show in the St. Leath Castle grounds, the Croquet Tournament, the Torchlight Procession. Arrangements progressed slowly; but just about this time tongues began to wag quickly—of course, no one really liked scandal, and this wasn't scandal—there was nothing in it—but a lady, Miss Stiles (quite remarkable for her deeds of charity) had noticed the oddest looks exchanged between Mrs. Brandon and—who d'you think—Mr. Morris. Of course, it was nothing. Mrs. Combermere said Miss Stiles had a nasty mind: "People can't even look at one another now. Why, you might as well say that I had been gazing at your Ronder when he came to tea the other day." "Perhaps I shall," said Miss Stiles, laughing.

Still, it so happened that on a Sunday morning the archdeacon was disturbed to find his wife in a strange mood—so ill—almost speechless, that she could not —would not—attend early service.

"There's your mother—I am bothered about her," said the archdeacon to Falk. "Have you noticed anything odd about her the last week or two?"

"Mother? No; in what way?"

"She's not herself. She's not happy. She's worrying about something."

"You're worrying, father. She's all right. Father, what would you say if I went up to London?"

"London? What for?"

"Oh, to do something, to get something to do."

"Not now—we'll talk about it in the autumn—" and he hummed "Onward Christian Soldiers," as he always did, a little out of tune. He went to the window and looked out on the green. "There are two of those choir boys on the grass again. If Ryle doesn't keep them in better order——"

The last talk of their lives together was ended.

Within a few days Falk is in London, and Annie is with him. With the news, a little later, of their marriage, they pass out of the tale. We are never taken for a moment away from Polchester, we never leave the shadow of the cathedral —except once, and that is to have lunch with the sweet-natured old bishop—he is nearly ninety. The shadow follows us even there, and mingles with the sunshine of the bishop's charming retreat at Carpledon; Brandon's visit is designed to influence the election of the archdeacon's pet candidate for the vacancy at Pybus—a living always regarded as a stepping-stone to diocesan preferment. Brandon flattered himself that he could twist the dear old bishop round his little finger—providing that no one else is there to spoil the ecclesiastical sport of catching the archdeacon's selected numbskull.

No sooner has the aged white-locked butler opened the door, and announced that his lordship will be down in a minute, than Brandon hears a footstep behind him, and turning round he sees—of all men—Ronder. Ronder was disastrous. Evidently that rubicund and smiling canon has caught wind of this visit; evidently he means to cut the ground from under Brandon's feet. The archdeacon's fingers twisted within one another as he considered how pleasant it would be to wring someone's ecclesiastical neck. Ah! he could have made the way smooth for his pet, Forsyth, one of the old, steady-going school. And who is the rival, backed by Ronder? A man named Wistons. "What!" cries Brandon, when he hears the name mentioned (oh! quite casually) by Ronder during this pleasant little ecclesiastical lunch: "What! The fellow who wrote that abominable book, The Four Creeds?" Ronder, rubbing his knees gently, thinks. Yes, it is the same. "That man! That atheist! The leading enemy of the Church! The man who would destroy every institution the Church possesses?"

On the way back to Polchester, riding in the dear bishop's little wagonette, Brandon and Ronder nearly come to blows. Indeed, Brandon climbs out—excited, distracted. A pain like a sword darts through his head, just like an active personal enemy. Why had God done this thing? He felt old, and sick, and weak.

As he trembled up the hill an enemy seemed to dog his footsteps.

The talk arising out of this unfortunate affair is drowned in the excitement of the great celebrations of Polchester loyalty. Ronder is uneasy at the turn events have taken; a little uneasy, also, as to whether he is quite wise in backing Wistons so heavily; perhaps, for the present, Brandon is enough to look after. As for Brandon, what does this man Hogg —Annie's disreputable parent (what a disgraceful connexion!)—mean by following him about? And that loafing, idle, drunken artist, Davray, who is always sketching and painting in the cathedral? Why are these things allowed? How dare Hogg speak to him! How dare Davray lecture *him* on the beauties of that great building! The chaste proprieties of the precincts invaded by these dark, sodden creatures from Seatown, indeed! "The cathedral is sick of you and your damned conceit, and is going to get rid of you, too!" Davray had said that to him—to Archdeacon Brandon!

How lonely he felt; the great Service at the Cathedral, the frail old bishop's sermon—his last, doubtless, in his long life—passed before his eyes like a dream. And the Ball at the Assembly Room; his pretty daughter Joan like a dream, fading away out of his life; and his wife, what's the matter with her? How ill he feels; he would die, were it not for Joan's faithful devotion—so faithful that, seeing the tragedy gathering round the old home, Joan has whispered to Johnny: "Hush! my darling boy—you must *wait!*" So Brandon wanders about, finds himself at the Fair Grounds among the waxworks and swings.

And then a terrible thing happens; in the throng he is attacked and badly mauled by Hogg and Hogg's confederates. Hogg calls him—him! "the villain whose son has ruined his daughter." He reaches home bruised, ill. Worse, that wretched Miss Milton, ex-librarian, has got hold of a letter from his wife to Morris:

Dearest. i am sending this by a safe hand to tell you that I cannot possibly get down to-night. I will explain everything when we meet to-morrow.

Of course, it is only by chance that this letter has fallen into Miss Milton's hands. For conscience sake she has taken it to Canon Ronder; naturally, too, she would like to obtain his advice on so delicate a subject. The canon's dictum is explicit —Burn it! Her principles revolt at the idea of so weak an action; so she lays it before the archdeacon's eyes; of course he can destroy it if he likes; but there are so many wickednesses going on in the town—well, her conscience—oh yes; she had shown it to Canon Ronder, and *he* had advised her to show it to the arch-deacon. But is it in his wife's handwrit-ing? Brandon thinks it is not, and Miss Milton is aware of the penalties for forgery? Penal servitude. Miss Milton smiles; she only requires full investiga-tion; she has only done her duty; she wishes him good-evening.

It is late when he reaches home that evening, for he has been to the good bishop, and the good bishop has given him spiritual advice. The ways of God are mysterious; even he, the bishop, had once upon a time lost all faith in God; had come out of that dreadful darkness believing only in the beauty of Christ's life. "Look up, my son; bear this with patience. God is standing at your shoul-der. This trouble is training for you." Strange peace came to Brandon's heart, not from the old man's words so much as from the touch of his thin, frail hand. Ronder was of little importance, after all. The cathedral faded.

Mrs. Brandon was in bed, staring straight in front of her. He wanted to have a talk with her; she has been un-happy; he wanted the trouble cleared away so that they can be as they were before. Before! The irony of it! Falk's going must have made her miserable. No; she is just tired, as she was that morning when she couldn't attend the Holy Communion. No; it won't do; peo-ple are talking—

"Some one brought me a letter, Amy. They said it was a letter of yours."

She did not move or stir. Then—"Let me see it—to whom do you suppose it was written?"

"To Morris of St. James'."

She nodded her head. "Ah yes, we're friends. Of course, it's a forgery; a very clever one. You have enemies, you know that; they are jealous."

"One enemy," he replied, "Ronder. The woman has been to him with this letter."

"What woman?"

"Miss Milton."

"And she had been with this letter to Canon Ronder before she came to you?"

"Yes."

"Ah!" Then she said very quietly, "And what do you mean to do about this letter?"

Whatever she wishes; but he would like to bring the wretches to justice. But what good can it do to follow it up, she asks.

Oh, to get away from this scan-dalous town!

"And we will," he cried eagerly. "Give me that letter; I'll destroy it."

She gave him the letter. "Look at it before you tear it up," she said, staring at him as though she would not miss any change in his features. "You are sure it *is* a forgery?"

"Why, of course."

"Nothing like my handwriting?"

"Nothing at all."

"Look well at that letter. You are wrong. It is not a forgery. I did write it."

Yes, it was true, she loved Morris, had loved him from the first moment she saw him. She had been unfaithful to her husband. At first Morris wouldn't. But she would; she had hated Brandon for years.

Then Brandon's hands met round her throat, and his knees were over her; then suddenly his eyes recognized hers; his hands dropped, he crawled from the bed; then felt his way blindly from the room.

The Last Stand

Mrs. BRANDON fades away from the scene, and the shade of Morris disappears with her. The great Jubilee week is over, and Canon Ronder has come through it magnificently. He is firmly established now as the leading man in Polchester; if only the Pybus living goes the right way he will have nothing more to wish for. Wistons is not quite the ascetic mixture of Dante and Savonarola expected by Ronder—at any rate, in looks. He is indeed thin, but he is little, almost deformed; his face is positively ugly, redeemed, however, by splendid and penetrating eyes. And he is going to have no nonsense about this appointment; he knows that there is opposition, and he will have no false pretences. He knows that there is a battle waging between the older, more conservative body of opinion, and the more modern school.

But did Ronder really think him the best man? An impertinent question, perhaps—and Ronder really thinks it *is* impertinent. Ronder had been so pleased with himself up to this point that a pleasant vision of distributing pennies to all the children in his immediate neighbourhood had been floating through his mind. For a time this pretty picture becomes clouded; still, no doubt, Wistons is the right man; he honestly thinks so. Of course, Brandon is a splendid fellow, and has done splendid work for the Church, but now he is behind the time, out of date, too obstinate to change. Besides, certain family misfortunes have hit him hard, and his health, alas, is not what it was.

"I want you to understand the kind of man I am, Canon Ronder, before you propose me for this post," said Wistons. "I come, if I come at all, to fight the cathedral—that is, to fight everything in it, round it, about it, that prevents men from seeing clearly the figure of Christ. I believe, Canon Ronder, that before many years are out it will become clear to the whole world that there are now two religions—the religion of authority and the religion of the spirit—and if in such a division I must choose, I am for the religion of the spirit every time."

"Exactly!" said Ronder, suddenly turning his eyes full on Wistons. "The Christian Church has made a golden calf of its dogmas. The calf is worshipped, the cathedral enshrines it."

Before the Chapter meets to decide the Pybus appointment the archdeacon deals out one strong blow straight from the shoulder—but not an ecclesiastical blow; one straight on the jaw of Hogg, whom he encounters in the High Street. It only remains now for him to put up a final fight for the cathedral—and himself. But, still physically strong under excitement, he is breaking down under the mental strain of the events of a few weeks. Indeed, it is hardly expected that he will be present at this historic meeting.

But he comes; careworn, but with the old important look. But not so confident. He apologises for being late; his watch, he fears. The meeting opens with prayer, and Brandon's head remains bowed longer than the others. Then to business. Pybus and its incumbent is an important matter in this diocese; everyone knows that. Certain names have been proposed; the two most favourably considered by the Chapter are those of the Rev. Rex Forsyth, chaplain to Bishop Clematis, and the Rev. Ambrose Wistons, of St. Edwards, Hawston. The first gentleman is known to most of the Chapter; the second is known chiefly through his writings.

WILL Canon Ronder say something? Yes; but the canon is some minutes—or it seems so—before he can say very much. The ghastly white face of Brandon is watching him—yet, what had he done that he could have left undone? Wistons is the man: ". . . our cathedral, that we all so deeply love, is waiting for just such a man. Then—although his opinions are not precisely those . . ." Brandon was staring at his long, nervous fingers. He speaks without looking up—almost in a whisper come broken words. Horrified—horrified at this acceptance of a man who is a declared atheist before God! "Yes, gentlemen—I am not very well. I have learnt many things under God's hand in the last six months. He has shown me some weaknesses and failings. But—have you read this man's books. Do you know that he questions the Divinity of Christ Himself?"

There is interruption; that is not true. Well, if they will only give him time, he will prove everything. Do not decide hastily. The dean, very gently, points out that the living has been vacant for some months; they must decide now.

"You against me. Every man's hand is now against me. Nevertheless, what I say is right and true . . . I have seen God, I have walked with God, I shall walk with him again. He will lead me out of these sore distresses and take me into green pastures. . . ."

The rain drizzles thick on the panes; the room is so dark that lights are called for. They are grateful to the archdeacon for what he has done. Any further name suggested? None. Pens and paper are put before everyone present; the little voting slips are slowly unrolled and counted. "One vote has been recorded for Mr. Forsyth, the rest for Mr. Wistons." Brandon was on his feet at once. "No—no——. Oh, God, help me now!" He fell, and in a minute was dead.

◆

THE WEAKER SEX

DANIEL GEARHART had just settled his bride in a log cabin on the edge of town, when the Revolution broke out. He embraced her, saying, "I shall return to thee soon. Meanwhile, fear not, and trust in God." Susan shed a few tears, and Daniel seized his musket and went out.

For three weeks Susan performed her daily tasks, prayed frequently, and in the evening by candlelight read a bit in her Bible.

On a Saturday evening she sat at the window watching the dusk change to darkness, when she looked up and saw a hand, quite evidently masculine, moving slowly over the window ledge. Susan made not a sound, but thought, "All the faith in the world will not stop that hand

from coming farther"; reaching up, she took down the hatchet from the wall. She neatly chopped off the fingers of the hand, slammed the casement shut, and barred it. Then, motionless for a moment, she listened, but heard nothing. She swept up things and retired without her usual prayer.

Sunday morning a shadow fell across the doorway and Susan looked up into the eyes of her husband. She went to him, and again two tears rolled down her cheeks. Daniel wiped them away and shook his head, saying: "What a pity thou art not made of stronger stuff! Man must always fight while woman sits at home and weeps."

Susan kissed him.

—JANE E. YOUNGMAN

JULIA PETERKIN

SCARLET SISTER MARY

JULIA PETERKIN was born in Laurens County, South Carolina, attended Converse College at Spartanburg, from which she holds A.B., A.M., and D.Litt. degrees. She married a South Carolinian and lives now on Lang Syne Plantation, Fort Motte, South Carolina. Her books for the most part deal with plantation negroes. "Scarlet Sister Mary" was awarded the Pulitzer Prize in 1928.

Mary's Wedding Day

MARY'S wedding-day had dawned, but instead of being up at first fowl crow and running around helping Maum Hannah get everything ready, she lay still on her bed in the shed room, thinking, pretending to sleep.

Mary was happy over her wedding. God knew she had loved July all of her life; yet, when she thought of leaving Maum Hannah and Budda Ben and this kind old house where she had been born and where she had spent most of her life, something inside her breast ached. Finally Sister Mary stood up and slipped out of her night-gown, which dropped near to the pot Maum Hannah was stirring. Mary laughed and stretched out her long slim body until every muscle was taut. What did she care if Maum Hannah saw her buck naked now when she had seen her so a thousand times?

Maum Hannah was leaning forward with her eyes blinking and gazing as if they could not see quite clearly. She was searching Mary's body from head to foot, marking each line, each curve, as if something astonished and distressed her. Her piercing eyes cut into Mary's heart.

"May-e, you an' July is been a-havin sin, enty?"

It fell so sorrowfully, with such pity, that Mary hung her head low. She could not even say, "Yes."

Maum Hannah shook her head.

"Why couldn' you wait for de preacher to read out de book over you

an' make you July's lawful wife? Lawd, gal, I'm dat sorry, I could pure cry like a baby. I could, fo-true. Some sin is black, an' some ain' so black, but dis sin you had is pure scarlet."

Mary sat on the floor speechless. Here, on her wedding-morning, all the joy in the world was gone. She wanted to be good. She tried to be kind, never to hurt anything or anybody; yet she had become a sinner because she loved July so much. And the worst of it was that Maum Hannah had found it out.

As the wedding-time drew near, the house and yard were jammed with people. July came, all clean shaved, with a fresh haircut, dressed up in fine new clothes his brother June's money bought him. No man on earth ever had a handsomer body or one so supple and straight and strong. Mary's second cousin, Cinder, had tried hard to get him, but she was not the bride, thank God.

Mary's voice was low and husky when she answered, "I will," but July spoke clear and loud and ahead of time. Everybody laughed when Reverend Duncan gave Mary a sudden smacking kiss. The ceremony was over and July was her lawful wedded husband, until Death came to part them. Then the people surged forward to kiss the bride and groom; to wish them joy and a gal and a boy.

MARY had kissed everybody there and answered every greeting with some pleasant word. Her feet, unaccustomed to shoes, had begun to ache, but the crowd was thinning out. Most of the people were going down the street to a leaning old house where the sinners had dances. The big drum was beating and calling everybody to come on to a dance and hot supper which Cinder was having there.

July loved to dance and pleasure himself, and even on his wedding-day he hated to miss any fun. This was no time to be thinking of hurting feet or weariness. She was a church-member and she could not dance, but she could eat rice and hash and drink some of the sweetened water.

Every corner was packed tight and the walls were lined with onlookers, but a place was quickly made for the bride and groom. Cinder came up and murmured something to July who smiled brightly at her, then said to Mary, "I'll be right back, honey, as soon as I lead off dis set wid Cinder. You wait here till I come."

Instead of leading the dance off and then stepping right back to stand beside Mary, July danced on. He must have forgotten what he was doing. Cinder clung to him and her small eyes were sparkling as she glanced sidewise at Mary. Cinder was shameless to keep July dancing when his lawful wife had to stand by the wall. Cinder cared nothing for what anybody thought of her. She was showing Mary she could make July pleasure himself even on his wedding night.

MARY had not seen June, July's brother, until she felt a hot hand on her shoulder, and he whispered in her ear. "Come on, Si May-e, dance a set wid me. Le's show de people how you an' me can take all de shine off o' July an' Cinder."

She could feel her body yielding. She placed her hands on her hips and with a laugh stepped out into the firelight. July watched her with a look that she had never seen before. Without looking up she knew that all the people were staring at her watching every move. All of them were marveling that she had fallen into sin on her wedding-night.

The crowd seized Mary and held her fast, but July fought for her bravely until he had her tight in his arms, and gathering her up off her feet, cleared a way through the jam of people and hurried down the street through the darkness. He soon had her home with the door shut and barred behind them.

Unexpected

THE days ran swiftly and happily. They spent many a happy evening together in front of the fire whose pleasant gleam was bright enough to let them see each other. Mary had been turned out of the church, but when July praised her housekeeping she could hardly have been happier, for July's smiles meant more to her than God or Jesus or any hope of Heaven.

Cinder had gone away to town on the riverboat, not very long after the wedding. A good thing. Not that July would ever look at Cinder again or at any other woman on earth but Mary.

July laughed when he noticed her growth, and warned her to have a boy-child. No girl-child for him. He had a lot of projects to carry out when he got a little money ahead, and he would need a son to help him. Mary laughed back and promised, and happiness filled her heart.

One morning while she was hurrying home from Grab-All, where she had been to buy a few more lengths of cloth to finish some of her baby's clothes, a terrible spasm of pain seized her body. It scarcely passed before it came back and seized her again, tearing her bones and sinews apart, fairly cutting at her very heart-strings. Lord, how scared she was! She cried for help as loud as she could, but nobody was in hearing distance, and her child was born right there in the middle of the road. The poor little creature set up such a pitiful wailing that she had to forget her own troubles and pick him up and wrap him in her apron and hurry home to Maum Hannah.

The old woman shook her head and looked very stern. "Dis child ain' no seven months' child. Look at de hair on his head. 'E got toe-nails an' finger-nails good as my own. You might could fool de people, but you can' fool me, gal, an' you can' fool God."

But what if she had been married only half a year? What difference did it make? July was her lawful, wedded husband, now, and her baby's father. What more could they ask?

July was as pleased as he could be.

He hurried to Grab-All for the castor oil Maum Hannah said Mary must have and he not only brought back a jug of whiskey for everybody to take a drink, but a piece of fine cloth for a dress for Mary. He named his son Unexpected. Mary had never heard that name before, but July explained to her that it meant coming as a great surprise. The baby had done that very thing. They would call him Unex for short; a nice name, a pleasant-sounding name.

Blessed little Unex, a better baby never came into the world. Happiness filled Mary's heart. Life was full of joy.

Trouble Catches Her

Night fell and the baby had gone back to sleep, but July had not come home. Mary drew the pots a little farther away from the fire so the food they held would not scorch or become dry. One by one the houses grew dark and silent, tears rolled out of her eyes and fell in her lap. July had forgotten her. A puff of cool air pushed in with him when he opened the door. Mary sniffed it softly for a faint scent of Cinder's perfume came with it on July's clothes. Anger stirred her. "Whe you been? What de matter ail you? Worryation kills me. Whyn' you tell me you was gwine off an' not a-comin' home?"

Mary could not tell if he heard her or not for he made no sign that he did. Then he straightened up. "Nuttin' ain' de matter ail me. I been in de woods shootin' a little crap, dat's all. You ought not to quarrel if I pleasure myse'f a lil."

"I can smell de stench o' Cinder's scent on you, so you needn' lie to me. I ain' no fool. I got some sense—some sense—"

July shrugged. "If you got so much sense, whyn' you bank de fire last night? E's dead as a wedge. Now I got to go borrow a piece from somebody to hotten me some victuals to eat."

Mary wept quietly for she could think of no words to tell July how hurt she

was, how utterly grieved at the way he was doing her now. She'd forgive him if he would only come and sit on the bed beside her and hold her hand and ask her pardon. But he didn't. He ate some food and left her without saying good-by.

Mary was unhappy, restless, disturbed, uncertain what to do. She must make up her mind to something for she could not go on any longer pretending she did not feel things that were breaking her heart.

Today, instead of being noisy and gay with fun, the plantation quarters were silent as on Sunday. Everybody who could raise the price of a round-trip ticket had gone to town, on the Saturday excursion. Instead of staying at home with her and the baby, July had gone on the excursion and left them behind, all by themselves. He could have taken them along and found them no trouble for the baby was as good as gold. But he said women and babies were better off at home, and they had no business gallivanting around on excursions.

The baby, Unex, was six months old today, yet he was able to creep across the floor and say things that sounded like words. He had more teeth than he was due to have and his head was covered with crinky little wool. The baby's eyes fairly danced whenever July came near him, and July's funny motions and talk made him shriek out with pleasure.

But now, in spite of Unex's nice ways, July had gone off on the excursion and Mary was down-hearted and weary.

The people in the quarters were careful what they said when she was around, but she was not blind or deaf. She knew more than they thought. She was no fool.

When she married July everybody said she was the prettiest bride that ever stepped in the quarters. Now she was withered and ugly with no way to stop being so. Trouble had caught her as a cat catches a mouse.

Saturday passed, then Sunday. All the excursion people were back home except July and Cinder and nobody knew what had become of them or where they had gone. Mary was so miserable she scarcely knew what to do.

ON MONDAY morning, Maum Hannah came in for a talk. Jesus was the onliest one who could help Mary now. Nobody else could. Nobody else.

"You ax Jedus to help you to forgive Cinder. Gawd is a strange Gawd. You better pray to Him instead o' frettin so hard fo July. Stead o' lookin down, you better look up. Git out and work. Sweat some evy day. It'll help you to shed a lot o' misery."

Maum Hannah declared she was wasting her life, losing her friends and her health and everything else she had left. Even if July had tricked her and broken her heart, she was not the first woman to have her heart broken by a low-down man. She would not be the last either. The best thing she could do was to put July clean out of her mind.

When she had finished she said very kindly, "Now, Si-Maye, I'm a done-talk woman. I hope I ain' wasted my breath."

Mary tried to smile and to sound brave as she answered, "No, Maum Hannah you ain' wasted em. I know good an' well what you say is de Gawd's truth. I know I ain' doin right. I'm gwine to learn to smoke. Smokin will help me to stop bein so nervish an' down-hearted."

She would learn to rule herself. She would not let another tear fall.

After Maum Hannah had left, Mary was startled by a deep voice: "Si May-e—" Her heart leaped into her throat, it sounded so much like July. "Dis is me, June. If you needs anyting, any time, please call on me."

"Tank you kindly, June," she answered huskily.

As he sat beside her the narrow step creaked with his weight. Mary couldn't talk, and they sat silent until June had cleared his throat.

"I doubt if July is gwine to get away from Cinder anytime soon, Si May-e. I draws wages and rations too, evy Sat'day. I ain' got a soul but myself and I'd give em to you if you'll take em."

"Tank you kindly, June." She slipped a hand through his big arm next to her cheek against his shoulder. "Plenty o willin gals in de quarters, June. Whyn' you marry one an' settle down an' have a home o' you own."

June turned and looked in Mary's eyes. "I'd been a-married an' settled down long time ago if I could a had my way. But July got my gal." He spat and sighed deep. "What is done is done. I'm gwine off on the boat dis evenin."

She rested her fingers on his shouder. "June," she said in a voice that was husky and low, "Please don' go. Seems like if you was to leave home, I couldn' hardly stand it."

"Den, I'll stay, Si May-e. I didn' know you'd feel so bad about my gwinen."

Mary Gets to Know Men

FIFTEEN years passed and although everything on the plantation looked much the same, many changes had crept in. The pots on Mary's hearth were al-ways full; a flock of hens clucked and cackled around her door and greens kept her vegetable garden lively.

Food was plentiful, but money was

scarce, for the cotton-fields which had always provided enough for outside needs were cursed with the most terrible pest the plantation had ever known.

For a few years June struggled on trying to fight weevils and make a crop. But fall after fall came and found him with nothing to show for his whole year's work. He got discouraged and gave up and went away to find something else to do. He could not write so no letter ever came to tell Mary where he went or what he was doing.

Unex had grown up tall like July. At last he gave up too and left to find better work, and easier money somewhere out in the world. Only God knew if he was alive or not.

Mary had reared every child she had brought into the world, for she knew how to start them off right. Her house was full of them, little and big, but Unex was her only lawful child.

She was able to laugh and dance and sing again, her flesh had got back its old smoothness, her old sadness and weariness and bitterness were left behind. Thank God, she knew men at last, and she knew that not one of them is worth a drop of water that drains out of a woman's eye.

Once, long ago, she used to think that Cinder was a mean, low-down hussy, but now she knew Cinder was not to blame for July's sins. Cinder's heart got broken too, for July left her to run off with another woman. Deep down in Mary's heart she thanked God for all the other strong men that were in the world. July was not the only one. And June wasn't either.

As the years passed life seemed to divide most of the people Mary knew into two groups; men and women; and the women were all her rivals and competitors, except Maum Hannah. Even

her oldest girl child, Seraphine, was pitted against her for the first place in the heart of Budda Ben.

WHEN Mary first began sinning openly, Budda Ben tried his best to stop her, then when he found that nothing he said made her change her ways, he began defending her and holding that whatever people crave to do is good for them to do. If Mary fed her children and clothed them and trained them to be brave-hearted, to work, and to have manners, that was enough to expect of her. She was not a member of any lodge or society or church, and she had a right to live her own life as she liked.

Mary was the best woman on the plantation. She understood folks. She had sympathy for them. She knew their needs and sufferings and forgave their mistakes because she knew that blunders are easy to make. Her children were not full kin, but they grew up together in peace as brothers and sisters of one family, working, pleasuring, growing up strong and more able than any lawful children in the quarters.

The quarter women muttered dark things about Mary and prophesied dark things for her. They feared the little charm she wore around her neck—the love-charm Old Daddy Cudjoe had given her to make her powerful over men.

Hard work had kept Mary lean and hard muscled. She was still keen-eyed and erect while they were paunchy in the middle and saggy in the cheeks. If getting men, taking them from their rightful owners, had been hard work she would never have bothered about it; but it was such an easy thing. All she had to do was to wear that little charm around her neck and they came a-runnin.

"Who Birthed Dis Baby?"

"LAWD, we had a time!" Mary said to Maum Hannah when all was over. Then she looked at two new-born sons and said gently, "De pain hit me so hard,

I couldn't pray not to save my life! No Jedus!"

Mary and the new-born babies were in the big room bed. Mary was too tired

Illustration for Julia Peterkin's
"SCARLET SISTER MARY"

even to talk to Seraphine who had un-expectedly come to the landing on the boat that afternoon. Maum Hannah was mortified for the girl to find Mary like this. She had been away with fine town people trying to make something of her-self, while her mother lived in sin. Mary ought to quit her ways. She had a daugh-ter almost grown now.

Gradually Maum Hannah's dronings tapered off and she settled down to sleep a little. She had hardly dozed when something roused Mary. She opened her eyes and peered through the dim light at her two babies. They were sound asleep. But certainly she had heard a baby's voice. One had waked her.

Maum Hannah sighed, then turned in her chair suddenly. She heard a baby too and she was not dreaming. Mary was sure it was in the room but Maum Hannah waited to hear it again. Some-thing strange was in that corner by the shed-room door.

Maum Hannah leaned and picked up something, then she hurried to the fire with it.

"Great Gawd! What is dis?"

Mary jumped up out of bed herself.

"Fo Gawd's sake, Auntie, who had dat baby?"

"Gawd knows, gal. I found em in dat corner."

Mary took the child in her arms. The two women looked at each other. Whose child was this girl-child?

"May-e—you reckon you could-a had dis chile an' didn't know?" Maum Hannah suggested.

"No, Jedus, when I birth chillen, I know it. Mebbe you had em, Auntie."

"Shut you mout', Si May-e, don' gi' me none o you' slack talk! Whose baby is dis?"

"I declare to Gawd, Auntie, e ain' my own. But three ain' no worse dan two. E's a fine child, Auntie. Git someting to wrop em up in."

Mary lay back down, and Maum Hannah covered her up with the three babies.

"Auntie, go in de shed room an' see

if Seraphine is wake," Mary whispered. "Wake em all up."

"Don' make dem lil chillen come, May'e, not dem boy-chillen. Dey so sleepy," Maum Hannah interceded.

Mary reflected a moment, then called sternly. "Evy one got to come! You Seraphine come stand close to dis bed. You low-down no-manners gal. You gone an' had a gal-child right here in my house, an' den lay down in de bed and make out it my own! I good mind to lick you till I scorch you gown-tail."

Seraphine denied most positively any knowledge of the extra child. "E ain' my own," Seraphine declared. "I know e ain' my own."

A good long sleep calmed Mary's anger, and the morning light showed that the girl-child was the prettiest one of the babies. Mary began feeling as proud of it as she was of her boys.

Seraphine woke with a fearful tooth-ache. Her throat was sore, too, and Mary made her stay in the house while the ground was so wet.

MARY mended fast and before long she was her strong able self. Every morning she thanked God that she was well again, and that the babies were all three thriving.

Not a soul in the whole world but Maum Hannah knew that the nice little girl-baby was not Mary's own. It was a nice little child. Seraphine ought to be proud of it.

Seraphine listened with a solemn face, tears began pouring out of her eyes. Mary put both arms around her and drew her up close.

"Now, honey, don' cry so hard. Si May-e loves you just de same as e ever did."

Instead of helping, this kind of talk made Seraphine cry more. So she tried different talk. She drew her arms away and stood Seraphine on her feet. "Look at me, gal. You think I don' know what ails you? I do. You ain' frettin because you done wrong. No. You's frettin be-cause one o' dem town mens tricked you

and dropped you. You is a fool. It don'
pay to love no one man too much. It's
all right to like em. But don' never let
yousef think on one man all de time.
It'll run you crazy if it don' kill you."

Seraphine was almost crying, yet ready
to smile again, as she gave Mary a hug.

"Si May-e, you's de best ting ever wa
yes, you is. I love you too good, S
May-e."

"I'm glad, honey, I need a lot o' lovin
Now, le's go home and milk de cow ar
de goat an' give all dem babies a goo
supper."

A Lonely Soul Climbs Home

LATE that night Sister Mary sat down
to smoke one last pipeful before
she went to bed. It was good to be under
shelter with all the children well and
safe and out of the cold black rain. Lord,
what a night!

She looked up at the enlarged picture
of Unex hanging on the wall. How much
like July he was. The same high bony
forehead and full eyes, the same broad
mouth. If the picture could talk, it might
tell her where he was, how he was; then
she could be happy and satisfied. But it
could only stare and stay dumb.

Somebody stumbled up the steps and
made a loud knock and called, "Si May-e,
is you home? Do, fo Gawd's sake, open
de door. Dis is me, Unex, Si May-e. Do
le me in—"

Mary dropped the door-bar. Her brain
felt addled, her knees shook, she could
not speak a word. She took off his hat
and pushed his head back and stroked
his chin cheeks. "Whe in Gawd's world
is you come from, son? Put you bundle
down an' get off dem wet clothes."

Unex held tight to his wet bundle with
both his arms and smiled a slow sad
smile. "Dis is a present I brought you,
Si May-e! Look at em and see how you
like em."

Unex bent over it saying, "Is you
wake, Emma? Look, Si May-e. E's you
gramma, honey."

Mary shifted her weight unsteadily
from one knee to the other. "Who had
em for you son?" she whispered.

"E mammy is dead, Si May-e," the boy
answered simply. "I couldn' raise em
mysef."

Mary brushed her tears away and
patted Unex's shoulder briskly. "Gi me
de child, son. Po lil creeter. Put some

wood on de fire. I bet dis baby i
hungry as e only can be."

The news of Unex's arrival sprea
with speed, and all the quarter peopl
hastened to greet him and bid him wel
come home. Everybody brought some
thing; the cabin table was full of goo
things, but he ate nothing. Unex crave
no food, he wanted cool spring water
not sweetened water or hot table tea
Soups and gruels and smelly high-sea
soned food made him retch.

Mary's heart turned cold. Unex wa
sick. His body was hot, his hands an
feet were cold. His eyes burned red, a
oil lamps burn just before they go out

He lay gazing at her, his big pitifu
eyes asking dumbly for help. She mus
not let him see how sad she felt, tha
would be against him. She must smile
and be cheerful, make him believe h
would soon be well.

Day after day melted into long black
night, and Unex grew steadily worse
An agony of dread chilled her every time
she leaned low to hear his whispered
words, for his breath had the faint swee
smell that always comes ahead of Death

For all her trying and loving and
pleading with God to leave him here
with her, he went. God knew he wa
the only heart-child she had. The others
were the fruit of eye-love, the children
of her flesh, yet they were strong and
hearty; but her joy-child was gone.

Grief smothered her. She hurried out
side and looked up at the sky where her
precious child's soul was wandering
about seeking its way to Heaven and
God. The stars were pale and dim, poo
lamps to light a lonely soul climbing tha
steep road trying to find the long way
home.

Mary is Reborn

SLEEP must have fallen heavily on her for she saw her own soul, walking in and out among the pines trying to find the way home. It was dark and a high wind from the sea lashed the tree-tops. Unex called her, but when she turned her head to find him she saw an open grave. Her naked soul stepped down into it. Unex spoke:

"Looka dat white cloth on de ground."

There it was, right at her feet and there were ten stripes, red like blood across the width of the white cloth.

"You see dem stripes on de cloth, enty, Si May-e?" he said, weeping. "Dem scarlet stripes is Jedus' blood. Every sin you had laid a open cut on Jedus' back. You had nine chillen, enty, Si May-e?"

"All was born in sin, enty?"

She bowed her head low. But she had only nine children. Why were there ten stripes?

"Seraphine had a sin child, Si May-e. Gawd holds you responsible for Seraphine's sin. You set de pattern and Seraphine followed em. You is to blame."

Mary knew that Unex spoke the truth.

"Prayin is all de hope you got so pray widout ceasin until dem stripes come clean and you soul gets white as snow."

The grave melted, Unex was gone.

Voices called to her all through the long night, but she did not answer them. She could not as long as that cloth lay there striped with Jesus' blood. In her misery she rolled over and over on the ground, her fists beat on her head and breast, but the stripes stayed pure scarlet.

She must try some other plan or she would die unforgiven. Maybe if she took them one sin at a time, that would help. She began with Unex, her first scarlet sin and prayed for it until that stripe slowly faded and was finally gone.

Next, Seraphine's stripe was changed into whiteness. One by one all the stripes were gone and the cloth became shining and beautiful. It was white as snow. Whiter than snow, and so shining her eyes could not face it.

THE deacons appointed Wednesday night for Mary to come and give in her experience and they invited all the people to hear them decide if her vision meant that her sins were forgiven, or if Satan had sent a dream to deceive her.

Before first dark she dressed herself carefully in a new black and white checked homespun dress and a large white apron which covered the whole front of her skirt. Should she wear her charm? Would it be sinful to wear it to-night? The deacons were men who needed to be ruled in her favor tonight.

When the hymn was sung, Brer Dee read out of the Book how the angels in Heaven rejoice over one sinner who repents; then he prayed a short prayer.

When Mary got to her feet to speak, the room grew so quiet she could hear her own quickened breath. She could feel how eagerly the people listened, how they leaned forward trying not to miss a word she said.

Brer Dee listened eagerly too, but when she finished, he got to his feet and said solemnly, "Brudders an' sisters, Si May-e has been a turrible sinner. E has sent many mens to Hell. His soul might be clean but his body ought to be baptized again befo we receives em into Heaven's Gate Church."

The deacons talked on and on, the members said what they thought. Most of them agreed that Brer Dee was right; Mary should be baptized again. Mary bowed her head meekly and said she was willing.

Meeting was over and the people came up to welcome Mary back into the fold.

Old Daddy Cudjoe came last.

"If you gwine to quit wid mens now, Si-Maye, do gi me you love-charm. E's de best charm I ever made."

Mary looked straight into his eyes and smiled as she shook her head.

"I'll lend em to you when you need em, Daddy, but I couldn't gi way my love-charm. E's all I got now to keep me young."

Booth Tarkington

SEVENTEEN

W HEN he first received the Pulitzer Prize in 1919, Booth Tarkington's name was well-known to American readers, young and old, for a trilogy of novels based on Middle-Western youth: "Penrod" (1914), "Penrod and Sam" (1916), and "Seventeen" (1916). All the realism, sensibility for the tender years, and the whimsy of this novelist and dramatist delight us in "Seventeen." Now, in his seventieth year, Booth Tarkington will see this story reproduced on the screen.

William

W ILLIAM SYLVANUS BAXTER paused for a moment of thought in front of the drug-store at the corner of Washington Street and Central Avenue. He had an eternal question to settle before he entered the store. Finally he decided upon chocolate and strawberry, mixed, before approaching the fountain. Once there, however, and a large glass of these flavors and diluted ice-cream proving merely provocative, he said, languidly—an affectation, for he could have disposed of half a dozen with gusto: "Well, now I'm here, I might as well go one more. Fill 'er up again. Same."

Emerging to the street, penniless, he bent a fascinated and dramatic gaze upon his reflection in the drug-store window, and then, as he turned his back upon the alluring image, his expression altered to one of lofty and uncondescending amusement. That was his glance at the passing public. From the heights, he seemed to bestow upon the world a mysterious derision—for William Sylvanus Baxter was seventeen long years of age, and learned to present the appearance of one who possesses inside information about life and knows all strangers and most acquaintances to be of inferior caste, costume and intelligence.

He lingered upon the corner a while, not pressed for time. Indeed, he found many hours of these summer months heavy upon his hands, for he had no important occupation, unless some intermittent dalliance with a work on geometry (anticipatory of the distant autumn) might be thought important, which is doubtful, since he usually went to sleep on the shady side porch at his home, with the book in his hand. So, having nothing to call him elsewhere, he lounged before the drug-store in the early afternoon sunshine, watching the passing to and fro of the lower orders and bourgeoisie of the middle-sized mid-land city which claimed him (so to speak) for a native son.

He was roused by the bluff greeting of an acquaintance not dissimilar to himself in age, manner, and apparel.

"H'l, Silly Bill!" said this person, halting beside William Sylvanus Baxter. "What's the news?"

W ILLIAM showed no enthusiasm; on the contrary, a frown of annoyance appeared upon his brow. The nickname "Silly Bill"—long ago compounded by merry child-comrades from "William" and "Sylvanus"—was not to his taste, especially in public, where he preferred to be addressed simply and manfully as "Baxter."

"Don't know any," William replied, coldly.

"Dull times, ain't it?" said Mr. Watson, a little depressed by his friend's manner. "I heard May Parcher was comin' back to town yesterday. They said she was goin' to bring a girl to visit her," Johnnie began in a confidential tone. "They said she was a reg'lar ringdinger and—"

"Well, what if she is?" the discouraging Mr. Baxter interrupted. "Makes little difference to me, I guess. I never saw one in my life I'd care whether she lived or died!"

"Honest?" asked Johnnie, struck by the conviction with which this speech was uttered. "Why I didn't know you felt that way about 'em, Silly Bill. I always thought you were kind of—"

"Well, I do feel that way about 'em!" said William Sylvanus Baxter, and, outraged by the repetition of the offensive nickname, he began to move away. "You can tell 'em so for me, if you want to!" he added over his shoulder. And he walked haughtily up the street, leaving Mr. Watson to ponder upon this case of misogyny, never suspected.

The Unknown

WILLIAM, meanwhile, made his way toward the "residence section" of the town, and presently—with the passage of time—found himself eased of his annoyance. He walked in his own manner, using his shoulders to emphasize an effect of carelessness which he wished to produce upon observers. For his consciousness of observers was abnormal, since he had it whether any one was looking at him or not, and it reached a crucial stage whenever he perceived persons of his own age, but of opposite sex, approaching.

A person of this description was encountered upon the sidewalk within a hundred yards of his own home, and William Sylvanus Baxter saw her while yet she was afar off. The thoroughfare was empty of all human life, at the time, save for those two; and she was upon the same side of the street that he was; thus it became inevitable that they should meet, face to face, for the first time in their lives.

He had perceived even in the distance, that she was unknown to him, a stranger, because he knew all the girls in this part of town who dressed as famously in the mode as that! And then, as the distance between them lessened, he saw that she was ravishingly pretty; far far prettier, indeed, than any girl he knew. At least it seemed so, for it is, unfortunately, much easier for strangers to be beautiful.

His heart—his physical heart—began to do things the like of which, experienced by an elderly person, would have brought the doctor in haste. In addition, his complexion altered—he broke out in fiery patches. He suffered from breathlessness and from pressure on the diaphragm. He felt that his agitation was ruinous and must be perceptible at a distance of miles, not feet. And then, in the instant of panic that befell, when her dark-lashed eyelids slowly lifted, he had a flash of inspiration.

HE OPENED his mouth somewhat, and as her eyes met his, full and startlingly, he placed three fingers across the orifice, and also offered a slight vocal proof that she had surprised him in the midst of a yawn.

For the fraction of a second, the deep blue spark in her eyes glowed brighter—gentle arrows of turquoise shot him through and through—and then her glance withdrew from the ineffable collision. But just at the moment when he and the lovely creature were side by side, and her head turned from him, she spoke —that is, she murmured, but he caught the words.

"You Flopit, wake up!" she said, in the tone of a mother talking baby-talk. "So indifferink!"

William's feet and his breath halted spasmodically. For an instant he thought she had spoken to him, and then for the first time he perceived the fluffy head of the dog bobbing languidly over her arm, with the motion of her walking; and he comprehended that Flopit, and not William Sylvanus Baxter, was the gentleman addressed. But—but had she *meant* him?

" '*So* indifferink' " murmured William. And, repeating the honeyed word, so entrancingly distorted, he fell into a kind of stupor; vague, beautiful pictures rising before him, the one least blurred being of himself, on horseback, sweeping between Flopit and a racing automobile.

And then having restored the little animal to its mistress, William sat carelessly in the saddle (he had the Guardsman's seat) while the perfectly trained steed wheeled about, forelegs in the air, preparing to go. "But shall I not see you again, to thank you more properly?" she cried, pleading. "Some other day—perhaps," he answered.

And left her in a cloud of dust.

Mr. Baxter's Evening Clothes

THAT evening, at about half-past seven o'clock, dinner being over and Mr. and Mrs. Baxter (parents of William) seated in the library, Mrs. Baxter said:

"I think it's about time for you to go and dress for your Emerson Club meeting, papa, if you intend to go."

"Do I have to dress?" Mr. Baxter asked, plaintively.

"I think nearly all the men do, don't they?" she insisted.

"But I'm getting old enough not to have to, don't you think mamma?" he urged, appealingly. "When a man's my age—"

"Nonsense." she said. "Your figure is exactly like William's. Go along like a good boy and get it over!"

Mr. Baxter rose submissively and went upstairs to do as he was bid. But, after fifteen or twenty minutes, he called down over the banisters.

"I can't find my evening clothes. They aren't anywhere in the house."

"Where did you put them the last time you wore them?" she called.

"I don't know. I haven't had 'em on since last spring."

"All right; I'll come," she said, putting her sewing upon the table and rising. "Men never can find anything," she observed. "Especially their own things!"

On this occasion, however, as she was obliged to admit a little later, women were not more efficacious than the duller sex. Search high, search low, no trace of Mr. Baxter's evening clothes were to be found. "Perhaps William could find them," said Mrs. Baxter, a final confession of helplessness.

But William was no more to be found than the missing apparel. William, in fact, after spending some time in the lower back hall, listening to the quest above, had just gone out through the kitchen door. After some ensuing futile efforts, Mr. Baxter was forced to proceed to his club in the accountrements of business.

He walked slowly, enjoying the full moon, which sailed up a river in the sky—the open space between the trees that lined the street—and as he passed the house of Mr. Parcher he noted the fine white shape of a masculine evening bosom gleaming in the moonlight on the porch. A dainty figure in white sat beside it, and there was another white figure present, though this one was so small that Mr. Baxter did not see it at all. It was the figure of a tiny doglet, and it reposed upon the black masculine knees that belonged to the evening bosom.

Mr. Baxter heard a dulcet voice.

"He is indifferink, isn't he, sweetest Flopit? Seriously, though, Mr. Watson was telling me about you today. He says you're the most indifferent man he knows. He says you don't care two minutes whether a girl lives or dies. Isn't he a mean old wicked sing, p'eshus Flopit!"

The reply was inaudible, and Mr. Baxter passed on, having recognized nothing of his own.

"These young fellows don't have any trouble finding their dress-suits, I guess," he murmured. "Not on a night like this."

Jane

Mrs. Baxter was pleasantly engaged with a sprinkling-can and some small flower-beds in the shady back yard, and her daughter, Jane, having returned from various sidewalk excursions, stood close by as a spectator, her hands replenished with bread-and-butter and apple sauce, sprinkled with powdered sugar. Upon this calm scene came William, plunging round a corner of the house, furious yet plaintive.

"You've got to do something about that child!" he began. "I cannot stand it!"

Jane looked at him dumbly, not ceasing however, to eat; while Mrs. Baxter thoughtfully continued her sprinkling.

"You've been gone all morning, Willie," she said. "I thought your father mentioned at breakfast that he expected you to put in at least four hours a day on your mathematics and—"

"That's neither here nor there," William returned, vehemently. "*Look* at her, I ask you! That's just the way she looked half an hour ago, out on the public sidewalk in front of the house, when I came by here with Miss Pratt! That was pleasant, wasn't it? To be walking with a lady on a public street and meet a member of my family looking like that!"

In the anguish of this recollection his voice cracked, and though his eyes were dry, his gestures wept for him. Plainly, he was about to reach the most lamentable portion of his narrative. "And then she *hollered* at me! She hollered, 'Oh, *Will-ee!*' Here he gave an imitation of Jane's voice, so damnatory that Jane ceased to eat for several moments and drew herself up with a kind of dignity.

"She hollered, 'Oh, Will-ee,' and she rubbed her stomach and slushed apple sauce all over her face, and she kept hollering, 'Will-ee.' with her mouth full. 'Will-ee, look! Good! Bread-and-butter and apple sauce and sugar! I bet you wish you had some Will-ee!' "

Mrs. Baxter laughed. "I really don't think people notice—"

" 'Notice!' " he wailed. "I guess Miss Pratt noticed! She wanted to know who 'that curious child' was, and I had to tell her that it was only my *sister.*"

"Willie, who is Miss Pratt?" asked Mrs. Baxter, mildly. "I don't think I've ever heard of—"

Jane had returned to an admirable imperturbability, but she chose this moment to interrupt her mother, and her own eating, with remarks delivered in a tone void of emphasis or expression.

"Willie's mashed on her," she said casually. "And she wears false side-curls. One almost came off."

At this unspeakable desecration William's face was that of a high priest stricken at the altar.

"She's visitin' Miss May Parcher," added the deadly Jane. "But the Parchers are awful tired of her. They wish she'd go home, but they don't like to tell her so."

One after another these insults from the *canaille* fell upon the ears of William. He became icily calm. "*Now* if you don't punish her," he said, deliberately, "it's because you have lost your sense of duty!"

Having uttered these terrible words, he turned upon his heel.

Little Sisters Have Big Ears

"What made you say that" Mrs. Baxter asked Jane curiously. "Where did you hear such things?"

"At the Parchers. I ate too many cookies at the Sunday-school class party and Miss Parcher said I better lay down—"

"Lie down, Jane!"

"Yes'm. On the sofa in the library, and Mrs. Parcher an' Mr. Parcher came in there an' sat down, and they didn't hardly notice me, or I guess they thought I was asleep, maybe. Mr. Parcher said he wished he knew when he was goin' to have a home again. Then Mrs. Parcher said May had to ask her Sunday-school class, but he said he never meant the Sunday-school class.

"He said since Miss Pratt came to visit, there wasn't anywhere he could go, because Willie Baxter an' Johnnie Watson an' Joe Bullitt an' all the other ones like that were there all the time, an' it made him just sick at the stummick, an' he did wish there was some way to find out when she was goin' home, because he couldn't stand much more talk about love.

"An' he said the reason they were all so in love of Miss Pratt was because she talks baby-talk, an' he said he couldn't stand much more baby-talk. Mamma, she has the loveliest little white dog, an' Mr. Parcher doesn't like it. He said he couldn't go anywhere around the place without stepping on the dog or Willie Baxter. An' he said he couldn't sit on his own porch any more; he said he couldn't sit even in the liberry but he had to hear baby-talk goin' on somewheres an' then either Willie Baxter or Joe Bullitt or somebody or another arguin' about love. Mamma, he said"— Jane became impressive—"he said, mamma, he said he didn't mind the Sunday-school class, but he couldn't stand those dam boys!"

"JANE!" Mrs. Baxter cried, "you mustn't say such things!"

"I didn't, mamma. Mr. Parcher said it. He said he couldn't stand those da—"

"Jane! No matter what he said, you must never again use such a terrible and wicked word."

"I won't, mamma," Jane said, meekly. Then she brightened, "Oh, I know! I'll say 'word' instead. Won't that be all right?"

"I—I suppose so."

"Well, Mr. Parcher said he couldn't stand those word boys. That sounds all right, doesn't it, mamma?"

Mrs. Baxter hesitated, but she was inclined to hear as complete as possible a report of Mr. and Mrs. Parcher's conversation, since it seemed to concern William so nearly and she well knew that Jane had her own way of telling things— or else they remained untold.

"I—I suppose so," Mrs. Baxter said again.

"Well Mr. Parcher said when he was young he wasn't any such a—such a word fool as these young word fools were. He said in all his born days Willie Baxter was the wordest fool he ever saw."

Willie Baxter's mother flushed a little. "That was very unjust and very wrong of Mr. Parcher," she said, primly.

"Oh no, mamma!" Jane protested. "Mrs. Parcher thought so, too. Only she didn't say word or wordest or anything like that," Jane explained. "She said it was because Miss Pratt had coaxed him to be so in love with her; an' Mr. Parcher said he didn't care whose fault it was, Willie was a—a word calf an' so were all the rest of 'em, Mr. Parcher said. He said he guess' pretty soon he'd haf to be in the lunatic asylum if Miss Pratt stayed a few more days with her word little dog an' all the other word calfs.

"Mrs. Parcher said he oughtn't to say 'word,' mamma. She said, 'Hush, hush!' to him, mamma. He talked like this mamma: he said, 'I'll be word if I stand it!' An' he kept gettin' crosser, an' he said 'Word! Word! Word! WOR—'"

"There." Mrs. Baxter interrupted, sharply. "That will do, Jane! We'll talk about something else now, I think."

The Truth Will Out

THE confidential talk between mother and daughter at noon was not the last to take place that day. At nightfall Jane was saying her prayers while her mother stood close by waiting.

"An' bless mamma and papa an'—' Jane murmured, coming to a pause. "An —an' bless Willie," she added, with a little reluctance.

"Go on, dear," said her mother.

"I know it, mamma," Jane looked up to say, "I want to tell you about somep'm."

"Finish your prayers first, Jane."

Jane obeyed with a swiftness in which there was no intentional irreverence. Then she jumped into bed and began a fresh revelation.

"It's about papa's clo'es, Mamma. His evening clo'es. Willie's got 'em on."

"What!"

"Yes, he has!" Jane assured her with emphasis. "I bet you he's had 'em on every single evening since Miss Pratt come to visit the Parchers! Anyway, he's got 'em on now, 'cause I saw 'em."

Mrs. Baxter bit her lip and frowned. "Are you sure, Jane?"

"Yes'm. I was in my bare feet after I got undressed—before you came upstairs—mamma, an' I was kind of walkin' around in the hall—"

"You shouldn't do that, Jane."

"No'm. He was standin' up there in papa's clo'es before the lookin'-glass, an' first he'd lean his head over on one side, an' then he'd lean it over on the other side, an' then he'd bark, mamma."

"He'd what?"

"Yes'm!" said Jane. "He'd give a little, teeny bark, mamma—kind of like a puppy, mamma. He said, 'Berp-werp. Berp-werp-werp!' You could tell he meant it for barkin', but it wasn't very good, mamma. What do you think he meant, mamma?"

"Heaven knows!" murmured the astonished mother.

"I think he was kind of pretendin' he was talkin' to Miss Pratt, or at a party, maybe. Anyways, he spoke out loud after while—not just exactly loud, I mean, but anyway so's I could hear what he said. Mamma—he said, 'Oh, my baby-talk lady!' just like that, mamma. Listen, mamma, here's the way he said it: *'Oh, my baby-talk lady!'*" cooed the terrible Jane.

Jane's voice, in this impersonation, became sufficiently soft and tremulous to give Mrs. Baxter a fair idea of the tender yearning of the original.

"Mercy!" Mrs. Baxter exclaimed. "Perhaps it's no wonder Mr. Parcher—" She broke off abruptly, then inquired, "What did he do next, Jane?"

"Next," said Jane, "he went out to the back stairs, an' went down the stairs tiptoe, mamma. You know what I think, mamma? I think he goes out that way an' through the kitchen on account of papa's clo'es."

Mrs. Baxter paused, with her hand upon the key of the shaded electric lamp. "I suppose that we better keep this a secret between you and me for a little while, Jane, and not say anything to papa about the clothes."

"Yes'm."

Mrs. Baxter turned out the light, then came and kissed Jane in the dark. "Good night, dear."

Mr. Parcher and Love

JANE might almost have been gifted with clairvoyance, for at that very moment William was barking. He was not barking directly at Mr. Parcher, it is true, but within a short distance of him and all too well within his hearing.

"Berp-werp! Berp-werp!" came the voice of William Sylvanus Baxter.

And in the library "Plutarch's Lives" moved convulsively, while with writhing lips Mr. Parcher muttered to himself.

"More, more!" cried Miss Pratt, clapping her hands. "Do it again, ickle-boy Baxter!"

"Berp-werp! Berp-werp-werp!"

"*Word!*" muttered Mr. Parcher.

Miss Pratt's voice became surcharged with honeyed wonder. "How did he learn such marv'lous, *marv'lous* imitation of darlin' Flopit? He ought to go on the big-big stage, and be a really actor, oughtn't he darlin' Flopit? He could make milyums and milyums of dollardies, couldn't he, darlin' Flopit?"

William's modest laugh disclaimed any great ambition for himself in this line. "Oh, I always could think up imitations of animals; things like that—but I hardly would care to—to adop' the stage for a career. Would—you?" (There was a thrill in his voice when he pronounced the ineffably significant word "You.")

"It is my *dream!*" she said.

"You would make a glorious actress!" he said.

AT THAT the mood changed. She laughed a laugh like a sweet little girl's laugh (not Jane's) and, setting her rocking-chair in motion, cuddled the fuzzy white doglet in her arms. "Ickleboy Baxter t'yin' flatterbox us, tunnin' Flopit! No'ty, no'ty flatterbox!"

"No, no!" William insisted earnestly. "I mean it. But—but—"

"But whatcums?"

"What do you think about actors and actresses making love to each other on the stage? Do you think they have to really feel it, or do they just pretend?"

"Well," said Miss Pratt, weightily, "sometimes one way, sometimes the other."

William's gravity became more and more profound. "Yes, but how can they pretend like that? Don't you think love is a sacred thing?"

"Ess," said Miss Pratt. "Do Flopit again. Be Flopit!"

"Berp-werp! Berp-werp-werp."

And within the library an agonized man writhed and muttered:

"Word! Word! WORD!"

This hoarse repetition had become almost continuous.

BUT out on the porch, that little, jasmine scented bower in arcady where youth cried to youth and golden heads were haloed in the moonshine, there fell a silence. It was William who broke the silence. "How—" he began, and his voice trembled a little. "How—how do you—how do you think of me when I'm not with you?"

"Think nice-cums," Miss Pratt responded. "Flopit an' me think nice-cums."

"No," said William; "I mean what name do you have for me when you're—when you're thinking about me?"

Miss Pratt seemed to be puzzled, perhaps justifiably, and she made a cooing sound of interrogation.

"I mean like this," William explained. "F'rinstance, when you first came, I always thought of you as 'Milady'"

"Ess. Boo'fums."

"But now I don't," he said. "Now I think of you—I call you—'My Baby-Talk Lady.'"

Bang!

They were startled by a crash from within the library; a heavy weight seemed to have fallen (or to have been hurled) a considerable distance. Stepping to the window, William beheld a large volume lying in a distorted attitude at the foot of the wall opposite to that in which the reading lamp was a fixture. But of all human life the room was empty; for Mr. Parcher had given up and was now hastening to his bed.

Beginning a True Friendship

MR. PARCHER was walking home from his office the next day and he walked slowly, gulping from time to time. As he approached the dwelling he had once thought of as home, he became aware of a little girl in a checkered dress approaching him. Mr. Parcher looked upon her, and he shivered slightly; for he knew her to be Willie Baxter's sister.

Unaware of the emotion she produced in him, Jane halted. "G'd afternoon, Mister Parcher," she said gravely.

"Good afternoon," he returned, without much spirit.

"My brother Willie's been at your house all afternoon," she remarked.

He repeated, "I suppose so," but in a tone which combined the vocal tokens of misery and of hopeless animosity.

"My brother Willie isn't comin' back to your house tonight, but he doesn't know it yet."

"What!" exclaimed Mr. Parcher, gazing fixedly at the wonderful child, and something like a ray of sunshine flicker ing over his seamed and harried face. "Are you *sure* he isn't? What makes you think so?"

"I know he isn't," said demure Jane. "It's on account of somep'm I told mamma."

And upon this a gentle glow began to radiate through Mr. Parcher. A new feeling budded throughout Mr. Parcher. A new feeling budded within his bosom; he was warmly attracted to Jane. She was evidently a child to be cherished, and particularly to be encouraged in the line of conduct she seemed to have adopted.

"He'll come in the afternoons, I guess," said Jane. "But you aren't home then, Mr. Parcher, except late—like you were that day of the Sunday-school class. It was on account of what you said that day. I told mamma."

"Good heavens!" Mr. Parcher, summoning his memory, had placed the occasion and Jane together. "Did you hear all that?"

"Yes." Jane nodded. "I told mamma all what you said."

"Murder!"

"Well," said Jane, "I guess it's good I did, because look—that's the very reason mamma did somep'm so's he can't come any more except in daytime."

"What? What did she do?"

"It's a secret," said Jane "I could tell you the first part of it—up to where the secret begins, I expect."

"Do!" Mr. Parcher urged.

"WELL, it's about somep'm Willie's been wearin'," Jane began, moving closer to him as they slowly walked onward. "I can't tell you what they were, because that's the secret—but he had 'em on him every evening when he came to see Miss Pratt, but they belong to papa. The secret was gettin' a little teeny bit too tight for papa and mamma said she

guessed it was already pretty loose for Willie; so she wrapped it up, an' I went with her, an' we took 'em to a tailor, an' she told him to make 'em bigger, for a surprise for papa, 'cause then they'll fit him again. I guess Willie would look too funny in 'em after they're fixed; and' anyway, Mr. Parcher, the secret won't be home from the tailor's for two weeks, an' maybe by that time Miss Pratt'll be gone."

They had reached Mr. Parcher's gate; he halted and looked down fondly upon this child who seemed to have read his soul. "Jane," said Mr. Parcher, "I should like to do something for you."

Jane looked down, and with eyes modestly lowered she swallowed the last fragment of the bread-and-butter and apple sauce and sugar which had been the constantly evanescent companion of their little walk together. She was not mercenary; she had sought no reward.

"Well, I guess I must run home," she said. And with one lift of her eyes to his and a shy laugh, she scampered quickly to the corner and was gone.

Jane did not appear at the table the next evening. "Poor child! she's sick in bed," Mrs. Baxter explained to her husband. "I was out, this afternoon, and she ate a five-pound box of candy."

Both the sad-eyed William and his father were dumbfounded. "Where on earth did she get a five-pound box of candy?" Mr. Baxter demanded.

"I'm afraid Jane has begun her first affair," said Mrs. Baxter. "A gentleman sent it to her."

"What gentleman?" gasped William.

And in his mother's eyes, as they slowly came to rest on his in reply, he was aware of an inscrutability strongly remindful of that inscrutable look of Jane's.

"Mr. Parcher," she said, gently.

Foreshadowings

Now the last rose had blown; the dandelion globes were long since on the wind; gladioli and golden-glow and salvia were here; and the season moved

toward asters and golden rod. The haloed summer still idled on its way, yet all the while sped quickly; like some languid lady in an elevator.

Then came a Sunday—very hot.

Mr. and Mrs. Baxter, having walked a scorched half-mile from church, drooped thankfully into wicker chairs upon their front porch. For a time, the two were content to sit in silence, nodding to occasional acquaintances who passed in the desultory after-church procession. But as a group of five young people passed along the other side of the street Mr. Baxter abruptly stopped fanning himself, and, following the direction of his gaze, Mrs. Baxter ceased to rock.

"My soul!" said William's father. "Hasn't that girl gone home yet?"

"You mean Miss Pratt?" she inquired dreamily, her eyes following the progress of her son.

"Look at that boy!" the father grumbled. "Mooning along with those other moon-calves—I wonder how many weeks of time, counting it out in hours, he's wasted that way this summer. My soul! What do they say?"

"I think she is going soon," said Mrs. Baxter. "The Parchers are to have a dance for her Friday night."

"That's one mercy, anyhow."

"And if you wonder what they say," she resumed. "Well what does anybody say? Jane for instance,—she's always fascinated by that darky, Genesis, when he's at work here in the yard, and they have long, long talks. If you went out to the back porch you'd find them talking steadily—but what on earth about I couldn't guess to save my life!"

And yet nothing could have been simpler; as a matter of fact Jane and Genesis were talking about society—specifically of the *beau monde*.

"Yes'm," said Genesis. "Now I'm in 'at Swim—flyin' roun' ev'y night wif all lem blue vein people—I say, Mus' go buy me some blue-vein clo'es! 'Nen I got me this here suit o' clo'es—*oh,* oh! Sign on 'em in window: 'Ef you wish to be bes'-dress' man in town take me home for six dolluhs ninety-sevum cents.' 'At's kine o' suit Genesis need,' I say. 'Ef Genesis go'n' a start dressin' high, might's well start top!'"

Jane nodded gravely, comprehending the reasonableness of this view. "What made you decide to start, Genesis?"

"Well, suh, I'z waitah for Fanny, the kaytliss now an' I roun' right in amongs' big doin's mos' ev'y night. Yes'm. But ain' got no mo' kaytun till nex' Friday even."

"Oh, I bet that's the party for Miss Pratt at Mr. Parcher's!" Jane cried. "Didn't I guess right?"

"Yes'm. I reckon I'm a go'n' a see one of you fam'ly 'at night."

"Oh, Willie's invited," said Jane. "Only I think maybe he won't go." She told him about Willie and his father's evening clothes and concluded: "Willie's been gettin' paler and paler everyday since he heard about the party. Mamma says he's pale some because Miss Pratt's goin' away, but she thinks it's a good deal more because, well, if he could wear those evening clo'es just to go callin', how would it be to go to that party an' not have any!"

Genesis chuckled. "They's a secon'-han' sto' ovuh on the avynoo, where they got swaller-tail suits all way f'um sevum dolluhs to nineteem dolluhs an' ninety-eights cents. I'm a—"

Jane started, interrupting him. "'Sh!" she whispered, laying a finger warningly upon her lips. William had entered the yard and arrived at the steps of the porch before Jane perceived him. She gave him an apprehensive look, but he passed into the house absent-mindedly.

"I guess he didn't hear us," said Jane, when he had disappeared into the interior.

She was mistaken in part. William had caught no reference to himself, but he had overheard something and he was now alone in his room, thinking about it almost feverishly.

"A secon'-han' sto' ovuh on the avynoo, where they got swaller tail suits all way f'um sevum dolluhs to nineteem dolluhs and ninety-eight cents."

As Jane had so precociously understood, unless he could somehow manage to obtain the proper draperies he could not go to the farewell dance for Miss Pratt. Other unequipped boys could go in their ordinary "best clothes," but William could not; for alack! he had dressed too well too soon!

He was in desperate case.

He had pleaded strongly for a "dress-suit" as a fitting recognition of his seventeenth birthday anniversary, but he had been denied by his father with a jocularity more crushing than rigor. The harried self of William was no longer debating a desperate resolve, but had fixed upon it.

Clothes Make the Man

Mrs. Baxter was troubled. During the following Friday afternoon she glanced often from the open window of the room where she had gone to sew, but the peaceful neighborhood continued to be peaceful, and no sound of the harassed footsteps of William echoed from the pavement. However, she saw Genesis arrive to do some weeding, and Jane immediately skip forth for mingled purposes of observation and conversation.

After an exciting half-hour Jane came flying to her mother, breathless. "Mamma," she cried, "I know where Willie is! Genesis told me, 'cause he saw him an' he talked to him while he was doin' it."

"Doing what? Where?"

"Willie's sittin' in a lumber-yard that Genesis comes by on his way from over on the avynoo where all the colored people live—an' he's countin' knot-holes in shingles. Every time he comes to a bad shingle, mamma, he puts it somewheres else, or somep'm like that, mamma, an' every time he's put a thousand bad shingles in this other place, they give him six cents. That's what he's been doin' all day!"

"Good gracious!"

"Oh, but that's nothing, mamma—just you wait till you hear the rest. *That* part of it isn't anything a *tall*, mamma."

"I want to know everything Genesis told you," said her mother, "and I want you to tell it as quickly as you can."

"Yes'm Genesis knows all about a second hand store over on the avynoo: an' it keeps 'most everything. It keeps waiter suits all the way up to nineteen dollars and ninety-nine cents.

Well, an' Genesis wants to get one of those suits, so he goes in there all the time. The man that keeps the store name's One-eye Beljus, mamma. This morning One-eye Beljus showed Genesis Willie's name written down in this book, an' One-eye Beljus asked Genesis if he knew anybody by that name an' all about him. One-eye Beljus said Willie came in there an' tried on the coat of one of those waiter suits.—"

"Oh no!" gasped Mrs. Baxter.

"Yes'm, an' One-eye Beljus said there was only one suit that would fit Willie and the suit was worth fourteen dollars, an' Willie said he didn't have any money, but he'd like to trade something else for it. Willie said he'd go an' get everything that b'longed to him, an' One-eye Beljus could pick out enough to make fourteen dollars' worth, an' then Willie could have the suit. Well, an' so Willie came home an' put everything he had into those two baskets mamma—that's just what he did.

"An' he told One-eye Beljus to pick out fourteen dollars worth an' One-eye Beljus ast Willie if he didn't have a watch. Well, Willie took out his watch, an' One-eye Beljus said it was an awful bad watch, but he would put it in for a dollar: and One-eye Beljus said that he would take all the things in the baskets and the watch and that would leave just three dollars an' sixty cents more for Willie to pay before he could get the suit."

Mrs. Baxter's face had become suffused with high color but she wished to know all that Genesis had said, and, mastering her feelings with an effort, she told Jane to proceed—a command obeyed after Jane had taken several long breaths.

"Well, an' so the worst part of it is,

Genesis says, it's because that suit is haunted."

"What!"

"Yes'm," said Jane, solemnly: "Genesis says it's haunted. Genesis says everybody over on the avynoo knows all about that suit, an' he says that's why One-eye Beljus never could sell it to a colored man for three dollars, but the man said he wouldn't put it on for three hundred dollars. It's cause it belonged to a Dago waiter that—that—took a case-knife he'd sharpened—*an' he cut a lady's head off with it!*"

Mrs. Baxter screamed faintly.

"An' he got hung, mamma! An' he sold this suit to One-eye Beljus when he was in jail. He sold it to him before he got hung, mamma."

"Hush, Jane!"

But Jane couldn't hush now. "An' he had that suit on when he cut the lady's head off, mamma, an' that's why it's haunted. They cleaned it all up excep' a few little spots of bl—"

"That will do!" Mrs. Baxter's voice was sharper than it had ever been in Jane's recollection. "I don't need to hear any more—and I don't want to hear any more!"

Jane was justly aggrieved. "But, mamma, it isn't my fault!"

Mrs. Baxter's lips parted to speak, but she checked herself. "Fault?" she said, gravely. "I wonder whose fault it really is!"

Three quarters of an hour later she was unburdening the contents of the two baskets and putting the things back in place, illuminating these actions with an expression of strong distaste—in spite of broken assurances that Mr. Beljus had not more than touched any of the articles offered to him for valuation.

Masculine Cinderella

WILLIAM had retired to his own room after dinner, where he lay upon his bed in the darkness. He heard the evening noises of the house faintly through the closed door: his father seemed to be in distress about something. William heard him complaining to Mrs. Baxter, and though the words were indistinct, the tone was vigorously plaintive. Mrs. Baxter laughed and appeared to make light of his troubles, whatever they were—and presently their footsteps were audible from the stairway; the front door closed emphatically, and they were gone.

As he lay on his dreary bed he thought of brightly lighted rooms where other boys were dressing eagerly, faces and hair shining, hearts beating high—boys who would possess this last evening and the "last waltz together," the last smile and the last sigh.

It did not once enter his mind that he could go to the dance in his "best suit," or that possibly the other young people at the party would be too busy with their own affairs to notice particularly what he wore. It was the unquestionable and granite fact, to his mind, that the whole derisive World would know the truth about his earlier appearances in his father's clothes. And that was a form of ruin not to be faced.

In the protective darkness and seclusion of William's bedroom it is possible that smarting eyes relieved themselves by blinking rather energetically; it is even possible that there was a minute damp spot upon the pillow. Seventeen cannot always manage the little boy yet alive under all the coverings.

Now arrived that moment he had most painfully anticipated, and dance-music drifted on the night—but there came a tapping upon his door and a soft voice spoke.

"Will-ee! I haf to tell you a joke on mamma."

"I don't want to hear any jokes."

"Well, I haf to tell you this one 'cause she told me to."

"I don't care if—"

"Papa went in his regular clothes to the card-party," whispered Jane triumphantly. "An' this is the joke on mamma: you know that tailor that let papa's dress-suit 'way, 'way out; well, mamma thinks the tailor must think she's crazy, or somep'm, 'cause she took papa's dress-suit to him last Monday to get it pressed for this card-party, and she guesses he must of understood her to tell him to do lots besides just pressin' it. Anyway, he went an' altered it, an' he took it 'way, 'way in again; an' this afternoon when it came back it was even tighter in what it was in the first place, an' papa couldn't begin to get into it! Well, an' so it's all pressed and ev'ything and it's layin' right on her bed this very minute!"

In one bound William leaped through the open door. Two seconds sufficed for his passage through the hall to his mother's bedroom—and there, neatly spread upon the lace coverlet and brighter than the coronation robes, fairer than Joseph's holy coat, It lay!

As a hurried worldling, in almost perfectly fitting evening clothes, passed out of his father's gateway and hurried toward the place whence faintly came the sound of dance music, a child's voice called sweetly from an unidentified window of the darkened house behind him:

"Well, *anyway*, you try and have a good time, Willie!"

William made no reply but Jane's friendly but ill-chosen "anyway" touched doubts already annoying him. He was certain to be late to the party—so late, indeed, that it might prove difficult to obtain a proper number of dances with the sacred girl in whose honor the celebration was being held.

His apprehensions fell away, and a glamorous excitement took their place, as he turned a corner and the music burst more loudly upon his tingling ear. Spellbound groups of uninvited persons, most of them colored, rested their forearms upon the upper rail of the Parchers' picket fence, offering to William's view a silhouette like that of a crowd at a fire.

Upon one of the posts there rested the elbow of a contemplative man, middle aged or a little worse. Of all persons having a pleasure of business within the bright inclosure, he was, that evening, the least important; being merely the background parent who paid the bills. However, even this unconsidered elder shared a thought in common with the Augustan now approaching. The preoccupying subject was the imminence of Miss Pratt's departure; neither Mr. Parcher nor William forgot it for an instant. No matter what else played upon the surface of their attention, each kept saying to himself, underneath: "This is the last night—the last night! Miss Pratt is going away—going away tomorrow!"

The unuttered words advanced tragically toward the gate in the head of William at the same time that they moved contentedly away in the head of Mr. Parcher; for Mr. Parcher caught sight of his wife just then, and went to join her as she sank wearily upon the front steps.

"They all seem to want to dance with her all the time," said Mrs. Parcher. "I heard her telling one of the boys, half an hour ago, that all she could give him was either the twenty-eighth regular dance or the sixteenth 'extra.'"

"The what?" Mr. Parcher demanded, whirling to face her. "Do they think this party's going to keep running till day after tomorrow?" And then, as his eyes returned to the group on the platform, "that Baxter boy seems to have quite a touch of emotional insanity," he remarked "What is the matter with him?"

"Oh, nothing," his wife returned. "Only trying to arrange a dance with her. He seems to be in difficulties. Look at him there."

Nothing could have been more evident than William's difficulties. He couldn't stand it, he told himself, even if he wanted to—not tonight! He had "been through enough" in order to get to the party and now he couldn't get a dance with Miss Pratt. Now that he was here he would dance and dance, on and on, with Miss Pratt. Anything else was unthinkable. He *had* to.

Marooned

"DON'T you want to dance?" said Mrs. Parcher coming up to him. "You come with me I'll fix you up."

Mrs. Parcher conducted him across the yard to a girl sitting alone by a tree. "Miss Boke, this is Mr. Baxter," said Mrs. Parcher, and she added, with what seemed to William hideous garrulity, "He and you both came late, dear, and he hasn't any dances engaged, either. So run and dance, and have a nice time together."

He had to give form to the fatal invitation. "M'av this dance 'thyou?" he muttered, doggedly.

"Vurry pleased to!" Miss Boke responded, whereupon they walked in silence to the platform, stepped upon its surface, and embraced.

They made a false start.

They made another.

She was a large, ample girl, weighing more than William (this must be definitely claimed in his behalf), and she had been spending the summer at a lakeside hotel where she had constantly danced "man's part." To paint William's predicament at a stroke, his partner was a determined rather than a graceful dancer—and their efforts to attune themselves to each other and to the music were in a fair way to attract general attention.

"Oh, you mustn't be discouraged with yourself," said Miss Boke, genially. "I've met lots of Men that had trouble to get started and turned out to be right good dancers, after all. It seems to me we're kind of workin' against each other. I'll tell you—you kind of let me do the guiding and I'll get you going fine. Now! One, *two,* one, *two!* There!"

William ceased to struggle for dominance, and their efforts to "get started" were at once successful. With a muscular power that was surprising, Miss Boke bore him out into the circling current, swung him round and round, walked him backward half across the platform, then swung him round and round again.

More than once he tried to assert himself and resume his natural place as guide, but each time he did so he immediately got out of step with his partner, their knees collided embarrassingly, they staggered and walked upon each other's insteps—and William was forced to abandon the unequal contest.

"I just love dancing," said Miss Boke, serenely. "Don't you, Mr. Baxter?"

"What?" he gulped. "Yeh."

"It's a beautiful floor for dancing, isn't it?"

"I just love dancing," Miss Boke thought proper to declare again. "Don't you love it, Mr. Baxter?"

This time he considered his enthusiasm to be sufficiently indicated by a nod. He needed all his breath.

So passed five dances. Long, long dances.

Likewise five encores. Long encores.

Catastrophe

AT LAST, at last, he sat beside the fairy-like creature, and filled his lungs with infinitesimal particles of violet scent. More; he was no sooner seated than the little blonde head bent close to his: the golden net brushed his cheek. She whispered:

"No'ty ickle-boy Batster! Lola's last night, an' ickle-boy Batster fluttin'! Flut all night wif dray bid dirl.'"

Her cruelty was all unwitting; she intended to rally him sweetly. But seventeen is deathly serious at such junctures, and William was in a sensitive condition. He made no reply in words. Instead, he drew himself up (from the waist, that is, because he was sitting) with a kind of proud dignity. And that was all.

"Oo be so tross" she said, "Lola talk to nice Man uvver side of her!"

With that she turned her back upon him and prattled merrily to the gentleman of sixteen upon her right.

Still and cold sat William. And

although Miss Pratt continued to make merry with the Man upon her right, it seemed to William that this was but outward show. He had a strange, subtle impression that the mysterious superiority which set him apart from others was becoming perceptible to her—that she was feeling it, too.

Alas! Such are the moments Fate seizes upon to play the clown!

Over the clatter and laughter of the guests rose a too familiar voice. "Lemme he'p you to nice tongue samwich, lady. No'm? Nice green lettuce sam—"

Genesis came suddenly to a dramatic dead-stop as he beheld William sitting before him wearing that strange new dignity and Mr. Baxter's evening clothes. "Name o'goo'ness." Genesis exclaimed, so loudly that every one looked up. "How in the livin' worl' you evuh come to git here? You' daddy sut'ny mus' 'a' weakened 'way down 'fo' he let you wear his low-cut ves' an' pants an' long-tail coat! I bet any man fifty cents you gone an' stole 'em out aftuh he done went to bed!"

And he burst into a wild, free African laugh.

At seventeen such things are not embarrassing; they are catastrophical. But, mercifully, catastrophes often produce a numbness in the victims. More as in a trance than actually William heard the outbreak of his young companions; and, during the quarter of an hour subsequent to Genesis's performance, the oft-renewed explosions of their mirth made but a kind of horrid buzzing in his ears. Like sounds borne from far away were the gaspings of Mr. and Mrs. Parcher, striving with all their strength to obtain mastery of themselves once more. A flourish of music challenged the

dancers. Couples appeared upon the platform. The dreadful supper was over. The ineffable One, supremely pink, rose from her seat at William's side and moved toward the platform with the glowing Joe Bullitt.

Then William, roused to action by this sight, sprang to his feet and took a step toward them. But it was only one weak step. A warm and ample hand placed itself firmly inside the crook of his elbow. "Let's get started for this one before the floor gets all crowded up," said Miss Boke.

Miss Boke danced and danced with him; she danced him on—and on—and on—

AT HALF past one the orchestra played "Home, Sweet Home." As the last bars sounded, a group of earnest young men who had surrounded the lovely guest of honor, talking vehemently, broke into loud shouts, embraced one another and capered variously over the lawn. Mr. Parcher beheld from a distance these manifestations, and then, with an astonishment even more profound, took note of the tragic William, who was running toward him, radiant—Miss Boke hovering futilely in the far background.

"What's all the hullabaloo?" Mr. Parcher inquired.

"Miss Pratt!" gasped William. "Miss Pratt!"

"Well, what about her?"

"She's going to stay!" shouted the happy William. "She's promised to stay another week!"

And then, mingling with the sounds of rejoicing, there ascended to heaven the stricken cry of an elderly man plunging blindly into the house in search of his wife.

OUR grand business undoubtedly is, not to *see* what lies dimly at a distance, but to *do* what lies clearly at hand.—*Carlyle.*

THE best way to keep good acts in memory is to refresh them with new.—*Attributed to Cato by Bacon.*

PAUL H. BUCK

THE ROAD TO REUNION
1865–1900

PROFESSOR BUCK is a Middle-Westerner, a graduate of Ohio State University. He took his graduate studies at Harvard University, where he has been a member of the faculty of History since 1926. The Pulitzer Prize in History for 1937 was awarded him for "The Road to Reunion." His treatment of the cultural conflict, the propaganda, and the political forces of the post-Civil War period of our history has been lauded for its objectivity. For sympathetic understanding of the South this book has been likened to "Gone With the Wind."

Victory

As THE last winter of the Civil War was drawing to a close and the promise of victory grew momentarily brighter, the Northern public began to speculate as to the sequel of the bitter conflict. For the first time it occurred to some that the hostility which existed between the sections would be an embarrassment if not a danger now that it was about to be decreed the two must live together in one union. The Civil War like all modern wars had been waged as much by propaganda as by armies in the field. The morale of each section had been maintained largely by emphasizing the so-styled irrepressible antagonisms of the respective rivals. As a consequence the war had left not only the necessity of rebuilding an exhausted and impoverished South, but also the unfamiliar task of reforming habits of thought that had been fixed in strife.

Lincoln was among the first to appreciate the necessity of removing the war psychosis. In the cabinet meeting of April 14, 1865, he uttered the well remembered words, "We must extinguish our resentments if we expect harmony and union." The query on every lip was, in the Lincolnian phrase, have these honored dead died in vain? All recognized three general positions as logical consequences of the war. First, the doc-trine of secession was renounced and the Union was recognized, in the spirit of Webster, to be one and indissoluble. Secondly, the institution of slavery was forever destroyed. And thirdly, it was more or less tacitly recognized that the pre-war leadership of the Southern slavocrat in national politics was permanently to be replaced in favor of Northern direction. But each of these general positions had in itself logical consequences, and it was in the unraveling that disputes arose.

The Union was preserved, but how could the tension and conflict within the Union be removed? The Negro was a freeman, but what was necessary to safeguard him in his new estate and to whom was the safeguarding to be entrusted? The Southern oligarchy had been overthrown, but how could the destruction be made complete and what was to take its place? The emotional relief, for it was basically that, with which large numbers of Northerners turned to the twin solution of the radicals—the enfranchisement of the Negro and the mortgaging of the nation's future to the Republican party—is evidence of the widespread neurosis of a people who had emerged from war.

THE assassination of Abraham Lincoln at the very moment of national rejoicing was interpreted generally as a divine caution to the North. The great body of Northern clergymen passed through the experience to a result disastrous to any hope of reconciliation. The misunderstanding and distrust engendered in the war lived on in part because the reporting of Southern conditions to the Northern reading public continued bad. And finally, the exigencies of the political situation proved an added hindrance to conciliatory influences. Just as in the crisis of 1860-61 the political chieftains found it impossible to retreat from the extreme positions they had assumed, so now in the crisis of 1865-66 the idea of partisan supremacy dictated intrenchment deep in the divisions of the period. The major parties acted not as unifying forces, but as divisive forces.

The unlaid ghosts of old disputes thus stalked the stage. The drama began in confusion and proceeded unplanned through perplexing shifts until the unintentioned climax of vindictiveness triumphing over magnanimity was reached. Reconciliation was to come only after the Northern program was firmly implanted in the South. So again the North sent its armies into the South, this time to overthrow the moderate Reconstruction governments established under the auspices of Lincoln and Johnson, and to rule by martial law until new structures based upon Negro rule and directed by Republican chieftains might make a conquest of the Southern spirit. The result was disorder worse than war, and oppression unequaled in American annals. Yet the North continued to cherish a belief in its own supposed leniency. In reviewing such a situation, it would seem the part of wisdom to understand rather than to blame. The victorious are as deserving of pity as the defeated. Few in the America of 1865 could have envisioned the arduous road that must be traversed to true peace.

Defeat

THE defeated South stretched more than twelve hundred miles from the ancient settlement of Jamestown to the open frontier in Texas. In the Northern mind this South of majestic distances was generalized as a formula or idea that must be combated and destroyed. The South did in fact assume a unity in face of Northern hostility. But in reality the situation was not so simple. The South was a vast congeries in which geographic variations, cultural deviations, and conflicting currents of historical development rested in yet imperfect adjustment.

The Civil War was no war of professional soldiers who made a business of fighting. Even in the South, with its outdoor background, men went into the army as amateurs. Each felt "the fate of the nation resting on his shoulders. It was the burden of responsibility which killed—killed and weakened—more than shot and shell and frost and heat together." Back of the soldier stood a nation socialized for purposes of waging war. To maintain the morale of such an army and such a so-

BROADWAY LANDING, APPOMATTOX RIVER

ciety the motives for fighting had to be translated into ideals. The Southern cause was preached as a soul-absorbing aspiration for an independent existence. Consequently defeat when it came was more than merely the loss of an armed contest.

It was a crushing of the spirit.

The forced remaking of a society is never pleasant to envision. The South faced a prospect made grimmer still by the heritage of hate and bitterness. Little sympathy could be expected from the North. The South emerged from the war with a strengthened conviction of Northern wickedness and a sense of having been unduly persecuted by the vindictive malignity of the Federal power. The sentiment hardened into unyielding prejudice. Lost were the dreams of greatness. Yet ruin, poverty, and defeat could not altogether destroy memory of the aspiration. The yearning for the vanished beauty of the past became a part of the Southern heart. Never was it more beautifully expressed than in the poem of Timrod, which itself became part of the tradition.

Sleep sweetly in your humble graves,
Sleep, martyrs of a fallen cause;

Though yet no marble column craves
The pilgrim here to pause.

Timrod dying from undernourishment himself, personified the spirit that slept beneath the Southern ashes.

The South did develop general acquiescence in the political consequences of the war. The apprehensive North little appreciated the completeness of its triumph, missed the extent to which the bankruptcy of Southern morale went, and so found it difficult to receive without some questioning the many assurances that the South "accepted the situation." "I am satisfied," wrote General Grant, "that the mass of thinking men of the South accept the present situation of affairs in good faith." But the North itself was so preoccupied with the issue of deciding a Reconstruction policy that everything Southern was distorted. And while the dominant section was active in its interest, the South was mainly passive. The people had had their fill of politics. Let the conqueror solve the problem of the nation's future. The South had a more intimate task to meet, an immediate one that engrossed every energy. That task was the personal one of salvaging a livelihood.

There Is No Peace
1865-1880

IN THE years that followed the Civil War, much was said about the need of healing the wounds of strife. Actually the war had ended only on the battlefield. In the minds of men it still persisted. Memories of the past and issues living in the present combined to perpetuate and perhaps enlarge the antagonism that victory and defeat had created.

Deeply engraven on the Northern heart was the conviction that the Confederacy had deliberately maltreated the prisoners of war captured by its armies. The Southern prisons were at best what one Confederate surgeon described as a "gigantic mass of human misery." A war-crazed public could not dissociate this suffering from deliberate intent of the enemy. Considering the emotions of the time it is surprising that of the men who had been most prominent in the management of the prisons on the Confederate side only two were punished. An obscure private was convicted of manslaughter and sentenced to a term in prison. And the arch-fiend of iniquity, for so the North regarded him, Major Henry Wirz, was hanged as a murderer in November 1865. Other trials all ending in acquittal continued into August 1866. But if the peak of frenzy passed, the issue continued to divide the sections.

If the prisons constituted a Northern grievance the South likewise had its hurtful memories. While Northerners blamed the evil genius of slavery for the war, Southerners pointed the finger

CIVIL WAR IN COLUMBIA, SOUTH CAROLINA

of responsibility to "those men who preached the irrepressible conflict to the Northern people" and "helped to bring on that unlawful and unholy invasion of the South." The South felt that it had been betrayed. The ineradicable sense of injury felt by the South took concrete form in condemning the ravages committed by General Sherman's army in Georgia and South Carolina.

Moreover, it was impossible for moderation to flourish in such an atmosphere, on either side. The unreconciled impressions were kept alive in the earliest memoirs written by the leading actors in the conflict, such men as: Admiral Semmes, General Sherman, and clergyman Henry Ward Beecher. The same was true of the psychology dominating a "History of the American Civil War" by John W. Draper. Unreconciled views entered into the textbooks used in the schools and were so transmitted to the youth of the country.

MORAL agitation over the Negro in slavery had been a vital factor in sectionalizing the nation. When emancipation came as a consequence of the war many professed to see in it the end of sectionalism. The history of the fifteen years after 1865 was to demonstrate that the freedman was to be a source of sectional strife almost as baneful as the slave. The problem of the Negro remained a rock separating the current of national life in angry currents. Emanci-

pation dictated that the Negro was to have a new status without defining what that status was to be. The determination of the Negro's future thereupon became the issue. A bitter competitive struggle was precipitated in which the true interests of the Negro disappeared. The South maintained that the problem was a domestic one in which it alone should participate. The North in reply pointed to the responsibility it had assumed when it suddenly bestowed freedom upon the Negro. The Negro and all that pertained to him accordingly formed a continuance of hostilities between the victors and the vanquished. Folly and passion characterized the approach to a problem that would yield only to the most considerate cooperation. The Negro himself fell the prey first to the Carpetbagger who seduced him with the suffrage and then to Ku Kluxism of an aroused white population which beat him back into discipline. Mistakes, misjudgments, heartburnings, alienation of races, and division of North and South, were the consequences of this first essay in race relations under freedom.

The injuries then experienced became a tradition. "Whether right or wrong," said General Gordon before a Congressional Committee in 1871, "it is the impression of the Southern mind—it is the conviction of my own mind, in which I am perfectly sincere and honest —that we have not been met in the proper spirit." And there is not a page written in the vast literature of war and Reconstruction literature which does not corroborate Gordon's judgment.

For the issue of whether the Negro should be the ward of the South or the ward of the Nation, took on a more sinister expression when the Republican party asserted a proprietary interest in the freedman. It is a truism of Reconstruction history that the Radicals enfranchised the Negro in order to build a Republican party in the South. This leads to a study of politics as the most important of all the divisive forces separating the sections and preventing the realization of harmony.

Politics as a Sectional Divisor
1865-1880

THE practice of American politics in the years that followed the Civil War seemed based upon a theory that the two great parties were hostile armies in camps irreconcilably divided. Democrats were to Republicans, and Republicans were to Democrats, not opponents to be persuaded, but enemies to be remorselessly pursued and destroyed. The condition primarily responsible for this hostility was the unhappy fact that party divisions coincided with the sectional dualism whose corrosive influence ate into the vitals of every phase of national life.

The Republican party was born in strife on issues that won support only in the North. It was a party of sectional-consciousness. As such it operated to split asunder the fabric of national life. Yet the party itself was in constant danger of factional disruption. There were rivalries within the party based upon diverging economic interests. At any time Northeast and Northwest might divide on tariff or finance and in doing so precipitate the party out of power.

The Republican party took glory in the Union victory it had conducted. This refusal to let the past fade into history, the exploitation of war issues that were settled, the inherent selfishness of the practice, all received censure from those outside the Republican party. A phrase of opprobrium was coined, "waving the bloody shirt," and applied to this feature of Republican politics. But the "bloody shirt" was possibly the greatest weapon any American party ever possessed and the Republican party would have been an unusual assemblage of politicians in-

deed if it had not exploited this instrument which was both a sword of offense and a shield of defense.

Handicapped by its war record, embarrassed by the forcefulness of the "bloody shirt" attack, the Democratic party was for more than a decade compelled to remain on the defensive. During these years it made painful and for the most part unsuccessful efforts to find an issue substantial enough to carry the party back into the confidence of the Nation. The first tactics assumed by the party chieftains was resistance to the Republican program of Reconstruction. True to the tactics of non-acceptance of Reconstruction the Democrats pictured themselves before the public throughout the elections of 1866 and 1868 as men of peace and reunion fighting hatred and vengeance. Bright as seemed its prospects the tactics of non-acceptance proved an unwise step. Pressure from outside solidified the Republican party, and, during the elections at least, moderates cooperated with Radicals. A consolidated Republican party was the result.

THE Republicans were assured of four more years in power. It did not seem possible to undo in 1872 what could not be undone in 1868. Consequently "reconciliation by acceptance" became the future basis of action. In the political parlance of the day this change of front was styled the "New Departure" of the Democratic party. It was a shrewd manoeuvre which promised to win accretions to the party ranks. At the same time the evils they attacked, corruption of the Grant regime and carpetbag excesses in the South, threatened seriously to disrupt the unity of their opponents. The nation-wide Liberal Republican movement seemed to promise the necessary accretions for Democratic control.

The Liberal Republican movement was the first great event in the political narrative which made an appreciable number of Republicans soften the harshness of their attitude toward Democrats and the South. Not merely did men like Schurz, Greeley, Julian, Sumner, David Davis, Charles Francis Adams, Jacob D. Cox, and Lyman Trumbull, politicians whose loyalty and integrity were unassailable in the North, henceforth speak the language of harmony. The Liberal Republican movement also brought into the same position the most powerful journals and the ablest editors in the North.

The Republican party fought the "New Departure," the Liberal Republican movement, and the Greeley campaign by the familiar methods of the "bloody shirt." When the Liberal Republicans secured endorsement from the Democrats, the Republicans could argue that peace on Greeley's lips was surrender, while peace from Grant meant that reconciliation would wait upon the right settlement of basic issues. Thus it was the suspicion that the restoration of the Democratic party to power notwithstanding its assurances of acquiescence would imperil Northern interests and disturb the war settlement that explained Grant's second presidential victory in 1872. Possibly it weakened the cause of reconciliation thus to have made it an issue. Certainly it did little good to have again the friendly gestures of Southerners spurned. But still the impression remains that Greeley's work was not all in vain. Emotion is an elusive thing, often impossible to analyze. Greeley's defeat was a personal tragedy made complete by his death shortly after the election. A universal sense of pity stilled for a moment the indecent abuse that had made the preceding six months a turmoil of strife.

FOUR more years of Grant demonstrated the futility of expecting peace through the Republican policy of pacification. Evils of carpetbag misrule in the South grew worse and the administration bogged in a morass of confusion that made more convincing the Democratic argument that solution could be realized only after "home rule" was restored to the South. Four more years of Grant also demonstrated the futility of expecting reform from within the ranks of the administration and raised again the possibility of using the Democratic party as a broom to sweep clean the filth of office. As a consequence the Democrats gained strength in the years from 1873 to 1876. Throughout the years when criticism of Republican policy was developing, Republicans clung to the practice of interpreting Southern news so as to maintain the fierce war spirit of the North. In 1876 the party met the reform issue by going outside the administration circle and nominating a "pure" candidate, Rutherford B. Hayes, of Ohio. But to meet the growing Northern sentiment against Southern abuses, the party had only the "bloody shirt" for defense.

The election ended a deadlock in which it was impossible to decide whether the people wanted Hayes or Tilden. The resulting Compromise of 1877 pleased those Northerners who still dreaded the prospect of a national Democratic administration, by placing Hayes in the White House to purify the Republican party. The removal of Federal troops from the South by a Republican President and the restoration of home rule to Southern whites had important consequences in shaping the future course of the sectional issue in politics. The three great political factors that had rent the nation asunder (the debate over slavery, the struggle for Southern independence, and the trials of Reconstruction) no longer existed. The hurt was in the past, and, while the South remained a problem often vexatious, the proportions of that problem were never

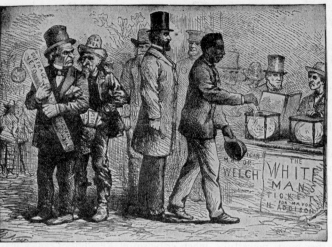

A SLAVE VOTES—UNDER THE DIRECTION OF CARPET-BAGGERS

ruin. Even the campaign of 1880 began, as one commentator observed, with "looseness of opinion on all questions except the condition of the South." On this issue the Republicans sought purposely to foster strife, while the Democrats made no honest effort at any solid solution, contenting themselves with continued repeal of Republican safeguards for the Negro. Between these two positions there was little comfort for the moderate who again saw the extremes triumph over the middle. Again the nation participated in the old, prolonged debate as to whether the people of one half the country were or were not to be trusted in their fidelity and patriotism. So far as the reconciliation of North and South was concerned politics were ever a negative force. It is time that we turn to some of the positive influences that even in the turbulent fifteen years after 1865 were raising the promise of ultimate peace.

again to reach the degree where they would overwhelm the good sense of the country.

Not all, however, felt inclined to soften the issues between the sections. In fact the major portions of both parties sought to keep alive old issues and rekindle the fire of the people. By 1878 it was apparent that the Congressional elections of that year were to be fought on lines of the ancient antagonisms and not under the new dispensation of peace and harmony. The tug of war within the Republican party was decided. So the projected bridging of the chasm collapsed in

Let Us Have Peace
1865-1880

Through the long years of controversy that bred in North and South an unyielding sense of difference, there could also be found a persistent desire for peace. Grant's "Let us have peace," while prostituted to party ends, nevertheless demonstrated that the North, too, sought surcease from strife. Confronted by the prejudices and passions of the war and postwar periods, this sentiment often seemed hopeless. But good will is a slow distillation of many inchoate promptings. Its workings are rarely so dramatic or capable of such neat analysis as dissen-

sion. Often it is taken for granted as though it needed no explanation. It came to a yearning people with no sudden realization, but quietly permeated the humblest folkways of the nation. Thus it was that the desire for peace found its first outlet in reconciling those who mourned at the graves of their dead soldiers. This is the origin of Memorial Day.

In another respect the sections were nearer together than surface trends seemed to indicate. This was in regard to amnesty. The President was granted power to amnesty offenders by proclamation and both Lincoln and Johnson liberally exercised the pardoning power. The Fourteenth Amendment, on the other hand, placed the former Confederate in a condition of political disability. The question of amnesty after 1868 became thereby a matter for Congressional debate. Acts of amnesty were passed during the second session of the Fortieth Congress even before the Amendment was proclaimd in force on July 28, 1868. Later, the General Amnesty Act of 1872 reduced the number of Southerners disqualified from holding office to less than five hundred men. Within the next eight years Congress removed disqualifications from more than one hundred Southerners excluded by the Act of 1872. It became a truism that any man the South elected to office could, if he needed it, receive amnesty from Congress, Jefferson Davis alone excepted. Thus pressure of public sentiment won an important concession and one hurt of Reconstruction was early remedied. But in a more positive manner amnesty also proved wise statesmanship. It permitted the return to national life of the respected and natural leaders of the South.

Public sorrow revealed a national heart throbbing in the South as well as in the North. On the second of July 1881 President Garfield was shot by an assassin. A long painful struggle with death resulted as the poison of the bullet slowly wore down the resistance of a strong physique. For eleven weeks the country stood watch over the bed of the sufferer, noting every fluctuation in his condition. Newspapers printed daily reports which frequently occupied an entire sheet. When the contest drew to a close on the night of September 19-20 the death was attended by universal grief.

What more do these disconnected episodes reveal than that the popular inclination was to forgive, to stress the things that made for peace, and to forget the unpleasant features of the past? The yearning for peace could not in itself, however, effect release from the hostility that divided North and South. A void existed. There was not enough in common in the social and economic structures of the sections to permit a true integration of interests and attitudes. Yet more important, sentiment North and South had turned definitely toward reconciliation.

Economic and Social Contacts
1865-1880

IN MOST respects the South that had sought independence had been attuned to ideals that sharply diverged from Northern aspirations. The agriculture of great estates, staple export crops, and enslaved labor had developed antagonisms with both the homestead farming of the Northwest and the business enterprise of the Northeast. Planters had waged war on one front against free homesteads of the new agricultural domain of the Mississippi Valley, while on another they contested with bitterness and suspicion the demands of industrialists for protective tariffs, centralized banking institutions, and subsidies for commerce. Moreover, the predilections of an aristocratic society for stability had not harmonized with Northern inventiveness and social experimentation. Basically the War for Southern Independence was the armed phase of an "irrepressible conflict" between these divergent objectives. More than any other factor they had constituted the most potent influence in widening the chasm between the North and the South.

The destruction of slavery, the humbling of the planting aristocracy, and the unimpeded sweep permitted Northern enterprise as a consequence of the war seemed to presage the removal of the major cause which had made for separateness. Many expressed the belief that the centrifugal force had been destroyed and now the centripetal force would operate unimpeded to unify the nation. It was obvious that the South faced an economic and social, as well as a political, reformation as a consequence of its defeat.

The revolution was not slow in materializing. Emancipation of the Negro removed the cornerstone of ante-bellum Southern society. In spite of the low price of land and the small acreage in which it could be acquired, few Negroes or white farmers were financially capable of purchasing farms and becoming actual owners. The split-up of the plantation did not result in a land-owning, independent and sturdy yeomanry. A system of tenancy, in which the laborer worked assigned tracts and shared the produce with the owner, developed and became permanent. The abounding poverty depressed the tenant into a status approximating peonage. Lacking sufficient savings to live through a season of growing crops without borrowing, he discovered that credit was an expensive luxury. By 1880 approximately three-fourths of the agricultural classes in the South were chronic debtors, and the merchants through their control of credit were the dominant factor in the new economic structure. At the same time the dirt farmers of the South found a community of interest with the farmers of the West. In time common needs would operate as a bond of union.

New ties were also established with the commercial centers of the Northeast. Now the planter no longer had dependent workers. He purchased only for his household. Former slaves, grouped in families, made their own purchases. Likewise the more progressive status of the white farmer made for a larger market. Retail trading grew up where wholesale trading had prevailed. A more intimate nexus of trade was thus woven into the fiber of national life.

Because of the insecure agricultural and industrial future of the South, the interest of Northern banking houses in the section during the fifteen postwar years was limited primarily to financing railroad securities and issues of State bonds. Until 1873 the situation was favorable for promoting railroads wherever located if the slightest promise of eventual profit could be shown. Of permanent value to national integration was the fact that the resultant vast railroad-building tended more than ever to absorb the South into the transportation system of the country. Much of importance in the later wedding of the sections—tourist travel, truck farming, grain shipments from the upper Mississippi Valley to the Gulf, cotton shipments by rail, as well as a greater interchange of articles of every sort—was to proceed from this railroad activity and its continuance.

It would be an exaggeration to say that the Northern church and charity workers in the South were adjusted to their environment by 1880, or that Southern opinion accepted them in intimate communion. But it is true that the trend was toward improved understanding. Better-minded Northerners were beginning to realize that their work must be subordinate and supplementary to what the white South did. In fact the North by 1880 was willing to retire from the field of combat, no longer apprehensive of the Union or zealous for the rights of Negroes, and confident in its own political and economic dominance. Indeed, the South now had within itself all the elements for deciding whether it would merge its future in a common Americanism or remain aloof, loyal to a tradition which seemed discarded and destroyed by the remainder of the world. The New South was the South's own responsibility.

Young Men Growing Up

One thing was still required for the revolution in Southern attitude to be complete. The New must breed a faith and confidence in itself. That faith and confidence was the contribution of young men growing up to manhood in the eighties, young men demanding the right to live a life of action and fulfillment rather than a life of wearing sackcloth amid the ashes of past grandeur.

To equip themselves for life in the future rather than for defense of the past, the young men accepted and made basic in their creed the revised judgment of Southern history which the more progressive of their elders had so painfully elaborated. Typical of the prevailing opinion was the speech of a young Virginian whose boyhood had been spent in South Carolina, Woodrow Wilson. In this speech, delivered in 1880, he asserted: "I yield to no one precedence in love for the South. But *because* I love the South, I rejoice in the failure of the Confederacy. . . . The perpetuation of slavery would, beyond all question, have wrecked our agricultural and commercial interests, at the same time that it supplied a fruitful source of irritation abroad and agitation within. We cannot conceal from ourselves the fact that slavery was enervating our Southern society and exhausting to Southern energies. . . . Even the damnable cruelty and folly of reconstruction was to be preferred to helpless independence." Again, Woodrow Wilson, after condemning the institution of slavery and the policy of Southern independence, paid "loving tribute to the virtues of the leaders of secession, to the purity of their purposes, to the righteousness of the cause which they thought they were promoting—and to the immortal courage of the soldiers of the Confederacy."

The new spirit and the new energy found complete expression in the industrial transformation of certain areas of the South during the decade of the eighties. So rapidly did manufactures develop that it seemed as though the South was undergoing a complete economic revolution. The number of factories, furnaces, and forges multiplied, giving the South again something to boast about. By 1890 a firm and permanent basis for a variety of manufactures was established, and the wealth and prosperity of Dixie no longer depended solely upon agriculture. It proceeded from a more diversified economy. Though it seems a paradox, the South became more nationally minded in direct ratio to the extent it achieved a degree of industrial self-sufficiency. The business brains, capital, and technology of North and South found a community of interest politicians had never known.

The South Begins to Write

IN THE realm of literature even more than in the field of business the New South demonstrated its capacity to participate completely in the life of the nation. American literature underwent important changes after the Civil War. War had been influential in broadening interest in American themes and in inspiring a buoyant pride in native life. Fiction became almost a matter of human geography, for the new writers seemed intent upon doing little more than describing in simple language the many local diversities of the national scene. And the South was admirably situated to participate in a prose fiction of local types and dialect. No section of America had such an abundance of picturesque detail.

Yet it took a very brief period to demonstrate that Southern writers could not find in Dixie enough patronage to survive, and that unless Southern literature became sufficiently American in tone to appeal to Northern readers there would be no Southern literature. The brief life of Sidney Lanier (1842-81) bridged the transition and best exemplified the course that Southern literature followed. Raised in the best Old South traditions, Lanier served the Confederacy in the war at the expense of shattered health, and then encountered adversity in Reconstruction so harsh as to justify his own statement that "pretty much the whole of life has been merely not dying." Yet in "Tiger Lilies" (1867) he recognized the futility of the war, in "Corn" (1875) he argued against the tyranny King Cotton had exercised over the South, in the "Centennial Cantata" (1876) he espoused the doctrine of Americanism, and in an article for *Scribner's Monthly* on the New South (1880) he opened his mind to the brightness of the future. It was from Lanier and Hayne that the young men of the new school received the double legacy of respect for the tradition of Dixie and belief in the South as an integral part of the nation.

Moreover, in the end, there was not an important writer of this new school who did not believe the South better off within the restored Union. This was one of the most important adaptations made in the postwar South. A civil war in literature had been an important phase of the "irrepressible conflict." But by 1880 the North too had lost its apprehension and Northern writers ceased to have any incentive to write in a spirit of hostility towards Dixie. A culture which in its life was anathema to the North, could in its death be honored.

Thus as far as reconciliation is concerned, the important feature of this literature is the picture of the Old South it conveyed to Northern readers. It is apparent that, on the part of the Southern writers, the Negro was primarily a device by which a white philosophy of race relations was advanced. Descriptions of the kindly and affectionate relations of the races under slavery were made the basis for a proper solution of the problem of races. Here, indeed, was a startling answer to the abolitionists.

The North Feels the Power of the Pen

JOEL CHANDLER HARRIS is a good illustration of how Northern editors and publishers encouraged the Southern group to write their "epitaph of a civilization." In the case of this shy Georgian they dragged him from obscurity and placed him blushing on a pedestal of fame. Harris had grown up in poverty, was trained in the office of a plantation newspaper, and then graduated to the growing city of Atlanta where he found a position on the *Constitution*. On the 18th of January 1877 Uncle Remus made his first appearance in the columns of this newspaper. For several years the stories continued in the *Constitution*. Then in 1880 Harris was surprised by a suggestion from D. Appleton and Company that the legends be collected and given permanent form in a book. Thus began a series which continued through five volumes published over a period of twenty-five years. Immediately after the publication of the first Uncle Remus volume, Harris was besieged with letters from Northern editors asking for material.

Certain of the younger writers in the North endeavored to share in the triumph of the Southern school by ventures of their own in the "undiscovered country." For the most part these Northern imitators were second-rate hacks without especial insight or capacity for expression. They exploited without adorning or improving the conventional types and themes. If there was nothing that was new and little that was felicitous in their output, they nevertheless served the purpose of effecting further the shift from hostile to sympathetic portraiture of the South.

Indeed, the efforts of Northern writers to duplicate the successes of Harris, Page, and Cable produced no masterpiece in the realm of fiction in the theater, however, Northerners working with Southern material had unquestioned supremacy. Yet no Civil War drama achieved real success until the middle eighties. From that time past the turn of the century there is no gainsaying the popularity of the Civil War dramas. They were the greatest "hits" of the time, and no American play except "Uncle Tom's Cabin" has ever aroused the popular enthusiasm caused by "Shenandoah" which brought the thrill of battle to the very stage and in the end made certain the future safety of the nation by uniting five (no less!) pairs of lovers whose loyalties had been divided by the war.

In place of the discarded image—the unfriendly picture of the South implanted in the Northern mind in the days of strife—these dramas generally fixed a far more friendly conception of a land basically American and loyal to the best traditions of the nation, where men and women had lived noble lives and had made heroic sacrifices to great ideals, where Negroes loved "de white folks," where magnolias and roses blossomed over hospitable homes that sheltered lovely maids and brave cadets, where romance of the past still lived, a land where the nostalgic Northerner could dwell in a Dixie of the storybooks which had become the Arcady of American tradition.

The Veteran Mind

THE organization properly claiming to be most representative of the Union veteran was the Grand Army of the Republic. The Grand Army soon arrogated to itself the special prerogative of maintaining inviolate the tradition of national patriotism. The fact that in the end even the Grand Army fell into the habit of extending friendly overtures to the men they had fought in war is indicative perhaps of the fact that "time has softened our griefs, healed our sorrows, and obliterated sectionalism."

The problem of the Southern veteran was one of adjustment. All the essentials of the solution may be found in the official report of the sixth reunion of the United Confederate Veterans, in 1896, which declared that the Confederate veteran "returned to the Union as an equal, and he remained in the Union as a friend. With no humble apologies, no unmanly servility, no petty spite, no sullen treachery, he is a cheerful, frank citizen of the United States, accepting the present, trusting the future, and proud of the past."

Meanwhile one by one the "lofty actors" of the great drama were leaving the stage and becoming memories. We take our heroes and bend them to our wishes. Before the century closed Lincoln and Lee, Davis and Grant, were idealizations and apostles of fraternity.

The Passing of the Sectional Issue in Politics
1880-1898

DESPITE the potency of the new forces that were transforming American life the activity of the major political parties remained rigidly fixed in patterns established by the bitter controversies of the Civil War and Reconstruction. Control of Congress fluctuated between narrow margins and no President from Hayes to McKinley enjoyed more than four continuous years in office. Groups of discontented reformers and new voters held the balance of power, and each recurrent election saw them make a "choice of evils" between an errant Republicanism and a still discredited Democracy. The only issue that made division between Democrats and Republicans intelligent was the North-South rivalry. On the issues of tariff, control of corporations, railroad regulation, finance, civil service reform, honesty in politics, and labor organization, the divisions were intra-party rather than inter-party.

Nevertheless the early eighties gave ample evidence that the nation was growing weary of the sectional issue in politics. President Arthur's first annual message to Congress in December 1881 made no reference of any sort to the South, a fact which caused many commentators to observe that this had not occurred before in any presidential message for over a quarter of a century. Those who had supported Cleveland in the campaign of 1884 widely proclaimed that his election marked an epoch in reconciliation. Southern newspapers were unanimous in expressing the opinion that the return of the Democratic party to power "swept away all sectional distinctions," "brought the South back into the Union," and "gave it the opportunity of impressing itself upon the national policy."

Yet the vacuity of national politics in this era is perfectly demonstrated in the fact that, except in the matter of honest administration where Cleveland proved an able and sturdy champion, the restoration of the Democrats made no appreciable change in any national policy. At every other stage in our history when a new party or an old party long out of power won the presidency far-reaching reversals of policy ensued. The election of Jefferson in 1800 was spoken of as a "revolution." Jackson's victory in 1828 resulted in dynamic alterations which indicated that the apprehensions of his conservative opponents were not without a basis of fact. Lincoln's election in 1860 changed the course of American history. Wilson in 1913 and F. D. Roosevelt in 1933 came to the presidency with programs of radical reform. But Cleveland's administration proved not unlike those of Hayes and Arthur. He was a perfect choice to dissipate the superstition that the Democratic party with its Southern wing would disturb the existing order.

Until Cleveland sent his message to Congress in December 1887 asking for a reduction in the tariff, there was no real issue upon which he as a Democrat could divide with the Republicans. Real issues were hard to find and Republican chieftains were desperately in need of ammunition.

From this unhappy dilemma Cleveland himself inadvertently rescued his opponents. His annual message to Congress in December 1887 broke all precedents in that it was devoted to a single topic, the urgent need of tariff reduction. Here was unexpected ground upon which to fight a decisive battle. The sec-

tional issue dropped into the background until it almost completely faded from the picture. When the votes were counted in November and Harrison emerged the victor, the Republican party had at last elected a President without the aid of the "bloody shirt."

In fact, the decade of the nineties gave a new fixation to American politics. The tremendous development of national wealth and power brought about one of those recurrent periods in our history when social and economic maladjustments demanded readjustment. Prosperity and depression, tariff and silver coinage, agrarian unrest and labor turmoil, foreign markets and world diplomacy—such issues of the new day did not conform to the old North-South alignment of political forces. The South remained solid as a legacy of the past and Southerners continued to wear the label of Democrats. But in the practical matter of voting for what they wanted in Congress their representatives divided on economic lines and sought support in union with kindred interests in the East and West.

Thirty years after Appomattox there remained no fundamental conflict between the aspirations of North and South. The people of the United States constituted at last a nation integrated in interests and united in sentiment. In spite of differences in past traditions and continuing regional divergences, the controlling influences which shaped national destiny operated in one section as freely as in the other. The remarkable changes that had taken place within the short span of a single generation had created a national solidarity hitherto unknown in American life. The reunited nation was a fact.

The applause of a single human being is of great consequence.—*Samuel Johnson.*

The improvement of the understanding is for two ends: first, for our own increase of knowledge; secondly, to enable us to deliver and make out that knowledge to others.—*Locke.*

Joseph Conrad

THE NIGGER OF THE NARCISSUS

"As an artist, I am willing to stand or fall on 'The Nigger of the Narcissus'," said Joseph Conrad. "Its pages are the tribute of my unalterable and profound affection for the ships, the seamen, the winds and the great sea—the moulders of my youth and the companion of the best years of my life." Perhaps Conrad (Polish-born Teodor Josef Konrad Korzeniowski), is better known for such novels as "Lord Jim," "The Heart of Darkness" and "Victory," but the story presented here is generally regarded as one of the greatest sea stories ever written. Conrad died, an English citizen, in 1924 at the age of 67.

Mustering at Bombay

Mr. BAKER, the Chief Mate, was mustering the crew. As he read out a name, one of the men would answer: "Yes, sir!" and, detaching himself from the shadowy mob of heads visible above the blackness of the bulwarks, would step barefooted into the circle of light, and in two noiseless strides pass into the shadows on the port side of the quarterdeck.

They answered in divers tones; in thick mutters, in clear, ringing voices; and some, as if the whole thing had been an outrage on their feelings, used an injured intonation: for discipline is not ceremonious in merchant ships, where the sense of hierarchy is weak, and where all feel themselves equal before the unconcerned immensity of the sea and the exacting appeal of work.

Mr. Baker read on steadily:—"Belfast—Singleton—Donkin . . . O Lord!" he involuntarily ejaculated as the last incredibly delapidated figure appeared in the light. It stopped; it uncovered pale gums and long, upper teeth in a malevolent grin.

"Is there anythink wrong with me, Mister Mate?" it asked, with a flavour of insolence in the forced simplicity of its tone. On both sides of the deck subdued titters were heard.

"That'll do. Go over," growled Mr. Baker. There was a moment of silence

while the mate peered at his list. "Sixteen, seventeen," he muttered. "I am one hand short, bo'sen," he said aloud.

"Wait!" cried a deep ringing voice. They saw a tall figure standing on the rail. It came down and pushed through the crowd, marching with a heavy tread towards the light on the quarter-deck. The whites of his eyes and his teeth gleamed distinctly, but the face was indistinguishable.

Mr. Baker advanced intrepidly. "Who are you? How dare you . . ." he began. He raised a light to the man's face. It was black. A surprised hum—a faint hum that sounded like the suppressed mutter of the word "Nigger"—ran along the deck and escaped out into the night.

After a moment the nigger said calmly: "My name is Wait—James Wait." He was calm, cool, towering, superb. "I belong to the ship," he enunciated distinctly. "The captain shipped me this morning. I couldn't get aboard sooner."

He held his head up in the glare of the lamp—a head vigorously modelled into deep shadows and shining lights—a head powerful and misshapen with a tormented and flattened face—a face pathetic and brutal; the tragic, the mysterious, the repulsive mask of a nigger's soul.

Mr. Baker, recovering his composure, looked at the paper close. "Oh, yes;

371

that's so. All right, Wait. Take your gear forward," he said.

Suddenly the nigger's eyes rolled wildly, became all whites. He put his hand to his side and coughed twice, a cough metallic, hollow, and tremendously loud; it resounded like two explosions in a vault; the dome of the sky rang to it, and the iron plates of the ship's bulwarks seemed to vibrate in unison, then he marched off forward with the others.

Stalking Death

THE passage had begun, and the ship, a fragment detached from the earth, went on lonely and swift like a small planet. Round her the abysses of sky and sea met in an unattainable frontier. A great circular solitude moved with her, ever changing and ever the same.

She drove foaming to the southward, as if guided by the courage of a high endeavor. The smiling greatness of the sea dwarfed the extent of time. The days raced after one another, brilliant and quick, like the flashes of a lighthouse, and the nights, eventful and short, resembled fleeting dreams. The men had shaken into their places, and the half-hourly voice of the bells ruled their life of unceasing care.

In the evening the cleared decks had a reposeful aspect, resembling the autumn of the earth. Donkin, solitary and brooding over his wrongs on the forecastle-head, moved closer to catch the drift of a discussion below him. Suddenly his face became grave. Something like a weak rattle was heard through the forecastle door. It became a murmur; it ended in a sighing groan.

In the blackness of the doorway a pair of eyes glimmered white, and big, and staring. Then James Wait's head, protruding, became visible, as if suspended between the two hands that grasped a doorpost on each side of the face.

The men waited in fascinated dread. He said ironically, with gasps between the words:—"Thank you . . . chaps. You . . . are nice . . . and . . . quiet . . . you! Yelling so . . . before . . . the door . . . Leave me alone. It won't be long. I'll soon die . . ."

Men stood around very still and with exasperated eyes. It was just what they had expected, and hated to hear, that idea of stalking death, thrust at them many times a day like a boast and like a menace by this obnoxious nigger. He seemed to take a pride in that death which, so far, had attended only upon the ease of his life; he was overbearing about it, as if no one else in the world had ever been intimate with such a companion; he paraded it unceasingly with an affectionate persistence that made its presence indubitable, and at the same time incredible. Was he a reality—or was he a sham—this ever-expected visitor of Jimmy's?

IT INTERFERED daily with our occupations, with our leisure, with our amusements. We had no songs and no music in the evening, because Jimmy (we all lovingly called him Jimmy, to conceal our hate of his accomplice) had managed, with that prospective decease of his, to disturb even the mental balance of our concertina player.

We ate our meals in silence and dread, for Jimmy was capricious with his food, and railed bitterly at the salt meat, at the biscuits, at the tea, as at articles unfit for human consumption—"let alone a dying men!" He would say: "Can't you find a better slice of meat for a sick man who's trying to get home to be cured—or buried?"

We did not know what to do. At every insignificant turn of our humble life, we met Jimmy overbearing and blocking the way, arm-in-arm with his awful and veiled familiar. It was a weird servitude.

He coughed often, but the most prejudiced person could perceive that, mostly, he coughed when it suited his purpose. He wouldn't, or couldn't, do his work—and he wouldn't lie-up. One day he

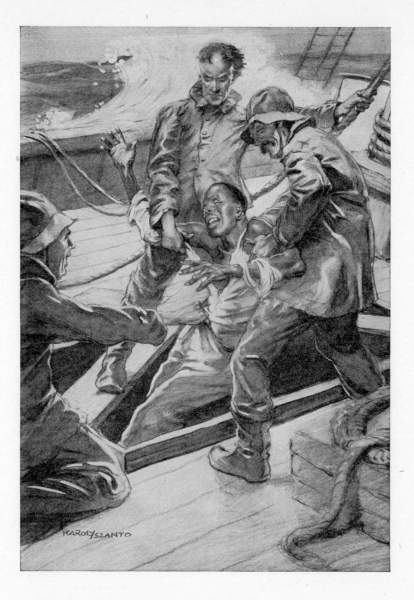

We swung him up like a lot of drunken
men embarrassed with a stolen corpse.

would skip aloft with the best of them, and the next time we would be obliged to risk our lives to get his limp body down. He was reported, he was examined; he was remonstrated with, threatened, cajoled, lectured.

But he was scornful and brooding; and no one could tell what was the meaning of that black man.

Invulnerable in his promise of speedy corruption, he trampled on our self-respect; he demonstrated to us daily our want of moral courage; he tainted our lives. Had we been a miserable gang of wretched immortals, unhallowed alike by hope and fear, he could not have lorded it over us with a more pitiless assertion of his sublime privilege.

Storm at Sea

THE thirty-second day out of Bombay began inauspiciously. In the morning a sea smashed one of the galley doors. Then, twice running, as though she had been blind or weary of life, the ship put her nose deliberately into a big wave which swept the decks from end to end.

Jimmy had shut his door, of course. We knew he was dry and comfortable within his cabin, and in our absurd way were pleased one moment, exasperated the next, by that certitude. Donkin skulked shamelessly, uneasy and miserable. He grumbled:—"I'm perishin' with cold outside in bloomin' wet rags, an' that 'ere black sojer sits dry on a blamed chest full of bloomin' clothes; blank his black soul." But we took no notice of him; we hardly gave a thought to Jimmy and his bosom friend.

There was no sleep on board that night. Most seamen remember in their life one or two such nights of a culminating gale. Nothing seems left of the whole universe but darkness, clamour, fury—and the ship. And like the last vestige of a shattered creation she drifts, bearing an anguished remnant of sinful mankind, through the distress, tumult, and pain of an avenging terror.

In the bed-places men lay booted, resting on elbows and with open eyes. Hung-up suits of oil skin swung out and in, lively and disquieting like reckless ghosts of decapitated seamen dancing in a tempest. No one spoke and all listened. Outside the night moaned and sobbed to the accompaniment of a continuous loud tremor as of innumerable drums beating far off. Shrieks passed through the air. Tremendous dull blows made the ship tremble while she rolled under the weight of the seas toppling on her deck.

THE next morning they could see the ship putting her side in the water, and they shouted all together:—"She's going!" Forward the forecastle doors flew open, and the watch below were seen leaping out one after another, throwing their arms up; and, falling on hands and knees, scrambling aft on all fours along the high side of the deck, sloping more than the roof of a house.

The immense volume of water thrown forward by the last scend of the ship had burst the lee door of the forecastle. They could see their chests, pillows, blankets, clothing, come out floating upon the sea. While they struggled back to windward they looked in dismay. The straw beds swam high, the blankets, spread out, undulated; while the chests, waterlogged and with a heavy list, pitched heavily like dismantled hulks, before they sank.

Hours passed. They were sheltered by the heavy inclination of the ship from the wind that rushed in one long unbroken moan above their heads, but cold rain showers fell at times into the uneasy calm of their refuge. Under the torment of that new infliction a pair of shoulders would writhe a little. Teeth chattered.

Suddenly some one cried:—"Where's Jimmy?" and we were appalled once more. Voices exclaimed dismally:— "Drowned—is he? . . . No! In his cabin! bloomin' rat in a trap . . .

Couldn't open his door . . . Aye! She went over too quick and the water jammed it . . . Poor beggar! . . . Let's go and see . . ."

"Damn him, who could go?" screamed Donkin.

"Nobody expects you to," growled the man next to him: "You're only a thing."

A sickening, sly lurch of the ship nearly sent them overboard. Together they shouted: "Jimmy! Jim!"

In a lull the sound of screaming and hammering sounded thin and distinct—like a solo after a chorus. He was alive. He was screaming and knocking below us with the hurry of a man prematurely shut up in a coffin.

As they crept below they could hear Jimmy screaming piercingly, without drawing breath, like a tortured woman; he banged with hands and feet. The agony of his fear wrung our hearts so terribly that we longed to abandon him, to get out of his hearing, back on the poop where we could wait passively for death in incomparable repose.

Three times a sea leaped over the high side and flung bucketfuls of water on our heads. Then Jimmy, startled by the shock, would stop his noise for a moment—waiting for the ship to sink, perhaps—and begin again, distressingly loud, as if invigorated by the gust of fear.

The *Narcissus* had the stoutest planks ever put into a ship's bulkhead—we thought—and then we perceived that, in our hurry, we had sent all the tools overboard. Groaning, we dug our fingers in, and very much hurt, shook our hands, scattering nails and drops of blood.

We could hear the object of our exasperated solicitude darting to and fro under the planks. He had cracked his voice at last, and could only squeak miserably. His back or else his head rubbed the planks, now here, now there, in a puzzling manner. He squeaked as he dodged the invisible blows.

Suddenly Archie produced a crowbar.

We howled with satisfaction as he struck mighty blows. The planks cracked. Then the crowbar went halfway in through a splintered oblong hole. Quickly that infamous nigger rushed at the hole, put his lips to it, and whispered "Help" in an almost extinct voice; he pressed his head to it, trying madly to get out through that opening one inch wide and three inches long. It seemed impossible to drive him away.

"If ye don't clear oot I'll drive the crowbar thro' your head," Archie shouted in a determined voice.

Jimmy disappeared suddenly, and we set to prising and tearing at the planks with the eagerness of men trying to get at a mortal enemy, and spurred by a desire to tear him limb from limb.

The wood split, cracked, gave way. "I've got 'im! Got 'im," Belfast shouted. "Pull at his legs . . . Pull."

We flew at him with brutal impatience, we tore the shirt off his back, we tugged at his ears, we panted over him; and all at once he came away in our hands as though someone had suddenly let go of him. With the same movement, without pause, we swung him up.

With burning faces we shivered to the very marrow of our bones. Never before had the gale seemed to us more furious, the sea more mad, the position of the ship more hopeless and appalling. Every movement of her was ominous of the end of her agony and of the beginning of ours.

Jimmy had completely collapsed now. Sheltering him, we swung him; and on the very brink of eternity we tottered all together, like a lot of drunken men embarrassed with a stolen corpse. We had so far saved him; and it became a personal matter between us and the sea.

How we hated James Wait! We could not get rid of the monstrous suspicion that this astounding black-man was shamming sick, had been malingering heartlessly in the face of our toil, of our scorn, of our patience—and now was malingering in the face of our devotion—in the face of death.

No! It couldn't be. He was all extremity. His cantankerous temper was only the result of the provoking invincibleness of that death he felt by his side.

He began to mutter. We were always incurably anxious to hear what he had to say: "It took you some time to come. I began to think the whole smart lot of you had been washed overboard. What kept you back? Hey?"

We said nothing.

After sunset the wind eased a little, but the sea ran as high as ever. The desire of life kept us alive, apathetic and enduring under the cruel persistence of wind and cold; while the bestarred black dome of the sky revolved slowly above the ship that drifted bearing our patience and our suffering.

Mutiny!

The hours of ineffective turmoil were forgotten; the fear and anguish of these dark moments were never mentioned in the glowing peace of fine days. Yet from that time our life seemed to start afresh as though we had died and had been resuscitated.

We boasted of our pluck, of our capacity for work, of our energy. We remembered honourable episodes; our devotion, our indomitable perseverance—and were proud of them as though they had been the outcome of our unaided impulses. We decried our officers—who had done nothing—and listened to the fascinating Donkin.

Our contempt for him was unbounded—and we could not but listen with interest to that consummate artist. He told us we were good men—a "bloomin' condemned lot of good men." Who thanked us? Who took any notice of our wrongs? Didn't we live a "dorg's loife for two poun' ten a month?" Did we think that miserable pay enough to compensate us for the risk of our lives and for the loss of our clothes? He made us forget that he, at any rate, had plenty.

He strutted with assurance in clothes that were much too big for him as though he had tried to disguise himself. These were Jimmy's clothes mostly; for nobody except Jimmy had anything to spare.

Donkin's devotion to Jimmy was unbounded. Nothing could keep him away from the pious work of visiting the sick, especially when there was some heavy hauling to be done on deck.

In the evening, in the dog-watches, and even far into the first night watch, a knot of men could always be seen congregated before Jimmy's cabin. Jimmy affected the languor of extreme weakness, so as to make it manifest to us that our delay in hauling him out from his horrible confinement, and then that night spent on the poop among our selfish neglect of his needs, had "done for him."

Donkin gave a sidelong glance at Jimmy.

"Look at 'im! Wish I was 'arf has 'ealthy as 'ee is—I do." He jerked a short thumb over his shoulder toward the after end of the ship. "That's the blooming way to do 'em!" he yelped with forced heartiness.

Belfast, rubbing his shoulder against the doorpost, remarked shrewdly:—"We can't all go an' be took sick—it would be mutiny."

"Mutiny—gawn!" jeered Donkin, "there's no bloomin' law against bein' sick."

"There's six weeks' hard for refoosing dooty," argued Belfast.

A voice far off cried, "Helm up!" another, more faint, answered, "Hardup, sir!" The voice in the night cried loud and commanding: "Haul the spanker out."

The group before the door vanished out of the light. They could be heard tramping aft while they repeated with varied intonations:—"Spanker out!" . . . "Out spanker, sir!"

Donkin remained alone with Jimmy. There was a silence. Jimmy opened and shut his lips several times as if swallowing draughts of fresher air:

"Ain't you going to give them a hand with the sail?" asked Jimmy.

"No. If six of 'em ain't 'nough beef to set that blamed, rotten spanker, they ain't fit to live," answered Donkin in a bored, far-away voice.

Jimmy considered the conical, fowl-like profile with a queer kind of interest.

"The mate will miss you—and there will be ructions."

Donkin got up to go. "I will do for 'im some dark night; see if I don't," he said over his shoulder.

In the shadows of the fore rigging a dark mass stamped, eddied, advanced, retreated. There were words of reproach, encouragement, unbelief, execration. Donkin got clear and saw three indistinct figures standing alone in the fainter darkness under the arched foot of the mainsail, that rose above their heads like a convex wall of a high edifice.

Donkin, agile and thin, flitted past with his right arm going like a wind-mill—and then stood still suddenly with his arm pointing rigidly above his head. The hurtling flight of some heavy object was heard; it passed between the heads of the two mates, bounded heavily along the deck, struck the after hatch with a ponderous and deadened blow.

In the morning the men were pressed three deep abreast of the mainmast and opposite the cabin-door. They were shuffling, pushing and had an irresolute mien and stolid faces.

Suddenly the Captain came out on the quarter-deck. He had his right hand in the side pocket of his jacket and also something heavy in there that made folds all down that side. He faced them with his worn, steely gaze, that by a universal illusion looked straight into every individual pair of the twenty pairs of eyes before his face.

What did they want? They shifted from foot to foot. Some pushed back their caps, scratched their heads. What did they want?

They wanted great things. And suddenly all the simple words they knew seemed to be lost for ever in the immensity of their vague and burning desire. They knew what they wanted, but they could not find anything worth saying.

"What is it—food?" asked the master "You know the stores were spoiled off the Cape."

"We know that, sir," said a bearded shell-back in the front row.

"Work too hard—eh? Too much for your strength?" he asked again. There was an offended silence.

"Tell you what's the matter? Too big for your boots. Think yourselves damn good men. Do half your duty. Think it too much. If you did ten times as much it wouldn't be enough. You can do no more? No, I know, and say nothing But you stop your caper or I will stop it for you. I am ready for you! Stop it!"

There was a moment of profound silence. "There is another thing," said the master, calmly. He made a quick stride and with a swing took an iron belaying pin out of his pocket. "This!" His movement was so unexpected and sudden that the crowd stepped back. He gazed fixedly at their faces, and some at once put on a surprised air as though they had never seen a belaying pin before. The master watched them attentively. "Donkin," he called out in a short, sharp tone.

Donkin dodged behind one, then behind another, but they looked over their shoulders, and moved aside. The ranks kept on opening before him, closing behind, till at last he appeared alone before the master.

"You know this?" asked the master.

"No, I don't," answered the other with cheeky trepidation.

"Take it," said the Captain, making a menacing gesture.

Donkin snatched at the pin as though his intention had been to run away with it, and remained stock still holding it like a candle.

"Put it back where you took it from," said the Captain, looking at him fiercely.

Donkin stepped back, opening wide eyes. "Don't tech me," snarled he, backing away.

"Then go. Go faster!"

"Don't yer 'it me . . . I will pull yer up afore the magistryt . . . I'll show yer up."

The Captain made a long stride, and Donkin, turning his back fairly ran off a little, then stopped and over his shoulder showed yellow teeth. "Are yer goin' to stand by and see me bullied?" he screamed at the silent crowd that watched him.

He started off again violently, with a leap, dashed at the fore-rigging, rammed the pin into its hole violently. "I'll be even with yer yet," he screamed at the ship at large and vanished beyond the foremast.

"Die—you beggar—die!"

A HEAVY atmosphere of oppressive quietude pervaded the ship. Very little was said. The problem of life seemed too voluminous for the narrow limits of human speech, and by common consent it was abandoned to the great sea that had from the beginning enfolded it in its immense grip; to the sea that knew all, and would in time infallibly unveil to each the wisdom hidden in all the errors.

Jimmy's steadfastness in the face of the inevitable truth had the proportions of a colossal enigma—of a manifestation grand and incomprehensible that at times inspired a wondering awe. He was becoming immaterial like an apparition; his cheekbones rose, the forehead slanted more; and the fleshless head resembled a disinterred black skull, fitted with two restless globes of silver in the sockets of eyes.

Old Singleton said that Jimmy was the cause of head winds. Mortally sick men —he maintained—linger till the first sight of land, and then die; and Jimmy knew that the very first land would draw his life from him. It was so on every ship. We were weary, hungry, thirsty; we commenced to believe Singleton, but with unshaken fidelity dissembled to Jimmy. But we looked to westward over the rail with longing eyes for a sign of hope, for a sign of fair wind; even if its first breath should bring death to our reluctant Jimmy.

One evening land was reported from aloft. Donkin chafed at the peace. Here was land already—home very soon—a bad pay-day—no clothes—more hard work. How offensive all this was. Land. The land that draws away life from sick sailors. That nigger there had money—clothes—easy times; and would not die. Land draws life away . . . He felt tempted to go see whether it did.

He opened the door of the cabin and had a shock. Sure enough, Jimmy was dead. Donkin glared with avidity. Then, Jimmy, without stirring, blinked his eyelids, and Donkin had another shock. Those eyes were blinking, startling.

Jimmy did not move but glanced languidly out of the corner of his eyes— "Land?" he asked.

"Yuss," said Donkin, very disappointed, and sat down on the box. He was thinking sadly of going out when Jimmy spoke again.

"Time we did get home . . . to get something decent to eat . . . I am always hungry."

Donkin felt angry all of a sudden.— "What about me?" he hissed, "I am 'ungry too an' got ter work. You, 'ungry!"

"Your work won't kill you," commented Wait, feebly; "There's a couple of biscuits in the lower bunk there— you may have one. I can't eat them."

Donkin dived in, groped in the corner and when he came up again his mouth was full. He munched with ardour.

DONKIN felt like a blind man feeling in his darkness the fatal antagonism of all the surrounding existence. He had a desire to assert his importance, to break, to crush; to be even with everybody for everything; to tear the veil, unmask, expose, leave no refuge—a perfidious desire of truthfulness!

He laughed in a mocking sputter and said: "You will be dead by this time tomorrow p'r'aps." He waited for a while. "Blame if yer don't look dead already."

Wait must have been collecting his strength, for he said almost aloud— "You're a stinking, cadging liar. Every one knows you." And sitting up, against all probability, startled his visitor horribly.

But very soon Donkin recovered himself and blustered.

"What? What? Who's a liar? You are—the crowd are—the skipper—everybody. I ain't. Who's yer? Who's yer to put on airs?" he repeated trembling. "'Ave one—'ave one, says 'ee—an' cawn't eat 'em 'isself. Now I'll 'ave both. By Gawd—I will! Yer nobody."

He plunged into the lower bunk, rooted in there and brought to light another dusty biscuit. He held it up before Jimmy—then took a bite defiantly. "Can yer stop me? Try. Come on. Try."

JIMMY was clasping his legs and hiding his face on the knees. His shirt clung to him. Every rib was visible. His emaciated back was shaken in repeated jerks by the panting catches of his breath. His lips moved rapidly; and hollow, moaning, whistling sounds filled the cabin with a vague mutter full of menace. It was incomprehensible and disturbing; a gibberish of emotions, a frantic dumb show of speech pleading for impossible things, promising a shadowy vengeance. Donkin, as if fascinated by the dumb eloquence and anger of that black phantom, approached, stretching his neck out with distrustful curiosity: "I've been treated worser'n a dorg by your blooming backlickers. They clouted me, kicked me—an' yer laffed—yer black, rotten incumbrance, you! You will pay fur it. Yer will pay fur it with yer money. I'm goin' ter 'ave it in a minyte; as soon has ye're dead. That's the man I am. An' ye're a thing—a bloody thing. Yah —you corpse!"

He flung at Jimmy's head the biscuit he had been all the time clutching hard but it only grazed, and striking against the bulkhead beyond burst into a thousand pieces. James Wait, as if mortally wounded, fell back on the pillow.

Donkin was surprised. After a moment, he began to mutter to himself, "Die, you beggar—die . . . That's where yer bound to go. Feet fust, through a port . . . Splash. Overboard! . . . Good 'nuff fur yer."

James Wait was mute. A tear, a big solitary tear, escaped from the corner of his eye and, without touching the hollow cheek, fell on the pillow. His throat rattled faintly.

Donkin, instinctively, glanced over his shoulder and then began to feel under the pillow for a key. He got it at once and for the next few minutes remained on his knees shakily but swiftly busy inside the box. When he got up, his face—for the first time in his life—had a pink flush—perhaps of triumph.

He turned his back squarely from the bunk, and started to the door. He clutched the handle cautiously, but at that moment he received the irresistible impression of something happening behind his back. He spun round. He was just in time to see Wait's eyes blaze up and go out at once, like two lamps overturned together by a sweeping blow. Something resembling a scarlet thread hung down his chin out of the corner of his lips—and he had ceased to breathe.

ON TWO planks nailed together and apparently resigned and still under the folds of the Union Jack with a white border, James Wait, carried aft by four men, was deposited slowly, with his feet pointing at an open port.

Everyone was there but Donkin, who was too ill to come. The Chief Mate began to read in a low tone: "To the deep—"

Yet James Wait seemed to cling to the ship with the grip of an undying fear.

"Higher! Lift!" whispered the boatswain, fiercely.

"He won't go," stammered one of the men shakily, and both appeared ready to drop everything.

"Jimmy, be a man!" shrieked Belfast, passionately. He stared wildly, twitching all over; he bent his body forward like a man peering at an horror. "Go!" he shouted, "Go, Jimmy! Jimmy, go! Go!"

His fingers touched the head of the body and the grey package started to whizz off the lifted planks all at once with the suddenness of a flash of lighting.

Mr. Baker, perspiring abundantly, read out the last prayer in a deep murmur of excited men, and fluttering sails. "Amen!" he said in an unsteady growl, and closed the book.

That night, while the ship rushed foaming to the Northward before a freshening gale, the boatswain unbosomed himself to the petty officers' berth:—"The chap was nothing but trouble," he said. "From the moment he came aboard—d'ye remember—that night in Bombay? Been bullying all that soft crowd—cheeked the old man—we had to go fooling all over a half-drowned ship to save him. Dam' nigh a mutiny —and now the mate abused me like a pickpocket for forgetting to dab a lump of grease on them planks. So I did, but you ought to have known better, too, than to leave a nail sticking up—hey, Chips?"

A WEEK afterwards the *Narcissus* entered the chops of the Channel. Under white wings she skimmed low over the blue sea like a great tired bird speeding to its nest. The clouds raced with her mastheads; they rose astern enormous and white, soared to the zenith, flew east, and falling down the wide curve of the sky, seemed to dash headlong into the sea—the clouds swifter than the ship, more free, but without a home.

The *Narcissus* came gently into her berth; the shadows of soulless walls fell upon her, the dust of all the continents leaped upon her deck, and a swarm of strange men, clambering up her sides, took possession of her in the name of the sordid earth. She had ceased to live.

The crew of the *Narcissus* drifted out of sight. I never saw them again. The sea took some, the steamers took others, the graveyards of the earth will account for the rest. And Donkin, who never did a decent day's work in his life, no doubt earns his living by discoursing with filthy eloquence upon the right of labour to live. So be it! Let the earth and the sea each have its own.

THE RAINBOW

MY HEART leaps up when I behold
A rainbow in the sky:
So was it when my life began;
So is it now I am a man;
So be it when I shall grow old,
Or let me die!
—*William Wordsworth*
(1770-1850).

H. G. WELLS

MR. BRITLING SEES IT THROUGH

For most people war comes as a "multitude of incoherent, loud, and confusing impressions." To Mr. Britling, like his creator H. G. Wells (1866-   ), war is the quintessence of human failure. In the last war he could not stand on the side lines, watching it come closer and closer, without trying to rise above the multitude and analyze it until it could be understood as something epic and explicable, as a stateable issue. The result is "Mr. Britling Sees It Through," published in 1916, as dramatic and fascinating a book as Mr. Wells has ever written.

Waste, Waste, Waste

Mr. BRITLING was entangled in a love affair. It was, to be exact, and disregarding minor affinities, his eighth. And the peculiar relations that existed between Mr. Britling and the second Mrs. Britling tended inevitably to make these love affairs troublesome, undignified and futile.

Mr. Britling's first marriage had been a passionately happy one. He had married in the glow of youth, he had had two years of clean and simple loving, helping, quarrelling and the happy ending of quarrels. Something went out of him into all that, which could not be renewed again.

There had been a child—a boy—to whose future career Mary and he had brought considerable imagination and humour. Mr. Britling's mind blossomed with wonderful schemes for his education. All that mental growth, no doubt, contributed greatly to Mr. Britling's peculiar affection for Hugh and with it there interwove still tenderer and subtler elements, for the boy had a score of Mary's traits.

He had met Edith under circumstances that did not in any way recall his lost Mary. Edith was a Bachelor of Science of London University and several things like that, and she looked upon the universe with quiet watchful eyes that had nothing whatever to hide,

a thing so incredible to Mr. Britling that he had loved and married her very largely for the serenity of her mystery. And for a time after their marriage he sailed over those brown depths plumbing furiously.

Of course he did not make his former passion for Mary at all clear to her. Without any deliberate intention he created an atmosphere between himself and Edith in which any discussion of Mary was reduced to a minimum and in which Hugh was accepted rather than explained.

They were profoundly incompatible. In all things she was defensive. She never came out; never once had she surprised him halfway upon the road to her. He had to go all the way to her and knock and ring, and then she answered faithfully. He piped and she did not dance. That became the formula of his grievance. For several unhappy years she thwarted him and disappointed him while he distressed her inexplicably.

Only very slowly did they realise the truth of their relationship and admit to themselves that the fine bud of love between them had failed to flower, and only after long years were they able to delimit boundaries where they had imagined union, and become—allies.

If it had been reasonably possible for them to part without mutual injury and recrimination they would have done so, but two children presently held them nd gradually they had to work out the road mutual toleration of their later elations.

If there was no love and delight between them there was a real habitual ffection and much mutual help. She vas proud of his steady progress to disinction, proud of each intimation of repect he won; she admired and respected is work; she recognized that he had ome magic of liveliness and unexpectedess that was precious and enviable.

So far as she could help him she did. Her practical capacity was for him a natter for continual self-congratulation. He marked the bright order of her ousehold, her flowering borders, the rosperous high-born roses of her garen with wondering appreciation. He ad never been able to keep anything a order. He relied more and more upon er. He showed his respect for her by scrupulous attention to her dignity, nd his confidence by a franker and ranker emotional neglect. Because she xpressed so little he succeeded in supoosing she felt little, and since nothing ad come out of the brown depths of er eyes he saw fit at last to suppose o plumb-line would ever find anything here.

So. Mr. Britling trod the path of his ighth digression, rather overworked in ne matter of flowers and the selection f small jewellery.

Had every man this sort of crowded atalogue? Was every forty-five-year-old nemory a dark tunnel receding from the ar of youth? It is surely a pity that fe cannot end at thirty. It comes to one ean and in perfect order . . .

Is experience worth having?

WHAT a clean straight thing the spirit of youth is! It is like a bright new spear. It is like a finely tempered sword. The figure of his boy took possession of his mind, his boy who looked out on the world with Mary's dark eyes, the slender son of that wholehearted first love. He was a being at once fine and simple, an intimate mystery. Must he in his turn get dented and wrinkled and tarnished?

He thought of the strenuous intentions of his own youth, before he had got into this turmoil of amorous experiences, while he was still out there with the clean star of youth. As Hugh was . . .

In those days he had had no amiable doctrine of compromise. He had truckled to no "domesticated God," but talked of the "pitiless truth"; he had tolerated no easy-going pseudo-aristocratic social system, but dreamt of such a democracy "mewing it mighty youth" as the world had never seen. He had thought that his brains were to do their share in building up this great national *imago,* winged, divine, out of the clumsy, crawling, snobbish, comfort-loving caterpillar of Victorian England.

With such dreams his life had started, and the light of them, perhaps, had helped him to his rapid success. Indeed, he counted as a success among his generation. He was widely known, reputably known; he prospered. Much had come, oh! by a mysterious luck, but everything was doomed by his invincible defects. Beneath that hollow, enviable show there ached waste. Waste, waste, waste—his heart, his imagination, his wife, his son, his country—

War Stands Unveiled

FOR days the broader side of Mr. Britling's mind, as distinguished from s egotistical edge, had been reflecting nore and more vividly and coherently ne spectacle of civilization, casting aside ne thousand dispersed activities of eace, clutching its weapons and setting s teeth for a supreme struggle against militarist imperialism. From the point of view of Matching's Easy that colossal crystallising of accumulated antagonisms was for a time no more than a confusion of headlines and a rearrangement of columns in the white windows of the newspapers through which those who lived in the securities of England looked out upon the world. It was the spectacle of the world less real even to most imaginations than the world of novels or plays. People talked of these things always with an underlying feeling that they romanced, and intellectualized.

On Thursday, July 23rd, the Austro-Hungarian minister at Belgrade presented his impossible ultimatum to the Serbian government, and demanded a reply within forty-eight hours.

On Thursday, the 30th of July, all the common topics of life had been swept out of the front pages of the paper altogether; the stock exchanges were in a state of wild perturbation, and food prices were leaping fantastically. Austria was bombarding Belgrade, contrary to the rules of war hitherto accepted; Russia was mobilising; and the Vienna Conference of Peace Societies was postponed.

"I do not see why a conflict between Russia and Austria should involve Western Europe," said Mr. Britling. "Our concern is only for Belgium and France."

But Herr Heinrich, his children's tutor, knew better. "No," he said. "It is war. It has come. I have heard it talked about in Germany many times. But I have never believed that it was obliged to come. Ach! It considers no one."

The hands of fate paused not for Herr Heinrich's distresses. He fretted from his room downstairs and back to his room, he went out upon mysterious and futile errands towards the village inn, he prowled about the garden. His head and face grew pinker and pinker; his eyes were flushed and distressed. Everybody sought to say and do kind and reassuring things to him.

"Ach!" he said to Mr. Britling; "You are a civilian. You live in a free country. It is not your war. You can be amused at it. . . ."

Something but very dimly apprehended at Matching's Easy, something methodical and compelling away in London, seemed to be fumbling and feeling

after Herr Heinrich, and Herr Heinric it appeared was responding. Sunday post brought the decision.

"I have to go," he said. "I must g right up to London today. To an addres in Bloomsbury. Then they will tell m how to go to Germany. I must pack an I must get the taxi-cab from the junctio and I must go."

At lunch he talked politics. "I am e tirely opposed to the war," he said. ' am entirely opposed to any war."

"Then why go?" asked Mr. Britlin "Stay here with us. We all like yo Stay here and do not answer you mobilisation summons."

"But then I shall lose all my countr I shall lose my papers. I shall be outcas I must go."

"I suppose a man should go with h own country," Mr. Britling reflected.

"If there was only one language i all the world, none of such thing would happen," Herr Heinrich declare "There would be no English, no Ge mans, no Russians."

"Just Esperantists," said Mr. Britlin

"Or Idoists," said Herr Heinrich. ' am not convinced of which. In som ways Ido is much better."

"Perhaps there would have to be war between Ido and Esperanto to settl it," said Mr. Britling.

"All this morning," said Herr Heir rich, expanding in the warmth of syn pathy, "I have been trying to pack an I have been unable to pack. My min is too greatly disordered. I have bee told not to bring much luggage. If could leave my violin, it would be great convenience. I do not care to b mobilized with my violin."

"If you could leave your things packe up. And afterwards they could be sent.

THE taxi-cab came presently to carr him off, and the whole famil gathered about it to see him off.

"Write and tell us how you get on, cried Mrs. Britling.

"We'll come to the village corner wit you, Herr Heinrich," cried the boys.

"No," said Herr Heinrich, sitting down in the automobile, "I will part with you altogether. It is too much . . ."

"*Auf Wiedersehen!*" cried Mr. Britling. "Remember, whatever happens here will be peace at last!"

"Then why not at the beginning?" Herr Heinrich demanded with a reasonable exasperation and repeated his maturer verdict on the whole European situation; "*Verdammte Bummelei!*"

"Go," said Mr. Britling to the taxi driver.

"*Auf Wiedersehen,* Herr Heinrich!"

"*Auf Wiedersehen!*"

"I do hope they won't hurt him," said Mrs. Britling.

"Oh, they won't put a youngster like that in the fighting line," said Mr. Britling. "He's had no training yet. And he has to wear glasses. How can he shoot?"

"He hasn't packed at all," said Mrs. Britling to her husband. "Just come up for an instant and peep at his room. It's—touching."

It was touching.

It was more than touching; in its minute, absurd way it was symbolical and prophetic, it was the miniature of one small life uprooted.

Instead of packing, the young man had evidently paced up and down in a state of emotional elaboration; the bed was disordered as though he had several times flung himself upon it, and his books had some little commencements of packing in a borrowed cardboard box. The violin lay as if it lay in state upon the chest of drawers, the drawers were all partially open, and in the middle of the floor sprawled a pitiful shirt of blue, dropped there, the most flattened and broken-hearted of the garments. The fireplace contained an unsuccessful pencil sketch of a girl's face, torn across . . .

In this fashion it was that the great war began in Europe and came to one man in Matching's Easy, as it came to countless intelligent men in countless pleasant homes that had scarcely heeded its coming through all the years of its relentless preparation. The familiar scenery of life was drawn aside, and War stood unveiled. "I am the Fact," said War, "and I stand astride the path of life. I am the threat of death and extinction that has always walked beside life, since life began. There can be nothing else and nothing more in human life until you have reckoned with me."

Through A Glass Darkly

ALL Mr. Britling's mental existence was soon threaded on the war. His more or less weekly *Times* leader became dissertations upon the German point of view; his reviews of books and Literary Supplement articles were all oriented more and more exactly to that one supreme fact.

It was rare that he really seemed to be seeing the war; few people saw it; for most of the world it came as an illimitable multitude of incoherent, loud, and confusing impressions. But all the time he was at least doing his utmost to see the war, to simplify it and extract the essence of it until it could be apprehended as something epic and explicable, as a stateable issue.

He had always hated conflicts and destruction, and felt that war between civilised states was the quintessential expression of human failure, it was a stupidity that stopped progress and all the free variation of humanity, a thousand times he had declared it impossible, but even now with his own country fighting he was still far from realising that this was a thing that could possibly touch him more than intellectually.

He did not really believe with his eyes and finger-tips and backbone that murder, destruction, and agony on a scale monstrous beyond precedent was going on in the same world as that which slumbered outside the black ivy and silver shining window-sill that framed his peaceful view.

War had not been a reality of the daily life of England for more than a thousand years. War that calls upon every man and threatens every life in the land, war of the whole national being, was a thing altogether outside English experience and the scope of the British imagination.

It was still incredible, it was still outside the range of Mr. Britling's thoughts all through the tremendous onrush and check of the German attack in the west that opened the great war. Through those two months he was, as it were, a more and more excited spectator at a show, a show like a baseball match, a spectator with money on the event, rather than a really participating citizen of a nation thoroughly at war.

IT was only after the near capture of Paris that Mr. Britling accepted the truth.

"One talks," he said, "and then weeks and months later one learns the meaning of the things one has been saying. I was saying a month ago that this is the biggest thing that had happened in history. I said that this was the supreme call upon the will and resources of England. I said there was not a life in all our empire that would not be vitally changed by this war. I said all these things; they came through my mouth; I suppose there

was a sort of thought behind them . . Only at this moment do I understand what it is that I said. Now—let me say it over as if I had never said it before this is the biggest thing in history, tha we are all called upon to do our utmos to resist this tremendous attack upon th peace and freedom of the world. Well doing our utmost does not mean stand ing about in pleasant gardens waiting fo the newspaper. Every man ought to b in training. Every one ought to be par ticipating. In some way. We have to bea them. It has to be done. And every on has to take a share."

Suddenly Mr. Britling started; fo Hugh had come into the room. He ha been speaking—generally. For the mo ment he had forgotten about Hugh Hugh was seventeen.

"You can't possibly go out for tw years," said Mr. Britling, as if he r gretted it.

A slight hesitation appeared in Hugh eyes. "I suppose not," he said.

"Things ought to be over by then anyhow," Mr. Britling added, betrayin his real feelings.

A pause had the effect of closing th theoretical side of the question, "Wher do you propose to enlist?"

Men Face to Face

HUGH came along one day in October in an ill-fitting uniform, looking already coarser in fibre and with a nose scorched red by the autumnal sun. He said the life was rough, but it made him feel extraordinarily well; perhaps man was made to toil until he dropped asleep from exhaustion, to fast for ten or twelve hours and then eat like a wolf. He was acquiring a taste for Woodbine cigarettes and a heady variety of mineral waters called Monsters. He feared promotion; he felt he could never take the high line with other human beings demanded of a corporal.

When Hugh had gone, the craving for a personal share in the nation's physical exertions became overpowering in Mr. Britling. So he became a special consta-

ble. The duties of a special constabl were chiefly not to understand what wa going on in the military sphere, and t do what he was told in the way o watching and warding conceivably vul nerable points. He had also to be avai able in the event of civil disorder. M Britling was provided with a truncheo and sent out to guard various culvert bridges, and fords in the hilly countr to the north-westward of Matching Easy.

As he prowled the countryside und the great hemisphere of Essex sky, leant against fences or sat drowsily upo gates or sheltered from wind and rai under ricks or sheds, he had much tim for meditation, and his thoughts we down and down below his first surfac npressions of the war. He thought no onger of the rights and wrongs of this articular conflict but of the underlying orces in mankind that made war possible; he planned no more ingenious eaties and conventions between the nations, and instead he faced the deeper riddles of essential evil and of conceivable hanges in the heart of man.

And one night in April he was perplexed by a commotion among the pheas-ants and a barking of distant dogs, and then to his great astonishment he heard noises like a distant firework display and saw something like a phantom yellowish fountain-pen in the sky far away to the east lit intermittently by a quivering search-light and going very swiftly. And after he had rubbed his eyes and looked again, he realized that he was looking at a Zeppelin—a Zeppelin flying Londonward over Essex.

Two Pictures

CERTAIN things had to be forced upon Mr. Britling because they jarred so greatly with his habits of mind that he could never have accepted them if he could have avoided doing so.

Notably he would not recognise at first the extreme bitterness of this war. He believed—and many people in England believed with him—that a great section of the Germans would welcome triumphant Allies as their liberators from intolerable political obsessions.

All the habits of the English inclined them to fight good-temperedly and comfortably, to quarrel with a government and not with a people. It took Mr. Britling at least a couple of months of warfare to understand that the Germans were fighting in an altogether different spirit.

And then came stories of atrocities, stories of the shooting of old men and the butchery of children by the wayside, stories of wounded men bayoneted or burnt alive, of massacres of harmless citizens, of looting and filthy outrages.

Mr. Britling did his utmost not to believe these things. They contradicted his habitual world. They produced horrible pains in his mind. They might, he hoped, be misrepresented so as to seem more violent or less justifiable than they were. They might be the acts of stray criminals, and quite disconnected from the normal operations of the war.

It was only after the war had been going on some months that Mr. Britling's fluttering, unwilling mind was pinned down by official reports and a cloud of witnesses to a definite belief in the grim reality of systematic rape and murder, destruction, dirtiness and abominable compulsions that blackened the first rush of the Prussians into Belgium and Champagne.

"You see," said Mr. Britling, trying to get it into focus, "I have known quite decent Germans. There must be some sort of a misunderstanding . . . I wonder what makes them hate us. There seems to me no reason in it."

"I think it is just thoroughness," said his friend. "They are at war. To be at war is to hate."

"That isn't at all my idea."

"We're not a thorough people. When we think of anything, we also think of its opposite. When we adopt an opinion we take in a provisional idea that it is probably nearly as wrong as it is right. We are—atmospheric. They are concrete . . . All this filthy, vile, unjust and cruel stuff is honest genuine war. We pretend war does not hurt. They know better."

AT TIMES young Heinrich alone stood between Mr. Britling and the belief that Germany and the whole German race was essentially wicked, essentially a canting robber nation. Young Heinrich became a sort of advocate for his people before the tribunal of Mr. Britling's mind. Heinrich's fresh, pink, sedulous face, very earnest, adjusting his glasses, saying, "Please," intervened and insisted upon an arrest of judgment.

Since the young man's departure he had sent two postcards of greeting directly to the "Familie Britling," and one letter through the friendly intervention of Mr. Britling's American publisher. Once also he sent a message through a friend in Norway.

The postcards simply recorded stages in the passage of a distraught pacifist across Holland to his enrolment. The letter by way of America came two months later. He had been converted into a combatant with extreme rapidity. He had been trained for three weeks,

had spent a fortnight in hospital with severe cold, and had then gone to Be gium as a transport driver. "If anythin happens to me," he wrote, "please sen my violin, at least, very carefully, to m mother."

And then abruptly all news from hi ceased.

"I hope our little Heinrich hasn't g seriously damaged . . . He may ▌ wounded . . ."

"Or perhaps they stop his letters . .

"Anatomy of Hate"

"Life had a wrangling birth. On the head of every one of us rests the ancestral curse of fifty million murders."

So Mr. Britling's thoughts shaped themselves in words as he prowled one night in March, chill and melancholy, across a rusty meadow under an overcast sky. The death squeal of some little beast caught suddenly in a distant copse had set loose this train of thought. "Life struggling under a birth curse?" he thought. "How nearly I come back at times to the Christian theology! And then, Redemption by the shedding of blood.

"Life is a rebellious child, struggling out of the control of the hate which made it what it is."

Has hate been necessary and is it still necessary, and will it always be necessary? Is all life a war forever? The rabbit is nimble, lives keenly, is prevented from degenerating into a diseased crawling eater of herbs by the incessant ferret. Without the ferret of war, what would life become? War is murder truly, but is not Peace decay?

It was during these prowling nights in the first winter of the war that Mr. Britling planned a new writing called the "Anatomy of Hate." It was to deal very faithfully with the function of hate as a corrective to inefficiency.

In spite of his detestation of war Mr. Britling found it impossible to maintain that any sort of peace state was better than a state of war. If wars produced destructions and cruelties, peace could

produce indolence, perversity, greedy a cumulation and selfish indulgences. Wa is discipline for evil, but peace may ▌ relaxation from good. The poor ma may be as wretched in peace time as ▌ war time. The gathering forces of an ev peace, the malignity and waste of wa are but obverse and reverse of the med of ill-adjusted human relationships.

Was there no Greater Peace possibl not a mere recuperative pause ▌ killing and destruction, but a phase ▌ noble and creative living, a phase ▌ building, of discovery, of beauty and r search? He remembered, as one remem bers the dead, dreams he had on dreamt of the great cities, the splend freedoms, of a coming age, of marvello enlargements of human faculty, of ▌ coming science that would be light a▌ of art that could be power . . .

But would that former peace ha ever risen to that?

After all, had such visions ever be more than idle dreams? Had the w done more than unmask reality?

The darkness drizzled about him; ▌ turned up his collar and watched t▌ dim shapes of trees and hedges gath out of the night to meet the dism dawn.

He may have drowsed; at least he h a vision, very real and plain, a visi very different from any dream Utopia.

It seemed to him that suddenly a mi burst under a great ship at sea, that m houted and women sobbed and cowered, nd flares played upon the rain-pitted lack waves; and then the picture hanged and showed a battle upon land, nd searchlights were flickering through he rain and shells flashed luridly, and nen darkly seen in the silhouette against

the red flames ran with fixed bayonets and slipped and floundered over the mud, and at last, shouting thinly through the wind, leapt down into the enemy trenches.

And then he was alone again staring over a wet black field.

"Forgive Them, Father . . ."

THE night was cold and bleak, but full of stars. Mr. Britling had already nastered the local topography, and he :new now exactly where all the bombs hat had been showered upon the place .ad fallen. Here was the corner of lackened walls and roasted beams where hree wounded horses had been burnt live in a barn, here the rows of houses, ome smashed, some almost intact, where mutilated child had screamed for two ours before she could be rescued from he débris that had pinned her down nd taken to the hospital. Everywhere y the dim light of the shaded street amps he could see the black holes and aps of broken windows; sometimes bundant, sometimes rare and excep-ional, among the otherwise uninjured welllings.

Altogether fifty-seven people had been illed or injured in this brilliant German ction. They were all civilians, and only welve were men. A third at least of the njured people had been in bed when estruction came upon them.

The story was like a page from some antastic romance of Jules Verne's; the eace of the little old town, the people oing to bed, the quiet streets, the quiet tarry sky, and then for ten minutes an proar of guns and shells, a clatter of reaking glass, and then a fire here, a re there, a child's voice pitched high by ain and terror, scared people going to nd fro with lanterns, and the sky empty gain, the raiders gone.

For the first time it seemed to Mr. Britling he really saw the immediate orror of war, the dense cruel stupidity f the business, plain and close. It was as he had never perceived anything of 1e sort before, as if he had been deal-

ing with stories, pictures, shows and representations that he knew to be shams.

And for a while Mr. Britling could do nothing but rage.

"Devils they are!" he cried to the stars. "Devils." Devilish fools rather. Cruel blockheads. Apes with all science in their hands! My God! but *we will teach them a lesson yet!*

And at last, sick and wretched, he sat down on a seat upon a deserted parade under the stars, close to the soughing of the invisible sea below.

Is the whole scheme of nature evil? Is life in its essence cruel? Is man stretched quivering upon the table of the eternal vivisector for no end—and without pity?

THESE were thoughts that Mr. Brit-ling had never faced before the war. They came to him now, and they came only to be rejected by the inherent quality of his mind. For weeks, con-sciously and subconsciously, his mind had been grappling with this riddle.

He found himself asking himself whether it was possible for a human being to do any cruel act without an excuse—or, at least, without the feeling of excusability. And in the case of these Germans and the outrages they had com-mitted and the retaliations they had pro-voked, he perceived that always there was the element of a perceptible if inade-quate justification.

Is there not, he now asked himself plainly, a creative and corrective impulse behind all hate? Is not this malignity indeed only the ape-like precursor of the great disciplines of a creative state?

Already he had been on the verge of

this phrase while wandering across the rushy fields towards Market Saffron; now it came to him again like a legitimate monarch returning from exile.

"When hate shall have become creative energy . . .

"Hate which passes into creative power; gentleness which is indolence and the herald of euthanasia . . .

"Pity is but a passing grace; for mankind will not always be pitiful."

But meanwhile, meanwhile . . . How long were men so to mingle wrong with right, to be energetic without mercy and kindly without energy?

He was no longer thinking of the Germans as diabolical. They were human; they had a case. It was a stupid case, but our case, too, was a stupid case. How stupid were all our cases! What was it we missed? Something, he felt very close to us, and very elusive. Something that would resolve a hundred tangled oppositions.

Some train of subconscious suggestion brought a long forgotten speech back into Mr. Britling's mind, a speech that is full of that light which still seeks so mysteriously and indefatigably to break through the drabness and thickness of the human mind.

He whispered the words. He whispered it of those men whom he still imagined flying far away eastward through the clear freezing air beneath the stars, those muffled sailors and engineers who had caused so much pain and agony in this little town.

"Father, forgive them for they know not what they do."

"And We Won't Get Back 'Til . . ."

Hugh was to stop the night. He spent what seemed to him and every one a long, shy, inexpressive evening. Only the small boys were really natural and animated. They were much impressed and excited by his departure, and wanted to ask a hundred questions about the life in the trenches. Many of them Hugh had to promise to answer when he got there. Then he would see just exactly how things were. Mrs. Britling was motherly and intelligent about his outfit. "Will you want winter things?" she asked.

But when he was alone with his father after every one had gone to bed they found themselves able to talk.

Mr. Britling spoke almost resentfully. "The older men ought to go before you boys. Who is to carry on if a lot of you get killed?"

Hugh reflected. "In the stiffest battle that ever can be the odds are against getting killed," he said.

"I suppose they are."

"One in three or four in the very hottest corners."

Mr. Britling expressed no satisfaction.

"I've never seen a dead body yet. In Dower-House land there aren't dead bodies."

"We've kept things from you—horrid things of that sort."

"I'm not complaining," said Hugh. "But—Master Hugh—the Master Hugh you kept things from—will never come back."

He went on quickly as his father raised distressed eyes to him. "I mean that anyhow *this* Hugh will never come back. Another one may. But I shall have been outside, and it will all be different when I come back to stay."

He paused. Never had Mr. Britling been so disposed to take up the discourse.

For some moments neither father nor son said anything more. They had a queer sense of insurmountable insufficiency. Neither was saying what he had wanted to say to the other, but it was not clear to them now what they had to say to one another.

Hugh could only manage: "The world has turned right over . . ."

"The job had to be done," said Mr. Britling.

"The job has to be done," said Hugh.

The pause lengthened.

"You'll be getting up early tomorrow," said Mr. Britling.

The Best Game

Hugh's letters divided themselves pretty fairly between two main topics; the first was the interest of the art of war, the second the reaction against warfare.

"After one has got over the emotion of it," he wrote, "and when one's mind has just accepted and forgotten (as it does) the horrors and waste of it all, then I begin to perceive that war is absolutely the best game in the world. It's such a big game. Instead of being fenced into a field and tied down to one set of tools, as you are in almost every other game, you have all the world to play with, and you may use whatever you can use. You can use every scrap of imagination and invention that is in you.

"Real soldiers aren't cruel. And war isn't cruel in its essence. Only in its consequences. Over here one gets hold of scraps of talk that light up things. Most of the barbarities in the early stages of the war were done—it is quite clear—by an excited civilian sort of men, men in a kind of inflamed state. The great part of the German army was really an army of demented civilians. They lived in a kind of nightmare. They didn't know what they were doing. They did horrible things just as one does them sometimes in dreams."

He flung out his conclusions with just his mother's leaping consecutiveness. Conscript soldiers are the ruin of war . . . Half the Germans and a lot of the French ought never to have been brought within ten miles of a battlefield.

"What makes all this so plain are the diaries the French and English have been finding on the dead. You know at the early stage of the war every German soldier was expected to keep a diary. He was ordered to do it. The idea was to keep him interested in the war. Consequently, from the dead and wounded our people have got thousands. It helps one to realise that the Germans aren't really soldiers at all. They are

obedient, law-abiding, intelligent people, who have been shoved into this.

"Diary hunting makes this war intellectually fascinating. But what the men put down aren't the beautiful things they ought to put down: most of them shove down lists of their meals, and a lot of them have written the most damning stuff about outrages and looting. Which the French are translating and publishing. The Germans would give anything now to get back those silly diaries.

"Our people got so keen on documenting and the value of chance writings that one of the principle things to do after a German attack had failed had been to hook in the documentary dead, and find out what they had on them.

"One does not think of the dead body as a man recently deceased, who had perhaps a wife and business connections and a weakness for oysters or pale brandy. Or as something that laughed and cried and didn't like getting hurt. That would spoil everything. One thinks of him merely as a uniform with marks upon it that will tell us what kind of stuff we have against us, and possibly with papers that will give us a hint of how far he and his lot are getting sick of the whole affair.

"There's a kind of hardening not only of the body but of the mind through all this life out here.

"It's only by an effort that I can recall how life felt in the spring of 1914. Do you remember Heinrich and his attempt to make a table chart of the roses, so that we could sit outside the barn and read the names of all the roses in the bar court?

"What an inconceivable thing that is now. For all I know I shot Heinrich the other night. For all I know he is one of the lumps that we counted after the attack went back.

"You once wrote that all fighting ought to be done nowadays by metal soldiers. I perceive, my dear Daddy, that all real fighting is . . ."

Lost and Found

And then as if it were something that everyone in the Dower House had been waiting for, came the message that Hugh had been killed.

Mr. Britling opened the telegram, hoping as he had hoped when he opened any telegram since Hugh had gone to the front that it would not contain the exact words he read; that it would say wounded, that at the worst it would say "missing," that perhaps it might even tell of some pleasant surprise, a brief return to home such as the last letter had foreshadowed. He read the final, unqualified statement, the terse regrets. He stood quite still for a moment or so, staring at the words . . .

Killed.

Then his own voice, hoarse and strange to his ears, spoke his thought.

"My God! how unutterably silly . . . Why did I let him go? Why did I let him go?"

Mrs. Britling did not learn of the blow that had struck them until after dinner that night. She was so accustomed to ignore his incomprehensible moods that she did not perceive that there was anything tragic about him until they sat at table together. She was stabbed to the heart to see a haggard white face and eyes of deep despair regarding her ambiguously.

"Hugh!" she said, and then with a chill intimation, *"What is it?"*

They looked at each other. His face softened and winced.

"My Hugh," he whispered, and neither spoke for some seconds.

"Killed," he said, and suddenly stood up whimpering.

He thrust his chair back clumsily and went hastily out of the room. She heard him sob.

The parlour maid came into the room. "Clear the dinner away!" said Mrs. Britling, standing at her place. "Master Hugh is killed . . ." And then wailing: "Oh! what can I *say?* What can I *say* to you?"

That night Mrs. Britling made the supreme effort of her life to burst the prison of self-consciousness and inhibition in which she was confined. Never before in all her life had she so desired to be spontaneous and unrestrained; never before had she so felt herself hampered by her timidity, her self-criticism, her deeply ingrained habit of never letting herself go.

It was late that night and after an eternity of resolutions and doubts and indecisions that Mrs. Britling went to her husband. He was sitting close up to the fire with his chin upon his hands, waiting for her; he felt that she would come.

She came and stood beside him. She ventured to touch him very softly, and to stroke his head. "My dear," she said. My poor dear!"

And then she went on saying "poor dear," saying it presently because there was nothing more had come into her mind. And suddenly her stroking hand ceased. Suddenly the real woman cried out from her.

"I can't *reach* you!" she cried aloud. "I can't reach you. I would do anything . . . You! You with your heart half broken . . ."

She turned towards the door. She moved clumsily, she was blinded by her tears.

Mr. Britling uncovered his face. He stood up astonished, and then pity and pitiful understanding came storming across his grief. He made a step and took her in his arms. "My dear," he said, "don't go from me . . ."

She turned to him weeping, and put her arms about his neck, and he too was weeping.

"My poor wife!" he said, "my dear wife. If it were not for you—I think I could kill myself tonight. Don't cry, my dear. Don't, don't cry. You do not know how you comfort me. You do not know how you help me."

He drew her to him; he put her cheek against his own . . .

Opened By Censor

IT WAS some weeks later. It was now the middle of November, and Mr. Britling, very warmly wrapped in his thick dressing gown and his thick llama wool pyjamas, was sitting at his night desk, and working ever and again at an essay, an essay of preposterous ambitions, for the title of it was "The Better Government of the World."

Latterly he had had much sleepless misery. In the day life was tolerable, but in the night—unless he defended himself by working, the losses and cruelties of the war came and grimaced at him, insufferably. Now he would be haunted by long processions of refugees, now he would think of the dead lying stiff and twisted in a thousand dreadful attitudes.

At other times he thought of wounds and the deformities of body and spirit produced by injuries. And sometimes he would think of the triumph of evil. Stupid and triumphant persons went about a world that stupidity had desolated, with swaggering gestures, with a smiling consciousness of enhanced importance, with their scornful hatred of all measured and temperate and kindly things turned now to scornful contempt.

And mingling with the soil they walked on, lay the dead body of Hugh, face downward. At the back of the boy's head, rimmed by blood-stiffened hair— the hair that had once been "as soft as the down of a bird"—was a big red hole. That hole was always pitilessly distinct. They stepped on him—heedlessly. They heeled the scattered stuff of his exquisite brain into the clay . . .

From all such moods of horror Mr. Britling's circle of lamplight was his sole refuge. His work could conjure up visions, like opium visions, of a world of order and justice. Amidst the gloom of world bankruptcy he stuck to the prospectus of a braver enterprise—reckless of his chances of subscribers . . .

BUT this night even this circle of lamplight would not hold his mind. On the top of Mr. Britling's desk, beside the clock, lay a letter, written in clumsy English and with its envelope resealed by a label which testified that it had been "OPENED BY CENSOR."

The friendly go-between in Norway had written to tell Mr. Britling that Herr Heinrich also was dead; he had died a wounded prisoner in Russia some months ago. Before he died he had written to his parents, and once again he had asked that the fiddle he had left in Mr. Britling's care should if possible be returned to them.

The letter would have to be answered, and the potentialities of the answer were running through Mr. Britling's brain to the exclusion of any impersonal composition. He thought of the old parents away there in Pomerania—he believed but he was not quite sure, that Heinrich had been an only son—and of the pleasant spectacled figure that had now become a broken and decaying thing.

He found himself thinking of young Heinrich in the very manner, if with a lesser intensity, in which he thought about his own son, as of hopes senselessly destroyed.

By no conceivable mental gymnastics could he think of the two as antagonists. Between them there was no imaginable issue. They had both very much the same scientific dispositions; with perhaps more dash and inspiration in the quality of Hugh; more docility and method in the case of Karl. Until war had smashed them one against the other . . .

They Live!

HE PUSHED aside the manuscript of "The Better Government of the World," and began to write rather slowly, shaping his letters roundly:

Dear Sir,

I am writing this letter to you to tell you I am sending back the few little things I had kept for your son at his request when the war broke out. Especially I am sending his violin which he asked me to convey to you. Either it is a gift from you or it symbolised many things for him that he connected with home and you. I will have it packed with particular care, and I will do all in my power to ensure its safe arrival.

I want to tell you that all the stress and passion of this war has not made us here in Matching's Easy forget our friend your son. He was one of us, he had our affection, he had friends here who are still his friends. So we share something of your loss.

I have got together for you a few snapshots I chance to possess in which you will see him in the sunshine, and which will enable you perhaps to picture a little more definitely than you would otherwise do the life he led here. There is one particularly that I have marked. Our family is lunching out-of-doors, and you will see that next to your son is a youngster, a year or so his junior, who is touching glasses with him. I have put a cross over his head. He is my eldest son, he was very dear to me, and he too has been killed in this war. They are, you see, smiling very pleasantly at each other.

THREE hours later Mr. Britling was working by daylight, though his study lamp was still burning. It was clear to him now that he was no longer writing as his limited personal self to those two personal selves grieving, in the old, large, high-walled, steep-roofed household amidst pine woods, of which Heinrich had once shown him a picture. He knew them too little for any such personal address.

He was writing, he perceived, not as Mr. Britling but as an Englishman—that was all he could be to them—and he was writing to them as Germans; he could apprehend them as nothing more. He was just England bereaved to Germany bereaved . . .

He sat back in his chair wearily, with his chin sunk upon his chest. For a time he did not think, and then, he read again a sentence in front of his eyes.

"*These boys, these hope, this war has killed.*"

The words hung for a time in his mind.

"No!" said Mr. Britling stoutly. "They live!"

And suddenly it was borne in upon his mind that he was not alone. There were thousands and tens of thousands of men and women like himself, desiring with all their hearts to say, as he desired to say, the reconciling word. It was not only his hand that thrust against the obstacles . . . Frenchmen and Russians sat in the same stillness, facing the same perplexities; there were Germans seeking a way through to him. Even as he sat and wrote.

And for the first time clearly he felt a Presence of which he had thought very many times in the last few weeks, a Presence so close to him that it was behind his eyes and in his brain and hands. It was no trick of his vision; it was a feeling of immediate reality.

And it was Hugh, Hugh that he had thought was dead, it was young Heinrich living also, it was himself, it was those others that sought, it was all these and it was more, it was the Master, the Captain of Mankind, it was God, there present with him and he knew that it was God.

It was as if he had been groping all this time in the darkness, thinking himself alone amidst rocks and pitfalls and pitiless things and suddenly a hand, a firm strong hand, had touched his own. And a voice within him bade him be of good courage.

GOD was beside him and within him and about him . . . It was the crucial moment of Mr. Britling's life. It was a thing as light as the passing of a cloud on an April morning; it was a thing as great as the first day of creation.

God was with him indeed, and he wa

with God. The King was coming to his own. Amidst the darknesses and confusions, the nightmare cruelties and the hideous stupidities of the great war, God, the Captain of the World Republic, fought his way to empire. So long as one did one's best and utmost in a cause so mighty, did it matter though the thing one did was little and poor?

"I have thought too much of myself," said Mr. Britling, "and of what I would do by myself. I have forgotten *that which was with me* . . ."

He forgot the Pomeranians for a time. He murmured to himself. He turned over the conviction that had suddenly become clear and absolute in his mind.

"Religion is the first thing and the last thing, and until a man has found God and been found by God, he begins at no beginning, he works to no end. He may have his friendships, his partial loyalties, his scraps of honour. But all these things fall into place and life falls into place only with God. Only with God. God, who fights through men against Blind Force and Night and Non-Existence; who is the end, who is the meaning. He is the only King . . .

Of course I must write about Him. I must tell all my world of Him. And before the coming of the true King, the inevitable King, the King who is present whenever just men foregather, this blood-stained rubbish of the ancient world, these puny kings, tawdry emperors, these wily politicians and artful lawyers, these men who claim and grab and trick and compel, these war makings and oppressors, will presently shrivel and pass—like paper thrust into a flame . . ."

Then after a time he said:

"Our sons who have shown us God . . ."

Blow, Blow, Thou Winter Wind

Blow, blow, thou winter wind,
Thou art not so unkind
    As man's ingratitude;
Thy tooth is not so keen,
Because thou art not seen,
    Although thy breath be rude.
Heigh ho! sing, heigh ho! unto the green holly:
Most friendship is feigning, most loving mere folly:
    Then heigh ho, the holly!
    This life is most jolly.

Freeze, freeze, thou bitter sky,
That dost not bit so nigh
    As benefits forgot:
Though thou the waters warp,
Thy sting is not so sharp
    As friend remember'd not.
Heigh ho! sing, heigh ho! unto the green holly:
Most friendship is feigning, most loving mere folly:
    Then heigh ho, the holly!
    This life is most jolly.
                              —*William Shakespeare*

EDWARD STREETER

DERE MABLE

THIS was the big best seller of the war year 1918. It is an amusing account of the trials and tribulations of a "Rookie" in training camp, which so caught the imagination of other "Rookies" and the folks at home that they bought over a million copies. After Edward Streeter had written several sequels and produced a play about Mable and her boy friend, he went into banking. He is now vice-president of a bank in New York, and has recently published another best seller called "Daily Except Sundays," about the trials and tribulations of a commuter.

DERE MABLE:

I guess you thought I was dead. Youll never know how near you was to right. We got the tents up at last, though, so I got a minit to rite. I guess they choose these camps by mail order. The only place there flat is on the map. Where our tents is would make a good place for a Rocky Mountain goat if he didnt break his neck. The first day the Captin came out an says "Pitch your tents here." Then he went to look for someone quick before anyone could ask him how. I wish I was a Captin. I guess he thought we was Alpine Chasers. Eh, Mable? But you probably don't know what those are.

Honest, Mable, if Id put in the work I done last week on the Panamah Canal it would have been workin long before it was. Of course there was a lot of fellos there with me but it seemed like all they did was to stand round and hand me shovels when I wore em out.

The Captin appresheates me though. The other day he watched me work awhile and then he says "Smith." He calls me Smith now. We got very friendly since I been nice to him. I noticed none of the other fellos had much to say to him. I felt kind of sorry for him. Hes a human bein even if he is a Captin, Mable. So every time I saw him I used to stop him and talk to him. Democratic. Thats me all over, Mable. "Smith" he says "If they was all like

you round here war would be hell, no joke." By which he meant that we would make it hot for the Boshes.

I been feelin awful sorry for you Mable. What with missin me and your fathers liver gone back on him again things must have been awful lonesome for you. It isnt as if you was a girl what had a lot of fellos hangin round all the time. Not that you couldnt have em Mable, but you dont an theres no use makin no bones about it. If it hadnt been for me I guess things would have been pretty stupid though I dont begrudge you a sent. You know how I am with my money. I guess you ought to any way. Eh, Mable? Never talk of money matters in connexun with a woman. Thats me all over.

Now I got started an found a fountain pen an the Y.M.C.A. givin away paper like it does Im goin to rite you regular. They say there goin to charge three sents for a letter pretty soon. That aint goin to stop me though, Mable. There aint no power in heavin or earth, as the poets say, as can come between you and me Mable. You mite send a few three sent stamps when you rite. That is if your fathers able to work yet. And willin, I should add.

Of course it aint nothin to me but Id keep these letters what you get from me as a record of the war. Some day you can read em to your granchildren an say "Your Granfather Bill did all these things." Aint I the worst, Mable? Serious though I havnt found noone so fa what has thought of doin this except the newspapers. I guess Ill get a lot of inside stuff that theyll never see. So this may be the only one of its kind. But it doesnt matter to me what you do with them, Mable.

Later Ill tell you all about everything but I guess you wont understand much cause its tecknickle. Lots of the fellos are gettin nitted things and candy and stuff right along. Dont pay no attenshun to that, though, or take it for a hint cause it aint. I just say it as a matter of rekord. Independent if nothin. Thats me all over.

Yours till the war ends

Bill

DERE MABLE:

I havnt rote for sometime I had such sore feet lately. When they broke up our regiment and sent me over to the artillery I thought I was goin to quit usin my feet. That was just another roomor.

Thanks for the box of stuff you sent me. I guess the brakeman must have used it for a chair all the way. It was pretty well baled but that dont matter. And thanks for the fudge too. That was fudge wasnt it, Mable? And the sox. They dont fit but I can use them for somethin. A good soldier never throws nothin away. An thank your mother for the half pair of gloves she sent me. I put them away. Maybe sometime shell get a chance to nit the other half. Or if I ever get all my fingers shot off theyll come in very handy.

The artillerys a little different from the infantry. They make us work harder. At least theres more work on the skedule. I know now what they mean when they say that the "artillerys active on the western front."

I dont care much for horses. I think they feels the same way about me. Most of them are so big that the only thing there good for is the view of the camp you get when you climb up. They are what they call hors de combat in French. My horse died the other day. I guess it wasnt much effort for him. If it had been he wouldnt have done it.

The horses has the softest of anyone, Mable. They dont even have to get up for breakfast in the morning. We bring it to em in a little bag filled with cereul. You tie this on there face. I guess they aint never been fed before the war broke out. When they see you comin they start jumpin round like starvin sailurs. I dont guess they like cereul. I wouldnt ether three times a day. I thought theyd give em somethin different Thanksgivin but not a chance. There always hopin it ull be somethin else I guess. When they see the same old thing they get sore and try to step on your feet.

The sargents stand way behind an say "Go on in. They wont hurt you." An then when they land on your corn they say "Thats to bad. You didnt do it right." I dont like sargents any better than horses.

An I dont kno as Im going to like the Captin much better ether. The other day I got laffin while I was standin in line. Just laffin to myself. Not disturbin nobody. The Captin turns round an says "Smith are you laffin at me?" I says no sir an he says "Well what else was there to laff at?" Thats the kind of a fello he is. I didn't sass him back or nothin, Mable. Just looked at him an made him feel cheap. I saw him again in the afternoon. Course I didnt salute. He says "What do you mean by not salutin?" I told him I thought he was mad. Im glad Im not his wife, Mable. You never know how to take a fello like that.

If I hadnt knowed they needed me Id have given him two weaks notise on the spot. Duty before pleasure though. Thats me all over.

Well I got to quit now an rite a bunch of other girls. Thanks again for the box although it was so busted that it wasnt much good but that dont matter.

Yours till you here otherwise,

Bill.

DERE MABLE:

Rainin today. No drill so Im going to rite you. If I dont get no exercise I go all to pieces. Im back from the artillery into the infantry. Captin an I had different ideas about runnin things. One of us had to leave. Hed been there longest. I left. Hot headed. Thats me all over.

Were doin baynut drill now. I cant say nothin about it. Its not for wimens ears. We have one place where we hit the Hun in the nose an rip all the decorashuns offen his uniform all in one stroke. Then theres another where you give him a shave an a round hair cut an end by knocking his hat over his eyes. Then the wiperzup come over with a lot of bums an do the dirty work. I an the rest of the fellos go ahead an take another trench. I havent been able to find out yet where we take it.

Its all worked out cientifick. The fello who doped it out had some bean. The principul of the thing is to get the other fello an not let him get you. If the allys had doped out some skeme like this the war would have been over now. There wouldnt have been no Huns left. It takes us Uncle Sammies. Eh Mable?

There gettin up a thrift campain now, Mable. First they sell us enough Liberty Bonds to buy a brand new army an let us go home. Then they cram a lot of insurence at you what wont never do you no good after your killed. Then I guess they found that someone still had a couple of dollars left so they made us send that back home. Now there gettin up a thrift campain Mable. They dont want us to spend our money foolish sos we can buy the Singer Buildin or a Ford or somethin like that when the war is over.

Some one say that we was the highest payed army in the world. Besides all this money we get our bed and board. I guess they dont know that in the army bed and board mean the same thing.

Went to a dance the other night and met some swell girls. I made em all laff. I says I guess I got the instinks of a soldier all right. The minit I smell powder Im right on my tows.

I havent been very well lately. I guess Ill cut out eatin at meals. It spoils my appetite for the rest of the day. I kno youll be glad to kno my feet aint hurtin so much. Remember me to the hired girl and your mother.

Yours through the winter,
Bill.

CHAIR MABLE:

Thats French. I didnt expect you to kno what it meant though. The Y.M.C.A. are learnin me French now. I only had three lessons so far but I can talk it pretty good. You know how quick I am at pickin up any kind of trick stuff like that. The only difference between French and English is that there pretty near alike but the French don pronounce there words right.

When I use French words Ill under line them. Thatll give you some ide of the languige.

When we get voila as the French sa for over there itll come handy to be abl to sit down and have a dosy dos witl them poilus. (That means chew the ra in English.) A poilus Mable is a Frencl peasant girl an they say that they ar very belle. (Now don't mispronounc things an get sore till you know. Yo pronounce that like the bell in push bu ton. It means good lookers.) There craz about us fellos. They call us Sammie: They named one of there rivers for u You have heard of the battle of th Samme. But I don't suppose you have.

Its getting frappayer and frappaye down here (meaning colder and colder Washington will never know how luck he was that he got assigned to Valle Forge instead of here. It got so cold tha I put on those sox that you nitted me. guess I wont any more though. I gue my feet are going to look like corderc the rest of my life. Youll understand n hard feelin I know. You know how del cate my feet is an how I cant afford prennez a hazard with them.

Thank your mother for the flannel p jammas. I wear them every night ov my uniform. I got to quit now an rea some pictur post cards.

Good night
(or as the French say Robe de Nuit

Dᴇʀᴇ Mᴀʙʟᴇ:

I havnt rote for some time because I been made an officer.—a corperal. I admit I deserved it. I didnt apply for it or nothin though. They just come and told me.

Bein corperal means I dont have nothin more to do with details. An at the same time I got more details than ever. Thats a sort of a joke that us military men understand. You couldnt get it probably Mable. Its tecknickle.

Two of my men has gone home on furlos. Me bein corperal I took all there blankets. The men didnt like it but I got a squad of men to look out for an my first duty is to keep fit. Duty first. Thats me all over. I got so many blankets now that I got to put a book mark in the place I get in at night or Id never find it again.

I bought a book on Minor Tackticks the other day. Thats not about underaged tacks that live in ticks as you might suppose, Mable. Its the cience of movin bodies of men from one place to another. I thought it might tell of some way of gettin the squad out of bed in the mornin but it doesnt. All the important stuff like that is camooflaged.

Camooflage is not a new kind of cheese Mable. Its a military term. Camooflage is French for cauliflower which is a disguised cabbage. It is the same thing as puttin powder on your face instead of washin it. You deceive Germans with it. For instance you paint a horse black and white stripes an a German comes along. He thinks its a picket fence an goes right by. Or you paint yourself like a tree an the Germans come an drink beer round you an tell military sekruts.

Well I guess its time to say Mery Xmas now Mable. I guess it wont be a very Mery Xmas withut me there, eh? Cheer up cause Im goin to think of you whenever I get time all day long. Im pretty busy nowdays. I got to watch the men work. It keeps a fello on the jump all the time. I like it though, Mable. Thats me all over. Isnt it?

Dont send me nothin for Christmas, Mable. I bought somethin for you but Im not going to tell you cause its a surprize. All that I can say is that it cost me four eighty seven ($4.87) which is more than I could afford. An its worth a lot more. But you know how I am with money. A spend drift. So dont send me anything please although I need an electric flash light, some cigarets, candy an one of them sox that you wear on your head. Ill spend my last sent on anyone I like but I dont want to be under no obligations. Independent. Thats me all over.

You might read this part to your mother. I dont want nothin from her ether.

Rite soon an plain Mable, cause I dont get much chance to study.

Yours till the south is warm,
Bill.

Your mothers present cost me three seventy seven ($3.77).

Mᴏɴ Cʀᴏǫᴜᴇᴛᴛᴇ:

Thats not the kind with the evenin dress tooth pick in the top, Mable. A croquette is a French society woman. Study these letters of mine an see how I use the words. You ought to be able to pick up enough French to understand me talkin it when I come home.

Well, Mable, New Years are behind us again. Once more I made a lot of revolushuns. Its no use sayin there wasnt nothin for me to change. Youre prejudiced. I can see falts where others cant. Underneath a pleasant exterior I am made of sterner stuff, as the poets say. I have gave up frivolity with the exception of goin into town once in a while to take a bath. Im strong for this sanity stuff under any conditions.

Im makin a study of war. Im goin to tell you a sekrut. Im workin on a plan to end the war. I got thinkin, as I will, an it struck me that no one had gone into this at all. There all figurin how to go on with it but none of em how to quit it. Dont say nothin till I get it worked out. I guess you always knew youd here from me when I got goin, eh Mable?

I got that watch your father sent me for a New Years present. Tell him thanks very much an not to feel bad because he forgot to send me a Christmas present cause this wipes out the debt entirely. He said it was a military watch an the latest thing out. I guess they call it a military watch cause it works two hours and stops four. Its the latest thing round here. If I answered call by that watch Id be fallin in for retreat round taps. Its so slow it cant stop quick.

I got asked to a dinner New Years night. I sat next to a Colonels wife. It was kind of embarrassing at first. I put her easy though. I says whose that funny lookin old bird sittin across the room with a head like an egg. Hes very chic isnt he? (Thats a French joke Mable.) She says "Thats my husband." As soon as Id stopped laffin I started right in an told her the history of every man in the company beginnin with the As. You know me when I get started. I didnt give her no chanst to get embarrassed. When she started to say somethin I just kept right on talkin just to show her that bein a Colonels wife she wasnt expected to make no effort.

I made good, Mable. I guess you kno I would. After dinner I heard her ask somebody who invited me. Then she said somethin like "Hed ought to be known better." Never miss a chance. Thats me all over. It may mean promoshun or anything. It may be that shell have me sent to Fort Silly to learn somethin. You cant tell.

You keep menshuning a fello named Broggins in your letters. Now I aint got a spark of jelusy in my nature. Big. Thats me all over, Mable. But I warn you frankly. If I ever catch one of those ailin enemies windin up your victrola Ill kick him out of the house. Thats only fair. It isn't that I care a snap. Theres plenty of girls waitin for me. Its just the principul of the thing.

Yours till you here otherwise,
Bill.

DERE MABLE:

I been thinkin of you a lot durin the last weak, Mable, havin nothin else to do. I been in the hospital with the Bronxitis. I guess I caught it from Joe Loomis. He comes from there. Id have rote you in bed but I dropped my fountin pen on the floor an bent it. Im all right now.

I got some news for you, Mable. The cook says we only drew ten days supply of food last time. He says he guesses when we et that up well go to France. Hes an awful smart fello the cook. Hes got a bet on that if the allys dont buck up an win the Germans is comin out ahead. Max Glucos, a fello in the tent, is refere. Were all eatin as fast as we can. Perhaps we can eat it all in less than ten days. So maybe well be gone, Mable, before I rite you from here again.

Theres a French sargent comes round once in a while an says the war is goin to be over quick. He ought to know cause hes been over there an seen the whole thing. He smokes cigarets something awful an dont say much. Thats because the poor cus cant talk much English. It must be awful not to talk English. Think of not bein able to say nothin all your life without wavin your arms round an then lookin it up in a dickshunary.

I feel so sorry for these fellos that Im studiin French a lot harder sos theyll have someone to talk to when we get over there. Im readin a book now thats rote all in French. No English in it anywhere, Mable. A fello told me that was the only way to talk it good. I dont understand it very well so far. The only way I kno its French is by the pictures. Some day Im goin to find out what the name is. Then I'm goin to get the English of it. Those are some picturs. Aint I fierce, Mable? I guess thats why I get on with wimen so well.

I gave up readin it out loud cause the fellos said it made em think they was in Paris so much they got restles. I cant speak no better yet. I guess that comes all at once at the end of the book.

I keep herein more about this fello Broggins. I suppose he belongs to the Home Guards an wares his uniform round in the evenin. An I suppose he has an American flag on his ritin paper. It dont mean nothin in my life. I aint goin to put up no arguments or get nasty like most fellos would. Dignity. Thats me all over, Mable. Let me tell you though if I ever come home and find him shinin his elbos on the top of your baby grand Ill kick him down the front steps if I only have one leg to do it with.

As ever,
on guard,
Bill.

Dere Mable:
This is the last time I will ever take my pen in hand for you. All is over among us.

Today among some letters that I got from girls was one from a girl what knos you well. She told me all about this fello Broggins. She says you take him around with you everywhere. Thats the kind of a fello I thought he was, Mable, but Im surprized at you. She says your awful fond of him hes so cute. I aint cute an aint never pretended to be. A mans man. Thats me all over. Mable. She says she went up to your house the other night an he was sittin in your lap stickin his tongue out at my pictur on the mantlepiece. After that, Mable, theres nothin to say. So I repeat, its all over among us.

Im returnin today by parcels post the red sweter an the gloves that has no fingers an the sox that you wear over your head an your pictur. Most of the stuff aint been used much. The pictur has some mud on it cause I had to keep it in the bottom of my barrak bag an my shoes came next.

The stuff that you sent me to eat I havent kept. I guess you wouldnt want that anyway Mable. The stuff that your mother sent me Im going to keep. She wasnt my girl an she didnt have to send all that stuff if she didnt want to.

As for all the things I have give you, Mable, keep em. I dont want em no more. I aint even goin to menshun all the money Ive spent on you for movies an sodas an the Lord knows what not. I aint the kind of a fello to throw that up to a fello or even menshun it in no ways. I kept track of it though in a little book. It comes to $28.27 and some odd sense.

And now, Mable, Im closin for the last time. It wont be no use runin to the door when you here the postman no more cause he wont have nothin but the gas bill. From now on the only way youll here from me is in the papers perhaps when we get over there.

Now Im going to ask you a favor, Mable, for old times sake. Take the pictur I had taken pointin to the American flag an burn it up. You cant have that to show your friends no more an I aint goin to have no flat foot makin faces at it. I may be selfish, Mable, but a girl cant make a cake an eat it too as the old sayin is.

Give my best to your father an mother. Tell em I sympathize with them in there loss. Its no use ritin any more cause Im firm as the rock of Gibber Alter. Concrete. Thats me all over, Mable.

as ever
yours no longer
Bill

WESTERN UNION TELEGRAM

RECEIVED AT Philopolis, N. Y.

Miss Mable Gimp
106 Main Street
Philopolis, N. Y.

Dere Mable: How was I to know Broggins was a dog. You can send back all your stuff and make me some more if you want to. This telegram is costing me nine cents a word so I cant say no more now. Thrifty. Thats me all over, Mable.

Bill.

Lloyd C. Douglas

GREEN LIGHT

Lloyd C. Douglas is by profession a clergyman, born in Indiana and educated in Ohio. He has held Lutheran pastorates in Indiana, Ohio, Washington, D. C., Michigan, and Canada. He now devotes his time to writing and lecturing. His better known novels include: "Magnificent Obsession" (1929); "Green Light" (1935); "White Banners" (1936); "Disputed Passage" (1939). Mr. Douglas at present makes his home in California.

Death in the Operating Room

By admonition and example, Dr. Bruce Endicott — elsewhere genial and talkative—had discouraged all unnecessary conversation in his operating-rooms at Parkway Hospital. He did not like to be distracted during the preparatory business of scrubbing-up.

On this eventful Wednesday the pantomime had been in progress for fifteen minutes unattended by any noise but the scuffing of competent rubber-shod feet on the tiled floor when the anxious face of the chief's secretary appeared in the crack of the corridor door.

"Could Dr. Endicott answer the telephone?" queried the girl nervously.

"Certainly not!" snapped the chief nurse through her gauze. "You ought to know that much."

"I told them," explained the secretary defensively. "But they said that Dr. Endicott would be seriously disadvantaged if the message was not delivered at once. It's his broker."

"Very well then, I'll go," boomed Dr. Endicott. "Sorry, Dr. Paige. I shall not be long."

Abstractedly stoking his gloves, Paige walked through the alcove, passing the operating table, and entered the adjacent chamber. Mrs. Dexter, with the customary modicum of morphine to reduce her active interest in the occasion, spread out her hand apathetically and signed that she was too drowsy to offer it.

Leaning over Mrs. Dexter, he whispered something in her ear which she approved with a contented sigh and several reassuring little nods. She closed her eyes, and the slightly smiling lips relaxed.

Presently the door opened and the chief appeared, quite plainly upset about something. Paige watched him anxiously as he resumed his washing with nervous haste.

Endicott's face was flushed and the muscles of his cheeks twitched. Everybody in the room knew that he had been engaged in an emergency conversation with his brokers and he knew that they all knew. At length, in spite of his haste, he was ready. They filed into the operating-room and gathered about the table.

The hands of the surgeons opened and whatever they required was instantly thrust into them; the others hovering close, alert, lynx-eyed. A clamp for Paige, a long-handled scissors for Endicott—a tense pause, quiet and stiff as a tableau.

The chief nurse offered the handles of a secondary clamp. Endicott shook his head. That meant he couldn't use it because there was no room to apply it.

Paige realized that the pedicle had been cut too short for safe ligation. He adjusted the ligature with difficulty and drew it as tightly as possible. Endicott slowly and with apparent reluctance relaxed the clamp and withdrew it. They waited. The chief breathed as if he had recently been running uphill.

H<small>E HAD</small> made two grave mistakes. In his nervous excitement he had neglected to dissect the pedicle—sheath of the renal artery—with sufficient care, and had severed it too short for a secure tie . . . The pedicle slowly rejected the ligature.

"My fault!" gasped Paige, as the flood broke. "I should have drawn it tighter. *My God!"*

The hemorrhage was instantly out of control. Sponges would have been equally serviceable at a crumbled dam. The increasing tempo of the splash of big drops falling from the table to the floor quickened to a brisk patter and accelerated to a steady stream.

The chief seemed suddenly to go to pieces—a shocking sight to those who had never seen him panic-driven. He panted for breath and his hands shook. "A donor—immediately!" he commanded hoarsely. "Here, Paige," handing him the clamp, "see what you can do." The frenzied grappling continued.

The hemorrhage was subsiding now. It had almost stopped. There was no further energy driving it.

Paige made a quick task of his ablutions, dashed to the dressing-room, and changed to his street clothes. Nothing seemed to matter now but a prompt escape from this place at top speed.

The chief nurse was waiting for him when he came out into the corridor.

"Wait!" she cried. "I know exactly what happened and I'm going to tell everybody the truth."

"You're going to mind your own business," retorted Paige, measuring his words. "And keep your mouth shut."

On the trip home in the taxicab, the one blistering fact that mattered most was the wanton destruction of his idol. As he and Dr. Endicott had stood there, side by side, almost touching elbows, scrubbing off the blood that had been so needlessly shed, he had momentarily expected the big, dynamic, generous-hearted fellow to turn to him and say, courageously: "I was to blame, Newell. We both know that. I'll clear you of any responsibility, you may be sure." And he had already composed the quick reply, "Better let the matter rest the way it is."

But Endicott—damn him!—had buried his hairy arms and pallid face in the square porcelain tub, splashing and sputtering, without a single glance, much less a friendly word.

Paige realized that Endicott's moral disaster had not been entirely unpredictable. He had seen the big man slipping, slipping, day after day. Too much fretting about investments. Too many business conferences downtown. Paige admitted to himself now that he had been afraid to see the chief operate on Mrs. Dexter.

The Enduring Vision

T<small>O HIS</small> amazement the thought of Mrs. Dexter calmed him somewhat. He had anticipated that the recollection of her tragedy would haunt him for life. Strangely enough, the painful sight of her on the operating table, was rapidly driven away by the enduring vision of her in her room.

For their professional acquaintance had ripened into an unusual comradeship. Sometimes Dr. Paige would stay with Mrs. Dexter for an hour or more. No one of her family had been in town. Her husband would come when the operation had been decided upon and

her daughter, Phyllis, was in Europe for the summer with a party of Vassar classmates.

Sometimes, seated at ease in her tranquil presence, he had found himself smiling indulgently as she talked of "the things that made for personal adequacy."

"You are a very fortunate woman," Newell Paige had told her once. "Last night when I was mulling over some of the things you had said about Dean Harcourt and the philosophy of life which he has taught you, it occurred to me that if somehow it could be reduced to simple terms and communicated, it would practically revolutionize the whole problem of human happiness. But I doubt whether it could ever be made elementary enough for the ordinary intellect."

"No." Mrs. Dexter's negative was accompanied by a slow shake of her head on the pillow. "No—it isn't a matter of mental capacity or even of temperament. The trouble is that the average individual leaves most of his tasks unfinished, his mental tasks in particular. Most people try to get along with a vocabulary of about six hundred words. This enables them to understand what is going on in the kitchen, the shop, and on the street. Any idea that can't be translated into kitchen-lore or shop-lore or street-lore is dismissed."

"Did Dean Harcourt ever try to put this into print?"

"No—nor has he more than hinted at it in public addresses. He does it all by the case-method. People in trouble come to him and he tells them. It's really amazing what happens to them."

Well she would be an everlasting inspiration. Tomorrow or the next day they would carry her out to some shady spot and leave her there to become one with the soil. That grisly aspect of human mortality was made strangely unrepellent as he remembered her self-confessed integration with "a planned universe" which in her opinion, was every way sound and worthy.

Sylvia, his dog, licked his hand when he opened the door of his apartment. She followed him closely into the library and when he slumped down to his desk she sniffed his fingers with quivering nostrils and whined.

Paige wrote a brief, business-like letter to the firm of attorneys who handled his affairs, confident that his secret would be kept and his instructions meticulously obeyed.

He left the letter, sealed and stamped, on the library table, and dressed quickly in a rough suit of tweeds and well-worn hiking shoes while the dog followed him about closely from room to room, sitting on her haunches directly before him while he laced his shoes, studying his face with a somewhat annoyed solicitude.

"No—you can't go, Sylvia," he said gruffly, patting her on the head. "Not where I'm going. You're still alive. Try to make the most of it."

It was dark in the street and nobody in the vicinity was astir. But Sylvia was trotting at his heels when he turned south on Elm Street.

In the Cathedral

LEARNING after breakfast that Dean Harcourt was available for private interviews between ten and noon, Paige had set out for the Cathedral early, arriving as the clock struck ten. He had taken Sylvia with him, knowing that she would wait interminably for him outside wherever she was told to remain.

Sauntering into the reception room quietly, Paige noticed that he was not alone. A young woman stood in the bay, at the far end of the room, looking out through the window. She was without coat or hat and evidently belonged to the establishment. At length she seemed to sense that she was not alone and slowly turned her head. Paige caught his breath at the sight of her profile. She was the living image of Mrs. Dexter as she might have appeared in her youth!

Just how long they stood there staring at each other neither of them knew. At length, the girl stirred, smiled tentatively and said in a low voice, "You came to see Dean Harcourt?"

"Yes," replied Paige, still searching her eyes—same heavy lashes, same patrician arch of the brows—same dark-amber iris. "My name is Parker," he added. "I am a stranger to the Dean."

"I shall tell Dean Harcourt you are here." She took a few steps toward the door. Apparently on impulse, she halted and said, "I am Miss Dexter."

Paige bowed and replied, almost inaudibly, "Yes . . . Miss Dexter."

A moment or so later she reappeared. "He will see you now," she said, leading the way.

Dean Harcourt did not extend his hand or offer any word of conventional greeting. There was something uncannily prescient in his eyes. They were dark, almost cavernous. A veritable sunburst of crow's feet at the outer corners gave the effect of a residual smile of compassion which softened the penetrating search and interpreted it as a comradely quest. His thick white hair shone silver in the single light suspended above his head, a light that intensified the deep lines of a face which bore unmistakable evidences of suffering. For Dean Harcourt was a cripple.

"And what brings you in out of the sunshine, Mr. Parker?" he asked quietly.

However difficult it had been to look down into the long-lashed, amber-tinted Dexter eyes and lie about his identity, it was even harder to face the analytical gaze leveled at him from beneath the serious brows of Dean Harcourt.

"My name is Paige, sir," he replied, after a moment's hesitation. "Newell Paige."

"I beg your pardon," Dean Harcourt answered. "I must have misunderstood."

"There was no misunderstanding," he found himself confessing. "I did tell the young lady that my name was Parker. There are reasons why I have—"

"I dare say your reasons are not dishonorable, else you would not have confided your real name . . . Tell me why you wanted to see me."

"Well, sir—I came to talk to you about the terms of a stabilized life which you mentioned in your sermon yesterday. I am quite in need of knowing something more about them."

On the Highway Through History

"Sometimes it is helpful to attempt a mental reconstruction of a highway from the very beginning and trace it forward through human history," said the Dean.

"Let us begin, then with the hypothesis that from the very dawn of animate life there was a potential man-in-the making, related to present-day man much as an acorn is related to the oak it is to be. At one phase of this creature's progress, he closely resembled what we know as the harbor seal. Dissatisfied with his ocean, he climbed up on a rock and at the cost of who knows how much agony—achieved a capacity for recovering oxygen from the air instead of the water. It is quite conceivable that of all these creatures who made the experiment, only a comparatively few had the fortitude to see it through.

"The harbor seal who, at a frightful price, learned to breathe, but who—at the one critical hour of deciding whether to justify this suffering by going on—inland—to possess the earth—is now sadly imitated by the people who have endured pain and grief and anxiety of their existence, but lack the courage to proceed toward the achievement of that peace and personal power which is their rightful wage. Many people who have fully paid for it, have no awareness of their own *personal adequacy*."

"That phrase stirs me, sir," muttered Paige. "I have heard it before. The person who used it said she had got it from you, sir."

"Would you like to tell me," said the Dean searchingly.

"I had it from Mrs. Dexter—in Parkway Hospital—a few days before I helped to—to take her life."

Dean Harcourt looked Paige squarely in the eyes for a moment. "I was never satisfied with the story, Dr. Paige," he declared firmly. "There was something very mysterious about it, even though the responsibility seemed to rest on you—when you ran away. I have often worried about you, my son, wondering where you were, and if you were still alive. I confess it was a bit of a shock when you told me your name, a while ago."

"I should like to talk to you about it. Would it be impertinent if I asked you to promise me that you will keep my secret."

"No, Dr. Paige, I will keep your secret."

"Forgive me for asking. I didn't want to risk an accident that might inform Miss Dexter of my identity. By the way, would she recognize my name?"

"Yes . . . she would."

"She thinks I was responsible for the death of her mother?"

"Yes . . . she does," replied the Dean reluctantly. "But I don't. *You took the blame!* I strongly suspected it all along. Endicott as much as told me. You were a brave fellow! I'm proud of a chance to talk with you. My sympathy is all with you, Dr. Paige. Perhaps, if I were in your place, I might find it very difficult to think of any extenuation for your chief.

"I think that we may say that Endicott's development came to an abrupt halt on the day he lacked the courage necessary to the carrying-on of his evolution. Up to that hour, we may say, he had fulfilled the requirements to be a real man. Figuratively speaking, he had gone through all the pain and fatigue of crawling up out of the ocean. He had walked on the bleeding stubs of his flippers into the forest. He had succeeded in climbing the tree, but—"

"But flunked on the day he should have climbed down," ventured Paige.

"It would seem so. Now will you try to look at it that way? It will ease your mind. I promise you."

The Cathedral clock tolled noon. Paige suddenly realized that he had monopolized all of Dean Harcourt's morning. He rose.

"Just a moment!" The Dean's gesture commanded him to be reseated. His tone was vibrant as he proceeded.

"For your comfort, my son, let me tell you that I have laid hold upon a truth powerful enough to sustain me until I die! I know that, in spite of all the painful circumstances I have met, *my course is upward*. I know that the Universe is on my side. It will not let me down. I have been detained at times—but eventually—*I go on through!*

"I get the signal to go forward! I have been delayed—long—long—long—but—at length—I get the GREEN LIGHT."

Paige's voice sounded very unlike his own when he impulsively broke the silence which followed. "God!—I wish I had that!"

Sylvia Does the Honors

NEWELL had taken his departure through the Cathedral nave, and was seated on a bench in Madison Park, waiting until he could control the emotions which had overcome him. Then he would go back for Sylvia.

About to rise, he saw Phyllis Dexter and Sylvia entering the park; Sylvia walking so close that she brushed her tawny flank against Phyllis's dress. Very odd of Sylvia and quite out of keeping with her habits. His heart pounded as he watched them approaching. He strolled to meet them.

"I waited for you," she said companionably. "Did you forget the dog?"

"No. To be quite honest, I wasn't up to seeing anyone—after I left Dean Harcourt. I was going back, a little later, for Sylvia."

"Funny name for a dog," laughed Phyllis. Then soberly, she said, half to herself, "Where was it? Somewhere I've heard of another dog whose name was Sylvia." Then she murmured almost inaudibly, "I remember now," and apparently dismissed whatever serious recollection had been stirred. "Now that Sylvia and you are reunited, I shall go to my luncheon."

She turned away in the direction from which she had come. Sylvia, probably presuming her master expected to rejoin her new friend, trotted on ahead and was presently at Phyllis' side. Then, much disturbed at seeing Paige remain

"Read that letter"

behind, the dog slowly retraced her steps to half the distance between them, looking from one to another. Phyllis laughed.

"Let's all go to luncheon together," called Parker, "and afterward Sylvia can decide what she wants to do. I want to say this is a very discriminating dog, very fussy about her friends, and a little inclined to be a snob." He fell into step with Phyllis and they walked slowly toward the park entrance.

At length as they were moving slower in the congestion of the downtown area, she said abruptly: "I have remembered, Mr. Parker, where I heard about the other dog—Sylvia. My mother, who died a few months ago, wrote to me about it. I was in London at the time, not aware that my mother was so ill. And she needn't have died. They operated on my mother and a Dr. Paige assisted. He made some frightful mistake that cost her life. Of course"—she went on, brokenly—"it was just a dreadful accident and he must have been terribly sorry. He ran away. They never saw him again."

She lifted her swimming eyes to Parker's face. It was white and haggard. For a long moment, Phyllis stared, frightened. Then she buried her face in her arms and shuddered. In an undertone she said: "Would you be—just awfully hurt—if I were to stop here. I know I can't possibly go on with it . . . I'm sorry."

It had all happened so quickly that, before he realized he was losing her, Phyllis had murmured good-bye and sped away.

Letter from Oblivion

D R. STAFFORD'S lengthy letter was, Dean Harcourt felt, the most interesting communication he had ever received. And this was saying much, for no small part of Dean Harcourt's daily labor was the handling of correspondence voluminous in bulk and confidential in character.

He had almost given up hope of hearing from Stafford. Two months had gone by since his mystified receipt of a newspaper clipping.

As for the clipping, the deduction was simple enough. Paige had evidently fallen in with another gentleman-vagabond who had met with an accident forcing them into the nearest hospital. They had refused to give their names, which seemed unnecessarily imprudent in Paige's case.

It was obvious that Paige had not voluntarily provided his address. What other conclusion could be arrived at but that the name had been found on Paige's person and probably used without his knowledge.

And now—two months afterward— Dr. Stafford had written this unusual letter from Wembelton, Montana. On the first page he explained that he was working with Dr. Paige in a Government Research Laboratory, investigating the cause of the deadly spotted fever.

"I think you, as his friend, have a right to know that Paige is usefully employed on a loathsome, poorly paid, hazardous job, and apparently happy in it. At present, Paige and I are the only ones here. In the past four years, men have come and gone—three to their graves. We have a three-room shack on the top of Boone Mountain, seven miles from Wembelton.

"In the opinion of Wembelton we are hunters and loafers living a worthless existence as hermits. For it would be difficult to make them believe that we are not carriers and are harmless to other people.

"The only man in town who knows about our affairs is the mayor and superintendent of the most important gold mine in this region. Gibson is very well-to-do and has a beautiful home.

"Now for the real purpose of this letter. Frank Gibson has told me that about a dozen families of the more prosperous sort who have daughters approaching school age are thinking seriously of organizing a private school and want to find some well educated, socially experienced young woman, recently graduated from a high-grade university. I told him that I would write to you, feeling quite sure that you might make a suggestion."

Dean Harcourt put down the letter. A happy twinkle began playing about the corners of his deep-set eyes . . . Phyllis!—why not?

Phyllis had written lengthily to her roommate Sonia of her first impressions. She had been met by the Gibsons —delightful people.

"And what do you think was the first thing I saw when I went into the house. Well, if you'll believe it, a red setter scrambled to its feet and began to jump up on me. Mrs. Gibson seemed terribly embarrassed for she said that Sylvia never paid any attention to anybody.

"Mrs. Gibson explained that the dog had been left in their care by a friend of Mr. Gibson's who is up in the mountains hunting. This doesn't sound quite right. Why should a hunter park his dog? They don't seem to want to talk about it. . . . Of course I'm consumed by curiosity."

On the Rugged Flanks of Boone

It was the last Sunday of October and the air was already crisp with the feel of winter stealthily slipping down the heavily wooded slopes of Mount Boone into the snug pocket that was Wembelton.

Phyllis—restless and lonesome—decided to take a walk. Sylvia noted with mounting interest the change of costume and could hardly contain herself when the heavy-soled tramping shoes came out of the closet.

One didn't have to walk very far in Wembelton to reach the suburbs and the open country. Phyllis's favorite course was a wagon-road which wound circuitously up the rugged flanks of Boone, the highest mountain in that region. This time she was venturing a little farther than usual.

Suddenly Sylvia cocked her head on one side attentively and lifted one front paw a little, as if she were signaling for complete silence.

But presently the dog, with a bound and a bark, was off, over the rocks through the woods and had disappeared. Phyllis stood with a dry throat, listening to Sylvia who was barking her head off for joy.

Presently she saw them coming. He was roughly clad in heavy corduroy trousers, a leather jacket, and an old, battered, gray felt hat drawn well down over his eyes. His lean face was deeply

tanned. But he had the same hurt look in his eyes that had haunted her ever since they parted.

A wave of contrition swept over Phyllis. His eyes quickly responded to the overture of conciliation, and when she extended her hand he grasped it tightly.

Fortunately for both of them at this trying moment, Sylvia lost her patience and began bounding up and down before them, pawing at Paige's leather-clad arm.

"She's happy to see you again," said Phyllis.

"Yes—it's a long time. No way to treat a friend, but—" He stooped and quieted the dog with his hand; then, straightening, he faced Phyllis with a troubled look. "I don't like your being up here alone. All sorts of people prowling in these woods. You must never do it again, my friend."

It was queer about words. She had been hearing the word "friend" all her life. But it was quite another word now, perhaps because it had been spoken so tenderly, so protectingly.

"Very well, Dr. Paige," she agreed respectfully, "I shall not do it again."

"There's no danger now. I'll walk down with you, if I may." He did not smile, but his eyes quietly entreated.

Paige looked at her attentively and she had a sudden suspicion that he was about to re-open the subject she had been trying valiantly to avoid.

"Phyllis—" His voice was very tender.

She slowly shook her head, and turned toward him with eyes half-closed and lips parted to ask him not to go on.

The conversation was choppy, inconsequential, unsatisfactory. He gave so poor an account of himself that Phyllis had some difficulty keeping back her impatience and disappointment in him.

"I would think," she did venture to say, rather crisply, "that one would be frightfully bored—doing—what you seem to be doing. Have you anything up there to read—just to while away the time?"

"Oh, yes," he answered, as if it didn't matter much.

The frowsy outskirts of Wembelton lay in plain sight only five minutes away. Neither of them had reckoned on Sylvia's dilemma. For a moment she stood at Paige's side, giving short barks directed toward the receding Phyllis. Then she bounded down the path and blocked Phyllis's way.

This disconcerting incident seemed likely to alter the nature of their leave-taking. They had parted with such an air of hopeless finality, and here they were with a comomn problem on their hands.

"Come, Sylvia," she said, suddenly depressed. "He doesn't need you." Her eyes were hot with tears of disappointment. What a mess they had made of everything.

A FEW days later Phyllis received a letter from her roommate, Sonia. She tore open the unusually bulky script—Sonia's letter had never been more than two pages long—and began to read with widening eyes and racing heart.

"We know now to a certainty that the mistake made in your mother's operation was Doctor Endicott's fault! The chief nurse, who saw it all, told my young cousin, Clay Block, who is interning in Parkway Hospital."

As she read, there was an occasional long "Oh!" articulated in a gasp of sheer delight. Newell Paige hadn't done it. Newell Paige had taken the blame to protect his senior whom he loved! Sonia was going to see whether Dr. Endicott would respond to the situation. Sonia hadn't decided exactly what course to pursue—but she was going to do *something!*

The light of a sudden, happy decision shone in Phyllis's eyes.

"I'm going out for a little tramp," she explained, meeting Mrs. Gibson ten minutes later in the lower hall.

Phyllis and Sylvia took the familiar path which Sunday's events had mapped indelibly. When they came to the spot where she had first met him, Phyllis paused.

"Sylvia!" she shouted, pointing up the path. "Go—find him!"

Then she turned and walked swiftly, resolutely, down the path. Hearing no sound behind her, she glanced back over her shoulder. Sylvia had disappeared.

An End and a Beginning

PAIGE patted the sand and gravel down evenly with the flat of his spade, and walking a little way apart, sat rather preoccupiedly gazing at the small rectangular mound he had made.

Stafford had generously volunteered to do it, gruffly counselling his associate researchist to "get the hell out o' here and take a walk" while he disposed of poor Sylvia who last night was a wretched little bundle of hot misery and his morning was cold and stiff.

Sylvia was nearly seven. He mustn't pretend it was out of the natural course of things for her to die. One thing had troubled Paige more than a little. He should have been more prudent about safeguarding Sylvia. When she had come bounding into the shack a few days ago, he had been so happy to see her that he hadn't reckoned seriously on the danger of spotted fever. Well, what happened, had happened, and there wasn't anything to be done about it.

But you could be as unsentimental as you pleased, the fact remained that the death of Sylvia marked the end of an epoch in which life had been lived to the full. . . . But had it been lived to the full? Honesty obliged him to confess that he hadn't really lived until the day he met Phyllis.

There had been plenty of time for thinking about her. His censor mind cynically suggested that he had probably idealized the girl out of all proportion to her actual gifts. But—last Sunday—Phyllis had not only justified all his day-dreaming: she had disclosed some charming little tricks of manner, gesture, inflection, that had made him want her with a longing too deep to be trusted to any words that might attempt to define his feeling.

He HAD dreamed about her so much, and longed for her so passionately, that he was distrustful of his own sight. No—there she was, sitting exactly where they had met a few days before. Phyllis leaped to her feet and was running toward him with all the abandon of an ecstatic child. She was flourishing an open letter.

"Read it!" she commanded. "It's wonderful!" Then, impulsively, she laid a hand over the letter and faced him. "What is it that's so dangerous on Boone Mountain?"

His promise to Stafford seemed to give way to the prior privilege of this question. She had a right to know.

"Well"—he explained, hesitatingly—"the Government Research Laboratory for the investigation of spotted fever is up there: is that what you mean?"

There were two big, hot tears on her cheeks. "Please forgive me—for what I said to you the other day." And then when she had recovered her voice a little, "Did Sylvia get there safely? I should love to see her."

"Yes," he replied mechanically, "and she would have loved to see you."

"Newell!" It was the first time she had spoken his name. "Is Sylvia sick?"

"Yes," he admitted, adding, "that is—she was sick."

Phyllis pressed her forehead against his shoulder and wept like a little child. He laid his hand tenderly upon her yellow-gold head.

"You must not blame yourself, dear," he said consolingly. "Sylvia would have been glad to know that her death had—"

He felt the yellow-gold head nod an affirmation against his arm. Presently Phyllis straightened, rubbed the tears out of her eyes and said thickly: "Read that letter!"

To Newell's amazement she snuggled very close to his side—so close that he could feel her soft contours and the beating of her heart against the arm she held tightly.

"God!" he shouted. "The good old duffer's going to come through! He's going to set me free!"

Thoroughly shaken with excitement he tossed the letter aside, and catching Phyllis in his arms, hugged her so tightly that her cheek touched his. Sometimes, when half-mad with loneliness and desire for her, he had indulged himself in a fleeting speculation on the ecstasy of having Phyllis in his arms. But his imagination had never pictured the confident and tender response she made to his kiss.

"Tell me something," said Newell finally. "How did you happen to come out here to Wembleton?"

"Dean Harcourt," she replied smiling.

"But you didn't know I was here, did you?"

Phyllis shook her head, the smile deepening her dimples.

"So—it was just a marvelous accident—our coming together here."

On the way down they met Stafford.

"Congratulations," the other doctor grunted. "By the way, Paige, here's a letter for you I picked up at the Post Office."

Newell inspected the handwriting on the envelope.

"It's from Dr. Endicott!" he said.

Albert Bigelow Paine

MARK TWAIN

S AMUEL CLEMENS (Mark Twain) saw history in the making not only in the pioneer American West but in the European courts of kings. It is therefore not surprising that the same man could have written "Roughing It" and "A Connecticut Yankee in King Arthur's Court," each of which illustrates the two distinct phases in his career. The first could be made into a companion piece for the recent stage and screen success "Abe Lincoln in Illinois" and it is with this thought in mind that we have drafted our condensation of Albert Bigelow Paine's biography which is regarded by William Lyon Phelps as the "best biographical work ever written in America." Certainly it is the period about which Mark Twain's best and most distinctive books were written. His marriage and rise to phenomenal world-wide popularity made a gentleman and a scholar out of Samuel Clemens although his wife and literary friends were never able to completely tame him. The anecdotes which complete the condensation illustrate his temperament and mental attitude, which made him loved and feared, and set him apart from all other novelists and humorists.

The Good Omen

I T WAS on a bleak day, November 30, 1835, that he entered feebly the domain he was to conquer. He was a seven-months child, and there was no fanfare of welcome at his coming. Perhaps it was even suggested that, in a house so small and so sufficiently filled, there was no real need of his coming at all.

Still, John Clemens must have regarded with favor this first gift of fortune in the new land of Missouri, for he named the little boy Samuel, after his father, and added the name of an old and dear Virginia friend, Langhorne. The family fortunes seemed to be improving at this time, and he may have regarded the arrival of another son as a good omen.

It was not a robust childhood. The new baby managed to go through the winter—a matter of comment among the family and neighbors. Added strength came, but slowly; Little Sam, as they called him, was always delicate during these early years.

It was a curious childhood, full of weird, fantastic impressions and contradictory influences. John Clemens seldom devoted any time to the company of his children and he rarely, or never, laughed. The problem of supplying food was a somber one to John Clemens; also, he was working on a perpetual motion machine at this period, which absorbed his spare time, and, to the inventor at least, was not a mirthful occupation.

Jane Clemens was busy, too. Her sense of humor never died, but with added cares and years her temper as well as her features became sharper, and it was just as well to be fairly out of range when she was busy with her employments.

It was Jennie, the house slave, and Uncle Ned, the negro of all work, who were in real charge of the five children and supplied them with entertainment. Wonderful entertainment it was. Old tales were repeated over and over, with adornments and improvements suggested by immediate events. At evening the Clemens children, big and little, gathered about the great open fireplace while Jennie and Uncle Ned told tales and hair-lifting legends. Even a baby of two or three years could follow the drift of this primitive telling and would shiver and cling close with the horror and delight of its curdling thrill.

But if the negroes were the chief companions and protectors of the children, they were likewise one of their discomforts. The greatest real dread children knew was the fear of meeting runaway slaves. A runaway slave was regarded as worse than a wild beast, and treated worse when caught. Once the children saw one brought into town by six men who took him to an empty cabin, where they threw him on the floor and bound him with ropes. His groans were loud and frequent. Such things made an impression that would last a lifetime.

WHEN Sam was four his family moved to Hannibal, Missouri. It was a town with a distinct Southern flavor, though rather more astir than the true Southern community of that period; more Western in that it planned, though without excitement, certain new enterprises and made a show, at least, of manufacturing. Mark Twain remembered it as "the white town drowsing in the sunshine of a summer morning, . . . the great Mississippi, the magnificent Mississippi, rolling its mile-wide tide along; . . . the dense forest away on the other side."

The river, of course, was the great highway. Rafts drifted by; steamboats passed up and down and gave communication to the outside world; St. Louis, the metropolis, was only one hundred miles away.

Hannibal was inclined to rank itself as of next importance, and took on airs accordingly. It had society, too—men who wore tall hats, ruffled shirt-fronts, and swallow-tail coats, usually of some positive color—and lived in colonnaded mansions. It was to this grade of society that Judge Clemens and his family belonged, but his means no longer enabled him to provide either the comforts or the ostentation of his class.

The Original Tom Sawyer

IT WAS in 1844 that the *Tom Sawyer* days may be said to have begun. Up to that time he was just Little Sam, a child—wild, and mischievous, often exasperating, but still a child. Now at nine, he had acquired health, with a sturdy ability to look out for himself, as boys will, in a community like that, especially where the family is rather larger than the income and there is still a younger child to claim a mother's care. So Sam grew up.

Once he saw an old man shot down on the main street, at noonday. He saw them carry him home, lay him on the bed, and spread on his breast an open family Bible which looked as heavy as an anvil. He thought if he could only drag that great burden away, the poor, old dying man would not breathe so heavily.

He saw a young emigrant stabbed with a bowie-knife by a drunken comrade, and noted the spurt of life-blood that followed; he saw two young men try to kill their uncle, one holding him while the other snapped repeatedly an Allen revolver which failed to go off.

Many such instances happened in a town like that in those days. And there were events incident to slavery. He saw a slave struck down and killed with a piece of slag for a trifling offense. He saw an abolitionist attacked by a mob, and they would have lynched him had not a Methodist minister defended him on a plea that he must be crazy.

Fortunately there were pleasanter things than these. There were picnics sometimes, and ferry-boat excursions. Once there was a great Fourth-of-July celebration at which it was said a real Revolutionary soldier was to be present. But this feature proved a disappointment; for when the day came and he was triumphantly brought in he turned out to be a Hessian, and was allowed to walk home.

But it was the river that meant more to him than all the rest. Its charm was permanent. It was the path of adventure, the gateway to the world. He would sit by it for hours and dream. He learned to know all its moods and phases. He felt its kinship. His hunger for the life aboard the steamers became a passion.

He was not a particularly attractive lad. He was not tall for his years, nd his head was somewhat too large or his body. He had a great ruck of ght, sandy hair which he plastered own to keep it from curling; keen blue-ray eyes, and rather large features. He id not speak much, and his mental at-inments were not highly regarded.

His brother Henry was regarded as a ar more promising lad. He was a lov-ble, obedient little fellow whom the ischievous Sam took delight in teasing. Ienry Clemens became the Sid of Tom awyer.

The home incidents in Tom Sawyer, iost of them, really happened. Sam lemens did clout Henry for getting him ito trouble about the colored thread ith which he sewed his shirt when he came home from swimming; he did in-veigle a lot of boys into whitewashing a fence for him.

As for escaping punishment for his misdeeds in the manner described in that book, this was a daily matter, and the methods adapted themselves to the con-ditions. In the introduction to Tom Sawyer Mark Twain confesses to the general truth of the history, and to the reality of its characters. "Huck Finn was drawn from life," he tells us. "Tom Sawyer also, but not from an individual —he is a combination of the character-istics of three boys whom I knew." The three boys were himself, chiefly, and in a lesser degree John Briggs and Will Bowen. As for Huck Finn, his original was Tom Blankenship, neither elabo-rated nor qualified.

Huckleberry Finn

There were several of the Blanken-ships: there was old Ben, the father, ho was the town drunkard; young Ben, ie eldest son—a hard case with certain ood traits; and Tom—that is to say, uck—who was just as he is described Tom Sawyer; a ruin of rags, a river-t, an irresponsible bit of human drift, nd of heart and possessing that price-ss boon, absolute unaccountability of nduct to any living soul.

He could come and go as he chose, he ever had to work or go to school; he uld do all things, good or bad, that the her boys longed to do and were for-dden. He represented to them the very nbodiment of liberty, and his general nowledge of important matters, such as hing, hunting, trapping, and all man-r of signs and spells and hoodoos and cantations, made him immensely valu-le as a companion. The fact that his ciety was prohibited gave it a vastly lded charm.

The Blankenships picked up a pre-rious living fishing and hunting, and ed at first in a miserable house of rk, under a tree, but later moved into ramshackle building back of the new emens home. Old drunken Ben Blank-enship never dreamed that pieces of his house would be carried off as relics be-cause of the literary fame of his son Tom.

Sam was likely to be at the Blanken-ships' any hour of the day, and he and Tom had cat-call signals at night which would bring him out on the back single-story roof, and down a little arbor and flight of steps to the group of boon com-panions which, besides Tom, included John Briggs, the Bowen boys, Will Pitts, and one or two other congenial spirits.

Sam Clemens was the leader of this unhallowed band and all the others looked to him for ideas and organization, whether the undertaking was to be real or make-believe. When they played "Bandit" or "Pirate" or "Indian," Sam Clemens was always chief; when they became real raiders it is recorded that he was no less distinguished. Like Tom Sawyer he loved the glare and trappings of leadership.

The cave supplied the background for the gang's activities. It was a real cave; not merely a hole, but a subterranean marvel of deep passages and vaulted chambers that led away into the bluffs, even below the river, some said. For Sam

Clemens the cave had a fascination that never faded. In Tom Sawyer Indian Joe dies in the cave. He did not die there in real life, but was lost there once, and was living on bats when they found him.

The treasure digging adventure in the book had a foundation in fact. Tom Blankenship one morning came to Sam Clemens and John Briggs and said he was going to dig up a treasure. He said that he had dreamed just where it was, and said that if they would go with him and dig, he would divide up. They followed Tom willingly to the place with some shovels and a pick and he showed them where to dig. Then he sat down under the shade of a papaw-tree and gave orders. He had done the dreaming which entitled him to an equal share, he said.

They did not find it that day or the next. The second day the boys declared they would not dig any more. But Tom had another dream. He dreamed the gold was exactly under the little papaw tree. This sounded so circumstantial that they went back and dug another day. It was hot weather too, August, and that night they were nearly dead. Even Tom gave it up, then. He said there was something the matter with the way they dug.

This differs considerably from the digging incident in the book, but it gives us an idea of the respect the boys had for the ragamuffin original of Huckleberry Finn.

Tom Blankenship's brother, Ben, was also drawn upon for the creation of Huck Finn, at least so far as one important phase of Huck's character is concerned. He was considerably older, as well as more disreputable, than Tom. But somewhere in Ben Blankenship there was a fine generous strain of humanity that provided Mark Twain with that immortal episode in the story of Huck Finn—the sheltering of Nigger Jim. This is the real story:

A slave ran off from Monroe County, Missouri, and got across the river into Illinois. Ben used to fish and hunt over there in the swamps, and one day found him. It was considered a most worthy act in those days to return a runaway slave; in fact, it was a crime not to do it. Besides, there was for this one a reward of fifty dollars, a fortune to ragged outcast Ben Blankenship. That money and the honor he could acquire must have been tempting but it did not outweigh his human sympathy. Instead of giving him up and claiming the reward, Ben kept the runaway over there in the marshes all summer. The negro would fish and Ben would carry him scraps of other food. Then, by and by, it leaked out. Some woodchoppers went on a hunt for the fugitive, and chased him to what was called "Bird Slough." There, trying to cross a drift, he was drowned.

In the book, the author makes Huck's struggle a psychological one between conscience and the law, on one side, and sympathy on the other. With Ben Blankenship the struggle—if there was struggle—was probably between sympathy and cupidity. He would care very little for conscience and still less for law. His sympathy with the runaway, however, would be large and elemental, and it must have been very large to offset the lure of that reward.

There was a gruesome sequel to the incident. Some days following the drowning of the runaway, Sam Clemens, John Briggs, and the Bowen boys went to the spot and were pushing the drift about, when suddenly the negro rose before them, straight and terrible, about half his length out of the water. He had gone down feet foremost, and the loosened drift had released him. The boys did not stop to investigate.

It is not easy to curtail these boyhood adventures of Sam Clemens and his scapegrace friends, but one might go on indefinitely with their mad doings. They were an unpromising lot. Ministers and other sober-minded citizens freely prophesied sudden and violent ends for them, and considered them hardly worth praying for.

They must have proven a disappointing lot to those prophets. The Bowen boys became fine river pilots; Will Pitts was in due time a leading merchant and bank director; John Briggs grew into a well-to-do and highly respected farmer; even Huck Finn—that is to say, Tom Blankenship—is reputed to have ranked as an honored citizen and justice of the peace in a Western town.

A Printer By Trade

JUDGE CLEMENS, who time and again had wrecked or crippled his fortune by devices more or less unusual, now adopted the one unfailing method of achieving disaster. He endorsed a large note for a man of good repute, and the payment of it swept him clean: home, property, everything vanished. A St. Louis cousin took over the home and agreed to let the family occupy it on payment of a small interest. But disaster overtook them again; for Judge Clemens died.

The boy Sam was fairly broken down. Remorse, which had always dealt with him unsparingly, laid a heavy hand on him now. Wildness, disobedience, indifference to his father's wishes, all were remembered; a hundred things, in themselves trifling, became ghastly and heart-wringing in the knowledge that they could never be undone. Seeing his grief, his mother took him by the hand and led him into the room where his father lay.

"It's all right, Sammy," she said. "What's done is done and it does not matter to him any more; but here by the side of him now I want you to promise me—"

He turned, his eyes streaming with tears, and flung himself into her arms.

"I will promise anything," he sobbed, "if you won't make me go to school!"

"No, Sammy; you need not go to school any more. Only promise me to be a better boy. Promise not to break my heart."

So he promised her to be a faithful and industrious man, and upright, like his father.

A year and perhaps part of another passed along before Mrs. Clemens and her son Samuel had another sober talk, and, realizing that the printing trade offered opportunity for acquiring further education as well as a livelihood, they agreed that he should be apprenticed to a printer. The apprentice terms were not over-liberal. They were the usual thing for the time: board and clothes—"more board than clothes, and not much of either."

When he had been there little more than a year Sam had become office favorite and chief standby. Whatever required intelligence and care and imagination was given to Sam Clemens. He could set type accurately and rapidly; he could wash up the forms a good deal better than the printer himself; and he could run the job-press to the tune of "Annie Laurie" or "Along the Beach at Rockaway," without missing a stroke or losing a finger. It is not believed that Sam had any writing ambitions of his own. His chief desire was to be an all-round journeyman printer.

He Sees the "World"

AFTER he had finished his apprenticeship he found a job in the composing room of the St. Louis *Evening News*. He remained on the paper only long enough to earn money with which to see the world. The world was New York City, where the Crystal Palace Fair was then going on. The railway had been completed by this time, but he had not traveled on it. It had not many comforts; several days and nights were required for the New York trip; yet it was a wonderful and beautiful experience.

On the whole there was not much inducement to remain in New York after he had satisfied himself with its wonders. He lingered, however, through the hot months of 1853 and presently went on to Philadelphia where he found work "subbing" on a daily paper, the *Inquirer*. Days and evenings when there was no vacant place for him to fill he visited historic sites, the art-galleries, and the libraries.

In January, when the days were dark he grew depressed and made a trip to Washington to see the sights of the capital. His stay was comparatively brief, and he did not work there. He returned to Philadelphia, working for a time on the *Ledger* and *North American*.

It was late in the summer of 1854, when he finally set out on his return to the West. His *Wanderjahr* had lasted nearly fifteen months.

After a short visit with his family he decided to go back to Cincinnati, which would be on the way either to New York or New Orleans. He secured work at his trade in Cincinnati at the printing office of Wrightson & Co., and remained there until April, 1857.

That winter in Cincinnati was eventless enough, but it was marked by one notable association—one that beyond doubt forwarded Samuel Clemens' general interest in books, influenced his taste, and inspired in him certain views and philosophies which he never forgot.

He lodged at a cheap boarding house filled with the usual commonplace people, with the exception of a Scotchman named Macfarlane. Macfarlane was a veritable storehouse of abstruse knowledge; a living dictionary and a thinke[r] and philosopher besides. He had at leas[t] one vanity: the claim that he kne[w] every word in the English dictionar[y] and he made it good. The younger ma[n] tried repeatedly to discover a word tha[t] Macfarlane could not define.

THIS Scotch philosopher did no[t] always reflect the conclusions o[f] others; he had speculated deeply an[d] strikingly on his own account. Tha[t] was a good while before Darwin an[d] Wallace gave out their conclusions o[f] the Descent of Man; yet Macfarlane wa[s] already advancing a similar philosoph[y] He went even further: he said that th[e] evolutionary scheme had failed wit[h] man; that man had retrograded; tha[t] man's heart was the only bad one in th[e] animal kingdom: that man was the onl[y] animal capable of malice, vindictivenes[s] drunkenness—almost the only anima[l] that could endure personal uncleanlines[s] He said that man's intellect was a de[-] praving addition to him which, in th[e] end, placed him in a rank far below th[e] other beasts, though it enabled him t[o] keep them in servitude and captivit[y] along with members of his own race.

They were long, fermenting discours[es] that young Samuel Clemens listened [to] that winter in Macfarlane's room, an[d] those who knew the real Mark Twai[n] and his philosophies will recognize th[at] those evenings left their impress up[on] him for life.

Life on the Mississippi

IN THE spring of 1857 he bade good-by to Macfarlane and set out on a voyage that was to continue for four years —four marvelous, sunlit years, the glory of which would color all that followed them. Mark Twain tells us in "Life on the Mississippi" that he "ran away," vowing never to return until he could come home a pilot, shedding glory. This is a literary statement. The pilot ambition had never entirely died; but it was coca and the Amazon that were uppermost in his head when he engaged passage on the *Paul Jones* for Ne[w] Orleans, and so conferred immortality [on] that ancient little craft. Nevertheless the little boat made its drowsy way dow[n] the river into lands that grew eve[r] pleasanter with advancing spring, t[he] old "permanent ambition" of boyho[od] stirred again, and the call of the far-aw[ay] Amazon grew faint.

Horace Bixby, the pilot of the *Pa[ul] Jones,* agreed to teach young Cleme[ns] his profession. In his Mississippi bo[ok] Mark Twain has given us a marvelo[us]

:position of the science of river pilot-
g, and of the colossal task of acquiring
.d keeping a knowledge requisite for
.at work. He has not exaggerated this
.rt of the story of developments in any
:tail; he has set down a simple con-
ssion.

Serenely enough he undertook the
sk of learning twelve hundred miles
 the great changing, shifting river as
:actly and as surely by daylight or
.rkness as one knows the way to his
vn features. Horace Bixby was a "light-
ng" pilot with a method of instruc-
on as direct and forcible as it was
fective.

"My boy, you must get a little memo-
ndum-book, and every time I tell you
thing put it down right away. There's
.ly one way to be a pilot, and that is
 get this entire river by heart. You
.ve to know it just like your A B Cs."

So Sam Clemens got the little book,
.d presently it "fairly bristled" with the
.mes of towns, points, bars, islands,
.nds, and reaches, but it made his heart
-he to think that he had only half of
.e river set down; for as the "watches"
.ere four hours off and four hours on,
.ere were long gaps during which he
.d slept. It would take days for the
-erage mind to remember even a page
 such statistics.

There is but one way to account for
.e fact that the man whom the world
.ew as Mark Twain—dreamy, unprac-
.al and indifferent to details—ever
-rsisted in acquiring knowledge like
.at. It lies in the fact that he loved the
ver in its every mood and aspect and
.tail. Wherever he has written of the
ver—we feel the claim of the old cap-
.vity and that it still holds him.

N "Huckleberry Finn" during those
 nights and days with Huck and
.igger Jim on the raft—whether in
.rmlit blackness, still noontide, or the
.ting mists of morning—we can fairly
.mell" the river, as Huck himself
.ould say, and we know that it is
.cause the writer loved it with his heart

of hearts and literally drank in its environment and atmosphere during those
halcyon pilot days.

The demands of the Missouri River
trade took Horace Bixby away from the
Mississippi, somewhat later, and he con-
signed his pupil, accordingly, to another
pilot—a man named Brown. Brown was
a fault-finding, tyrannical chief, ignorant,
vulgar and malicious. His subordinate
soon learned to detest him thoroughly.
Once when Brown had been more insulting than usual his subordinate went
to bed and killed him in "seventeen
different ways—all of them new."

He had been on the river nearly a
year now, and, though universally liked
and accounted a fine steersman, he was
receiving no wages. In New Orleans the
young pilot found that he could get
night employment, watching freight on
the levee at three dollars a night.

"It was a desolate experience," he said,
long afterward, "watching there in the
dark among those piles of freight; not
a sound, not a creature astir. But it was
not a profitless one; I used to have inspirations as I sat there. I used to imagine all sorts of situations and possibilities.
Those things got into my books by and
by and furnished me with many a chapter. I can trace the effect of those nights
through most of my books in one way
and another."

Many of the curious tales in the latter half of the Mississippi book came
out of those long night-watches. It was
a good time to think of such things.

Finally he became a pilot. In eighteen
months he had packed away in his head
all the multitude of volatile statistics and
acquired that confidence and courage
which made him one of the elect. He
could smell danger in the dark; he could
read the surface of the water as an open
page. At twenty-three he had acquired
a profession which yielded an income
equal to that then earned by the Vice
President of the United States. He had
plenty of money now. He could help
his mother with a liberal hand, and he
did it.

Roughing It

THE inauguration of Abraham Lincoln brought the Civil War. Samuel Clemens was of the less radical element. He knew there was a good deal to be said for either cause; furthermore, he was not then bloodthirsty. A pilot-house with its elevated position and transparency made him a good target for either side. So he went into retirement in St. Louis.

The inauguration of Lincoln also brought a friend of his older brother, Orion, into the cabinet. Orion applied for something and got an appointment as Territorial secretary in Nevada. He needed only money to carry him to the scene of new endeavor.

Sam had accumulated money out of his pilot's salary and there was no comfortable place just then in the active Middle West for a man who wanted to stay out of the service. So he agreed that if Orion would overlook this defection and appoint him secretary, he would supply the funds for both overland passages and they would start with no unnecessary delay.

In the briefest possible time he had packed his belongings and the brothers were on their way to the great mysterious land of the Pacific West. From St. Louis they took the boat for St. Jo, whence the Overland stage started. At St. Jo they paid one hundred and fifty dollars apiece for their stage fare and on the twenty-sixth of July, 1861, set out on that long, delightful trip behind sixteen galloping horses never stopping except for meals or to change teams. From horizon to horizon they went over the billowy plains, across the snow-clad Rockies, covering the seventeen hundred miles between St. Jo and Carson City (including a two-day halt in Salt Lake City) in nineteen glorious days.

In "Roughing It" he tells it all, and says: "Even at this day it thrills me through and through to think of the life, the gladness, and the wild sense of freedom that used to make the blood dance in my face on those fine Overland mornings."

IT WAS a hot, dusty August 14th that the stage reached Carson City. It was known that the Territorial secretary was due to arrive; and something in the nature of a reception had been planned. When the committee saw two wayworn individuals climb down from the stage, unkempt, unshorn—clothed in the roughest of frontier costumes—the reception plan faded out and was not heard of again. Soap and water and fresh garments worked a transformation; but that first impression had been fatal to the welcoming festivities.

Within a brief time Sam Clemens was about the most conspicuous figure on the Carson streets. Lately a river dandy, in fancy percales and patent leathers, he had become the roughest of rough-clad pioneers, in rusty slouch hat, flannel shirt, coarse trousers slopping half in and half out of the heavy cowskin boots. Always something of a barbarian in love with the loose habit of unconvention, he went even further than others and became a sort of paragon of disarray.

Samuel Clemens did not catch the mining fever immediately; there was too much to see at first to consider any special undertaking. His chief purpose was to see the world beyond the Rockies, to derive from it such amusement and profit as might fall in his way. The war would end, by and by, and he would go back to the river, no doubt.

It was not until early winter that Samuel Clemens got the real mining infection. Everybody had it. The wildest stories of sudden fortune were in the air, some of them undoubtedly true. Men had gone to bed paupers and awakened to find themselves millionaires. Others had sold for a song claims that had been suddenly found to be fairly stuffed with precious ores.

In the midst of these things report came from the newly opened Humboldt

egion of mountains literally bursting
with gold and silver. He joined an expedition at once.

"I confess with shame," says the author of "Roughing It," "that I expected
to find masses of silver lying all about
the ground." And he adds that he
slipped away from the cabin to find a
claim on his own account and tells how
he came staggering back under a load of
golden specimens; also how his specimens proved to be only worthless mica;
and how he learned that in mining
nothing that glitters is gold. His account in "Roughing It" of the Humboldt
mining experience is sufficiently good
history to make detail here unnecessary.

He had about exhausted his own
funds by this time and it was necessary
that Orion should become the financier.
The brothers owned some mining claims
in the Esmeralda district in partnership
and it was agreed that Orion should
furnish the means, and Sam would go
actively into the field and develop their
riches. Neither had the slightest doubt
but that they would be millionaires
presently.

IT was February when the printer-pilot-
miner arrived in Aurora, that rough,
turbulent camp of the Esmeralda district
lying about one hundred miles south of
Carson City, on the edge of California.
The new arrival camped with Horatio
Phillips (Raish), in a tiny cabin and
they cooked and bunked together and
combined their resources in a common
fund.

When he lacked for other employment
and was likely to be discouraged a desire to set things down for their own
sake began to stir. One or two of his
earlier letters home had found their way
into a Keokuk paper. Copies containing
them had gone back to Orion, who had
shown them to a representative of the
Territorial Enterprise. The *Enterprise*
reprinted at least one of these letters,
and with this encouragement the author
of it sent an occasional contribution
direct to that paper over the pen-name
"Josh." He did not care to sign his own
name. He was a miner who was soon to
be a magnate.

The "Josh" letters to the *Enterprise*
awakened at least a measure of interest
and Orion did not fail to identify their
author when any promising occasion
offered. As a result certain tentative overtures were made for similar material.
Orion eagerly communicated such
chances, for the money situation was becoming desperate.

At the end of July, 1862 the editor of
the *Enterprise* wrote to the author of the
Josh letters offering him a job at twenty-
five dollars a week. In "Roughing It" we
are led to believe that the author regarded this as a gift from heaven and
accepted it straightaway. As a matter
of fact, he fasted and prayed a good
while over the "call." There was no
desperate eagerness to break into literature, even under urgent financial conditions. It meant the surrender of all hopes
in the mines.

But at last on a hot and dusty August
day a worn and travel-stained pilgrim
drifted into the office of the Virginia
City *Enterprise*. A tangle of reddish-
brown hair fell on his shoulders, and a
mass of tawny beard, dingy with alkali
dust, dropped half way to his waist.

"My name is Clemens, and I've come
to write for the paper," he said.

It was the master of the world's widest
estate come to claim his kingdom.

Mark Twain

THE *Territorial Enterprise* was one of
the most remarkable frontier papers
ever published. Its editor-in-chief was a
man of rare appreciation, wide human
understanding, and a comprehensive
newspaper policy. His instructions were:

"Never say we learn so and so, or it is
rumored, or we understand so and so;
but go to headquarters and get the
absolute facts; then speak out and say it
is so and so. In the one case you are
likely to be shot, and in the other you

are pretty certain to be; but you will preserve the public confidence."

It was a sort of free ring, with every reporter for himself. The publisher let the boys write and print in accordance with their own ideas and upon any subject. Often they wrote about each other —squibs and burlesques. The indifference to "news" was noble. They would dismiss a murder with a couple of inches and sit down and fill up a column with a fancy sketch.

The author of "Roughing It" has given us a better picture of the Virginia City of those days and his work there than any one else will ever write. He has made us feel the general spirit of affluence that prevailed; the problem was not to get money, but to spend it. He has told us of the desperadoes and their trifling regard for human life, and preserved other elemental characters of those prodigal days. The funeral of Buck Fanshaw—that amazing masterpiece—is a complete epitome of the social frontier.

Clemens' articles were copied and quoted all along the Coast. They were easily identified with one another, but not with a personality. He realized that to build a reputation it was necessary to fasten it to an individuality, a name. He tried a good many combinations in his mind but none seemed as convincin[g] as Mark Twain, the pen name of an ol[d] Mississippi pilot who was given to wri[t]ing tall tales about himself. News cam[e] just at that time that the old pilot ha[d] died. Clemens decided that he woul[d] give Mark Twain a new meaning an[d] a new association in this far-away lan[d.] He went up to see his boss.

"Joe," he said. "I want to sign m[y] articles so that I can be identified to [a] wider audience. How about Mar[k] Twain? It is an old river term, a lead[s]man's call, signifying two fathoms— twelve feet. It has a richness about i[t] it was always a pleasant sound for [a] pilot to hear on a dark night; it mean[t] safe water."

Mark Twain was first signed to a[n] article bearing the date of February [3,] 1863, and from that time was attache[d] to all Samuel Clemens's work. The wor[k] was neither better nor worse than be[-]fore, but it had suddenly acquired iden[-]tification and special interest. Member[s] of the legislature and friends in Virgini[a] and Carson immediately began to ad[-]dress him as Mark. The papers of th[e] Coast took it up, and within a period t[o] be measured by weeks he was no longe[r] Sam or Clemens or that bright chap o[f] the *Enterprise,* but "Mark Twain."

The Jumping Frog

IT was in the same year that Artemus Ward came to Virginia City. He made the *Enterprise* office his headquarters, and fairly reveled in the company he found there. He and Mark Twain became boon companions. Each recognized in the other a kindred spirit.

Those were three memorable weeks in Mark Twain's life. Artemus Ward was in the height of his fame as a humorist and he encouraged his new-found brother humorist.

With Artemus Ward's encouragement, Clemens began to think of extending his audience eastward. Ward urged him to try this market and promised to write a special letter to some editors, introducing Mark Twain and his work.

In Mark Twain's old note-book occur[s] a memorandum—a mere casual entry[:] "Coleman with his jumping frog—be[t] stranger $50—stranger had no frog, an[d] C. got him one—in the mean tim[e] stranger filled C's frog full of shot an[d] he couldn't jump. The stranger's fro[g] won."

It seemed unimportant enough, n[o] doubt, at the time; but it was the nucleu[s] around which was built a surpassin[g] fame. For one night Mark Twain tol[d] the jumping frog story to Artemu[s] Ward, who was delighted with it. H[e] urged him to write it and send it to h[is] publisher.

"Jim Smiley and His Jumping Frog["] appeared in the *Saturday Press* of N[ew] vember 18, 1865, and was immediately copied and quoted far and near. It brought the name of Mark Twain across the mountains, bore it up and down the Atlantic coast, and out over the prairies of the Middle West. Now every one who took a newspaper was treated to the tale of the wonderful frog, and received a mental impression of the author's signature. The name Mark Twain was hardly an institution, as yet, but it made a strong bid for national acceptance.

Whether the story of "Jim Smiley's Frog," offered for the first time today, would capture the public, and become the initial block of a towering fame, is another matter. That the author himself under-rated it is certain. That the public, receiving it at what we now term the psychological moment, may have over-rated it, is by no means impossible. In any case, it does not matter now. The stone rejected by the builder was made the cornerstone of his literary edifice.

Innocents Abroad

IT HAD been more than thirteen years since he had been to New York. Now, a veteran, he had decided to return. However he stopped there only long enough to see Charles Henry Webb, late of California, who had put together a number of Mark Twain sketches, including "The Jumping Frog," for book publication. When the publishing formalities had been concluded he started for St. Louis and was soon with his mother and sister, whom he had not seen since that eventful first year of the war.

He went up to Hannibal to see old friends, and delivered a lecture there. He was the center of interest and admiration—his welcome might have satisfied even Tom Sawyer. From Hannibal he journeyed to Keokuk, where he lectured again to a crowd of old friends and new, then returned to St. Louis for a more extended visit.

It was while he was in St. Louis that he first saw the announcement of the *Quaker City* Holy Land Excursion, and was promptly fascinated by what was then a brand new idea in ocean travel. Henry Ward Beecher was advertised as one of the party; General Sherman as another; also ministers, high-class journalists—the best minds of the nation. He lost no time in writing to the steamship company, proposing that they send him in this select company. The management was staggered by the proposition but finally decided that the investment in Mark Twain would be sound. A letter was accordingly sent, stating that a check for his passage would be forwarded in due season.

Later while waiting for attention in the shipping office he heard a newspaper man inquire what notables were going. A clerk, with evident pride, rattled off the names: "Lieutenant-General Sherman, Henry Ward Beecher, and Mark Twain; also probably General Banks."

So he was billed as an attraction. It was his first surreptitious taste of fame on the Atlantic coast.

THEY were not all ministers and deacons aboard the *Quaker City*. Clemens found other congenial spirits besides his "splendid immoral roommate," Dan Slote (Dan of "The Innocents Abroad"). There was the ship's surgeon, Dr. A. Reeves Jackson (the guide-destroying Doctor of "The Innocents"), Jack Van Nostrand, of New Jersey (Jack); Julius Moulton, of St. Louis (Moult) and Charles J. Langdon of Elmira, New York, a boy of eighteen, who had conceived a deep admiration for the brilliant writer.

Sometimes young Langdon invited the journalist to his cabin and, boy-like, exhibited his treasures. He had two sisters at home, and of Olivia, the youngest, he had brought a dainty miniature done on ivory in delicate tints. Each time Clemens came he asked to see the picture, and once he begged to be allowed to take it away with him. The boy would not agree to this, and the elder man looked long and steadily at the miniature, resolving in his mind that some day he would meet the owner of that lovely face.

When they returned to America on November 19, 1867, young Langdon was especially anxious to bring his distinguished *Quaker City* friend and his own people together, and two days before Christmas Samuel Clemens was invited to dine at the hotel. He went very willingly. The lovely face of that miniature had been often a part of his waking dreams. For the first time now he looked upon its reality. Long afterwards he said:

"It is forty years ago. From that day to this she has never been out of my mind."

THE engagement of Samuel Langhorne Clemens and Olivia Lewis Langdon was ratified on February 2, 1869. The revised proofs of "The Innocents Abroad" were coming now, and he and gentle Livy Langdon read them together. He realized presently that with her sensitive nature she had also a keen literary perception. What he lacked in delicacy—and his lack was likely to be large enough in that direction—she detected, and together they pruned it away. She became his editor during those happy courtship days—a position which she held to her death.

The world owes a large debt of gratitude to Mark Twain's wife, who from the very beginning, inspired him to give only his worthiest to the world, whether in written or spoken word, in counsel or in deed. Those early days of their close companionship, spiritual and mental, were full of revelation to Samuel Clemens, a revelation that continued from day to day, and from year to year, even to the very end.

"The Innocents Abroad" was a success from the start. The machinery for its sale and delivery was in full swing by August 1, and five thousand one hundred and seventy copies were disposed of that month—a number that had increased to more than thirty-one thousand by the first of the year. It was a book of travel; its lowest price was three and a half dollars. No such record had been made by a book of that description; none has equaled it since.

If Mark Twain was not already famous, he was unquestionably famous now. He was swept into the domain of letters as one riding at the head of a cavalcade—doors and windows wide with welcome and jubilant with applause.

"There have been greater writers than Mark Twain, but none of his peculiar gifts, temperament, and mental attitude. It is impossible to compare him with any other humorist or any other novelist; he resembles no one except himself." The following anecdotes will illustrate this statement which William Lyon Phelps makes in his introduction to this biography.

MARK TWAIN'S father-in-law, Mr. Langdon, gave him a completely furnished house in Buffalo as a wedding present. This was kept as a surprise until the young author had entered it with his wife. Nobody quite remembers what was the first remark that Mark Twain made; but either then or a little later he said:

"Mr. Langdon, whenever you are in Buffalo, if it's twice a year, come right here. Bring your bag and stay overnight if you want to. It sha'n't cost you a cent!"

The Rev. T. DeWitt Talmage, an immensely popular clergyman of the day, had delivered from his pulpit an argument against workingmen occupying pews in fashionable churches, on the basis that their smell would drive the rich parishioners away. Mark Twain's remarks on the subject, in which he compares the Rev. Talmage with the disciples of Christ, appeared in the *Galaxy* in 1870.

"If the subject of these remarks had been chosen among the original Twelve Apostles he would not have associated with the rest, because he could not have stood the fishy smell of some of his comrades who came from around the Sea of Galilee. He would have resigned his commission with some such remark as he has lately made: 'Master, if thou art going to kill the church thus with bad smells I will have nothing to do with this work of evangelization.' He is a disciple, and makes that remark to the Master; the only difference is that he makes it in the nineteenth instead of the first century."

On the back of an old envelope Mark Twain set down this literary declaration in 1874:
"I like history, biography, travels, curious facts and strange happenings, and science. And I detest novels, poetry, and theology."

Mark Twain regarded himself as the first person to apply the typewriter to literature and believed that the story of *Tom Sawyer* was the first typewriter-copied manuscript.

It was during a trip to Boston that he first saw a typewriter. He bought one for $125 and was practicing on it on December 9, 1874 when he wrote the following letter to William Dean Howells, errors and all:
"You neednt answer this; I am only practicing to get three; *anothe slip-up there;* only practici?ng ti get the hang of the thing. I am simply using you for a target to bang at. Blame my cats, but this thing requires genius in order to work it just right."

THE efforts of Mrs. Clemens to make a gentleman out of her husband led to many a domestic *impasse*. He used to tell how, for a long time, he concealed his profanity from her; how one morning, when he thought the door was shut between their bedroom and the bathroom, he was in there dressing and shaving, accompanying these trying things with language intended only for the strictest privacy; how presently, when

he discovered a button off the shirt he intended to put on, he hurled it through the window into the yard with appropriate remarks, followed it with another shirt that was in the same condition, and added certain collars and neckties and bathroom requisites, decorating the shrubbery outside, where the people were going by to church; how in the extreme moment he heard a slight cough, and turned to find that the door was open and a voice repeating his last terrific remark. He turned to see her sitting up in bed, regarding him with a look as withering as she could find.
"Livy," he said, "did it sound like that?"
"Of course it did," she said, "only worse. I wanted you to hear just how it sounded."
"Livy," he said, "it would pain me to think that when I swear it sounds like that. You got the words right, Livy, but you don't know the tune."

Letters came queerly addressed. There is one envelope still in existence which bears Clemens's name in elaborate design and a very good silhouette likeness, the work of some talented artist. "Mark Twain, Somewhere," mailed in a foreign country, reached him promptly, and "Mark Twain, Anywhere," found its way to Hartford in due season.

Then there was a letter (he was abroad at the time) mailed by Brander Matthews and Francis Wilson, addressed, "Mark Twain, God Knows Where." It found him after traveling half around the world and in his answer he said, "He *did*." Then some one sent a letter addressed, "The Devil Knows Where." Which also reached him, and he answered, "*He* did, too."

Harriet Beecher Stowe was leaving for Florida one morning, and Clemens ran over early to say good-by. On his return Mrs. Clemens regarded him disapprovingly:
"Why, Youth," she said, using her pet name for him, "you haven't on any collar and tie."

He said nothing, but went up to his room, did up these items in a neat package, and sent it over by a servant, with a line:

"Herewith receive a call from the rest of me."

ADVANCING years did little toward destroying Mark Twain's interest in human affairs. At no time in his life was he more variously concerned and employed than in his sixty-seventh year. The following document, whose publication Mrs. Clemens never permitted, indicates his then unorthodox attitude toward imperialism.

THE STUPENDOUS PROCESSION

At the appointed hour it moved across the world in the following order:

The Twentieth Century

A fair young creature, drunk and disorderly, borne in the arms of Satan. Banner with motto, "Get What You Can, Keep What You Get."

Guard of Honor—Monarchs, Presidents, Tammany Bosses, Burglars, Land Thieves, Convicts, etc., appropriately clothed and bearing the symbols of their several trades.

Christendom

"A majestic matron in flowing robes drenched with blood. On her head a golden crown of thorns; impaled on its spines the bleeding heads of patriots who died for their countries—Boers, Boxers, Filipinos; in one hand a slingshot, in the other a Bible, open at the text, 'Do unto others,' etc. Protruding from pocket, bottle labeled 'We bring you the blessings of civilization.' Necklace—handcuffs and a burglar's jimmy.

Supporters—At one elbow Slaughter, at the other Hypocrisy.

Banner with motto—'Love your Neighbor's Goods as Yourself.'

Ensign—The Black Flag.

Guard of Honor—Missionaries and German, French, Russian and British soldiers laden with loot.

"And so on, with a section for eac nation of the earth, headed each by th black flag, each bearing horrid emblem instruments of torture, mutilated pri oners, broken hearts, floats piled wit bloody corpses. At the end of all, ba ners inscribed;

'All White Men are Born Free and Equal.'
'Christ died to make men holy,'
'Christ died to make men free.'
with the American flag furled an draped in crêpe, and the shade of Lin coln towering vast and dim toward th sky, brooding with sorrowful aspect ove the far-reaching pageant."

SHORTLY before he died (April 2 1910) Mark Twain wrote dow some advice concerning deportment upo reaching the Gate which St. Peter supposed to guard. This is his last b of continued writing:

"Upon arrival do not speak to S Peter until spoken to. It is not your plac to begin.

"Do not begin any remark with 'Say

"When applying for a ticket avoi trying to make conversation. If you mus talk let the weather alone. St. Pete cares not a damn for the weather. An don't ask him what time the 4.30 trai goes; there aren't any trains in heaven except through trains, and the less in formation you get about them the bette for you.

"You can ask him for his autograph— there is no harm in that—but be carefu and don't remark that it is one of th penalties of greatness. He has hear that before.

"Don't try to kodak him. Hell is ful of people who have made that mistake.

"Leave your dog outside. Heaven goe by favor. If it went by merit you woul stay out and the dog would go in.

"You will be wanting to slip dow at night and smuggle water to those poo little chaps (the infant damned), bu don't you try it. You would be caught and nobody in heaven would respect yo after that."

EDNA FERBER

SO BIG

"THERE are people who write Best Sellers as a matter of business. But occasionally some one comes along who commits a Best Seller in all innocence. Of such am I," says Edna Ferber (1887-   ). It is safe to say that at least several million people have enjoyed and profited by the reading of "So Big" which was published in 1924. Edna Ferber has achieved an even wider audience through the successful movie versions of "Show Boat" and "Cimarron" and her ability as a playright was established by the long Broadway runs of "The Royal Family," "Dinner at Eight," and "Stage Door." Recently she published her autobiography, "A Peculiar Treasure," which followed her other works into Bestsellerdom.

Plunged into Life

JULIE HEMPEL and Selina Peake, both finished products of Miss Fister's school, were of an age—nineteen. Selina, on this September day, had been spending the afternoon with Julie, and now, adjusting her hat preparatory to leaving, she clapped her hands over her ears to shut out the sound of Julie's importunings that she stay to supper. Certainly the prospect of the usual Monday evening meal in Mrs. Tebbit's boarding house (her father's luck at gambling was momentarily low) did not present sufficient excuse for Selina's refusal.

"Well then, silly, why not stay!" asked Julie.

"Father comes home at six. If I'm not here he's disappointed. He hates it here."

"Then I don't see why you stay. I think it's horrid and stuffy."

"Father has had some temporary business setbacks."

Selina's costume testified to that. True, it was modish, and bustled, and basqued, and flounced; and her high-crowned hat with its trimming of feathers and flowers and ribbons had come from New York. But both were of last spring's purchasing, and this was September.

Now Julie, fond though defeated, kissed her friend good-bye and Selina walked quickly the short distance to the boarding house. Up in her second floor room she took off her hat and called to her father, but he had not yet come in. She was glad of that. She had been fearful of being late.

Then she heard a sound. She had never heard that sound before—that peculiar sound—the slow, ominous tread of men laden with a heavy inert burden; bearing with infinite care that which was well beyond hurting. Selina had never heard that sound before, and yet, hearing it, she recognized it by one of those pangs, centuries old, called woman's instinct. Thud—shuffle—thud—shuffle—up the narrow stairway, along the passage.

She flung open the door. A flat still burden partially covered with an overcoat carelessly flung over the face. The feet, in their square-toed boots, wobbled listlessly. Selina noticed how shiny the boots were. He was always very finicky about such things.

SIMEON PEAKE had been shot in Jeff Hankin's place at five in the afternoon. The irony of it was that the bullet had not been intended for him at all.

Simeon Peake left his daughter Selina a legacy of two fine clear blue-white diamonds (he had had a gambler's love of them) and the sum of four hundred and ninety-seven dollars in cash.

To Selina fell the choice of earning her

own living or of returning to a Vermont village and becoming a withered and sapless dried apple, with black fuzz and mould at her heart, like her aunts, the Misses Sarah and Abbie Peake. She did not hesitate.

"But what kind of work?" Julie Hempel demanded. "What kind of work can you do?" Women—that is, the Selina Peakes—didn't work.

"I—well, I can teach."

"You have to do something first—go to Normal, or teach in the country, don't you?"

Selina rallied to Julie's onslaught. "Then I'll just teach a country school."

"You! Teaching a country school."

She looked at Selina. She saw a mis leading delicate face, the skull small an exquisitely formed. The cheek bone rather high—or perhaps they looked s because of the fact that the eyes, dark soft, and luminous, were unusually deep set in their sockets. The face, instead o narrowing to a soft curve at the chin, de veloped unexpected strength in the jav line. That line, fine, steel strong, shar and clear, was of the stuff of whic pioneer women are made. Julie, inex perienced in the art of reading the hu man physiognomy, did not decipher th meaning of it.

School Marm

SELINA had thought herself lucky to get the Dutch school at High Prairie, ten miles outside of Chicago. Thirty dollars a month. She was to board at the house of Klaas Pool, the truck farmer. It was August Hempel, Julie's father, who had brought it all about; or Julie, urging him.

Selina went about her preparations in a singularly clear-headed fashion, considering her youth and inexperience. She sold one of the blue-white diamonds, and kept one. She placed her inheritance of four hundred and ninety-seven dollars, complete, in the bank. She bought stout sensible boots, two dresses, one a brown lady's cloth which she made herself, finished with white collars and cuffs, very neat; and a wine-red cashmere (mad, but she couldn't resist it) for best.

When she thought back, years later, on that period of her High Prairie experience, stoves seemed to figure with absurd prominence in her memory. From the first the schoolhouse stove was her bête noir. Those children who sat near this monster baked; those near the windows froze. Sometimes Selina felt she must go mad beholding the writhings and contortions of a roomful of wriggling bodies scratching at backs, legs, and sides as the stove grew hotter and flesh rebelled against the harsh contact with the prickling undergarments o an over-cautious day. From eight-thirty until four Selina ruled this grubby do main; a hot-and-cold roomful of sneez ing, coughing, wriggling, shuffling, doz ing children, toe scuffling on agonized heel, and heel scrunching on agonized toe, in a frenzy of itching.

It had been Roelf Pool, the eldest sor of the Klaas Pools with whom she lived, who had taught Selina to build the schoolhouse fire. He had gone with her on that first morning, had started the fire, filled the water pail, initiated her in the rites of kerosene, and dampers. A shy, dark, silent boy. She set out deliberately to woo him to friendship.

"Roelf, I have a book called 'Ivanhoe.' Would you like to read it? You wouldn't have to hurry. And there's another called 'The Three Musketeers'."

He was trying not to look pleased; to appear stolid and Dutch, like the people from whom he had sprung. Some Dutch sailor ancestor, Selina thought, or fisherman, must have touched at an Italian port or Spanish and brought back a wife whose eyes and skin and feeling for beauty had skipped layer on layer of placid Netherlanders to crop out now in this wistful sensitive boy.

Selina had spoken to the Pools about a shelf for her books and her photographs. They had put up a rough bit of board, very crude and ugly, but it had served. She had come home one snowy afternoon to find this shelf gone and in its place a smooth and polished one, with brackets intricately carved. Roelf had cut, planed, polished, and carved it in many hours of work in the cold little shed off the kitchen.

This sort of thing was looked upon by Klaas Pool as foolishness. Roelf's real work in the shed was the making and mending of coldframes for the early spring plants. Whenever possible Roelf neglected this dull work for some fancy of his own. To this Klaas Pool objected as being "dumb." For that matter, High Prairie considered Pool's boy "dumb like."

Once when he had come home from the market in town he shyly laid before her a torn sheet of coarse brown paper on which he had sketched crudely, effectively, a melée of great-haunched horses; wagons piled high with garden truck; men in overalls and corduroys; flaring gas torches. He had drawn it with a stub of pencil exactly as it looked to him. The result was as startling as that achieved by the present-day disciples of the impressionistic school. Selina was enchanted. She recognized that here was something rare, something precious.

One night Roelf had knocked at her door. He wore his best suit—his first suit of store clothes. He put down his cheap yellow suitcase.

"I am going away. I can't stand it here."

She nodded. "Where?"

"Away. Chicago maybe." He was terribly moved, so he made his tone casual. "I have got some books that belong to you." He made as though to open the suitcase.

"No, no! Keep them."

"Good-bye."

"Good-bye, Roelf." She took the boy's dark head in her two hands and, standing on tiptoe, kissed him. He turned to go. "Wait a minute. Wait a minute." She had a few dollars—in quarters, dimes, half dollars—perhaps ten dollars in all—hidden away in a canister on the shelf. She reached for it. But when she came back with the box in her hand he was gone.

Farmer's Wife

ON HER fifth Sunday in the district she accompanied the Pools to the morning service at the Dutch Reformed Church. Selina's appearance had made quite a stir, of which she was entirely unaware. She would have been aghast to learn that High Prairie, inexplicably enough, knew all about her from the color of the ribbon that threaded her neat little white corset covers to the number of books on her shelf.

In the midst of the drab assemblage of churchgoers there entered late and rustlingly a tall, slow moving woman in a city bought cloak and bonnet. As she came down the aisle Selina thought she was like a full-sailed frigate.

"Who's that?" whispered Selina to Mrs. Pool.

"Widow Paarlenberg. She is rich like anything. Look once how she makes eyes at Pervus DeJong."

Selina craned, peered. "The—oh—he's very good looking, isn't he?"

Selina decided she'd come to church oftener. The service went on, dull, heavy. It was in English and Dutch. She heard scarcely a word of it. The Widow Paarlenberg and this Pervus DeJong occupied her thoughts.

Mrs. Pool told her about him with a good deal of savour. Pervus DeJong had been left a widower two years before. Within a month of that time Leendert Paarlenberg had died, leaving to his widow the richest and most profitable farm in the whole community. Pervus DeJong, on the contrary, possessed a scant twenty-five acres of the worst lowland. The acreage was notoriously barren.

Luck and nature seemed to work against him. His seedlings proved unfertile; his stock was always ailing; his cabbages were worm-infested; snout-beetle bored his rhubarb. To complete his discomfort, his household was inadequately ministered by an elderly and rheumatic female connection whose pies and bread were the scandal of the neighboring housewives.

It was on this Pervus DeJong, then, that the Widow Paarlenberg of the rich acres had set her affections. She wooed him openly, notoriously, and with a Dutch vehemence that would have swept another man off his feet.

Knowing well that the entire community was urging him toward this profitable match with the plump, rich, red-lipped widow, Pervus set his will like a stubborn steer and would have none of her. He was uncomfortable in his untidy house; he was lonely, he was unhappy. But he would have none of her. Vanity, pride, resentment were all mixed up in it.

The very first time that Pervus DeJong met Selina he had a chance to protect her. With such a start, the end was inevitable.

THEY were married the following May. Selina was at once bewildered and calm; rebellious and content. Overlaying these emotions was something like grim amusement. Beneath them, something like fright.

Selina had never known spring in the country before. It made her ache with an actual physical ache. She moved with a strange air of fatality. It was as if she were being drawn inexorably, against her will, her judgment, her plans, into something sweet and terrible.

There had been days when the feeling of unreality possessed her. She, a truck farmer's wife, living in High Prairie the rest of her days! Why no! No! Was this the great adventure that her father had always spoken of? She, who was going to be a happy wayfarer down the path of life—any one of a dozen things. This High Prairie winter was to have been only an episode. Not her life!

In the midst of the ceremony Selina had her moment of panic when she actually saw herself running shrieking from the company, the man, the house, down the road, on, on toward—toward what? The feeling was so strong that she was surprised to find herself still standing there in the Dutch wedding gown answering "I do" in the proper place.

Next morning it was dark when he awakened her at four. She started up with a little cry and sat up, straining her ears, her eyes. "Is that you, Father?" She was little Selina Peake again, and Simeon Peake had come in, gay, debonair, from a night's gaming. Then she remembered.

Pervus DeJong laughed and came toward her. "Get up, little lazy bones. It's after four. All yesterday's work I've got to do, and all today's. Breakfast, little Lina, breakfast. You are a farmer's wife now."

Living From the Earth

PERVUS DEJONG loved his pretty young wife, and she him. But young love thrives on colour, warmth, beauty. It becomes prosaic and inarticulate when forced to begin its day at four in the morning by reaching blindly, dazedly, for limp and obscure garments dangling from bedpost or chair, and to end that day at nine, numb and sodden with weariness, after seventeen hours of physical labor.

She had married in May. From May until October it was necessary to tend the fields with a concentration amounting to fury. Selina had never dreamed that human beings toiled like that for sustenance. Toil was a thing she had never encountered until coming to High Prairie. Now she saw her husband wrenching a living out of the earth by sheer muscle, sweat, and pain.

During June, July, August, and September the good black prairie soil for miles around was teeming, a hotbed of plenty. There was born in Selina at this time a feeling for the land that she was never to lose. She was aware of a feeling of kinship with the earth; an illusion of splendour, of fulfilment.

But it had not taken her long to discover that the great broad-shouldered man she had married was a kindly creature, tender and good, but lacking any vestige of initiative, of spirit. One day she had sketched some of her plans in large dashing strokes.

"Pervus, we must paint the house in October, before the frost sets in, and after the summer work is over. White would be nice with green trimmings. A lovely background for hollyhocks. Then that west sixteen. We'll drain it. You've got to use tile drainage. All it needs is draining and manure. With potash, too, and phosphoric acid."

Pervus laughed a great hearty laugh that Selina found surprisingly infuriating. "Well, well, well! School teacher is a farmer now, huh? Tell me, little

Lina, from where did you learn all this about truck farming?"

"Out of a book," Selina said, almost snappishly. "I sent to Chicago for it."

"A book! A book." He slapped his knee. "A vegetable farmer out of a book."

"Why not! The man who wrote it knows more about vegetable farming than anybody in all High Prairie. He knows about new ways. You're running the farm just the way your father ran it."

"What was good enough for my father is good enough for me."

"It isn't!" cried Selina, "It isn't! The book says clay loam is all right for cabbages, peas, and beans. It tells you how. It tells you how!"

Pervus stared straight ahead. "Fine talk. Fine talk."

"Oh!" Selina beat her knee with an impotent fist.

So Big

By october High Prairie housewives told each other that Mrs. Pervus DeJong was "expecting." Dirk DeJong was born in the bedroom off the sitting room on the fifteenth day of March, of a bewildered, somewhat resentful, but deeply interested mother; and a proud, foolish, and vainglorious father whose air of achievement, considering the really slight part he had played in the long, tedious, and racking business, was disproportionate. The name Dirk had sounded to Selina like something tall, straight, and slim. Pervus had chosen it. It had been his grandfather's name.

But So Big was the name that stuck to him until he was almost ten. The nickname had sprung from the early and idiotic question invariably put to babies and answered by them, with infinite patience, through the years of their infancy. Selina had little time for the expression of affection. Yet, in that moment, as the woman looked at the child there in the warm moist spring of the Illinois prairie land, or in the cluttered kitchen of the farmhouse, there quivered

and vibrated between them and all about them an aura, a glow, that imparted to them and their surroundings a mystery, a beauty, a radiance.

"How big is baby?" Selina would demand, senselessly.

The child would momentarily cease to poke plump fingers into the rich black loam. He would smile a gummy though slightly weary smile and stretch wide his arms. She, too, would open her tired arms wide, wide. Then they would say in a duet, his mouth a puckered pink petal, hers quivering with tenderness and a certain amusement. "So—o-o—big!" with the voice soaring on the prolonged vowel and dropping suddenly with the second word. Then he would throw back his head and laugh a triumphant laugh. She would run to him and bury her flushed face in the warm moist creases of his neck, and make as though to devour him. "So big!"

But of course he wasn't. He wasn't as big as that. In fact, he never became as big as the wide-stretched arms of her love and imagination would have him.

No Time for Tears

Dirk was eight; Little Sobig DeJong, in a suit made of bean-sacking sewed together by his mother. A brown blond boy with mosquito bites on his legs and his legs never still.

Dirk went to school from October until June. Pervus protested that this was foolish. The boy could be of great help in the fields from the beginning of April to the first of November, but Selina fought savagely for his schooling, and won.

"Reading and writing and figgering is what a farmer is got to know," Pervus argued. "What good does it do a truck farmer when he knows Constantinople is the capital of Turkey? That don't help him raise turnips."

"Sobig isn't a truck farmer."

"Well, he will be pretty soon. Time I was fifteen I was running our place."

"You're all alike. Look at Roelf Pool! They tried to make a farmer of him, too. And ruined him."

"What's the matter with farming? What's the matter with a farmer? You said farm work was grand work, once."

Verbally Selina did not combat this. But within her every force was gathering to fight it when the time should come. But this particular struggle never materialized.

That September, usually a succession of golden days and hazy opalescent evenings on the Illinois Prairie land, was disastrously cold and rainy that year. Pervus's great frame was racked by rheumatism. This brought on pneumonia. In a locality that advised closed windows and hot air as a remedy, Pervus's battle was lost before the doctor's hooded buggy was seen standing in the yard for long hours through the night.

Perhaps the most poignant and touching feature of the days that followed was not the sight of this stricken giant, lying majestic and aloof in his unwonted black; nor the boy Dirk, mystified but elated, too, with the unaccustomed stir and excitement; nor of the shabby little farm that seemed to shrink and dwindle into further insignificance beneath the sudden publicity turned upon it. No; it was the sight of Selina, widowed, but having no time for decent tears. The farm was there; it must be tended, the vegetables pulled, hauled to market, sold. Upon the garden depended the boy's future, and hers.

For the first few days following the funeral one or another of the neighbouring farmers drove the DeJong team to market, aided Jan Steen, the blundering hired man, in the fields. But each had his hands full with his own farm work.

On the fifth day Jan Steen had to take the garden truck to Chicago, though not without many misgivings on Selina's part, all of which were realized when he returned late next day with half the load still on his wagon and a sum of money representing exactly zero in profits. The wilted left-over vegetables were used later as fertilizer.

"I'll go myself Monday."

Jan stared. "Go? Go where, Monday?"

"To market."

His horror and unbelief were shared by the rest of High Prairie when on Monday Selina literally took the reins in her own slim work-scarred hands.

"To market!" argued Jan as excitedly as his phlegmatic nature would permit. "A woman she don't go to market. A woman—"

"This woman does."

The Future and the Past

It would be enchanting to be able to record that Selina had phenomenal success, disposing of her carefully bunched wares to great advantage, driving smartly off up Halsted Street toward High Prairie with a goodly profit jingling in her scuffed leather purse. The truth is that she had a day so devastating as would have discouraged any woman less desperate.

The pedlers looked at her bunched bouquets, glanced at her, passed her by. It was not unkindness that prompted them, but a certain shyness, a fear of the unaccustomed. They saw her pale fine face with its great sombre eyes; the slight figure in the decent black dress; the slim brown hands clasped so anxiously together. Her wares were tempting but they passed her by with the instinct that the ignorant have against that which is unusual.

By nine o'clock trading began to fall off. In a panic Selina realized that the sales she had made amounted to little more than two dollars. In desperation she harnessed the horses, threaded her way out of the swarming street.

There were groceries near Eighteenth, and at the other cross-streets—Twenty-second, Twenty-sixth, Thirty-first. They were passing the great stone houses of Prairie Avenue of the '90s. Her vegetables, canvas covered, were fresher than those in the near-by markets. Why not try to sell some of them here, in these big houses? In an hour she might earn a few dollars this way at retail prices slightly less than those asked by the grocers of the neighborhood.

She filled a large market basket with the finest and freshest of her stock and with this on her arm, started down the street. "I can't! I can't," cried all the prim dim Vermont Peakes, in chorus. "All right. Starve to death and let them take the farm and Dirk, then."

Up one side of the street, and down the other. Four times she refilled her basket. At one house she sold a quarter's worth. Fifteen at another. Twenty cents here. Almost fifty there. "Good morning," she always said at the door in her clear, distinct way. They stared, usually. But they were curious, too, and did not often shut the door in her face.

The last house. She had almost five dollars, earned in the last hour. "Just five minutes," she said to herself. Her arms were full of vegetables which she was about to place in the basket at her feet when she heard at her elbow:

"Now, then, where's your license?"

She turned. A policeman at her side. She stared up at him.

"License? Why, no. No." She stared at him, still.

"Well, say, where d'ye think you are, peddlin' without a license. A good mind to run you in. Get along out of here. Leave me ketch you around here again!"

"What's the trouble, Officer?" said a woman's voice.

"Woman peddling without a license, Mrs. Arnold," said the policeman turning to a modish woman who was just stepping from a victoria. "You got to watch 'em like a hawk. . . . Get along wid you, then." He put a hand on Selina's shoulder and gave her a gentle push.

A passion shook Selina from head to foot. "How dare you touch me! How dare you!" The blazing eyes in the white mask. He took his hand from her shoulder.

Julie Hempel Arnold had known her by her eyes. And she had stared and then run to her in her silk dress and her plumed hat, crying, "Oh, Selina! My dear! My dear!" with a sob of horror and pity and had taken Selina, beets, corn, and radishes in her arms.

The vegetables lay scattered all about them on the sidewalk in front of Julie Hempel Arnold's great stone house on Prairie Avenue. But strangely enough it had been Selina who had done the comforting, patting Julie's plump silken shoulder and saying, over and over, as to a child. "There, there! It's all right, Julie. Don't cry. Sh-sh! It's all right."

I. O. U.

The best thing for Dirk. The best thing for Dirk. It was the phrase that repeated itself over and over in Selina's speech during the days that fol-

lowed. Julie Arnold was all for taking him into her gray stone house, dressing him like Lord Fauntleroy and sending him to the north-side private school attended by Eugene, her boy, and Paula, her girl.

In this period of bewilderment and fatigue Julie had attempted to take charge of Selina much as she had done a dozen years before at the time of Simeon Peake's dramatic death. And now, as then, she pressed into service her wonder-working father and bounden slave, August Hempel.

"You want to drain and tile. Plant high-grade stuff. You got to have a man on the palce that knows what's what, not that Rip Van Winkle. New horses. A wagon." His eyes narrowed speculatively. Shrewd wrinkles radiated from their corners. "I betcha we'll see the day when you truck farmers will run into town with your stuff in big automobile wagons that will get you there in under an hour. It's bound to come. The horse is doomed, that's chust what." Then, abruptly, "I will get you the horses, a bargain, at the yards." He took out a long flat check book. He began writing in it. He tore off the check with a clean rip. "For a starter," he said. He held it out to Selina.

But Selina did not take it. She sat very still in her chair, her hands folded. "That isn't the regular way," she said. "I'm borrowing this money, not taking it. In five years—seven—I'll pay it back. I want a—" she was being enormously businesslike, and unconsciously enjoying it—"a—an I.O.U. A promise to pay you back just as—as soon as I can. That's business, isn't it? And I'll sign it."

Ten years later Selina had that original I.O.U. with its "Paid In Full. Aug Hempel," carefully tucked away in the carved oak chest together with other keepsakes that she foolishly treasured—ridiculous scraps that no one but she would have understood or valued: a bustled and panniered wine-red cashmere dress, absurdly old-fashioned; a pair of men's old side-boots with mud caked on them; a crude sketch, almost obliterated now, done on a torn scrap of brown paper and showing the Haymarket with the wagons, vegetable-laden, and the men gathered beneath the streetflares—Roelf's childish sketch.

Among this rubbish she rummaged periodically in the years that followed. Indeed, twenty years later Dirk, coming upon her smoothing out the wrinkled yellow creases of the I.O.U. or shaking the camphor laden folds of the wine-red cashmere, would say, "At it again! What a sentimental generation yours was, Mother. If the house caught fire you'd probably run for the junk in that chest. It isn't worth two cents, the lot of it."

"Perhaps not," Selina said, slowly. "Still, there'd be some money value, I suppose, in an early original signed sketch by Roelf Pool. At a sale in New York last week one of his sketches—not a finished thing at all, brought one thous—"

"Oh, well, that—yes. But the rest of the stuff you've got there—funny how people will treasure old stuff like that. Useless stuff. It isn't even beautiful."

"Beautiful!" said Selina, and shut the lid of the old chest. "Why, Dirk—Dirk! You don't even know what beauty is. You never will know."

The Splendours of Achievement

SELINA thought constantly of Dirk's future. A thousand other thoughts might be racing through her mind during the day—plans for the farm, for the house—but always, over and above and through all these, like the steady beat of a drum penetrating sharper and more urgent sounds—was the thought of Dirk. It was during those careless years of Dirk's boyhood between nine and fifteen that Selina changed the DeJong acres from a worn-out and down-at-heel truck farm whose scant products brought a second-rate price in a second-rate market to a prosperous and blooming vegetable garden whose output was sought a year in advance by the South Water Street commission merchants. DeJong asparagus with firm white thick stalk bases tapering to a rich green streaked with lavender at the tips. DeJong hothouse tomatoes in February, plump, scarlet, juicy. You paid for a pound a sum Pervus had been glad to get for a bushel.

These six or seven years of relentless labor had been no showy success with Selina posing grandly as the New Woman in Business. No, it had been a painful, grubbing, heart-breaking process as is any project that depends on the actual soil for its realization. She drove herself pitilessly. She literally tore a living out of the earth with her two bare hands.

Yet there was nothing pitiable about this small energetic woman of thirty-five or forty with her fine soft dark eyes, her clean-cut jaw-line, her shabby decent clothes that were so likely to be spattered with the mud of the road or fields, her exquisite nose with the funny little wrinkles across the bridge when she laughed. Rather, there was something splendid about her; something rich, prophetic. It was the splendour and richness that achievement imparts.

T̲HOUGH it was her busiest time on the farm Selina went to Cornell for Dirk's college graduation in 1913. He was twenty-two and, she was calmly sure, the best-looking man in his class. Undeniably he was a figure to please the eye; tall, well-built, as his father had been, and blond, too, like his father except for his eyes. These were brown—not so dark as Selina's, but with some of the soft liquid quality of her glance. They strengthened his face, somehow; gave him an ardent look.

Selina, in her black silk dress, and her plain black hat, and her sensible shoes was rather a quaint little figure amongst all those vivacious, beveiled, and beribboned mammas. But a distinctive little figure, too. She eyed the rather paunchy, prosperous, middle-aged fathers and thought, with a pang, how much handsomer Pervus would have been than any of these, if only he could have lived to see this day. Then, involuntarily, she wondered if this day would ever have occurred, had Pervus lived. Chided herself for thinking thus.

When he returned to Chicago, Dirk went into the office of Hollis & Sprague, Architects. He thought himself lucky to work wth this firm. But his work there was little more than that of a draughtsman, and his weekly stipend could hardly be dignified by the term of salary.

"Oh, you don't know, Mother. It's so damned slow. What am I! An office boy—or little more than that—at Hollis's."

"Never mind," Selina assured him, happily. "Beauty needs time to perfect it. Maybe some day I'll be driving down Michigan Boulevard with a distinguished visitor—Roelf Pool, perhaps. And he'll say, 'Who designed that building—the one that is so strong and yet so light? So gay and graceful, and yet so reticent! And I'll say, 'Oh, that! That's one of the earlier efforts of my son, Dirk DeJong.'"

A Great Mistake

D̲URING his university years Dirk had seen much of Julie's children, Eugene and Paula, but it sometimes seemed to Selina that he avoided these meetings. Paula's fascination for Dirk was strong. Selina knew that, too. In the last year or two he had talked very little of Paula and that, Selina knew, meant that he was hard hit.

Sometimes Paula and Eugene drove out to the farm, making the distance from their new north shore house to the DeJong place, far south, in some breathtaking number of minutes. Eugene would appear in rakish cap, loose London coat. Paula did not affect sports clothes for herself. She was not the type, she said. Slim, dark, vivacious, she wore slinky clothes—crêpes, chiffons. Her eyes were languorous, lovely. She worshipped luxury and said so.

"I'll have to marry money," she declared. "Now that they've finished calling poor Grandpa a beef baron and taken millions away from him, we're practically on the streets."

"You look it," from Dirk; and there was bitterness beneath his light tone. "You don't really mean that rot about marrying a rich man."

"Of course I mean it. What other sort of man do you think I ought to marry?" He looked at her, silently. She smiled. "Yes, wouldn't I make an ideal bride for a farmer?"

"I'm not a farmer."

"Well, architect then . Your job as draughtsman at Hollis & Sprague's must pay you all of twenty-five a week."

"Thirty-five," said Dirk, grimly. "What's that got to do with it!"

"Not a thing, darling." She stuck out one foot. "These slippers cost thirty."

"Oh, forgive me. But—listen, Paula— you know I'm—gosh!— And there I am stuck in an architect's office and it'll be years before I—"

"Yes, but it'll probably be years before I meet the millions I require, too. So why bother? And even if I do, you and I can be just as good friends."

Six months later Paula Arnold was married to Theodore A. Storm, a man of fifty, a friend of her father, head of so many companies, stockholder in so many banks, director of so many corporations that even old Aug Hempel seemed a recluse from business in com-parison. She never called him Teddy. No one ever did.

He built for Paula a town house on the Lake Shore Drive in the region known as the Gold Coast. The house looked like a restrained public library. There was a country place beyond Lake Forest far out on the north shore, slop-ing down to the lake and surrounded by acres and acres of fine woodland, ex-pertly parked.

Within three years Paula had two children, a boy and a girl. "There! That's done," she said.

Her marriage was a great mistake and she knew it. For the war, coming in 1914, a few months after her wedding, sent the Hempel-Arnold interests sky-rocketing. Millions of pounds of Ameri-can meat were shipped to Europe. In two years the Hempel fortune was greater than it ever had been.

Dirk had not seen her in months. She telephoned him unexpectedly one Friday afternoon in his office.

"Come out and spend Saturday and Sunday with us, won't you? We're run-ning away to the country this afternoon."

"I don't think I—"

"I'll call for you at four. I'll be at the curb. Don't keep me waiting, will you? The cops fuss so if you park in the Loop after four."

"Success" Story

Paula was lovely in her Red Cross uni-form. She persuaded Dirk to go into the Liberty Bond selling drive and he was unexpectedly effective in his quiet, serious way; most convincing and unde-niably thrilling to look at in uniform. Paula's little air of possession grew until it enveloped him. She wasn't playing now; was deeply and terribly in love with him.

When, in 1918, Dirk took off his uni-form he went into the bond department of the Great Lakes Trust Company in which Theodore Storm had a large in-terest. He said that the war had disillu-sioned him.

"What did you think war was going to do?" said Selina. "Purify! It never has yet."

It was understood, by Selina at least, that Dirk's abandoning of his profes-sion was a temporary thing.

"Steel and stone and brick, with en-gines throbbing inside it like a heart, and people flowing in and out. Part of a city. A piece of actual beauty conceived by you! Oh, Dirk!" To see her face then must have given him a pang, it was so alive, so eager.

He found excuses for himself. "Selling bonds that make that building possible isn't so dull, either."

But she waved that aside almost con-temptuously. "What nonsense, Dirk. It's like selling seats at the box office of a theatre for the play inside."

Dirk had made many new friends in the last year and a half. From the start he was a success. Within one year he was so successful that you could hardly distinguish him from a hundred other successful young Chicago business and professional men whose clothes were made at Peel's; who kept their collars miraculously clean in the soot-laden atmosphere of the Loop; whose shoes were bench-made; who lunched at the Noon Club on the roof of the First National Bank where Chicago's millionaires ate corned-beef hash whenever that plebeian dish appeared on the bill of fare.

Two years and Dirk had learned to "grab the Century" in order to save an hour or so of time between Chicago and New York. He had been abroad twice. He learned to call it "running over to Europe for a few days." It had all come about in a scant two years, as is the theatrical way in which life speeds in America.

Selina was a little bewildered now at this new Dirk whose life was so full without her. Sometimes she did not see him for two weeks, or three. He sent her gifts which she smoothed and touched delightedly and put away; fine soft silken things, hand-made—which she could not wear. The habit of years was too strong upon her. Though she had always been a woman of dainty habits and fastidious tastes the grind of her early married life had left its indelible mark.

Now, as she dressed, you might have seen that her petticoat was likely to be black sateen and her plain durable corset cover neatly patched where it had worn under the arms. She employed none of the artifices of a youth-mad day. Her skin was tanned, weather-beaten; her hair rough and dry. Her eyes, in that frame, startled you by their unexpectedness, they were so calm, so serene, yet so alive. They were the beautiful eyes of a wise young girl in the face of a middle-aged woman. Life was still so fresh to her.

"I don't know how you do it," Julie Arnold complained one day as Selina was paying her one of her rare visits in town. "Your eyes are as bright as a baby's and mine look like dead oysters." Julie was massaging. Her eyes had an absent look. Suddenly: "Listen, Selina. Dirk and Paula are together too much. People are talking."

"Talking?" The smile faded from Selina's face. "Goodness knows I'm not strait-laced. You can't be in this day and age. If I had ever thought I'd live to see the time when— Well, since the war of course anything's all right, it seems. But Paula has no sense. Everybody knows she's insane about Dirk. They're together all the time, everywhere. I asked her if she was going to divorce Storm and she said no, she hadn't enough money of her own and Dirk wasn't earning enough. His salary's thousands, but she's used to millions. Well!"

"They were boy and girl together," Selina interrupted, feebly.

"They're not any more. Don't be silly, Selina. You're not as young as that."

No, she was not as young as that.

When Dirk next paid one of his rare visits to the farm she called him into her bedroom—the cool, dim, shabby bedroom with the old black walnut bed in which she had lain as Pervus DeJong's bride more than thirty years ago.

She looked up at him. "Dirk, why don't you marry?"

"Why—there's no one I want to marry."

"No one who's free, you mean?"

He stood up. "I mean no one." He stooped and kissed her lightly. Her arms went round him close. Her hand with the thick gold wedding band on it pressed his head to her hard. "Sobig!" He was a baby again.

"You haven't called me that in years." He was laughing.

She reverted to the old game they had

played when he was a child. "How big is my son! How big?" She was smiling, but her eyes were sombre.

"So big!" answered Dirk, and measured a very tiny space between thumb and forefinger. "So big."

She faced him, sitting up very straight in bed, the little wool shawl hunched about her shoulders. "Dirk, are you ever going back to architecture? Pretty soon it will be too late. Are you ever going back to architecture? To your profession?"

A clean amputation. "No, Mother."

She gave an actual gasp, as though icy water had been thrown full in her face. She looked suddenly old, tired. Her shoulders sagged. He stood in the doorway, braced for her reproaches. But when she spoke it was to reproach herself. "Then I'm a failure."

"Oh, what nonsense, Mother. I'm happy. You can't live somebody else's life. You used to tell me, when I was a kid I remember, that life wasn't just an adventure, to be taken as it came, with the hope that something glorious was always hidden just around the corner. You said you had lived that way and it hadn't worked. You said—"

She interrupted him with a little cry.

"I know I did. I know I did." Suddenly she raised a warning finger. Her eyes were luminous, prophetic. "Dirk, you can't desert her like that."

"Desert who?" He was startled.

"Beauty! Self-expression! Whatever you want to call it. You wait! She'll turn on you some day. Some day you'll want her, and she won't be there."

Inwardly he had been resentful of this bedside conversation with his mother. She made little of him, he thought, while outsiders appreciated his success. He had said, "So big," measuring a tiny space between thumb and forefinger in answer to her half-playful question, but he had not honestly meant it. He thought her ridiculously old-fashioned now in her viewpoint, and certainly unreasonable. But he would not quarrel with her.

"You wait, too, Mother," he said now, smiling. "Some day, your wayward son will be a real success. Wait till the millions roll in. Then we'll see."

She lay down, turned her back deliberately upon him, pulled the covers up about her.

"Shall I turn out your light, Mother, and open the windows?"

"Meena'll do it. She always does. Just call her. . . . Goodnight."

Unsight, Unseen

HE KNEW that he had come to be a rather big man in his world. Influence had helped. He knew that, too. But he shut his mind to much of Paula's manoeuvring and wire pulling—refusing to acknowledge that her lean, dark, eager fingers had manipulated the mechanism that ordered his career. Paula herself was wise enough to know that to hold him she must not let him feel indebted to her. She knew that the debtor hates his creditor. She lay awake at night planning for him, scheming for his advancement, then suggested these schemes to him so deftly as to make him think he himself had devised them.

Paula had a scheme for interesting women in bond buying. It was a good scheme. She suggested it so that Dirk

thought he had thought of it. Dirk was head now of the bond department in the Great Lakes Trust Company's magnificent new white building on Michigan Boulevard north.

It was decided that for the national advertising there must be an illustration that would catch the eye of women, and interest them. The person to do it, Dirk thought, was this Dallas O'Mara whose queer hen-track signature you saw scrawled on half the advertising illustrations that caught your eyes.

Dirk sent for Dallas O'Mara. She replied, suggesting an appointment two weeks from that date at four-thirty.

The female of forty, as he had conceived her, with straggling hair and a bundle of drawings under her arm, was announced at four-thirty to the dot. Dirk let her wait five minutes and at four thirty-five there entered his private office a tall slim girl in a smart little broadtail jacket, fur-trimmed skirt, and a black hat at once so daring and so simple that even a man must recognize its French nativity. She carried no portfolio of drawings under her arms.

Through the man's mind flashed a series of unbusinesslike thoughts such as: "Gosh! . . . Eyes! . . . That's way I like to see girl dress . . . Pretty ... : No, she isn't . . . yes, she . . ." Aloud he said, "This is very kind of you, Miss O'Mara." Then he thought that sounded pompous and said, curtly, "Sit down."

Miss O'Mara sat down. Miss O'Mara said nothing. Now, this was a new experience for Dirk DeJong. Usually women spoke to him first and fluently. Quiet women waxed voluble under his silence; voluble women chattered. Paula always spoke a hundred words to his one. But here was a woman more silent than he; not sullenly silent, nor heavily silent, but quietly, composedly, restfully silent.

"I'll tell you the sort of thing we want, Miss O'Mara." He told her. When he had finished she probably would burst out with three or four plans. The others had done that.

When he had finished she said, "I'll think about it for a couple of days while I'm working on something else. I always do. I can begin work on yours Wednesday."

"But I'd like to see it—that is, I'd like to have an idea of what you're planning

to do with it." Did she think he was going to let her go ahead without consulting his judgment!

"Oh, it will be all right. But drop into the studio if you like. It will take me about a week, I suppose. I'm over on Ontario in that old studio building. You'll know it by the way most of the bricks have fallen out of the building and are scattered over the sidewalk." She smiled a slow wide smile. He found himself smiling, too, sociably. Then he became businesslike again. Very businesslike.

"How much do you—what is you—what would you expect to get for a drawing such as that?"

"Fifteen hundred dollars," said Miss O'Mara.

"I'm afraid we can't pay that, Miss O'Mara."

Miss O'Mara stood up. "That is my price." She was not at all embarrassed. He realized that he had never seen such effortless composure. "Goodbye, Mr.—DeJong." She held out a friendly hand. He took it.

"Well, if that's your price, Miss O'Mara. I wasn't prepared to pay any such—but of course I suppose you top-notchers do get crazy prices for your work. Fifteen hundred dollars is quite a lot of money."

"I think so, too. But then, I'll always think anything over nine dollars is quite a lot of money. You see, I used to get twenty-five cents apiece for sketching hats for Gage's."

She smiled again her slow wide smile; turned and went out.

Wanted: A Splash of Splendour

In the next few days he learned that a surprising lot of people knew a surprisingly good deal about Dallas O'Mara. She hailed from Texas, hence the absurd name. She was twenty-eight—twenty-five—thirty-two—thirty-six. She was beautiful. She was ugly. She was an orphan. She supported an assortment of unlucky brothers and spineless sisters.

She had worked her way through art

school. Two years ago she had achieved sudden success with her drawings. She toiled like a galley-slave; played like a child; had twenty beaux and no lover; her friends, men and women, were legion and wandered in and out of her studio as though it were a public thoroughfare.

The picture was finished and delivered within ten days. In that time Dirk went twice to the studio in Ontario Street. Dallas did not seem to mind. Neither did she appear particularly interested. She was working hard both times. It was practically impossible to get a minute with her alone. That irritated him. People were always drifting in and out—queer, important, startling people; little, dejected, shabby people.

"Look here, Miss O'Mara," he had got her alone for a second. "Look here, will you come out to dinner with me some time? And the theatre?"

"Love to."

"When?" He was actually trembling.

"Tonight." He had an important engagement. He cast it out of his life.

They went to the Blackstone. The head waiter knew him. "Good evening, Mr. DeJong." Dirk was secretly gratified. Then, with a shock, he realized that the head waiter was grinning at Dallas and Dallas was grinning at the head waiter. "Hello, André," said Dallas.

He began to talk about himself. He felt relaxed, at ease, happy.

"You know I'm an architect—at least, I was one. Perhaps that's why I like to hang around your shop so. I get sort of homesick for the pencils and the drawing board—the whole thing."

"Why did you give it up, then?"

"Nothing in it."

"And then you became a banker, h'm? Well, there ought to be money enough in a bank." Her brows met in a little frown. "I'd rather plan one back door of a building that's going to help make this town beautiful and significant than sell all the bonds that ever floated—whatever it is that bonds are supposed to float."

He defended himself. "I felt that way, too. But you see my mother had given me my education, really. She worked for it. I couldn't go dubbing along, earning just enough to keep me. I wanted to give her things. I wanted—"

"Did she want those things? Did she want you to give up architecture and go into bonds?"

"Well—she—I don't know that she

exactly—" He was too decent—still too much the son of Selina DeJong—to be able to lie about that.

HE LEANED toward her, suddenly. "Listen, Dallas. What do you think of me, anyway." He wanted to know. He couldn't stand not knowing any longer.

"I think you're a nice young man."

That was terrible. "But I don't want you to think I'm a nice young man. I want you to like me—a lot. Tell me, what haven't I got that you think I ought to have? Why do you put me off so many times? I never feel that I'm really near you. What is it I lack?" He was abject.

"Well, if you're asking for it. I do demand of the people I see often that they possess at least a splash of splendour in their makeup. Some people are nine-tenths splendour and one-tenth tawdriness and some are nine-tenths tawdriness and one-tenth splendour. But some people are all just a nice even pink without a single patch of royal purple."

"And that's me, h'm?"

He was horribly disappointed, hurt, wretched. But a little angry, too. His pride. Why, he was Dirk DeJong, the most successful of Chicago's younger men; the most promising; the most popular.

"Is it because I'm a successful business man that you don't like me?"

"But I do like you."

"That you don't find me attractive, then?"

"But I think you're an awfully attractive man. Dangerous, that's wot."

"You know damned well what I mean. You've got me and you don't want me. If I had been a successful architect instead of a successful business man would that have made any difference?"

"Good Lord, no! Some day I'll probably marry a horny-handed son of toil, and if I do it'll be the horny hands that will win me. If you want to know, I like 'em with their scars on them. There's something about a man who has fought for it—I don't know what it is—a look in his eye—the feel of his hand. I'm not very good at this analysis stuff. I only know—well, you haven't a mark on you. Not a mark. You quit being an architect, or whatever it was, because architecture was an uphill disheartening job at the time. I don't say that you should have kept on. For all I know you were a bum architect. But if you had kept on—if you had loved it enough to keep on—fighting, and struggling, and sticking it out—why, that fight would show in your face today—in your eyes and your jaw and your hands and in your way of standing and walking. Listen, I'm not criticizing you. But you're all smooth. I like 'em bumpy."

He sat looking down at his hands—his fine strong unscarred hands. Suddenly and unreasonably he thought of another pair of hands—his mother's—with the knuckles enlarged, the skin broken—expressive—her life written on them. Scars. She had them. "Listen, Dallas. If I thought—I'd go back to Hollis & Sprague's and begin all over again at forty a week if I thought you'd—"

"Don't."

Auld Lang Syne

GENERAL GOGUET and Roelf Pool had been in Chicago one night and part of a day. Dirk had not met them —was to meet them at Paula's dinner that evening. He was curious about Pool but not particularly interested in the warrior. Restless, unhappy, wanting to see Dallas (he admitted it bitterly) he dropped in her studio at an unaccustomed hour after lunch.

Dallas in a grimy smock and the stuffed kid slippers was entertaining the two truants from Chicago society—General Emile Goguet and Roelf Pool. They seemed to be enjoying themselves hugely. She had never mentioned them to him. Yet now: "This is Dirk DeJong—General Gouguet. We were campaigners together in France. Roelf Pool. So were we, weren't we, Roelf?"

Roelf Pool's dark face had lighted up with such a glow of surprise and pleasure as to transform it. He strode over to Dirk, clasped his hand. "You're Selina's Dirk. Aren't you? My Selina. I'm driving out to see her this afternoon. She's one of my reasons for being here. She doesn't know we're coming, but she'll be there, won't she? I've a feeling she'll be there, exactly the same."

"She'll be there," answered Dirk cordially. It was early spring; the busiest of seasons on the farm.

She was not on the porch, or in the yard, when they got there. She was out in the west sixteen—the west sixteen that used to be unprolific, half-drowned muckland. Dirk felt a little uneasy, and half ashamed that he should feel so.

Then they saw her coming, a small dark figure against the background of sun and sky and fields. As she came nearer they saw that she was wearing a dark skirt pinned up about her ankles to protect it from the wet spring earth and yet it was spattered with a border of mud spots. A rough heavy gray sweater was buttoned closely about the straight slim body.

She was coming up the path now. She could distinguish their faces. Then she stopped, suddenly, and her hand went to her heart as though she had felt a great pang, and her lips were parted, and her eyes enormous. As Roelf came forward swiftly she took a few quick running steps toward him like a young girl. He took the slight figure in the mud-spattered skirt, and rough gray sweater into his arms.

Revelations

THEY had had tea in the farm sitting room. Selina had entertained them with the shining air of one who is robed in silk and fine linen. She and General Goguet had got on famously from the start, meeting on the common ground of asparagus culture.

"But how thick?" he had demanded,

for he, too, had his pet asparagus beds on the farm in Brittany. "How thick at the base?"

Selina made a circle with thumb and forefinger. The General groaned with envy and despair. He was very comfortable, the General. He flattered Selina with his eyes. She actually dimpled, flushed, laughed like a girl.

But it was to Roelf she turned; it was on Roelf that her eyes dwelt and rested. It was with him she walked when she was silent and the other talked. It was as though he was her own son, and had come home. Her face was radiant, beautiful.

Seated next to Dirk, Dallas said, in a low voice: "There, that's what I mean. That's what I mean when I say I want to do portraits. Not portraits of ladies with strings of pearls and one lily hand half hidden in the folds of a satin skirt. I mean character portraits of men and women who are really distinguished looking—distinguishedly American, for example—like your mother. She's beautiful. She'd make me famous at one leap. You'd see!"

Dirk stared at her. It was as though he could not comprehend. Then he turned in his chair to stare at his mother. Selina was talking to Roelf.

"And you've done all the famous men of Europe, haven't you, Roelf? To think of it! You've seen the world, and you've got it in your hand. Little Roelf Pool. And you did it all alone. In spite of everything."

Roelf leaned toward her. He put his hand over her rough one. "What a fine life you've had, too, Selina. A full life, and a rich one and successful."

"I!" exclaimed Selina. "Why, Roelf, I've been here all these years, just where you left me when you were a boy. I think the very hat and dress I'm wearing might be the same I wore then. I've been nowhere, done nothing, seen nothing. When I think of all the places I was going to see! All the things I was going to do!"

"You've been everywhere in the world," said Roelf. "You've seen all the places of great beauty and light."

The General was interested but uncomprehending. He glanced now at the watch on his wrist and gave a little exclamation. "But the dinner! Our hostess, Madame Storm! It is very fine to run away but one must come back. Much rather would I remain here on this quiet and beautiful farm."

At the porch steps he turned, brought his heels together with a sharp smack, bent from the waist, picked up Selina's rough work-worn hand and kissed it. And then, as she smiled a little, uncertainly, her cheeks pink, Roelf, too, kissed her hand tenderly.

"Why," said Selina, and laughed a soft tremulous little laugh. "Why, I've never had my hand kissed before."

She stood on the porch steps and waved at them as they were whirled swiftly away, the four of them. A slight straight little figure in the plain white blouse and the skirt spattered with the soil of the farm.

Inside Dirk something was saying, over and over, "You're nothing but a rubber stamp, Dirk DeJong. You're nothing but a rubber stamp." Over and over.

Now as the four were whirled back to Chicago over the asphalted road they were relaxed, a little tired. They yielded to the narcotic of spring that was in the air.

Roelf Pool took off his hat. In the cruel spring sunshine you saw that the black hair was sprinkled with gray. "On days like this I refuse to believe that I'm forty-five. Dallas, tell me I'm not forty-five."

"You're not forty-five," said Dallas in her leisurely caressing voice.

Roelf's lean brown hand reached over frankly and clasped her strong white one. "When you say it like that, Dallas, it sounds true."

"It is true," said Dallas.

They dropped Dirk at his smart little apartment and went on.

WILLIAM J. LOCKE

THE ROUGH ROAD

CAN good things come out of war? "The Rough Road," published in 1917, holds out the reassuring affirmative that war is not all bad. William J. Locke (1863-1930), its author, was one of the leaders of his age in the art of fiction. He was not only a born story teller and character creator but his works abound in a practical philosophy which is often quoted. You will find "The Rough Road" particularly interesting reading today.

Toy Pom

THE brutal of his acquaintance g a v e him the name of "Doggie" years before the War was ever thought of, because he had been brought up from babyhood like a Toy Pom. The almost freak offspring of elderly parents, he had the rough world against him from birth. His father died before he had cut a tooth. His mother was old enough to be his grandmother. She wrapped Doggie—his real name was James Marmaduke—in cotton-wool and kept him so until he was almost a grown man. Doggie had never a chance.

His cousin Oliver had the profoundest contempt for Marmaduke. Being two years older, he kicked him whenever he had a chance. Marmaduke loathed him. Marmaduke shrank into Miss Gunter, the governess's, skirts whenever he saw him.

To preserve him from persecution Mrs. Trevor jealously guarded him from association with other boys. He neither learned nor played any boyish games. In defiance of the doctor, whom she regarded as a member of the brutal anti-Marmaduke League, Mrs. Trevor proclaimed Marmaduke's delicacy of constitution. He must not go out into the rain lest he should get damp, nor into the hot sunshine lest he should perspire. She kept him like a precious plant in a warmed conservatory. Doggie, used to it from birth, looked on it as his natural environment.

Under feminine guidance and tuition he embroidered and painted screens and played the piano and the mandolin. Without doubt his life was a happy one. All that he asked for was sequestration from Oliver and his associates.

When Oliver went to Rugby, happier days than ever dawned for Marmaduke. There were only the holidays to fear. But as time went on the haughty contempt of Oliver, the public school boy, for the home bred Doggie forbade him to notice the little creature's existence; so that even the holidays lost their gloomy menace and became like the normal halcyontide.

When he reached the age of fourteen, his uncle, the Dean of the Cathedral, by strenuous endeavour, rescued him from the unavailing tuition of Miss Gunter. But school for Marmaduke Mrs. Trevor would not hear of. Marmaduke—so sensitive and delicate—school would kill him. It would undo all the results of her unceasing care. It would make him coarse and vulgar like other horrid boys. She would sooner see him dead at her feet than at a public school.

IT WAS true that he ought to have the education of a gentleman. She would engage a private tutor. It was Phineas McPhail who got the position. He saw eye to eye with her in every detail of Marmaduke's upbringing. Mr. McPhail did not encourage him to play rough games, or take long walks, or row on the river, because he appreciated his constitutional delicacy.

His reading was selected like that of

a young girl in a convent: he was taken only to the most innocent of plays: foreign theatres, casinos, and such like wells of delectable depravity existed almost beyond his ken. Until he was twenty it never occurred to him to sit up after his mother had gone to bed.

During his seven years of soft living Phineas McPhail scientifically developed an original taste for whisky. He seethed himself in it as the ancients seethed a kid in its mother's milk. He had the art to do himself to perfection. Never had Mrs. Trevor the slightest suspicion of evil courses.

If Phineas had maintained the wily caution which he had exercised up to her death, all might have been well. But he lost grip of himself. He became the scarlet scandal of Durdlebury and the terror of Doggie's life. The Dean came to the rescue of a grateful nephew. A swift attack of delirium tremens crowned and ended McPhail's Durdlebury career.

"My boy," said the Dean on the day of Phineas's expulsion, "I don't want to rub it in unduly, but I've warned your poor mother for years, and you for months, against this bone-idle worthless fellow. Neither of you would listen to me. But you see that I was right. Perhaps now you may be more inclined to take my advice."

"Yes, Uncle," replied Doggie, submissively.

If ever young man heard that which was earnestly meant for his welfare, Doggie heard it from his Very Reverend Uncle's lips.

"And now, my dear boy," said the Dean by the way of peroration, "you cannot but understand that it is your bounden duty to apply yourself to some serious purpose in life."

"I do," said Doggie. "I've been thinking over it for a long time. I'm going to gather material for a history of wallpapers."

White Feather

DOGGIE, being comfortably off, continued the maternal tradition and kept on bringing himself up like a Toy Pom. He did not know what else to do. Then, when he was six-and-twenty, he found himself at the edge of the world gazing in timorous starkness down into the abyss of the Great War.

He received an anonymous letter, "For little Doggie Trevor from the girls of Durdlebury," enclosing a white feather. The cruelty of it broke Doggie down. He sat in his ivory and peacock room and nearly wept. Then he plucked up courage and went to Peggy, his fiancée. She was rather white about the lips as she listened.

"I'm sorry," she said, "but I expected something of the sort to happen."

"It's brutal and unjust."

"Yes, it's brutal," she admitted, coldly.

"I thought you, at any rate, would sympathise with me," he cried.

She turned on him. "Do you ever give a moment's thought to what I've had to go through the last few months. 'Why isn't Marmaduke in khaki?' 'Why isn't Doggie fighting?' 'I wonder how you can allow him to slack about like that!' —I've had a pretty rough time fighting your battles."

"My dear," said Doggie, feeling very much humiliated. "I never knew. I never thought. But," he added eagerly, "you told them the real reason?"

"What's that?" she asked, looking at him with cold eyes.

Then Doggie knew that the wide world was against him. "I'm not fit. I've no constitution. I'm an impossibility."

"What does your doctor say?"

DOGGIE was taken aback. He had no doctor. He had not consulted one for years, having no cause for medical advice. There was only one person familiar with his constitution, and that was himself. He made confession of the surprising fact. Peggy made a little gesture.

"That proves it."

Some men would have taken deep offence and, consigning Peggy to the devil, have walked out of the room. But Doggie, a conscientious, even though a futile human being, was gnawed for the first time by the suspicion that Peggy might possibly be right. He desired to act honourably.

"I'll do," said he, "whatever you think proper."

"Good," she said, with her first smile of the day. "Get Dr. Murdock to overhaul you thoroughly with a view to the army. If he passes you, take a commission. Dad says he can easily get you one through his old friend, General Gadsby, at the War Office. If he doesn't, and you're unfit, I'll stick to you through thick and thin, and make the young women of Durdlebury wish they'd never been born."

She put out her hand. Doggie took it.

The next day Doggie submitted to a physical examination. "You're flabby," said Dr. Murdock. "But that's merely a matter of unused muscles. Physical training will set it right in no time. Otherwise, my dear Trevor, you're in splendid health. Not only are you a first class life for an insurance company, but you're a first class life for the Army—and that's saying a good deal. There's not a flaw in your whole constitution."

Doggie regarded him blankly as the Pronouncer of Doom.

Death Warrant

THE fateful letter burdening Doggie with the King's commission arrived a few weeks later: a second lieutenancy in a Fusilier battalion of the New Army. Dates and instructions were given. The impress of the Royal Arms at the head of the paper, with its grotesque, perky lion and unicorn, conveyed to Doggie a sense of the grip of some uncanny power.

He looked around. All these daintinesses and prettinesses had a meaning. They signified the magical little beauties of life—things which asserted a range of spiritual truths, none the less real and consolatory because vice and crime and ugliness and misery and war co-existed in ghastly fact on other facets of the planet Earth. The sweetness here expressed was essential to the world's spiritual life as the sweet elements of food-stuffs to its physical life.

And he was going to leave it all. All that it meant in beauty and dignity and ease of life. For what? For horror and filthiness and ugliness, for everything against which his beautiful peacock and ivory room protested. Doggie's last night at Denby Hall was a troubled one.

DOGGIE wrote regularly. His letters were shy and conveyed little information. The work was hard, the hours long, his accommodation Spartan. Some-times·he confessed himself too tired to write more than a few lines. He had a bad cold in the head. He was better.

It was a very strange life—one which he never dreamed could have existed. "Fancy me," he wrote, "glad to sleep on a drenched bed!" There was the riding school. Why hadn't he learned to ride as a boy? He had been told that the horse was a noble animal and the friend of man. He was afraid he would return to his dear Peggy with many of his young illusions shattered. The horse was the most ignoble, malevolent beast that ever walked, except the Sergeant-Major in the riding school. His letters contained simple statements of fact, but not a word of complaint.

Then there came a time when his letters grew rarer and shorter. One evening an unstamped envelope addressed to Peggy arrived containing a copy of a cutting from the "Gazette." A sentence was underlined and adorned with exclamation marks at the sides.

"R. Fusiliers. Temp'y 2nd Lieutenant J. M. Trevor resigns his commission."

The Colonel dealt with him as gently as he could in that final interview. He put his hand in a fatherly way on Doggie's shoulder and bade him not take it too much to heart. Soldiers in high command, with great reputations, had already been scrapped. In Doggie's case there was no personal discredit. He had always conducted himself like a gentleman and a man of honour, but he had not the qualities necessary for the command of men. He must send in his resignation.

The Colonel knew that Doggie's life had been a little hell on earth from the first day he had joined. He was very sorry for the poor Little Toy Pom in his pack of hounds. It was scarcely the Toy Pom's fault that he had failed. But the Great Hunt could have no use for Poms.

Out of the Past

HE dallied with thoughts of suicide. Drowning was not so difficult. Any fool could throw himself into the water. With a view to the inspection of a suitable spot, Doggie wandered idly, in the dusk of one evening, to Waterloo Bridge, and turning his back to the ceaseless traffic, leaned his elbows on the parapet and stared in front of him.

At this point he became aware of a presence by his side. He turned his head and found a soldier, an ordinary private, very close to him, also leaning on the parapet.

"I thought I wasn't mistaken in Mr. Marmaduke Trevor."

Doggie started away, on the point of flight, dreading the possible insolence of one of the men of his late regiment. But the voice of the speaker rang in his ears with a strange familiarity.

"Yes, laddie. It's your old Phineas. Phineas McPhail, Esq., M.A., defunct. Now 33702 Private P. McPhail."

He warmly wrung the hand of the semi-bewildered Doggie, who murmured "Very glad to meet you, I'm sure."

Phineas, gaunt and bony, took his arm. He laughed, as though it had been a playful freak of destiny. Doggie laughed too. But for the words he had addressed to hotel and lodging-house folk, he had spoken to no one for over a fortnight. The instinctive craving for companionship made Phineas suddenly welcome.

"Yes. Let us have a talk," said he. "Come to my rooms, if you have the time. There'll be some dinner."

"Will I come? Will I have dinner? Will I re-enter once more the Paradise of the affluent? Laddie, I will."

A few minutes later they reached Woburn Place. Phineas looked round him in surprise.

"Laddie," said he gravely. "It cannot be that you've come down in the world?"

"To bed-rock," said Doggie.

The sight of the man, smug, cynical, shameless, sprawling luxuriously on the sofa unbuttoning his tunic, filled Doggie with a sudden fury.

"Yes, and I'll tell you," he cried, "I've reached the bed-rock of myself—the bed-rock of humiliation and disgrace. And it's all your fault. Instead of training me to be a man, you pandered to my poor mother's weaknesses and brought me up like a little toy dog—the infernal name still sticks to me wherever I go. You made a helpless fool of me, and let me go out a helpless fool into the world. And when you came across me I was thinking whether it wouldn't be best to throw myself over the parapet. A month ago you would have saluted me in the street—"

"Eh? What's that, laddie?" interrupted Phineas, sitting up. "You've held a commission in the army?"

"Yes," said Doggie fiercely. "And I've been chucked. I've been thrown out as a hopeless rotter. And who is most to blame—you or I?"

"Laddie, laddie," said Phineas reproachfully, "the facts of my being a guest beneath your roof and my humble military rank, render it difficult for me to make an appropriate reply."

Doggie's rage had spent itself. "I'm sorry, Phineas. As you say, you're my guest. And as to your uniform, God knows I honour every man who wears it."

The Only Alternative

"THAT's taking things in the right spirit," Phineas conceded graciously, helping himself to another glass of wine. "And the right spirit is a great healer of differences. I'll not go so far as to deny that there is an element of justice in your apportionment of blame."

Doggie lit a cigarette. His fingers were still shaking. "I'm glad you own up. It is a sign of grace."

"Ay," said Phineas. "No man is altogether bad. In spite of everything I've always entertained a warm affection for you, laddie, and when I saw you staring at bogies about the dome of St. Paul's cathedral, my heart went out to you. You didn't look happy. If you call upon me to put my almost fantastically variegated experience of life at your disposal and advise you in this crisis, I must ask you to let me know the exact conditions in which you find yourself at this moment."

Then Doggie broke down, and with a gush of unminded tears found expression for his stony despair. His story took a long time in the telling; and Phineas interjecting an occasional sympathetic "ay, ay!" and a delicately hinted question, extracted from Doggie all there was to tell, from the outbreak of the war to their meeting on Waterloo Bridge.

"And now," cried he, at last, "what the hell am I going to do?"

"Laddie," said Phineas, "if you had posed the question in the polite language of the precincts of Durdlebury Cathedral, I might have been at a loss to reply. But the manly invocation of hell shows me that your foot is already on the upward path. Why don't you enlist?"

Doggie stared at him wildly. "Enlist?" he repeated. "As a Tommy? My God!"

He lit a cigarette and after a few puffs flung it into the grate. He stared at the alternatives.

Flight, which was craven—a lifetime of self-contempt. Durdlebury, which was impossible. Enlistment—?

YET what else was a man incapable yet able-bodied, honourable though disgraced, to do?

A few days later the Dean, Peggy's father, received a letter bearing the pencilled address of a camp on the South Coast, written by 35792 prte James M. Trevor, A Company 2/10th Wessex Rangers. It ran:

"I hope you don't think it heartless of me to have left you so long without news of me; but until lately I had the same reasons for remaining in seclusion as when I last wrote. Even now I'm not asking for sympathy or reconsideration of my failure or desire in any way to take advantage of the generosity of you all.

I have enlisted in the 10th Wessex. Phineas McPhail, whom I met in London and whose character for good or evil I can better gauge now than formerly, is a private in the same battalion. I don't pretend to enjoy the life any more than I could enjoy living in a kraal of savages in Central Africa. But that is a matter of no account. I don't propose to return to Durdlebury till the end of the war.

Please ask anybody who might care to write to address me as 'James M.' and not as 'Marmaduke'."

The Dean read the letter aloud to the family who were at breakfast. Mrs. Conover began to cry.

"Oh, the poor boy! It will be worse than ever for him."

"It will," said Peggy. "But I think it splendid of him to try. How did he bring himself to do it?"

"Breed tells," said the Dean. "That's what everyone seems to have forgotten. He's a thoroughbred Doggie."

"What can we do for the poor boy?" asked his wife.

"We can cut out the slanderous tongues," he said.

"It will all come right, dear old thing," Peggy wrote to Doggie. "It's a cinch, as the Americans say. You'll soon get used to it—especially if you can realise what it means to me. 'Saving face' has been an awful business. Now it's all over. The engagement stands and all Durdlebury knows it . . ." and so on, and so on.

The Long, Long Trail

HE READ Peggy's letter several times. He recognized her goodness, her loyalty. The grateful tears even came to his eyes, and he brushed them away hurriedly with a swift look round. But his heart beat none the faster.

So they were both "sports" now. There she was wrong; Doggie shook his head. In her sense of the word he was not a "sport." A sport takes chances, plays the game with a smile on his lips. There was no smile on his. He loathed the game with a sickening shivering loathing. He was engaged in it because a conglomeration of irresistible forces had driven him into the mêlée. It never occurred to Doggie that he was under orders of his own soul. This simple yet stupendous fact never occurred to Peggy.

From the language of the canteen he recoiled in disgust. He could not reconcile it with the nobler attributes of the users. It was in vain for Phineas to plead that he must accept the *lingua franca* of the British Army like all other things appertaining thereto. Doggie's stomach revolted against most of the other things. The disregard (from his point of view) of personal cleanliness universal in the ranks, filled him with dismay.

The meals—the rough cooking, the primitive service—the table-manners of his companions, offended his delicate senses. He missed napkins. Never could he bring himself to wipe his mouth with the back of his hand and the back of his hand on the seat of his trousers. Nor could he watch with equanimity an honest soul pick his teeth with his little finger. But Doggie knew that acquiescence was the way of happiness and protest the way of woe.

He tried to be friendly; and if he met with no great positive success, he at least escaped animosity. In his spare time he mooned about by himself, shy, disgusted, and miserable.

A penny whistle was the cause of a little revolution in Doggie's regimental life. One of the men was an earnest though indifferent performer on this instrument. It was his constant companion, the solace of his leisure moments and one of the minor tortures of Doggie's existence. His version of the *Marseillaise* was peculiarly excruciating.

One day when he was playing it with dreadful variations of his own to an admiring group in the Y.M.C.A. hut, Doggie, his nerves rasped to the raw by the false notes and maddening intervals, snatched it out of his hand and began to play himself. Hitherto, shrinking morbidly from any form of notoriety, he had shown no sign of musical accomplishment. But today the musicians' impulse was irresistible. He played the *Marseillaise* as no one there had heard it on penny whistle before. The hut recognised a master's touch, for Doggie was a fine executant musician. When he stopped there was a roar: "Go on!" Doggie went on. They kept him whistling till the hut was crowded.

Thenceforward he was penny-whistler, by excellence, to the battalion. He whistled himself into quite a useful popularity.

In the Trenches

DOGGIE went to France: a France hitherto undreamed of either by him or by any young Englishman; a France cleanswept and garnished for war, a France, save for the ubiquitous soldiery, of silent towns and empty villages and deserted roads; a France of smiling fields and sorrowful faces of women and drawn, patient faces of old men.

The world upheaval had thrown Doggie from his peacock and ivory room into a horrible, fetid hole in the ground in Northern France. It had thrown not the average young Englishman of comfortable position who had toyed with aesthetic superficialities as an amusement, but a poor little by-product of cloistered life who had been brought up from babyhood to regard these things as the nervous texture of his very existence. He was wrapped from head to heel in a fine net, to every tiny mesh of which he was acutely sensitive.

A hole in the ground in Northern France. The regiment, after its rest, moved on and took its turn in the trenches. Four days on; four days off. Four days on, of misery inconceivable. Four days on, during which the officers watched the men with the unwavering vigilance of kindly cats.

"How are you getting along, Trevor?"

"Nicely thank you, sir."

"Feet all right?"

"Yes, thank you, sir."

"Sure? If you want to grouse, grouse away. That's what I'm talking to you for."

"I'm perfectly happy, sir."

"Darn sight more than I am!" laughed the subaltern and with a cheery nod in acknowledgment of Doggie's salute, splashed down the muddy trench.

But Doggie was chilled to the bone, and he had no feeling in his feet which were under six inches of water, and his woollen gloves, being wet through, were useless, and prevented his numbed hands from feeling the sandbags with which he and the rest of the platoon were repairing the parapet; for the Germans had just consecrated an hour's general hate to the vicinity of the trench, and its exquisite symmetry, pride of the platoon commander, was disturbed.

There had also been a few ghastly casualties. Something that looked like half a man's head and a bit of shoulder had dropped just in front of the dug-out where Doggie and his section was sheltering. Doggie staring at it was violently sick. In a stupefied way he found himself mingling with others who were engaged in clearing up the horror.

The bombardment over, he had taken his place with the rest in the reparation of the parapet; and as he happened to be at the end of the line, the officer had spoken to him. If he had been suffering tortures unknown to Attila and unimagined by his successors, he would have answered just the same.

A Woman's Knowledge

After one of the spells in the trenches, the worst he had experienced, 'A' Company was marched into new billets some miles below the lines, in the once prosperous village of Frélus. There he saw a barn full of fresh straw, and when somebody pointed to a vacant strip, he fell down, with many others, and went to sleep.

The reveille sounded a minute afterwards, though a whole night had passed; and there was the blessed clean water to wash in—he had long since ceased to be fastidious in his ablutions—and there was breakfast, sizzling bacon and bread and jam.

Kit inspection, feet inspection, all the duties of the day and dinner were over. Most of the men returned to their billets to sleep. Some, including Doggie, wandered about the village, taking the air, and visiting the little modest cafés and talking with indifferent success, so far as the interchange of articulate ideas was concerned, with shy children.

He was passing a large and comfortable house. The front door stood wide open, giving the view of a neat, stiff little hall. An article of furniture caught his idle eye. He crossed the road in order to have a nearer view. It was a huge, polished mahogany cask standing about four feet high, bound with shining brass bands, such as he remembered having seen once in Brittany.

He advanced still closer, and suddenly a slim dark girl appeared and stood in the doorway and looked frankly and somewhat rebukingly into his inquisitive eyes. Doggie sketched a vague salutation halfway between a salute and a bow, and began a profuse apology. Mademoiselle must pardon his curiosity, but as a lover of old things he had been struck by the beautiful *tonneau*.

An amused light came into her sombre tragic eyes. "There is no reasons for excuses, Monsieur," she said. "The door was open to the view of everybody. You can enter and examine the *tonneau,* if you wish."

"Mademoiselle was very amiable," said Doggie. Mademoiselle moved aside and Doggie entered taking off his helmet and holding it under his arm like an opera-hat.

In the course of the next three days Doggie managed on one pretext or another to enter that house several times and pass the time of day with Mademoiselle Jeanne. Once he found her sewing.

"May I move the lamp slightly," he asked, for it hid her from his view.

He moved it somewhat to her left. It threw shadows over her features, accentuating their appealing sadness. He watched her and thought of ghosts behind her eyes.

"You seem to have suffered greatly, Mademoiselle Jeanne," he said softly.

Her lips quivered. *"Mais oui, Monsieur."*

She put her hands and needlework in her lap and looked at him full.

"And you too have suffered."

"Oh, no."

"But yes, I have seen too much of it not to know. I see in the eyes. Your comrades—they are good fellows—but they have not suffered. You are different."

"Not a bit," he declared. "We're just little indistinguishable bits of the conglomerate Tommy."

"And I, Monsieur, have the honour to say that you are different."

This was very flattering. More—it was sweet unction, grateful to many a bruise.

"How?" said he.

"You do not belong to their world. I am only an ignorant girl, half bourgeoise, half peasant, Monsieur, but I have my woman's knowledge—and I know there is a difference between you and the others. You are a son of good family. It is evident. You have a delicacy of mind and of feeling. You were not born to be a soldier."

"You are quite right. But it's not a question of what I was born to be—but what I was trained to be. I wasn't trained to be a soldier. But I do my best."

"You abandoned everything to fight for your country?"

Under the spell of her dark eyes Doggie said, as he had once said to Phineas: "I think, Mademoiselle Jeanne, it was rather to fight for my soul."

She resumed her sewing. "That's what I meant long ago," she remarked with the first draw of the needle. "No one could fight for his soul without passing through suffering." She went on sewing. Doggie, shrinking from a reply that might have sounded fatuous, remained silent; but he realised a wonderful faculty of comprehension in Jeanne.

After a while he said: "Where did you learn all your wisdom, Mademoiselle Jeanne?"

"At the convent, I suppose. My father gave me a good education."

"An English poet has said 'Knowledge comes, but wisdom lingers'"—Doggie had rather a fight to express the meaning exactly in French—"You don't gather wisdom in convents."

"It is true. Since then I have seen many things." She stared across the room, not at Doggie, and he thought again of the ghosts.

"Tell me some of them, Mademoiselle Jeanne," he said in a low voice.

She shot a swift glance at him, and met his honest brown eyes. "I saw my father killed in front of me," she said in a strange, harsh voice.

"My God!" said Doggie.

Mademoiselle Jeanne's Story

"IT was on the Retreat. When we heard the Germans were coming, father, somewhat of an invalid, decided to fly. The roads were full of the English in retreat. I shall not tell you what I saw of the wounded by the roadside. I sometimes see them now in my dreams. And we were helpless. We thought we would leave the main roads, and at last we got lost and found ourselves in a little wood. We sat down to rest and to eat. We had scarcely begun when a body of cavalry with strange pointed helmets rode along the path and, seeing us, halted. My mother, half dead with terror, cried out, *'Mon Dieu, ce sont des Uhlans!'*

"The leader, I suppose an officer, called out something in German. My father got up and stood in front of his horse shouting back. The officer shot him through the heart, and he fell dead.

"My mother became mad. She screamed and clung to the bridle of the horse. And he rode her down and the horse trampled on her. Then he pointed at me, who was supporting the body of my father, and three men dismounted. But suddenly he heard something, gave an order and the men mounted again, and they all rode away laughing and jeering, and the last man, in bad French, shouted at me a foul insult.

"I was overwhelmed with grief and horror. Some hours afterwards a small body of English infantry came—many of them had bloodstained bandages. An officer, who spoke a little French, questioned me. I told him what had happened. He spoke with another officer and I recognised the word 'Uhlans.' Then they dug a little grave with their bayonets for my father. Some soldiers took a rope and pulled our hand cart, with my mother lying on top of our little possessions, and I walked with them, until the whole of my life was blotted out with fatigue. In the night, as we were still marching, there was a halt. I went to my mother. She was cold, Monsieur, cold and stiff. She was dead.

"I fainted. I do not know what happened till I recovered consciousness at dawn. I found myself wrapped in one of our blankets lying under the handcart. The English had carried me, I suppose, on the handcart, all night, they who were broken with weariness. I owe them my life and my reason."

"You have paid me a great compliment, Mademoiselle." Then after a while

he asked, "And then you found means to come here?"

"Alas, no!" she said, putting her work in her lap again. "I made my way to our original destination, a little farm belonging to the eldest brother of my father. The Farm of La Folette. We thought we were safe. Alas! news came that the Germans were always advancing. We had time to fly. All the farmhands fled, except Père Grigou, who loved my uncle.

"It was Père Grigou who forced us to hide. That lasted two days. There was a well in the farm, and one night Père Grigou tied up my money and my mother's jewelry and my father's papers, *enfin,* all the precious things we had, in a packet of waterproof and sank it with a long string down the well so that the Germans could not find it. It was foolish, but he insisted.

"We lay hidden until it was dark— how they did not find us I don't know— and then we escaped across country. I came here to my Aunt Morin—it is not far from La Folette. I help my aunt, who is ill and has lost her son, because I don't wish to live on the charity of my friends. I am without a sou—all my money having been hidden in the well by Père Grigou."

Doggie leant his elbows on the table. "And you have come through all that. Mademoiselle Jeanne, just as you are— so gentle and kind and comprehending."

Her cheek flushed. "I am not the only French woman who has passed through such things and kept herself proud. But the struggle has been very hard."

Doggie rose and clenched his fists and began to swear incoherently in English. She smiled sadly.

"Ah, mon pauvre ami!"

He wheeled round: "Why do you call me *'mon pauvre ami'*?"

"Because I see that you would like to help me, and you can't."

IT WAS dark when 'A' Company marched away. Doggie had seen nothing more of Jeanne. At the north end of the village the road took a sharp twist, skirting a bit of rising ground. There was just a glimmer of a warning light which streamed athwart the turning ribbon of laden ants. And as Doggie wheeled through the dim ray, he heard a voice that rang out clear.

"*Bonne chance!*"

He looked up swiftly. Caught the shadow of a shadow. But it was enough. It was Jeanne. The men responded incoherently, waving their hands, and Doggie's shout of "*Merci!*" was lost. But though he knew, with a wonderful throbbing knowledge, that Jeanne's cry was meant for him alone, he was thrilled by his comrades' instant response to Jeanne's voice. The company paid homage to Jeanne. Jeanne who had come out in the rain and the dark, and had waited, waited.

He ploughed on. Left, right! Thud, thud! Left, right! Jeanne, Jeanne!

And that night Jeanne prayed for the little soldier who was facing Death.

Something to do with Destiny

A WEEK later a dusty car with a military chauffeur at the wheel drove into Frélus and stopped before the Morin house. On the appearance of Jeanne, they saluted politely and introduced themselves as Intelligence officers. She bade them be seated.

"Mademoiselle, we are told that you billeted here last week a soldier by the name of Trevor."

Jeanne's lips grew white.

"Did you tell him about your private affairs?"

"Much, Monsieur."

He held out a strange twisted packet to her. "Mademoiselle, do you recognise this?"

She looked at it dully for a moment; then suddenly sprang to her feet and clenched her hands and stared open-mouthed. She nodded. She could not speak. Her brain. They must have come to tell her that Doggie was dead and now they showed her Père Grigou's packet. What was the connection

"If this is your property, Mademoiselle, you have your friend Trevor to thank for restoring it to you."

She put both hands to her reeling head.

"But is he dead, Monsieur?"

"Not a bit of it. He's just as much alive as you or I."

Jeanne swayed, tried to laugh, threw herself on a chair and broke down in a passion of tears.

"He is wounded?" she asked suddenly after a few moments.

"Not very seriously, Mademoiselle. A Boche sniper got him in the leg. It will put him out of service for a month or two. But there is no danger."

"*Grâce à Dieu!*" said Jeanne. "I ask your pardon, Messieurs, but sometimes sudden happiness is more overwhelming than misfortune. I am now quite at your service."

"I must ask you, Mademoiselle, some formal questions. Where was the packet when you last saw it?"

She made her statement, calmly. A few minutes later she signed a paper and thus entered into possession of her heritage.

THE officers were about to depart when Jeanne detained them. "But, Monsieur. How did he reach the well of La Folette? I don't comprehend it all."

"We had taken over a new sector and I was getting the topography right with a map," replied one of the officers. "I asked Trevor to help me. There was the site of the Folette farm marked by name and the ruined well away over to the left in No Man's Land. I remember the beggar calling out 'La Folette!' in a startled voice, and when I asked him what was the matter, he said 'Nothing sir!'

"A friend of mine about three miles further up the line told me that just before dawn yesterday morning, a man rolled over the parapet into our trench and promptly fainted. Under his tunic was this package—a fortune in loot or his person. Things looked mighty suspicious. As soon as he was fit to be interrogated, the C.O. took him in hand and he told him about you and your story. He regarded the nearness of the well as something to do with Destiny, and resolved to get you back your property. The opportunity occurred when he was out on a wiring party. He crept out to the ruins by the well, fished out the packet, and a sniper got him. He managed to get back to our lines, having lost his way a bit."

"But he was in danger of death all the time," said Jeanne, losing the steadiness of her voice.

"He was. Every second. It was one of the most dare-devil, scatter-brained things I've ever heard of. And I've heard of many, Mademoiselle. I must congratulate you on the restoration of your fortune and the possession of a very brave friend."

For the first time since she left her old home a smile came into Jeanne's eyes, together with grateful tears.

"*Il a fait cela pour moi! Il a fait cela pour moi!*"

Blighty

"How are you feeling, Trevor?"

"Nicely, thank you, Sister."

"Glad to be in Blighty again?"

Doggie smiled. "Good old Blighty!"

Blighty was a very desirable country, but in it you were compelled to think. And enforced thought was an infernal nuisance. The beastly trenches had their good points, after all. There you were not called upon to think of anything; the less you thought, the better for your job.

Now that he came to look at it in proper perspective, it wasn't at all a bad life. There were his friends: the humorous, genial, deboshed, yet ever kindly Phineas; dear old Mo Shendish whose material feet were hankering after the vulgar pavement of Mare Street.

It was strange to realise how the tentacles of his being stretched out gropingly towards these (from the old Durlebury point of view) impossible friends. They had grafted themselves on to his life. Or had they not rather, all grafted themselves on to a common stock of life, so that the one common sap ran through all their veins?

He had lived the Tommy life intensely. He was living it now. And the extraordinary part of it was that he didn't want to be anything else but a Tommy. From the social or gregarious point of view his life for the past year had been one of unclouded happiness. The realisation of it, now that he was clearly sizing up the ramshackle thing which he called his existence hit him like the butt-end of a rifle. Hardship, cold, hunger, fatigue, stench, rats, the dread of inefficiency—all these had been factors of misery which he could never eliminate from his soldier's equation; but such free, joyous, intimate companionship with real human beings he had never enjoyed since he was born.

Although his future was as nebulous as the planetary system in the Milky Way, at the back of his mind was a vague conviction that it would be connected somehow with the welfare of those men whom he had learned to know and love; the hemi-demi-semi-educated men, whose crude socialistic opinions, the open lessons of history and the eternal facts of human nature derisively refuted; the men who had sweated and slaved in factory and in field to no other purpose than to obey the biological laws; yet men with the sweet minds of children and the hearts of lions.

The Prodigal Son Returns

THE day of his discharge came in due course. A suit of khaki took the place of the hospital blue. He received his papers, the seven days sick furlough, shook hands with nurses and comrades, and sped to Durdlebury in the third class carriage of the Tommy.

Peggy was waiting for him at the

station yard. "Where's your luggage?" she asked him after hearty greeting.

"Haven't got any, thank God! If you knew what it was to hunch a horrible canvas sausage of kit about, you'd appreciate feeling free."

"Can't you forget you're a Tommy for a few days because Oliver is here," she said, as soon as the car had cleared the station gates and was safely under way.

Doggie laughed at the queer little social problem that seemed to be worrying her. Of course his old tormentor was a Major and he was in the ranks. "I think you'll find blood is thicker than military etiquette," he reassured her. "After all, Oliver is my first cousin."

Oliver, a tall lean figure in uniform, waved at them as they drew up to the Deanery steps.

"Hello, old chap!" he greeted Oliver as he stepped from the car. "My hat! you do look fit." He turned to Peggy. "A hundred times the man he was."

When they sat down to tea it appeared to Doggie that he had returned to some forgotten former incarnation. The delicate china cup in his hand seemed too frail for the material usages of life, and he feared lest he should break it with rough handling. The talk lay chiefly

between Oliver and himself. For the first time in his life Doggie began really to like Oliver. He stood out as an officer trusted and beloved by his men and his heart went out to him.

After much further talk the dressing gong boomed softly through the house. His valet welcomed him with tears of joy and a display of all the finikin luxuries of the toilet and adornment which he had left behind at Denby Hall. Doggie waved him away.

"Are you sure you can manage, sir?" Peddle asked anxiously, for time was when Doggie couldn't stick his legs into his trousers unless Peddle held them out for him.

"Quite," said Doggie.

"It seems rather roughing it here, Mr. Marmaduke, after what you've been accustomed to at the Hall."

"That's so," said Doggie. "And it's martyrdom compared with what it is in the trenches. There we always have a Major-General to lace up our boots, and a Field-Marshal's always hovering round to light our cigarettes."

Peddle, who had never known him to jest, or his father before him, went out in a muddled frame of mind, leaving Doggie to struggle into his dress trousers.

Happiness For Three

DOGGIE strode downstairs and opened the drawing room door and strode in. His entrance was so swift, so protected from sound, that the pair had no time to start apart before he was there. Peggy's hands were on Oliver's shoulders, and Oliver's arms were around her.

"I beg your pardon, sir," Doggie said with imperturbable irony, and turned.

Oliver rushed across the room. "It's my fault, Doggie. Everything's on me. Peggy's as true as gold."

"A triangular explanation is scarcely decent. Perhaps you might let me have a word or two with Peggy."

"I'll be in the dining room if you want me," said Oliver and went out.

Doggie took Peggy's hand and very gently led her to a chair. "First, before

we touch on this situation, let me say something to you. It may ease things. You see, I have made up my mind definitely, if I'm spared, not to live in Durdlebury after the war. I know that this won't please you—that you may have something very serious to say about it."

Peggy twisted a rag of a handkerchief and wavered for a moment. "You're a dear to put it that way, but I'm not going to step out of our engagement by the side door. We're all honourable people and Oliver"—she drew a sharp little breath—"Oliver will go out of our lives."

"Look here, Peggy, let's face it out. If you'll confess that you and Oliver are in love with each other, I'll confess to a girl in France."

"Oh?" said Peggy, with a swift change

to coolness. "How long has this been going on?"

"The last four days in billets before I got wounded," said Doggie. Then he laughed out loud and kissed her the heartiest, honestest kiss she had ever had from man, and rushed out of the room. Presently he and the Major returned. Oliver had cried:

"Doggie, you're the best and finest of dear old chaps in the world."

Now that Doggie had gained his freedom, Jeanne ceased to be a wraith. She became once again a wonderful thing of flesh and blood towards whom all his young, fresh instinct yearned tremendously. One day it struck his ingenuous mind that, if Jeanne were willing, there could be no possible reason why he should not marry her. All he had to do was to seek out Jeanne and begin his wooing in earnest. The simplest adventure in the world for a well-to-do and unattached young man—if only that young man had not been a private soldier on active service.

That was the rub. How on earth could he get to Frélus again? Not till the end of the war, at any rate, which might be years hence. There was nothing for it but a resumption of intimacy by letter.

Lost: One Girl

So HE wrote to Jeanne. But no answer came. Then he wrote another letter telling her of Peggy and his freedom, and his love and his hopes, and to that there came no reply. A prepaid telegram produced no result. Doggie began to despair. What had happened to Jeanne? Why did she rule him out of her existence?

And Jeanne? Well, Jeanne was no longer at Frélus; for there came a morning when her aunt was found dead in her bed. All her property had been left to a son, including the house. The result was that Jeanne was homeless.

With heavy heart she set out for Paris. She wrote, indeed, to Phineas, and weeks afterwards Phineas, who was in the thick of the Somme fighting, wrote to Doggie telling him of her departure from Frélus; but regretted that, as he had lost her letter, he could not give him her Paris address.

And in the meantime the bureaucratically minded old Postmaster at Frélus, who had received no instructions from Jeanne to forward her correspondence, handed Doggie's letters and telegrams to the aged postman, who stuck them into the letter box of the deserted house.

At last, Doggie, fit again for active service, went out with a draft to France, and joined Phineas and Mo, almost the only survivors of the cheery, familiar crowd that he had loved, and the grimness of battles such as he had never conceived possible took him in its grip.

Yet there were rare times of relief from stress, when he could gropingly string together the facts of a pre-Somme existence. And then he would curse Phineas lustily for losing the precious letter.

"Man," Phineas once replied, "don't you see that you are breaking a heart which, in spite of its apparent callosity, is as tender as a new-made mother's? Tell me to do it, and I'll desert and make my way to Paris and—"

"And the military police will see that you make your way to hell via a stone wall. Don't be a blithering fool," said Doggie.

Phineas Crashes Through

THE fighting went on, and to Doggie the inhabitants of the outside world became almost phantasmagorical. Then to Doggie came a heartbroken letter from the Dean. Oliver had been killed in action. Peggy was frantic with grief. The new glory of life that Peggy had found, Death had blackened out in an instant. Doggie looked again at the old man's letter and forgot for a while the familiar things around him, and lived with Peggy in her sorrow.

One day, after a successful raid, Doggie tumbled back with the rest of the men into the trench and, looking about, missed Phineas. Presently the word went round that "Mac" had been hit, and later the rumour was confirmed by the passage down the trench of Phineas on a stretcher, his weather-battered face a ghastly ivory.

"I'm alive all right, laddie," he gasped, contorting his lips into a smile. "I've got it clean through the chest like a gentleman. But it gars me greet I canna look after you any longer." He made an attempt at waving a hand, and the stretcher-bearers carried him away, out of the army for ever.

Doggie missed Phineas beyond all his conception of the blankness of bereavement. Like himself, Phineas had found salvation in the army. Doggie realised how he had striven in his own queer way to redeem the villainy of his tutorship. No woman could have been more gentle, more unselfish.

"What the devil am I going to do?" said Doggie.

Meanwhile Phineas, lying in a London hospital with a bullet through his body, thought much and earnestly of his friend, and one morning Peggy got a letter, asking her to come and see him. The next morning Peggy set out for London. Just before she started for the hospital a telegram arrived from the Dean.

"Just heard that Marmaduke is severely wounded."

She scarcely recognised the young private tutor of Denby Hall in the elderly man with the deeply furrowed face, who smiled as she approached his bed. She had brought him flowers, cigarettes of the exquisite kind that Doggie used to smoke, chocolates . . . .

"All this is more than gracious, Mrs. Manningtree," said Phineas. "I'm grateful to you for concerning yourself about my entirely unimportant carcass. But, as Virgil says, 'we must sing of somewhat greater things.'"

In his pedantic way he went on to tell her the story of Jeanne, so far as he knew it. He told her of the girl standing in the night wind and rain on the bluff by the turning of the road. He told her of Doggie's insane adventure across No Man's Land to the Farm of La Folette. Tears rolled down Peggy's cheeks.

"Doggie did that? For a woman? If a man had done a thing like that for me, I should have crawled after him to the ends of the earth." Presently she looked up with a flash in her eyes. "Why isn't this girl doing it?"

"You must listen to the end of the story," said Phineas. He continued the story of Jeanne; how she had learned through him of Doggie's wealth and position and finally of the loss of the letter containing her address in Paris.

After he had finished, Peggy sat for a long while thinking. This romance in Doggie's life had moved her as she thought she could never be moved. Finally Phineas broke in on her thoughts.

"Mrs. Manningtree, can you find Jeanne for Doggie?"

Peggy bent forward with a queer light in her eyes. "Does she love him—really love him as he deserved to be loved?"

"It is not often, Mrs. Manningtree, that I commit myself to a definite statement. But to my certain knowledge, these two are breaking their hearts for each other. Couldn't you find her, before the poor laddie is killed?"

"He's not killed yet, thank God!" said Peggy, with an odd thrill in her voice. "But how can I find her—just a girl—an unknown Mademoiselle Boissière—among the millions of Paris?"

"I've been racking my brains all the morning," replied Phineas, "to recall the address, and out of the darkness there emerge just two words, Port Royal. That is the clue to the labyrinth," replied Phineas.

So it came to pass that while Doggie, with a shattered shoulder and a touched left lung, was being transported from a base hospital in France to a hospital in England, Peggy, armed with all kinds of passports and recommendations and a very fixed, personal sanctified idea, was crossing the Channel on her way to Paris and Jeanne.

It turned out to be no wild goose chase, but a very simple matter.

For Jeanne, the sight of the young English woman in black who was waiting to see her was unreasonably disquieting. Peggy advanced with outstretched hand.

"I am a cousin of Monsieur Trevor—"

"Ah, Madame"—Jeanne pointed to the mourning—"You do not come to tell me he is dead?"

Peggy smiled and said quietly, "No, this is for my husband."

Jeanne, in distress, asked her pardon. Then she added, "You have come from England perhaps to tell me that he is wounded?"

"Yes. I had a telegram this morning to say that he had arrived at a hospital in London. I want you to accompany me back to him."

"But Madame. How do you know that he desires my presence? He would have written to me if he desired that and I have never heard from him."

"He wrote many letters and telegraphed to Frélus."

"Madame," cried Jeanne, "I implore you to believe that not one of those letters has ever reached me. *Je le jure, Madame.*"

And Peggy believed her.

Jeanne said: "Madame, I am profoundly moved by what you have told me. I have only to confess that I love Doggie with all my heart, with all my soul"—with her two clenched hands she smote her breast—and Peggy noted it was the first gesture that she had made. "I feel the infinite need, Madame—you will understand me—to care for him, to protect him—"

"Protect him?" Peggy interrupted. "Why, hasn't he shown himself to be a hero?"

Jeanne leant forward and there was a wonderful light behind her eyes.

"It is only the little ready-made heroes who have no need of a woman's protection. But it is a different thing with the great heroes who have made themselves without the aid of a *bon Dieu*, from little dogs of no account to what Doggie is at the moment. The woman then takes her place. She fixes things for ever. She alone can understand."

Peggy gasped as at a new Revelation. The terms in which this French girl expressed herself were far beyond the bounds of her philosophy.

"But what would you protect him from?" she protested in order to see more clearly.

"From want of faith in himself; from want of faith in his destiny, Madame. Once he told me he had come to France to fight for his soul. It is necessary that he should be victorious. It is necessary that the woman who loves him should make him victorious."

Peggy put out her hand and touched Jeanne's wrist.

"I'm glad I didn't marry Doggie, Mademoiselle," she said simply. "I couldn't have done that."

Doggie lay in a long, pleasant ward of a great London hospital, the upper left side of his body a mass of bandaged pain. No more fighting for Doggie this side of the grave. But the grave was as far distant as it is from any young man in his twenties who avoids abnormal peril.

Today he felt wonderfully strong in spite of the unrelenting pain, and the nurse had said: "I shouldn't wonder if you had some visitors this afternoon." Peggy, of course. And sure enough, as he looked round contentedly he saw Peggy and a companion coming down the ward, together. With her was a girl in black.

He raised himself, forgetful of exquisite pain, on his right elbow, and stared in a thrill of amazement.

And Jeanne came to him, and there were no longer ghosts behind her eyes, for they shone like stars.

BESS STREETER ALDRICH

SONG OF YEARS

Few American novelists are as dearly beloved as Bess Streeter Aldrich (1881—). Most of her books including "A Lantern in Her Hand" and "Spring Came on Forever" have been outstanding bestsellers and "Song of Years" is no exception. This is a story of pioneer life on the Prairies at the time of the Civil War and more particularly of two young people who fell in love. It is rich in the "never say die" American spirit which is still with us.

SUZANNE

BELOVED WIFE

OF

But what else it says you cannot know because a thick growth of old clinging wood-bine and a clump of sweet-william covers the secret of whose beloved she was.

Reading the inscription chiseled long ago, it seems of such small consequence whose name is hidden under the vines. But, to Suzanne it mattered so very much.

This is the love story of the Suzanne who lies here by the side of the curving graveled path.

It begins, perhaps, on a June day in 1854 with a young man walking steadily to the west in the light-footed rhythmic way of the prairie-wolf. Once or twice he reached in his pocket to make sure that the paper they had given him was still there—the list of un-patented and unsold lands out here in the Valley of the Red Cedar in the new state of Iowa. And for the hundreth time he touched the ridge of his waist-line which was the quilted belt containing money for a portion of that land.

For the first time in his life he felt entirely free, completely his own boss. For the first time he would own prop-erty-rich land out here in this new raw state. A great many people thought it would never be settled. It was true there were no railroads, no big towns, only a few settlements clinging to rivers.

Once his mind dwelt on another memory—a girl. He had no hankering for a sweetheart, would have none for many years. When he did . . . if he ever did . . . his mind formed a very indistinct picture of some beautiful un-known creature in a nebulous mist of white, a soft blurred outline of a wing-less angel floating in clouds. Anyway, he would know her when he saw her.

Then quickly he tossed this sketchy and imaginative picture aside as lightly as crumpled paper. No time to think about girls out here. He desired nothing so much as land and crops and stock, freedom to come and go as he wished, to get rich and perhaps parade his suc-cess a bit back home.

Abruptly he turned off the trail and followed the creek bed to the northwest. This now—about here . . . ended the preempted claims. That which extended beyond was all government land.

The young man drew a quick excited breath. Wood . . . creek . . . gravel . . . sand . . . glowing spring . . . rich loam . . . only a mile to the north of the beaten track, about five from Prairie Rapids . . . only about three, probably, from Sturgis Falls. *This was it.* For this he had come the long miles by steam-cars, stage, and foot.

It was something like the sudden meeting with a person of whom you had long heard but whose face you had never seen. It was almost—why it came pretty near to being like the first meeting with that girl he'd sometimes imagined.

He took off his cap and the sun brought out the glints in his yellow hair. "Wayne Lockwood," he grinned widely, "do you take this land to be your lawfully wedded own, to have and to hold in sickness and in health?"

Jocularly he made his answer in a feminine voice: "I do."

"I pronounce you mine," he said boyishly.

A Challenge

THE gay words died in the utterance for not a half-dozen rods away to the east, a top-buggy with glistening body, pulled by a sleek pair of prancing bay horses was coming directly toward him through the prairie grass.

Apparently seeing that Wayne was not making any move to come to them, one of the men in the buggy said affably: "Little off the trail, aren't you? Looking for land? My name's Bedson—Cady Bedson."

"Yes, sir."

"Good land up this way. We've located several fine sections. You will probably find something you like."

"Yes . . . I've found it."

The young man was not quite so cordial now. "Not this section?"

"This *quarter*-section."

"Oh, no . . . this one is mine . . . this half."

Wayne looked down at the paper still in his hand. "I made this out from a government map . . . and it's not filed on yet, according to this," he said quietly.

"No." The young chap admitted it readily enough. "We're driving back to Dubuque, though, tomorrow to attend to that matter."

He smiled with such oily condescension that Wayne took an immediate dislike to him. And when he asked: "Did you walk out from Dubuque?" it seemed to take on the tone of a superior addressing an inferior.

"Yes."

"I thought I didn't see any conveyance about."

That was perilously close to a sneering comment. When Wayne remained silent, the stranger volunteered affably enough: "Well . . . we'll go on. We're staying at a tavern in Sturgis Falls but will be driving back to Dubuque tomorrow."

Not particularly versed in the nuances of the human voice, still Wayne thought he detected the semblance of a threat in the statement. The stranger could well afford to be pleasant, though, with those prancing bays, ready to take him back to the land-office one hundred miles away. So he was saying cheerfully: "Better luck in your next choice."

WAYNE threw himself on the creek's bank. He was disappointed and chagrined. If that smart Aleck had really owned that land, he would have walked on with no thought of covetousness. But after all, it was not yet the other fellow's any more than his. Only by virtue of owning that swift team would the stranger be able to claim it.

Dubuque! One hundred miles. It might as well have been half a world away.

But the men would have to spend the night at Sturgis Falls. It might be late in the morning when they would get started. There was just a chance he himself might be overtaken by some one with whom he could ride.

He looked down at his strong young limbs incased in calfskin boots as though there he might find the answer to his questioning. A deep longing for the real ownership of that which had already taken on familiar lines and an obstinacy within him, as well as an intuitive dislike of the young stranger's condescending tones—all of these feelings, which could not take the decision calmly, spurred him on.

Suddenly he turned and, in that light Indian-footed way of his, strode back toward the east.

Setting Up Housekeeping

ONE week later found Wayne Lockwood nearing the end of his second journey to the Valley of the Red Cedar, nearly back, to the quarter-section he had chosen with such swiftness of decision, and tramped a hundred weary miles to obtain.

It gave him a queer feeling in which pride and a sense of responsibility were the leading emotions, but running through both, like a scarlet thread in a gray coat, was the boyish jubilation over winning out in the entry of it. All he needed to cheer him in any moment of homesickness or fear for his ultimate success in the new country was to recall that look of amazement and chagrin which had come over the face of that dapper young fellow, Cady Bedson, whom he had beaten out of it. Even now as the new wagon jolted over the trail he laughed aloud at the remembrance.

Yes, it was his all right, thanks to a quick decision and two good legs, and no finer land lay anywhere in the new state, he would wager.

And now he was almost home. *Home!* That was a queer word to apply to the prairie grass and the creek and the clump of timber lying off there to the north. But in no time at all he would have a good snug cabin. He would break out the sod, raise fine crops, stock his farm, bring in sheep, buy more land. Ten years from now he would have a transplanted New England home, but larger and finer.

IT was far into the forenoon of the next day when from the southeast he saw two horses galloping toward him. As they approached he made out that one was ridden by a man, but that skirts were billowing out, balloon-like, at the side of the other.

When they rode close and reined in, the man proved to be middle-aged, black-whiskered, shaggy-browed and dark-skinned. He sat on his horse with ease, the trunk of his body erect as the tree Wayne had just marked for the next cutting, but his head drooped forward as though he must be forever urging his mount on.

The billowing skirt belonged to a young girl who might have been any age from twelve to sixteen; it was difficult to tell it, clothed as she was in the full-skirted, tight-waisted garment of the prairie female person. Her hair was reddish-brown, vaguely wavy, he could see, for it had partially tumbled out from a black net in the swift riding over the prairie. Her gray-blue eyes looked too large for the slim oval of her face and too mature for a certain childishness.

"Well . . . what's goin' on here?" was the man's bluff and hearty greeting as soon as he had dismounted.

Wayne met him pleasantly enough with: "Oh, I'm sort of setting up housekeeping. I take it you're one of my neighbors."

"You took it right. Jeremiah Martin's my name. I'm an old time settler, now, came two years ago this month. Live over there at the edge of that grove on the trail."

"My name is Wayne Lockwood."

"Glad to make your acquaintance, Mr. Lockwood, and welcome you to Red Cedar Valley."

They shook hands and when Wayne unconsciously glanced at the young girl, high on her tall horse, Jeremiah Martin said: "That's one of my girls. Let's see now, slips my mind at this time just which one she is." His blue eyes were twinkling behind their black bushes. "Oh, yes, now I recollect . . . this one's Suzanne."

"I'm pleased to make your acquaintance, Suzanne."

"Howdydo." She was neither forward nor shy, merely matter-of-fact, as though strangers were an everyday occurrence.

There was conversation between the two men about the land, the number of sections taken, prospects of other land-seekers coming in and, surprisingly to Wayne, the offer from Mr. Martin in behalf of himself and the other settlers, to help build the cabin. When Wayne protested that he had expected to do everything himself, wouldn't want to take them from their own work, Jeremiah Martin broke in with: "We'll all be ready to help cut tomorrow mornin'."

He turned 'his mare preparatory to riding back toward his home, and then said casually: "We'll look for you to supper tonight."

"Oh, but . . . I've got supplies."

"Just as important to break bread together out here as to break sod. Friendship is one of the most necessary things in this world anywhere, my lad, but you'll need it out here more than you ever have back home."

"Well, I thank you . . . of course . . ."

They were starting away. The girl looked back over her shoulder and spoke for the first since her brief salutation. "We eat about sun down," she called back.

Many Martins

THE long table had been set with a nice white cloth, one of the good ones which Sarah Martin had owned back in York State. Against it the sand-polished steel knives and forks with their black handles looked very fine. In the center of the table was a mass of wild bouncing-Bets in the old tureen, their shaggy pale-pink blossoms lovely against the delft blue of the bowl.

"Suzanne always drags flowers into the house," one of the girls was saying, so that Suzanne hid her red face in her hands. And her father said, "Any of you make sport of Suzanne and her flowers I'll thump you."

They shouted with laughter and Sabina explained to Wayne: "Ever since I was a little girl he's said that . . . 'I'll thump you' . . . and he's never touched one of us yet."

"But Ma has," Jeanie said, and they all laughed again.

"Don't you go to makin' sport of Ma, either, or . . ."

"'I'll thump you,'" they mimicked in chorus.

The most unusual family he had ever known, Wayne thought, saying bold, mean-sounding things to each other, but seemingly having bonds of affection underneath.

Jeremiah, the father, sat at one end of the table and Sarah, the mother, at the other. On one side were Henry, Phoebe Lou, Wayne Lockwood, Melinda, and Emily; on the other, Phineas,

Sabina, Celia, Jeanie and Suzanne. At both ends of the table were platters of steaming stewed prairie-chicken. Several large bowls held white-flour saleratus biscuits in prairie-chicken gravy. Wayne knew just how those shepherd-dogs felt licking their chops outside the door. He felt like doing it himself.

AND now Jeremiah's head was bowed and there was a slow trickling off of that constant feminine chatter as though it were as hard to stop as vinegar dripping from a barrel's bung hole.

"Thank Thee for this food and bless it," Jeremiah's voice rumbled into his big black beard. He did not call the Lord by name, merely addressed himself humbly to some great Unseen Power who was the woods, the prairies, the moon, the sun, the winds, the rains. "And bless the stranger within our gates as he now becomes our friend. Amen."

Chatter broke forth immediately like the cider that must flow again from the barrel after being held back a moment by a wooden plug. Constantly Wayne was on the alert to get this family straight in his mind. He had not known any one just like them, could see plainly that although he might admire them as friends and neighbors, there was not the slightest chance of ever feeling anything else toward any one of them. There was no lovely creature floating in a white veil of cloud here among these healthy and hearty girls.

A Magic World

SUZANNE was picking berries in the far end of the Martin property. She was also thinking of Wayne Lockwood. Suzanne thought she had never seen so good-looking a young man. Something made you like just everything about him, the way his wavy light hair went back from his forehead, his direct looking blue eyes, the way he held his head, the way his mouth pulled up at the corners when he smiled, that light-footed way of his walking. Even his strong brown hands pleased her.

Suzanne had a game of her very own which no one of the family knew anything about. She had a secret gift whereby she could live in either one of two worlds, just as she chose, and she scarcely knew which one she liked better. It was no trouble at all to change from one to the other, as easy, almost, as opening the wooden door between the main room and the lean-to.

She went into her other world whenever she chose. All you had to do was to open the door . . . and there you were.

Now she had a new person to inhabit this country which no one entered but herself—Wayne Lockwood. This was the first time a real person had ever been admitted, the only time that any one of flesh and blood was nice enough and handsome enough to mingle with all those other people who lived in her fancy.

There were no sounds now in the sleepy warmth of the day excepting a few plaintive mourning-doves' calls and the occasional plop of some water animal. And then suddenly she heard movement in the bushes as of light-footed walking, and her heart stood still with fright. Her body turned cold and she shook a little in the summer heat. Then Wayne Lockwood, gun in hand, came through the underbrush.

"Well, hello, there," he was saying. "Where'd you come from? Are you lost?"

"Oh, no." Suzanne, relieved and happy, laughed aloud at that. "This place belongs to me."

She had never been one moment alone with him. The few times she had seen him the whole family had been around, as like as not plaguing her, too. For the first time she felt at ease in his presence.

"So this is yours, is it?" Then I must be trespassing. "Well. Prin-*cess* Suzanne"—he swept off his cap, placed it across his breast, and bowed low in mock homage—"will you kindly allow me to cross your domain so that I can get to my castle on the other side of the Black Forest?"

Suzanne's eyes were wide with astonishment and she could not know how the playful words had lighted the candles that lay behind them. No one had ever said anything like that but her secret people. That was the way they talked. That was the way they acted. Her face grew pink with the excitement and embarrassment of it, and her voice trembled when she said shyly, "Yes, I guess I'll let you this once."

Long after he had gone on, turning around to laugh that he was walking here only by her permission, she remembered just how he looked and what he said.

It was going to be very, very easy after this to live in that magic world.

Six Years Later

SO MANY changes in the Valley as there had been during the six years since the youthful Wayne Lockwood walked into it across the prairies from Dubuque that sunlit afternoon!

The railroad creeping within twenty-four miles of town and met by the stage was one change. Eight, ten, a dozen passengers sometimes alighted—new-comers, visiting politicians, an occasional returned resident who had been visiting "back home." All brought news of antislavery agitation in the East and threats of secession in the South.

There were changes, too, in Wayne. He was twenty-four now, a man, his own boss, a respected settler. He had raised as good crops as any one, owned a nice flock of sheep for which he had built a shelter bigger than his cabin, so that people joked him about treating his stock better than himself.

His cabin was neat even though there were no softening touches. More than one young woman in the Valley would have been glad to add that touch.

But to all these Wayne was impervious. For how could he say that marriage meant more to him than that the work in his cabin should be done and a woman lie by his side? How could he tell them that always he carried within himself the thought of a girl who was the face of a girl in a cloud?

And sometimes in the evening after the day's work was done, when he went down the lane road, he let his voice out to its fullest, putting into a melody all this that he carried in his heart but would never tell.

He could not know that his voice, carrying across the north prairie its unconscious longing as the bittern calls for its mate, unaccountably stirred the pulses and brought an unwanted mist of tears to the eyes of a young girl. For whenever Suzanne heard that voice singing up the lane road she would slip away from the others—to the loft bedroom or into the edge of the grove—drinking in the song alone, for fear some one would notice that which she must conceal.

THEN, on a late August afternoon with a peculiarly cool tinge in the air vaguely reminiscent of past falls, Jeremiah ordered Suzanne and Celia to go over to the school house to scrub it and wash the four glass windows. School would take up after a bit now and he wasn't going to have the new teacher think the director who had a school house right under his nose couldn't get it ready.

They were almost through, with the benches piled neatly and the windows clean of their summer cobwebs, when Wayne Lockwood rode up on horseback. Without dismounting, he leaned in the window and said: "The people are moving into the big new house you all are so curious about. You can satisfy your curiosity about them right now if you like."

The three could get a view of the open carriage stopping at the corner close to the school. Suzanne did not know which was more exciting, the arriving Scotts or the nearness of that masculine presence of which she was always so keenly aware.

Mr. Scott got out. He turned to assist a lady—a young girl in summer blue, her skirts fashionably full, and on her head a little white straw bonnet from which a blue plume and a long white veil dropped. She stepped down, and in doing so, turned her head toward the school house so that they could see her pale delicate features. As she stood there looking toward the east and yet not seeing them, a breeze picked up the long white veil and whipped it high about her head.

Involuntarily Suzanne glanced up at Wayne. He was staring at the new girl with a queer expression on his face, so that Suzanne's pounding pulses stopped in sudden questioning of the strange look.

And Suzanne, you had reason to question. For, peculiarly, at just that moment, the girl's face in the flowing white veil looked like the face of a girl in a cloud.

Crashing Air Castles

ONE day Suzanne slipped down to the garden patch, and through the side gate, and stopped at the stake-and-rider fence, deciding it was too near supper time to go on. There was no one in sight and because she still had on hoops from visiting in town, she pulled them and her skirts high and climbed to the top of the fence, releasing them then so they sprang out into their round fullness, giving her the apearance of a blue mushroom growing like a parasite on the bark of the rail fence.

Suppose, just suppose, that Wayne Lockwood should come through the woods now, while she was sitting elegantly here in her best dress, and say right out of a clear sky: "Suzanne, I've known you for a long time. I love you. I've loved you ever since I saw you the first day I came to the Valley. Will you marry me, Suzanne, dear one?"

So far, the scene involving the ardent proposal had been confined to that vague locality known to Suzanne's past childhood as her magic world, always a place of silence. But now in the warmth of the loved one's fervor and her own reaction to his imagined emotions, it broke bounds and said aloud: "Yes . . oh, yes, I will."

"Will what?"

Twigs were snapping. A branch was crackling. And Wayne Lockwood came through the underbrush.

No longer was Suzanne sitting elegantly, for in wide-eyed and open-mouthed terror, she promptly and completely fell off the fence. Not gracefully, but in an awkward, sidewise tumble, with her hoops catching on one of the stakes and her best ruffled pantalets a prominent part of the picture.

Wayne threw back his head and laughed heartily. Even so he was hurrying to disengage the wire-and-elastic skeleton structure and its disconcerted owner from their perilous position.

When the robust laughter died away, he said, "Anyway, I'm glad I ran across you here alone." He had put a foot up on the log of the fallen hickory tree trunk and was facing her. "Suzanne. . ." He was all seriousness now. "I've known you a long time . . . ever since the first day I came to the Valley . . . And I want to ask you something."

An unseen force was performing a miracle for her. From out of the world of imagination by some unknown means

she had called an exquisite reality. Her pulses were pounding so loudly that she was afraid he must be hearing them.

"I wonder," Wayne's deep resonant voice went on, "would you go down to the Scotts' on some excuse when you have a chance and find out more about the daughter?"

Like the shocked silence after crashing thunder on the prairie, Suzanne's beating pulses were numbed.

"You want me . . . ?"

"I hate to ask you. It seems cowardly and underhanded, but I want to get acquainted with her and they seem so stiff and unfriendly, I thought maybe if you could go first and find out a little more about her and tell me. . . You're the only one I felt I could trust to do it . . . and keep it confidential."

Suzanne moistened her dry lips. "And you . . . trust me?"

"Yes. I don't know just why, Suzanne, but of all you girls . . . you're the one who seems most . . ." his voice trailed away in a half-abashed silence.

Suzanne said quietly: "All right, Wayne, I will."

They walked on up to the house together, the deepening prairie twilight thrown over them like a gray veil.

THE day before the County Fair, making an invitation to attend it the excuse for her going and thus keep her promise to Wayne, Suzanne dressed in her blue poplin and rode Jupiter down the field road to the Scotts'.

No ambassador to a foreign court ever went in such a mixed mental state including, as did Suzanne's mind, timidity, curiosity, envy, and disrelish.

When she beheld Miss Carlie Scott coming down the stairway only the thought of Pa's being the Honorable Jeremiah Martin bolstered her courage.

"My name's Suzanne Martin," she said and knew her voice sounded pinched and squeaky. "I thought I'd come over and tell you about the County Fair tomorrow, and urge you to go."

Miss Carlie Scott said that was nice

for her to come and to sit down here where it was cool. She was pretty and so pale that her sister Celia would certainly take a back seat. Her mouth was a pouting pink which gave her the appearance of a small child.

The black woman brought in cookies and glasses of something that tasted to Suzanne partly like wild grapes and partly like apple cider. But even eating together did not make the call a complete success as Pa said breaking bread always did. Something between them seemed never to be overcome.

Reporting all about it at home, she said, "I can't tell you what it was, but I don't believe I'd ever feel acquainted with them. I don't believe they ever have fun and I bet they don't know what a joke is."

The next day Wayne Lockwood thanked her for calling on the Scotts. "I wouldn't have needed to ask you, but I appreciated it. You see I got acquainted with her anyway. Suzanne, she's . . ." his voice wrapped itself about the words, folding them in tenderly . . . "she's like a flower."

"A flower?" Suzanne repeated stupidly.

"Yes . . I guess one of these . . . little wind flowers . . . you know, dainty and delicate." He laughed suddenly. "Funny I could say that out loud to any one. Sounds pretty foolish, doesn't it?"

THE next day Suzanne said suddenly to her father: "Pa, I want to go to this new Female Seminary in Prairie Rapids when it opens. Do you think I could?"

Jeremiah appraised his youngest with a critical if furtive eye. "Well, those are legitimate desires, I'd say. But just why are you anxious to go this week and was lukewarm last?"

"I've been thinking . . . and I've made up my mind to be a teacher. If I go there this winter I guess I could pass the teacher's examinations and get a school instead of just helping Ma."

"Or gettin' married and settlin' down?"

"Oh, don't say that. I wouldn't marry anybody if . . . if every man in the country wanted me."

"Well . . to save you the possible embarrassment o' giving 'em all the mitten, I guess maybe you better go. It's fifty cents a week tuition. That comes pretty often for a half a dollar. I'd want you to make the most of your time."

"Oh, I will, Pa. I want to spend my whole life studying!"

War Beyond the Horizon

ALL the rest of the year Suzanne went back and forth to the Seminary—home Friday nights, back to Prairie Rapids Sunday night, or so early Monday morning that the pale December sun was not yet up.

Life now to Suzanne was divided, like that Gaul Miss Anna Field told about, into three parts: I, School. II, War talk. III, Wayne Lockwood.

She had too much pride to ask any one about Wayne and Carlie Scott when she was home, but, even so, there was no need, for Celia and Melinda volunteered glibly as soon as she arrived that often Wayne passed the house on the way to the Scotts', and that he sat by Carlie Scott's side at singing school and sang,

"Thou only hast my heart," like to raise the dead.

The war was a monster that lay in wait over there to the south beyond the horizon. Here they were safe, for it could never come to the Valley. Lying in bed these nights next to Celia, Suzanne would try to think what it meant. Valley Forge . . . Bunker Hill . . . Yorktown . . . they were paragraphs in the history book and dates to recite to Miss Libbie Field.

But war was something more than paragraphs and dates. It was her brothers and brothers-in-law and all the Pioneer Grays. There was even talk that maybe Lincoln might call for more than these first boys. If he did . . . She would lie quietly, staring into the blackness of the logs. "Don't let Wayne Lockwood go," she would petition some unseen force. "Even if he belongs to Carlie Scott, keep him safe here."

By September she was getting the home school ready for her first teaching. Seeing Wayne Lockwood ride down the field road toward the Scotts' she would put him out of her mind for days. Then he would ride up, as she was leaving perhaps, stop a few minutes to chat, maybe swing off the horse and stand near her, and the door of that magic world would fly open as easily as though some impish creature, inserting the key with invisible hands, had pushed it ajar in wicked glee.

When the second call came for troops, she was almost sure that Wayne would volunteer. No family, no responsibilities excepting those he made for himself, he was just the kind of young man to go.

B<small>UT</small> Wayne did not go. He thrashed his wheat, put up tons of hay in his new frame barn, so much larger than his cabin, brought in more sheep, built another new shelter for them, said casually to Suzanne one day as though his thoughts, long-harbored, were involuntarily forming speech: "When I build my new house, Suzanne, it shall be something like my grandfather's old home near the sea . . . wide clapboards painted white . . . and green blinds . . . and a built-in seat on both sides of the stoop."

Hearing it, Suzanne locked the door of her fancy once more and threw the key away—threw it blindly and far this time as one would toss a little unwanted thing into the green sea of the pasture grass.

Wayne Lockwood felt almost money-mad, angered that the war was intruding itself just when his prospects were so good. A fragile dainty girl must have everything nice . . . all the fine things that money could buy. His deepest hope at every dawn's rising was that the next battle would be the last, so he might settle down to work without prick of conscience or goading thought of obligation to his country. Never had he felt completely at ease with himself since that first voluntary contingent of soldiers, the Pioneer Grays, had pulled out from the new depot the June before.

Seldom did he sing. For some reason, even though the flowerlike face of Carlie Scott was often in his thoughts, he was not letting out his melodious voice there in the Valley as of old. For how could one sing of war with thoughts of love stealing through the martial strains? And how could one sing of love with the guns of war drowning out the melody?

Lost and Found

S<small>UZANNE</small> had dismissed the children and was ready to leave the school herself one Friday afternoon when she looked up quickly to see Carlie Scott standing in the entry way. Suzanne was startled that there should be anyone there at all so that it was Carlie Scott who was now saying: "Oh, I thought you'd be gone."

Plainly Carlie was disturbed. Something was not turning out as she had planned, and Suzanne felt intuitively that the something was her presence. Finally she put her muff down and said—"I guess I'll just have to throw myself on your mercy and ask you to promise not to tell anything about seeing me here."

Suzanne's heart stood still with fright and the pain of what Carlie was to say. "If it's . . . necessary . . . I promise."

"Some one is coming for me," Carlie explained hurriedly. "By the time it's found out . . . I'll be gone."

"Wayne Lockwood . . . is coming?"

Carlie gave a short laugh that held irritation in it as well as faint amusement.

"Oh, no . . . How stupid! The man I love . . . that they didn't want me to see any more . . . that they thought they were separating me from for always. Well, they'll find they couldn't do that."

For a time they stood in awkward silence and then there was the sound of floundering horse hoofs and squeaking runners, and Carlie Scott was out the door. She turned back and laughed nervously, her pale cheeks flushed. "Now, you can have your big solemn farmer. Maybe, you think I haven't guessed. I wasn't blind. Well, that's all I wanted of him . . . to throw them off the scent . . . keep them from knowing my real feeling and what was going to happen. Good-by."

For long moments Suzanne stood unmoving, eyes to the door beyond which Carlie Scott had disappeared. Still in a daze she finished fastening her galoshes and put on her mittens. Mind in a turmoil at the knowledge of this devastating thing that had happend to Wayne, she lowered her head and walked into the cold wind across the schoolyard.

From the sight of low rolling grayish-white clouds, high above the horizon now, her eyes suddenly caught a glimpse of that which caused her to stop short in her tracks. Other grayish white clouds were rolling along on the ground. They were Wayne's sheep, drifting foolishly ahead of the storm as sheep will, heading straight for the river.

To GET to Wayne's cabin and tell him about his sheep was the least she could do for him. Otherwise they were heading straight for the broken ice, which meant the utter destruction of all his work. He must not have this loss on top of his loss of Carlie.

To the north she could see his cabin standing but it looked silent and desolate. There was no use wasting time. Cutting across the field, herself, to head off the sheep was clearly the only thing to do. The grayish white sheep were not far away—she could hear their bleating but suddenly they were no longer visible. The darkness and the storm had leagued together to obliterate them. And now she lived in a world of ice and snow in which no other thing existed.

"I'm in real danger," she thought. "I've got to keep my head. It's getting worse and I've got to get home."

Quite suddenly her mind was clear and she knew what to do. Follow the creek bed. It might take hours in the darkness of the storm feeling the way along the ice . . . but she would make it unless . . . like the sheep in those open places . . .

There was another sound now, one of breaking snow crust and a thrashing creature coming close. Wayne Lockwood, trying to trace the path of his sheep through the storm, had run onto her. "Suzanne . . . good God! What are you doing here?"

The next thing she knew she was in his arms and up on the horse. Laboriously he retraced the path through the crashing sleet and howling wind to the light in his cabin window.

Wayne put the half-frozen girl down in a chair by the fire. He hung her soggy garments up to dry and then brought her some soup. When he came to take the bowl he stopped a moment and looked down at her. "Now tell me why you did that dangerous darn-fool thing?"

"I saw your sheep heading for the creek . . . and I couldn't bear to think of your losing them, too."

It was out before she realized she had said it. That little word "too," so innocent and so guilty, gone into the air with all the things that have been spoke which never should have been said.

But he did not question her. She felt that he knew. He had heard. She could tell by his attitude and the strange baffled look on his face.

Sometime in the night she woke with a start, incredulous and half frightened to find herself here. He was still there in front of the fire with his head forward in his hands so that she wished with every fiber of her being she might comfort him. It was of Carlie he was thinking and it was for Carlie he was grieving. Of that Suzanne had no doubt.

For how could she know that queer things were running through Wayne's mind, crazy, confused thoughts he had never harbored before, perplexing questions with no answers. "Oh, Suzanne, what shall I do? I've been hurt and disillusioned. I don't know where to turn but to you. More than anything in the world I want to tell you about it. I want your comfort and sympathy. And I want you. You're the one real thing in life, Suzanne. But you wouldn't understand that. You have your pride, too . . ."

Song of Strength and Love

SUZANNE, leaning against the doorway, had been hearing something in the stillness. Wayne Lockwood who had not sung for so long a time was singing as he rode home from town. It was a new song—"The Song of A Thousand Years."

Singing, Wayne Lockwood rode in more light-hearted mood than for many months. He had enlisted and felt cleansed of some former defilement, rid of an undesirable part of himself because of his decision. Peace followed in the wake of right decisions. Stoutness of character included following one's duty. And just now duty led to war. Doing one's duty made one strong. The song of years was a song of strength.

The resonant voice died away up the lane road and Suzanne thought:

"I'll not try to evade it any more," she thought. "I'm no longer a child with dreams. I'm a woman. I love him and always shall. That he doesn't care the slightest thing for me doesn't enter into it any more. But I'm willing . . . and reconciled . . . Just that and nothing more."

To Suzanne there was never any doubt that the song of years was a song of love.

THERE were only five of the very smallest children in school. The others had gone to town with their folks to see the soldiers entrain. Wayne Lockwood would be among the men leaving.

Constantly her eyes went to the rails over there to the north of the school house. High on the graveled embankment the track shone in the morning sun.

It was time now.

"We'll go up the lane road," she told the five, "and watch the train go by with the soldiers on it."

Now they could see the flat gravel cars, blue with uniforms. The bell was ringing, the steam-whistle shrieking. But what was the matter? It was not coming at its usual mad pace, roaring its way across the prairie. It was slowing down. What was happening?

Wayne Lockwood was swinging off the last of the flat cars. Wayne in his blue uniform coming toward them. And now he had Suzanne in his arms, was straining her body to his own, his lips to hers for one long moment.

"Good-by."

With no word other than that he released her and was up the graded bank again. Hands were reaching for him, pulling him onto the flat car.

The children were excited. *The train had stopped.* It was the wonder of the year.

"Miss Martin," one of them asked. "Did the train stop just because he wanted to say good-by to you?" And then a new and pleasant thought struck: "Why did he want to? Is he your lover?"

Suzanne's hands were at her throat and she was crying.

"Yes . . . he's my lover."

Dead from Wounds

IF IT could only be over before anything happened to Wayne. Pictures marched across her mind day and night in one endless procession of imagined horrors. Over there to the south and east was the unknown, too far away for one to hear the booming of cannon, to see the gaping wounds or smell the fetid odors. But they did not escape her. To the extent that her imagination led, she saw and smelled and heard with an inner sensitiveness that could not be evaded.

"Let it be over before something happens to Wayne. Bring him safe home and I'll ask nothing more of life."

Thus did Suzanne daily try to bargain with God, promising blandly to free Him from other obligations if He would grant her this one boon.

But God was not to be bargained with, not to be cajoled into favoring Suzanne Martin above other women.

Lockwood, Wayne, wounded, died

When the news came there was not so much the shock of what it was, as that now it was happening. That sensitive inner sight had made her know this was to come some day, prepared her to meet it. She could not even cry like other people did.

The family had never known that there was anything between them unless perchance by guessing so. They did not talk about him. For that she was grateful.

Sometimes when company came and the others launched out into their old time way of talking and laughing, Suzanne would slip away and go down to the gate and look up the lane road, as though there she might see a horse and rider, or catch, perhaps, a wild sweet strain of singing in the moonlight.

ONE September evening Cady Bedson, driving past with his spanking bays, pulled up short when he saw Suzanne at the gateway to tell her Atlanta had fallen. Then suddenly in a show of warm interest he wanted to know if she wouldn't like to drive over to Sturgis Falls with him to see her sister.

It turned out to be rather pleasant riding up the river road and cooling in the humid summer night. On the way home Cady said: "There's something I'd like to ask you, Suzanne. Were you betrothed to Wayne Lockwood?"

Bethrothed? What could she say to that but the truth which was no truth at all.

"No," she said in a peculiarly thin voice so that Cady, thinking she was provoked at the inference, said he didn't mean anything much by it.

Her father joked her at breakfast. "Well . . . Cady Bedson. That is a beau for you, Suzanne."

Her mother sniffed. "Been taking awful good care of his own hide, though, I must say."

Jeremiah said nothing to that. The truth was he would have been ashamed if he had been Cady Bedson—unmarried, no responsibilities, and yet he had never volunteered, hiring a substitute to go when his name was drawn at the time of the draft.

IN NOVEMBER with the roads froze into hard ruts Cady and Suzanne rode home from Sabina's. When they drove into the yard Cady said: "Suzanne, I admired you very much in the summer. Then my admiration turned to affection and I am sure now it is something more. Will you be my wife?"

And Suzanne, whose world now was a real one in which nothing stirred her pulses or gave her throat any throbbing for either its sorrows or its joys, said quietly:

"Why, yes, Cady, I suppose I could if you want me to."

Suzanne did not go into the house immediately after Cady left. Instead she picked her way down the front path to the gate.

Jeremiah who had waited up for her watched her until she stopped, and then walked down to where she stood. He was disturbed by her attitude as though she were looking for something that was not there.

She turned on him suddenly. "Why, Pa. You scared me. How does it happen you're up?"

"Never mind. How you and Cady comin'?"

"I guess we'll be married about the last of May."

"That'll be fine. Cady'll probably be well-to-do one of these days. You're going to be happy, ain't you, Suzanne?"

"Yes. I'll be happy."

It was too acquiescent, too gently agreeable. She used to be so excited over everything, her eyes, so shining.

But he had only one thought in his mind and he did not know how to approach her about it. Finally he put his big hand over her small one lying on the railing of the gate. "Suzy, I guess I should tell you. I didn't aim to blurt it out before every one . . . if it meant more to you than just ordinary. But with you . . . I didn't quite know . . . Suzanne, Wayne Lockwood is alive."

She gazed up at him so long, the moon picking out the dark of her eyes, that he thought she had not comprehended. And when she remained silent, only gazing at him with that queer look on her face, he grew confused. He tried to find refuge again in the commonplace.

"If you had any little-girl notions about him, ever, don't you get it into your bonnet that you can do anything about it now. You're rightly betrothed. It can't make any difference now."

"No," she said, not taking her eyes from old Jeremiah's, her lips moving dryly. "No, it can't make any difference now."

The Lady in the Cloud

WAYNE LOCKWOOD was crossing the Iowa prairies between Dubuque and the Cedar Valley. The steam cars were filled with humanity.

Here he was going over the same trail from Dubuque to the Valley which he had taken ten years before. He recalled the days when he had swung along the grassy trail, his head full of dreams about riches and lands and freedom. Now he was riding on the steam cars over the same grassy trail. And where were his riches and lands?

He had bungled some things. And the war had stepped in and bungled others.

Like a fanatic who inflicts his own punishment he turned to thoughts of Suzanne. He tried to analyze the stupidity with which he had been enveloped in those days when he had not realized how dear to him she was. In self-flagellation he went over it all, chin in palm, looking out at the prairie, so peaceful appearing to the returned soldiery, so uninteresting to one who had nothing but bitterness in his heart.

Cady Bedson had won after all. Cady Bedson had won her—the girl who had been meant for him but whom he had lost forever.

JEREMIAH told himself that he might as well face the truth. Up to this evening, the night Suzanne was going to be married, he had not thought much about how she would take it when Wayne came home. She would be married to Cady Bedson, and married women tended to their own affairs. But here Wayne was home and some one naturally would say so, and if Suzanne looked at the bearer of the news the way she had looked at him that night . . . Cady's eyes on her too, like as not . . . Cady and every one would know.

He was at her bedroom door. Was that some one laughing or crying? Sounded like crying. He rattled the knob. "Girls, can I come in?"

"You look pretty fine, Suzanne." The sight of her in the white dress ready to marry Cady cleared his mind. Out with it now, just as natural as talking about the weather.

"Suzy, I thought maybe . . ." Already he felt himself floundering under the keenness of those gray-blue eyes ". . . you'd like to know."

"He's come," she said so suddenly and definitely that it startled him immeasurably.

"Well, if you're meanin' Wayne Lockwood . . . yes, tonight."

When she did not move or say more he went on spiritedly: "Some one could get out to his cabin on horseback and ask him to the wedding. There's still time. Good neighbor like he was . . . used to be at our house so much."

Old Jeremiah stopped talking again.

ime now, stood there distressed, wonder-
ng if after all he should not have evaded
he responsibility and left the whole
hing to Fate. And then the spell broke.
Now he knew for a certainty. Suzanne,
his youngest, had sorrow and disappointment, a mental agony and a hurt heart.
And she could not cover it with laughter.

"Suzanne, *go yourself*. I'll get your
cape. Come down the back way," he
said.

IN THE soft dusk Wayne Lockwood
walked out the river road—no longer
n the light footed rhythmic way of the
prairie-wolf, but heavily, doggedly, like
a man who had marched through mud
and dust, swamp, clay and mire. He
wanted nothing tonight but his old cabin
up the lane road, darkness and the bed
and comforting sleep. Tomorrow he
would meet old friends, look over his
land, lay his future plans.

A gleam of light flickered in the direction of the cabin. It proved to be a light
in his cabin. For the first time he
grinned. It would be a bit of a joke
to walk quietly in on some one and give
him a scare. He put his hand quietly
on the wooden latch with its leather
thong, hesitated a moment, and then
flung back the door.

Across the room a girl in a long dark
cape was placing a candle on the fireplace mantel. At the swinging of the
door she whirled so suddenly that the
unfastened wrap slipped to the floor.
There stood Suzanne Martin in the white
cloud of her wedding dress.

There was no sound anywhere. There
was no moan of prairie wind or song of
timber bird. Nothing but silence about
them, deep and immeasurable, pregnant
with unspoken things.

The girl's hands fluttered from her
throat and the man's white-knuckled
fists relaxed.

"Suzanne."

"Wayne."

THE early settlers lie there together
in friendly silence on a hillside in
the Valley. The graveled walks between
the tall tombstones cross each other
primly at right angles, quite as the miles
of midwestern sections now cross the
old prairie, the main one long and
curving a little at the end like the old
river road.

SUZANNE
BELOVED WIFE
OF

and under the old vines the name that
meant so much to her—

WAYNE LOCKWOOD

———◆———

LATE LEAVES

THE leaves are falling; so am I;
The few late flowers have moisture in the eye;
    So have I too.
Scarcely on any bough is heard
Joyous, or even unjoyous, bird
    The whole wood through.

Winter may come: he brings but nigher
His circle (yearly narrowing) to the fire
    Where old friends meet,
Let him; now heaven is overcast,
And spring and summer both are past,
    And all things sweet.

—Walter Savage Landor

ELIZABETH

THE ENCHANTED APRIL

THE book is as charming as its title. The setting is an Italian castle on the Mediterranean and the characters are modern women, bowed down by everyday cares, who find life and love there. No one but Elizabeth (1866—) can so convincingly fuse high romance and caustic humor. Her first highly successful book, "Elizabeth and her German Garden," was published in 1898 when she was the wife of the German, Count Arnim. After he died she married the late Earl Russell (d. 1931), brother of the present Earl (Bertrand) Russell, the philosopher. Her most recent book is "Mr. Skeffington."

The Rainy Day

IT BEGAN in a woman's club in London on a February afternoon— an uncomfortable club, and a miserable after- noon—when Mrs. Wil- kins took up *The Times* from the table in the smoking-room, and running her listless eye down the Agony Column saw this:

> To Those who Appreciate Wistaria and Sun- shine. Small medieval Italian Castle on the shores of the Mediterranean to be Let Fur- nished for the month of April. Necessary servants remain. Z., Box 1000, *The Times.*

Mrs. Wilkins dropped the newspaper with a gesture that was both irritated and resigned, and went over to the win- dow and stared drearily out at the drip- ping street. Not for her the shores of the Mediterranean in April, and the wis- taria and sunshine. Such delights were only for the rich. Yet the advertisement had been addressed to persons who ap- preciate these things, so that it had also been addressed to her, for she certainly appreciated them; more than anybody knew.

But she was poor. In the whole world she possessed of her very own only ninety pounds, saved from year to year, put by carefully pound by pound, out of her dress allowance, as a shield and refuge against a rainy day. So Mrs. Wilkins's clothes were what her hus- band, urging her to save, called modest and becoming and her acquaintances, to

each other, when they spoke of her at all, which was seldom, for she was very negligible, called a perfect sight.

She turned away from the window with the same gesture of mingled irrita- tion and resignation with which she had laid down *The Times,* and crossed the room with the intention of getting her mackintosh and umbrella and fighting her way into one of the overcrowded omnibuses. Then she beheld Mrs. Arbuthnot, a woman she knew by sight as also living in Hampstead sitting at a table in the middle of the room, ab- sorbed, in her turn, in the first page of *The Times.*

Mrs. Wilkins had never yet spoken to Mrs. Arbuthnot, who belonged to one of the various church sets, and who ana- lyzed, classified, divided and registered the poor; whereas she and Mellersh, when they did go out, went to the par- ties of impressionist painters, of whom in Hampstead there were many. Mel- lersh had a sister who had married one of them and because of this alliance Mrs. Wilkins was drawn into a circle which was highly unnatural to her, and she had learned to dread pictures.

NOBODY took any notice of Mrs. Wil- kins. She was the kind of person who is not noticed at parties. Her clothes, infested by thrift, made her prac- tically invisible; her face was non-arrest- ing, her conversation was reluctant; she was shy. Also she was always overshadowed by her husband, that clean-shaven, fine-looking man, who gave a party, merely by coming to it, a great air.

Wilkins was very respectable. Being a solicitor, he could not afford to miss church, and it was there that Mrs. Wilkins became familiar, though never through words, with Mrs. Arbuthnot.

Obeying an impulse she wondered at even while obeying, Mrs. Wilkins, the shy and reluctant, sat down exactly opposite Mrs. Arbuthnot, to whom she had never yet spoken in her life. Mrs. Arbuthnot, however, did not look up. She continued to gaze, with eyes that seemed to be dreaming, at one spot only of *The Times*.

Suddenly Mrs. Wilkins found herself leaning across the table. "Are you reading about the medieval castle and the wistaria?" she heard herself asking.

Naturally, Mrs. Arbuthnot was surprised; for she had been reading about the medieval castle and the wistaria; but she was not half so much surprised as Mrs. Wilkins was at herself.

"Why do you ask me that?" Mrs. Arbuthnot said in her grave voice, for her training of and by the poor had made her grave and patient.

Mrs. Wilkins flushed and looked excessively shy and frightened. "Oh, only because I saw it too, and I thought perhaps—I thought somehow—" she stammered and although she was at least thirty, wriggled in her chair with the movement of an awkward and embarrassed schoolgirl. "It seems so wonderful and it is such a miserable day. . . ." And then she sat looking at Mrs. Arbuthnot with the eyes of an imprisoned dog.

"This poor thing," thought Mrs. Arbuthnot whose life was spent in helping and alleviating, "needs advice." She accordingly prepared herself patiently to give it.

"Were you reading it?" insisted Mrs. Wilkins.

"Yes," said Mrs. Arbuthnot, her eyes going dreamy again.

"Wouldn't it be wonderful," murmured Mrs. Wilkins.

"Wonderful," said Mrs. Arbuthnot. Her face, which had lit up, faded into patience.

BUT Mrs. Wilkins was not listening; for just then, absurd as it seemed, a picture had flashed across her brain, and there were two figures in it sitting together under a great trailing wistaria that stretched across the branches of a tree she didn't know, and it was herself and Mrs. Arbuthnot—she saw them—she saw them. And behind them, bright in sunshine, were old grey walls—the medieval castle—she saw it—they were there . . .

She leaned across the table. "Why don't we try and get it?" she whispered.

Mrs. Arbuthnot became wide-eyed. "Get it?" she repeated.

"Yes," said Mrs. Wilkins, as though she were afraid of being overheard. "Not just sit here and say, How wonderful, and then go home to Hampstead without having put out a finger—go home just as usual and see about the dinner and the fish just as we've been doing for years and years and will go on doing for years and years. In fact," said Mrs. Wilkins, flushing, "I see no end to it. There is no end to it. So that there ought to be a break, there ought to be intervals—in everybody's interests. Why it would really be being unselfish to go away and be happy for a little, because we would come back so much nicer. You see, after a bit everybody needs a holiday."

"But—how do you mean, get it?" asked Mrs. Arbuthnot.

"Rent it. Hire it. Have it."

"Why, but we don't know each other."

"But just think how well we would if we went away together for a month! And I've saved for a rainy day, and I expect so have you, and this is the rainy day—look at it—"

"She is unbalanced," thought Mrs. Arbuthnot; yet she felt strangely stirred.

Bled White By Prayers

Mrs. Arbuthnot's balance was returning, hand in hand with her compassion. Such fleeting things did not make one happy. Mrs. Arbuthnot had learned in her long life with Frederick —he was her husband—where alone true joys are to be found. They are to be found, she now knew, only in daily, in hourly, living for others; they are to be found only—hadn't she over and over again taken her disappointments and discouragements there, and come away comforted?—at the feet of God.

Frederick had been the kind of husband whose wife betakes herself early to the feet of God. The way Frederick made his living was one of the standing distresses of her life. He wrote immensely popular memoirs, regularly, every year, of the mistresses of kings. Mrs. Arbuthnot, who had no money of her own, was obliged to live on the proceeds of Frederick's activities, and her very nest-egg was the fruit, posthumously ripened, of ancient sin. Convinced that morality is the basis of happiness, the fact that she and Frederick should draw their sustenance from guilt, however much purged by the passage of centuries, was one of the secret reasons of her sadness.

At least she had persuaded Frederick, when first he began his terrible successful career—he only began it after their marriage; when she married him she had been a blameless official attached to the library of the British Museum—to publish the memoirs under another name, so that she was not publicly branded.

Hampstead read the books with glee, and had no idea that their writer lived in its midst. Frederick was almost unknown, even by sight, in Hampstead He never went to any of its gatherings Whatever it was he did in the way of recreation was done in London, but he never spoke of what he or whom he saw; he might have been perfectly friendless for any mention he ever made of his friends to his wife.

She had long since found peace. And Frederick, from her passionately loved bridegroom, from her worshipped young husband, had become second only to God on her list of duties and forbearances. There he hung, the second in importance, a bloodless thing bled white by her prayers.

For years she had been able to be happy only by forgetting happiness. She wanted to stay like that. She wanted to shut out everything that would remind her of beautiful things, that might set her off again longing, desiring . . .

"I'd like so much to be friends," said Mrs. Arbuthnot earnestly. "Won't you come and see me, or let me come to you sometimes." She held out a card.

Mrs. Wilkins ignored the card.

"It's so funny," said Mrs. Wilkins, just as if she had not heard her, "but I see us both—you and me—this April in the medieval castle. I shall write and find out about it."

The Path Made Straight

The owner of the medieval castle was an Englishman, a Mr. Briggs, who was in London at the moment and wrote that it had beds enough for eight people, exclusive of servants, three sitting-rooms, battlements, dungeons, and electric lights. The rent was £60 for the month, the servants' wages were extra, and he wanted references.

Mrs. Arbuthnot, who was now a vic- tim to the idea, and Mrs. Wilkins had not thought of references, and they had not dreamed a rent could be so high. Before Mrs. Arbuthnot's eyes rose up boots: endless vistas, all the stout boots that sixty pounds would buy and besides the rent there would be the servants' wages, and the food, and the railway journeys out and home. While as for references, these did indeed seem a stumling block; it did seem impossible to give any without making their plan more public than they had intended.

Then Mrs. Arbuthnot, whose mind was trained in the finding of ways out of difficulties, found a way out of the reference difficulty; and simultaneously Mrs. Wilkins had a vision revealing to her how to reduce the rent.

Mrs. Arbuthnot's plan was simple, and completely successful. She took the whole of the rent in person, drawing it out of her Savings Bank; went to the owner and presented it to him. And when he saw her, and her parted hair and soft dark eyes and sober apparel, and heard her grave voice, he told her not to bother about writing round for those references.

Thomas Briggs would have liked to ask her to lunch with him. "I hope you'll like the old place," he said, holding her hand a minute at the door. "You'll fit in very well. There are several portraits of you there."

"Portraits?"

"Madonnas, you know. There's one on the stairs really exactly like you."

Mrs. Arbuthnot smiled and said goodbye and thanked him. He wished that she hadn't gone. Rose Arbuthnot. Pretty name.

THAT difficulty, then, was overcome. But there still remained the other one, the really annihilating effect of the expense on the nest-eggs. This in its turn was overcome by the vision vouchsafed to Mrs. Wilkins. They in their turn would advertise in the Agony column of *The Times,* and they would inquire after two more ladies, of similar desires to their own, to join them and share the expenses.

There seemed to be only two ladies in England at that moment who had any wish to join them, for they only had two answers to their advertisement. A Lady Caroline Dester and a Mrs. Fisher, whom they interviewed.

Lady Caroline came to the club in Shaftesbury and appeared to be wholly taken up by one great longing, a longing to get away from everybody she had ever known. When she saw the club, and Mrs. Arbuthnot, and Mrs. Wilkins, she was sure that here was exactly what she wanted. She would be in Italy with a company of strangers who would never mention a single person she knew, for the simple reason that they had not, could not have, and would not come across them. She asked a few questions about the fourth woman, and was satisfied with the answers—Mrs. Fisher, of Prince of Wales Terrace, a widow.

Mrs. Fisher had been unable to come to the club because, she explained by letter, she could not walk without a stick; therefore Mrs. Arbuthnot and Mrs. Wilkins went to her. She was much older than they or Lady Caroline—Lady Caroline had informed them she was twenty-eight—but not so old as to have ceased to be active minded.

Her house was full of signed photographs of illustrious Victorian dead, all of whom she said she had known when she was little. Carlyle had scowled at her; Matthew Arnold had held her on his knee; Tennyson had sonorously rallied her on the length of her pig-tail. Quite a good part of the interview was taken up by reminiscent anecdote—her very abstractedness was a recommendation. She only asked, she said, to be allowed to sit quiet in the sun and remember. That was all Mrs. Arbuthnot and Mrs. Wilkins asked of their sharers.

THERE were disagreeable incidents towards the end of March, when Mrs. Wilkins, her heart in her mouth and her face a mixture of guilt, terror, and determination, told her husband that she had been invited to Italy, and he declined to believe it. Of course he declined to believe it. Nobody had ever invited his wife to Italy before. There was no precedent. He required proofs.

The only proof was Mrs. Arbuthnot, and Mrs. Wilkins had produced her; but after what entreaties, what passionate persuading! For Mrs. Arbuthnot had not imagined she would have to face Mr. Wilkins and say things to him that were short of the truth, and it brought home to her what she had for some time suspected, that she was slipping more and more away from God.

Indeed, the whole of March was filled with unpleasant, anxious moments. It was an uneasy month. Mrs. Arbuthnot's conscience, made super-sensitive by years of pampering, could not reconcile what she was doing with its own high standard of what was right. It gave her little peace. She was going off, spending precious money on going off, simply and solely to be happy. One woman. One woman being happy, and these piteous multitudes . . .

Nor did it help her or quiet her that, having actually told Frederick, in her desire to make up for what she was squandering, that she would be grateful if he would let her have some money, he instantly gave her a check for £100. He asked no questions. It was a relief to Frederick that she should take some money. She gave it all immediately to the organization she worked with, and found herself more tangled in doubts than ever.

Alive to Such Beauty

WHEN Mrs. Wilkins woke the first morning in Italy, she lay in bed a few minutes before getting up and opening the shutters. It was delicious to lie there thinking how happy she was, but outside those shutters it was more delicious still. She jumped up, ran to the window and threw open the shutters.

All the radiance of April in Italy lay gathered together at her feet. The sun poured in on her. The sea lay asleep in it, hardly stirring. Across the bay the lovely mountains, exquisitely different in colour, were asleep too in the light, and underneath her window, at the bottom of the flowered-starred grass slope from which the wall of the castle rose up, was a great cypress, cutting through the delicate blues and violets and rose-colours of the mountains and the sea like a great black sword.

She stared. Such beauty; and she there to see it. Such beauty; and she alive to feel it. According to everybody she had ever come across she ought at least to have twinges. She had not one twinge. Something was wrong somewhere.

Wonderful that at home she should have been so good, so terribly good, and merely felt tormented. Twinges of every sort had there been her portion; aches, hurts, discouragements, and she the whole time being steadily unselfish. Now she had taken off all her goodness and left it behind her like a heap of rain-sodden clothes, and she only felt joy. And there, away in the dim mugginess of Hampstead, was Mellersh being angry.

She tried to visualize Mellersh, she tried to see him having breakfast and thinking bitter things about her; and lo, Mellersh himself began to shimmer, became rose-colour, became delicate violet, became an enchanting blue, became formless, became iridescent. Actually Mellersh was lost in light.

She moved about with quick, purposeful steps, her long thin body held up straight, her small face, so much puckered at home with effort and fear, smoothed out. All she had been and done before this morning, all she had felt and worried about, was gone. Each of her worries behaved as the image of Mellersh had behaved, and dissolved into colour and light.

And she noticed things she had not noticed for years,—when she was doing her hair in front of the glass she noticed it, and thought, "Why, what pretty stuff." Now she suddenly saw it, and she twisted it round her fingers before the glass, and was glad it was so pretty.

When she was ready she opened her door to go across to see if Rose were awake.

"Were you ever, ever in your life so happy?" asked Mrs. Wilkins, catching Mrs. Arbuthnot by the arm.

"No," said Mrs. Arbuthnot. Nor had she been; not ever; not even in her first love days with Frederick. Because always pain had been close at hand in that other happiness ready to torture her with doubts, to torture even with the very excess of her love; while this was simple happiness of complete harmony with her surroundings, the happiness that asked for nothing, that just accepts, just breathes, just is . . .

Arm in arm they went along the hall, and their husbands would not have known them, their faces were so young with eagerness, and together they stood at the open window, and when their eyes wandered further among the beauties of the garden, they saw sitting on the low wall at the east edge of it, gazing out over the bay, her feet in lilies, Lady Caroline.

She had on a white frock, and her head was bare. They had no idea that day in London, when her hat was down to her nose and her furs were up to her ears, that she was so pretty. She was exceedingly pretty.

Lady Caroline turned her head. She looked up at them a moment, surprised to see them so much younger than they had seemed that day at the club, and so much less unattractive. Indeed, they were really almost quite attractive, if any one could ever be really quite attractive in the wrong clothes. As she got off the wall and came towards the window, it seemed a restful thing to know she was going to spend an entire month with people in dresses made as she dimly remembered dresses used to be made five summers ago.

"I got here yesterday morning," she said looking up at them and smiling. She really was bewitching.

That day at that queer club Lady Caroline had had merely a blurred impression of Mrs. Wilkins, for it was the other one who did all the talking, and her impression had been of somebody so shy, so awkward that it was best to take no notice of her. Therefore she now looked at her in some surprise when Mrs. Wilkins said with great conviction: "I didn't realize you were *so* pretty."

She stared at Mrs. Wilkins. She was not usually told this quite so immediately and roundly.

"It's very kind of you to think so," she said.

"Why, you're lovely," said Mrs. Wilkins. "Quite, quite lovely."

Then Lady Caroline began to be afraid she was an original. Perhaps she had better be a little less encouraging. If they had got out of their shells so immediately, at the very first contact, unless she checked them they would soon begin to press upon her, and then goodbye to her dream of thirty restful silent days, lying unmolested in the sun, not grabbed at and monopolized, but just recovering from the fatigue, the deep and melancholy fatigue, of the too much.

Besides, there was Mrs. Fisher. Mrs. Fisher had arrived at the same time she had. Because of Mrs. Fisher's stick, Lady Caroline had to see about everything. She had been obliged to take care of her as if she had been her own grandmother, and listen to her everlasting anecdotes about the great Victorians. Yes, Mrs. Fisher would have to be checked. And so would these two up at the window. She had better begin at once.

So she said with marked coldness—at least, she tried to make it sound marked —that she supposed they would be going to breakfast, and that she had had hers; but it was her fate that however coldly she sent forth her words they came out sounding quite warm and agreeable. And if she stared icily it did not look icy at all, because her eyes, lovely to begin with, had the added loveliness of very long, soft, dark eyelashes so that persons stared at merely thought they were being regarded with a flattering and exquisite attentiveness. So she could never be disagreeable or rude without being completely misunderstood.

Recovering from Too Much

LADY CAROLINE began to consider her position. It was very curious, and no one in the world could have been more surprised than she herself, but she wanted to think. She had that really rather disgusting suspicion that her life till now had not only been loud but empty. Well, if that were so, and if her first twenty-eight years—the best ones —had gone just in meaningless noise, she had better stop a moment and look round her; pause, as they said in tiresome novels, and consider.

Her mother would have been concerned if she had known. Her mother doted. Her father would have been concerned too, for he also doted. Everybody doted. And when, melodiously obstinate, she had insisted on going off to entomb herself in Italy for a whole month with queer people she had got out of an advertisement, refusing even to take her maid, the only explanation her friends could imagine was that poor Scrap— such was her name among them—had overdone it and was feeling a little nervy.

Her mother had been distressed at her departure. The thinking of the beautiful would be bound to result in hesitations, in reluctances, in unhappiness all round. And here, if she could have seen her, sat her Scrap thinking quite hard. And such things.

The war had finished Scrap. It killed the one man she felt safe with, whom she would have married, and it finally disgusted her with love. Since then she had been embittered. It gave her no pleasure to outdo other women; she didn't want their tiresome men. None of them would talk to her of anything but the things of love, and how foolish and fatiguing that became after a bit. It was as though a healthy person with a normal hunger was given nothing whatever to eat but sugar.

"*Why* should I love you? *Why* should I?" she would ask, amazed, sometimes when somebody was trying—somebody was always trying—to propose to her. But she never got a real answer, only further incoherence.

A deep cynicism took hold of the unhappy Scrap. Her inside grew hoary with disillusionment, while her gracious and charming outside continued to make the world more beautiful. What had the future in it for her? She would not be able, after such a preparation, to take hold of it. She was fit for nothing; she had wasted all this time being beautiful. Presently she wouldn't be beautiful, and what then?

Stupid, stupid. Everything was stupid. There wasn't a thing she wanted to do. There were a thousand things she didn't want to do.

Goodness Attained Violently

MRS. WILKINS said she was going down to the village to find out where the post-office was and post her letter to Mellersh, and would Rose go too. "I've been thinking about Mellersh," said Mrs. Wilkins.

"Have you?" said Rose Arbuthnot, a faint distaste in her voice, for her experiences with Mellersh had not been of a kind to make her enjoy remembering him. She had deceived Mellersh; therefore she didn't like him. And yet how wrong to feel that, she rebuked herself, and how presumptuous. No doubt

Lotty's husband was far, far nearer to God than she herself was ever likely to be. Still, she didn't like him.

"I've been a mean dog," said Mrs. Wilkins.

"A *what?*" asked Mrs. Arbuthnot, incredulous of her hearing.

"All this coming away and leaving him in that dreary place while I rollick in heaven."

Whenever Lotty had begun to blurt out things, Rose had swiftly changed the conversation. One husband led to another, in conversation as well as in life.

she felt, and she could not, she would not, talk of Frederick.

A great desire to be friends with everybody, seemed to be invading Lotty, —a desire for sheer goodness. Rose's own experience was that goodness, the state of being good was only reached with difficulty and pain. It took a long time to get to it; in fact one never did get to it, or, if for a flashing instant one did, it was only for a flashing instant. Desperate perseverance was needed to struggle along its path, and all the way was dotted with doubts. Could one really attain goodness so violently? Wouldn't there be an equally violent reaction?

"I shouldn't be sure of that too quickly," said Rose with caution.

"But I am sure of it, and I've written and told him so. And I've invited him to come and stay with us."

Rose could only stare.

"It's the least I could do. Besides, look at this." Lotty waved her hand. "Disgusting not to share it. I was a mean dog to go off and leave him, but no dog I've ever heard of was ever as mean as I'd be if I didn't try and persuade Mellersh to come out and enjoy this too. It's barest decency that he should have some of the fun out of my nest-egg. After all, he has housed me and fed me for years. One shouldn't be churlish."

"But—do you think he'll come?"

"Oh, I hope so," said Lotty with the utmost earnestness; and added, "Poor lamb."

At that Rose felt she would like to sit down. Mellersh at San Salvatore? Mellersh, from whom Lotty had taken such pains so recently to escape?

"I see him here," said Lotty, as if in answer to her thoughts.

But how she wished, oh how Rose wished, that she too could write to her husband and say "Come." The Wilkins *ménage*, however pompous Mellersh might be, and he had seemed to Rose pompous, was on a healthier, and more natural footing than hers. Lotty could write to Mellersh and would get an

answer. She couldn't write to Frederick, for only too well did she know he wouldn't answer.

"I don't think I'll come down to the village with you today," she said, looking up at Lotty with eyes suddenly gone dim. "I think I want to think."

"All right," said Lotty, at once starting off briskly down the path. "But don't think too long," she called back over her shoulder. "Write and invite him at once."

"Invite who?" asked Rose, startled.

"Your husband."

LOTTY had spoilt her day—Lotty with her invitation to her husband, with her suggestion that she too should invite hers. How could she invite him? It had gone on so long, their estrangement, such years; she would hardly know what words to use: and besides, he would not come. Why should he come? He didn't care about being with her.

Rose felt right down to her very roots that if you have once thoroughly bored somebody it is next to impossible to unbore him. Once a bore always a bore—certainly, she thought, to the person originally bored.

Then, thought she, looking out to sea through eyes grown misty, better cling to her religion. But oh, she wanted to cling to something tangible, to love something living, something that one could hold against one's heart, that one could see and touch and do things for.

Such were Mrs. Arbuthnot's reflections and emotions that first day at San Salvatore. She went back to tea dejected as she had not been for years. San Salvatore had taken her carefully built up semblance of happiness away from her, and given her nothing in exchange. Yes, —it had given her yearnings in exchange, this ache and longing, this queer feeling of bosom; but that was worse than nothing.

Then came Lotty, back to dinner, incredibly more freckled, exuding the sunshine she had been collecting all day, talking, laughing, being tactless, being unwise, being without reticence; and Lady Caroline woke up to animation, and Mrs. Fisher was not so noticeable, and Rose was beginning to revive a little,

for Lotty's spirits were contagious as sh described the delights of her day.

She suddenly said, catching Rose' eye, "Letter gone?"

Rose flushed. This tactlessness . . .

Etiquette Under Difficulties

By THE end of the week Mr. Wilkins arrived; even as his wife had fore-seen he would, so he did. And there were signs almost of eagerness about his acceptance of her suggestion, for he had not waited to write a letter in answer to hers, but had telegraphed.

All three who were not Mellersh's wife had breakfast in bed on the day of his arrival, moved by a common instinct to take cover. Scrap always breakfasted in bed and she made plans for spending the whole day in bed on this particular day.

But perhaps today wasn't as dangerous as tomorrow; for today would be pro-vided for. He would want to have a bath, and having a bath at San Salvatore was an elaborate business, a real adven-ture if one had a hot one in the bath-room. Having it, Scrap calculated, would keep him busy for a long while. Then he would unpack, and then, after his night in the train, he would probably sleep till the evening. So Scrap decided to get up.

There—she could hear Mr. Wilkins' educated voice asking his way to the bathroom.

Mr. Wilkins in the meantime had gotten into the bath and turned off the tap. Naturally he turned off the tap. It was what one did. But on the instruc-tions, printed in red letters, was a para-graph saying that the tap should not be turned off as long as there was still fire in the stove or the stove would blow up.

Mr. Wilkins got into the bath, turned off the tap and the stove blew up, ex-actly as the printed instructions said it would. It blew up, fortunately, only in its inside, but it blew up with a terrible noise, and Mr. Wilkins leapt out of the bath and rushed to the door, and only the instinct born of years of training

made him snatch up a towel as h rushed.

Scrap, half way across the landing o her way out of doors, heard the ex plosion, And she ran towards the hea of the stairs to call the servants, an as she ran, out ran Mr. Wilkins clutch ing his towel, and they ran into eacl other.

"That damned bath!" cried Mr. Wil kins, perhaps for the only time in hi life forgetting himself; but he was up set.

Here was an introduction. Mr. Wil kins imperfectly concealed in hi towel, his shoulders exposed at one en and his legs at the other, and Lady Caroline Dester, to meet whom he hac swallowed all his anger with his wife and come out to Italy.

For Lotty in her letter had told him who was at San Salvatore besides her self and Mrs. Arbuthnot, and Mr. Wil kins at once perceived that this was ar opportunity which might never recur Lotty had merely said, "There are two other women here, Mrs. Fisher and Lady Caroline Dester," but that was enough He knew all about the Droitwiches, their wealth, their connections, their place in history, and the power they had, should they choose to exert it, of making yet another solicitor happy by adding him to those they already employed.

Directly his wife's letter reached him he telegraphed and packed. This was business. He was not a man to lose time when it came to business; nor was he a man to jeopardize a chance by neglect-ing to be amiable. He met his wife perfectly amiably, aware that amiability under such circumstances was wisdom. Besides, he actually felt amiable—very. For once, Lotty was really helping him.

In the train he had selected the words of his greeting, going over them with care—some slight reference to her distinguished parents and the part her family had played in the history of England—made, of course, with proper tact and the first steps towards what might well be the turning point in his career would have been taken.

And here he was . . . no, it was too terrible, what could be more terrible? Only a towel on, water running off his legs, and that exclamation. He knew at once the lady was Lady Caroline—the minute the exclamation was out he knew it. It would be impossible to live this down.

B UT Mr. Wilkins was reckoning without Scrap. After she had choked the laughter down and got her face serious again, she said composedly as if he had had all his clothes on, "How do you do."

Overwhelmed with gratitude he took her offered hand and said "How do you do," in his turn; and merely to repeat the ordinary words seemed magically to restore the situation to normal.

"Allow me to introduce myself," said Mr. Wilkins, with the ceremony of the drawing room. "My name is Mellersh-Wilkins." And he instinctively held out his hand a second time at the words.

"I thought perhaps it was," said Scrap, a second time having hers shaken and a second time unable not to smile.

He was about to proceed to the first of the graceful tributes he had prepared in the train, oblivious, as he could not see himself, that he was without his clothes, when the servants came running up stairs and, simultaneously, Mrs. Fisher appeared in the doorway of her sitting room.

Mrs. Fisher did not know what the noise could be, and coming out of her room to inquire stood rooted on the door-sill. It was enough to root anybody. Lady Caroline shaking hands with what evidently, if he had had clothes on, would have been Mrs. Wilkins' husband, and both of them conversing just as if—

Then Scrap became aware of Mrs. Fisher. "Do let me," she said gracefully, "introduce Mr. Mellersh-Wilkins. He has just come. This," she added, turning to Mr. Wilkins, "is Mrs. Fisher."

And Mr. Wilkins, nothing if not courteous, reacted at once to the conventional formula. First he bowed to the elderly lady in the doorway, then he crossed over to her, his wet feet leaving footprints as he went, and having got to her he politely held out his hand.

"It is a pleasure," said Mr. Wilkins in his carefully modulated voice, "to meet a friend of my wife's."

Scrap melted away down into the garden.

The Divine Infection

T HE strange effect of this incident was that when they met that evening at dinner both Mrs. Fisher and Lady Caroline had a singular feeling of secret understanding with Mr. Wilkins. He could not be to them as other men. He could not be to them as he would have been if they had met him in his clothes. There was a sense of broken ice; they felt at once intimate and indulgent; almost they felt to him as nurses do—as those feel who have assisted either patients or young children at their baths. They were acquainted with Mr. Wilkins' legs. Now that he was dressed they took

an almost paternal pride in everything he said.

Lotty, for her part, looked on with round eyes. She had expected Mellersh to take at least two days before he got to this stage, but the San Salvatore spell had worked instantly. It was not only that he was pleasant at dinner, for she had always seen him pleasant at dinners with other people, but he had been pleasant all day privately,—so pleasant that he had complimented her on her looks while she was brushing out her hair, and kissed her. And it was neither good morning nor good night.

And so the second week began, and all was harmony. The arrival of Mr. Wilkins, instead of, as three of the party had feared and the fourth had only been protected from fearing by her burning faith in the effect on him of San Salvatore, disturbing such harmony as there was, increased it. He fitted in. He was determined to please, and he did please.

He was most amiable to his wife. And the more he treated her as though she were really very nice, the more Lotty expanded and became really very nice, and the more he, affected in his turn, became really very nice himself; so that they went round and round, not in a vicious, but in a highly virtuous circle.

Lotty's belief in the irresistible influence of the heavenly atmosphere of San Salvatore being thus obviously justified, and Mr. Wilkins being so evidently a changed man, both Rose and Scrap began to think there might after all be something in what Lotty insisted on, and that San Salvatore did work purgingly on the character.

T HEY were more inclined to think so in that they too felt a working going on inside themselves; they felt more cleared, both of them, that second week —Scrap in her thoughts, many of which were now quite nice thoughts, really amiable ones about her parents and relations, with a glimmer in them of recognition of the extraordinary benefits she had received at the hands of what? Fate. Providence?—anyhow of something, and of how, having received them, she had misused them by failing to be happy; and Rose in her bosom, which though it still yearned, yearned to some purpose, for she was reaching the conclusion that merely inactively to yearn was no use at all; and that she must either by some measure stop her yearning or give it at least a chance—remote, but still a chance —of being quieted by writing to Frederick and asking him to come out.

Was not Lotty right when she said the other day that nothing at all except love mattered? Nothing certainly seemed

much use unless it was built up on love. But once frightened away, could it eve come back? Yes, it might in that beauty it might in the atmosphere of happines Lotty and San Salvatore seemed betweer them to spread round like some divin infection.

She had, however, to get him ther first, and he certainly couldn't be go there if she didn't write and tell him where she was. She got up quickly. Yes she would write. She would go and writ to him at once.

On the first day of the third week Rose wrote to Frederick. A thousand times a day Rose wished she had le Frederick alone. Lotty, who asked he every evening whether she had sent he letter yet, exclaimed with delight wher the answer at last was "yes", and threw her arms round her. "Now we shall b *completely* happy!" cried the enthusiasti Lotty.

But nothing seemed less certain to Rose, and her expression became mor and more the expression of one who ha something on her mind.

Two days later Mr. Wilkins brough her a telegram. She stared at him, her mouth open. Of course. She knew it She had been sure of it all the time Bright and burning, Youth in that in stant flashed down again on Rose. Why but if things could happen like this— why, but there was no end to—why, she and Frederick—they were going to be —again—at last—

"No bad news, I trust?" said Mr. Wil kins. For when she had read the tele gram she stood staring at it and her face went slowly white. She turned and looked at Mr. Wilkins as if trying to re member him. "Oh no. On the con trary—" She managed to smile. "I'm go ing to have a visitor," she said, holding out the telegram.

Mr. Wilkins read the telegram. I had been sent that morning from Mez zago, and was:

AM PASSING THROUGH ON WAY TO ROME MAY I PAY MY RESPECTS THIS AFTERNOON

THOMAS BRIGGS

"Who is Thomas Briggs?" he asked, following her into the dining room. "He is the owner. This is his house.

He is very nice. He is coming this afternoon," she told him after collecting her thoughts.

The Collapse of Mr. Briggs

Thomas Briggs was at that very moment coming. He had been thinking so much of Rose Arbuthnot since that day. Such a pretty name. And such a pretty creature. He longed to see her in his house. Had she seen the portrait of herself on the stairs? He wondered if she liked it.

He looked up at the sound of footsteps, and there she was, coming down the stairs just as he had imagined her in that place, dressed in white. He watched her coming down the stairs with the utmost eager interest. In a moment she would be level with her portrait.

"How do you do," said Rose, intent only on a decent show of welcome. She did not welcome. He was here, she felt, the telegram bitter in her heart, instead of Frederick, doing what she had longed Frederick would do, taking his place.

"Just stand still a moment—"

She obeyed automatically.

"Yes—quite astonishing. Do you mind taking off your hat?"

Rose, surprised, took it off obediently.

"Yes—I thought so—I just wanted to make sure."

Rose's surprise became amusement, and she could not help smiling.

"Come and show me all the views," he said eagerly; and it was plain, even to the self-deprecatory Rose, that she did not bore Mr. Briggs.

They had a very pleasant walk, with a great deal of sitting down in warm thyme-fragrant corners, and if anything could have helped Rose to recover from the bitter disappointment of the morning it would have been the company and conversation of Mr. Briggs. He did help her to recover, and the same process took place as that which Lotty had undergone with her husband, and the more Mr. Briggs thought Rose charming, the more charming she became.

She came back to tea, bringing Mr. Briggs, and looking quite different, Mr. Wilkins noticed, from what she had looked till then. Trouble here, trouble here, thought Mr. Wilkins, mentally rubbing his professional hands. He could see himself being called in presently to advise. Well, he was the man for trouble. He regretted, of course, that people should get into it, but being in it he was their man.

It was decided after the very amiable tea that Briggs should spend the night there.

"How kind of you all," he said, his face broad with smiles. "I'd love to be a guest here. What a new sensation. And with three such—I say, oughtn't I to have a fourth hostess?"

"Yes. There's Lady Caroline," said Lotty.

"The daughter of the Droitwiches, Briggs," said Mr. Wilkins, "is not likely to be wanting in the proper hospitable impulses."

"The daughter of the—" repeated Briggs; but he stopped dead, for there in the doorway was the daughter of the Droitwiches herself; or rather, coming towards him out of the dark doorway into the brightness of the sunset, was that which he had not in his life yet seen but only dreamed of, his idea of absolute loveliness.

From a cheerful, chatty, happy young man, overflowing with life and friendliness, he became silent, solemn, and with little beads on his temples.

A deep melancholy invaded Scrap. The symptoms of the incipient grabber were all there and only too familiar, and she knew that if Briggs stayed her rest cure might be regarded as over.

Briggs had not supposed or hoped that any one as beautiful as his dream of beauty existed. He had never till now met even an approximation. Pretty women, charming women by the score had he met and properly appreciated, but never the real, the godlike thing itself. He used to think, "If ever I saw a perfectly beautiful woman I should die"; and though, having now met what to his ideas was a perfectly beautiful woman, he did not die; but became very nearly as incapable of managing his own affairs as if he had.

It was a sad sight to see the collapse of Briggs. Everybody noticed it, even Rose.

Before Dinner at Eight

SCRAP felt melancholy. Here she was shut up in her bedroom, which was stuffy from the afternoon sun that had been pouring into it, instead of out in the cool garden, and all because of Mr. Briggs.

Intolerable tyranny, she thought, flaring up. She wouldn't endure it; she would go out all the same. She snatched up a wrap, for she did not mean to come back for a long while, perhaps not even to dinner—it would be all Mr. Briggs's fault if she went dinnerless and hungry—and with another glance about to see if she was safe, stole out and got away to the sheltering trees of the zig-zag path.

Ah, this was lovely, thought Scrap with a sigh of relief. How cool. How good it smelt. Ah, this was—What was that? Footsteps. Footsteps from the village. The next moment the footsteps turned the corner of her bit of path, and stood still. Then as they stopped, she turned her head, and beheld with astonishment a person she had seen a good deal of lately in London, the well-known writer of amusing memoirs, Mr. Ferdinand Arundel.

He looked ashamed and entreating, like a guilty but devoted dog. "You must forgive me," he said. "Lady Droitwich told me where you were, and as I happened to be passing through on my way to Rome I thought I would look in and see how you were."

Scrap, who had become melancholy at the sight of Briggs, became philosophical at the sight of Arundel. Here he was. She couldn't send him away till after dinner. He must be nourished. This being so, she had better make the best of it, and do that with a good grace which anyhow wasn't to be avoided. Besides, he would be a temporary shelter from Mr. Briggs.

She therefore prepared herself for friendliness. "I'm to be fed," she said, "at eight, and you must come up and be fed too. Sit down and get cool and tell me how everybody is."

TIME flew, and it grew quite dusk and it grew nearly dark, and Mr. Arundel still went on amusing her with news of London. It was a quarter to eight before she suddenly remembered dinner.

And she was gone up the path with the swiftness of a young, slender deer. Arundel followed.

Having shown him where he could wash she put him in the empty drawing room. The house was quiet with the hush that precedes dinner, when the inhabitants are all shut up in their rooms dressing.

Briggs in his room was throwing away spoilt tie after spoilt tie; Scrap in hers was hurrying into a black frock with a vague notion that Mr. Briggs wouldn't be able to see her so clearly in black; Mrs. Fisher was fastening the lace shawl which nightly transfomed her day dress into her evening dress, with the brooch Ruskin had given her on her marriage; Mr. Wilkins was sitting on the edge of his bed brushing his wife's hair—thus far in this third week had he progressed in demonstrativeness—while she, for her part, sitting on a chair in front of him, put his studs in a clean shirt, and Rose, already dressed, sat at her window considering her day.

Rose was quite aware of what had happened to Mr. Briggs. If she had had ny difficulty about it, Lotty would have emoved it by the frank comments she nade while she and Rose sat together fter tea on the wall. Lotty was delighted t more love being introduced into San alvatore, even if it were only one-sided, nd said that when once Rose's husband vas there there wouldn't be another lace in the world more swarming with appiness than San Salvatore.

Rose sat at her window thinking of hese things. On one thing she was determined: the first thing she would do vhen she got home would be to have it ut with Frederick. This separate life, his freezing loneliness, she had enough f it.

Tired of staying in her bedroom she lecided to go out on the battlements and vatch the moon rise out of the sea. On aer way along the deserted hall she was attracted by the firelight shining through he open door of the drawing room.

Firelight and flowers; and outside aung the blue curtain of the night. How oretty. And those gorgeous lilacs on the able—she must put her face in them . . .

BUT she never got to the lilacs. She went one step towards them, and hen stood still, for she had seen the figure looking out of the window in the arther corner, and it was Frederick.

Her thoughts wouldn't go on. Her mind stammered. She couldn't think. She could only see and feel. She didn't know how it had happened. It was a miracle. God could do miracles. God had lone this one. God could—God could— could—

"Frederick," she whispered, hardly able even to whisper, choked by the beating of her heart.

He spun round on his heels.

"Rose!" he exclaimed, staring blankly. But she did not see his stare, for her arms were round his neck, and her cheek was against his, and she was murmuring, her lips on his ear, "I knew you would come—in my very heart I always, always knew you would come—"

Now Frederick was not the man to hurt anything if he could help it; besides, he was completely bewildered. Not only was his wife here—here, of all places in the world—but she was clinging to him as she had not clung for years, and murmuring love, and welcoming him. If she welcomed him she must have been expecting him.

Frederick was bewildered. But not being the man to hurt anything if he could help it, he too put his arms round her, and having put them round her he also kissed her; and presently he was kissing her quite as tenderly; and again presently he was kissing her more tenderly, and just as if he had never left off.

He was bewildered, but he still could kiss. It seemed curiously natural to be doing it. It made him feel as if he were thirty again instead of forty, and Rose were his Rose of twenty, the Rose he had so much adored before she began to weigh what he did with her idea of right, and the balance went against him, and she had turned strange, and stony, and more and more shocked, and oh, so lamentable.

And as he held her close to his heart and her arms were soft round his neck, he felt stealing over him a delicious sense of—at first he didn't know what it was, this delicate, pervading warmth, and then he recognized it as security. Yes; security. With her he was safe. To her he was her lover, as he used to be; and she would never notice or mind any of the ignoble changes that getting older had made in him and would go on making more and more.

The Spell of Happiness

BUT at dinner Frederick knew he was in for it. He would look like an ass to Lady Caroline, the most absolute as well as deceitful ass. When she introduced him as her friend whom she had invited to dinner—well, God alone knew what would happen.

But he was reckoning without Scrap.

That accomplished and experienced young woman slipped into the chair Briggs was holding for her, and on Lotty's leaning across the table eagerly, and saying before any one else could get a word in, "Just fancy, Caroline, how quickly Rose's husband has got here!" turned to him without so much as the faintest shadow of surprise on her face, and held out her hand, and smiled like a young angel, and said, "And me late your very first evening."

The daughter of the Droitwiches . . . San Salvatore, Lotty would say, was working its spell of happiness. Scrap could quite believe in its spell. Even she was happier there than she had been for ages and ages. The only person who would go empty away would be Mr. Briggs.

Poor Mr. Briggs. It seemed out of the picture that the owner of the place, the person to whom they owed all this, should be the only one to go away from it unblessed.

Compunction seized Scrap. What very pleasant days she had spent in his house, lying in his garden, enjoying his flowers, loving his views, using his things, being rested,—recovering, in fact. Oh, she knew she paid him some ridiculous small sum a week, out of all proportion to the benefits she got in exchange.

Compunction laid its quick, warm hand on Scrap. Impulsive gratitude flooded her. After dinner she went straight up to Briggs: "I owe you so much," she said overcome by the sudden realization of all she did owe him, and

ashamed of her churlishness in the afternoon.

He looked at her in wonder. "You owe me?" he said. "But it's I who—I who—"

"Unwise," thought Mr. Wilkins, who was standing there too, while Lotty sat on the wall. He was surprised, he was concerned, he was shocked that Lady Caroline should thus encourage Briggs.

Lotty, on the other hand chose this moment when Lady Caroline needed special support and protection, to draw him away.

"I cannot" said Mr. Wilkins, trying to draw back, "leave Lady Caroline alone in the garden.

"Don't be silly, Mellersh—she isn't alone. Besides, I want to tell you something."

"Well, tell me, then."

"Indoors."

With a reluctance that increased at every step Mr. Wilkins was taken farther and farther away from Lady Caroline. He believed in his wife now and trusted her, but on this occasion he thought she was making a terrible mistake.

"I'm sorry, Mellersh," said Mrs. Wilkins, "if you don't like it, but—" Her grey eyes shone, and her face rippled with the light and conviction that had so much surprised Rose the first time they met. She looked into his alarmed solemn face and laughter as well as light flickered and danced over her.

"I *see* them being the Briggses," said Mrs. Wilkins.

A Tear Is An Intellectual Thing

But vain the sword and vain the bow,
They never can work War's overthrow.
The hermit's prayer and the widow's tear
Alone can free the world from fear.
For a tear is an intellectual thing,
And a sigh is the sword of an angel king,
And the bitter groan of the martyr's woe,
Is an arrow from the Almighty's bow.

— *W. Blake*

DOROTHY CANFIELD

HILLSBORO PEOPLE

Is LIFE most deeply and fully lived in a city or a country village? Dorothy Canfield (1879—), whose fame as a novelist would make her a distinguished resident of any large city in America, chooses to live in the village of Arlington, Vermont. Here, as Mrs. John Fisher, she has reared her son and daughter, has written a score of successful books and has given her time and energy to many worthwhile nation-wide educational enterprises. In "Hillsboro People," she shows how ordinary village people (unlike herself) have attacked and mastered the problems of life and have thus achieved the fullness of life.

The Vitalizing Stream of Humanity

Sometimes people from Hillsboro leave our forgotten valley, high among the Green Mountains, and "go down to the city," as the phrase runs. They always come back exclaiming that they should think New Yorkers would just die of lonesomeness, and crying out in an ecstasy of relief that it does seem so good to get back where there are some folks. After the desolate isolation of city streets, empty of humanity, filled only with hurrying ghosts, the vestibule of our church after morning service fills one with an exalted realization of the great numbers of the human race. It is like coming into a warmed and lighted room, full of friendly faces, after wandering long by night in a forest peopled only with flitting shadows. In the phantasmagoric pantomine of the city, we forget that there are so many real people in all the world, so diverse, so unfathomably human as those who meet us in the little post-office on the night of our return to Hillsboro.

All that we hear from that part of America which is not Hillsboro is the wild yell of excitement going up from the great cities, where people seem to be doing everything that was ever done or thought of except just living. City dwellers make money, make reputations (good and bad), make museums and subways, make charitable institutions, make with a hysteric rapidity, like excited spiders, more and yet more complications in the mazy labyrinths of their lives, but they never make each others' acquaintances . . . and that is all that is worth doing in the world.

We who live in Hillsboro know that they are to be pitied, not blamed, for this fatal omission. We realize that only in Hillsboro and places like it can one have "deep, full life and contact with the vitalizing stream of humanity." We know that in the very nature of humanity the city is a small and narrow world, the village a great and wide one, and that the utmost efforts of city dwellers will not avail to break the bars of the prison where they are shut in, each with his own kind. They may look out from the windows upon a great and varied throng, as the beggar munching a crust may look in at a banqueting hall, but the people they are forced to live with are exactly like themselves; and that way lies not only monomania but an ennui that makes the blessing of life savorless.

There can be no city dweller of experience who does not know the result of this herding together of the same kind of people, this intellectual and moral inbreeding. To the accountant who knows only accounts, the world comes to seem like one great ledger, and account-keeping the only vital pursuit in life. To the banker who knows only bankers, the world seems one great bank filled with money, accompanied by people. The prison doors of uniformity are closed inexorably upon them.

And then what happens? Why, when anything goes wrong with their trumpery account books, or their trashy money, these poor folks are like blind men who have lost their staves.

We in Hillsboro are sorry for the account keepers who disappear forever, fleeing from all who know them because their accounts have come out crooked; we pity the banker who blows out his brains when something has upset his bank.

Life is not accounts, nor banks, and it is a sign of inexperience to think so. The trouble with the despairing banker is that he has never had a chance to become aware of the comforting vastness of the force which animates him in common with all the rest of humanity, to which force a bank failure is no apocalyptic end of Creation, but a mere incident or trial of strength like a fall in a slippery road. Absorbed in his solitary progress, the banker has forgotten that his business in life is not so much to keep from falling as to get up again and go forward.

The pathetic feature of this universal inexperience among city dwellers of real life and real people is that it is really entirely enforced and involuntary. At heart they crave knowledge of real life and sympathy with their fellow men as starving men do food. In Hillsboro we explain to ourselves the enormous amount of novel-reading and play-going in the great cities as due to a perverted form of this natural hunger for human life. If people are so situated they can't get it fresh, they will take it canned, which is undoubtedly good for those in the canning business; but we feel that we who have better food ought not to be expected to treat their boughten canned goods very seriously.

To tell the truth, all novels seem to us badly written, they are so faint and faded in comparison to the brilliant colors of the life which palpitates up and down our village street, called by strangers, "so quaint and sleepy-looking."

What does the author of a novel do for you, after all, even the best author? He presents to you people not nearly so interesting as your next-door neighbors, makes them do things not nearly so exciting as what happened to your grandfather, and doles out to you in meager paragraphs snatches of that comprehending and consolatory philosophy of life, which long ago you should have learned to manufacture for yourself out of every incident in your daily routine.

Romances, adventures, tragedies, and farces . . . why, we are the characters of those plots. Every child who runs past the house starts a new story, every old man whom we leave sleeping in the burying-ground by the Necronsett River is the ending of another . . . or perhaps the beginning of a sequel.

A Drop in the Bucket

THERE is no need to describe in detail the heroine of this tale, because she represents a type familiar to all readers of the conventional New-England-village dialect story. She was for a long time the sole inhabitant of Hillsboro, who came up to the expectations of our visiting friends from the city, on the lookout for Mary Wilkins characters.

On the way to the other end of the street, where Cousin Tryphena's tiny, two-roomed house stood, we always laid bare the secrets of her somnolent, respectable, unprofitable life; we always informed our visitors that she lived and kept up a social position on two hundred and fifteen dollars a year, and that she had never been further from home than to the next village.

She always drew attention to her one treasure, the fine Sheraton sideboard that had belonged to her great-grandfather, old Priest Perkins; and, when we walked away from the orderly and empty house we were sure that our friends from the city would always exclaim with great insight into her character, "What a charmingly picturesque life! Isn't she perfectly delicious!"

Next door to Cousin Tryphena's minute, snow-white house is a forlorn old building, one of the few places for rent in our village, where nearly everyone owns his own shelter. It stood desolately idle for some time until a burly, white-bearded tramp moved in with his stick and bundle and sent away for the rest of his belongings, that is to say, an outfit for cobbling shoes. Then he announced himself ready to do all the cobbling and harness-repairing he could get . . . and a fine workman he showed himself to be.

Although, from his name, as from his strong accent, it was evident that old Jombatiste belonged, by birth, to our French-Canadian colony, he never associated himself with that easy-going, devoutly Catholic, law-abiding and rather unlettered group of our citizens. He allied himself with quite another class, making no secret of the fact that he was an out-and-out Socialist, Anti-clerical, Syndicalist, Anarchist, Nihilist. . . .

In fact, the central article of Jombatiste's passionately held creed seemed to be that everything was exactly wrong, and that, while the Socialist party was not nearly sweeping enough in its ideas, it was, as yet, the best means for accomplishing the inevitable, righteous, overturning of society. Accordingly, he worked incessantly, not only at his cobbling, but at any odd job he could find to do, lived the life of an anchorite, went in rags, ate mainly crackers and milk, and sent every penny he could save to Socialist Headquarters.

He took two Socialist newspapers, and nobody knows how many queer little inflammatory magazines from which he read aloud selections to anyone who did not run away. Naturally enough, from his point of view, he began with his neighbor, Cousin Tryphena.

WHAT Cousin Tryphena did not know about the way the world outside of Hillsboro was run would have made a complete treatise on modern civilization. She never took a newspaper, only borrowing, once in a while, the local sheet to read the news items from Greenford, where she had some distant cousins; and, though she occasionally looked at one of the illustrated magazines, it was only at the pictures.

It is therefore plain that old Jombatiste could not have found a worse listener for his bellowed statements that ninety per cent. of the money of this country was in the hands of two per cent. of the population; that the franchise was a farce because the government was controlled by a Wall Street clique; and that any man who could not earn a good living for his family had a moral right to shoot a millionaire.

For the most part, Cousin Tryphena counted her tatting stitches and paid not the least attention to her malcontent neighbor. When she did listen, she did not believe a word he said. She had lived in Hillsboro for fifty-five years and she knew what made people poor. It was shiftlessness. There was always plenty of work to be had at the brush-back factory for any man who had the sense and backbone to keep at it.

It is proverbial that people who are mostly silent often keep for some time a reputation for more wisdom than is theirs. Cousin Tryphena unconsciously profited in the estimation of her neighbor by this fact of psychology. Old Jombatiste had thundered his per cents. of the distribution of capital for many months before he discovered that he was on the wrong track.

After he did, he made no more remarks about industrial slavery, nor did he begin, as was his wont, with the solemnly enunciated axiom, "Wealth comes from labor alone!" He laid down, on the Sheraton sideboard, an armful of his little magazines, and settled himself in a chair and began to read the story of a man who was burned to death in molten steel because his employers did not install a rather expensive safety device, and who left a young widow and three children. These tried to earn their livings by making artificial flowers. They could earn, all of them working together, three cents an hour. When the last dollar of the dead father's savings was used up, and there was talk of separating the family so that the children could be put in an asylum, the mother drowned the three little ones and herself after them. Cousin Tryphena dropped her tatting, her country-bred mind reeling. "Didn't she have any folks to help her out?"

Jombatiste explained that she came from East Poland so that her folks, if indeed she had any, were too far away to be of use. He struck one fist inside his palm with a fierce gesture and cried, ". . . and that in a country that produces three times the food it consumes." For the first time, a statistical statement awoke an echo in Cousin Tryphena's atrophied brain.

Cousin Tryphena sat rigid, her tatting fallen to the floor, her breath coming with difficulty. It is impossible for the average mind, calloused by promiscuous reading, to conceive the effect upon her primitive organism of this attack from the printed page. She not only did not dream that these stories might not be true, they seemed as real as though she had seen the people.

Jombatiste read on . . . the story of a decent, ambitious man, employed in a sweatshop tailoring establishment, who contracted tuberculosis from the foul air, and who dragged down with him, in his agonizing descent to the very depths of misery, a wife and two children. He was now dead, and his wife was living in a corner of a moldy, damp basement, a pile of rags the only bed for her and her children, their only heat what fire the mother could make out of paper and rubbish picked up on the streets.

Jombatiste read no more that day, for Cousin Tryphena had put her gray head down on the center-table and wept as she never had done in her life. Jombatiste rose softly and tiptoed out of the room.

The tap-tap-tap of his hammer rang loud and fast the rest of that day. He was exulting over having aroused another bourgeois from the sleep of greasy complacency. He had made a convert. To his dire and utter pennilessness, Cousin Tryphena's tiny income seemed a fortune. He had a happy dream of persuading her to join him in his weekly contributions to the sacred funds.

B Y NOON of the next day, everyone in the village was thrilling with wild surmise. Cousin Tryphena had gone over to Graham and Sanders', asked to use their long distance telephone and had telephoned to Putnam, the antique dealer in Troy to come and get her Sheraton sideboard. After this strange act, she had passed Albert Graham with so wild a mien that he had not ventured to make any inquiries. But he took pains to mention the matter to everyone who happened to come in, that morning; and, by dinner, every family in Hillsboro was discussing the possibility that the well-known queer streak, which had sent several of Cousin Tryphena's ancestors to the asylum, was suddenly making its appearance in her.

I was detained, that afternoon, and did not reach her house until nearly four; and I was almost the last to arrive. I appealed directly to Cousin Tryphena for information as to what the trouble was.

"There ain't any trouble 's I know of," she answered in a shaking voice. "I've heard of a widow woman, down in the city, who's bringin' up her two children in the corner of a basement where the green mold stands out on the wall, and I'm goin' down to fetch her an' the children up here to live with me."

"Dear Cousin Tryphena," I said as gently as I could, "you haven't had a very wide experience of modern industrial or city conditions and there are some phases of the matter which you don't take into consideration." Then I brought out the old, wordy, eminently reasonable arguments we all use to stifle the thrust of self-questioning: I told her that it was very likely that the editor of that newspaper had invented, or at least greatly exaggerated those stories, and that she would find on investigation that no such family existed.

"I don't see how that lets me out of lookin' for them," said Cousin Tryphena. "If I'd ha' had the money, I'd ha' gone on the noon train!"

At this point, the man from Putnam's came with a team from our livery to carry away the Sheraton sideboard. Cousin Tryphena bore herself like a martyr at the stake, watching, with dry eyes, the departure of her one certificate to dear gentility and receiving with proud indifference the crisp bills of a denomination most of us had never seen before.

"You won't need all that just to go down to the city," I remonstrated.

She stopped watching the men load her shining old treasure into the wagon and turned her anguished eyes to me. "They'll likely be needing clothes and things."

I gave up. She had indeed thought it all out.

It was time for us to go home to prepare our several suppers and we went our different ways, shaking our heads over Tryphena's queerness. I stopped a moment before the cobbler's open door. When he looked up at me from his work, I said with some acerbity, "Well, Jombatiste, I hope you're satisfied with what you've done to poor old Miss Tryphena . . . spoiling the rest of her life for her!"

"Such a life, Madame," said Jombatiste, dryly, "ought to be spoiled, the sooner the better."

"She's going to start for the city tomorrow," I said, supposing of course he had heard all the news. "She's gone daft over those bogie stories of yours . . . she's looked the list over and picked out the survivors, the widow of the man who died of tuberculosis, and so on, and she's going to bring them back here to share her luxurious life."

Jombatiste bounded into the air as if a bomb had exploded under him, scattering his tools. He rushed past me out of the house and toward Cousin Tryphena's. She opened the door in answer to his battering knocks, frowned, and began to say something to him, but was fairly swept off her feet by the torrent of his reproaches.

"How dare you take the information I give you and use it to betray your fellow-man! You call yourself a nurse . . . what would you think of a mother who hid an ulcer in her child's side from the doctor because it did not look pretty! What else are you planning to do? You with your plan to put court-plaster over one pustule in ten million and thinking you are helping cure the patient! You are planning simply to please yourself. There are hundreds of others . . . why, I could read you a thousand stories of worse—"

Cousin Tryphena's limit had been reached. She advanced upon the intruder with a face as excited as his own . . . "Jombatiste Romotte, if you ever dare to read me another such story I'll go right out and jump in the Necronsett River!" The mania which had haunted earlier generations of her family looked out luridly from her eyes.

I felt the goose-flesh stand out on my arms, and even Jombatiste's hot blood was cooled. Finally he turned to me with a bewilderment almost pathetic, "Did you hear that . . . what sort of logic do you call—"

Cousin Tryphena started off on her crack-brained expedition, the very next morning, on the six-thirty train. I happened to be looking out sleepily and saw her trudging wearily past our house in the bleak gray of our mountain dawn, the inadequate little, yellow flame of her old-fashioned lantern like a glowworm at her side. It seemed somehow symbolical of something. I did not know what.

Eight days after Cousin Tryphena had gone away, I had a telegram from her, which read, "Build fires in both my stoves to-morrow afternoon."

The morning after she arrived I went to see her. Cousin Tryphena saw me coming and opened the door. She did not smile, and she was still very pale, but I saw that she had regained her self-control. "Come right in," she said, in rather a tense voice, and, as I entered she added, in our rustic phrase for introduction, "Make you 'quainted with my friend, Mrs. Lindstrom. She's come up from the city to stay with me. And this is her little boy, Sigurd, and this is the baby."

Cousin Tryphena was evidently afraid that I would not take her cue and sound the right note, for she went on hastily, "Mrs. Lindstrom has been real sick and kind o' worried over the baby, so's she's some nervous. I tell her Hillsboro air is thought very good for people's nerves. Lots of city folks come here in summer time, just for that. Don't you think Sigurd is a real big boy for only six and a half? He knows his letters too! He's goin' to school as soon as we get settled down. I—"

The other woman was openly crying now, clinging to her benefactress' hand and holding it against her cheek as she sobbed. My heroic old cousin patted her hair awkwardly, but kept on talking in her matter-of-fact manner, looking at me sternly as though defying me to show, by look or word, any consciousness of anything unusual in the situation; and we fell at once, she and I, into a commonplace conversation about the incidents of the trip up.

When I came away, half an hour later, Cousin Tryphena slipped a shawl over her head and came down the walk with me to the gate. The happy ending of her adventure filled me with a cheerful wonder at the ways of Providence which I tried to pass on to her in the exclamation, "Why, Cousin Tryphena, it's like a story book. You're going to enjoy having those people. The woman is as nice as she can be, and that's the brightest little boy! He's as smart as a whip!"

I was aware that the oddness of Cousin Tryphena's manner still persisted even now that we were alone. She sighed heavily and said, "I don't sleep much better nights now I've done it!" Then facing me, "I hadn't ought to have brought them up here! I just did it to please myself! Once I saw 'em . . . I wanted 'em!"

This seemed to me the wildest possible perversion of the Puritan instinct for self-condemnation and, half-vexed, I attempted some expostulation.

She stopped me with a look and gesture Dante might have had, "You ain't seen what I've seen."

I was half-frightened by her expression but tried to speak coolly. "Why, was it as bad as that paper said?" I asked.

She laid her hand on my arm, "Child, it was nothing like what the paper said . . . it was so much worse!"

"Oh . . ." I commented inadequately.

"I was five days looking for her . . . they'd moved from the address the paper give. And in those five days, I saw so many others . . . *so many others* . . ." her face twitched. She put one lean old hand before her eyes. Then, quite unexpectedly, she cast out at me an exclamation which made my notion of the pretty picturesqueness of her adventure seem cheap and trivial and superficial.

"Jombatiste is right!" she cried to me with a bitter fierceness: "Everything is wrong! Everything is wrong! If I can do anything, I'd ought to do it to help them as want to smash everything up and start over! What good does it do for me to bring up here just three out of all I saw . . . Jombatiste is right . . . what I'm doin' now is only a drop in the bucket!"

She started from her sombre reverie at the sound of a childish wail from the house . . . "I knew the cat would scratch him!" she told me with instant, breathless agitation, as though the skies were falling, and darted back. After a moment's hesitation, I, too, went back and watched her bind up with stiff unaccustomed old fingers the little scratched hand, watched the frightened little boy sob himself quiet on her old knees that had never before known a child's soft weight, saw the expression in her eyes as she looked down at the sleeping baby and gazed about the untidy room so full of life, which had always been so orderly and so empty. There was a look in her eyes, a gloomy austerity which forbade me to sentimentalize over the picture she made.

"But, Cousin Tryphena," I urged, "it is a drop in the bucket, you know, and that's something!"

She looked down at the child on her knee, she laid her cheek against his bright hair, but she told me with harsh, self-accusing rigor, " 'Tain't right for me to be here alive enjoying that dead man's little boy."

The Bedquilt

OF ALL the Elwell family Aunt Mehetabel was certainly the most unimportant member. It was in the New England days, when an ' unmarried woman was an old maid at twenty, at forty was everyone's servant, and at sixty had gone through so much discipline that she could need no more in the next world. Aunt Mehetabel was sixty-eight.

She had never for a moment known the pleasure of being important to anyone. Not that she was useless in her brother's family; she was expected, as a matter of course, to take upon herself the most tedious and uninteresting part of the household labors. Aunt Mehetabel did not resent this treatment; she took it quite as unconsciously as they gave it. It was to be expected when one was an old-maid dependent in a busy family. She gathered what crumbs of comfort she could from their occasional careless kindnesses and tried to hide the hurt which even yet pierced her at her brother's rough joking about her maidenhood.

Her sister-in-law, a big hearty housewife, who ruled indoors with as autocratic a sway as did her husband on the farm, was rather kind in an absent, offhand way to the shrunken little old woman, and it was through her that Mehetabel was able to enjoy the one pleasure of her life. Even as a girl she had been clever with her needle in the way of patching bedquilts and in this work she enjoyed a tepid importance. Sometimes the neighbors would send over and ask "Miss Mehetabel" for such and such a design. It was with an agreeable flutter at being able to help someone that she went to the dresser, in her bare little room, under the eaves, and extracted from her crowded portfolio the pattern desired.

She never knew how her great idea came to her. She never admitted to herself that she could have thought of it without other help; it was too great, too ambitious. At first it seemed to her only like a lovely but quite unreal dream. But so curiously does familiarity accustom us even to very wonderful things, that as she lived with this astonishing creation of her mind, the longing grew stronger and stronger to give it material life with her nimble old fingers.

She gasped at her daring when this idea first swept over her and put it away as one does a sinfully selfish notion, but she kept coming back to it again and again. Finally she said compromisingly to herself that she would make one "square," just one part of her design, to see how it would look.

She had but little time from her incessant round of household drudgery for this new and absorbing occupation, and she did not dare sit up late at night lest she burn too much candle. It was weeks before the little square began to take on a finished look, to show the pattern. Then Mehetabel was in a fever of impatience to bring it to completion.

Finally she could wait no longer, and one evening ventured to bring her work down beside the fire where the family sat, hoping that some good fortune would give her a place near the tallow candles on the mantelpiece.

UP TO that moment Mehetabel had labored in the purest spirit of disinterested devotion to an ideal, but as Sophia held her work toward the candle to examine it, and exclaimed in amazement and admiration, she felt an astonished joy to know that her creation would stand the test of publicity.

By the end of the summer the family interest had risen so high that Mehetabel was given a little stand in the sitting-room where she could keep her pieces, and work in odd minutes. She almost wept over such kindness, and resolved firmly not to take advantage of it by neglecting her work, which she performed with a fierce thoroughness. But the whole atmosphere of her world was changed. Things had a meaning now. Through the longest task of washing milk-pans there rose the rainbow of promise of her variegated work. She took her place by the little table and put the thimble on her knotted, hard finger with the solemnity of a priestess performing a sacred rite.

A year went by and a quarter of the quilt was finished; a second year passed and a half was done. The third year Mehetabel had pneumonia and lay ill for weeks and weeks, overcome with terror lest she die before her work was completed. A fourth year and one could really see the grandeur of the whole design; and in September of the fifth year, the entire family watching her with eager and admiring eyes, Mehetabel quilted the last stitches in her creation.

The girls held it up by the four corners, and they all looked at it in a solemn silence. Then Mr. Elwell smote one horny hand within the other and exclaimed: "By ginger! That's goin' to the county fair!" Mehetabel blushed a deep red at this. It was a thought which had occurred to her in a bold moment, but she had not dared to entertain it. The family acclaimed the idea, and one of the boys was forthwith dispatched to the house of a neighbor who was chairman of the committee for their village. He returned with a radiant face. "Of course he'll take it. Like's not it may git a prize, so he says; but he's got to have it right off, because all things are goin' tomorrow morning."

EVEN in her swelling pride Mehetabel felt a pang of separation as the bulky package was carried out of the house. As the days went on she felt absolutely lost without her work. For years it had been her one preoccupation, and she could not bear even to look at the little stand, now quite bare of the litter of scraps which had lain on it so long. The family noticed the old woman's depression, and one day Sophia said kindly, "You feel sort o' lost without the quilt, don't you, Mehetabel?"

"They took it away so quick!" she said wistfully: "I hadn't hardly had one real good look at it myself."

Mrs. Elwell made no comment, but a day or two later she asked her if she would like to go to the fair.

Mehetabel looked at her with incredulity. It was as though someone had offered her a ride in a golden chariot up to the gates of heaven. "Why, you can't *mean* it!" she cried, paling with the intensity of her emotion. Her sister-in-law laughed a little uneasily. Even to her careless indifference this joy was a revelation of the narrowness of her life. "Oh, 'tain't so much to go to the fair. Yes, I mean it. Go git your things ready, for you're goin' to start tomorrow morning with Tom Ralston."

ON HER return home the next evening she was very pale, and so tired and stiff that her brother had to lift her out bodily, but her lips were set in a blissful smile. They crowded around her with thronging questions.

Mehetabel drew a long breath. "It

was just perfect!" she said; "finer even han I thought. They've got it hanging up in the very middle of a sort o' closet made of glass, and one of the lower corners is ripped and turned back so's to show the seams on the wrong side. There are a whole lot of other ones in hat room, but not one that can hold a candle to it, if I do say it who shouldn't. I heard lots of people say the same thing. You ought to have heard what the women said about that corner, Sophia. They said—well, I'd be ashamed to tell you what they said. I declare if I wouldn't!"

Mr. Elwell asked, "What did you think of that big ox we've heard so much about?"

"I didn't look at the stock," returned his sister indifferently.

"Did any of the horses in our town race?" asked young Thomas.

"I didn't see the races."

"How about the preserves?" asked Sophia.

"I didn't see the preserves," said Mehetabel calmly. "You see, I went right to the room where the quilt was, and then I didn't want to leave it. It had been so long since I'd seen it. And then the people begun comin' in and I got so interested in hearin' what they had to say I couldn't think of goin' any-

wheres else. I ate my lunch right there too, and I'm glad as can be I did, too; for what do you think?"—she gazed about her with kindling eyes—"while I stood there with a sandwich in one hand didn't the head of the hull concern come in and open the glass door and pin 'First Prize' right in the middle of the quilt!"

There was a stir of congratulation and proud exclamation. Then Sophia returned again to the attack, "Didn't you go to see anything else?" she queried.

"Why, no," said Mehetabel. "Only the quilt. Why should I?"

She fell into a reverie where she saw again the glorious creation of her hand and brain hanging before all the world with the mark of highest approval on it. She longed to make her listeners see the splendid vision with her. She struggled for words; she reached blindly after unknown superlatives. "I tell you it looked like—" she said, and paused hesitating. Vague recollections of hymn book phraseology came into her mind, the only form of literary expression she knew; but they were dismissed as being sacrilegious, and not sufficiently forcible. Finally, "I tell you it looked real *well!*" she assured them, and sat staring into the fire, on her tired old face the supreme content of an artist who has realized his ideal.

Finis

To old Mrs. Prentiss, watching apprehensively each slow mountain dawn, the long, golden days of the warm autumn formed a series of blessed reprieves from the doom which hung over her. With her inherited and trained sense of reality, she could not cheat herself into forgetting, even for a moment, that her fate was certain, but, nevertheless, she took a breathless enjoyment in each day, as it passed and did not bring the dreaded change in her life. She spoke to her husband about this feeling as they sat on the front step one October evening, when the air was as mild as late May, breaking the calm silence in which they usually sat, by saying, "Seems as

though this weather was just made for us, don't it, father?"

The old man stirred uneasily in his chair. "I dun'no'—seems sometimes to me as though I'd ruther have winter come and be done with it. If we've got to go as soon as cold weather sets in, we might as well go and have it over with. As 'tis, I keep on saying good-by in my mind to things and folks every minute, and get up in the morning to begin it all again. And yet I suppose we are real lucky to have such a good son as Hiram, now that the others are all gone. I dun'no' what we'd do if 'tweren't for him."

"Do!" cried his wife bitterly. "We

could go on living right in this valley where we belong, if 'twas only in the poor house!"

The old man answered reasonably, as though trying to convince himself, "Well, I suppose it's really lying in the face of Providence to feel so. The doctor says your lungs ain't strong enough to stand another of our winters in the mountains, fussing over stove fires, and zero weather and all, and I'm so ailing I probably wouldn't last through, either. He says it's a special dispensation that we've got such a nice place to go where there's steam heat, and warm as summer, day and night."

"Nathaniel!" exclaimed his wife, attempting to turn her bulky body toward him in the energy of her protest, "how can you talk so! We've visited Hiram and we know what an awful place he lives in. I keep a-seeing that little narrow room that's to be all the place you and I'll have, with the one window that gets flapped by the wash of the Lord knows who, and that kitchen as big as the closet to my bedroom here, and that long narrow hall—why, it's as much as ever I can walk down that hall without sticking fast—and Hiram's queer Dutch wife—"

She stopped, silenced by the scantiness of her vocabulary, but through her mind still whirled wordless out-cries of rebellion.

The gaunt old man turned toward her, a helpless sympathy twisting his seamed and weather-marked face. "It's too bad, mother," he said. "I know just how you feel about it. But Hiram's a good son, and"—he hesitated, casting about for a redeeming feature—"there's always the Natural History Museum and the birds."

"That's just it, Nathaniel," returned the old rebel against fate. "You have something there that's going on with *one* thing you've done here. You've always noticed birds and studied 'em in the woods, and you can go on doing it in a museum. But there ain't a thing for me! All I've ever done is live right

here in this house ever since I was born, and look out at the mountains and the big meadows and the river and the churchyard, and keep house and take care of the children.

"Now the children are all gone, and I haven't the strength to take care of you the way you need; my life is all done—there ain't no more to it!

"It's like a book—there's still a chapter *you* can write, or one you can finish up; but me—I've come right down to *Finis*, only the Lord won't write it for me. It's as if somebody wanted to scrawl on the back flyleaf something that hasn't a thing to do with the rest of the book, some scratching stuff in a furrin' language that I can't even understand."

Her husband did not contradict her. He sighed heavily and they both fell again into a cheerless silence.

THE NEXT morning there was a foot of snow and the thermometer was going steadily down. When the doctor arrived, red-nosed and gasping from the knife-like thrusts of the wind over Eagle Rock, he announced that it was only eight above zero, and he brought a kindly telegram from Hiram, saying that he had started for the mountains to accompany his parents back to the city."

"I envy you!" said the doctor, blowing on his stiff fingers. "Think of the bliss of being where you have only to turn a screw in your steam-radiator to escape from this beastly cold."

Mrs. Prentiss did not answer. She was so irrationally angry with him that she could not trust herself to speak.

Then she heard the doctor saying, "I'm coming over here myself when you start for the station, to see that you're well wrapped up. The least exposure—" He looked at Mrs. Prentiss's broad and obstinate back, turned to her husband, and tapped his chest significantly.

An instant later, like an echo, a fiercer gust than usual swept down off the ledge of rock above the little house, rattled the loose old window, and sent a sharp blade of icy air full in the old woman's eyes. She gasped and started back. And then, all in a breath, her face grew calm and smooth, and her eyes bright with a sudden resolve. When the doctor was out of sight, she turned to her husband and said in a tone more like her old self than he had heard for some time, "Father, I wish you'd go over to Mrs. Warner's and take back that pattern. If we're going to leave tomorrow, you know—"

The old man rose obediently, and began putting on his wraps. His wife helped him, and hurried him eagerly off. When she was alone, she tore at the fastening of her gown in a fury of haste, baring her wrinkled old throat widely. Then without a glance about her, she opened the door to the woodshed, stepped out, and closed it behind her. The cold clutched at her throat like a palpable hand of ice, and her first involuntary gasp set her into a fit of coughing.

She sat down on the stump where kindlings were always split and opened her gown wider. She noticed how fair and smooth the skin on her shoulders still was and remembered that her husband had always been proud of her pretty neck. She had worn a low-necked dress when he had told her he loved her. That had been in a garden, into which she could now look as she sat on the stump. She had been picking currants for tea, and he had gone out to see her. The scene came up before her so vividly that she heard his voice and felt herself turn to him with the light grace of her girlhood and cry again, in an ecstasy of surprised joy, "Oh, *Nathaniel!*"

A gust of wind whirled a handful of snow against her and some of it settled on her bare shoulders. She watched it melt and felt the icy little trickle with a curious aloofness. Suddenly she began to shiver, griped by a dreadful chill, which shook her like a strong hand. After that she was very still again, the death-like cold penetrating deeper and deeper until her breath came in constricted gasps. She did not stir until she heard the front door bang to her husband's return. Then she rose with infinite effort and struggled back into the kitchen. When he came in, she was standing by the sink, fumbling idly with the dishes. Already her head was whirling, and she scarcely knew what she was doing.

IN THE nightmare of horror which his wife's sudden sickness brought upon him, old Mr. Prentiss felt that he could bear everything except the sight and sound of his wife's struggles for breath. He hardly heeded the doctor's desperate attempts with all varieties of newfangled scientific contrivances to stay the hand of death. He hardly knew that his son had come, and in his competent, prosperous way was managing everything for him.

On the third day he was left alone with her, by some chance, and suddenly her dreadful, heaving gasp was still. He sprang to the bedside, sick with apprehension, but his wife looked up at him with recognition in her eyes. "This is the end, Nathaniel," she said in so low a whisper that he laid his ear to her lips to hear. "Don't let anybody in till I'm gone. I don't want 'em to see how happy I look." Her face wore, indeed, an unearthly look of beatitude.

"Nathaniel," she went on, "I hope there's no life after this—for me anyway. I don't think I ever had very much soul. It was always enough for me to live in the valley with you. When I go back into the ground I'll be where I belong. I ain't fit for heaven, and, anyway, I'm tired. We've lived hard, you and I, Nathaniel; we loved hard when we were young, and we've lived all our lives right out to the end. Now I want to rest."

The old man sat down heavily on a chair by the bed. His lips quivered, but he said nothing. Then he stepped to the door and locked it. As he came back, the sick woman motioned him to come closer. "Natty, I thought I could keep it, but I never did have a secret from you, and I can't die without telling you. If there *is* a heaven and hell— Oh, Natty, I've done a wicked thing, and I'm dying without repenting. I'd do it again. That time you went to Mrs. Warner's with the pattern—this cold I got that day I went out—"

Her husband interrupted her. For the first time in years he did not call her "mother," but used the pet name of their courtship. The long years of their parenthood had vanished. They had gone back to the days when each had made up all the world to the other. "I know, Matey," he said. "I met young Warner out in the road and give the pattern to him, and I come right back, and see you out there. I knew what 'twas for."

His wife stared at him, amazement silencing her.

"I thought it was the only thing left I could do for you, Matey, to let you stay there. You know I never wished for anything but that you should have what you wanted." He had spoken in a steady, even tone, which now broke into an irrepressible wail of selfish, human anguish. "But you leave me all *alone,* Matey! How can I get on without you! I thought I'd die myself as I sat inside the house watching you. You're all I ever had, Matey! All there has ever been in the world for me!"

The old woman stopped her gasping by a superhuman effort. "Why, Natty, I never supposed you thought so much of me still. I thought that had gone when we got old. But, oh, my dear! I'm afraid I've dragged you down with me to destruction. It wa'n't any matter about me, but I'm afraid you've lost your soul. That was a wicked thing for us to do!"

Her husband lifted his tear-stained, old face and laid it on the pillow beside her. He did not put his arms about her, as a younger lover or one of another country might have done, but because he was a man who had loved deeply all his life, his answer came with the solemn significance and sincerity of a speech before the Judgment Seat. "I ain't afraid of hell if you're there, Matey," he said.

His wife turned her head and looked at him, her whole face transfigured. She was no longer a fat old woman on her deathbed. Before his very eyes she grew again to be the girl among the currant bushes, and with the same amazed intonation of incredulous joy she cried his name aloud. "Oh, Nathaniel!" she said, and with the word the longed for *Finis* was written to her life.

Mutability

From low to high doth dissolution climb,
And sink from high to low, along a scale
    Of awful notes, whose concord shall not fail;
A musical but melancholy chime,
Which they can hear who meddle not with crime,
    Nor avarice, nor over-anxious care.
    Truth fails not; but her outward forms that bear
The longest date do melt like frosty rime,
That in the morning whiten'd hill and plain
And is no more; drop like the tower sublime
    Of yesterday, which royally did wear
His crown of weeds, but could not even sustain
    Some casual shout that broke the silent air,
Or the unimaginable touch of Time.
               —*William Wordsworth*

LOUIS BROMFIELD

THE GREEN BAY TREE

LOUIS BROMFIELD has published fourteen books in as many years. "The Green Bay Tree" which made his reputation as a leading American novelist gives us much food for thought on the questions of war and labor trouble today. "The Rains Came," a story of India where the author has spent much time, has recently been made into a successful movie. Bromfield won the *Croix de Guerre* while serving in the French Army during the World War and now has a home near Paris besides a farm in Ohio. He is married and has three children.

What the Town Never Knew

UNDER the wistarias on the wrought iron piazza Julia Shane surveyed the bright garden party and her departing guests. She wondered where Irene, Lily and the Governor could have hidden themselves.

When the last guest had gone, she pulled out a cigarette. No one in the Town had ever seen her smoke. It was well enough to smoke at Biarritz or Monte Carlo; smoking in the Town was another matter. The diamonds and amethysts on her thin fingers glittered in the fading light. She was angry and the unmistakable signs of her anger were present—the flash in her bright blue eye, the slight trembling of the veined hands. As Irene entered she didn't move or shift for a second the expression of her face.

"And where are they?—Have you found them?"

The girl's lips grew pale, and when she replied, she trembled with the awful consciousness of lying to her mother.

"I cannot find them. I have looked everywhere."

The mother frowned. "That man is a fool. He has offended a dozen important men, after I took the trouble to invite them here. God knows, I didn't want them."

The sound of footsteps came from the open gallery that ran along the far side of the drawing-room and two figures appeared at the windows moving toward the doorway. They were the missing Lily and the Governor.

Lily was taller than her sister and two years older; yet there was an enormous difference between them, which had to do less with age than with manner. There was about Irene something childish and undeveloped. Lily was a woman, tall and lovely. Her hair was the color of honey. It held bright copper lights; and she wore it low on a lovely neck that carried a warning of wilfulness. Her skin was the transparent sort which artists love for its green lights, and her eyes were of a shade of violet which in some lights appeared a clear blue.

THE Governor followed her, a tall man of perhaps forty, strongly built with a fine chest and broad shoulders. He was angry now with a primitive, boiling anger which threatened to burst the bonds of restraint.

"Madame," he said, "Your daughter has refused to marry me. It is serious, Madame, I promise you. I love your daughter. She has told me that she loves me." He turned to Lily suddenly. "It is true, isn't it?"

The girl nodded. "Yes, I have told you that . . . But I will not marry you."

The Governor came over and stood before her. "Lily," he said and then halted as though uncertain how to continue. "Lily . . . I don't believe you realize what has happened. I don't believe you understand."

The girl smiled faintly. "Oh, yes . . . I know . . . I am not a child, you know . . . certainly not *now*. You needn't fear a scandal. I know . . . I know . . . You're afraid there might be a child. Even if there was it would make no difference."

"But why . . . why won't you marry him?" asked her mother.

"I can't tell you why . . . I don't know myself. I only know that I don't want to marry him, that I want to be as I am . . ."

"Please . . . please, Lily," the man cried.

"It is no use. Two days ago I might have married you. I cannot now, because I know. I wanted to know, you see." She looked up suddenly with a strange smile. "Would you have preferred me to take a lover from the streets?"

He trembled. His face grew scarlet. At last with a terrible effort he turned suddenly from her.

In the Town the tidings of Lily's sudden departure followed the course of all bits of news from Shane's Castle. It created for a time a veritable cloud of gossip. Again when it became gradually known that she intended living in Paris, heads wagged for a time. Her name became the center of myriad tales such as accumulate about beautiful women who are also indifferent.

But of one fact the Town learned nothing. It had no knowledge of a cablegram which arrived at Shane's Castle containing simply the words, "John has arrived safely and well." Only the telegraph operator saw it and to him the words could have meant nothing.

The Lady with a Light

Meanwhile the Town grew. Houses, uniform and unvaryingly ugly in architecture and cheap in construction, sprang up in clusters like fungi to house the clerks and petty officials of the Mills. In the Flats, which included all that district taken over by the factories, hundreds of alien workmen drifted in to fill the already overcrowded houses.

In Halsted street, next door to the corner saloon, a handful of worthy citizens, moved by the gravity of conditions in the district, opened an establishment to which they gave the sentimental name of Welcome House, using it to aid the few aliens who were not hostile and suspicious of volunteer workers from the Town.

All this, Julia Shane, living in another world, ignored. She saw nothing of what happened beneath her very windows.

It was true that she found no satisfaction in her daughter Irene. On the return of the girl from a long rest at the convent, there took place between mother and daughter a terrible battle, which did not end in a sudden, decisive victory, but dragged its length across many weeks.

On the first evening at home, the mother and daughter sat until midnight in the library. "Mother," began Irene gently, "Mother, I've decided to enter the church."

The mother's face grew stern, almost hard. "I won't hear of it." She spoke with a rising intensity of feeling that was akin to hatred. "You shall not do it as long as I live and never after I am dead, if I can help it."

For days a silent struggle between the two continued, a struggle which neither admitted, yet one of which they were always conscious, sleeping or waking. At last the mother gained from the tormented girl a promise—that she would never enter the church so long as her mother was alive.

Shrewdly Julia Shane roused the interest of the girl in the families of the mill workers who dwelt at the gates of Cypress Hill. Among these Irene found a place. Like a sister of charity, she went into their homes, facing all the deep rooted hostility and the suspicions of Shane's Castle. She even went by night to teach English to a handful of laborers in the school at Welcome House. For three years she labored thus, and at the end of that time she seemed happy, for there were at least a few among the aliens who trusted her.

It was this pale, devout Irene that Lily found when she returned home after four years to visit her mother at Cypress Hill.

"How long has Irene been behaving in this fashion?" she asked her mother.

"It is more than three years now. I don't interfere because it gives her so much pleasure. It saved her, you know, from entering the church. Anything is better than that."

"You might as well let her enter the church," said Lily. "She already behaves like a nun. A woman has no right to make herself look hideous. There's something sinful in it. No man would look at her."

"Irene will never marry. . . . It is no use speaking to her. I have seen the type before, Lily . . . the *religieuse*. It takes the place of love. It is just as ecstatic."

So THERE they remained while the tall candles burned lower and lower. Suddenly after a brief pause in the talk, the mother turned to Lily and said, "Et toi?"

Lily shrugged her shoulders. "Moi? Moi? Je suis contente."

"Et Madame Gigon, et le petit Jean."

"They are well . . . both of them."

"The boy," the mother said, "should have a father. You should marry for his sake, Lily."

"He shall have . . . in time. There is no hurry. Besides, his position is all right. I am Madame Shane, a rich American widow. Madame Gigon has taken care of that. My position is excellent."

Gradually she drifted into an account of her life in Paris. The house in the Rue Raynouard was big and old. It had been built before the Revolution at a time when Passy was a suburb surrounded by open meadows. As for friends, there were plenty of them . . . more than she desired. There were the respectable baronnes and comtesses of Madame Gigon's set. To be sure, they were fuddy-duddy, but their sons and daughters were not so bad.

"After all," she concluded, "I am not clever or brilliant. I am content with them. I am really happy."

They sat talking thus until the candles burnt low, guttered and began to go out, one by one, and at last the distant tinkle of a bell echoed through the house. Lily got up languidly saying, "It must be Irene."

Lily made her way through the hall and boldly opened the door to discover that she was right. Irene stood outside covered with snow. As she stepped in, her sister caught a glimpse through the mist of falling snow of a tall man, powerfully built, walking down the long drive.

"Who is the man?" asked Lily with an inquisitive smile.

Her sister, pulling off her heavy overshoes, answered without looking up: "His name is Krylenko. He is a Ukrainian . . . a mill worker. I've taught him English. . . . He's trying to introduce the union now."

The Great Strike

IN THE flats, as the years passed, new tides of immigrants swept in, filling the abominable dirty houses to suffocation, adding to the garbage and refuse which already clogged the sluggish water of the Black Fork. The men worked twelve hours and sometimes longer in the Mills. The women wore shawls over their heads and bore many children, most of whom died amid the smoke and filth.

Welcome House, the tentative gesture of a troubled civic conscience, went down beneath the waves of prosperity. Volunteer citizens no longer ventured into the troubled area of the Flats. Money ceased to flow in for its support. It dropped at length from the rank of an institution supported by a community to the rank of a school supported by one woman and one man. The woman was Irene Shane.

The man was Stepan Krylenko. The woman was rich. The man was a mill worker who toiled twelve hours a day and gave six hours more to the education of his fellow workers.

T HE years and the great progress had been no more kind to Irene than they had been to the Town. She aged . . . dryly, after the fashion of spinsters who have diverted the current of life from its wide course into a single narrow channel of feverish activity. She grew thinner and more pale. Her pale blond hair lost its luster and grew thin and straight, because she had no time and even less desire to care for it. Yet she retained a certain virginal look, and in her eye there was a queer exalted light. She must have found peace in her work and satisfaction in the leader she had molded from the tow-haired boy.

For Krylenko had grown into a remarkable man. He spoke English perfectly. He worked with Irene, a leader among his own people. He taught the others. He read Jean Jacques Rousseau, John Stuart Mill, Karl Marx, and even Voltaire . . . books which Irene bough him in ignorance of their flaming con tents. At twenty-five Stepan Krylenke was a leader in the district, and in the Town there were men of property whe had heard vaguely of him as a disturber an anarchist, a madman, a Socialist, criminal.

Trouble became more frequent nowa days. A barricade of barbed wire sur rounded the Mills on all sides, impreg nable, menacing. It crowded the dead hedges of arbor vitae that enclosed the park at Shane's Castle. It was waiting.

W HEN it came it was known as the Great Strike and it served to mark an epoch. As the strike progressed and the violence increased, other ma chines of warfare were set up . . . such things as machine guns and searchlights which at night fingered the Flats and sky above with shafts of white light, rigid and unbending as steel.

Free At Last

I N THE house at Cypress Hill the world of Julia Shane narrowed from the castle itself to a single room and at last to the vast Italian bed. It was seldom that she gathered sufficient strength to struggle to her feet and make her way, leaning on an ebony and silver cane, to the window where the Mill yards and Flats lay spread out beneath her gaze.

Then there came a day, after the sights and sounds of the Mill yard had become a matter of indifference to the old woman, when the doctor forbade her to leave her bed if she wished to survive the day set for Lily's arrival.

Irene, so capable in succoring the miserable inhabitants of the Flats, grew helpless when death peered in at the tall windows of Shane's Castle. Besides, she had her own work to do. As the strike progressed, she came to spend days and nights in the squalid houses of Halsted Street, returning at midnight to inquire after her mother.

T HE arrival of Lily brought a certain repose to the household. The servants who behaved so sulkily under the shifting dominations of the anemic Irene, began slowly to regain their old respectful attitudes. For a time the household took on the order and dignity which it had known in the days of Julia Shane's domination.

Although her arrival worked many a pleasant change in the house, there was one thing which she was unable, either consciously or unconsciously, to alter in any way.

This then was the position of Irene. The sister remained an outsider. Lily, to be sure, made every effort to change the condition of affairs; but her efforts, it appeared, only drove the sister more deeply into the shell of taciturnity and indifference.

So it was not until Irene returned one midnight that she learned her mother was dead. She received the news coldly enough, perhaps because in those days death and suffering meant so little to her; but even Lily must have seen the faint glimmer of triumph that entered her sister's pale, red-rimmed eyes at the news that she was free at last.

Pageant In the Park

THE business of the will was virtually settled. Lily had announced her intention of leaving within a day or two. Two of her bags were already packed. One of them she had not troubled herself to unpack because she hadn't the faintest need of clothes. Being indolent, she preferred to lounge about comfortably in the black kimono embroidered in silver with a design of wistaria.

She was sitting thus when she turned at the sound of shuffling footsteps and saw one of the servants coming softly towards her. The countenance of the mulatto carried a vague, indefinable expression of terror.

"What is it, Sarah?" asked Lily. "In the name of Heaven, what is the matter?"

The woman trembled. "There's trouble a-brewin', Miss Lily," she said. "The park is full of men. They've been comin' in at the gate and they're all over the place."

"The best thing to do," said Lily softly, "is for you to go to bed and forget about it. I'll go up to my own room . . . You might see that all the doors are locked."

Upstairs in her own room, she drew up the chaise longue and pulled aside the curtains from the window. The glass ran to the floor so that she was able, lying down, to watch everything that took place in the park.

OUTSIDE a strange pageant continued to grow in size and animation. Sometimes the searchlight, swinging low in its course, flashed swiftly across the park, revealing for an instant a hundred swarthy faces and as many figures wrapped in heavy coats, bits of old blanket, rags . . . anything to shut out the bitter cold. Above each figure hung a little cloud of steaming breath, a soul hovering above a body.

Somewhere in their midst a light began to glow, increasing slowly in volume until the tongues of red flame showed above the black heads of the mob. They had built a great fire for warmth, and near it some one had set up a barrel for the speakers to stand on.

A moment later a man climbed to the top of the barrel. He was an enormous fellow, a veritable giant who towered above the mob.

At the sight of the speaker the strikers cheered wildly. The flames leaped higher and, in the wild light, doubt was no longer possible. It was Krylenko who harangued, feverishly and desperately, the threatening sullen mob.

Suddenly above the crackling of the fire and the voice of the speaker the air was ripped abruptly by a solitary rifle shot; then another and another in quick succession, until the air became alive and vibrant with the sound of guns. From the mob rose a solitary scream, followed by a groan or two and the confused, animal cries of a mob suddenly striken by a panic. The figure on the barrel disappeared, engulfed by a swarming mass of terrified humanity. The Mill guards, from the security of the barrier, had fired upon the helpless mob. The innocent plan of Irene had been, after all, nothing but a trap.

Lily Comes to Earth

THE French traveling clock struck eleven and at the same time a new sound, a distant unearthly creaking, came faintly through the open door of Lily's room. It was an indistinct scraping sound as if some one were trying a key in a lock.

Lily made her way quietly into the hall until she reached the top of the stairway where she leaned over the rail

LOUIS BROMFIELD

white as Lily's own soft body. The man's whole figure carried an air of freedom of a certain fierce desire to burst through the shabby, stained clothing.

Lily sat by him clad in the black and silver kimono, seductive, beautiful, perfect. The kimono had come open at the neck and left her white soft throat exposed. Krylenko was watching her now in a puzzled fashion. He behaved almost as if she terrified him in some new indefinable way. It was the manner of a man unused to women's company, or a man who had never before addressed a great lady; for Irene could not properly be called either a woman or a great lady. She was, rather, the embodiment of an idea.

For a long time they remained thus, and presently Krylenko, opening his eyes looked up at her with a puzzled expression. "You are not the same as Miss Irene," he said in a low voice.

and flashed the light. The glare illuminated all the lower hall. Everything was the same, save that on a chest with his head resting on his hands, sat Krylenko, hatless, his coat all torn, the blood streaming down the side of his face.

"I am Lily," she said. "Lily . . . Miss Irene's sister."

With one arm Krylenko wiped the blood from his eyes. "Then you don't know me," he said weakly. "I am not a thief . . . breaking in."

"Come," she said, "this is no place for you. There is a divan in the drawing room."

She made him comfortable, piling the brocade pillows carelessly beneath his bloody head. Then she filled a white basin with water and brought out a pair of linen pillow cases and a small silver flask.

Lily, tearing the linen pillow cases into long strips, watched him narrowly. Where the coat was torn and the dark flannel shirt ripped from the throat, the powerful muscles of the arm and shoulder lay exposed.

She saw that the fair skin was as

THE minutes passed and then suddenly, sharply, there are a loud uproar, the sound of angry knocking and a hand rattling the big outer door.

"It's the police!" said Lily, and stood up. "Come with me. Bring the bowl . . . the bandages!"

She turned the brocade cushions so that the bloody side was concealed and led the way through the hall. She turned into a storeroom where a great box stood in a corner.

"I'll hide you in this box," she said. "They'll never find you. It is full of books." Krylenko climbed in.

As Lily ran back through the corridor the knocking increased in violence. Outside on the snow covered piazza stood a half dozen men in the uniforms of the constabulary. At the apparition of the beautiful woman in the doorway they remained for an instant silent, startled.

"What is it you want?" she asked.

One of the men, a burly fellow with a brutal jaw, stepped forward. "We want to search the house. We're looking for a man named Krylenko. We're going to have a look."

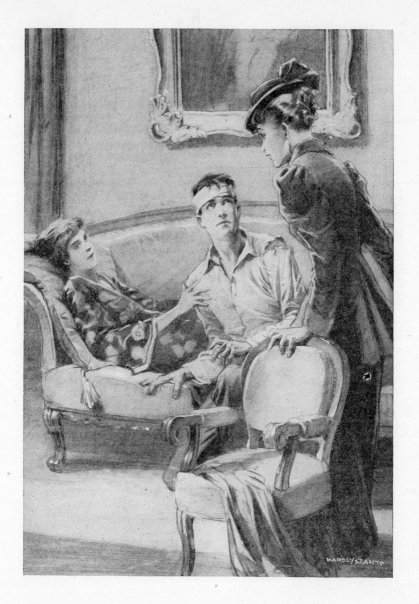

It was not until she gave a low convulsive cry that
Lily and Krylenko discovered Irene was watching them.

Illustration for Louis Bromfield's
"THE GREEN BAY TREE"

"Oh, no, you're not," she said. "It is my house. You have no right to enter it. You have no warrant. It is mine. You cannot enter it."

The man, it seemed, was baffled. If the woman in the doorway had been the wife of a workman, a simple Italian or Slovak, he undoubtedly would have brushed her aside, shot her if necessary, trampled her under foot. But this woman in the doorway was a lady. She was not a poor foreigner. She was more American than himself.

He turned away and began a low conversation with his companions. As he talked, the door was closed suddenly and locked, shutting him out in the darkness, leaving him no choice in the matter.

Some Things Are Impossible

INSIDE the house, she listened until the creak of boots on the snow died away. Then she moved off along the corridor. She walked uncertainly and from time to time leaned against the wall for support. Finally she came to the storeroom door. "It's all right, now. I've sent them away."

The books in the great box stirred and Krylenko emerged, pale and shaken. He climbed out and as his foot struck the floor, Lily gave a little cry and pitched forward so that he caught her suddenly. She did not faint. In a moment she recovered herself and managed to stand upright, but she did not move away from Krylenko. Slowly his powerful arms closed about her with the vague gesture of a man wakening from a profound sleep. He kissed with a strange, awed gentleness the white line of her bare throat and, stroking her hair gently, tried to quiet the violent trembling which had taken possession of her.

Presently he lifted her easily and gently and bore her down the dark corridor to the drawing room sofa. She lay quietly, sobbing in a heartbroken fashion. Silently he knelt beside the sofa and rested his blond head on her breasts. Neither of them spoke a word, but Lily's hand returned once more to the old gentle caressing motion across his tired eyes.

THEY were, it seemed, oblivious to everything until suddenly there stepped through the doorway the thin figure of Irene. It was not until she gave a low convulsive cry that Lily and Krylenko discovered she was watching them.

Irene had become hideous. When she spoke her voice was cold with an insane, unearthly hatred.

"So," she said bitterly, "it has happened! I might have known it . . . I should have guessed . . ." And then her voice rose to a suppressed scream. "You are no better than a street walker! You are damned forever! I have prayed . . . I have prayed, but God himself could not save you . . . He would not want you . . . a vile creature . . . a strumpet! . . . to destroy all that I have spent my life to create."

She began to sob wildly. "To destroy in a night what cost me years." She suddenly began moaning and rocking. "In the Flats they're dying . . . and you two up here, like beasts all the time . . . like beasts!"

It was Krylenko who solved the difficulty. He bent over Irene and picked her up despite her protests. He turned to Lily. "Where is her bed?"

Silently Lily led the way up the long stairs while he followed bearing Irene who moaned like a wounded animal. Together they laid the sister upon the narrow white bed. At the door of her own room Lily halted. "Wait," she said and returned in a moment with her arms burdened with blankets. "Take these, it will be cold in the drawing room."

KRYLENKO was the only one who slept. With the coming of dawn he sank into a deadening thick slumber among the stained brocade pillows of the rosewood sofa. When at last he did waken, he found on the lacquer table beside him a note, which read:

"There are some things in this world which are impossible, things fate herself will not permit. This you will understand, I am sure. I have gone away. Irene has gone too. Where she has gone I do not know. Perhaps it does not matter. There is small chance of our meeting again. Our paths lie too far apart. I have arranged for you to remain in the house, as long as you desire it. It would please me to think of you here. My blessings are with you and your cause."

The note was signed with Lily's name, and underneath it in the same sprawling hand was written, "O God! I love you. Good-by."

He got up and began pacing the floor angrily, up and down, up and down, scarring the polished floor at each step. And then all at once he went down upon his knees before the sofa and seizing one of the stained cushions in his arms, he kissed it again and again as if it were Lily instead of a feather-stuffed bit of brocade which he held in those muscular arms of his.

The Aftermath

HE DID not quit the old house. He remained there in hiding to direct the strike. From the old house he sent out to the strikers message after message of encouragement and exhortation, until, at last, the strike was lost and there was no longer either need or place for him in the Mills or in the Town. No one knew when he went away.

Day in and day out Lily's life followed its easy, happy course. Always there were diversions, always gaiety, always people. Yet there were times now—indeed they seemed to have begun upon her return from America following her mother's death—when a cloud of sadness descended upon her, times when she would withdraw suddenly to her room as if something had set fire to a train of secret memories.

Undoubtedly she was no longer in her first youth. This may have depressed her, for she was a woman to whom beauty and youth were the beginning and the end. Yet the fits of melancholy had something to do with a more definite and tangible thing. They were associated in some way with a little enameled box in which she kept a growing bundle of clippings from American newspapers.

In the solitude of her room, she opened the box and reread the clippings many times, over and over again, until the edges became frayed and the print blurred from much fingering. They had to do with the career of a certain labor leader, a man named Krylenko. Slowly, clipping by clipping, the battle he fought was being won. The unions penetrated now this steel town, now that one. He was so strong that great newspapers printed editorials against him and his cause. They called him an "anarchist," "an alien disturber," "a peril to the great American nation," and most frequently of all, "a menace to prosperity and the inalienable rights of property."

Lily kept the enameled box locked in a drawer of her writing desk. No one had ever seen it. No one would see it until she died. It had been there for seven years.

Flashes on the Horizon

LILY and Madame Gigon passed the summer of 1914 at Germigny l'Evec in the lodge of a chateau above the winding Marne. Although Madame Gigon's health was none too good and might have benefited by sea air, she preferred this house where she had always spent her summers, and Lily was content to remain there as the weeks passed through June.

For diversion the pair were visited by Jean who came ramping down from St. Cyr for a brief holiday now and then, always looking handsome and behaving with the ferocity of a cavalryman.

But it so happened that Lily and Madame Gigon were alone on the peaceful summer evening when the red-cheeked farmer's boy brought the final edition of *Figaro*.

Madame Gigon, hearing the rustle of the paper, stirred and said peevishly, "What is new today?"

"Not much of importance," said Lily, and after a pause, "the Archduke of Austria has been assassinated. Shall I read you that?"

"Certainly," replied the old woman with a fierce impatience.

So LILY read of the Archduke's assassination and Madame Gigon listened, thoughtfully, interrupting her occasionally with a clucking sound to indicate how terrible the affair really was. It was the natural result of the Republican movement, of Socialism, which was, after all, the same thing. Just another example of what these wild ideas might lead to!

Upon Germigny l'Evec, removed from the highroad and the railway, the war descended at first slowly, with the unreality of a vague dream and then with a gathering ponderous ferocity.

Lily left Madame Gigon and set out to walk the white tow-path at the edge of the river. On the far side the farm appeared deserted, as if suddenly its occupants had been overcome by the sleep of enchantment. For the farmer's family had joined the straggling columns of refugees which had appeared like magic during the early morning. There could be no doubt. The farm and the chateau were empty. At Germigny only Lily and Madame Gigon remained.

It appeared that the discovery made no impression upon Lily, for she continued on her way along the deserted river path without stopping. "Me . . . myself . . . Do they think that I am afraid?" She laughed suddenly. "Afraid of what?" Besides it was impossible to flee with a sick old woman and no means of conveyance. She laughed again and said bitterly, "What do they think . . . that I am a magician?"

She regarded the distant horizon and the queer flashes of color like heat lightning which appeared at intervals. Sometimes the rising night wind bore toward her a faint sound like that of distant thunder. On the way to the bridge the alder branches stirring softly in the breeze, whispered together in a vague, ghostly fashion. She walked slowly in the same tired fashion until she reached the little white house by the church.

Inside, the old priest at the sound of her knock looked up from his reading and took off his spectacles. "Come in," he said. M. Dupont, regarding her with an expression of amazement, rose from his chair. "Why are you here? You know the Germans may come any time now. Surely before morning."

"There is Madame Gigon," she said. "I could not go if I chose. Madame Gigon, you understand, has given up her life to me . . . It would be impossible to desert her now. She has been everything to me. You understand . . . a friend . . . a companion . . . even a mother"

And then, without warning, she poured out the whole story of her life, incident by incident, chapter by chapter, reserving nothing, disguising nothing. She told him of Jean. She told him that in her heart she had even sinned for the sake of a common laborer . . . Krylenko.

The torrent of her revelations flowed on. Instead of confession, she appeared to be pouring out to the trembling old man secrets, too long confined, which she found herself driven to reveal. "You see," she ended brokenly, "Madame Gigon is dying. The war has taken everything . . . my son . . . You understand I shall be alone . . . completely alone."

M. Dupont made no reply. He kept his head bowed. He was repeating a prayer.

He prayed for Lily Shane who had not been inside a church for more than seven years.

"Come," said the old priest finally. "If Madame Gigon is dying we must waste no time," in so gentle a voice that tears welled in Lily's eyes. (Lily who never wept.)

Conversation at Midnight

WITH the falling of night, Germans were in possession of the chateau and the gardens. Lily, sitting quietly inside the darkened lodge by the side of Madame Gigon, heard their shouts and the stamping of their horses in the stables.

Thus passed three hours.

It was the sound of knocking which aroused Lily, a violent imperious sort of knocking. From one of the lower windows of the chateau streamed a path of light which illuminated faintly the terrace, the front of the lodge and a Uhlan officer. He was not tall and was not in the least savage in appearance. On the contrary his face was smooth shaven and narrow, rather the face of scholar than a soldier.

"Were you sleeping?" he asked.

"Yes."

"Extraordinary. You must be a woman of great nerve."

"No . . . not at all. I have not slept in thirty-six hours."

He hesitated. "I have been riding for that length of time . . . and still I cannot sleep. I have tried . . ." The Uhlan laughed. "I might as well talk with you . . . since you too suffer from insomnia." Then he continued. "Do you fancy I like this war? . . . I am not pleased with killing men. Why should I? I do not hate them. How is it possible? How can you even hate me?"

She stirred impatiently. "No. It is impossible to hate genuinely . . . without a reason one can put one's finger on. All the same you are my enemy," she added stubbornly.

The Uhlan laughed. "Who has made me so, Madame? Not myself, surely," and then added with a kind of desperation, "No, I am like all the others. I have nothing to do with it. We are all caught, Madame . . . hopelessly caught in one great web spun by a monster. Ah, what Monsters! Commerce, industry, wealth, power."

He tossed away his cigarette and lighted another. "When this is over, who do you think will have gained? Not the peasant, Madame. Not the shepherd, not the poet. Ah, no! They will be shoveled under the earth . . . whole bodies and pieces of bodies because they are no longer of any use. Not the worker, Madame, whom the Monster devours. Ah, no."

His voice rose suddenly. "It is the Monster who will have gained . . . the Monster and the men whose pockets he fills with gold . . . the Monster of material, of industry. He will destroy us. He will devour us."

FOR a time Lily remained thoughtful and silent. At last she said, "I can understand the bravery of fighting for what you believe. I cannot understand yielding without a fight to the monster you despise. I knew a man . . ." For a second she hesitated. "He fought for what he believed. He gave up everything for the fight . . . his health, his friends, his work, his money. He would have given his life if it had been necessary. I am telling you this because he is fighting the very Monster that you hate. In the end he will win. But there are not many like him. There are too many like you."

Suddenly she covered her face with her hands. "In times like this," she said, "I think of him. It helps one to live." And after a moment, she added bitterly, "He would not have gone off to kill!"

She had scarcely finished speaking when the air was shattered by the terrific rattle of a dozen rifles fired simultaneously below the terrace.

The Uhlan officer did not move but Lily sat up suddenly. The stranger watched her as if fascinated and unable to remove his eyes from her face. "What was that?" she asked in a breathless whisper.

Slowly his lips began to move. "It is the Priest, Madame. They have shot the Priest." The voice carried the hard mocking cruelty of indifference. "They caught him signaling with his lantern from the steeple of the church."

Without a sound Lily lay back once more and buried her face in her cloak.

"I could do nothing else," continued the smooth voice. "It was not I who killed. I had nothing to say in the matter. I did what I could not help doing. *Enfin*, it was the Monster!"

Peace that Passeth Understanding

LILY sat alone watching the procession of figures, confused, grotesque, in the long crystal-hung corridors. There were British, French, Belgians, Italians, triumphant Japanese. There was, of course, a vast number of Americans, . . . politicians, senators, congressmen. In all the crowd, so merry, so talkative over victory, the figure of Lily, withdrawn and silent, carried an inexpressible air of loneliness.

She must have been sitting there for half an hour when her face assumed an expression of rigidity, the look of one who has seen something in which he is not quite able to believe. Moving towards her down the long vista of crystal and brocade curtains came a man. He was a big man, tall, massive, handsome in a florid way.

Then above the subdued murmur, the sound of his booming voice reached her.

"Well, well, well! . . . And what are you doing in this wicked Paris? Come to fix up the peace, I suppose!"

His whole figure betrayed an enormous self-satisfaction. It was impossible any longer to doubt. The man was the Governor. For a second she leaned against the wall and then, as if she could no longer resist the temptation, she moved quickly forward and touched his shoulder.

"Henry," she said softly and waited.

"Lily . . . !" he said. "Lily Shane . . . For the love of God!"

AND then she led him back to the corner by the tall window overlooking the misty square. There they settled themselves to talk.

"Tell me," she said, "tell me about everything. I haven't read an American newspaper in years."

"We're a rich country, Lily," he said. "The war has made us powerful. We can rule the world and do as we please. It's ours from now on. That is, the future is ours if these fools on the American commission don't spoil everything. We've got to put an end to this League of Nations nonsense. We won the war and now they're trying to wriggle out. There's no reason we should be mixed up in their troubles. I have no intention of seeing the American nation being made a dupe just because we're rich and prosperous and the others have ruined themselves."

Lily glanced at her watch. "I shall be forced to leave soon," she said. "My husband will be waiting for me."

"So you're married," he said. "And you never told me. How long has it been?"

"Not for long . . . three months."

"And what is his name?"

"De Cyon . . . René de Cyon. He is in the new ministry . . . You see I married a politician after all." She laughed in a mysterious half-mocking, half-cynical fashion.

Here a deadlock rose in their conversation. The Governor turned suddenly and said, "Tell me . . . Where's Irene?"

"She's buried . . . She's been buried these eleven years."

The Governor frowned. "I'd no idea," he stammered. "I wouldn't have asked if I had known."

Lily smiled. "Oh, she's not dead. She's a nun. She's in the Carmelite convent at Lisieux." All at once she cast down her eyes and shuddered. "Perhaps she is dead . . . When one's faith is killed one is not alive any more. You see, I killed her faith in this world. That's all I meant. She's really buried . . . alive, you understand."

The Governor made a low whistling sound. Then he did a fantastic thing. He bent over his own fat stomach and raised her hand gently to his lips. It was the simple gesture of a man who made speeches before thousands and became helpless and mute before one woman.

As Lily turned away, she saw that he was still watching her, shyly, wistfully, with head bent a little.

ONE bright October day of the same year Lily was running through a pile of newspapers when a name, buried in one corner in the smallest print, caught her attention. It must have struck her suddenly with all the force of a blow in the face, for she closed her eyes and leaned back in her chair.

It was a brief paragraph, not more than three or four lines. It recounted the death of one Stepan Krylenko, a man well known as a leader in international labor circles. He died, according to the despatch, of typhus in Moscow whither he had been deported by the American government.

Perhaps, after all, the Uhlan was right. The monster would devour them all in the end.

Last Lines

No COWARD soul is mine,
No trembler in the world's storm-troubled sphere:
　　I see Heaven's glories shine,
And faith shines equal, arming me from fear.

　　O God within my breast,
Almighty, ever-present Deity!
　　Life—that in me has rest,
As I—undying Life—have power in Thee!

　　Vain are the thousand creeds
That move men's hearts: unutterably vain;
　　Worthless as wither'd weeds,
Or idlest froth amid the boundless main,

　　To waken doubt in one
Holding so fast by Thine infinity;
　　So surely anchor'd on
The steadfast rock of immortality.

　　With wide-embracing love
Thy Spirit animates eternal years,
　　Pervades and broods above,
Changes, sustains, dissolves, creates and rears.

　　Though earth and man were gone,
And suns and universes cease to be,
　　And Thou were left alone,
Every existence would exist in Thee.

　　There is not room for Death,
Nor atom that his might could render void:
　　Thou—Thou art Being and Breath,
And what Thou art may never be destroyed.

　　　　　　　　　　—Emily Brontë

JOHN ERSKINE

THE PRIVATE LIFE OF HELEN OF TROY

THIS version of "The Private Life of Helen of Troy," published in 1925, is distinctly unorthodox for it presents a very modern Helen voicing very modern ideas about life and love. As such it has been phenomenally popular and ranks with the biggest bestsellers of recent years. John Erskine (1879-   ), its author, has also written many books of a serious nature on literature and music. Mr. Erskine is now president of the Juilliard School of Music in New York.

WHEN the war ended in Troy, with the fall of the city, Menelaos went looking for Helen, with a sword in his hand. He was undecided whether to thrust the blade through her alluring bosom, or to cut her swan-like throat. He hadn't seen her for some time. She was waiting, as though they had appointed the hour. With a simple gesture she bared her heart for his vengeance, and looked at him. He looked at her. The sword embarrassed him.

"Helen," he said, "it's time we went home."

"MENELAOS," said Eteoneus, the old gate-keeper, "I've hoped for a few minutes of your time ever since you came home. You've been absent a long while, and I dare say you'll want a report of the household."

"Nothing wrong, is there?" said Menelaos.

"Orestes has been here."

"Oh—my brother's son," said Menelaos.

"Yes," said Eteoneus, "and I might add, your wife's sister's son."

"What do you mean by that?" said Menelaos.

"I mean," said Eteoneus, "I had some doubt whether I ought to let him in. When Paris came, I let him in. What happened afterward we all know. You entertained him, of course, without question as to what he came for, and he stole your wife. Naturally you went off for your revenge, and I may say that none of us who stayed at home expected to see Helen again, certainly not restored to your esteem."

"You were about to speak of Orestes," said Menelaos.

"I was," said Eteoneus. "When you went away, you told me to look after the house with peculiar vigilance, since your strongest men were with you, and your daughter Hermione remained here. Then Orestes appeared. Perhaps I should have asked him in, but in your absence I couldn't take the risk. I assured him, however, that with us nothing was more sacred than the rights of a guest, but that recently we had become interested in the rights of the host, also, and that since these had been ignored once in this house, we were a bit nervous about good looking and anonymous young men; in these upset times we felt that unusual caution on our part should not be misinterpreted."

"I see nothing in that speech to insult him," said Menelaos.

"Well," replied the gate-keeper, "I inquired after his mother's health."

"That's sometimes done," said Menelaos, "even among the polite."

"I mean," said the gate-keeper, "I asked him whether it wasn't more delicate to leave your husband's roof before you betrayed him, than to be false by his own fireside while he happened to be absent. Orestes got the point—that's why he was angry."

"If Orestes understood you," said Menelaos, "it's more than I do."

"I suppose you haven't heard," said Eteoneus, "but all Sparta knows the scandal. Your sister-in-law, Clytemnestra —your double sister-in-law, I might say, your wife's sister and your brother's wife —has been living with Aegisthus ever since Agamemnon went to Troy."

"There! I never liked her!" exclaimed Menelaos. "I'm shocked but not surprised, except for the man. Aegisthus will regret his daring. Agamemnon has had considerable practise recently in dealing with men who steal other people's wives."

"What Sparta is curious about," said the gate-keeper, "is whether he has had enough practise in dealing with Clytemnestra. She is a formidable woman and she is making no secret of her present way of life. She thinks she is justified because Agamemnon sacrificed their daughter Iphigeneice, in order to get a favorable wind for his trip to Troy."

"This is terrible!" groaned Menelaos. "I don't wonder that Orestes was angry. Frankly Eteoneus, I should like to hear his side of the story.

"You may, easily enough," said the gate-keeper, "for he's been here right along. He never asked permission again. He just came in. I ought to add that he came always to see Hermione, and she arranged it somehow."

"I can't believe anything scandalous of my daughter," said Menelaos, "and you made a grave error in introducing the idea. Of course I've been away a long time and she's now quite grown up, but her character seems to me essentially unchanged. I've always thought her propriety itself."

"So do I, so do I," said the gate-keeper. "She was rather pathetic, I thought, circulating stories about her absent mother, stories which if we were deceived by them would make Helen out quite innocent, rather a victim than —well, we'll leave it there. I admired the daughter's loyalty, though it took a fantastic form, and I was sure, of course, she didn't believe her own yarns.

"But now Orestes has put ideas into her head which once would have troubled you. I had a talk with her one day about him—told her what was going on between Clytemnestra and Aegisthus, and warned her against compromising herself with that branch of the family. If you'll believe it, she actually defended Clytemnestra. I could guess she had the argument from Orestes."

"I won't say I like these ideas of Orestes, but they don't scare me," said Menelaos. "Before I went to Troy, if you had told me that Achilles would give back Hector's body to be buried by his relatives, and would stop the war for twelve days so the funeral would not be interrupted, I shouldn't have believed you; but that's what he did. When Helen went off with Paris I followed to kill them both. Now here she is home with me again and not in the cemetery. I'm rather surprised myself, but not so much as you are."

"The parallel between Hector's corpse and your wife escapes me," said the gate-keeper, "but I gather, Menelaos, that you think a great deal of good has come out of the war for you. The logic of your position, I suppose, is that your wife did you a good turn when she ran away with another man."

"I don't know that my gate ever needed watching so much as it does at this moment," said Menelaos. "Did you happen to favor my wife with any of your conversation just before she left the house for Troy? I've often wondered what drove her away; Paris was never reason enough."

Hermione was Helen's child, but Menelaos was her father. She had his dark hair, his black eyes, and his kind of regal bearing. She had the manner of knowing who she was. Hele was queenly by birth, Hermione by inheritance. She stood before Helen now, tall and slender, much at ease, wondering why her mother had sent for her.

"Hermione, I find certain scandalous rumors circulating about me here in Sparta. Perhaps you can explain them."

"There's a legend," said Hermione, "that you deserted your husband and ran away with Paris to Troy. I first heard of it right after you went."

"But that's not scandal," said Helen, "that's the truth."

"If that's not scandal, I don't know what is."

"I see you don't," said her mother. "In scandal there's always some falsehood, something malicious and defamatory. Paris didn't steal me, as you have been telling everybody, I was quite willing."

"Mother, this is a terrible subject—I'd rather avoid it," said Hermione. "But if I must speak plainly, I realize without the slightest shame that I'm more old-fashioned than you are; I like the respectability you seem to dread, I want a lover I can settle down with and be true to, I'm going to have an orderly home. I'm sorry I tried to save your reputation for you, since you prefer it the other way, but no great harm was done,—none of your friends really believed me. What I did was out of duty. I have no reason to love you, I owe you gratitude for nothing. You never made me happy, you never made any one happy, not even those who loved you—not my father nor Paris, nor any of them. Paris must have seen—he was a fool to take you."

Hermione was a bit amazed, and on the whole gratified, at her own indignation and spirit. She felt it was a big moment. Helen too, strange to say, seemed pleased.

"Correct at every point; you have no reason to love me, and none to be grateful. As for Paris, I've often wondered why he loved me. For the same reason, I suspect, that your father didn't kill me, that night in Troy. I told Paris precisely what you have said—that I had made no one happy. I also told him that no man had made me happy—that what promised to be immortal ecstasy would prove but a moment, brief and elusive, that our passion would bring misery after it, that for him it would probably bring death. With his eyes open, and I can't say he was a fool, he chose our love. Or perhaps there was no choice. But surely your father knew the worst when he came to find me, sword in hand and murder in his heart. He had good right to kill me, and I thought he would."

"Don't you think you're a peculiar case?" said Hermione. "To you love may be this uncertain kind of trouble, but to other people, as far as I've observed them around here, it's a fairly normal, reliable happiness. At least they don't talk as you do, they look comfortable, and they congratulate the young who have agreed to marry."

"My dear child," said Helen, "I am a peculiar case—every one is who has known love. You'll have to learn for yourself when you fall in love."

"I am in love," said Hermione,—"with Orestes."

"Yes, child, in love—but not very far in. I dare say he has never disappointed you, as yet."

"Never!"

"The early state," said Helen. "We have to build up the illusion before we can be disappointed."

"Has love for you always been a mistake?" asked Hermione.

"Never a mistake," said Helen, "always an illusion."

"So when you ran off with Paris, it wasn't really Paris you loved—as you found out later?"

"You might say that—it wasn't the real Paris. It's the illusion you fall in love with. And no matter how often it occurs, no matter how wise you are as to what the end will be, one more illusion is welcome—for only while it lasts do we catch a vision of our best selves. In that sense, as I understand it, love is a disease, and incurable."

"I don't think all the people I know think their happiness is an illusion. For myself I want the kind of happiness I believe they really have. I shall never understand how you, so beautiful and so clever, with a husband you had chosen yourself from so many splendid suitors, could throw yourself away on that person from Asia. I've tried to imagine just what was your state of mind when you ran off with him, but I can't."

"No, in that direction," said Helen, "you failed rather notably."

"Hermione, my child, come here," said Menelaos. "I must ask you a question. Sit down. Have you the love of life?"

"Oh, yes indeed!" said Hermione.

"We will now apply the test," said Menelaos. "Do you earnestly desire to marry Orestes?"

"Yes, I do," said Hermione.

"That answers it. You haven't the love of life. Your mother says that if you have it, you may marry any time, even if it's the wrong man, but if you haven't, you must postpone the wedding, even if it's the right one."

"I wish you'd tell me what you are talking about," said Hermione.

"All in good season," said Menelaos. "I must first ask you another question or two. Is there any one you would like to elope with?"

"I don't want to elope! I want to marry Orestes."

"Hasty again," said Menelaos. "You should elope first. Your mother says you should, though she fears you won't. I believe the idea is that sooner or later one elopes, and your mother, having tried it later, thinks it had better be sooner. Enough of that. Would you like to see Pyrrhus for a few days?"

"Who's Pyrrhus?"

"You know—Achilles' son."

"Why should I want to see him for a few days?"

"It would be good for you—for your acquaintance with the world at large.

Pyrrhus is the cure for your sheltered life. If our high opinion of you is justified, you would fall in love with him."

"I'm already in love with Orestes!"

"Then you might elope with Pyrrhus, discover your mistake, and marry Orestes afterward."

"I won't have Pyrrhus," said Hermione. "I'll tell mother that again the moment I see her."

"I'm glad you mentioned Pyrrhus," said Helen; "I want to talk to Hermione about him, and it saves time to come straight to the point. I will not ask Hermione to marry him. She may marry whom she chooses. She will, anyway. Indeed, I've never mentioned him to her, but I was about to tell her she ought to make his acquaintance before she chooses finally. You've been reporting our conversation, have you?"

"Yes," said Menelaos. "I told her you wanted Pyrrhus for a son-in-law, and you suggested having him here for a visit. To practice some of your frankness, I don't think that she would get much out of a visit from Pyrrhus. With you here, she wouldn't see much of him. He'd be charmed, of course—so deeply enchanted that he mightn't notice there was such a person as your daughter—or your husband. It won't do, Helen. You've come out all right so far, but from now on we'll leave well enough alone!"

"Go on, Menelaos," said Helen.

"There's nothing more," said Menelaos.

"There must be," said Helen. "No man can speak so to his wife and before his daughter, without a great deal more. This is the way you insulted me the last time we discussed this subject. I told you then I would not stay with you if you repeated the offense. Now I shall go. We've come to the end, Menelaos. I'll go my way, and you go yours. Hermione, I ask you, on your honor, not to let your father start any story about a love-affair with Achilles, or any other falsehood to account for my leaving. I go because your father has his kind of mind."

"You mustn't go, Helen," said Menelaos, "you really must not."

"If you'll stay," said Hermione, "I'll do what you ask about Pyrrhus. I'll welcome him here, in this house, before I marry Orestes."

"If you'll stay, Helen, I'll send the invitation to Pyrrhus at once," said Menelaos.

"You have made a wise decision," said Helen, "and you'd better go now and send the messenger."

"And you'll stay? That's the whole point!" said Menelaos.

"Oh, is it?" said Helen, "then it was a bargain, after all? In that case I won't stay."

"My word, what a woman!" said Menelaos. "I'll go send the messenger."

"WE HAVE news," said Eteoneus, "and I don't like to tell it."

"Tell us, Eteoneus," said Helen; "don't keep us waiting. We can stand the news, good or bad!"

"Agamemnon is dead," said Eteoneus.

"My brother is dead!" repeated Menelaos.

"I didn't like to tell you," said Eteoneus.

"Who—how did he die?" asked Menelaos.

"He was killed," said Eteoneus. "Aegisthus killed him."

"Never!" said Menelaos. "It's a mistake. Aegisthus couldn't stand a moment before my brother in a fair fight!"

"No, he couldn't," said Eteoneus, "but it wasn't a fair fight. Agamemnon went into his house, and thinking himself safe at home, he took off his armor and hung up his sword. Then they killed him."

"They? Who were they?" cried Helen.

"The messenger says Clytemnestra was implicated."

"My sister, my sister! I knew it!" cried Helen. "I knew in my heart she would murder him some day. She's the one, not Aegisthus! Eteoneus is trying to spare me, but I'm sure that's the fact."

"Clytemnestra must know that there will be some sort of revenge for this murder," said Hermione. "Orestes will exact a terrible penalty from Aegisthus, but if Clytemnestra were implicated, he would have to punish her too—the murderers, in fact. She understands where such a deed would end."

"Orestes wouldn't kill his mother," said Menelaos. "I think Helen is unjust to her sister . . . Eteoneus, did the messenger give you any further details?"

"There are details," said Eteoneus. "The messenger says Agamemnon went into the house and after a while the people who came to welcome him went away, not seeing more entertainment in prospect. Then Clytemnestra had them all called back, and she came out and made them a speech. She said she had enjoyed such admirable relations with her neighbors that there was no reason why she should not take them into her complete confidence. She had, she said, just killed her husband. They probably knew that Aegisthus and she had been living together, and considered themselves man and wife in the eyes of the gods, if the gods had noticed it. She had doubted that Agamemnon would return—rather hoped that he wouldn't, for he had murdered their daughter, and she was bound by every pious obligation, as they would readily appreciate, to slay the murderer of her child.

"She wished it understood that she had killed Agamemnon to avenge Iphigeneia, their daughter, not in order to pursue her love for Aegisthus; that love, in fact, had come about of itself as an indirect consequence of what Agamemnon had done. She confessed that the duty to avenge her child had been complicated by the fact that he was her legal husband, and she had once loved him.

"She wished them all to know, first, that she had done it herself, without aid from anybody; and secondly, that she was proud of it and had nothing to apologize for. She would now take Aegisthus as her lawful second husband; she had accepted no aid from him in killing Agamemnon, for after all the feud had to do with her daughter and not with her love affairs."

"THE messenger considered it quite a speech," said Eteoneus, "and at first it was well received, but the people began to notice, as they thought it over, that she really was shielding Aegisthus, and trying to lay the blame where no vengeance could strike. The messenger says that Orestes will have the people with him if he succeeds in killing Aegisthus, but if he fails, they'll probably stand by Clytemnestra—she has the situation well in hand."

"Of course she has," said Helen. "She undoubtedly planned it all, even the speech, long ago. She leaves nothing to accident. She murdered him. I'm glad at least she didn't pretend otherwise."

"Don't you think you'd better go help Orestes," said Hermione.

"I'm going within the hour—I made up my mind to that while we were talking," said Menelaos.

"Bring Orestes back with you," said Helen, "and the wedding can take place without further delay. It will rehabilitate that branch of the family, socially I mean, to have the alliance with your daughter, and it will take the poor fellow's mind off his terrible troubles."

"That wedding can wait," said Menelaos.

"Of course it can," said Helen. "Meanwhile, what will you do if you meet Clytemnestra now? Won't it be rather awkward for you to pass the time of day while you're killing her lover? And won't it be still more awkward afterward? You ought to consider every side of it Menelaos. This time I'm not urging you to avoid danger or ridicule; I'm thinking that since Agamemnon is gone, you must approach Clytemnestra, as the surviving parent, when you arrange the details of Hermione's wedding, and perhaps it would therefore be wiser to keep out of this feud—especially since Orestes seems able to bear her wrath."

"I don't see that at all," said Hermione. "He can't keep out of the feud, mother; he can't talk to Clytemnestra about me, nor about anything else, without remembering who killed Agamemnon. He might just as well go now and help Orestes, and I can marry without Clytemnestra's approval."

"You can't ignore your mother-in-law," said Menelaos. "I'm glad you feel about her as you do, but it will be difficult for you to get on after you have given yourself to her son. I like Orestes better than ever, and all that sort of thing, but in marriage you have to reckon with the relatives."

"Father, are you going back on me, and on Orestes?" said Hermione.

"Suppose we let the whole subject drop for a while; Orestes is preoccupied, anyway, and there's no hurry."

"I can't let Orestes drop, if that's what you mean," said Hermione. "I'm committed to him—I'm engaged. When he's ready to take me, I'm his."

"Hermione," said Helen. "I'd like to remind you that you have my full permission to marry Orestes. I pleaded with you merely to see Pyrrhus; even about that I grew lukewarm. Marry Orestes when you like, so far as I'm concerned; it's for you and your father to work out."

"I've made up my mind, and I feel I belong to Orestes all the more because of the trouble he's in."

MENELAOS looked worried. It may have been the accumulation of domestic disaster, or it may have been that he was about to demonstrate his ability to make Helen do what he wanted, but whatever the reason, he was haggard and suddenly old. He walked up and down several times, without any gain of confidence. Helen seemed prepared for something. She had an indefinable air of being amused. She never looked better.

"I'd like to talk with you about something," he said. "I think it will please you. Pyrrhus accepts your invitation."

"Your invitation," said Helen.

"Well, he accepts the invitation, and will shortly be here. He probably is on the way now. I hope you are satisfied."

"What about?"

"If Orestes hears that I'm trying to marry Hermione to Pyrrhus, he'll say my objection to the murder is just a device to break his engagement and win a more celebrated son-in-law."

"Can the messenger reach him before he starts—or shortly after?" said Helen. "It wouldn't do to turn him back from your very door. If you could get word that your brother is dead, and that my sister killed him, Pyrrhus won't want to come, anyway, and he'll be glad to understand why we can't have him at present."

"I'll do that," said Menelaos. "I never wanted him, and it's not too late if the messenger hurries. . . ."

"May I come in?" said Eteoneus. "I don't wish to interrupt but I have some news."

"News about what?" said Menelaos.

"About Orestes. It's partly good news, and partly bad. In the first place, the young man has avenged his father's death. He has killed Aegisthus."

"That's something like it!" said Menelaos. "I thought Orestes could manage it alone, and there's a special satisfaction when the son can take care of his father's memory; it shows the line hasn't run out. That's very good news."

"What did Clytemnestra say?" said Helen.

"Nothing."

"And what did she do?"

"Nothing."

Helen looked at him so steadily that they all looked at her, and noticed that the color had left her face.

"You have bad news, too," she said. "Tell us everything."

"I see you've guessed it," said Eteoneus, "and that makes it easier to tell. Clytemnestra's dead."

Helen rose to her feet, as if she were about to leave. Then she said: "How did she die, Eteoneus?"

"Orestes killed her."

"No!" cried Hermione. "Not his own mother!"

"His own mother."

"Orestes!"

"Helen," said Menelaos, "this is a good deal worse than my brother's death. There is no forgiveness in Heaven or on earth for such a crime. Orestes is a lost soul. Clytemnestra, in comparison, was a good woman, I hope I may never see—"

"I think Hermione is fainting," said Helen.

"I'm all right," said Hermione. "I don't blame you, father—it's impossible —even if I had seen him do it, I'd say it's impossible. Orestes loved her, and he had the deepest sense of filial duty —it's simply impossible!"

"If you mean he didn't do it, you're wrong," said Eteoneus. "He killed her. It was one filial duty against another, and he took vengeance all round. He knows you won't like it."

"For the time only," said Helen. "I'm sorry for Orestes. Whatever emotions I have besides, I'm chiefly sorry for a serious and stupid boy who could do such a thing by way of being dutiful. He is a lost soul, Menelaos, but I don't want him to be more lost than necessary. Imagine how he will feel when he realizes what he has done! You had better send for him, Menelaos!"

"I don't want him to come," said Hermione. "It would be too terrible with the whole household around. I think I had better see him first alone."

"I was going to tell you, as another piece of news," said Eteoneus, "that Pyrrhus will probably be here in a day or two. He started more quickly than we expected."

"I think I'll retire, if you don't mind," said Hermione. "My head begins to ache terribly, and I must be alone."

"IT simply comes to this," said Menelaos, "that we can't find her."

"That's it," said Eteoneus. "The men have been everywhere in the neighborhood, then miles, I should say, in all directions, and no one has heard of her, or seen her go by."

"It's very strange that a young girl could walk out of a house in broad daylight, in a civilized country, and completely disappear!"

"My notion is that she didn't go far," said Eteoneus. "My idea isn't worth much, I confess, since I don't see how she could conceal herself nearby, but if she came in at any moment I shouldn't be over-surprised."

"I should," said Menelaos. "She's looking for Orestes, and he's not in this part of the world."

"How do you know he's not?"

"He wouldn't have the impudence," said Menelaos.

"On the other hand," said Eteoneus, "it's all that you need for your most exquisite embarrassment, to have him show up just as Pyrrhus arrives."

"That's not my worst embarrassment —the worst will be to welcome Pyrrhus with the news that my daughter has run away. We must find her—we must, Eteoneus. I'm known to Pyrrhus chiefly as the man whose wife ran off, and if I must tell him my daughter has gone too—I can't face it, I simply can't!"

"Well, Menelaos, I'd do anything in reason, but I'm very tired of my job, and I don't believe Hermione is ever coming back. You can't ask me to stay for life and look for her."

"That's really what I'd like to ask you but stay until Hermione is found, whether she comes back here or not; the moment we know positively where she is, you may go."

"Thank heaven, I can go now! What do you think of that! Here she is! Right behind you in the door."

"What does this mean, Hermione? Where have you been?"

"Ask that question some other time— it's irrelevant. I want to speak to you and mother."

"Your absence hasn't improved your manners," said Menelaos. "You need have no fear of Pyrrhus if you talk to

him as you do to your parents. He's a brave man, but he won't take that on for life."

"You still expect Pyrrhus to visit you?" said Hermione.

"Almost any time now."

"He isn't coming," said Hermione. "That's what I had to tell you."

"I'd like to know why not?"

"He insulted Orestes. Orestes and I met Pyrrhus on the road, and—"

"What were you doing with Orestes?" said Menelaos.

"That's of no importance now," said Hermione. "He and I were walking together when we met Pyrrhus. I guessed who it was, but said nothing. He stopped to inquire the way, and before I could do anything to prevent it, they found out each other's name. Pyrrhus stiffened up at once, and said that as he was to be your guest, he felt bound to offer me his protection. Orestes asked from whom he wanted to protect me, and Pyrrhus said, from a man who would lift his hand against his own mother. Before I realized what was happening, they had drawn their swords."

"They actually had a fight?" said Menelaos.

"I should say! Pyrrhus is dead."

"Hermione, Pyrrhus was my guest! Don't tell me Orestes killed a man coming to my house, on my invitation?"

"Orestes killed him, father, in the circumstances I have just reported."

"I see we've reached the end," said Menelaos. "If any new catastrophe can overtake my house, at least I don't know the name of it. There's nothing more to discuss; if Hermione wants Orestes after this, we'll have to admit she knows the worst about him, and they say there's no arguing in matters of taste. May I ask, Hermione, merely for information, if you dream of being the wife of this murderer?"

"I don't dream," said Hermione, "I am. I told you quite clearly I was going to marry him. We weren't married when we met Pyrrhus, and that was awkward, though the quarrel would not have been avoided, probably, even if we had been. But I showed Orestes that people would remark on our traveling together, when they spoke of the killing, and we ought to marry at once. So we did."

"You may leave the house!" said Menelaos. "Eteoneus, kindly open that door for her."

"I had no intention of staying so long: I've been keeping Orestes waiting. Good-by!"

"One moment!" said Helen. "Menelaos, we have reached the end, as you said. We have our opinion of what Hermione and Orestes have done, but since they did it on their own responsibility, we have no part in the consequences. There is nothing more to be said, and we might as well be friends."

"I'll never be friends with Hermione and Orestes!"

"Menelaos! Menelaos!" said Helen. "I don't want Hermione to go until she has promised to send her husband to see us. If she will do that, I rather think we can some day understand one another again—all of us. It isn't my sister's murderer I want to talk with—it's her son. If Hermione loves him so desperately, there must be good in him I knew nothing about."

"He is a splendid man—you couldn't help admiring him, if you knew what he really is. The trouble with you and father was that you didn't know him, and you didn't want to."

"The fact is as you said, daughter—we don't know Orestes. Will you ask him to come tomorrow?"

"I'll give him the invitation," said Hermione.

"It was good of you to come, Orestes," said Helen. "I understand you are very busy at present, but I wanted to see you as soon as Hermione told us of the marriage."

"I'd like to say, but I can't, that I'm glad to come," said Orestes. "You have very reason to hate me. I dreaded to meet you."

"I don't hate you," said Helen. "But don't misunderstand me, Orestes; what you have done seems to me inexpressibly horrible. You'll pay a heavy penalty for it, in the treatment most people will give you, and still more in your own thoughts. I can't say how sorry I am for you. I should have done anything to prevent you from such a course, just as I tried to prevent Hermione from marrying you. But what's done is done, and we are now free to enjoy each other's friendship, and to sympathize with each other in the consequences of our mistakes. On my own behalf I grieve over what you have done; for your sake too. The better friends we are, the more I shall regret your actions. I didn't want Hermione to assume a share in your misery."

"I did not wish to lay any of it upon her, but she would have it so," said Orestes. "There is a kind of justice in it since she is your child, for if we are talking of our wrong-doing, I may as well say that I blame you for the whole tragedy. That's how it all began—with your beauty. Agamemnon sacrificed his daughter to get the fleet started. I think my mother was justified in leaving him, after that. She felt she ought to avenge her child by killing him, if he should return.

"She was wrong, I am sure, but I respect her motives. That is why I found it so terribly hard to avenge my father —but of course I had no choice. Now I have quarreled fatally with your guest. Iphigeneia—Agamemnon—Clytemnestra —Pyrrhus. That is the sanguinary logic of your behavior. My mother felt you were to blame. She said you were inordinately beautiful. You are. But she said also that wherever you came, people began to do wrong. I can see that would be so.

"Can you sleep soundly? I can't. But what I have done seems, I suppose, amateurish and unimportant to you. That's why you can greet me so cheerfully. You have caused so many men to do awful things, who except for you would have led uneventful and innocent lives. All those men dead at Troy—their children slain or starved—the women captured and disgraced! We can never be very good friends; I couldn't bring myself to enjoy the sight of your loveliness while I knew the evil effects it had produced."

"WE SHAN'T quarrel over your opinion, Orestes," said Helen. "It is essentially my own opinion. It's what I expected you to think of me. Where I have been, disaster has always followed. If it had not been for me, your father would not have offered up his own child, my sister would not have slain her husband, you would not have killed your mother, nor Pyrrhus—and you wouldn't have married Hermione."

"Oh, I should have married Hermione anyway! That's not a catastrophe, and you are in no way responsible for it. I married Hermione because I love her. When you love as Hermione and I do, you can not help yourself."

"You never met Paris, did you? He felt the same way about it."

"Oh, I beg your pardon! Such a theory would make your passion for that Trojan rascal as sacred as my love for Hermione."

"I didn't mention any theory," said Helen. "I was citing a fact. You told me how you and Hermione felt; I told you how Paris and I felt. Why did you call him a rascal? You didn't know him. Our love was decidedly like any other love; it seemed to us sacred."

"If you could not have done otherwise," said Orestes, "you are logically not to blame for the miseries that followed. It's an ingenious point of view, but I don't think it will hold. Who is responsible for it all?"

"I've often wondered," said Helen, "but I still don't know. I could make an argument to show it was Menelaos' fault, but then I should have to explain Menelaos, and the deeper you get in, the more difficult it is. That is why I have learned to accept a thing once

done, as done; we must take the consequences, but there's no sense in debating it as though it were still to do, and I am disinclined to pass judgment on the doer."

"That's a most upsetting doctrine! That would leave all wrong-doers unpunished!"

"Never—unless you feel there is nothing ethical in life itself. I still like to believe you can find out whether an action is right or wrong by doing it— that a right action has better results."

"Of course, in general," said Orestes. "But in the practical world, in society, you've got to distinguish between criminals and others."

"I'd like to," said Helen, "but I doubt if any one can—that is, not until you have a long time to watch the result of their lives. Take yourself, for example: I don't know whether you are a murderer or an unusually dutiful son."

"I tried to do my duty," said Orestes, "but what I did makes me fiendishly unhappy."

"Exactly," said Helen. "You are probably something of both—I meant to say your deeds were both bad and good. You acted from the highest motives you had, but maybe they weren't high enough. Your morals are beyond criticism, but perhaps your information was inadequate. I notice that most people feel they may safely act when they know they are right. It strikes me, after a few experiments, that when we are sure we are right we had better be careful. We've probably overlooked something. In love, as you say, we can't help ourselves— I'm referring to everything else.

"You think I did wrong in going to Troy, though you understand, I'm grateful to know, that I couldn't have done otherwise," said Helen. "But I dare say you think Menelaos was compelled to bring on a great war, destroy a city, take hundreds to their death, all because his wife ran away. You think I'm to blame. Well, I don't see it. I think it was pride and a lack of imagination. He, not I, caused all those deaths, though he acted with a clear conscience and is rather satisfied with himself, and I knew I was doing a tragic thing, though I couldn't help it. Which of us is really responsible for the suffering that followed? I think a decent man could lose his wife without bringing on a war."

"Don't you think a wife should be punished for deserting her husband?"

"Perhaps I should be punished—perhaps I am punished, but not by Menelaos. He got his friends to destroy Troy and let themselves be killed, but here he and I are back again. I know he feels he accomplished something, and I think it best not to ask him what."

"Why not?"

"For the same reason that I should not ask you what you accomplished when you punished your mother, or what she accomplished when she killed your father. It's kind to ask people only their intentions; if we saw the true meaning of what we have done, perhaps we couldn't survive."

"You confuse me terribly—you can't know how terribly!"

"Yes, I can," said Helen. "I did it deliberately. You came here thinking me a bad woman, and yourself something of a martyr to duty. You were right about yourself; you are a martyr to what you thought was your duty. So was your mother. But after what I have said, you are not so sure. You probably continue to think me bad, but you see that it might not be so easy to prove, if we came to an argument about it. About my own conduct, Orestes, I have long been confused. But I won't hang my head over anything I've done. I'll take what retribution life has for me; if it has none, I'll be thankful that what I did isn't so bad as I feared."

"That's a terribly dangerous doctrine," said Orestes.

"I'm not trying to convert you to it," said Helen. "I merely wanted to explain myself, and perhaps to comfort you a little. Some of the wrong we do is crime, and some error; our mistakes ought to be less tragic than our sins, but it often turns out the other way. You, I think, have made some terrible mistakes, but that won't interfere with our friendship. Of course I do hope you won't repeat them."

"What you say sounds kind and I'm grateful for it, but it still seems immoral," said Orestes.

"Perhaps it is," said Helen. "It's the best I can do. At any rate, there are no hard feelings between us?"

"I don't approve of your visit to Troy, and all that," said Orestes, "but that's past."

"I'm afraid it is," said Helen.

"That doesn't sound like repentance," said Orestes.

"I hope it doesn't," said Helen.

To A Young Lady

SWEET stream that winds through yonder glade,
Apt emblem of a virtuous maid—
Silent and chaste she steals along,
Far from the world's gay busy throng,
With gentle, yet prevailing, force
Intent upon her destined course;
Graceful and useful all she does,
Blessing and blest where'er she goes,
Pure—bosomed as that watery glass,
And heaven reflected in her face.

—*W. Cowper*

IRVING BACHELLER
THE LIGHT IN THE CLEARING

THIS is the story of America one hundred years ago and more particularly of a states-man who like Washington and Lincoln earned the title of Great Commoner. Most people today have never heard of Silas Wright, but every school child would have known him if he had consented to be President of the United States. Irving Bacheller (1859-   ), the author of many successful novels on early America, puts himself in the place of a frontier boy who was befriended by Silas Wright and the resulting story (published in 1917) throws an interesting light on the character of the times.

THE Light in the Clearing shone upon many things and mostly upon those which, above all others, have impassioned and perpetuated the Spirit of America and which, just now, seem to me to be worthy of attention.

I believe that spirit to be the very candle of the Lord which, in this dark and windy night of time, has flickered so that the souls of the faithful have been afraid. But let us be of good cheer. It is shining brighter as I write, and under God, I believe it shall, by and by, be seen and loved of all men.

One self-contained, Homeric figure of the remote country-side in which I was born, had the true Spirit of Democracy and shed its light abroad in the Senate of the United States and the Capitol at Albany. He carried the candle of the Lord. It led him to the height of self-forgetfulness achieved by only two others—Washington and Lincoln.

Yet I have been surprised by the profound and general ignorance of this generation regarding the career of Silas Wright, of whom Whittier wrote:

"Man of the millions thou art lost too soon!
Portents at which the bravest stand aghast
The birth throes of a future strange and vast
Alarm the land. Yet thou so wise and strong
Suddenly summoned to the burial bed,
Lapped in its slumbers deep and ever long,
Hear'st not the tumult surging over head.
Who now shall rally Freedom's scattering host?
Who wear the mantle of the leader lost?"

The distinguished Senator who served at his side for many years, Thomas H. Benton of Missouri, has this to say of Silas Wright in his *Thirty Years' View:*

"He refused cabinet appointments under his fast friend Van Buren and under Polk, whom he may be said to have elected. He refused a seat on the bench of the Supreme Court of the United States; he rejected instantly the nomination of 1844 for Vice-President; he refused to be put in nomination for the Presidency. He spent that time in declining office which others did in winning it. The offices he did accept, it might well be said, were thrust upon him. He was born great and above office and unwillingly descended to it."

So much by way of preparing the reader to meet the great commoner in these pages.

Ominous Portents

AMOS GRIMSHAW was there in our dooryard the day that the old ragged woman came along and told our fortunes—she that was called Rovin' Kate, and was said to have the gift of "second sight," whatever that may be.

I remember how she shook her head and sighed and sat beating her forehead with the knuckles of her bony hands after she had looked at the palm of Amos. Swiftly the point of her pencil ran over and up and down the sheet like the movements of a frightened serpent.

My aunt exclaimed, "Mercy!" as she looked at the sheet; for while I knew not, then, the strange device upon the paper, I knew, by and by, that it was a gibbet. Beneath it were the words: "Money thirst shall burn like a fire in him."

She rose and smiled as she looked into my face. I saw a kind, gentle glow in her eyes that reassured me. She examined my palm and grew serious and stood looking thoughtfully and said:

"I see the longing of the helper. One, two, three, great perils shall strike at him. He shall not be afraid. God shall fill his heart with laughter. I hear guns, I hear many voices. His name is in them. He shall be strong. The powers of darkness shall fear him, he shall be a lawmaker and the friends of God and of many people, and great men shall bow to his judgement and he shall—"

She began shaking her head thoughtfully and did not finish the sentence, and by and by the notion came to me that some unpleasant vision must have halted her pencil.

A Great Man Meets Me

MY FIRST peril came when I ran away from home. When night fell I lay down by a water trough and went to sleep.

What happened that night I have wondered often. Kind hands had picked me up and carried me to a little veranda that fronted the door of a law office. There I slept peacefully until daylight, when I felt a hand on my face and awoke suddenly. I remember that I felt cold. A kindly faced man stood leaning over me.

"Hello, boy," said he. "Where did you come from and what is your name?"

"My name is Barton Baynes and I come from Lickitysplit," I replied sleepily.

"Where is your father?"

"In Heaven," I answered, that being the place to which he had moved, as I understood it.

"Why are you such a long way from home?" my new friend asked.

"I ran away," I replied. "They can't stand me any longer. Uncle Peabody's all tired out, and my Aunt Deel, too. I've tipped over every single thing on that place. I tipped over the honey yesterday—spillt it all over everything and rooend my clothes. I'm a regular pest."

"Well, pest or no pest, I think your aunt and uncle will be very glad to see you again. Suppose we both go and see them?"

I SHALL not try to describe that home coming. We found Aunt Deel in the road five miles from home. She had been calling and traveling from house to house most of the night. Uncle Peabody and one of our neighbors had also been out all night with pine torches. I recall how, although excited by my return, he took off his hat at the sight of my new friend and said:

"Mr. Wright, I never wished that I lived in a palace until now."

I knew that my new friend must be very great, for there was a special extravagance in their tone and manner toward him which I did not fail to note.

When the great man had gone Uncle Peabody said to Aunt Deel: "Do you remember what ol' Kate wrote down about him? This is his first peril an' he had met his first great man an' I can see that Sile Wright is kind o' fond o' him."

NEXT day the stage came to our house and left a box and a letter from Mr. Wright, addressed to my uncle, which read:

"DEAR SIR—I send herewith a box of books and magazines in the hope that you or Miss Baynes will read them aloud to my little partner and in doing so get some enjoyment and profit for yourselves.

"Yours respectfully,
"S. Wright, Jr."

I remember that I tried to walk and talk like Silas Wright after that day. He had a way of twisting little locks of his hair between his thumb and finger when he sat thinking. I practised that trick of his when I was alone.

One evening a neighbor brought the *Republican* from the post office. I opened it and read aloud these words, in large type at the top of the page:

SILAS WRIGHT ELECTED TO THE U. S. SENATE.

"Well I want to know!" Uncle Peabody exclaimed.

I read of the choosing of our friend and the part which most impressed us were these words from a letter of Mr. Wright to Azariah Flagg of Albany, written when the former was asked to accept the place:

"I am too young and too poor for such an elevation. I have not had the experience in that great theater of politics to qualify me for a place so exalted and responsible. I prefer therefore the humbler position which I now occupy."

"That's his way," said Uncle Peabody. "They had hard work to convince him that he knew enough to be Surrogate."

"Big men have little conceit—ayes," said Aunt Deel with a significant glance at me.

Evil Days of 1837

THEN came the evil days of 1837, when the story of our lives began to quicken its pace and excite our interest in its coming chapters.

Wild speculations in land and the American paper-money system had brought us into rough going. The banks of the city of New York had suspended payment of their notes. They could no longer meet their engagements. As usual, the burden fell heaviest on the poor.

Uncle Peabody had been silent and depressed for a month or more. He had signed a note for Rodney Barnes, a cousin, long before and was afraid that he would have to pay it.

"Bart," my uncle said one evening, as I took down a book to read. "I guess we'd better talk things over a little to-night. These are hard times. If we can find anybody with money enough to buy 'em I dunno but we better sell the sheep."

"I'll stay at home an' work," I proposed bravely.

"You ain't old enough for that," sighed Aunt Deel.

"I want to keep you in school," said Uncle Peabody, who sat making a splint broom.

While we were talking in walked Benjamin Grimshaw—the rich man of the hills. He didn't stop to knock but walked right in as if the house were his own. It was common gossip that he held a mortgage on every acre of the countryside.

"I see you've got one o' these new fangled stoves," said Mr. Grimshaw as he looked it over. "Huh! Rich folks can have anything they want."

Uncle Peabody had sat splintering the long stock of yellow birch. I observed that the jacknife trembled in his hand.

"When I bought that stove I felt richer than I do now. I had almost enough to settle with you up to date, but I signed a note for a friend and had to pay it."

"Ayuh! I suppose so," Grimshaw answered in a tone of bitter irony which cut me like a knife-blade, young as I was. "What business have you signin' notes an' givin' away money which ain't yours to give—I'd like to know? What business have you got enlargin' yer family—takin' another mouth to feed and another body to spin for? That costs money. I ain't no objection if a man can afford it, but the money it costs ain't yours to give. It looks as if it belonged to me. I want to tell you one thing, Baynes, you've got to pay up or git out o' here."

"Oh, I ain't no doubt o' that," said Uncle Peabody. "You'll have to have yer money—that's sure; an' you will have it if I live, every cent of it. This boy is goin' to be a great help to me—you don't know what a good boy he is and what a comfort he's been to us!"

"He'd 'a' been all right at the county house until he was old enough to earn his livin', but you was too proud for that—wasn't ye? I don't mind pride unless it keeps a man from payin' his honest debts. You ought to have better sense," said Mr. Grimshaw.

"An' you ought to keep yer breath to cool yer porridge," said Uncle Peabody.

Mr. Grimshaw opened the door and stood for a moment looking at us and added in a milder tone: "You've got one o' the best farms in this town an' if ye work hard an' use common sense ye ought to be out o' debt in five years— mebbe less."

He closed the door and went away.

Having recovered my composure I repeated that I should like to give up school and stay at home and work.

Aunt Deel interrupted me by saying: "I have an idee that Sile Wright will help us—ayes! He's comin' home an' you better go down an' see him!"

"Bart and I'll go down tomorrer," said Uncle Peabody.

A Good Bargain

THERE was a crowd of men and women in front of Mr. Wright's office and through its open door I saw many of his fellow townsmen. We waited at the door for a few minutes. Finally the Senator caught sight of me and came to my side and put his hand on my head and said:

"Hello, Bart! How you've grown! and how handsome you look!"

Mr. Wright was stouter and grayer and grander than when I had seen him last. He was dressed in black broadcloth and wore a big beaver hat and high collar and his hair was almost white. I remember vividly his clear, kindly, gray eyes and ruddy cheeks.

"Baynes, I'm glad to see you," he said heartily. "Did ye bring me any jerked meat?"

"Didn't think of it," said Uncle Peabody.

"But I'd like to bring it tomorrer— I want a chance to talk with ye for half an hour or such a matter," said my uncle. "I've got a little trouble on my hands."

"There's a lot of trouble here," said the Senator. "I've got to settle a quarrel between two neighbors and visit a sick friend and make a short address to the Northern New York Conference at the Methodist Church. I expect to get through about six o'clock and right after supper I could ride up to your place with you and walk back early in the morning. We could talk things over on the way up."

"That's first rate," said my uncle.

The Senator took us into his office and introduced us to the leading men of the county.

"Here," said the Senator as he put his hand on my head, "is a coming man in the Democratic party."

The great men laughed at my blushes and we came away with a deep sense of pride in us.

That evening Silas Wright rode back to the farm with us.

My uncle told him about the note and the visit of Mr. Grimshaw and of his threats and upbraidings.

"Did he say that in Bart's hearing?" asked the Senator.

"Ayes!—right out plain."

"Too bad! I'm going to tell you frankly, Baynes, that the best thing I know about you is your conduct toward this boy. I like it. The next best thing is the fact that you signed the note. It was bad business but it was good Christian conduct to help your friend. Don't regret it. You were poor and of an age when the boy's pranks were troublesome to both of you, but you took him in. I'll lend you the interest and try to get another holder for the mortgage on one condition. You must let me attend to Bart's schooling. I want to be the boss about that. We have a great schoolmaster in Canton and when Bart is a little older I want him to go there to school. I'll try to find him a place where he can work for his board."

"We'll miss Bart but we'll be tickled to death," said Uncle Peabody.

The Mark of Cain

For several years we had kept Grimshaw from our door by paying interest and the sum of eighty dollars on the principal. It had been hard work to live comfortably and carry the burden of debt. By the time I was sixteen, Grimshaw had begun to press us. My uncle wanted to get his paper and learn, if possible, when the Senator was expected in Canton. So he gave me permission to ride with our hired man to the post-office—a distance of three miles —to get the mail.

When we had come to the most desolate part of the road, we heard a quick stir in the bushes. Then promptly a voice broke the silence with these menacing words sharply spoken:

"Your money or your life!"

The hired man whirled his horse and lashed him up the hill. Glancing backward I saw him lose a stirrup and fall and pick himself up and run as if his life depended on it. I saw the stranger draw his pistol. A gun went off in the edge of the bushes close by. The flash of fire from its muzzle leaped at the stranger. The horses reared and plunged and mine threw me in a clump of small poplars by the roadside and dashed down the hill.

When I had collected my thoughts, I peered through the bushes. A stranger lay helpless in the road and a figure was bending over him. It was a man with a handkerchief hanging over his face with holes cut opposite his eyes. He had not seen my fall and thought, as I learned later, that I had ridden away.

His gun lay beside him, its stock toward me. I observed that a piece of wood had been split off the lower side of the stock. I jumped to my feet and seized a stone to hurl at him. As I did so the robber fled with gun in hand.

If the gun had been loaded I suppose that this little history would never have been written. Quickly I hurled the stone at the robber. I saw it graze the side of his head. He reeled and nearly fell and recovered himself and ran on, but the little stone had put the mark of Cain upon him.

The stranger lay still in the road. I lifted his head and dropped it quickly with a strange sickness. The feel of it and the way it fell back upon the ground when I let go scared me, for I knew that he was dead. There was nothing upon him to indicate his name or residence. Weeks passed with no news of the man who had slain him. I had told of the gun with a piece of wood broken out of its stock, but no one knew of any such weapon in or near Lickity-split.

It was a sunny day in late September on which Aunt Deel and Uncle Peabody took me and my little pine chest with all my treasures in it to the village where I was to go to school and live with the family of Mr. Michael Hacket, the schoolmaster.

The day after I arrived I learned that Amos Grimshaw had been arrested for the murder of the man who had tried to hold me up.

"But do you think that the son of Ben Grimshaw will receive his punishment even if he's proved guilty? Not at all. He will be protected—you mark my words," said Mr. Hacket.

My brain had gone back over the events of that tragic moment—the fall, the look of the robber in the dim light, the hurling of the stone. The man who fled was about the size of Amos, but I had never thought of the latter as the guilty man.

"You saw the crime, I believe," said

Mr. Hacket as he turned to me. "I think we should walk up to the jail and spend a few minutes with Amos."

We entered an ill-smelling, stone-floored room with a number of cells against its rear wall. The door was locked behind us. I saw a face and figure in the dim candle-light, behind the grated door of one of these cells. How lonely and dejected and helpless was the expression of that figure! The sheriff went to the door and unlocked it.

We shook Amos' hand and he said that he was glad to see us. I saw the scar under his left ear and reaching out upon his cheek which my stone had made and knew that he bore the mark of Cain.

We left him and went to our home and beds. I to spend half the night thinking of my discovery, since which, for some reason, I had no doubt of the guilt of Amos, but I spoke not of it to any one and the secret worried me.

Money Can't Buy It

I was called home a day or so later by Uncle Peabody who said that Mr. Grimshaw wanted to talk to us both.

Mr. Grimshaw came in soon after we had finished our lunch. "Tell me what you know about that murder," he demanded.

"Wal, I had some business over to Plattsburg," my uncle began. "While I was there I thought I'd go and see Amos. So I drove out to Beekman's farm. They told me that Amos had left there after workin' four days. He left some time in the night an' took Beekman's rifle with him, so they said. There was a piece o' wood broke out o' the stock o' the rifle. That was the kind o' gun that was used in the murder."

It surprised me that my uncle knew all this. He had said nothing to me of his journey or its result.

"How do you know?" snapped Mr. Grimshaw.

"This boy see it plain. It was a gun with a piece o' wood broke out o' the stock."

"Are you sure that the stock of the gun you saw was broken?" said Mr. Grimshaw, addressing me.

"Yes, sir—and I'm almost sure it was Amos that ran away with it."

"Why?"

"I picked up a stone and threw it at him and it grazed the left side of his face, and the other night I saw the scar it made."

My aunt and uncle and Mr. Dunkelberg moved with astonishment as I spoke of the scar. Mr. Grimshaw, with keen eyes fixed upon me, gave a little grunt of incredulity.

"Huh!—Liar!" he muttered.

I answered: "No, sir—I saw the stone hit and I saw him put his hand on the place while he was running. I guess it hurt him some."

"Look a' here, Baynes," Mr. Grimshaw began. "I know what you want an' we might jest as well git right down to business first as last. You keep this boy still an' I'll give ye five years' interest."

Uncle Peabody changed color as he rose from his chair. "Say, Mr. Grimshaw, I'm awful sorry for ye, but I've always learnt this boy to tell the truth an' the hull truth. I know the danger I'm in. It'll be hard to start over ag'in an' you can ruin us if ye want to. But I couldn't muzzle the boy if I tried—he's too much of a man. If you're scared o' the truth you must know that Amos is guilty."

"I see that I'm the mouse an' you're the cat," Mr. Grimshaw resumed, as that curious laugh rattled in his throat. "Look a' here. Baynes. I'll tell ye what I'll do. I'll cancel the hull mortgage."

Again Uncle Peabody rose from his chair with a look in his face which I have never forgotten. Then the fragments from the explosion began falling with a loud crash:

"No, sir! Ye can't buy the nail on my little finger or his with all yer money—damn you!"

Every member of that little group stood stock-still and breathless. Then Mr. Grimshaw shuffled out of the door, his cane rapping the floor as if his arm had been stricken with palsy in a moment.

I remember that my own eyes were wet as I went to my aunt and kissed her. She kissed me—a rare thing for her to do—and whispered brokenly but with a smile: "We'll go down to the poorhouse together, Bart, but we'll go honest."

BY AND BY the fall term of school ended. Uncle Peabody came down to get me the day before Christmas. I had enjoyed my work and my life at the Hackets', on the whole, but I was glad to be going home again. My uncle was in high spirits and there were many packages in the sleigh.

"We're goin' to move," said my uncle presently. "We've agreed to get out by the middle o' May."

"How does that happen?" I asked.

"I settled with Grimshaw and agreed to go. If it hadn't 'a' been for Silas Wright we wouldn't 'a' got a cent. They threatened to bid against him at the sale. So he settled. We're goin' to have a new home. We've bought a hundred an' fifty acres from Abe Leonard. Goin' to build a new house in the spring. It will be nearer the village."

He playfully nudged my ribs with his elbow. "We've had a little good luck, Bart," he went on. "An old uncle over in Vermont died three weeks ago and left us thirty-eight hundred dollars. It was old Uncle Ezra Baynes o' Hinesburg. Died without a chick or child. Your aunt and me slipped down to Potsdam an' took the stage an' went over an' got the money. It was more money than I ever see before in my life. We put it in the bank in Potsdam to keep it out o' Grimshaw's hands. I wouldn't trust that man as fur as you could throw a bull by the tail."

An Unmourned Death

THREE times that winter I had seen Benjamin Grimshaw followed by Rovin' Kate clothed in rags and pointing with her finger. When he came to town she followed. I always greeted the woman when I passed her, but when she was on the trail of the money-lender she seemed unaware of my presence, so intent was she on the strange task she had set herself. If he were not in sight she smiled when passing me, but neither spoke nor nodded.

Grimshaw had gone about his business as usual when I saw him last, but I had noted a look of the worried rat in his face. He had seemed to be under extreme irritation. The notion came to me that her finger was getting down to the quick.

The trial of Amos came on. He had had "blood on his feet," as they used to say, all the way from Lickitysplit to Lewis County in his flight, having attacked and slighty wounded two men with a bowie knife who had tried to detain him at Rainy Lake. He had also shot at an officer in the vicinity of Lowville, where his arrest was effected. He had been identified by all these men, and so his character as a desperate man had been established. This in connection with the scar on his face and the tracks, which the boots of Amos fitted, and the broken gun stock convinced the jury of his guilt.

Slowly the crowd moved out of the court room. Benjamin Grimshaw rose and calmly whispered to his lawyer. He had not spoken to his son or seemed to notice him since the trial had begun, nor did he now. Many had shed tears that day, but not he. Mr. Grimshaw never showed but one emotion—that of anger. He was angry now. His face was hard.

Rovin' Kate was waiting for him on the steps. Out went her bony finger as he came down. He turned and struck at her with his cane and shouted in a shrill voice that rang out like a trumpet and in his frenzy shouted:

*"Go 'way from me. Take her away,
somebody, I can't stan' it. She's killin'
me. Take her away!"*

His face turned purple and then
white. He reeled and fell headlong, like
a tree severed from its roots, and lay
still on the hard, stone pavement.

The Silent Woman stood as still as he,
pointing at him with her finger, her
look unchanged.

"Dead!" she muttered.

A lawyer who had come out of the
court room pressed near me and bent
over and looked at the set eyes of Benjamin Grimshaw and said:

"She floored him at last. I knew she
would. He tried not to see her, but I
tell ye that bony old finger of hers burnt
a hole in him. He couldn't stand it. I
knew he'd blow up some day under the
strain. She got him at last."

"She's got an evil eye. Everybody's
afraid o' the crazy ol' Trollope!"

"Nonsense! She isn't half as crazy as
the most of us," said the lawyer. "In my
opinion she had a good reason for pointing her finger at that man. She came
from the same town he did over in
Vermont. Ye don't know what happened there."

I learned later that he had been the
father of her child.

I Go to Washington

Swiftly now I move across the border
into manhood—a serious, eager, restless manhood.

I spent a summer of hard work in the
fields. Evenings I read the books which
Mr. Wright had loaned to me, Blackstone's *Commentaries* and *Greenleaf on
Evidence.*

Mr. Wright came up for a day's fishing in July. My uncle and I took him
up the river. I remember that after he
had landed a big trout he sat down and
held the fish up before him and looked
proudly at the graceful, glowing, arrowy
shape.

"I never did anything in the Senate
that seemed as important as this," he
said.

But I remembered a letter that my
schoolmaster, Mr. Hacket, had received
from his Harvard classmate George
Bancroft. I quote it from the original:

" 'Your fellow townsman, Silas
Wright, is now the largest figure in
Washington. We were all worried by
the resolution of Henry Clay until it
began to crumble under the irresistible
attack of Mr. Wright. On the 16th he
submitted a report upon it which for
lucid and accurate statements presented
in the most unpretending manner, won
universal admiration and will be remembered alike for its intrinsic excellence
and for having achieved one of the most
memorable victories ever gained in the
United States Senate. After a long debate Clay himself, compelled by the
irresistible force of argument in the report of Mr. Wright, was obliged to retire from his position, his resolution
having been rejected by a vote of
44 to 1.' "

While we ate our luncheon he described Jackson and spoke of the
famous cheese which he had kept on a
table in the vestibule of the White
House for his callers. He described his
fellow senators—Webster, Clay, Rives,
Calhoun and Benton. I remember that
Webster was, in his view, the least of
them, although at his best the greatest
orator. We had a delightful day, and
when I drove back to the village with
him that night he asked me to go with
him to Washington as his secretary. You
can imagine with what joy I accepted.

My mental assets would give me a
poor rating I presume in the commerce of modern scholarship when I
went to Washington that autumn with
Senator and Mrs. Wright. My best assets
were not mental but spiritual for I had
unusual strength of character gained
through my association with my aunt
and uncle.

Those days the candles were lighting
the best trails of knowledge all over the

land. Never has the general spirit of this republic been so high and admirable as then and a little later. It was to speak, presently, in the immortal voices of Whittier, Emerson, Whitman, Greeley and Lincoln. The dim glow of the candles had entered their souls and out of them came a light that filled the land and was seen of all men. What became of this mighty spirit of democracy? My friend, it broke down and came near its death in a long, demoralizing war which gave to our young men a thorough four-year course in the ancient school of infamy.

I was awed by the grandeur of Washington itself. It seemed to me that there was not room enough in my consciousness for the great public buildings and the pictures and the statues and the vast machinery of the government. Beauty and magnitude have a wonderful effect when they spring fresh upon the vision of a youth out of the back country.

One afternoon we went to hear Senator Wright speak. He was to answer Calhoun on a detail of the banking laws. The floor and galleries were filled. With what emotion I saw him rise and begin his argument as all ears bent to hear him. He aimed not at popular sentiments in highly finished rhetoric, as did Webster, to be quoted in the school books and repeated on every platform. But no words of mine are able to convey a notion of the masterful ease and charm of his manner on the floor of the Senate or of the singular modesty, courtesy, aptness and simplicity of the words as they fell from his lips.

He had a priceless and unusual talent for avoiding school-reader English and the arts of declamation and for preparing a difficult subject to enter the average brain. The underlying secret of his power was soon apparent to me. He stood always for that great thing in America which, since then, Whitman has called "the divine aggregate," and seeing clearly how every measure would be likely to affect its welfare.

Not much in my term of service there is important to this little task of mine. I did my work well, if I may believe the Senator, and grew familiar with the gentle and ungentle arts of the politician.

One great fact grew in magnitude and sullen portent as the months passed: the gigantic slave-holding interests of the South viewed with growing alarm the spread of abolition sentiment. Subtly, quietly and naturally they were feeling for the means to defend and increase their power. Straws were coming to the surface in that session which betrayed this deep undercurrent of purpose. We felt it and the Senator was worried I knew, but held his peace. He knew how to keep his opinions until the hour had struck that summoned them to service.

The winter wore away slowly in hard work. Mr. Van Buren came down to see the Senator one day from his country seat on the Hudson. The Ex-president had been solicited to accept the nomination again. I know that Senator Wright strongly favored the plan but feared that the South would defeat him in convention, it being well known that Van Buren was opposed to the annexation of Texas—a pet project of the slaveholders. However, he advised his friend to make a fight for the nomination and this the latter resolved to do. Thenceforward until middle May I gave my time largely to the inditing of letters for the Senator in Van Buren's behalf.

Into the Lives of Few Men . . .

THE time appointed for the convention in Baltimore drew near. I took the stage to Baltimore on the twenty-sixth of May. The convention thrilled me—the flags, the great crowd, the bands, the songs, the speeches, the cheering—I see and hear it all in my talk. The uproar lasted for twenty minutes when Van Buren's name was put in nomination.

Then the undercurrent! The slave interest of the South was against him as

Wright had foreseen. The deep current of its power had undermined certain of the northern and western delegations. Ostensibly for Van Buren and stubbornly casting their ballots for him, they had voted for the two-thirds rule, which had accomplished his defeat before the balloting began. It continued for two days without a choice. The enemy stood firm. After adjournment that evening many of the Van Buren delegates were summoned to a conference. I attended it.

The Ex-president had withdrawn and requested his friends in the convention to vote for Silas Wright. I was appointed to ride to Washington to see whether Silas Wright would accept the nomination.

Well, I reached Washington very sore, but otherwise in good form, soon after daybreak. I was trembling with excitement when I put my horse in the stable and rang the bell at our door. It seemed to me that I was crossing the divide between big and little things. A few steps more and I should be looking down into the great valley of the future. Yet, now that I was there, I began to lose confidence.

The butler opened the dor.

Yes, the Senator was up and had just returned from a walk and was in his study. I found him there.

"Well, Bart, how does this happen?" he asked.

"It's important business," I said, as I presented the letter.

Something in his look and manner as he calmly adjusted his glasses and read the letter of Judge Fine brought the blood to my face. It seemed to puncture my balloon, so to speak, and I was falling toward the earth and so swiftly my head swam. He laid the letter on his desk and, without looking up and as coolly as if he were asking for the change of a dollar, queried:

"Well, Bart, what do you think we had better do about it?"

"I—I was hoping—you—you would take it," I stammered.

"That's because the excitement of the convention is on you," he answered. "Let us look at the question. They have refused to nominate Mr. Van Buren because he is opposed to the annexation of Texas. On that subject the will of the convention is now clear. It is possible that they would nominate me. We don't know about that, we never shall know. If they did, and I accepted, what would be expected of me is also clear. They would expect me to abandon my principles and that course of conduct which I conceive to be best for the country. Therefore I should have to accept it under false pretenses. Is that right?"

"No," I answered.

Immediately he turned to his desk and wrote the telegram which fixed his place in history. It said no.

Into the lives of few men has such a moment fallen. I am sure the Lord God must have thought it worth a thousand years of the world's toil. It was that moment in the life of a great leader when Satan shows him the kingdoms of the earth and their glory.

I looked at him with a feeling of awe. What sublime calmness and serenity was in his face. As if it were a mere detail in the work of a day, and without a moment's faltering, he has declined a crown, for he would surely have been nominated and elected.

He rose and stood looking out of the open window. Always I think of him standing there with the morning sunlight falling upon his face and shoulders. He had observed my emotion and I think it had touched him a little. There was a moment of silence. A curious illusion came to me then, for it seemed as if I heard the sound of distant music.

He was one of a lean body and visage, as if his eager soul, biting for anger at the clog of his body, desired to fret a passage through it.—*Thomas Fuller.*

A Madonna Leads a Man through Adversity

Hervey Allen

ANTHONY ADVERSE

"Anthony adverse" needs no introduction. Everyone knows about this overpowering novel, even though he may not have had a chance to plough through its 1224 pages packed with adventurous romance and poetic glamour. It is a *tour de force* of Hervey Allen's imagination, for he has never actually visited many of the scenes of the novel, although he has travelled widely in the United States and Europe where he took an active part in the World War. Now he devotes himself to writing, his wife, two daughters and a farm in Maryland.

High on an Alpine pass on a wild night in the winter of 1776 an illegitimate man child was born. His mother, Maria Bonnyfeather, the unhappy girl wife of the Spanish Grandee, Don Luis, died giving him birth. Don Luis had already wrecked his vengeance on the child's charming Irish father in mortal sword combat and as he was no longer in a position to tyrannize over his erring wife he dumped the child into a satchel, with a madonna figurine which had belonged to the mother, and left it at the nearest convent. The child arrived on the day of St. Anthony and so the good sisters baptized him Anthony.

Anthony lived in this saintly atmosphere until he was ten. His bodily needs were well provided for by the sisters and his mental ones by a local priest who gave him the fundamentals of a fine education. When a new Mother Superior came, it was her idea to turn the convent into a school for girls, which policy made Anthony's position there somewhat embarrassing. So the good priest arranged to have the boy apprenticed to the rich merchant, John Bonnyfeather, of Livorno, Italy. Anthony was packed off to Livorno with the satchel and madonna which had come with him to the convent.

When Mr. Bonnyfeather first caught sight of the child he was astounded by the startling resemblance to his only child, Maria, who had died ten years ago giving birth to a child, who, he had understood from his son-in-law, Don Luis, had also died. When he saw the madonna which Anthony brought with him, he had little doubt that this was really Maria's child. However, Don Luis' strange behavior seemed to indicate the circumstances of Anthony's birth, and he resolved to keep the secret locked in his heart to guard the honor of his family.

Until that time the child bore but one name, so that his position among the clerks of Mr. Bonnyfeather's office was somewhat embarrassing. It was decided that because he had entered the world in great adversity, his surname should be Adverse.

As the years went by, Mr. Bonnyfeather came to treat Anthony as a son, with the result that he was able to spend more time acquiring an education from books and people than he spent over the books in the old merchant's office. When Anthony was about twenty, news came that Napoleon was on the way to Italy with conquest in his eye. Mr. Bonnyfeather decided to liquidate his holdings and draw up his will in favor of Anthony.

The largest bill outstanding on Mr. Bonnyfeather's ledgers was due from a concern of Cuban slave dealers. It was suggested that Anthony might like to go to collect it. Anthony readily fell in with the suggestion. Before he left, Mr. Bonnyfeather showed him a picture of his daughter. Anthony saw the significance, but asked no questions and promised to keep the secret. And so he set sail for Cuba with his mother's madonna wrapped up in his luggage.

When Anthony arrived in Havana he found not only a beautiful lady named Dolores but Mr. Bonnyfeather's corrupt and wily agent. It appeared that the only way he could get Mr. Bonnyfeather's money without having most of it deducted for fees and taxes was to go to Africa himself and bring back a cargo of slaves. Anthony left Cuba and the beautiful Dolores with regret, but not before the Cuban officials had shanghaied to his boat a Franciscan Brother who had interfered with their brutal treatment of the black slaves. Brother François had previously been deported from Paris where for two years he had stood by the Revolutionary guillotine, comforting those who were about to die. On the voyage Brother François was taken violently ill with the fever from which he miraculously recovered with the help of Anthony's ministrations. At last they reached Gallegos, a slave trading post on the African coast.

The Master of Gallegos

For all practical purposes the entire landscape Anthony now looked over, from the new veranda at Gallegos to the Mongo's fields six miles away across the bay, was a very—well, a very Adverse one. Yes, on the whole, a great deal had been accomplished since he had pulled in three years before—a great deal!

Fourteen ships in three years! And the fifteenth swinging at anchor below there now. Another caravan was due soon, despite the nearness of the rainy season, and the stock in the warehouse was low. The neighbouring country was pretty well worked out.

This rainy season would be better—the first in the new house since it was finished. It might even be comfortable, and there would be a let-up in the perpetual man-hunt. There would be time to devote to Neleta! They would live together in the same house. Brother François could look as sad as he wanted to. Neleta would be his housekeeper now. Housekeeper! He smiled, and drifted away in a vision that relaxed him in the chair.

That half-breed brother of hers, Ferdinando, could not expect him to marry her. Marry her? He laughed. He was master here. Master—a rich one, too. To think that only three years ago he had been trying to collect a debt for Mr. Bonnyfeather and now. . . . He let his eye wander over the ample plantation that lay just below the house.

To Anthony it seemed that he was at last finding himself; at least he told himself that. He was "doing things"; he was being a very practical and a successful man in a situation that had required courage, finesse, adaptability and a grim determination to carry through.

Yet there was a part of Anthony which seemed to be withering by the way. It was the part of him which lay locked up in the chest which had come from Livorno with Mr. Bonnyfeather's books, some more youthful clothes and his old madonna. Yet it was upon this part of him that his eyes looked when they turned inward. And it was the refusal to listen to certain old promptings that turned his pupils stony and had given him a fixed mask-like cast of countenance. It was all that which turned him white with fury when it had been suggested to him by his half-breed factor, Ferdinando, that what lay locked up in the fireproof store room might be his soul.

He had jumped the doubts as to which was the better man of the two, the old self or the new Master of Gallegos. His will was now all on the side of the latter and it took less and less willing, he thought, to keep himself the Master of Gallegos from day to day. Two things helped him maintain this conviction; intercourse with Neleta and what he poured into himself from a glass. With only a little stimulant, so far, he could attain for the time being what seemed at least to be a solid basis of personality.

Indeed, it was more than that: it was the sensation of a complete unity, of being absolutely physical. Tobacco soothed and allayed, wine stimulated and completed. Neleta was beyond all this, Neleta was indescribable consummation of the flesh alone. He did not need to think about her. He consumed with her.

Men For Sale

At the residence all was now final frantic activity, although Neleta had been actively preparing for the advent of the caravan since early dawn. The procession which now began to unroll itself through the gate and to advance down the slope toward the residence was bizarre, if not positively weird. So strange were the aspects of the men and beasts who walked and stalked in it that it might have been an embassy from another planet . . .

A crowd of painted Mandingo barkers preceded it. They were dressed only in breech-clouts, but were armed with the deadliest weapons of noise; cymbals, tom-toms, bull whistles, and gourd rattles on long sticks. These, and fifty other hellish devices, produced an atmospheric disturbance, that, added to the salvos from the cannon, raised the wild-fowl from the marshes for miles around.

Behind them, a long, dark, glistening body commenced to crawl through the gateway as though a legendary serpent were sliding into the stockade. It was seen to be composed of hundreds of naked, human bodies rubbed shiny with palm oil and rancid butter for their approaching sale. In the sun they glittered like ebony scales. Bamboo withes, stretched from one tight neck-fork to another, bound them together into one interminable twisting line.

Soon the small forms of children could be made out darkening the intervals between the passing legs of this huge millepede as it wound down the slope. Hovering about it, and along its flanks, were white-robed Arabs with rhinoceros-hide whips. An occasional report like a pistol-shot from one of these instruments helped to keep the worm crawling fairly rapidly.

THIS was the third caravan which the Mohammedan Amah had led to Gallegos. Anthony and he had entered into what amounted to a partnership based on a general admiration for each other's resourcefulness and the mutual advantages of cooperation. Amah watched the inland trails constantly and swept into his net all the small traders going to the coast, in the meanwhile carrying on a holy war against the heathen. In this way he was able to gather together large caravans of both slaves and traders, offering to the latter his "protection," for which he levied a tax. But unlike other leaders of caravans he collected the tax and no more. On the whole everybody was satisfied.

The swiftness and orderliness of trade had been considerably accelerated at Gallegos by reaching an agreement beforehand with the leaders of caravans as to the prices to be paid for various kinds of goods. This did away with endless chaffering over every oxhide and piece of ivory.

Slaves, however, were another matter. Profitable as the petty trade was, it was minor compared to the trade in man himself. Soon the barter for slaves began.

The inspections proceeded rapidly but meticulously. The slaves were stark naked, and from the crown of their head to their toe-nails they were thoroughly appraised. They were made to squat, to get up, to lean over; to dance and to walk about. They were asked a few swift questions and the tones and intelligence of their replies noted. Their mouths were pulled open and their teeth examined; the whites of their eyes, their pulses, and the colour and texture of their skins. A swelling, an unsoundness or a malformation was spotted by them off-hand. In particular they were on the watch for slaves who had been doctored up for the occasion. And there were a hundred clever tricks in that black art.

The number of those rejected was small but their plight was terrible. Indeed, the very worst that could happen to a slave was to be rejected as unfit; the best was to please both his old and new owners by being valuable. So nearly all of those who had wit enough to appreciate their predicament tried to appear attractive on the block.

Behind the Iron Mask

TO BROTHER FRANÇOIS, seated on a stool by a crack in Ferdinando's door, the barter of human bodies for goods piled just behind him in the sample-room was an experience of inexpressible pathos and agony.

It was not only that he believed that his Master had given His body for these dark children of the forests and that they were truly the sheep of His fold, but having been born where and when he had been in France, Brother François understood the meaning of the word "liberty" in both its practical and abstract sense. It was, in fact, the favourite word of his age.

Consequently, every one of these scenes was, for him at least, a Calvary. The perspiration ran down in his sleeves. If he had not believed that violence was always wrong and futile he would have rushed out and died fighting. But this belief and the glimpse of a certain face before him kept him temporarily inactive. The face was Anthony's.

At this game of human barter, Anthony's features registered what he wished he could feel about it, nothing at all. In the final analysis he did not really care for the goods which trade brought him. It was action and not gain which was his profit—the sense of power.

Yes, that was the masculine secret, deeper than love of women, or friendship—or God. Power is what a man keeps for its own sake and not for what it will do for him. Power he was determined he would trade for nothing at all, but he would trade all things, even men for it.

His association with Brother François had so far tended to confirm him in the opinion that even the "subjects of God" could do nothing about slavery. And one had to live as—to be a man. Be practical.

There was only one thing which kept Anthony from feeling entirely successful, practical—he could not entirely stifle his feelings. During a slave-barter he always became peculiarly aware of that. Somehow this trading in men seemed to be the whole crux of the matter.

As the afternoon advanced, Anthony's state of feeling became all but unbearable. He was now beholding, he knew very well, the inmost core, the essence of doing things in order to get them done. The process was as naked to him as the slaves who stepped onto the block. He was at once fascinated and tortured. What if his state of feeling should prevail over his will and become his whole state of being? What would he do then?

He must remain calm and sober, the Master of Gallegos, beginning with himself. By evening he would have dark circles under his eyes where the lower lids had set up a minute twitching. Going home up the hill he would suddenly feel small, and cold. Neleta would be waiting too, damn her!

While a caravan was at Gallegos, on those nights, even Neleta was no solace. After a day of burning he was left cold with her at night. The last time Amah had been here it was worse than ever. He had dreamed his old madonna was smothering in that chest where she was locked up. Somehow he was in there too and struggling desperately with her to get out. Neleta had wakened him, still struggling. It infuriated him to be going back to such dreams.

The Good Shepherd of Gallegos

To Brother François, watching from the crack behind Ferdinando's door, the expression on Anthony's face and the scenes on the block were complementary to each other. He understood the cause of that expression. He had seen the will and the emotions at war before, turning men either into jovial pigs or iron masks. It was, he felt, one of the commonest symptoms of the moral disease of the world he knew.

The slice of life he saw there seemed to him, although presented in primitive and uncomplicated terms, to be quite an ordinary one. It was merely another case where sympathy between men had become inoperative because greed for the possession of things and profit at the expense of others had reduced it to the state of being less valuable than things. In that case, what more natural than that some men, those who could not help themselves, should actually be traded for things? "Sambo for three kegs of rum and an ell of cloth."

But how does this differ from the universal commerce of the world for personal profit? Is it not all a trading of my brother for an ell of cloth or some more intoxicating substance? How many merchants and bankers and statesmen were doing the same thing! Because their system was more complex, was it essentially different? No. What he saw here, if it differed at all, differed in degree and not in kind.

The cure for all this, Brother François believed, was only to be brought about by awakening sympathy in the hearts of men, man by man. And there was only one way of doing that, he thought—by presenting them with the opposite example of the way of his Master and letting them see it work. Only the example itself, the way of his Master embodied in a man's life might avail.

In Gallegos his plan consisted in buying up, for whatever he could get together or beg, the slaves rejected on the block; nursing the sick ones till they died; or keeping the crippled and maimed in his garden where their light labours sufficed in that climate to support the little community. A few of these unfortunates he had even been able to rehabilitate completely, but not many. Most of them soon came to rest in the ever-growing graveyard. In particular, however, Brother François concerned himself with children.

Many an exhausted black child, unable to follow the caravan any longer, who had seen the long file in which its mother was yoked disappear into the shades of the forest, now owed its existence to him. Lying in the forest waiting for darkness and the inevitable end, dumb with exhaustion and fear, it had heard the leaves rustle, screamed—and found itself in the arms of the good shepherd of Gallegos.

"For I also," said Brother François, "hunt like a lion, and do seek my meat from God."

What extra goods and help he needed to carry out his plans in the valley, Brother François had always asked from Anthony. It was given to him without question, usually by a written order on Ferdinando.

Small as was the charity the priest required, the method of charging it on the books puzzled Ferdinando. The half-breed, although he had acquired most of the outward manners of civilization as a youth in Spain, had in reality only one vital touch with it. It was the very primitive and unemotional one of commercial bookkeeping. Except for his clothes, his European manners, and his always perfectly kept books, Ferdinando was a savage. He did not know to what account to charge the small sundries issued from time to time to Brother François.

But he had a scheme. Some day he would balance the books and show a profit. As yet he had not said anything about it to Anthony. It could wait.

Fire and Ice

For the rest of his life that long rainy season at Gallegos remained in Anthony's mind as a vague but horrible nightmare. Fever was in his bones, he felt his joints grind. The chills, the fever, and the rains came on. Malaria began to burn and freeze him.

He got steadily worse. It was always dark outside. But within him it was darker still. In a few weeks the world appeared as if he were sitting far back in a cave. At a great distance, and in a curiously blurred way, things went on happening at the entrance to the cavern. He himself was chained in there.

Neleta kept annoying him by trying to keep him in bed. He would fight with her, drive her off. Yet he knew he should not. She meant well. He hated her now because she loved him. She would not go away. Ferdinando he would not have in the room.

In Madrid he runs into Dolorez whom he knew in Cuba
and whom he unconsciously links with his Madonna image.

Illustration for Hervey Allen's
"ANTHONY ADVERSE"

The factor, however, took this philosophically enough. He was glad to find himself to all intents and purposes the master of Gallegos. He soon introduced certain minor practices about the place which Pharaoh would never have countenanced.

Brother François, for one, fared ill. Neither Ferdinando nor Neleta welcomed him at dinner. Indeed, he would have ceased coming to the house on the hill altogether if it had not been that he longed to do all he could for Anthony. He was not able to break the clutch of the fever. As he sat by Anthony's bed he was always conscious of Neleta's eyes resting on him. They were baleful. She managed on one pretext or another to exclude him as much as she could.

Brother François must frequently have sat by the bed of the sick man for hours, or with this memory alone was there afterward any voice. The import of it vanished but the comfort and refreshment remained. It was always Anthony's impression that it was this spiritual medicine which had permitted him to survive.

It was while he lay in what was all but a fatal lethargy after the third bleeding that Brother François came for the last time. Just that day it was too much trouble to move his eyes to one side or the other. Brother François seemed greatly excited, animated, protesting. He seemed to be trying to get the man on the bed to do something. Why did they trouble *him* this way? They might let him die in peace at least. He heard a sound of voices arguing.

Ferdinando and Neleta were in the picture now. Brother François was holding on to the bed pleading. Suddenly he saw him rise and turn away. He lay very still, on the balance, just breathing. Something terrible had happened, something for which he could not be forgiven. Brother François had gone. Well, he would go, too. He gave up.

Leg-Irons for Young Shins

THE poignant atmosphere of tragedy which had conveyed its emotional contagion to the sick man so near the brink as to be numb and insensate—lost, indeed, to all understanding of its cause and only dimly aware of its emotional effect—had been the doing of Ferdinando.

When the last ship had arrived at Gallegos she found the slave pens empty. Sóller, who was in charge of the schooner, was impatient to return. It was the middle of the rainy season and no new supplies of captives could be expected for some time. Yet both Sóller and Ferdinando were peculiarly anxious to make an excellent showing in the books for Anthony when he should recover.

Why not seize the children under Brother François's charge and so make up a full cargo? It would also immediately provide a way to balance that irritating open account on Ferdinando's books and show a nice profit on the goods supplied to Brother François for some years past, goods the half-breed considered to have been wasted.

Sóller was enthusiastic. He even saw an element of humour in carrying off the priest's flock. Healthy children brought from $25 to $50 apiece since the trade had been curtailed by the English war. Bueno!

Whereupon Ferdinando put the Gallegos blacksmith to work shrinking leg-irons to fit snugly about young shins.

The peaceful sound of the bell came to them through the trees as they neared Brother François' little establishment. They found the entire population of the beehive village gathered before the small chapel engaged in the simple service which always marked the end of their day.

"Never mind the irons, drive them down," cried Sóller. "Use the canes!" He broke off a section of bamboo and began to round up the flock. Some of them broke away and ran to the priest. He cried out without words and struggled. Presently he grew calm and stood weeping. Ferdinando cursed him.

UNFORTUNATELY most of the children had taken refuge in the little chapel. These were now driven forth in charge of several big Arabs with long sticks. The entire flock was then herded pell-mell downhill.

"You do not know what you are doing, do you, Sóller?" Brother François said, almost gently. A puzzled, clownish look spread half belligerently over Sóller's coarse features.

"Well, I guess I know my business," he blurted out. "I guess I do."

"May Christ forgive you," said Brother François and let his clenched hands fa by his side.

"Now that's what I call being a Chri tian," laughed Sóller, and set off dow the hill whistling. Feeling quite sure th he had frightened the priest into forgi ing him, he swaggered somewhat in h walk. Ferdinando had rushed off bathe his face.

Towards midnight Brother Franço rose and went into his chapel to be alon He lit the candles and celebrated mas It was the following morning that had gone to make his final plea to A thony. But Anthony had been too ill respond.

That night Brother François disa peared into the jungle.

The Resurrection of the Madonna

ANTHONY grew a little stronger day by day. Nevertheless, it was a long, tedious process. The man he saw looking back at him from the glass was more like the youth of four years ago than the bronzed Master of Gallegos who had greeted him there only a few months back. The hard lines in his face had relaxed. Yes, he was more like— "like Anthony,"—he thought. It reminded him of old times.

In this moody vein it comforted his reminiscent fancy to insist on having his madonna brought out.

Now she stood before him again. He had forgotten how beautiful she was. The blue of the heavenly little canopy, the gorgeous robe of the Virgin, and the mother-of-pearl at her feet glowed in the bare room. He almost felt like talking to her again as to an old friend; or that Brother François might come into the room at any moment. But where— Suddenly it struck him that he had not seen Brother François lately. Why didn't he come to visit him? How strange!

He had gone on a journey, said Neleta. Doubtless he would be back shortly. She put Anthony off as best she could. Brother François, he remembered, had often been away for as much as a week or two at a time.

In the midst of these recollections I suddenly remembered a promise he ha made to Amah to visit him in the mou tains in the spring. If he did not go would be a deadly affront—he w largely dependent on him for his trad Indeed, Gallegos might not be tenab without his friendship.

Despite that, Anthony hesitated. I was still weak and comparatively hel less. The journey might finish him.

But finally he sent for Ferdinando ar gave him off-hand but minute instru tions as to the conduct of affairs Gallegos during his absence. Ferdinand listened carefully, and decided to s nothing then about Brother Françoi leaving. He regarded Anthony's d parture as a solution to the difficulty.

That spring there was a good deal thumping and "wizard-talk" from villa to village, especially on dark nigh Ferdinando noticed it as he lay awa through the long night hours. The dru at Bangalang was interminable! Mnombibi, the witch doctor, howev came the news, tapped out and relay over miles of jungles that the wh witch doctor had settled down in a ne refuge in the hills. Runaway slaves we welcomed and protected there. Mnomb began to lay his plans.

Appeals from the Furnace

IN THE mountains a heavy stone seemed to have lifted off his chest. All the sensations of his body responded and became a joy to him again. "I have escaped all that fever in the furnace below," he thought,—"come up under the clean, clear stars again. I shall live and go on now. My other, my real self is not going to die."

For the first time in months he was able to merge into sleep happily. Like a healing spring he felt the waters of rest begin to permeate him. Presently he seemed to have made an unalterable decision—or it had been made for him. He was utterly content with it.

Six months of the barbaric but bountiful life in the hill-country more than put Anthony on his feet again. Indeed, it had put him on four feet for Amah had given him a splendid Arab horse. He had never known the dependence and devotion of animals before; how deeply it tried and tested a man. All that was wanting was a wife and children. Amah on more than one occasion had said so laughingly.

All this, however, was suddenly put an end to by the unexpected appearance of Juan with disconcerting news from Gallegos. Ferdinando had now seen fit to illuminate his employer about the departure of Brother François. Furthermore, the cargo of children had been sold at a considerable profit.

"And it is on the whole, senor, much better that we are rid of the padre once and for all here at Gallegos. He has attempted to set up again at some place about the headwaters of the Rio Pongo which has caused a great stir among the coast tribes whose slaves have been slipping off to his crazy settlement. . . .

So far has this matter gone since you left that a great gathering of the coast tribes has taken place and after a great deal of drumming and witch-finding set off yesterday inland. We wish him no harm, of course, but I did not think it necessary to interfere. Mnombibi, the witch doctor, is his enemy, and I did not desire to antagonize the natives so near at hand upon whom we must depend. What we now fear is that on the way back they will be crazed with the war fever and attack the settlement from the land side. We are short handed. . . ."

Anthony flung the letter on the ground with a curse and looked up to see Juan's eyes resting upon him.

"Si," said Juan looking at him reproachfully. "It is much worse than you think. That man Ferdinando is a half-breed wolf. He and his sister—caramba! If you are a man, senor, you will come back now. Brother François gave me this on the way up. I found him! He is well but . . ."

"You saw him!" cried Anthony. "Give it to me!"

He tore open the small scroll of native matting.

"*A moi, mon ame*, for the love of Christ—and the peace of your own soul. I appeal to the last. . . ."

The rest was a hopeless blur. But the import was like an explosion in Anthony's brain. "Mnombibi — Brother François."

"Can you still ride, Juan—after your long journey?"

"If it is with you—homeward."

Father François' Golgotha

ANTHONY pressed his men and horses to the limit. Following Juan's lead, they entered an open, bowl-shaped valley. At the upper end, the embers of what had been a cluster of huts only a few hours before still shimmered with heat and smoked hazily into the afternoon sunlight.

They were too late.

Anthony sat his horse drearily. He cursed himself and his luck darkly. Here and there in the grass he saw the glimmer of dark bodies. Several vultures flapped away. There was the busy noise of flies. Mnombibi's people must have raided the place some time that morning.

But Brother François, where was he?

Someone gave a dismal shout and pointed. Against a black outcrop of cliff several hundred yards away Anthony saw a white body apparently suspended in the air. It did not move. His spine crept.

He slid down the neck of his horse, and stumbled forward in a tumult of agonized horror. He looked for the rope. The arms were held out stiffly. At first he did not see the dark beams of the cross against the black rock in the cliff's shadow. Now they suddenly seared themselves in his mind forever—and the man hanging there.

"Father," he cried, and looked up.

There were none of the comforting conventions of the carved crucifix there. The naked body, welted from the shoulders down, was bound to the beams with thongs of rawhide. These had drawn tight in the morning sun, which passed slowly, blistering the tonsured head. The dark, clotted locks hung down before the face like a scorched curtain. Through the hands and feet were thrust long mimosa thorns that dropped slowly into black clots on the stones below.

THE man on the cross shivered and opened his eyes. He heard a voice below him. He saw dimly. After a while he remembered.

"Anthony," he whispered, "my son . . ."

The sound fell into the ears of the man below like dry burning leaves. "Alive yet!" cried Anthony. He stood up. He could do something. He looked.

Not too late . . . ? Yes—yes, too late —and forever too late . . . Oh!

"You are dying."

The leaves of sound began to fall again. The cross shook. The man on it was trying to speak to him. He looked up again at that agony. It was for him. *His*. The wind blew the hair back from the face. It was only the body fighting there he saw—fighting. Suddenly Brother François' face, the beloved face Anthony had known, peered through it. The lips moved to the music of the mind.

"It is you who are dying. Not I."

Anthony stood fixed, turned to stone. He saw that face lift to the sky.

"Remember me . . . Jesu . . . I still live . . .

"I LIVE," he cried with a triumphant voice.

"GO!"

The body of him leaped upward against the thongs and thorns. The cross rocked against the sky.

Now the entire universe seemed to be filled and to be thundering "GO" accompanied by speeding bolts of light that struck the hills themselves into day.

So ANTHONY goes back to Livorno to find his benefactor, Mr. Bonnyfeather, dead and himself the heir to his fortune. Meanwhile, Don Luis, his mother's husband, happens to pass the convent where years before he left his wife's child. Out of curiosity he drops in to see what has happened to him. He finds to his horror that he was apprenticed to his father-in-law and rushes to Livorno, just at the time Anthony arrives there. Don Luis is introduced as Mr. Bonnyfeather's son-in-law and Anthony recognizes, from the little he knows of his past and the man's attitude, a sworn enemy.

During his visit in Livorno, Anthony runs into his old friend Vincent Nolte, who has cornered most of the Mediterranean trade and since Europe is deeply involved in the Napoleonic Wars, he is doing a rushing financial business with all the warring governments. He explains that these governments are paying for the war with paper money without gold and silver to back it up. But he knows that there are enormous quantities of both in Mexico which are very difficult to get through the blockades. Vincent suggests that Anthony might like to go as his agent to New Orleans where he could receive the Mexican bullion and ship it to Europe as neutral goods.

Anthony accepts the offer and agrees to go with Vincent to Paris and London to arrange the transaction. On their way over the Alps, Anthony discovers that Don Luis has preceded them. The Spanish Grandee has carefully arranged with his coachman to force Anthony's carriage into an Alpine gorge. It is only through the luck of a forced stop that Anthony discovers the trap and foils the wily Don Luis completely.

After several months of negotiation in European capitals, including Madrid, where he runs into Dolores whom he knew in Cuba and whom he unconsciously links with his madonna image, Anthony sets sail for New Orleans.

Anthony Gropes For Reality

THE long voyage, conveying the impression that Europe was infinitely remote and all its experiences left behind him forever, the novel scenes and interest into which he was suddenly plunged, but above all, a determination to make the life of the new country into which he had come *his* life—and to look to the future rather than the past for guidance, all these things had their full effect upon Anthony. Within a few weeks after his arrival he found himself pushing forward the plans to transfer the bullion not as the end for which he had come, but merely as the means of weaving himself more deeply into the interests of the place.

To Anthony the game of finance was never in itself overpoweringly fascinating. By training and experience he understood its methods of procedure and it was only natural that he should enter into it rather than take up politics, or merely amuse himself going about spending. Like a great many other young men, then and since, he felt forced to go on doing something "real" even if his ideals remained locked up. He was not the only one whose madonna was in a bundle in the cupboard.

Yet with Anthony there remained in a peculiarly vivid manner the memory of another rôle, of another way of acting which implied a choice of his own

instead of a mere assignment by fate. It would turn the world from a place in which to write letters and speak lines and turn financial and other games into reality, and yet into a mystical city where one could be a whole man and act like one.

ANTHONY still hoped to work through one rôle into the other. In a curious way he entered upon this attempt by taking part in one of the greatest international financial intrigues of the time. It was a great plot. Through it he hoped to take his place in the world, and then . . .

In three years, a half million dollars from nowhere was pumped into New Orleans and became *real enough* to draw interest for the bank. A great many "gentlemen" of all kinds were "much obleeged" for loans.

Anthony himself now began to launch out. He looked around for land for a suitable plantation and house. In a short while he would settle down. On the first rising ground to the west of the city Anthony built and laid out the lovely plantation of "Silver Ho" upon which he lavished the fondest dreams of his soul and a wealth of hope. The outlay was in proportion. For the first time he opened the strings of his own purse indulgently and to his heart's content.

The Hyphenated Entirety of Existence

DURING the time the house was being built Anthony began to receive disconcerting letters from his agent, David Parish, in Philadelphia. Parish had married Florence Udney, an English girl whom Anthony had greatly admired when he was a boy in Livorno. The man seemed to be losing his grip. Never before had David become so personal—and so complaining.

"I shall soon be forced to make the arduous journey over the Alleghanies in order to obtain from one Blennerhassett, of Pittsburgh, an adequate mortgage security on his properties for

sums lent him on my account in Philadelphia. Since my health is precarious, Mrs. Parish has heroically decided to accompany me.

I mention this both to give you some idea of my many difficulties and to set your mind at rest in regard to a certain fact. You seem to have inferred from my last letter than we were expecting a domestic accretion. Alas, your felicitations are without justification. I should be more willing to gratify the natural longing of a woman to hold a child in her arms did I not feel that the duties of my wife require her to grace the board of her husband's establishment rather than to languish over the cradle of his heir."

It was some months later that Florence Parish arrived in New Orleans with news that her husband had died, financially ruined, and asking for help from her old friend, Anthony Adverse. Anthony saw in her a means of making his new plantation house a home. On their wedding night Anthony took his madonna from her wrappings and set her into the niche by the hearth.

THE days slipped into one another deep with peace and contentment, bright with hope for the future, pleasantly busy with the affairs of the great plantation. But above all, complete with that double-entity, that hyphenated entirety of existence between man and wife that makes home—and that makes all other places and conditions merely more or less tolerable by comparison.

The time of the coming of the child passed, a time infinitely close and dowered with peace, in which Florence drew nearer to the center and core of the mystery of life. Love and tenderness were having their fulfilment. It was Anthony's whim, he said, to call the child "Maria." And that name seemed good to both of them.

By the hearth in the great living-room the ancient statue of the madonna stretched forth her hands with the babe in them into the pleasant firelight and into the darkness. The figure of the man who sometimes came to kneel before her with a heart full of gratitude and unexpected contentment she may have known. For they had wandered together from the first and in many regions. He, on his part, was quite sure that he had looked upon the final and most benign expression of her face. Meanwhile, unchanging, she continued to stand there.

Fire From Heaven

AT SILVER Ho Florence finished a hand of whist and turned in. The wind bellowed in the chimney. A smouldering log leaped up and crackled. It spat a fat, live coal out onto the carpet. Presently the robe of the madonna, who stood holding the child out in the darkness, began to twinkle with little flames.

The wind in the chimney at Silver Ho and the orators at the Chamber of Commerce in New Orleans roared away till after midnight. The chimney at the plantation now had more than it could do. The windows on the lower floor began to help it out. Between speeches Anthony caught a little nap. . . . He was awakened by a rough hand on his shoulder.

"Fire!"

It was northward toward Silver Ho, and it hung with an appalling glow over the river.

"Oh, God!" he cried, and began to kill the horse with his spurs.

The light in the sky suddenly died down to a low, pink glow. There were no sparks over the top of the ridge any longer. Three miles more . . .

He galloped out of the last clump of oaks and came thudding over the lawn.

The house—

Nothing, nothing was left but a great bed of coals that shimmered like a lake of hell when the wind blew on them and made the spot in the sky above momentarily brighter. The terrible heat from the place where the great mansion had stood beat up in his face.

He had no doubt what had happened. He knew. Otherwise they would have come to meet him before this.

Fire had fallen from heaven upon Anthony and crisped his wife, his child. The same element also threatened to suffuse his brain with intolerably glowing images and memories. His heart went on. His body functioned. The event had not stopped them. He was left, left alone in the field of his own suffering, and he took shelter under the only available tree there, his own will.

Grief is a curious thing. It must reassure itself at last of the reality of the things for which it grieves. Had there ever been a place called Silver Ho; a man who had once been happy there? Perhaps? Almost he had convinced himself "No." No he must go and see. He *must* see it once again. In some way he must find surcease there, or—

Someone had left some garden roses and early spring wild-flowers at the foot of the chimney. "Probably some of the hands," he thought. "They loved her."

He walked over to the chimney and climbed up on the hearth where the blossoms lay on a rude, fire-scarred altar before the statue of his little madonna.

The Essence of Things Past and Present

HE LOOKED at her in doubtful amazement, where she still stood in the niche where he had last seen her—that night. And now—there was nothing left but the figure of the woman and the child. She stood there exactly as she had come from the hands of her maker millenniums ago. Only the fire had glazed her. It had annealed every crack and imperfection. But the golden Byzantine diadem, the gorgeous medieval robe, the heavens of art above her and the pearly steps beneath had sublimed in the furnace through which she had passed.

She stood there, rooted in the stone, still holding her son forth to the man who now lay before her on the cold hearth . . .

His vision as he looked at the madonna in the niche was peculiarly acute. The fire had cracked the chimney in places. An evil mouth of darkness yawned just beneath her. He caught the glimpse of something moving in this maw. Out of it, very slowly, as it were sick of life itself, came a filthy-looking snake. The thing was obviously in great trouble. It was a sickly-white like an old cocoon.

Presently the snake began to gasp and dart out its tongue as if to taste the sunlight for the last time. Its eyes looked seared. Then the skin of its throat parted and a new head came out of the old one. Its effort had been a violent one. Like the man on the hearth only a few feet away, it now lay very still.

THE man lay there for hours. The snake emerged. It stripped itself from head to tail. It lay in the sun while its new colours became more brilliant and it revived. It coiled and uncoiled and uncoiled itself, a glorious creature at last, the colour of flame. It flowed off

into the sunlight across the ashes and left its empty husk lying behind it on the stone.

Anthony rose, stiff in every joint, for he had been fascinated for hours. He took the statue out of the niche from the stone it had been standing on and went back to town.

The next morning after a few brief preparations he embraced his friends for the last time, stepped into a canoe with four voyageurs whom he had befriended in the old days and started up-river headed for the unknown.

As they passed Silver Ho he lay down and held the madonna close to him. There was nothing else in the craft to remind him of anything in the past.

"It is finished," he said. "I go."

THEY followed the river for five months. Anthony learned to give himself up to being nothing but muscles to paddle with and eyes to search the river ahead; to use every faculty to slay and keep from being slain by animals; to sharpen his five wits so keenly that the world without became the world within—and he had discovered how to master the world without and how to cope with it.

He had learned how to hunt and fish, how to make clothes for himself out of skins, the ways of a hundred animals and the uses of trees and plants. In short, how to get along in the wilderness without anything but a rifle, an axe, and a knife.

The madonna hung in a small deerskin bag tied close to the rafters. He had made it to contain her fire-scarred body. With a drawstring he tied the mouth of the bag fast.

He had come into the wilderness to let the scars of burning heal. He had also hoped to draw near to the All-

Father in nature by becoming one of his children. And he had become a child again, able to release himself into the world about him and to play there contentedly between sleep and sleep. But of the Causer of Dreams and of the nature of Nature he had learned nothing at all. Nature nobly sustained his body, and that was all.

Finally Anthony is captured by Indians who in turn are captured by Spaniards for slaves. Anthony is taken with them over the tortuous trail to Santa Fé where Don Luis is now the Spanish military governor. When they arrive Don Luis comes to pass judgment upon them. The sight of Anthony gives the old man a stroke which a few hours later brings death. But within those hours he sentences Anthony perpetually to the prison of St. Lazarus in Mexico City.

Hate's Eternal Opposite

A thorough examination standing on the block—"Now I know how the slaves felt at Gallegos," he thought.

Anthony found himself welcomed by the other prisoners, who had too many miseries of their own to be curious about his. Neither his fellow prisoners nor the guards knew exactly what to make of him. They looked somewhat askance upon the powerful man with the yellow beard tucked into his belt—with such a serene look upon his face. What made him so happy?

As for Anthony, he was glad to be back once more among the children of men.

"And there is only one way to live among them," he thought. "Brother François was right: 'Let us be kind to one another.' Now I am free of everything at last: of all my possessions; of sorrows and hates; of useless curiosity about the nature of God and the Universe. All that I have left is my life and the love of the Divine Child. I sought the Almighty One among the lonely hills for my own comfort, and this is the answer. 'Only among men can a man find Him!' The rest is mystery."

Don Luis had not triumphed. He had meant to leave the son of Maria a legacy of immortal hatred and despair, but once again he had failed. He had merely provided an opportunity for Anthony to understand and to participate in hate's eternal opposite. For it was in the prison of St. Lazarus that he was finally born again into freedom and new hope. He lost the fear of death. Here, where the bodies of men perished and withered horribly, he saw the spirit of love in them working. And he participated in that work. He became a part of it.

THE festival of San Lazaro takes place on the eleventh of March. For some days before that event the inmates of the prison spent their time and ingenuity in preparing for the only visitation of charity which they were genuinely enthusiastic about.

The lepers had decorated their room with festoons and flags; with bright, pathetic devices cut from all kinds of coloured papers. These were strung about the walls and streamed from the lamps and brackets. Even the bars of the windows were gaily trimmed.

The lepers' room was now aswirl with excitement and colours. The crowd ran the gamut of classes from a city where the diversity of population is as complex as any that exists. There were priests with shovel hats, and soldiers, gamblers and ragamuffins; ladies attired in mantillas, jewels and satins, and girls with hardly any dress at all. A party of highborn and fashionable women arrived with a meal which they served themselves.

The second hour of the afternoon marked the height of this orgy of charity. The table before Anthony was now heaped high. He made a last appeal and was about to go. "Forget not to the end the souls of thy poor."

A lady disengaged herself from the richly dressed group which surrounded her and approached his table. He saw her hand dropping a gold piece in the jar. It fell onto the floor.

"Is it possible?" she exclaimed.

"Not lost," he cried, "I'll find it for you!"

He got up and found himself face to face with Dolores.

He reached out impulsively and took her hands. She let them lie in his while in each other's faces they sought to read something of the story of the past. Then a look of horror came and she snatched them away.

"Señora, I am clean," he said.

They stood for awhile in eternity. The room vanished. Then she took his hands again.

"No matter," she exclaimed. "I shall never let go of them now."

The Madonna's Final Expression

DOLORES made her arrangements. She began to take a great interest in prisons in general. A number of other women were also interested. For a while it became the fashion to visit the oppressed. As a result of this, nearly fifty persons incarcerated by tyrannical measures during the Spanish regime found themselves blinking in the light of day again. Among them was a man with a long golden beard from the prison of St. Lazarus.

The unfortunate prisoner, whose patriarchal appearance had rather tended to fix attention upon him, then disappeared.

Anthony aroused a barber late that night to shave him and dress his hair. The next day there was no more reason to associate the quiet, well-dressed and dignified gentleman, who spoke a careful Castilian, but was thought to be an Englishman, with the late inmate of St. Lazaro than there was to connect this utter stranger with the name of Dona Dolores. Yet they met frequently.

A few weeks later Anthony and Dolores were married. And if Anthony remembered another "wedding breakfast," he did not show it. There was a calmness and an assured serenity about him which was reflected in the face of the noble woman who had become his wife.

They expected little; they hoped for much. They rode northward into the desert together, accompanied by a few of Dolores' people. Their objective was a certain detached mountain with a village on it. Dolores had once visited it years before and remembered it as an abode of peace.

ANTHONY and Dolores became a part of this village and its life. Gallegos and Silver Ho had taught him his lessons. He did not try to change the place, to improve it, and to tear from the earth a surplus and superabundance, which exhausts the soil upon which man stands. From too great abundance, he had discovered, came the chief curses to the bodies and spirits of men.

Their house built after the manner of those in the village was of stone and adobe. It contained all they needed and only a little more. Here Inez and Flora, their two daughters, were born and flourished through childhood.

Only once were they disturbed and then by a pilgrimage of Penitentes whipping themselves, walking upon glass and hot stones.

"Some of them," said Fray Pedro, "may crucify each other. I have heard of it. Just before a Penitente dies, those about him break his arms and legs. It ensures paradise, they think, for they say that those who are treated thus have suffered more than Christ who was not so broken when he descended from the cross. Is that not a cunning temptation for simple minds?" He sat for some time looking sad and perplexed. "I wish," he said at last, "I had a beautiful image of the Mother of God to hold up mercy before them in the chapel."

Anthony rose and taking the little madonna from the deerskin bag, gave it to Fray Pedro.

"Take it," said he, "I have kept her with me long. I can never lose her now."

And so with due festival the little madonna went home to the village church.

H. G. WELLS

A MODERN UTOPIA

SOCIAL philosophy, especially in so far as it bears on the evolution of mankind and its civilization, has always been regarded by Mr. Wells as the most important part of his literary work. In the semi-imaginary account of his coming Utopia, which Mr. Wells himself epitomizes here, he dwells on a favourite theme. In human development, he declares, success must eventually depend on "superiority of equipment in the hands of a certain type of man, a type that it becomes more and more impossible to improvise, that a country must live for through many years, and that no country on earth at present can be said to be doing its best possible to make."

I—The Planet Utopia

No LESS than a planet will serve the purpose of a modern Utopia. Out beyond Sirius, far in the deeps of space, blazes the star that is *our* Utopia's sun. It is a planet like our planet, the same continents, the same islands, the same oceans and seas.

Suppose that two of us were actually to find ourselves there! You figure us upon some high pass in the Alps. We have fallen into a talk of Utopias, and behold, in the twinkling of an eye, we are in that other world!

We should scarcely note the change. Not a cloud would have gone from the sky. And yet we might come slowly to feel a difference in things—an unfamiliarity, perhaps, in the grouping of the little towns below. And presently, amazed and amazing, we should happen on a man—no Swiss—dressed in unfamiliar clothing and speaking an unfamiliar speech.

We should start down the mountain and gather together a thousand factors for our impression of this more civilized world. A modern Utopia will have done with yapping about nationality, and so the ugly fortifications and military defilements of the earthly vale will be wanting. Instead, there will be a great multitude of gracious little houses clustering in college-like groups, no doubt, about their common kitchen and halls, down and about the valley slopes.

It is unlikely there will be any smoke-disgorging steam railway trains in Utopia, but a thin spider's web of inconspicuous special routes will cover the land of the world, pierce the mountain masses and tunnel under the seas. By means of them the Utopian, even the commonest, will travel about the earth from one chief point to another at a speed of two or three hundred miles or more an hour.

We should walk on the great road for a time, and note that the tramways, the train-road, the culverts and bridges, will all be beautiful things. There is nothing in machinery, there is nothing in embankments and railways and iron bridges and engineering devices to oblige them to be ugly.

IN UTOPIA a man who designs a tram-road will be a cultivated man, an artist craftsman; he will strive, as a good writer or a painter strives, to achieve the simplicity of perfection. He will make his girders and rails and parts as gracious as that first engineer, Nature, has made the stems of her plants and the joints and gestures of her animals. This tram-road beside us will be a triumph of design.

Indeed, the whole thing will be designed.

II—A Room in Utopia

WE NEED suppose no linguistic impediments to intercourse. The whole world will surely have a common language. Indeed, should we be in Utopia at all if we could not talk to everyone? We are helped by the good fortune of picking up a Utopian coin of gold, and at last we adventure into the Utopian inn.

The effectual abolition of a labouring and servile class will make itself felt in every detail of that inn. My bedroom is very clear and clean and simple, designed to economise the labour of cleaning just as much as possible. The room has no corners to gather dirt, and the apartment could be swept out effectually by a few strokes of a mechanical sweeper.

There is no fireplace, but there is a thermometer beside six switches on the wall. One switch warms the floor, which is covered by a substance like soft oilcloth, one warms the mattress, the others warm the wall in varying degrees. The casement does not open, but noiseless fans pump air in and out of the room.

There is a recessed dressing-room, equipped with a bath, and the water is warmed by passing it through an electrically heated spiral of tubing. A cake of soap drops out of a store machine on the turn of a handle, and when you have done with it, you drop that and your soiled towels and so forth, which also are given you by machines, into a box through which they drop and sail down a smooth shaft.

III—London in Utopia

LONDON will be the first Utopian city centre we shall see. We take the train at Lucerne.

When one travels over two hundred miles an hour, there is nothing but fatigue in looking out of windows, and this corridor-train, twice the width of its poor terrestrial brother, will have no need of that distraction. The simple device of abandoning any but a few windows, and those set high, gives the wall space of the long corridors to books; the middle part of the train is, indeed, a comfortable library with abundant armchairs and couches, each with its green-shaded light, and soft carpets upon the sound-proof floor. Behind we shall come to bedrooms, bath-rooms, the hairdresser and so forth.

No sea crossing breaks our journey— there is nothing to prevent a channel tunnel in that other planet; and I wake in London.

How will a great city of Utopia strike us?

Here will be one of the great races in the commonality of the World State, and here will be its social and intellectual exchange. There will be a mighty University here, with thousands of professors and tens of thousands of advanced students; and here great journals of thought and speculation, mature and splendid books of philosophy and science, and a glorious fabric of literature will be woven and shaped and, with a teeming leisureliness, put forth. Here will be stupendous libraries and a mighty organization of museums.

About these centres will cluster a great swarm of people, and close at hand will be another centre, where the ruling council of the world assembles. Then the arts will cluster round this city as gold gathers about wisdom, and here Englishmen will weave into wonderful prose and beautiful rhythms and subtly atmospheric forms, the intricate, austere and courageous imagination of our race.

EVERYONE is well grown and well nourished, everyone seems in good condition, everyone walks well and has that clearness of eye that comes with cleanness of blood. People here know better what to do and what to avoid, and how to evade and suppress the subtle poisons that blunt the edge of sensibility. They have put off the years of decay. They have extended the level years into the seventies, and age, when it comes, comes swiftly and easily. And amidst the men whose faces have been made fine by thought and steadfast living, among the serene-eyed women, comes youth, buoyantly healthy, with challenging eyes, with fresh and eager face.

There comes a dusky little Jewess, red-lipped and amber-clad, with a deep crimson flower in the dull black of her hair, and then I am looking at a brightly-smiling, blue-eyed girl, tall, ruddy and freckled warmly, clad like a stage Rosalind, and talking gaily to a fair young man. Then a grave man in a long, fur-trimmed robe, a merchant maybe, debates some serious matter with a white-tunicked clerk. And the clerk's face? I turn to mark the straight, blue-black hair. The man must be Chinese.

A very human crowd it has seemed to me. But I am seeing more and more clearly that there must be a will beneath this visible Utopia. Convenient houses, admirable engineering that is no offence amidst natural beauties, beautiful bodies and a universally gracious carriage, these are only the outward and visible signs of an inward and spiritual grace.

Such an order means discipline. Behind all this material order there must be men and women willing these things. In that crowd are there any who might be thought of as having a wider interest than the others, who seem in any way detached from the rest by a purpose that passed beyond the seen?

Then suddenly I come upon a well-built man of perhaps five and thirty, with the easy movement that comes with perfect physical condition and the firm mouth of a disciplined man. His legs are clad in some woven stuff deep red in colour, and over this he wears a white shirt fitting pretty closely, and with a woven purple hem. On his head is a cap of thin leather and still thinner steel.

I should note that there were other lithe and serious-looking people wearing the same uniform.

IV—The Samurai

IT MIGHT happen to me to talk with one of the wearers of that uniform, and I first question him on its significance. He tells me that it is the uniform of the order of the *samurai,* to which he belongs.

"The order is not hereditary," he explained. "The samurai are, in fact, volunteers. Any intelligent adult in a healthy and efficient state may at any age after five and twenty become one of the samurai, and take a hand in the universal control."

"Provided he follows the Rule?"

"Precisely. Practically the whole of the responsible work of the world is in their hands, all our head teachers, our judges, barristers, employers of labour beyond a certain limit, doctors, legislators, must be samurai, and all our executive committees are drawn from them."

I listen with wrapt attention to all he says. Yes, this is Utopia!

"Tell me about the Rule," I said.

"THE Rule aims to exclude the dull and base altogether, to discipline the impulses and emotions, to develop a moral habit and sustain a man in periods of stress, fatigue and temptation, to produce the maximum co-operation of all men of good intent, and to keep all the samurai in a state of bodily health and efficiency.

"Our founders made a collection of several volumes, which they called collectively the Book of the Samurai. It was to play the part for the samurai that the Bible did for the ancient Hebrews. From its beginning it has been constantly under revision, and now there is hardly anything in it that is not beautiful and perfect in form. The whole range of noble emotions finds expression there, and all the guiding ideas of our modern state.

"The samurai must study and have an exhaustive knowledge of that book. There are other intellectual qualifications which exact a little exertion. And the man who breaks the Rule after his adult adhesion is no more in the samurai."

"And what is forbidden?"

"We forbid a good deal. Many small pleasures do no great harm, but'we think it well to forbid them none the less, so that we can weed out the self-indulgent. We think that a constant resistance to little seductions is good for a man's quality.

"Originally, the samurai were forbidden usury, though now our commercial code practically prevents usury altogether. The idea of a man growing richer by mere inaction, and at the expense of an impoverishing debtor, is profoundly distasteful to Utopian ideas, and our state insists now upon the participation of the lender in the borrower's risks. It is felt that to buy simply in order to sell again brings out many unsocial human qualities; it makes a man seek to enhance profits and falsify values, and so the samurái are forbidden to buy or sell on their own account or for any employer save the state, unless some process of manufacture changes the nature of the commodity; and they are forbidden salesmanship and all its arts."

"But these rules," I said, "will work out as a vow of moderate poverty, and if your samurai are an order of poor men——"

"They need not be. Samurai who have invented, organized and developed new industries have become rich men. And wealth is no sort of power unless you make it one. You can, by subtle statesmanship, contrive what it shall buy and what it shall not. In your world, it would seem, you have made leisure, movement, any sort of freedom, life itself, purchaseable. The more fools you!"

I REFLECTED. "What else may not the samurai do?"

"Acting, singing, or reciting are forbidden them, though they may lecture or debate. Nor may the samurai do personal services, except in the matter of medicine or surgery. Nor may a man under the Rule be any man's servant, pledged to do whatever he is told. He may neither be a servant nor keep one; he must shave and dress and serve himself. And he is also forbidden to play games in public, or to watch them being played. Our founders made no peace with the organization of public sports. They did not spend their lives to secure for all men and women on the earth freedom, health and leisure in order that they might waste lives in such folly."

"Is there a vow of chastity?"

"There is a rule of chastity—but not of celibacy. We know that civilization is an artificial arrangement, and that all the physical and emotional instincts of man are too strong, and his natural instinct of restraint too weak, for him to live easily in the civilized state. Under the unnatural perfection of security, liberty and abundance our civilization has attained, the normal untrained human being is disposed to excess in almost every direction. He tends to eat too much, drink too much, becomes lazy and makes love too much.

"Our founders organized motives from all sorts of sources, but I think the chief source to give men self-control is pride. Pride may not be the noblest thing in the soul, but it is the best king there. They looked to it to keep a man clean and sound and sane. In all matters of natural desire they held no appetite must be -glutted, or artificially whetted, and equally that no appetite should be starved."

Then he would tell me of the things the samurai was obliged to do. There would be many precise directions regarding his health, and rules that would aim at that constant exercise of will that makes life good. But the full rule in these minor matters is voluminous detail, and it abounds in alternatives. Its aim is rather to keep before the samurai by a number of sample duties, as it were, the need of, and some of the chief methods toward, health of body and mind, rather than to provide a comprehensive rule, and to ensure the maintenance of a community of feeling and interests among the samurai through habit, intercourse and a living contemporary literature. Women samurai who are married must bear children, and I think that it is from samurai mothers that a very large proportion of the future population of Utopia will be derived.

V—The Religion of Utopia

BUT now he came to the heart of all his explanation, to the will and motives at the centre that made men and women ready to undergo discipline, to renounce the richness and elaboration of the sensuous life, to master emotions and control impulses, to keep in the key of effort while they had abundance about them to rouse and satisfy desires.

The leading principle of the Utopian religion is the repudiation of the doctrine of original sin; the Utopians hold that man, on the whole is good. Man has pride and conscience, they hold, that you may refine by training as you refine his eye and ear; he has remorse and sorrow in his being, coming on the heels of all inconsequent enjoyments. He is religious; religion is natural to him.

But, just as the language of Utopia will be a synthesis, even so will its God be. They will hold God to be complex and of an endless variety of aspects, to be expressed by no universal formula nor approved in any uniform manner. So far as the samurai have a purpose in common in maintaining the state, and the order and progress of the world, so far by their discipline and denial, by their public work and effort, they worship God together. But the fount of motives lies in the individual life, in silent and deliberate reflections, and at this the most striking of all the rules of the samurai aims.

For seven consecutive days in the year, at least, each man or woman under the Rule must go right out of the life of man into some wild and solitary place and have no sort of intercourse with mankind. They must go bookless and weaponless, without pen or paper or money. Provisions must be taken for the period of the journey, a rug or sleeping-sack (for they must sleep under the open sky), but no means of making a fire. They must study maps beforehand to guide them, showing any difficulties and dangers in the journeys, but they may not carry such helps. They must not go by beaten ways.

PARTLY, this discipline is to ensure good training and sturdiness of mind and body, but partly also it is to draw their minds for a space from the insistent details of life, from the intricate arguments and the fretting effort to work, from personal quarrels and personal affections, and the things of the heated room.

"There is time to think over a lot of things. One puts one's self and one's ambition in a new pair of scales. . . .

"You know, after these solitudes, I feel just the same queer disinclination to go back to the world of men that I feel when I have to leave it. This last journey I outstayed my time, camping in the pine woods for six days. Then my thoughts came round to my proper work again. I got keen to go on with it, and so I came back into the world. You come back physically clean, as though you had your arteries washed out. Your brain has been cleaned, too."

It came to me suddenly as very strange that, even as we sat and talked, across deserted seas, on burning sands, through the still aisles of forests, and in all the high and lonely places of the world, beyond the margin where the ways and houses go, solitary men and women sailed alone or marched alone, or clambered—quiet, resolute exiles; they stood alone amid wildernesses of ice on the precipitous banks of roaring torrents, in monstrous caverns, or steering a tossing boat in the little circle of the horizon amid the tumbled, incessant sea, all in their several ways communing with the emptiness, nearer God.

EDWARD BOK

THE AMERICANIZATION OF
EDWARD BOK

Tʜɪs book might also be called the "Edward Bokization of America," for from it one gathers that few persons have ever exerted a greater influence in changing the manners, morals and face of America than he has. Undoubtedly Edward Bok (1863-1930) was a tremendous power for good during his thirty years' editorship of *The Ladies Home Journal.* Certainly his achievements are all the more remarkable because he started out as a poor immigrant boy and grew up to realize his ideal of "making the world a better and more beautiful place to live in."

Message from the Past

Aʟᴏɴɢ an island in the North Sea, five miles from the Dutch Coast, stretches a dangerous ledge of rocks that has proved the graveyard of many a vessel sailing that turbulent sea. On this island once lived a group of men who, as each vessel was wrecked, looted the vessel and murdered those of the crew who reached shore.

The government of the Netherlands decided to exterminate the island pirates, and for the job King William selected a young lawyer at The Hague. By royal proclamation he was made mayor of the island, and within a year, a court of law being established, the young attorney was appointed judge; and in that dual capacity he "cleaned up" the island.

The young man now decided to settle on the island, and began to look around for a home. It was a grim place, barren of tree or living green of any kind; it was as if a man had been exiled to Siberia. Still, argued the young mayor, an ugly place is ugly only because it is not beautiful. And beautiful he determined this island should be.

"We must have trees," he said; "we can make this island a spot of beauty if we will!"

And for the fifty years that he lived on the island he planted trees. Now their verdure beautifully shades the quaint, narrow lanes, and transforms into cool wooded roads what once had been only barren sun-baked wastes.

Artists began to hear of the place and brought their canvases, and on the walls of hundreds of homes throughout the world hang today bits of the beautiful lanes and wooded spots. The American artist William M. Chase took his pupils there almost annually. "In all the world today," he declared to his students, as they exclaimed at the natural cool restfulness of the island, "there is no more beautiful place."

Aꜰᴛᴇʀ the young mayor-judge had been on the barren island two years he went to the mainland one day and brought back with him a bride. It was a bleak place for a bridal home, but the young wife had the qualities of the husband. "While you raise trees," she said, "I will raise our children." And within a score of years the young bride sent thirteen happy-faced, well-brought-up children over that island, and there was reared a home such as is given to few.

One day when the children had grown to man's and woman's estate the mother called them all together and said to them, "I want to tell you the story of your father and of this island," and she told them the simple story that is written here.

"And now," she said, "as you go out into the world I want each of you to take with you the spirit of your father's work, and each in your own way and place, do as he has done: make you the world a bit more beautiful and better because you have been in it."

The children and grandchildren have gone to the four corners of the globe, and are now the generation of workers —some in the far East Indies; others in Africa; still others in our own land of America. But each has tried, according to the talents given, to carry out the message of that day, to tell the story of the grandfather's work; just as it is told here by the author of this book, who, in the efforts of his later years, has tried to carry out, so far as the opportunity has come to him, the message of his grandmother:

"Make you the world a bit more beautiful and better because you have been in it."

American-To-Be

THE leviathan of the Atlantic Ocean, in 1870, was *The Queen,* and when she was warped into her dock on September 20 of that year, she discharged, among her passengers, a family of four from the Netherlands who were to make an experiment of Americanization.

Unwise investments had swept away the father's fortune, and in preference to a new start in his own land, he had decided to make the new beginning in the United States, where a favorite brother-in-law had gone several years before. But that, never a simple matter for a man who has reached forty-two, is particularly difficult for a foreigner in a strange land. This fact he and his wife were to find out.

There were two boys: the elder, William, was eight and a half years of age; the younger Edward was soon to celebrate his seventh birthday.

Thanks to the linguistic system that compels the study of languages, English was already familiar to the father and mother. But to the two sons, who had barely learned the beginnings of their native tongue, the English language was a closed book. It seemed a cruel decision of the father to put his two boys into a public school in Brooklyn, but he argued that if they were to become Americans, the sooner they became part of the life of the country and learned its language for themselves, the better.

At the best, they were difficult days at school. Fortunately the linguistic gift inherent in the Dutch race came to Edward's rescue and the conquest of English did not prove as difficult as he had expected.

But there were other problems. Like all healthy boys of his age he was fond of play and eager to join the boys of his neighborhood in their pastimes after school hours. He also wanted to help his mother, which meant washing dishes, cleaning the rooms, and running various errands for the needed household supplies. Then, too, he was not progressing as rapidly as he wished with his school studies, and he felt that he ought to do everything in his power to take advantage of his opportunity to get an education.

Methodically he worked out a plan which made it possible to accomplish all three objects. He planned that on one afternoon he should go directly home from school to help his mother and as soon as he had finished the necessary chores he could play for the rest of the afternoon. On the following day he would remain in school for an extra hour and would get the teacher's help on any lessons that were not clear to him. With that accomplished he would still have part of the afternoon to play in. Both his mother and teacher approved the idea and agreed that it had been well thought out.

Thus Edward Bok learned early in life the valuable lesson of a wise management of time. As his evenings were also devoted to various tasks and duties, this young American-to-be, by using each bit of spare time for some useful purpose, became early in life the busy person that he has remained to the present day.

THE elder Bok did not find his "lines cast in pleasant places" in the United States. He found himself, professionally, unable to adjust the methods of his own land and of a lifetime to those of a new country.

Then Edward and his brother decided to relieve their mother in the housework by rising early in the morning, building the fire, preparing breakfast, and washing the dishes before they went to school. After school they gave up their play to prepare the evening meal and wash the dishes afterward. It was a curious coincidence that it should fall upon Edward thus to get a first-hand knowledge of woman's housework which was to stand him in such practical stead in later years.

It was not easy for the parents to see their boys thus forced to do work which only a short while before had been done by a retinue of servants. And the capstone of humiliation seemed to be when Edward and his brother, after having for several mornings found no kindling wood or coal to build the fire, decided to go out of evenings with a basket and pick up what wood they could find in neighboring lots, and the bits of coal spilled from the coal-bin of the grocery-store, or left on the curbs before houses where coal had been delivered. The mother remonstrated with the boys, although in her heart she knew that the necessity was upon them.

But while the doing of these homely chores was very effective in relieving the untrained and tired mother, it added

little to the family income. Edward looked about and decided that the time had come for him, young as he was, to begin some sort of wage-earning. But when and where?

ONE evening Edward went to a party of young people, and his latent journalistic sense whispered to him that his young hostess might like to see her social affair in print. So he wrote up the party, being careful to include the name of every boy and girl present and took the account to the city editor of the *Brooklyn Eagle,* with the sage observation that every name mentioned in that paragraph represented a buyer of the paper, who would like to see his or her name in print. The editor was not slow to see the point and offered Edward three dollars a column for such reports.

Within a few weeks, Edward was turning in to *The Eagle* from two to three columns a week; his pay was raised to four dollars a column; the editor was pleased in having started a department that no other paper carried, and the "among those present" at the parties all bought the paper and were immensely gratified to see their names.

So everybody was happy, and Edward Bok, as a full-fledged reporter, had begun his journalistic career.

The American spirit of initiative had entered deep into the soul of Edward Bok. The brother had left school a year before, and found a place as messenger in a lawyer's office; and when one evening Edward heard that there was an opening as office boy at the Western Union office, he applied for and got the job. And so, at the age of thirteen, Edward Bok left school and entered upon his career with the salary of six dollars and twenty-five cents per week.

Self-Education Made Exciting

WITH school-days ended, the question of self-education became an absorbing thought with Edward Bok. He had mastered a schoolboy's English,

but seven years of public-school education was hardly a basis on which to build the work of a lifetime. He saw each day in his duties as office boy some

of the foremost men of the time. He
knew that some of these men, too, had
been deprived of the advantage of col-
legiate training, and yet they had risen
to the top. But how?

The boy decided to read about these
men and others, and find out. He could
not, however, afford the separate biographies, so he went to the libraries to
find a compendium that would authoritatively tell him of all successful men.
He found it in Appleton's *Encyclopaedia*. He was encouraged to find that
in many cases their beginnings had been
as modest as his own, and their opportunities of education as limited.

One day it occurred to him to test
the accuracy of the biographies he was
reading. James A. Garfield was then
spoken of for the presidency; Edward
wondered whether it was true that he
had once been a boy on a tow-path.
With simple directness characteristic of
his Dutch training, he wrote to General
Garfield, asking whether the boyhood
episode was true, and explaining why
he asked.

Of course any public man, no matter
how large his correspondence, is pleased
to receive an earnest letter from an
information-seeking boy. General Garfield answered warmly and fully.
Edward showed the letter to his father,
who told the boy it was valuable and he
should keep it. This was a new idea.
He followed it further: if one such letter
was valuable, how much more valuable
would be a hundred! Why not begin a
collection of autographed letters?

So he took his *Encyclopaedia*—its
trustworthiness now established in his
mind by General Garfield's letter—and
began to study the lives of successful
men and women. Then, with boyish
frankness, he wrote to famous persons
on some mooted question in their lives.

Most interesting were, of course, the
replies. General Grant sketched on an
improvised map the exact spot where
General Lee surrendered to him; Longfellow told him how he came to write
"Excelsior"; Whittier told the story of

"The Barefoot Boy"; Tennyson wrote
out a stanza or two of "The Brook,"
upon condition that Edward would not
again use the word "awful," which the
poet said "is slang for 'very'," and "I
hate slang."

ONE day the boy received a letter
from the Confederate general Jubal
A. Early, giving the real reason why he
burned Chambersburg. A friend visiting
Edward's father, happening to see the
letter, recognized in it a hitherto missing
bit of history, and suggested that it be
published in the *New York Tribune*.
The letter, when published, attracted
wide attention and provoked national
discussion.

Of course the *Tribune* at once saw a
"story" in the boy's other letters, and
within a few days it appeared with a
long article on its principal news page
giving an account of the Brooklyn boy's
remarkable letters and how he had
secured them. *The Brooklyn Eagle*
quickly followed with a request for an
interview; the *Boston Globe* followed
suit; the *Philadelphia Public Ledger*
sent its New York correspondent; and
before Edward was aware of it, newspapers in different parts of the country
were writing about "the well-known
Brooklyn autograph collector."

Edward Bok was quick to see the
value of the publicity which had so suddenly come to him. Several of his correspondents had asked Edward to come
and see them. Accordingly, when they
lived in New York or Brooklyn, or came
to these cities on a visit, he was quick
to avail himself of their invitation. He
began to note each day in the newspapers the "distinguished arrivals" at the
New York hotels; and when any one
with whom he had corresponded arrived, Edward would, after business
hours, go up-town, pay his respects and
thank him in person for his letters.

No person was too high for Edward's
boyish approach; President Garfield,
General Grant, General Sherman, President Hayes—all were called upon, and

all received the boy graciously and were interested in the problem of his self-education. It was a veritable case of making friends on every hand; friends who were to be of the greatest help and value to the boy in his after-years, although he had no conception of it at the time.

Into the Book World

EDWARD BOK had not been office boy long before he realized that if he learned shorthand he would stand a better chance for advancement. Before many weeks Edward could "stenograph" fairly well, and as the typewriter had not then come into its own, he was ready to put his knowledge to practical use.

Edward felt that his daytime hours would be best spent in a publishing atmosphere as stenographer. Accordingly he secured a job with Henry Holt and Company.

From his book-publishing association he became convinced that the American public as a whole, was not reading the number of books that it should, considering the intelligence and wealth of the people, and the cheap prices at which books were sold. He concluded to see whether he could not induce the newspapers to give larger and more prominent space to the news of the book world.

Owing to his constant contact with authors, he was in a peculiarly fortunate position to know their plans in advance of execution, and he was beginning to learn the ins and outs of the book-publishing world. He believed he could convince editors of the public interest in a newsy, readable New York literary letter, and he prevailed upon the editor of the *New York Star* to allow him to supplement the book reviews of George Parsons Lathrop in that paper by a column of literary chat called "Literary Leaves."

Occasionally he sent to an editor here and there what he thought was a particularly newsy letter just "for his information, not for sale." The editor of the *Philadelphia Times* was the first to discover that his paper wanted the letter, and the *Boston Journal* followed suit.

Then the editor of the *Cincinnati Times-Star* discovered the letter in the *New York Star* and asked that it be supplied weekly. These newspapers renamed the letter "Bok's Literary Leaves," and the feature started on a successful career.

EDWARD had been in the employ of Henry Holt and Company as clerk and stenographer for two years when he heard that there was an opening in the publishing house of Charles Scribner's Sons, if he wanted to make a change. Edward saw at once the large opportunities possible in a house of the importance of Scribners, and he immediately applied for and got the position of stenographer to the two senior members of the firm. He was to receive a salary of eighteen dollars and thirty-three cents per week, which was then considered a fair wage for stenographic work. He was twenty-one years of age at the time.

Edward was immediately brought into touch with the leading authors of the day, their works as they were discussed in the correspondence dictated to him and the authors' terms upon which books were published.

The Scribners had the foremost theological list of all the publishing houses; its educational list was exceptionally strong; its musical list excelled; its fiction represented the leading writers of the day; its general list was particularly noteworthy; and its foreign department, importing the leading books brought out in Great Britain and Europe, was an outstanding feature of the business. The correspondence dictated to Bok naturally covered all these fields and a more remarkable opportunity for self-education was never offered a stenographer.

Later, when the house decided to start *Scribner's Magazine,* all the preliminary correspondence was dictated to Bok through his employers, and he received a first hand education in the setting up of the machinery necessary for the publication of a magazine.

Then again he was fortunate in that his desk was placed in the advertising department of the house. Thus he had a chance to learn the art of advertising at first hand. Whenever his stenographic work permitted, he assisted in preparing and placing the advertisements.

Of course, his opportunities for making his literary letter interesting were unusual. Owing to his Scribner connection, however, he had taken his name from his literary letter and signed that of his brother. He had, also, constantly to discriminate between the information that he could publish without violation of confidence and that which he felt he was not at liberty to print. This gave him excellent experience; for the most vital of all essentials in a journalist is the ability unerringly to decide what to print and what to regard as confidential.

Woman Hater Edits Women's Magazine

THE market for Bok's literary letter finally expanded to some forty-five newspapers. One of these was the *Philadelphia Times.* In that paper, each week, the letter had been read by Mr. Cyrus H. K. Curtis, the owner and publisher of *The Ladies' Home Journal.* Mr. Curtis had decided that he needed an editor for his magazine, in order to relieve his wife, who was then editing it, and he fixed upon the writer of *Literary Leaves* as his man. He found that while the letter was signed by William J. Bok, it was actually written by his brother who was with Scribner's and it was there that he approached Edward.

Bok turned over in his mind the wisdom of interrupting his line of progress with Scribner's, and in New York, and began to contemplate the possibilities in Philadelphia and the work there.

He gathered a collection of the few domestic magazines then published, and found that they were of rather poor quality. Then he began to study himself, his capacity for the work, and the possibility of finding it congenial. He realized that it was absolutely foreign to his Scribner work: that it meant a radical departure. But the main question was: had he within him that peculiar subtle something that, for the want of a better phrase, we call the editorial instinct? That was all there was to it, and that decision had to be his and his alone.

Bok's instinct was strongly in favor

of an acceptance. He now consulted his business associates, and, to a man, they discouraged the step, but almost invariably upon the argument that it was suicidal to leave New York. Bok had experience enough to realize that a man could not be buried in any city, provided he had the ability to stand out from his fellow men.

Therefore on September 1, 1889, he wrote to Mr. Curtis, accepting the position in Philadelphia. On October 20, 1889, Edward Bok became the editor of *The Ladies' Home Journal.*

THE women's magazine field was wide open when Edward Bok entered it. It was not only wide open but fairly crying out to be filled. It was this consciousness of a void ready to be filled that made the Philadelphia experiment so attractive to the embryo editor.

He looked over the field and reasoned that if women were ready to buy the rather poor home magazines then in existence, how much greater response would there be to a magazine that would be an authoritative clearing house for all the problems confronting women in the home, that brought itself closely into contact with those problems and tried to solve them in an entertaining and efficient way; and yet a magazine of uplift and inspiration: a magazine, in other words, that would give light and leading in the women's world.

Edward Bok immediately encountered the popular misconception that if a man is the editor of a periodical with a distinctly feminine appeal, he must, as the term goes, "Understand women." No man, perhaps, could have been chosen for the position who had a less intimate knowledge of women. Bok had no sister, no women confidantes; he had lived with and for his mother. She was the only woman he really knew or who really knew him. Nor had he the slightest desire, even as an editor, to know them better, or to seek to understand them.

What he saw in the position was not the need to know women; he could employ women for that purpose. He perceived clearly that the editor of a magazine was largely an executive: his was principally the work of direction; of studying currents and movements, watching their formation, their tendency, their efficacy if advocated or translated into actuality; and then selecting from the horizon those that were for the best interests of the home.

For the home was something Edward Bok did understand. He had always lived in one; had struggled to keep it together, and he knew every inch of the hard road that makes for domestic permanence amid adverse financial conditions.

Advice to the Love-Lorn

IT was upon his instinct that he intended to rely rather than upon any knowledge of women. His first act in the editorial chair of *The Ladies' Home Journal* showed him to be right in this diagnosis of himself, for the incident proved not only how correct was his instinct, but how woefully lacking he was in any knowledge of the feminine nature.

He had divined the fact that in thousands of cases the American mother was not the confidante of her daughter, and reasoned if an inviting human personality could be created on the printed page that would supply this lamentable lack of American family life, girls would flock to such a figure. But it all depended on the confidence which the written word could inspire.

He tried several writers, but in each case the particular touch that he sought for was lacking. It seemed so simple to him, and yet he could not translate it to others. Then, in desperation, he wrote an instalment of such a department as he had in mind himself, intending to show it to a writer who might imitate it. But as time was short he decided to let the manuscript go into the magazine under the name of Ruth Ashmore. The day after publication two hundred letters were received for "Ruth Ashmore," with the mail clerk asking where they should be sent. On the following day the mail clerk handed him five hundred.

The editor now took two letters from the top and opened them. He never opened the third! His instinct had correctly interpreted the need, but he never dreamed how far the feminine nature would reveal itself on paper.

Bok finally secured Isabel A. Mallon to write the column. She became the most ridiculed writer in the magazine world, and yet the most helpful editor that ever conducted a department in a periodical. For sixteen years she conducted the department and in that time received one hundred and fifty-eight thousand letters; she kept three stenographers busy, and the number of girls who today bless the name of Ruth Ashmore is legion.

But newspaper humorists who insisted that Ruth Ashmore was none other than Edward Bok never knew the partial truth of their joke.

BY THIS time the editor had come to see that the power of a magazine might lie more securely behind the printed page than in it. He had begun to accustom his readers to writing to his editors upon all conceivable problems.

Step by step he built up a staff of thirty-five corresponding editors and before long the letters streamed in by the tens of thousands during a year. The editor still encouraged, and the total ran into the hundreds of thousands, until during the last year, before the service was finally stopped by the Great War of 1917-18, the yearly correspondence totalled nearly a million letters.

A World More Beautiful

THE influence of his grandfather and the injunction of his grandmother to her sons that each "should make the world a better or a more beautiful place to live in" now began to be manifest in the grandson.

Edward Bok was unconscious that it was this influence. What directly led to the signal piece of construction in which he engaged was the wretched architecture of small houses. As he travelled through the United States he was appalled by it.

He believed he might serve thousands of his readers if he could make it possible for them to secure at moderate cost, plans for well-designed houses by the leading domestic architects in the country. He consulted a number of architects, only to find them unalterably opposed to the idea. They disliked the publicity of magazine presentation; prices differed too much in various parts of the country; and they didn't care to risk the criticism of their contemporaries. It was "cheapening" their profession!

Bok saw that he should have to blaze the way and demonstrate the futility of these arguments. At last he persuaded one architect to cooperate with him, and in 1895, began the publication of a series of houses which could be built, approximately, for from one thousand five hundred dollars to five thousand dollars. The idea attracted attention at once, and the architect-author was swamped with letters and inquiries regarding his plans.

This proved Bok's instinct to be correct as to the public willingness to accept such designs; upon this proof he succeeded in winning over two additional architects to make plans. He offered his readers full building specifications and plans to scale of the houses with estimates from four builders, in different parts of the United States, for five dollars a set. The plans and specifications were so complete in every detail that any builder could build the house from them.

Slowly but surely he won the approval of the leading architects, who saw that he was appealing to a class of house-builders who could not afford to pay an architect's fee, and that, with his wide circulation, he might become an influence for better architecture through these small houses.

The sets of plans and specifications sold by the thousands. It was not long before the magazine was able to present small-house plans by the foremost architects in the country, whose services the average householder could otherwise never have dreamed of securing.

BOK then turned to the subject of the garden for the small house, and the development of the grounds around the homes which he had been instrumental in putting on the earth. He encountered no opposition here. The publication of small gardens for small houses finally ran into hundreds of pages, the magazine supplying planting plans and full directions as to when and how to plant—this time without cost.

Next the editor decided to see what he could do for the better and simpler furnishing of the small American home. He felt that the method of presentation for his interior furnishing plan would be to secure photographs of the most carefully furnished homes in America. He immediately employed the best available expert, and within six months there came to him an assorted collection of over a thousand photographs of well furnished rooms. The best were selected, and a series of photographic pages called "Inside of 100 Homes" was begun.

The editor followed this up with another successful series, again pictorial. He realized that to explain good taste in furnishing by text was almost impossible. So he started a series of all-picture pages called "Good Taste and Bad Taste." He presented a chair whose lines were bad and either useless or uncomfortable to sit in, and explained where and why it was bad; and then put a good chair next to it, and explained where and why it was good.

The lesson to the eye was simply and directly effective; the pictures told their story as no printed word could have done, and furniture manufacturers and dealers all over the country began to put on the market the tables, chairs, divans, bedsteads, and dressing-tables which the magazine was portraying as examples of good taste. It was amazing that, within five years, the physical appearance of domestic furniture in the stores completely changed.

It was a peculiar satisfaction to Bok that Theodore Roosevelt once summed up this piece of work in these words: "Bok is the only man I ever heard of who changed, for the better, the architecture of an entire nation, and he did it so quickly and yet so effectively that we didn't know it was begun before it was finished. There is a mighty big job for one man to have done."

Photographic Civics

In his travels Bok began to note the disreputably untidy spots which various municipalities allowed in the closest proximity to the centre of their business life, in the most desirable residential sections, and often adjacent to the most important municipal buildings and parks. It was decided to select a dozen cities, pick out the most flagrant instances of spots which were not only an eyesore and a disgrace from a municipal standpoint, but a menace to health and meant a depreciation of real-estate value.

Lynn, Massachusetts, was the initial city chosen, a number of photographs were taken, and the first of a series of "Dirty Cities" was begun in the magazine. The effect was instantaneous. The people of Lynn rose in protest, and the municipal authorities threatened suit against the magazine; the local newspapers were virulent in their attacks. Without warning, they argued, Bok had held up their city to disgrace before the entire country; the attack was unwarranted; in bad taste; every citizen in Lynn should thereafter cease to buy the magazine, and so the criticisms ran. In answer Bok merely pointed to the photographs; to the fact that the camera could not lie, and that if he had misrepresented conditions he was ready to make amends.

Of course the facts could not be gainsaid; local pride was aroused, and as a result not only were the advertised "dirty spots" cleaned up, but the municipal authorities went out and hunted around for other spots in the city, not knowing what other photographs Bok might have had taken.

Cities throughout the country now began to look around to see whether they had dirty spots within their limits, not knowing when the photographers might visit them. Bok received letters from various municipalities calling his attention to the fact that they were cognizant of spots in their cities and were cleaning them up, and asking that, if he had photographs of these spots, they should not be published.

It happened that in two such instances Bok had already prepared sets of photographs for publication. These he sent to the mayors of the respective cities, stating that if they would return them with an additional set showing the spots cleaned up there would be no occasion for their publication. In both cases this was done. Atlanta, Georgia; New Haven, Connecticut; Pittsburgh, Cincinnati, and finally Bok's own city of

Philadelphia were duly chronicled in the magazine; local storms broke and calmed down—with the spots in every instance improved.

It was an interesting experiment in photographic civics. The pity of it is that more has not been done along this and similar lines.

Death to Patent Medicines

IN 1892 *The Ladies' Home Journal* announced that it would thereafter accept no advertisements of patent medicines for its pages. Into an army of deceit and spurious medicines, *The Ladies' Home Journal* fired the first gun. Neither the public nor the patent-medicine people paid much attention to the first attacks. But as they grew, and the evidence multiplied, the public began to comment and the nostrum makers began to get uneasy.

The magazine attacked the evil from every angle. It aroused the public by showing the actual contents of some of their pet medicines, or the absolute worthlessness and even harmfulness of them. The Editor got the Women's Christian Temperance Union into action against the periodicals for publishing advertisements of medicines containing as high as forty per cent alcohol. He called the United States Post Office authorities to account for accepting and distributing obscene circular matter.

He cut an advertisement out of a newspaper which ended with the statement:

Mrs. Pinkham, in her laboratory at Lynn, Massachusetts, is able to do more for the ailing women of America than the family physician. Any woman, therefore, is responsible for her own suffering who will not take the trouble to write to Mrs. Pinkham for advice.

Next to this advertisement representing Mrs. Lydia Pinkham as "in her laboratory," Bok simply placed the photograph of Mrs. Pinkham's tombstone in Pine Grove Cemetery, at Lynn, showing that Mrs. Pinkham had passed away twenty-two years before! It was one of the most effective pieces of copy that the magazine used in the campaign. It told its story with absolute simplicity, but with deadly force.

The proprietors of "Mrs. Winslow's Soothing Syrup" had strenuously denied the presence of morphine in their preparation. Bok simply bought a bottle of the syrup in London, where, under the English Pharmacy Act, the authorities compelled the proprietors of the syrup to affix the following declaration on each bottle: "This preparation, containing, among other valuable ingredients, a small amount of morphine is, in accordance with the Pharmacy Act, hereby labelled 'Poison!'" The magazine published a photograph of the label, and it told its own convincing story. It is only fair to say that the makers of this remedy now publish their formula.

HE NOW engaged Mark Sullivan, then a young lawyer in downtown New York, induced him to give up his practice, and bring his legal mind to bear upon the problem. It was the beginning of Sullivan's subsequent journalistic career, and he justified Bok's confidence in him. He exposed the testimonials to patent medicines from senators and congressmen, then so widely published; showed how they were obtained by a journalist in Washington who made a business of it. He charged seventy-five dollars for a Senator's testimonial, forty dollars for that of a congressman, and accepted no contract for less than five thousand dollars.

Sullivan next exposed the disgraceful violation of the confidence of women by these nostrum vendors in selling their most confidential letters to any one who would buy them. Sullivan himself bought thousands of these letters and names, and then wrote about them in the magazine. One prominent firm indignantly denied the charge, asserting that whatever others might have done their names were always held sacred. In answer to this declaration Sullivan published an advertisement of this righteous concern offering fifty thousand of their names for sale.

Bok had now kept up the fight for over two years, and the results were apparent on every hand. Reputable newspapers and magazines were closing their pages to the advertisements of patent medicines; legislation was appearing in several States; the public had been awakened to the fraud practised upon it, and a Federal Pure Food and Drug Act was being talked about.

Today the pages of every newspaper and periodical of recognized standing are closed to the advertisements of patent medicines; the Drug Act regulates the ingredients, and post office officials scan the literature sent through the United States mails.

The Root of Evil

ONE day when Bok was at luncheon with Doctor Lyman Abbott, the latter expressed the wish that Bok would take up the subject of venereal disease as he had the patent-medicine question.

"Not our question," answered Bok.

"It is most decidedly your question," was the reply. "Read up on the subject and you will find that the evil has its direct roots in the home with the parents. You will agree with me before you go very far that it *is* your question."

Bok began to read on the unsavory subject. It was exceedingly unpleasant reading, but for two years he persisted, only to find that Doctor Abbott was right. The root of the evil lay in the reticence of parents with children as to the mystery of life; boys and girls were going out into the world blind-folded as to any knowledge of their physical selves. The results were appalling. Bok pursued his investigations from books direct into the "Homes of Refuge," "Doors of Hope," and similar institutions, and unearthed a condition, the direct results of the false modesty of parents, that was almost unbelievable.

Bok realized that for his magazine, of all magazines, to take up this subject would be like a bolt from the blue in tens of thousands of homes. But this very fact, the unquestioned position of the magazine, the remarkable respect which its readers had for it, and the confidence with which parents placed the periodical on their home tables—all this was, Bok thought, the more reason why he should take up the matter.

He consulted his friends, who advised against it; his editors were all opposed to the introduction of the unsavory subject into the magazine.

Mr. Curtis, alone, encouraged his editor. Bok called his attention to the fact that a heavy loss in circulation was a foregone conclusion; he could calculate upon one hundred thousand subscribers, at least, stopping the magazine. "It is a question of right," answered the publisher, "not of circulation."

And so, in 1906, with the subject absolutely prohibited in every periodical and newspaper of standing, never discussed at a public gathering save at medical meetings, Bok published his first editorial.

DAY after day, thousands of letters of protest came in. Thousands of subscriptions were stopped; advertisements gave notice that they would cancel their accounts; the greatest pressure was placed upon Mr. Curtis to order his editor to cease, and Bok had the grim experience of seeing his magazine, hitherto proclaimed over the land as a model advocate of virtues, refused admittance into thousands of homes, and saw his own friends tear the offending pages out of the periodical before it was allowed to find a place on their home tables.

But *The Journal* kept steadily on. Number after number contained some article on the subject, and finally such men and women as Jane Addams, Cardinal Gibbons, Margaret Deland, Henry van Dyke, President Eliot, the

Bishop of London, braved the public storm, came to Bok's aid, and wrote articles for his magazine heartily backing up his lonely fight.

The public, seeing this array of distinguished opinion expressing itself, began to wonder "whether there might not be something in what Bok was saying, after all." At the end of eighteen months, inquiries began to take the place of protests; and Bok knew then that the fight was won.

He employed two experts, one man and one woman, to answer the inquiries and he had published a series of little books, each written by a different author on a different aspect of the question. This series was *The Edward Bok Books.*

The Close of a Career

In 1918 he decided that he would ask his company to release him from the editorship of *The Ladies' Home Journal.* In October, 1919, he would reach his thirtieth anniversary as editor, and he fixed upon this as an appropriate time for the relinquishment of his duties.

He felt he had carried out the conditions under which the editorship of the magazine had been transferred to him by Mrs. Curtis. He had, too, realized his hope of helping to create a national institution of service to the American woman, and he felt that his part in the work was done.

In circulation it had not only outstripped that of any other monthly periodical, but it was still growing so rapidly that it was only a question of a few months when it would reach the almost incredible mark of two million copies per month. With its advertising patronage exceeding that of any other monthly, the periodical had become, probably, the most valuable and profitable piece of magazine property in the world.

The time might never come again when all conditions would be equally favorable to a change of editorship. Moreover, Bok wished to say good-bye to his public before it decided, for some reason or other, to say good-bye to him. He had no desire to outstay his welcome. The public had been wonderfully indulgent toward his shortcomings lenient with his errors, and tremendously inspiring to his best endeavor. He would not ask too much of it. Thirty years was a long tenure of office, one of the longest, in point of consecutively active editorship, in the history of American magazines.

He decided to round out his career with a series of articles on the problem of Americanization. The war and its after-effects had clearly demonstrated this to be the most vital need in the life of the nation, not only for the foreign born but for the American as well.

It was peculiarly gratifying to him that his editorial work should end with the exposition of that Americanization of which he himself was a product. It seemed a fitting close to the career of foreign born Americanized editor.

The question now naturally arises: To what extent, with his unusual opportunities of fifty years, has the Americanization of Edward Bok gone? How far is he, today, an American?

Where America Falls Short

When I came to the United States as a lad of six, the most needful lesson for me, as a boy, was the necessity for thrift. I had been taught in my home across the sea that thrift was one of the fundamentals in a successful life. Where the Dutchman saved, the American wasted. There was waste, and the most prodigal waste, on every hand.

At school, I quickly learned that to "save money" was to be "stingy"; as a young man, I soon found that the American disliked the word "economy," and on every hand as plenty grew spending grew. There was literally nothing in American life to teach me thrift or economy; everything to teach me to spend and to waste.

I saw men who had earned good
laries in their prime, reach the years
f incapacity as dependents. I saw fami-
es on every hand either living quite
p to their means or beyond them;
rely within them.

It was in this atmosphere of prodigal
xpenditure and culpable waste that I
as to practise thrift: a fundamental in
fe! And it is into this atmosphere that
1e foreign-born comes now, with every
1ducement to spend and no encourage-
1ent to save.

Is it any wonder, then, that in this,
1e of the essentials in life and in all
1ccess, America fell short with me, as
is continuing to fall short with every
reign-born who comes to its shores?

s a Dutch boy, one of the cardinal
truths taught me was that what-
/er was worth doing was worth doing
ell: that next to honesty came thor-
1ghness as a factor in success.

I came to America to be taught ex-
tly the opposite. The two infernal
mericanisms "That's good enough"
d "That will do" were early taught
.e, together with the maxim of quantity
ther than quality.

Thoroughness was at a discount on
ery hand; production at a premium.
made no difference in what direction
went, the result was the same; the cry
as always for quantity, quantity! And
to this atmosphere I brought my ideas
Dutch thoroughness and my convic-
on that doing well whatever I did was
count as a cardinal principle in life.

s a Dutch boy I was taught a wholesome respect for law and authority.
he fact was impressed upon me that
ws of themselves were futile unless the

people for whom they were made respected them, and obeyed them in spirit
more even than in the letter. I came to
America to feel, on every hand, that
exactly the opposite was true. There was
little respect for the law; there was
scarcely any for those appointed to enforce it.

The nearest that a boy gets to the law
is through the policeman. In the Netherlands a boy is taught that a policeman
is for the protection of life and property; that he is the natural friend of
every boy and man who behaves himself.

I came to America to be told that a
policeman is a boy's natural enemy; and
he is eager to arrest him if he can find
the slightest reason for doing so. A
policeman, I was informed, was a being
to hold in fear, not in respect.

Not a note of respect did I ever hear
for the law in my boyhood days. A law
was something to be broken, to be
evaded, to call down upon others as a
source of punishment, but never to be
regarded in the light of a safeguard. It
is a very unfortunate impression that
this American lack of respect for those
in authority makes upon the foreign-
born mind.

To the American, part and parcel of
his country, these particulars in which
his country falls short with the foreign
born are, perhaps, not so evident; they
may even seem not so very important.
But to the foreign-born they seem distinct lacks; they loom large; they form
serious handicaps which, in many cases,
are never surmounted; they are a menace to that Americanization which is, today, more than ever our fondest dream,
and which we now realize more keenly
than before is our most vital need.

America's Priceless Gift

HATEVER shortcomings I may
have found during my fifty-year
:riod of Americanization; however
merica may have failed to help my
ansition from a foreigner into an
merican, I owe to her the most price-

less gift that any nation can offer, and
that is opportunity.

As the world stands today, no nation
offers opportunity in the degree that
America does to the foreign born. It
may be that the foreign born, as in my

own case, must hold on to some of the ideals and ideas of the land of his birth; it may be that he must develop and mould his character by overcoming the habits resulting from national shortcomings. But into the best that the foreign born can retain, America can graft such a wealth of inspiration, so high a national idealism, so great an opportunity for the highest endeavor, as to make him the fortunate man of the earth today.

When I look around me at the American born I have come to know as my close friends, I wonder whether, after all, the foreign born does not make in some sense a better American—whether he is not able to get a truer perspective; whether his is not the deeper desire to see America greater; whether he is not less content to let its faulty institutions be as they are; whether in seeing faults more clearly he does not make a more decided effort to have America reach those ideals or those fundamentals of his own land which he feels are in his nature, and the best of which he is anxious to graft into the character of his adopted land?

It is naturally with a feeling of deep satisfaction that I remember two Presidents of the United States considered me a sufficiently typical American to wish to send me to my native land as the accredited minister of my adopted country. And yet when I analyze the reasons for my choice in both instances I derive a deeper satisfaction from the fact that my strong desire to work in America for America led me to ask to be permitted to remain here.

It is this strong impulse that my Americanization has made the driving power of my life. And I ask no greater privilege than to be allowed to live to see my potential America become actual: the America that I like to think of, the America of Abraham Lincoln—not faultless, but less faulty.

It is a part in trying to shape that America, and an opportunity to work in that America when it comes, that I ask in return for what I owe to her. A greater privilege no man could have.

THE HARP THAT ONCE THROUGH TARA'S HALLS

THE harp that once through Tara's halls
    The soul of music shed,
Now hangs as mute on Tara's walls
    As if that soul were fled.
So sleeps the pride of former days,
    So glory's thrill is o'er,
And hearts, that once beat high for praise,
    Now feel that pulse no more.

No more to chiefs and ladies bright
    The harp of Tara swells:
The chord alone, that breaks at night,
    Its tale of ruin tells.
Thus Freedom now so seldom wakes,
    The only throb she gives,
Is when some heart indignant breaks,
    To show that still she lives.

               —*T. Moore*

H. L. Davis

HONEY IN THE HORN

. . . He met her in the lane and he laid her on a board
And he played her up a tune called Sugar *in the Gourd,*
Sugar in the gourd, honey in the horn,
Balance to your partners, honey in the horn . . .

The inspiration and mood of our Pulitzer Prize Novel (1935) presentation comes from
this gusty ballad. It is a rugged tale of Oregon's homestead period which has all the vigor,
humor and pace of American frontier life.

The Proposed Bereavement

Public spiritedness about children who had been left orphaned or abandoned was one of Uncle Preston Shiveley's off-and-on interests. He hadn't been able to raise the two sons of his own to be anything but barrel-picking drunks and community nuisances, but that didn't hinder his freaks of adopting loose youngsters to try his system on again.

The newest of Uncle Preston's adoptions was Clay Calvert, and he was a drip-nosed youth of about sixteen, with a god-forsaken expression about him and a mean-spoken sassiness that kept people from being pleasant to him even when they wanted to.

His mother had borne him in some fence-corner, and when he was six years old had taken him with her while she looked for an outfit of harvest-campers. The harvesters broke up in a row somewhere near the bush cabin where Uncle Preston's two sons lived, and she stopped off and married one of them—which one, nobody had ever felt interested enough to look up. She hung on for nearly four years with them and then died, and her youngster stayed on with their fighting and helling and squaw-rolling for six years more, until Wade Shively killed his brother—supposedly in self-defense—in a row. Then Uncle Preston closed the bush cabin up and took Clay Calvert home.

One stormy night about four years after Clay's arrival Uncle Preston was disturbed by a wagon pulling up to the carriage-block in front of the house. Two half-drowned men got out.

"Press," one said. His voice was deep and mechanical, as if words were being blown through him by an outside blast of air. "This is Orlando Geary, Press. We want to see you about Wade Shiveley. He killed another man last night, it looks like. We found old Pappy Howell shot and layin' in the road yesterday mornin' on the way back from a horse-race. They claim he started from the race-track with about eight hundred dollars on him. Wade's tracks was around him, so it looks like Wade killed him and took it."

"What do you want me to do?" said Uncle Preston. The news didn't seem to faze him. "Do you want me to help you find him? Talk, damn it!"

Prepared speech number three sounded as if it had hit the line of conversation by accident. "This ain't got anything to do with arrestin' Wade Shiveley, Press," Geary answered. "We wouldn't ask you to do that, on account of your natural feelin's. We don't need to, anyway, because we caught him ourselves this mornin'."

His artless announcement had about the same effect as if he had yanked the roof off the house and galloped away with it. None of them spoke, and even

Uncle Preston was silent for some minutes. Then he brisked up. "Well, you've got him, and as far as I'm concerned you can keep him," he said.

Old Geary said no, the thing was that Wade had sent after Uncle Preston to come on the canter, and would he please get his coat and tell them where they could find fresh horses?

"I'll be damned if I go a step," said Uncle Preston. "I told Wade Shiveley a good long time ago that I didn't intend ever to see him again. You heard me, because you helped put him off the place. I've got work to do, and he's got no right to come botherin' me at it."

"Well then, Press, we'll take Clay Calvert if you'll fetch him. He used to live with Wade Shiveley."

Uncle Preston explained that they would have to wait until he came in as he was out cheering the last hours of a band of sheep. "He'll be all beat out when he gets here, and he don't like Wade Shiveley any better than I do. But I'll do what I can with him."

When Clay got back Uncle Preston called him in and shut the door behind him. He didn't look like a man about to be humiliatingly bereaved of his only surviving son.

"You've heard about it, I hear," Uncle Preston said. "Somebody has got to go, it looks like. I told Wade Shiveley ten years ago that I wouldn't ever look at him again, and I'll stand by that, by God, if they hang me along with him. So it's lucky you're here. There's something I want you to help me with when you talk to him."

Clay mumbled, "All right." He re-spected Uncle Preston, and he tried t[o] make a quick splice between his respec[t] and Uncle Preston's selfishness in send[-] ing him off to town without even a[n] apology for the extra work he ha[d] already done.

"That shows you're dependable, an[d] that's more than that son of mine wi[ll] ever be in a hundred years," said Uncl[e] Preston. "If I'd wrung his neck th[e] night he was born, everybody woul[d] have been better off. Well, now this so[n] of mine is in jail bellerin' for somebod[y] to rush in and hear how bad he don[t] want to be hung. I want to do som[e] thing for him, and I want you to tak[e] this gun. Pack it somewhere out of sigh[t] and if you can slip it to him when n[o] body's lookin', I want you to do it."

He slid an oily black pistol across th[e] table into the lamplight. Clay picked [it] up, noted that it was fully loaded, an[d] laid it down.

"You're certain you want him to hav[e] this thing?" Clay asked. "He'll kill some[-] body with it."

"He'll try to," said Uncle Presto[n] "Only the cartridges ain't got an[y] powder in 'em. I pulled all the bulle[ts] and emptied it out. Don't tell him th[at] when you give it to him."

"What do you expect him to do wit[h] a gun that won't shoot?" Clay inquire[d] "If he tries to use it, he'll git hurt."

Uncle Preston said, yes. "I remembe[r] the night he was born. I suppose ever[y] man's mind runs back like that whe[n] he's in a situation like this. I want hi[m] to get hurt. I want him to get kille[d] It'll be better for him and better f[or] everybody. You take this gun."

Killer and Accomplice Escape

THERE were three men in the sheriff's office around a desk. None of them said anything. It was exactly like a party sitting up with a dead person. Wade Shiveley was standing at the jail door, with his hands grasping the cross-bars. His face was swollen across the cheekbones, and perfectly bloodless except the eyes, which were red.

He pressed his face closer to the ba[rs] and gagged twice before he spoke. "Th[e] man didn't come," he said, hollowl[y] "He's against me like the rest of 'e[m] I suppose."

"If you've got anything to tell, tell to me," said Clay.

The hole in the cement floor was sti[ll] there. He sidled to it and planted h[is] foot on it. The gun came out his boot crosswise.

"I didn't kill Pap Howell, Clay," Wade said. "I swear to God, if they hang me for it they'll be committin' murder. You got to find 'em whoever it was that done it. Listen to me, Clay. That gun that shot Howell split the bullet-jacket. You can shoot mine at anything you want to, and it won't ever do that. I want you to tell the old man that if I ever git out of this, I'll be a good son to him and make up for—"

"He sent you this," Clay said, softly, and let out another loop of the cord. "Look down. When it's ready, pretend to drop something and pick this up with it. I'll tell you when."

"All right," Wade muttered. "If you see the old man before I do, you tell him thanks for this, and I'll see him in a couple of days. Yes, by God! And tell him I'll kick the stuffin' out of his low-down old hide for the way he's treated me, too. He owes me a damn sight more than this, and I'll collect it, too."

WADE SHIVELEY had broken out of jail. It had got around that Clay slipped him the gun to make his break with, and the solid citizens were all madder about it than fire. If they caught Clay they would raise hell with him.

"They're welcome to, if they can catch me," Clay said to the Indian boy who had come to him with the news. How did Wade Shiveley come to break jail? The gun I slipped him wouldn't shoot."

The Indian boy explained scornfully that Wade Shiveley hadn't found it necessary to shoot. He had merely pointed it at the two men in the sheriff's office, and they had trotted over and unlocked the door for him as eager as yet puppy-dogs. He took their guns away and locked them in, and then walked out.

Nobody was bothering much about catching Wade Shiveley, because Orlando Geary had claimed that job for himself. But there was a whole swad of men out after Clay because the story had got out that he had put one over on them by dropping a gun into jail from his pants leg, and it made them look foolish.

Clay didn't think about the luck that had changed him from an honest young work-hand to hideout and fugitive sneaking through the cold brush to steal venison so he wouldn't starve. He was too young and too afflicted with social conscience to feel any of the uneasiness of the hunted. As long as nobody caught or crowded him, dodging people was a game, like bull-pen or wounded soldier, only a good deal more gratifying to be ahead in.

A couple of days after he had started on his get-away he came to a wagon and a tent by the road side with twenty-odd horses grouped around it. Nobody was in sight except a tall colorless-haired man in carpet slippers hacking stove wood off a stump.

Then a girl came out of the tent. She had gray eyes, and she was barefooted and she laughed at Clay. The girl didn't look at all self-conscious or embarrassed. She turned so the light caught her face, and Clay saw that her gaiety was not so innocent and plum-bloom as the shadows had made it look. Her gray eyes held him and took his measure without flinching; she knew he was takings hers, and she was neither eager about it nor afraid of it.

The horses swung into a trot, the man picked up his ax and went to hacking the stump, and the girl came out of the tent with her shoes on and stood by the road, looking after him. She had not spoken one word to him and he never expected to see her again. But he felt glad over having seen her.

She was like an action; she was something that made mankind seem bigger and more credible than he had imagined; she was like one of the things that had happened in the night before he had to start thinking of lying and smuggling firearms and listening to Wade Shiveley in jail.

Refuge and Reunion

H E RODE along until old Flem Simmons came driving his sled-runner wagon up the road and pulled up almost in front of him.

"You can't stay out in this weather. Christ, it'll kill ye!" said old Simmons. "Why not come up to my place for the night."

"I'll go to your place," said Clay.

Flem Simmons' land-holding was a half-mile-square homestead claim astraddle of a creek bottom full of devils-club stalks and skunk cabbage and wild-currant bushes and alder saplings. Simmons had planted fruit trees and berry bushes in the yard outside his door. They weren't of any particular use to him, but he kept them because he had always been accustomed to seeing such things around where people lived. Close to the door, within easy reach in case of unexpected illness, was a chittim-tree, the bark of which, boiled in a tea, was a reliable and violent purgative if the patient was man enough to get it down.

There were certain rules for barking a chittim-tree for physic, and a good deal of hard luck was apt to hit the consti-pated sufferer who guzzled a dose that hadn't been peeled carefully from up to down. If stripped on the bias, or round and round, the bark would take one's innards in that direction too, and grind the patient back and forth and side-ways like gravel in a stamp-mill without ever turning anything loose. If peeled up, it was liable to fetch his entire sys-tem up, like turning a sock wrong side out.

Chittim-trees grew wild on that slope of the mountains, and Simmons made a considerable chunk of extra money every year by peeling the wild bark to ship to patent-medicine manufacturers in the East. Sometimes they didn't pay him much for it, and then he evened up, not by sulking and refusing to deal with them any more, but by selling them a shipment of bark that had been peeled round and sideways and hind side to.

The thought of the patent-medicine factory being jumped by indignant cus-tomers who had heaved up the insol of their boots getting rid of the medi-cine, and by others who hadn't been able to get rid of it at all, gave Simmons more genuine entertainment than he could have bought himself by getting a decent price for the chittim-bark.

His snickering himself through a whole winter with little actual informa-tion to go on showed how easy he was to entertain. Even his own conversation was enough to hold him spellbound.

A LONG in the high fever of one tale he stopped, noticing that Clay had gone to sleep on him. He was about to jolt him awake and resume his recita-tion when he heard a wagon rattling from the road up the mountain. He let Clay alone because he wanted the pleas-ure of meeting whatever traveler it might be himself. He shaded his eyes and saw that what was coming was the horse-trader and his outfit.

The noise of the wagon rattling as it turned through the gate woke Clay in the cabin. He got off the bench and took a sight out through the window and then went to the door and watched the horsetrader's outfit make its entrance. She was so far from the house that Clay could make out none of her features, but he recognized her. He ran out in the snow and started untangling tie-ropes to help her.

"I know you," she said, low.

Clay said yes.

Her name, she told him, was Luz, which is the Mexican word for light. But Luce was the right pronunciation. She seemed to feel no need to explain why she wanted him to know all about her. She went on talking because there were certain things he needed to know, and she wanted to get them out and done with. Horse-swapping was not their trade. Sometimes, when wages were high enough to make it worth the

Look down . . . drop something and pick this up.

Illustration for H. L. Davis'
"HONEY IN THE HORN"

trouble, they worked harvesting; sometimes when the demand for horses was slow they traveled around, working at whatever there was. All that she told in a kind of unstemmable rush, without giving Clay any chance to put in anything.

"I'm leavin' with these people tomorrow for the hop-fields," Clay told Old Simmons that night.

What Love Could Amount To

Picking hops was not grinding toil, and a young man could easily get through several weeks at it without having his emotional reflexes worn down a particle. Also, it was fairly profitable. A man with his mind on it could weigh in from three to five dollars' worth of picked hops in a day.

Luce worked by herself, and carried her basket around to the far side of the vines whenever Clay edged close enough to talk to her. In the evenings after work it was the same. She acted afraid of him, and took such elaborate pains to keep him from catching her alone that he stopped trying to. It was a strain, having to want her and dislike her at the same time, but it did teach him something about what love could amount to.

One day he set his basket down to rest and change holds, and saw that he was about to bump into visitors. They hadn't called out of neighborliness, for one of them showed a star on his suspender and then covered it with his coat. He was after somebody among the hop-pickers, because he handed down a paper with printing on it and the hop-yard owner read it and asked, indignantly, why the damnation he had come bothering a man's hired help.

"You all set around the office with your feet on the stove when that Wade Shiveley raises hell in another county," he roared. "But when it's some measly family row or other, out you rip to fetch the mallyfactor to justice if it wears out every horse in the livery-stable. Are any of your men out helpin' to catch Shiveley? No, you're damn right they ain't."

It had taken Clay very little time to decide that the warrant was for him. He was backing cautiously away.

Clay had to go sneaking his way around a strange wilderness, harassed, hunted, friendless, alone. It was an outrageous piece of blamed foolishness. Having figured it out that he had a right to feel injured, he fell into a deep sleep that ended in an alarmed start of wakefulness because he heard a horse rattling somewhere along the road. He told himself that there was nothing to be scared of yet, and turned over to listen which direction it was traveling in. A girl was leading a saddled horse through a dropped place in the fence, and she was Luce.

He wanted to get up, but the shock, partly fright, of seeing her took his strength so he couldn't. He sat helpless, and she sat down beside him and turned her pony loose to graze. She didn't look in the least out of temper. Her face was always alert and swift—strong, but changing so readily with her changes of thought that a man who was used to her could tell what was in her mind even when she wanted to conceal it.

"I saw your mare down the road through the trees," she said. "I traveled nearly all night after you."

Table, Fireplace and No Rats

Clay and Luce explored one of the canyons for an old cabin. They had to be choosy because they had no tent to patch breaks with. Luce found one close to a grove of crab-apple trees and refused to look farther.

"The roof sheds water," she said. "And there's benches and a table and a fireplace and no rats. When you've been wintering on what you can find as long as I have you'll learn not to expect much more than that. Get some wood, and we'll boil some water to scrub things up."

Her housekeeping fever was surprising. Clay had supposed women interested themselves in such matters mostly because they were too timid or too puny to do anything else. But she could herd, harness, and skin a team and ride as well as he could, and here she was talking about scrubbing and cooking and fruit-canning as whole-heartedly as if she had never ventured foot outside the scullery. She was downright exultant about discovering a case of empty fruit-jars.

They lived there from late September until the alder-buds began to crack open about the middle of May. There were a few weeks in October when the days were warm and still, when leaves browned and grass ripened in the sun and the reflection of light from the sea lasted until long after nightfall, as if the sun were shining back from some distant water. Afterwards the sky blackened and the snow fell, and from that time until spring the rain never totally stopped and the light never entirely started. Except on the line of surf, the sea itself was like ink, and the tremendous winds that blew out of it carried fierce twisters of rain that turned everything pitchy as they passed.

That was the time that wore people's nerves the hardest. But to Clay, it was the best time of all. It was the same with Luce, even during all those days when they had to burn candles at noon to read by.

The Stray Shot

ONE night late in May Clay spent putting on a jag with Clark Burdon. Burdon had busted the bomb shell about Wade Shiveley being in those parts. There was a dash of comfort in knowing where Wade was. It was easier to avoid a man when you knew in which direction to look for him, so that, strategically, the night's conversation had given Clay a distinct advantage.

He was not too full to walk straight, but the road showed a tendency to get out from under his feet and run him against unfamiliar landmarks. He looked over his camp for several minutes before he realized that it was his. The buckskin mare grazing close by convinced him that he belonged there.

The mare raised her head and stared inquiringly at the backend of the wagon. Clay stared, too, and the fly in the wagon canvas opened. A man climbed down over the end-gate, reached out a saddle. He was a big man, heavy-built, and his silhouette against the canvas showed that he had on a gray pony-express hat.

Councils to decide one's future conduct did very little good in pressing emergency. Clay, who had talked all night trying to decide what he should do about Wade Shiveley, ripped loose his pistol and drew a bead without even thinking it over. The light was too bad and Burdon's whiskey too conquering for any close marksmanship. His first shot plowed the dirt under the man's feet, his second glanced off the wagon wheel and went howling off over the hill. Clay gave up trying to hit him, but banged a third shot after him by way of helping him along.

Clay hurried the saddle back where it belonged before Luce came out. She was barefooted, and she had a rifle ready. "Nothing but a stray dog," he told her easily. "I smoked him up a little to scare him."

She took him by the shoulders, jiggled him back and forth until he was dizzy and said, "You're drunk. I knew you would be if that old ape of a Clark Burdon got hold of you. The mare ran away on account of the shots and you can go up and bring her down right now. It'll help you walk off your jag."

It didn't seem quite bright, after putting in the night getting a jag, to turn around and put in the morning getting rid of it. But she was set in the notion, and Clay, after puttering around for close to an hour to give the camp-prowler plenty of time to get out of the thicket and be on his way, took a halter and dragged up the hill with it.

He finally cornered her among some bushes and haltered her. Leading her out, he came to a deep little gully full of black mud, and in it there was a man lying face down. A pony-express hat was jammed crooked on his head with mud soaked gray felt, there was a dark wet patch on the back of his shirt, and flies were buzzing over it peacefully. He was dead and he wasn't Wade Shiveley.

It was Isaac Lund, a son of a neighboring settler. Clay unhobbled the horse and rode for Clark Burdon.

The Plot

"Don't bawl now," Burdon warned him when he arrived. "We've got to counsel this out sensibly. This Wade Shiveley might be an idea, if he was handled properly. You say he's killed two men already? You know the names and dates and places, and all that truck?"

Clay hung back. He began to see what emotional strain had hitherto kept him from noticing. Burdon was still pretty well ginned, and the vehemence of his grudge against Wade Shiveley brought it out on him. "If I testify against him, he'll bust loose and testify back against me. And then the court will hold me and look up my record across the mountains, and where will I be? And people know I shot this morning. Luce knows it."

"The court won't hold you, because there won't be any court," Burdon pointed out. "We can handle a case like this right out here, and if he don't like it, what did he come here for. He certainly wasn't invited. He won't accuse you of anything, either. I'll fix that after we catch him. Tell that girl of yours there's been a murder up in the pasture and you're deputized to help run in the man that did it. We'll teach that bushwacker that he can't go killing people around this train whenever he feels like it."

"Maybe we can turn up some other way to handle it, if we think it over a little," Clay said. "Maybe I can just pull out of this train."

"You damned little idiot," said Burdon, losing patience. "I've figured you out of one hole and, by God! you'd better let me do it! Are you goin' to pull out of this train, or ain't you? Are you goin' to do as I say, or not? Answer me!"

A shadow fell across them and Luce stepped in front of them. "So you're going to make him answer you, are you?" she said. Her voice had a tone that Clay had not heard in it before.

Burdon sat without moving until she had finished. "It wasn't anything," he said. "Nothing of any importance whatever. A little matter of—a little matter of— Well, it wasn't anything."

Possibly it was disappointment at his deciding not to tell that made her fiercer. "It wasn't anything, and you had it laid out to make trouble for him if he didn't promise to do it? Well Clark Burdon, I'll kill you if you ever come near him again. If he ever gets into any trouble I'll know you're back of it and I'll kill you for that. You'd better heed what I say. I'll do it."

Burdon got to his feet with his self-possession apparently restored. "I'm not in the least afraid of being killed," he said and left them alone.

Luce did not appear out of temper with Clay, but rather pleased that she had happened around in time to take a difficult piece of management off his shoulders.

"What was he arguing with you about? Some crookedness that he's afraid to undertake himself?"

"Well," said Clay. "Some things have changed since we hit this country, and he thinks if we pull off into another road—" She continued to look at him through lowered eyelids as he explained about the probability that some crossroads constable would see money in

Wade Shiveley and hold Clay himself for a witness. "Then we'd be stuck here till court term—two months, maybe more."

"Then they'll hang him," Luce put in, "and you can go where you please. We know he killed Isaac Lund. He's sure to be hanged."

"I didn't see him do it," Clay reminded her. "You can't tell anything in a court except what you've seen."

"Well, the two men he killed across the mountains, you can tell them about that, can't you? We're only guessing that they'll hold you for a witness at all, but if they do you can tell enough to make sure they won't turn him loose."

She had moved so that her lips were close to his ear, and her voice was saying something altogether different from what she said in words. He knew that this was going to bind him to something that was dangerous and dishonest, that it would have to be paid for by lying Wade Shiveley to death, that it would have to be paid for. But it would have been worse to leave.

Being sure of him, she let go all holds on herself and lay waiting, short-breathed, unable to move or speak. Not to take her would mean setting up enmity between them, and it would be an enmity of her body, which couldn't understand such matters as moral responsibility and ethical scruples. He dared not risk that.

The Lynching

THE hounds were casting on an open rise beyond the horseherd. They moseyed in circles, first wide and then short, and now and then a couple would meet, put their heads together, and discuss the prospects before going at it again.

Clay got his buckskin mare saddled, and Burdon led over and stood watching with him. "I was in hopes you'd come along," he remarked, cautiously. "Better if Shiveley gets clean away, but people would notice if you didn't help tag him. Take it easy now. The hounds may not find him within a mile of where they're workin'. The longer they take, the farther our man will travel, and it'll be a blamed sight better for you if we don't catch him at all."

In the silence, they heard the dogs yelling almost straight ahead. Not the long woo-woo-woo this time, but a short-spaced hubbub of yapping and yelping like coyotes after a rainstorm in summer. In the middle of that they heard a shot, and a long succession of echoes trading it back and forth like something falling downstairs. The trail was wide and well used, and they lit out at a gallop.

Wade Shiveley stood in front of a wickyup door, staring from one to another of the men as if waiting for them to start something; the men stared at one another as if in doubt what to start. Shiveley sat suddenly down in the dust and said they couldn't prove that he had ever killed anybody, not at any mark in his career. Burdon pushed Clay forward into the light, and he thought "now for it."

"I know that's a lie," he said. "I know he killed his brother in a fight, and I know he killed a man on the road and robbed him of eight hundred dollars. I know he broke jail. He'll lie about it, but he done it. Turn him loose and he'll do more."

His voice kept clear and steady and indifferent. This was easier than testifying in court. He was getting through it luckier than he had expected. Shiveley still made no break to get away, and he didn't interrupt Clay or accuse him. He sat stubbornly in the dust and said that this was the end. He knew, better even than Burdon did, that the men were there to finish him, and that the only thing they still balked at was the physical disagreeableness of the job.

Shiveley got up and stood while the rope was being fixed around his neck. "I want to say something to you men," he said. "All the trouble I've had with this outfit of yours has been on account of that kid. When you hear about it, when you hear what I've got to tell you, you'll wonder how I ever put up with half of it."

"You can say what you've got to say when you're on top of the haystack," Lavran Baker told him. "Come on, before you're tempted to kill somebody else without intendin' to."

Nobody said anything. Three men climbed up the haystack ladder, caught Shiveley's lead-rope when it was thrown, and hauled in as he came up.

"Well?" one of them said. "If you've got any talkin' to do, now's your time for it."

Nobody ever knew when or how the realization had got worked through to him that he was going to die there. It had worked through, and so had something else—something so wild and un-expected that Clay, who knew him best, was never able to think of it afterwards without feeling glad he had seen it. Of his own part in it he felt sick and ashamed. Shiveley's made it worth remembering.

"I know I did have something to say," Shiveley said. "But it don't make any difference now. Go ahead whenever you want to. I don't care."

Daylight came almost as he dropped— at least it must have, for the first thing anybody noticed after he died was that the clouds overhead had turned pink and the colors of objects were visible, as well as their shapes.

Clay had paid for Luce with the hanging. It had cost him scarcely anything; it had been easy when he expected it to be difficult, and yet it seemed to him that the account was squared and that he had at last got something without paying for it.

One Agony On Top of Another

All the wagons had pulled past Clay's encampment. He had told them to go ahead, rejecting the women's offers of help because he did not realize at the time that they could be of any.

He could hear Luce calling him, first low and indistinct, then rising into shrill terror at the thought that he might have left her alone. Her body was what frightened her. It had turned on her and set itself against her; it griped her with such a building up of one agony on top of another that she was afraid to trust herself with it alone, as if its system of torturing her was something secretive and intimate which the presence of somebody else could hold back.

She got no better, and one morning something happened that made them realize what the trouble was and how dangerous a thing they had been trying to cure with ginger and hot water. The hemorrhage turned to something that even they in their ignorance could not mistake or be cheerful about. Luce was going through a miscarriage.

"There's no use keepin' on with this,"

Clay said. "I can't do you any good stayin' here, and I may find somebody that can. A doctor, a woman, somebody. I'm goin' to look."

She clutched him and said in a shaking voice that he must not leave her, that this was a sickness he had helped to bring on her and that he must stand it with her. He pulled away, and she fell back and lay watching him. "If you leave now, it's for good," she said. "You'll never see me again, I promise you. Look now, because this will be your last time."

He saw a fire on the horizon about twelve miles off, and headed for it without knowing whether he would strike anything when he got there or not. It was not settlers' wagons and it was not a town, but it was the next best thing. It was an Indian village. A half a dozen buck Indians lay in their blankets by a fire with the bare soles of their feet turned to the warmth.

"Find me somebody that's got a little sense, can't you?" Clay said. "I've got a sick girl, and I want somebody to come and help me to tend to her."

A young squaw remarked diffidently that as her original idea of what he wanted had been quoted at two dollars, she thought this ought to be worth five, because it would take so much more of her work and time. He paid her and

she put the money away, and one of the men got up and caught her a horse.

When they got back to the camp there was the pile of ashes where he had heated water. She was gone, she had carried out her threat and left; she had told him it was the last time, and it had been.

"You'll Have to Shoot Him!"

LUCE wintered what was left of her father's horse-herd at a deserted mining-camp in the Strawberry Mountains. It was the first winter she had ever gone through entirely alone and it wore hard on her. The dry winds of Spring lifted her spirits and made her eager to be out in it and going somewhere.

Beyond Burnt River several of her horses went down from lack of feed. She had to leave them, and that, coming at the end of everything else, frightened her. Once, after she had left Clay and was getting well of her sickness, she had been glad to leave Burnt River, because it was monotonous and ugly and full of people who had no use for her father. But now she was alone, and she had counted on it as a place she could always go if the road got too hard. On the summit, she got packed into a column of waiting wagons a couple of miles behind the slide, in the midst of some people from Cherry Creek.

A committee of Cherry Creek dignitaries—the speech-making, know-it-all stripe of men that always float to the top of an American crowd when any sudden emergency hits—informed her that their driver wanted the loan of her chestnut stallion, and that she would have to hand it over in the public interest. The stallion meant considerable to her, and she didn't think much of

their driver's looks, but there was nobody to back her up if she refused. She cut the stallion loose and let them have him.

It was not the Cherry Creek spokesmen for the public interest who brought the news that the stallion had been hurt. The word was brought her by a slow-spoken man whom she had known at Burnt River and on the Coast.

"You oughtn't to loaned out that horse of yours," he informed her, breaking it easy. "You ought to told 'em no. That young feller of yours is along with us, so we'd have backed you up. Now you've lost him."

"Lost?" she said, and got down over the wheel in a leap. The man backed, fearing that she was after him, and went into details.

"He's all broke up in the rocks, and you'll have to shoot him," he explained, luminously. "I looked him over careful, and he's plumb done for. You better come. Bring your gun to finish him with. The horse, I mean."

Relief that it was only the horse showed on her when she went down the rocks with her rifle. If Clay was here and if Burnt River claimed him it might claim her, too. Maybe her days of fighting all communities and belonging to none were about done with. She hurried down, and he got up and opened on her before she could speak.

The Truth Outs

"THAT's the rifle you didn't want anybody to know you had," he accused her, glaring at it. "Give it here to me."

She looked at him and at the rifle, trying to understand what was so awful

about it. The end of lone traveling had seemed so close that she had been thinking of that and not of anything behind her. "This is our rifle," she said. "What do you want with it?"

"I want it to settle something with your old man," he said. "He bush-whacked old Howell with it, and all I need is his gun to prove it. It's got a swelled bore, and the bullets come apart in it. Hand it here or I'll take it away from you."

She tossed it to her shoulder and shot. The chestnut stallion laid his neck heavily flat on the ground and died. The size of the wound showed that the bullet had dumdummed when it hit. She looked at what she had done, and tossed the rifle at Clay's feet. "There it is, and there's how it shoots," she said. She was a little defiant, but not frightened or conscience-stricken. "Is that any proof against my father, and what good is it going to do you if it is? My father is dead. Did you know that? Also I want you to know that my father didn't kill anybody. I did."

She half shut her eyes to keep out the glare from the gray rocks and the frost-white dead grass, and talked, leaving out nothing. She began when the horse-trader owned that he had got cleaned out in a match-race with old Howell. The horse-trader's wife swore that she would get the money back from the for-sworn old pup, so she and Luce got on their horses and rode through the rain to head him off, and they waited in a patch of scrub-oak with dark coming on until he passed. The horse-trader's wife stepped out on him and fell down and called to Luce to stop him, and Luce shot. She stopped him. Then she lay and trembled while the horse-trader's wife collected his eight hundred dollars, and then they went back and moved their camp hurriedly, so the rain would wash out all their tracks.

Nothing happened to them for that, but what kept worrying them was that eight hundred dollars which was not only the money her father had gambled but also the money Howell had put up against him. They dared not send it back for fear it would be traced to them; she dared not take it with her for fear Clay would find it.

She left it with the horse-trader, and his wife promised to see that it was sent back as soon as it was safe to send it. But afterward she left, too, as she had often threatened to. The horse-trader was alone when he found Luce sick in Clay's encampment.

"So you went along with him to watch it," Clay said. "You got up and left me because you felt afraid he'd spend the money you'd stole?"

IT was his old habit of quarrelsomeness that made him throw that at her, and he felt sorry the minute it was out. But her leaving him was something he had to find out about.

"I wasn't afraid of that," she said. "I was only afraid I might get out of my head and say something that would drive you away for good. Something about what I'd done or about that Lund shooting of yours."

He said that she hadn't let out anything; the Lund business had been a pure accident.

"I did," she said. "I was standing in the tent door when it happened, and I heard your bullet hit him when he ran. When you wouldn't tell me about it I knew it must be dangerous. I didn't get over that for a long time, not till they ran that outlaw down and lynched him for it. I hated Clark Burdon because he knew about it and I wasn't supposed to. . . . Well, my father found me in the tent and took me along with him."

"Well, we're in it," Clay said. "I ought to tell you about the things that I've done. There was a jail break that I'd helped with across the mountains, but it's done with now and it wouldn't matter in a stampede like this, anyhow. That's one good thing about it. Nothing counts except what's goin' on around you."

"That's the way I've been trying to live ever since I saw you," she said.

"You'd better move your wagon over with ours," he said. "The people know you're here, and they'll expect you to be with me."

James W. Gerard

MY FOUR YEARS IN GERMANY

James w. gerard (1867-) was American Ambassador to Germany during the period in which the two countries hovered on the brink and then fell into the abyss of war. "My Four Years in Germany" published in 1917, is a keen analysis of why the Germans have always been disposed toward warfare, and a forewarning of their designs on the Western Hemisphere. In reading it, one has only to substitute Hitler's autocracy for the Kaiser's to make it appear as pertinent today as it was twenty years ago.

Porter of Hell

Invariable custom required a new Ambassador in Berlin to give two receptions, one to the Diplomatic Corps and the other to all those people who have the right to go to court.

At the reception for the court people Mrs. Gerard stood in one room and I in another, and with each of us was a representative of the Emperor's household to introduce our guests. The officer assigned to me had the extraordinary name of der Pfortner von der Hoelle, which means the "porter of Hell."

I have often wondered since by what prophetic instinct he was sent to introduce me to the two years and a half of world war which I experienced in Berlin.

The winter before the war was not all cakes and ale either. First, we were then engaged in our conflict with Huerta, the Dictator of Mexico, and it was part of my work to secure from Germany promises that she would not recognize this Mexican President.

During this trouble the German Press, almost without exception, and especially that part of it controlled by the Government and by the Conservatives or Junkers, was most bitter in its attitude towards America.

The reason for this was the underlying hatred of an autocracy for a successful democracy, envy of the wealth, liberty and commercial success of America, and a deep and strong resentment against the Monroe Doctrine which prevented Germany from using her powerful fleet and great military force to seize a foothold in the Western Hemisphere.

Germany came late into the field of colonization in her endeavour to find "a place in the sun." The colonies secured were not habitable by white men. Togo, the Kameroons, and German East Africa, are too tropical in climate, too subject to tropical diseases, ever to become successful German colonies. German Southwest Africa has a more healthy climate but is a barren land. About the only successful industry there has been that of gathering the small diamonds that were discovered in the sands of the beaches and of the deserts running back from the sea.

On the earnest request of Secretary Bryan, I endeavoured to persuade the German authorities to have Germany become a signatory of the so-called Bryan Peace Treaties. After many efforts and long interviews, von Jagow, the Foreign Minister, finally told me that Germany would not sign these treaties because the greatest asset of Germany in war was her readiness for a sudden assault, that they had no objection to signing the treaty with America, but that they feared they would then be immediately asked to sign similar treaties with Great Britain, France and Russia, that if they refused to sign with these countries the refusal would almost be equivalent to a declaration of war, and, if they did sign, intending in good faith to stand by the treaty, that Germany would be deprived of her greatest asset in war, namely, her carefully acquired readiness for a sudden and overpowering attack.

Why Germans Wage War

To the outsider, the Germans seem a fierce and martial nation. But, in reality, the mass of the Germans, in consenting to the great sacrifice entailed by their enormous preparations for war, have been actuated by fear.

This fear dates from the Thirty Years' War, the war which commenced in 1618 and was terminated in 1648. In 1648, when the Treaty of Westphalia was concluded, Germany was almost a desert. Its population had fallen from twenty millions to four millions. The few remaining people were so starved that cannibalism was openly practised. In the German States polygamy was legalized, and was a recognized institution for many years thereafter.

Of thirty-five thousand Bohemian villages, only six thousand were left standing. In the lower Palatinate only one-tenth of the population survived, in Württemberg, only one-sixth. Hundreds of square miles of once fertile country were overgrown with forests inhabited only by wolves.

A picture of this horrible period is found in the curious novel, "The Adventurous Simplicissimus," written by Grimmelshausen, and published in 1669, which describes the adventures of a wise peasant who finally leaves his native Germany and betakes himself to a desert island which he refuses to leave when offered an opportunity to go back to the Fatherland.

He answers those who wish to persuade him to go back with words which seem quite appropriate today: "My God, where do you want to carry me? Here is peace. There is war. Here I know nothing of the arts of the court, ambitions, anger, envy, deceit, nor have I cares concerning my clothing and nourishment. . . . While I still lived in Europe everything was (O, woe that I must appear witness to such acts of Christians!) filled with war, burning, murder, robbery, plundering and the shame of women and virgins."

After the conclusion of the Thirty Years' War, Germany was again and again ravaged by smaller wars, culminating in the Seven Years' War of Frederick the Great and the humbling of Germany under the heel of Napoleon. In the wars of Frederick the Great, one tenth of the population was killed. Even the great Battle of the Nations at Leipsic in 1813 did not free Germany from wars, and in 1866 Prussia and the smaller North German States, with Italy, defeated Austria.

I am convinced that the fear of war induced by a hereditary instinct, caused the mass of the Germans to become the tools and dupes of those who played upon this very fear in order to create a military autocracy. On the other hand, and, especially, in the noble class, we have in Germany a great number of people who believe in war for its own sake.

Early in the winter of 1913-14, the Crown Prince showed his collection of Napoleana to a beautiful American woman of my acquaintance, and said that he hoped war would occur while his father was alive, but, if not, he would start a war the moment he came to the throne.

Since writing the above, the American woman who had this conversation with the Crown Prince wrote out for me the exact conversation in her own words, as follows: "I had given him Norman Angell's book, 'The Great Illusion,' which seeks to prove that war is unprofitable. He (the Crown Prince) said that whether war was profitable or not, when he came to the throne there would be war, if not before, just for the fun of it. On a previous occasion he had said that the plan was to attack and conquer France, then England, and after that my country (the United States of America); Russia was also to be conquered, and Germany would be master of the world."

IT MUST not be forgotten that at all periods of history it seems as if some blind instinct had driven the inhabitants of the inhospitable plains of North Germany to war and to conquest. The Cimbri and Teutones—the tribes defeated by Marius; Ariovistus, who was defeated by Julius Caesar; the Goths and the Visi-Goths; the Franks and the Saxons; all have poured forth from this infertile country, for the conquest of other lands.

The heart of modern Germany is the great north central plain which comprises practically all of the original kingdom of Prussia, stretching northward from the Saxon and Hartz mountains to the North and Baltic seas. It is from this dreary and infertile plain that for many centuries conquering military races have poured over Europe. The climate is not so cold in winter as that of the northern part of the United States. There is much rain and the winter skies are so dark that the absence of the sun must have some effect upon the character of the people. The Germans of today express the longing of the North Germans for pleasanter climes in the phrase in which they demand "a place in the sun."

The Saxons inhabit a more mountainous country; Württemberg and Baden are hilly; Bavaria is a land of beauty, diversified with lovely lakes and mountains. The soft outlines of the vine-covered hills of the Rhine Valley have long been the admiration of travellers.

The inhabitants of the Rhine Valley drink wine instead of beer. They are more lively in their disposition than the Prussians, Saxons and Bavarians, who are of a heavy and phlegmatic nature. The Bavarians are noted for their prowess as beer drinkers, and it is not at all unusual for prosperous burghers of Munich to dispose of thirty large glasses of beer in a day; hence the cures which exist all over Germany and where the average German business man spends part, at least, of his annual vacation.

In peace times the Germans are heavy eaters. As some one says, "It is not true that the Germans eat all the time, but they eat all the time except during seven periods of the day when they take their meals." And it is a fact that prosperous merchants of Berlin, before the war, had seven meals a day.

Many of the doctors who were with me thought that the heavy eating and large consumption of wine and beer had unfavourably affected the German national character, and had made the people more aggressive and irritable and consequently readier for war. The influence of diet on national character should not be under-estimated. Meat-eating nations have always ruled vegetarians.

The Psychological Moment

IF the Germans' long preparations for war were to bear any fruit, countless facts pointed to the summer of 1914 as the time when the army should strike that great and sudden blow at the liberties of the world.

It was in June, 1914, that the improved Kiel Canal was reopened, enabling the greatest warships to pass from the Baltic to the North Sea.

In the Zeppelins the Germans had arms not possessed by any other country and with which they undoubtedly believed that they could do much more damage to England than was the case after the actual outbreak of hostilities. They had paid great attention to the development of the submarine. Their aeroplanes were superior to those of other nations. They believed that in the use of poison gas, which was prepared before the outbreak of the war, they had a prize that would absolutely demoralize their enemy. They had their flame throwers and the heavy artillery and howitzers which reduced the redoubtable forts at Liège and Namur to fragments witin a few hours, and which made the holding of any fortresses impossible.

There was a belief in Germany that the French nation was degenerate and corrupt and unprepared for war. This belief became conviction when, in the debates of the French Senate, Senator Humbert, early in 1914, publicly exposed what he claimed to be the weakness and unpreparedness of France.

Prince Lichnowsky, the German Ambassador in London, certainly reported to his government that England did not wish to enter the war. It was believed by the Germans that Ireland would rise in general rebellion the moment that war was declared. In the summer of 1914 Russia was believed to be on the edge of revolution.

THEN there was a movement of the German people against the militaristic autocracy which warned the government and military people that the mass of Germans were coming to their senses and were preparing to shake off the bogy of militarism and fear, which had roosted so long on their shoulders like a Prussian old-man-of-the-sea.

The fact that the Socialists, at the close of the 1913 session of the Reichstag, boldly remained in the Chamber and refused to rise or to cheer the name of the Emperor indicated a new spirit of resistance to autocracy; and autocracy saw that if it was to keep its hold upon Germany it must lead the nation into a short and successful war.

This is no new trick of a ruling class. From the days when the patricians of Rome forced the people into war whenever the people showed a disposition to demand their rights, autocracies have always turned to war as the best antidote against the spirit of democracy.

The Kaiser was implicitly believed when on the first day of the war, he appeared on the balcony of the palace and told the crowd who were keen for war, that "before the leaves have fallen from the trees you will be back home."

The army and all Germany believed him and believed, too, that a few short weeks would see the destruction of France and the consequent seizure of her rich colonies; that Russia could then be struck a good quick blow before she could concentrate her army and resources; that England would remain neutral; and that Germany would consequently become, if not the actual owner, at least the dictator of the world.

Some one has since said that the Emperor must have meant pine trees.

The Lusitania

I THOUGHT that America would break diplomatic relations and enter the war in 1915 with the killing of American women and civilians who were passengers on the *Lusitania*. I was prepared to leave Germany immediately.

During this period I had constant conversations with Foreign Minister Zimmermann. It was during the conversations about this submarine warfare that Zimmermann on one occasion said to me: "The United States does not dare to do anything against Germany because we have five hundred thousand German reservists in America who will rise in

arms against your government if your government should dare to take any action against Germany." As he said this, he worked himself up to a passion and repeatedly struck the table with his fist.

I told him that we had five hundred and one thousand lamp posts in America, and that was where the German reservists would find themselves if they tried any uprising; and I also called his attention to the fact that no German Americans making use of the American passports which they could easily obtain, were sailing for Germany by way of Scandinavian countries in order to enlist in the German army. I told him that if he could show me one person with an American passport who had come to fight in the German army I might more readily believe what he said about the Germans in America rising in revolution.

The climax was reached when medals celebrating the sinking of the *Lusitania* were sold throughout Germany. Even if the sinking of the *Lusitania* had been justified only one who has lived in Germany since the war can understand the disgustingly bad taste which can gloat over the death of women and babies.

It seemed as if the Government was anxious to cultivate the hate against America. Long before American ammunition was delivered in any quantity to England and long before any at all was delivered to France, not only did the Government influence newspapers, but the official *Communiqués* alleged that quantities of American ammunition were being used by the Allies.

The Government seemed to think that if it could stir up enough hate against America in Germany on this ammunition question the Americans would become terrorized and stop shipment.

Hymns of Hate

ON MY way from Berlin to America, in February, 1917, I met the celebrated Italian historian, Ferrero. He had written on America, and had stated that the thing that struck him most in the study of the American people was the absence of hate.

In the discussion which followed we agreed that the reasons why there was more hate in Europe were first, because the peoples of Europe were confined in small space, and, secondly, because the European, whatever his rank or station, lacked the opportunities for advancement and consequently the eagerness to press on ahead, and that fixing of the thought on the future, instead of the past, which formed part of the American character.

In a few hours in Europe it is pos-

THE GERMAN VIEW. The sinking of the Cunard liner *Lusitania* in May, 1915, is allegorized on this medal. On the obverse, ignoring warnings, crowds buy tickets from Death at the Cunard office, which bears the motto "Business above everything." On the reverse (right) the sinking ship is seen to carry airplanes and munitions in defiance of the "No contraband" declaration
British Museum; photo, Oxford University Press

sible to travel in an automobile across countries where the people differ violently from the countries surrounding them not only in language, customs and costumes, but also in methods of thought and physical appearance.

The day I left Berlin I went to see Herr von Gwinner, head of the Deutsche Bank, with reference to a charitable fund which had been collected for widows and orphans in Germany. In our talk, von Gwinner said that Europeans envied America because we seemed to be able to assimilate all those people who, as soon as they landed on our shores, sought to forget their old race hatreds and endeavoured, as speedily as possible, to adopt American clothes, and thought.

I told him I thought it was because in our country we did not try to force any one; that there was nothing to prevent a Pole speaking Polish and wearing Polish dress, if he chose; that the only weapon we used against those who desired to uphold the customs of Europe was that of ridicule; and that it was the repressive measures such as, for example, the repressive action taken by Prussia against the Poles and the Danes, the Alsatians and the Lorrainers, that had aroused a combative instinct in these people and made them cling to their former nationality.

At first, with the coming of war, the concentrated hate of the German people seemed to be turned upon the Russians. But later, and directed by the master hand of the governing class, all the hatred of the Germans was concentrated upon England.

The cartoon in *Punch* representing a Prussian family having its morning "Hate," was, in some aspects, not at all exaggerated. Hate in Germany is cultivated as a noble passion, and, during the war, divines and generals vied with each other in its praise. Early in 1917, the Prussian General in command at Limburg made a speech in which he extolled the advantages of hate and said that there was nothing like getting up in the morning after having passed a night in thoughts and dreams of hate.

The phrase "Gott strafe England" seemed to be all over Germany. It was printed on stamps to be affixed to the backs of letters like our Red Cross stamps. I even found my German body servant in the Embassy affixing these stamps to the back of all letters, official and otherwise, that were sent out. He was stopped when discovered. Paper money was stamped with the words: "Gott strafe England," "und America" being often added as the war progressed and America refused to change the rules of the game and stop the shipment of supplies to the Allies.

Every one is familiar with Lissauer's "Hymn of Hate." It is not extraordinary that one man in a country at war should produce a composition of this kind; but it is extraordinary as showing the state of mind of the whole country, that the Emperor should have given him the high order of the Red Eagle of the Second Class as a reward for having composed this extraordinary document.

The Treachery of Americans

As the Germans gradually awoke to the fact that President Wilson was not afraid of the German vote and that the export of supplies from America would not be stopped, this stream of hate was turned on America. There was a belief in Germany that President Wilson was opposed by a majority of people of the United States, that he did not represent the real sentiment of America,

and that the sentiment there was favourable to Germany.

Unfortunately many Americans in Germany encouraged the German people and the German Government in this belief. Americans used to travel about, giving lectures and making speeches attacking their own country and their own President, and the newspapers published many letters of similar import.

One of the most active of these was a man named Maurice Somborn, a German American, who represented in Germany an American business house. He made it a practice to go about in Berlin and other cities and stand up in cafes and beer halls in order to make addresses attacking the President of the United States.

So bold did he become that he even, in the presence of a number of people in my room, one day said that he would like to hang Secretary Bryan as high as Haman and President Wilson one foot higher. The American newspapers stated that I called a servant and had him thrown out of the Embassy. This statement is not entirely true: I selfishly kept that pleasure for myself.

The case of Somborn gave me an idea and I cabled to the Department of State asking authority to take up the passports of all Americans who abused their own country on the ground that they had violated the right, by their abuse, to the protection of a passport. The Department of State sustained my view and, by my direction, the consul in Dresden took up the passports of a singer named Rains and a gentleman of leisure named Recknagel who had united in addressing a letter to the Dresden newspapers abusing the President.

It was sometime before I got Somborn's passport and I later on received from him the apologies of a broken and contrite man and obtained permission from Washington to issue him a passport in order to enable him to return to America.

Of course, these vilifiers of their own country were loud in their denunciations of me, but the prospect of losing the protection of their passports kept many of these men from open and treasonable denunciation.

The League of Truth

THE Government actually encouraged the formation of societies which had for their very object the scattering of literature attacking the President of the United States. The most conspicuous of these organizations was the so-called League of Truth.

This organization worked with the express permission of the German authorities because during the war no societies or associations of any kind could meet, be formed or act without the express permission and superintendence of both the military and police authorities.

Any one who has lived in Germany knows that it would be impossible even in peace times to hang a sign or a wreath on a public statue without the permission of the local authorities; and yet on the Emperor's birthday, January twenty-seventh, 1916, this League of Truth was permitted to place an enormous wreath, over four feet high, on the statue of Frederick the Great, with an American flag draped in mourning attached, and a silk banner on which was printed in large letters of gold, "Wilson and his press are not America." The League of Truth then had a photograph taken of this wreath which was sent all over Germany, again, of course, with the permission of the authorities. The wreath and attachments, in spite of frequent protests on my part to Zimmermann and von Jagow, remained in this conspicuous position until the sixth of May, 1916.

Then I told von Jagow that if this continuing insult of our flag and President was not taken away that I would go the next day with a cinematograph operator and take it away myself. The next day the wreath had disappeared.

This League of Truth attacked me in a circular which they distributed shortly after my return from a trip to America in December, 1916. It stated, "What do you think of the American Ambassador? When he came to Germany after his trip to America he brought a French woman with him."

And the worst of this statement was that it was true. But the League, of course, did not state that my wife came with me bringing her French maid by the express permission of the German Foreign Office.

I have had occasion many times to wonder at the curious twists of the German mind, but I have never been able to understand on what possible theory the German Government permitted and even encouraged the existence of this League of Truth. Certainly the actions of the League would not terrorize the American Congress, President or me into falling in with all the views of the German Government, and if the German Government was desirous of either the President's friendship or mine, why was this gang of good-for-nothings allowed to insult indiscriminately their country and their President?

On the Brink of War

I REMEMBER on one evening Secretary Zimmermann asked me what America could do, supposing the almost impossible, that America should resent the commencement of ruthless submarine warfare by the Germans and declare war. I said that nearly all the great inventions used in this war had been made by Americans; that the very submarine which formed the basis of our discussion was an American invention, and so were the barbed wire and the aeroplane, the ironclad, the telephone and the telegraph, so necessary to trench warfare; that even that method of warfare had been first developed on something of the present scale in our Civil War; and that I believed that, if forced to it, American genius could produce some invention which might have a decisive effect in this war.

Zimmermann seemed inclined to believe that there was something in my contentions. But he said, "While possibly you might invent something in America, while possibly you will furnish money and supplies to the Allies, you have no men; and the public sentiment of your country is such that you will not be able to raise an army large enough to make any impression."

I said that possibly if hostilities once broke out with the Germans, the Germans might force us by the commission of such acts as had aroused Great Britain, to pass a law for universal military service. This proposition of mine was branded by the Chancellor as absolutely impossible; and therefore, I am sure that the adoption by the United States of universal service in the first round of the war struck a very severe blow at the morale of Germany.

DURING every crisis between America and Germany I had looked forward always to one object, namely, the preservation of peace between our respective countries. Many suggestions were made which, I think, materially aided up to that time in the preservation of peace.

The great question to be solved was whether the Germans were sincerely anxious for peace, or were only making general offers of peace in order to excuse in the eyes of the world a resumption of ruthless submarine warfare and to win to their side public opinion in the United States, in case such warfare should be resumed.

Had the decision rested with the Chancellor and with the Foreign Office, instead of with the military, I am sure that the decision would have been against the resumption of this ruthless war. But Germany is not ruled in war time by the civilian power.

In the meantime and in spite of the official assurance given to me certain men in Germany, in a position to know, warned me that the government intended to resume ruthless submarine war. Ludendorf, they said, had declared in favour of this war and, accordingly to them, that meant its adoption.

The military felt that three months' time was all that would be required to bring Great Britain to her knees and end the war. And in fact so cleverly did von Tirpitz, the Conservatives and the enemies of the Chancellor and other advocates of submarine war carry on their propaganda that the belief was ingrained in the whole of the German nation that a resumption of this ruthless war would lead within three months to what all Germans so ardently desired —peace.

But this peace, of course, meant only a German peace, a peace as outlined to me by the Chancellor; a peace impossible for the Allies and even for the world to accept; a peace which would leave Germany immensely powerful and ready immediately after the war to take up a campaign against the nations of the Western hemisphere; a peace which would compel every nation, so long as German autocracy remained in the saddle, to devote its best energies, the most fruitful period of each man's life, to preparations for war.

Breaking Diplomatic Relations

ON JANUARY thirtieth, I received a definite intimation of the coming Ultimatum and I telegraphed a warning to the American Ambassadors and Ministers as well as to the State Department. On January thirty-first at about four o'clock in the afternoon I received a letter from Zimmermann asking me to come and see him.

I went to the Foreign Office at six o'clock. Zimmermann then read to me in German a note from the Imperial Government, announcing the creation of the war zones about Great Britain and France and the commencement of ruthless submarine warfare at twelve p.m. that night. I made no comment, put the note in my pocket and went back to the Embassy. It was then about seven p.m. and, of course, the note was immediately translated and dispatched with all speed to America.

Saturday, February third, the President announced to Congress the breaking of diplomatic relations with Germany. The news of this did not reach Berlin until Sunday. On this Saturday evening Mrs. Gerard and I had a supper engagement with Zimmermann.

After supper, while I was talking to Zimmermann, he spoke of the note to America and said: "You will see, everything will be all right. America will do nothing, for President Wilson is for peace and nothing else. Everything will go on as before. I have arranged for you to go to the Great General Headquarters and see the Kaiser next week and everything will be all right."

The Berlin Sunday papers contained the authentic account of the breaking of diplomatic relations by America. On Monday I went over to see Zimmermann and told him that I had come to demand my passports.

Of course, Zimmermann by that time had received the news and had had time to compose himself. The American correspondents told me that when he saw them on the day before, he had at first refused to say anything and then had been rather violent in his language and had finally shown great emotion. I am sure, from everything I observed, that the break of diplomatic relations came as an intense surprise to him and to the other members of the government, and yet I cannot imagine why intelligent men should think that the United States of America had fallen so low as to bear without murmur this sudden kick in the face.

The Long View

I WAS credited by the Germans with having hoodwinked and jollied the Foreign Office and the Government into refraining for two years from using illegally their most effective weapon. This, of course, is not so. I always told the Foreign Office the plain simple truth and the events showed that I correctly predicted the attitude of America.

Our American national game, poker, has given us abroad an unfair reputation. We are always supposed to be bluffing. A book was published in Germany about the President called, "President Bluff."

I only regret that those high in authority in Germany should have preferred to listen to pro-German correspondents who posed as amateur super-Ambassadors rather than to the authorized representatives of America. I left Germany with a clear conscience and the knowledge that I had done everything possible to keep the peace.

When I returned to America, after living for two and a half years in the centre of world calamity, everything seemed petty and small. I was surprised that people could still seek little advantages, still be actuated by little jealousies and revenges. Freed from the round of daily work I felt for the first time the utter horror and uselessness of all the misery these Prussian military autocrats had brought upon the world; and what a reckoning there will be in Germany some day when the plain people realize the truth, when they learn what base motives actuated their rulers in condemning a whole generation of the earth to war and death!

Is it not a shame that the world should have been so disturbed; that peaceful men are compelled to lie out in the mud and filth in the depth of raw winter, shot at and stormed at and shelled, waiting for a chance to murder some other inoffensive fellow creature?

Why must the people in old Poland die of hunger, not finding dogs enough to eat in the streets of Lemberg? The long lines of broken peasants in Serbia and Roumania; the population of Belgium and Northern France torn from their homes to work as slaves for the Germans; the poor prisoners of war starving in their huts or working in factories and mines; the cries of the old and the children, wounded by bombs from Zeppelins; the wails of the mothers for their sons; the very rustling of the air as the souls of the ten million dead sweep to another world,—why must all these horrors come upon a fair green earth, where we believed that love and help and friendship, genius and science and commerce, religion and civilization, once ruled?

It is because in the dark, cold Northern plains of Germany there exists an autocracy, deceiving a great people, poisoning their minds from one generation to another and preaching the virtue and necessity of war; and until that autocracy is either wiped out or made powerless there can be no peace.

I have always stated that Germany is possessed yet of immense military power; and, to win, the nations opposed to Germany must learn to think in a military way. The mere entrance, even of a great nation like our own, into the war, means nothing in a military way unless backed by military power.

And there must be no German peace. The old régime, left in control of Germany, of Bulgaria, of Turkey, would only seek a favourable moment to renew the war, to strive again for the mastery of the world.

Fortunately America bars the way,— America led by a fighting President who will allow no compromise with brutal autocracy.

WHATEVER an author puts between the two covers of his book is public property; whatever of himself he does not put there is his private property, as much as if he had never written a word.—*Gail Hamilton.*

THE first (barbers) that entered Italy came out of Sicily and it was in the 454 yeare after the foundation of Rome. Brought in they were by P. Ticinius Mena as Verra doth report for before that time they never cut their hair. The first that was shaven every day was Scipio Africanus, and after him cometh Augustus the Emperor who evermore used the rasor.—*Pliny the Elder.*

Josephine Johnson

NOW IN NOVEMBER

THIS WINNER of the Pulitzer Prize in 1934 is not merely a farm story, any more than was "Ethan Frome" (Issue No. 10), with whose spirit it has much in common. It is a story of human beings caught in the clutches of land and the elements—of their unalterable loneliness and shattered emotions. In the hands of a less gifted writer the theme of "Now in November" would be maudlin; in the delicate fingers of Josephine Johnson (1910-), this novel becomes a tragic little epic of America.

Roots Struck in March

Now in November I can see our years as a whole. This autumn is like both an end and a beginning to our lives, and those days which seemed confused with the blur of all things too near and too familiar are clear and strange now. It has been a long year, longer and more full of meaning than all those ten years that went before it. There were nights when I felt that we were moving toward some awful and hopeless hour, but when that hour came it was broken up and confused because we were too near, and I did not even quite realize that it had come.

I can look back now and see the days as one looking down on things past, and they have more shape and meaning than before. But nothing is really finished or left behind forever.

I remember the day we came and the months afterward well enough. Too well. The roots of our life, struck in back there in that March, have a queer resemblance to their branches.

It was an old place and the land had been owned by Haldmarnes since the Civil War, but when we came no one had been living there for years. The land was stony, but with promise, and sheep grew fat in the pastures, where rock ledges were worn back, white like stone teeth bared to the frost. There were these great orchards planted up and down the hills, and

when Mother saw them that first day she thought of having to gather the crop and haul the apples up this steepness but she only said a good harvest ought to come, and the trees looked strong though old.

"No market even if they bear," I remember Father said and then,—"it's mortgaged land."

Mother sat there very quiet. He had not told her the place was mortgaged and the land at least, she had thought was unencumbered, and sanctuary though everything else was gone. But even in the moment when she saw that this, too, was uncertain and shifting ground, something she always had— something I didn't know then and may never know—let her take it quietly. A sort of inner well of peace. Faith, I guess it was.

BUT we could forget for the time this sense of impermanence and doubt which had come up from his words. Merle was ten then and I was fourteen, and it seemed to us that some great adventure had begun.

Father looked only at the old, year-rotted barns. He wasn't a man made for a farmer, although brought up on the land when a boy. He hadn't the resignation that a farmer has to have,—that resignation which knows how little use to hope or hate, or pray for even a bean before its appointed time.

My father's life had been a sort of fierce crawling to rid us of debt before hat time when even the effort would be too heavy for him. He wanted some safety for us, freedom from that fear and doubt he had always known himself. And he wanted time to look around and be still. He loved the land in a proud, owned way,—only because it was his, and for what it would mean to us.

It was cold that first March and the ploughing late, I remember. Kerrin, my eldest sister, complained of the raw coldness and the house was hard to keep warm enough. But I remember one day of God that came toward the last, when we lay down carefully on the grass so as not to smash the bluets, and smelled their spring-thin scent.

We watched a bluebird searching the trees and along the fence posts, and could see a long way off into the bottom land where the creek was and the maples that followed the water, long branched and bending down to its pools. There was a shrike in the crab branches and Kerrin said they were cruel things, impaling the field-mice and birds on locust thorns so that their feet stuck out stiff like little hands. I didn't think they were cruel things though—only natural. They reminded me of Kerrin, but this I had sense not to say aloud.

"Dad's birthday comes soon now," Merle said. "He'll be fifty-seven. We should have a party, I think—with presents."

"Where'll you get the money?" Kerrin asked. "I've got some, but you haven't any. I bought a knife that I'm going to give him."

I looked at Kerrin quick and jealous. "Where did you get money from?" I asked. I hadn't thought of a thing to give, and it made me angry at her.

"It's mine, Marget. I earned it!" Kerrin shouted. "I suppose that you think I stole or borrowed!" She got up and glared down on me. She was dark all over her long thin face, and I think she hoped that I did suspect her—she wanted to feel accused of dark and secret things.

I didn't have anything to say. I was afraid to start probing again about the knife. Nothing was changed, but the afternoon seemed cold and chilly.

Father's Birthday Party

We planned the party ourselves, how it was to be and what was to be made, and I taught Merle a long poem to say, and kept her in the chicken house for an hour a day sitting on the bran-bin to recite it off by heart. It was about a farmer, and we hoped that Father would laugh because it was supposed to be funny in some places, but we knew that Mother would, anyway.

Kerrin wouldn't tell us what it was she was going to do, but went off each day by herself in the woods. "It's going to be good," was all she'd say. "You-all will be shamed." Between milking and supper she would be gone off alone and come back sometimes singing.

Father's birthday came on the ninth of April. We had battered about all night scarcely asleep, and so heard Dad get up as he always did at four, and supposed that his heart was pounding like ours.

At six that evening Dad came in and shouted, "Where's the food, you women?" and sounded so young and cheerful that we climbed on him as we had not done in weeks. Mother looked suddenly younger, too, and Cale, our old blind dog, barked as loud as he would at some stranger. Mother brought in the ham stuck about with cloves and I saw her slip Cale a bit to calm him.

Then we let Merle bring the cake in on its platter, and her face looked like a big candle itself, looming above the little flames, and Dad grinned but didn't shout as we thought he should. He cut us big slices, and a bigger one for Mother, and then we thought it was time for the presents to be given.

"You be the first one, Kerrin," I said. Father looked pleased, but puzzled and wondering what was to come. Kerrin got up, fierce and excited in her eyes, and pulled a small heavy thing out of her sweater pocket. She held it out toward him but kept her fingers on it, and we could see that it was a folded knife tipped with silver on the end.

"This is supposed to be your present, Dad." She sounded excited and full of pride. "Watch what I've learned to do —taught myself how to do it." She opened the knife and aimed at a brown spot on the wall.

"Look out!" Dad shouted. "Stop!" He shoved back his chair and tried to snatch the knife, but jerked at her arm instead. Merle and I screamed out, and the knife went wild, straight at old Cale's blind head, and slashed across his nose.

"God damn you!" Father shouted. He grabbed at Kerrin and knocked her back against the wall.

Merle started to cry and Kerrin screamed out some horrible things. Only Mother had sense enough to run to Cale and slop at his nose with water. The cut was deep and slashed back i his head, and it bled as if every vei were opened. Kerrin was on her knee by Mother, trying to sop up the blood but Dad knocked her away.

It was terrible—the way she went ou in a black rage, crying, with her hand clenched and her eyes—I was scared an Merle screamed when we saw her eye and the awful hate in them. She slammed the door and rushed out in th dark, though it was beginning to rai and a cold wind had come up. I stood there dumb, not knowing what to do or say, and Merle kept on crying.

Then Dad said, "It's no use." He picked up Cale and started out toward the door. "The girl's killed him," he said.

Mother still held the cloth around Cale's mouth, and we heard her tell Dad that it was he who had shaken Kerrin' arm. But the door slammed after an we could not hear his answer except a a loud and angry sound.

Ten Years After

ON FATHER's birthday this year, I walked up near to the old stone fence where we'd buried Cale. Merle and I had piled some rocks into a sort of cairn on the top of his grave, and planted wild ginger there.

We used to see Kerrin going up the hill-path sometimes, and once, years ago, we found her crying on top of the cairn and sneaked away, pretending not to see. It seemed queer to us who had never cried afterward, but had loved him so much when alive—much more than she had, we thought. But now I'm sure of it: Kerrin had a strange way of not seeming to notice things or care about them, but years later we'd find the feeling was there, living and fierce, under a thin slab of indifference.

We did not celebrate Father's birthday any more. We let this day go by without saying much, and I think he himself had forgotten the meaning of it; but there was one thing at least this year that set it apart again from othe days.

FATHER came up tired that night while Merle was peeling potatoes. He turned toward Mother and threw his hat on the table, mopped at his damp and rutted face. "Max isn't coming back," he said "It seems not to pay to work for me!" He looked at Mother as if it were she who had driven Max off or else had failed through some fault to hold him here.

"Maybe Grant Koven could come," Mother said. She knew that nothing was ever as overwhelming or final as he seemed to think; that if he would wait, instead of shouting, there'd be less to shout over in the end.

"No," Father said. He shoved her suggestion away as though it were a stupid thought that had come to him hours ago and had been found of no use. He stared at his hands. Sullen and tired,

he anger going out. Then he jerked
his head toward Merle, saw the potatoes
half-peeled and asked when supper was
going to be. "If you'd have it any time
soon," he muttered, "I'd make it over
to Kovens' tonight."

Grant was about thirty-one, Mother
said, and had been away from home for
five years, working on ranches and in
the mines after he had finished school,
but had now come back to his father's
place. Bernard Koven had been a min-
ster once; then he bought this land of
his and went to farming. He did no
dairying, or any of all those things that

Father had started and was breaking his
back to keep on doing—each by itself
too much for one man alone.

I wondered a lot about Grant in those
days before he came. Merle seemed only
mildly interested, though, and hoped
that he wouldn't eat very much. Kerrin
said nothing at all about him and might
not even have known that he was coming. She was never around when things
were told, and then acted as if we had a
conspiracy of silence against her.

I felt excited, though, and full of a
kind of nameless hope. This year, I
thought, will be different . . . better.

Grant

THEN on a cold dry day toward the
middle of April, Grant came over.
He looked older than I had thought he
would be, and seemed at first a cragged
and strange-looking man. He was tall
and thin and we found ourselves staring
up at his face like children. When he
spoke, his voice had a kind sound,
almost old, and his smile was quick and
sudden. He was embarrassed, we could
see, but I noticed he had a quiet way
of standing, not stiff and awkward like
most men ill at ease.

"I'm glad you've come, Mr. Koven,"
Mother said. She spoke stiffly as though
he were the minister or sheriff, but she
smiled and a person could see she meant
it.

"It's good to have somebody new
around," Merle blurted out. *"Anything
new."*

Grant laughed then, a big hearty
sound, and looked much younger. "You
make it easy for me," he said. "I'm glad
that anything's going to do."

I like to remember that noon. Kerrin
did not come in and we felt, as always,
more free and at ease without her. Even
Father seemed less impatient and
screwed with worry, and ate two of the
pickled peaches, forgetting to ask how
many were left.

It wasn't that Grant was a man easy
to know and given to making much fun,
nor was he quick and loud like Merle.

But things struck him new and differently and he knew how to make his
tales come alive. He talked with Father
over all the old arguments and theories
that we knew too well to debate or even
to hear any longer; and Father felt that
he had a man to support him, though
Grant seldom agreed with him. Grant
had a kind of dry humor, too, bitter at
times, but never with any malice or
littleness.

I CAME to wonder how we had got
along alone in the days before Grant
had come. I wondered sometimes with
Merle how he moved all his dangling
knots and bones hard and together
enough to accomplish the things he did.
"He looks like a gaunt old long-legged
tree," she told me once.

Dad was around and turned fast on
her. "That ain't for you to say," he
shouted. "Grant's a good-enough looking man—better looking than most!"

Merle said maybe he was right and
as long as Grant did the work he could
look like a post or anything else and it
wouldn't matter to her."

"Men are all like each other," Merle
said. "We'll find him no different than
any other. They're like as pods. Seem to
think that just being born sets them
apart as gods!"

She talked like this, not with malice
but believing it, till one day that first

week when he came up at noon and found her washing. He came over and told her to let him do the rest. "I've got the time now," he said. "You let me finish up."

Grant pulled out three shirts at once and twisted them all together. Squashed the buttons in half. Then he slung them over the line and stood back grinning, red and embarrassed. She thought him a little mad, I guess, but hoped that he'd finish before the spell passed over. I could see her mind changing before my eyes, a hard core softening up.

"You're better than most," she told him. "Maybe just being a man isn't all the excuse you need for living."

"It's a good enough one," Grant said. He looked at her and laughed, and then asked why she didn't go in and start cooking.

I saw Grant watching her when she went away, a sort of pleased look on his tired face.

Grant was kind, very kind to me. I could not have asked for anything worse. Something snatched and blundered inside me when I heard his voice unexpectedly, but after a while the foolish ecstasy and fog dried up, and there was only the pain and the reality left.

I began to see clearly what I had already known, and yet had not gone far enough in thought to face. I think I knew it plainly, not through any word spoken, but from watching Grant's face when he was looking at Merle.

Kerrin wanted Grant, too, wanted him more than anything else she had ever snatched at. Because he was tangible, I suppose. It wasn't the real Grant that she wanted or cared about, because she had never known him underneath. She made me think of the carrion vine that move with a hungry aimlessness groping blindly in all directions till they find a stalk to wrap on.

I still had hope that Grant was not beyond me, because I could still see him and hear him at least. I was afraid though, and prayed. Lord, make me satisfied with small things. Make me content to live on the outside of life, God, make me love the rind!

There must be some reason why I was made quiet and homely and slow and then given this stone of love to mumble. Love *was* a stone!

And suddenly I wished to God that Grant had never come here at all.

The Long Drouth

May was a queer month. The beginning of understanding. A cold dry month. Rot-sweet smell of mandrakes on the air, but most things almost too chilled to bloom. No rain, and dust coming up behind the plough. Cold dust is a sort of ominous thing, and Father began to worry over the shrunken pond. These things were sourly appropriate to the month's end.

By June things were shriveling brown, but not everything dried and ugly yet. It was not so much the heat and dryness then as the fear of what they *would* do. I could imagine a kind of awful fascination in the very continuousness of this drouth, a wry perfection in its slow murder of all things.

By July half the corn was dead and flapped in the fields like brittle paper. The pastures burned to a cinder. I stumbled once in the woods and the ash of dry leaves flew up like a dust. Prices went up, we heard again, but Dad got no more for his milk and got less for the cows he sold, since nearly all other farmers were selling off.

I kept hearing the calves bawl all the time, hot and thirsty in the pastures, but we could only water them in the evenings.

When everything was finally dead, I thought that relief from hope would come, but hope's ponds will fill up again . . . the fall pastures might come back with rain . . . the cistern get deep again. There was still the awful torture of hope that would die only with life.

Merle alone didn't seem to mind the heat. She worked out in the fields with Grant and Dad, and was burned deep to a kind of smouldering brown. I noticed that she grew more quiet in those days from something that had started to worry her out of mildness. A sort of fear and responsibility.

She tried to avoid Grant, and talked to him with a queer mixture of hesitancy and frankness. I pitied Grant and wondered if he was learning, as I had, the numbness of patience made possible only by blindly shoving away all doubt. He never complained, and sometimes I wished that he would say more. Shout or curse. His silence seemed like a wall against some rising tide.

Because I was quiet and dull I noticed Grant more than the others did, and sometimes even in the middle of talking he would seem years away from us and gone into himself. But there was a dignity about him that I loved.

It came on me suddenly once, with no reason for knowing, but with a certainty nothing could shake or change, that neither Mother nor Grant looked up to or envied any man. It was not a self-pride or a feeling of being different. Not that at all. But a sort of faith in the dignity of the human spirit. I only stumble for words to make it plain. I only know it was there and gave them an inch of height beyond us; and that they were never petty or even ridiculous.

After a while we had less work, so much of the garden stuff having died, and the ground was too hard for ploughing. We sat out and talked on the nights too hot for sleep.

Kerrin would come these evenings and lie half asleep in the porch's shadow; some nights not saying a word, and other times very shrilly excited. She told us things she'd picked up around on the farms; scandals half true and half invented, of how old Leon Kind, who'd been going strange, had watered his dying garden with milk—poured out nine gallons still warm from the buckets over his shriveled beans. She had a way of retelling that made this seem strange and sinister and a little vile.

When she heard of a death or accident, she was never at peace until she knew every circumstance of how it had come to be. And somehow out of her words one got a picture of restlessness and fear, widening and spreading through all the farms. Out of poverty fear, and fear bringing hate; and out of hate a sly violence, and sometimes insanity or death. She slurred the patience we knew was there, and never spoke of a saner planning that might in time change all our shrunken lives.

Kerrin's Increasing Vagueness

In august the smell of grapes poured up like a warm flood through the windows. But they ripened unevenly, with hard green balls all through the purple.

I saw the early goldenrod bloom feebly, like drifts of yellow pollen along the fence rows, and I remembered that there was a time—it seemed a hundred years back—when the sight of goldenrod was enough to live and feed on. But now in these days it was only a blur beyond the thought of potatoes and the blasted fields and Kerrin's increasing vagueness.

Four years after we had come to the farm, Kerrin had started to teach at the Union County school, although she was only nineteen then. The board would never have thought of or considered her of their own accord, but when they heard she was through with high school, they took her for lack of knowing what else to do. We were glad, not only because of the money—which Kerrin kept to herself, knowing it gave her a kind of power even though she might have to lend it sometimes,—but glad because it took her away from home.

Even when she was quiet or reading, I could never find rest where Kerrin was. None of us could. No matter in what sort of a mood she was—and there were times when Kerrin was almost fiercely happy and kind—the tautness was never gone, the fear of what she might say or do.

She had begun to teach school in August, but seemed still uncertain of what she wanted, furious and balked that she could not reach or do things of which she had no clear idea herself.

And then when it seemed that no worse or more terrible thing could come to us, there was another.

THE Huttons called us one morning. Asked if we could get word sent over to Kerrin's school and have Whit Hutton come home. His uncle had been killed, they said. The hay-hoist had broken and fallen on top of him. No ma'am, there was nothing that we could do. Just tell Whit to come right home.

It was a long walk up to the school, and I wondered sometimes, plodding those miles of dust and living each moment only for the times when a tree cast its thin dry shade, why there was always such hurry with everyone to spread the news of a death. Time now, hours of time for Whit to see the splunged-in head of his uncle and fill his ears with the story of how it happened, muttered and shrilled to him in a dozen ways.

I had never been to Kerrin's school and she had refused to tell us how things went on, what the children said or did. "They learn. I see that they learn, all right. What else is there to say? What is it you want to know?— how the room smelt?—who kicked who?—how dumb Hutton's kids can be? Maybe you'd like a diagram of their dirt!" Then she'd go off.

And I wished to God sometimes afterward that there had never been any excuse for seeing her at work. Kerrin was at the desk, but didn't see me. She asked questions fast without looking up and not waiting to hear the answers given. "That's right," she'd say and go on to the next one.

The children squirmed or slept in their seats, but did not whisper. It was queer—their silence and Kerrin's not looking up. Even here in the shadowless light of full sun there was something about it all that made me cold and sick. It came to me that they were afraid to talk. They were used to her doing this!

Then she looked up and saw me without at first knowing who it was. I saw the blood wash up her face in a tide and go away leaving only the soiled, burnt color of her skin. "When did you sneak up here? Who sent you?" she kept asking before I said anything.

I explained to her why I'd come, and she called out to Whit to tell him. "Your folks called up. You've got to go home." The boy looked scared and sullen and didn't seem to believe her. "Your uncle's dead," she told him. "Hay-hoist knocked him off." She seemed to take a malicious delight in telling it to him that way.

Whit stared at us, then started off down the road like a crazy rabbit. I called out after him not to run, that he'd die in the sun, but he didn't hear.

When I told Mother what I'd seen, she didn't say anything at first, but just sat down on the porch, too tired and heavy to stand any longer. "We ought to tell them now," Mother said at last. "If she isn't teaching their children. If she isn't responsible any more."

Poor Dad, harassed with debt and drouth already, would have to find some substitute for her crabbed but welcome dole.

They let her go. Not only, I found, because of my going to the School Board, but because the children had talked about her and people were getting uneasy and restless. We had to take it and be quiet at Kerrin's rage when she came home confused with anger and humiliation.

The days seemed a long series of unfought battles, a walking between poison-thorns, and there was a need for patience that wore the endurance raw.

Dead of Her Own Hand

WHEN I remembered it afterward and the thought had grown more accustomed through necessity, and the need to keep a hard layer of calmness between me and the dark that kept coming up like a tide, I was glad this had happened when it did, and I knew after all that her death was the one good thing God did.

There was no place for her. If we had had money, we might have sent her away. She never belonged with us, and maybe there is no place on earth for people like her. I was glad she died.

It was the way we found her and the awful completeness of death that came as a shock. We found her back of the sheep barn and near the water-trough. It was after a long time of searching, and sometimes Grant called her but there was no answer, and we began to think she had gone off in the woods when suddenly we came on her lying against the barn wall, with one arm fallen across the trough, and the blood from her wrist staining the shallow water.

Dad took it hard; more for the swift, spectacular way she had done it, outraging decency and precedent, than because of any belated love. "Who did this, Marget?" he kept asking. He could not believe she had killed herself.

Late in the day the coroner came.

"Kerrin was sick," I told the man, "sick in her head. She'd been that way long time."

Father didn't say anything much, but sat and looked at the man, sullenly and defying him to find out more. Grant sat near Merle and watched him writing the paper out: *Kerrin Haldmarne . . . dead of her own hand . . . Admitted suicide.*

Kerrin was buried up in the old Haldmarne lot. There was no funeral, thank God.

THE NIGHT after she was buried, Grant came down while I was watering the sheep. He stood there watching and seemed a little at peace. It was quiet and getting dark. Then he spoke suddenly. He told me he was going to leave for good the next week.

"Why?" I asked.

"On account of Merle," he said.

I asked him where he would go. I can hear the words now,—quiet, standing off by themselves, having nothing to do with my hot, sick heart. "Where will you go, Grant? What will Dad do?"

"I'll go back up-state," he said. "Find a place somewhere. Max'll come back and help you. He's out of a job again."

"Max made a good worker sometimes," I said. I dribbled out the last bucket and hung it on the nail. I could not say "God keep you!" It kept getting darker there near the stalls, and something in me cracking and straining, wanting to touch him and get what sour comfort there might be in this awful love, the desire shut back, sick in the throat . . . Let me go—let me out! O God, please! And the mind sitting there cold and hard and yet fearful: you can't do this . . . you can't do it. . . .

It's a lie that the body is a prison! It's the mind. I tell you!—always the cold, strong mind that's jailer. I felt something hammering in my throat, and my hands were shaking together like old leaves. I ran out through the shed and left him. I don't know what he thought. I was crying, and it hurt to cry. I was sick and hating because I loved him.

Ordeal By Fire

THE DAYS were quiet with Kerrin and Grant gone. I felt lost. Only by getting away from the house and off in the fields sometimes could I keep sane and find life bearable. It was not a healing—neither from earth nor love nor from any one thing alone comes healing, —but without this I should have died.

I do not know how we should have gone on or how things would have been otherwise, but one night in August was the end and beginning to more than I had thought possible to endure.

The dryness had gone on worse than ever. A quiet and monotonous dying. Fires started up in the brush. Fires to the east and west of us had charred off acres. One August night we saw that our south field was on fire. We could see the red light, a wide wash of it along the field-edge, and the acrid smoke hot along the air.

Father was out first, stumbling and swearing, his face an awful muddle of fear and rage. He only stopped for a moment to hold back my mother. "Don't go," he begged her.

"I have to," Mother said. "It's coming fast." She dragged down a pile of sacks, and Merle helped her. We soaked them wet in the last of the barrels, and it hurt to see water splash out along the floor.

Father shoveled helplessly, trying to scrape out a path that the flames couldn't leap, and saw it sweep out beyond him, farther down, closing in on us with a great arc. There was no time for any thought, no time for fear. It was horrible, and too near for us even to realize what it meant.

Then suddenly—I don't know how, unless she stumbled and lurched sideways into the burning weeds—Mother fell and was lashed around with flames before she could drag herself up or

scream. Father saw her fall and ran ha' a field, throwing his shovel and shou' ing at us through the roar and smoke haze, and when we reached them h had dragged her out beyond the fire smothering the flames with his hand and the sack she'd held,—but too late t keep her from being burned.

He carried her back to the house an I followed them, not knowing what should do. Nothing seemed enough t cover all the terrible burns, and ther was no more salve on the shelf than little to spread on her face and hands.

Father went out leaving me alon with her. I was not able to do anything only praying and crying out to some thing or against everything—Chris please!

It was awful—horrible—to see he suffering. I think I would rather b racked than go through that night agai —the red light reflected hot on the win dowpanes, the choking air, and Mothe lying there on the bed, blotched re and half-crazy with pain . . .

Then suddenly the wind died down the flames came slower and smok drifted up instead of coming in blin clouds. We saw the moon paler, an there was a greyish light. It was th hour before dawn when the wind ha always stopped in those nights; and faint chill had come at last in the air In the gradual ceasing of sound w heard the cocks crow with a fresh eeri shrillness, startling as from anothe world.

Faith Swept Away

MOTHER got neither better nor worse. She just went on suffering. I do not think the doctor knew very much. When her skin turned black in one place, he began to look worried. "If she's healed," Merle said, "it'll come more of her own will than out of this stuff he uses." We hadn't the money to pay anyone else even if there had been anyone else to come. I used to sit up at night beside her, and at first it was almost too hard. It was awful—the pain she

suffered. Hours and days of agony enough to turn her mind, and yet sh seldom said anything aloud. I though sometimes I should scream out myself suffering for her and half crazy with pity and helplessness.

Our life seemed only a long waiting for her to get well—a vacuum in which we moved and did things, but nothing was the same. I felt lost and Merle seemed suddenly grown older, as i waked from a living sleep.

Not Grant's love or Kerrin's death
d changed her as much as this. She
issed Grant, but only as someone to
t against, missed his dry and gritty
mor. She knew why he'd gone but her
ind was too full of Mother to leave
y room for the thought of him.

Father was pitiful in a way. He asked,
low is she?" each morning, and
most demanded with his eyes that we
y she was well—entirely recovered. I
ink he expected it every morning. "No
tter" or "Just the same," Merle would
y, and he'd go out looking as though
e'd betrayed him in some way.

She died in early October, a month
;o, and the autumn storms began. The
rst rains since February . . . Once I
thought there were words for all things
except love and intolerable beauty. Now
I know that there is a third thing beyond expression—the sense of loss.
There are no words for death.

The night after her funeral I went
out and walked miles in the dark. I
don't know how far I went—hours
along the dim roads; but this time the
dark could not cover or fill the broken
emptiness. I could not pretend or hope
any longer, or believe blindly in any
goodness. I was all gone. Faith swept
away like a small mound of grass, and
nothing to live or wait for any longer.
God was only a name, and it was her
life that had been the meaning of that
name.

We Can Go Forward

T IS almost two months now since her
death, and we have gone on living.
is November and the year dying fast
the storms. The ploughed fields
arred around us on the hills. We have
ad our mortgage extended, but it does
ot mean that we are free or that much
really changed.

I do not see in our lives any great
b and flow or rhythm of earth. There
nothing majestic in our living. The
arth turns in great movements, but we
rk about on its surface like gnats, our
ays absorbed and overwhelmed by a
ass of little things—that confusion
hich is our living and which prevents
s from being really alive.

Our essential hours of life are snatched
om years of living. Intervals and
ings stolen between—between what?
—those things which are necessary to
ake life endurable?—fed, washed, and
othed, to enjoy the time which is not
ashing and cooking and clothing.

We have no reason to hope or believe,
ut do because we must, receiving peace
its sparse moments of surrender, and
eauty in all its twisted forms, not pure,
nadulterated, but mixed always with
our potato-peelings or an August sun.

There is no question of what we will
o. It is as plain before us as the dead
fields. We are not trapped any more
than all other men. Any more than life
itself is a trap.

How much of what came to us came
of ourselves? Was there anything that
we could have done that we did not
do? God—if you choose to say that the
drouth is God—against us. The world
against us, not deliberately perhaps,
more in a selfish than malicious way,
coming slowly to recognize that we are
not enemies or plough-shares. And we
against ourselves.

It is not possible to go on utterly
alone. Father may see this now, in a
furious and tardy recognition. We can
go forward; the way is plain enough.
But it is only that this road has too high
banks and too much dust . . .

Love and the old faith are gone. Faith
gone with Mother. Grant gone. But
there is the need and the desire left, and
out of these hills they may come again.
I cannot believe this is the end. Nor can
I believe that death is more than the
blindness of those living. And if this is
only the consolation of a heart in its
necessity, or that easy faith born of
despair, it does not matter, since it gives
us courage somehow to face the mornings. Which is as much as the heart can
ask at times.

Thornton Wilder

THE BRIDGE OF SAN LUIS REY

Graduating from Yale in 1920, Thornton Wilder continued his studies at the American Academy in Rome, and at Princeton. He has taught at Lawrenceville School and the University of Chicago. His "Bridge of San Luis Rey" (1927) won the Pulitzer fiction prize. In 1938 his play "Our Town" was awarded the same prize in drama. Mr. Wilder is now a resident of New Haven, where he writes books and prepares lectures, which he delivers in all parts of the United States.

On friday noon, July the twentieth, 1714, the finest bridge in all Peru broke and precipitated five travellers into the gulf below. St. Louis of France himself protected it, by his name and by the little mud church on the further side. The bridge seemed to be among the things that last forever; it was unthinkable that it should break.

Everyone was very deeply impressed, but only one person did anything about it, and that was Brother Juniper. It was very hot that fatal noon, and coming around the shoulder of a hill Brother Juniper stopped to wipe his forehead. Then his glance fell upon the bridge, and at that moment a twanging noise filled the air, as when the string of some musical instrument snaps in a disused room, and he saw the bridge divide and fling five gesticulating ants into the valley below.

Anyone else would have said to himself with secret joy: "Within ten minutes myself . . . !" But it was another thought that visited Brother Juniper: "Why did this happen to *those* five?" If there were any plan in the universe at all, if there were any pattern in human life, surely it could be discovered mysteriously latent in those lives so suddenly cut off. Either we live by accident and die by accident, or we live by plan and die by plan.

And on that instant Brother Juniper made the resolve to inquire into the secret lives of those five persons, that

moment falling through the air, and t surprise the reason of their taking off.

The result of his diligence was a enormous book, which, as we sha see later, was publicly burned in th great square. But there was a secret cop and after a great many years and with out much notice it found its way t the library of the University of Sa Marco. There it lies between two gre wooden covers collecting dust in a cup board.

It deals with one after another of th victims of the accident, cataloguin thousands of little facts and anecdote and testimonies, and concluding with dignified passage describing why Go had settled upon that person and upo that day for His demonstration of wis dom.

Yet for all his diligence Brothe Juniper never knew the central passio of Doña María's life; not of Uncle Pio' not even of Esteban's. And I, who clair to know so much more, isn't it possibl that even I have missed the very sprin within the spring?

Some say that we shall never kno and that to the gods we are like the flie that the boys kill on a summer day, an some say, on the contrary, that the ver sparrows do not lose a feather that ha not been brushed away by the finger o God.

It seemed to him that it was tim for theology to become an exact scienc The collapse of the bridge was a shee Act of God and provided a perfect lab oratory.

The Marquesa de Montemayor

ᴀɴʏ Spanish schoolboy is required to know today more about Doña María, Marquesa de Montemayor, than other Juniper was to discover in years research. Within a century of her ath her letters had become one of the monuments of Spanish literature and her life and times have ever since been the object of long studies.

She was the daughter of a cloth-erchant who had acquired money. Her childhood was unhappy: she was ugly; she stuttered; her mother persecuted her with sarcasms in an effort to arouse some social charms and forced her to go about the town in a veritable harness of jewels. She lived alone and she thought alone.

At last at twenty-six she found herself penned into marriage with a super-tious and ruined nobleman and the cathedral of Lima fairly buzzed with the sneers of her guests. Still she lived alone and thought alone, and when an exquisite daughter was born to her she fastened upon her an idolatrous love. But little Clara took after her father; she was cold and intellectual. At the age of eight she was calmly correcting her mother's speech and presently reminding her with astonishment and revulsion. The frightened mother became meek and obsequious, but she could not prevent herself from persecuting Doña Clara with nervous attention and a fatiguing love. From the offers of mar-ge that fell to her, Doña Clara delib-tely chose the one that required her removal to Spain. So to Spain she went, the land from which it takes six months to receive an answer to one's letter.

Doña maría's were the letters that in an astonishing world have become the text-book of schoolboys and the ant-of the grammarians. She would have resented her genius had she not been born with it, so necessary was it to her sake that she attract the attention, per-

haps the admiration, of her distant child.

She forced herself to go out into society in order to cull its ridicules; she insinuated herself into the company of those who were celebrated for their conversation. Night after night in her baroque palace she wrote and rewrote the incredible pages, forcing from her despairing mind those miracles of wit and grace, those distilled chronicles of the viceregal court. We know now that the daughter barely glanced at the letters and that it is to the son-in-law that we owe their preservation.

The Marquesa's knowledge that she would never be loved in return acted upon her ideas as a tide acts upon cliffs. Her religious beliefs went first, for all she could ask of a God, or of immortality, was the gift of a place where daughters love their mothers; the other attributes of Heaven you could have for a song.

And when on the balcony her thoughts reached this turn, her mouth would contract with shame for she knew that she sinned and that though her love for her daughter was vast enough to include all the colours of love, it was not without a shade of tyranny; she loved her daughter not for her daughter's sake, but for her own. She longed to free herself from this ignoble bond; but the passion was too fierce to cope with.

And then on the green balcony a strange warfare would shake the hideous old lady, a singularly futile struggle against a temptation to which she would never have the opportunity of succumbing. How could she rule her daughter when her daughter saw to it that four thousand miles lay between them? Nevertheless Doña María wrestled with the ghost of her temptation and was worsted on every occasion. She wanted her daughter for herself; she wanted to hear her say: "You are the best of all possible mothers"; she longed to hear her whisper: "Forgive me."

The Education for Greatness

THE person who saw most of the difficult hours of the Marquesa was her
little companion, Pepita. Pepita was an
orphan and had been brought up by
that strange genius of Lima, the Abbess
Madre María del Pilar. The only occasion upon which the two great women
of Peru (as the perspective of history
was to reveal them) met face to face
was on the day when Doña María called
upon the directress of the convent and
asked if she might borrow some bright
girl from the orphanage to be her
companion.

The Abbess gazed hard at the grotesque old woman. She asked her a
great many questions and then paused
to think. She wanted to give Pepita the
worldly experience of living in the
palace. She also wanted to bend the old
woman to her own interests. And she
was filled with a sombre indignation, for
she knew she was gazing at one of
the richest women in Peru, and the
blindest.

Her plain red face had great kindliness, and more idealism than kindliness,
and more generalship than idealism. All
her work, her hospitals, her orphanage,
her convent, her sudden journeys of
rescue, depended upon money. No one
harbored a fairer admiration for mere
goodness, but she had been obliged to
watch herself sacrificing her kindliness,
almost her idealism, to generalship, so
dreadful were the struggles to obtain
her subsidies from her superiors in the
church.

Lately she had felt not only t
breath of old age against her cheek, b
a graver warning. A chill of terror we
through her, not for herself, but for h
work. Who was there in Peru to valu
the things she had valued? And risin
one day at dawn, she had made a rap
journey through her hospital and co
vent and orphanage, looking for a so
she might train to be her successor. T
search ended with Pepita.

THE education for greatness is diffic
enough at any time, but amid t
sensibilities and jealousies of a conve
it must be conducted with fantastic
direction. Pepita was assigned to t
most disliked tasks in the House, b
she came to understand all the aspe
of its administration.

There were sudden interviews wh
the Abbess (not daring to wait until t
girl was older) had discussed with h
the duties of her office. She had talk
to Pepita as to an equal. Such spee
is troubling and wonderful to an in
ligent child and Madre María del Pi
had abused it. She had expand
Pepita's vision of how she should f
and act beyond her years. And she h
unthinkingly turned upon Pepita t
full blaze of her personality. Pepita v
frightened by her sense of insufficien
she did it and wept.

It was a step in this education
greatness that led to Pepita's enteri
upon the crazy duties of being D
María's companion.

Pepita

WHILE Doña María was passing the
late afternoon in the Church and
in the Square, Pepita was left to prepare
their lodging. She showed the porters
where to lay down the tapestries and
the portraits of Doña Clara. She descended into the kitchen and gave the
cook exact instructions as to the preparation of a certain porridge upon which
the Marquesa principally subsisted.

Then she returned to the rooms a
waited.

She resolved to write a letter to
Abbess. She hung for a long time o
the quill, staring into the distance v
trembling. Pepita longed for the d
presence, the only real thing in her l

She wrote a letter, all inkstains a
incoherence. Then she went downst
to taste the porridge.

The Marquesa came in and sat down
a table. Then a boy handed her a
rge packet wrapped in parchment and
angling some nuggets of sealing-wax.
owly she undid the wrappings. With
easured stoic gestures she read first
a affectionate and jocose note from her
n-in-law; then her daughter's letter.
was full of wounding remarks rather
illiantly said, perhaps said for the
eer virtuosity of giving pain neatly.
ach of its phrases found its way
rough the eyes of the Marquesa, then,
refully wrapped in understanding and
rgiveness it sank into her heart.
"I can do no more. What will be, will
," she whispered. "I can no longer
aim the least influence."

HE sat for a long time, her palms
against her cheeks, making a blank
her mind. Her eyes fell on Pepita's
ter. She opened it mechanically and
rted to read. She read a full half bere she was aware of the meaning.

"But all this is nothing if you like me
d wish me to stay with her. I oughtn't
tell you but every now and then the
d chambermaids lock me up in rooms
d steal things and perhaps My Lady
ll think that I steal them. I hope not.
m so much alone and not talking to
yone, and everything. Sometimes I do
t know whether you have forgotten
and if you could find a minute to
ite a little letter or something, I could
ep it, but I know how busy you
. . ."

Doña María read no further. She
ded the letter and put it aside. For a
ment she was filled with envy: she
nged to command another's soul as
mpletely as this nun was able to do.
st of all she longed to be back in
simplicity of love, to throw off the
den of pride and vanity that hers had
ways carried.

epita returned bringing the supper
her hands. "Your supper is ready, My
ly," she said.

DOÑA MARÍA had risen and approached
the table. "My dear child, I am
sending off a letter to Lima in the morning. If you have one you can enclose it
with mine."

"No, I have none," said Pepita.

"But, my dear, you have one for . . .
Madre María del Pilar. Wouldn't
you . . . ? I know she would like a
letter from you, Pepita."

Pepita was reddening. She glanced
hastily at the old woman and saw that
she had not ceased from staring at her
with sad inquiring eyes. Pepita was
willing to concede one more answer:
"No, it was a bad letter. It wasn't a
good letter. It wasn't brave." She carried the letter off into her own room and
could be heard tearing it up.

Doña María sat down to her dish
amazed. She had never brought courage
to either life or love. Her eyes ransacked
her heart.

But then she thought of her daughter.
She remembered the long relationship,
crowded with the wreckage of exhumed
conversations, of fancied slights, of in-
opportune confidences, of charges of
neglect and exclusion.

"But it's not my fault," she cried. "It's
not my fault that I was so. It was circumstance. It was the way I was brought
up. Tomorrow I begin a new life. Wait
and see, oh my child."

At last she cleared away the table and
sitting down wrote what she called her
first letter, her first stumbling misspelled
letter in courage. It is the famous letter
LVI, known to the Encyclopedists as her
Second Corinthians because of its immortal paragraph about love. It was
almost dawn when she finished the
letter.

Then she took a candle into the next
room and looked at Pepita as she slept,
and pushed back the damp hair from
the girl's face. "Let me live now," she
whispered. "Let me begin again."

Two days later they started back to
Lima, and while crossing the bridge of
San Luis Rey the accident which we
know befell them.

Esteban

ONE morning twin boys were discovered in the foundlings' basket
before the door of the Convent. Names
were found for them, but they were not
as useful to them as our names are to
most of us, for no one ever succeeded in
telling the boys apart.

From the years when they first learned
to speak they invented a secret language
for themselves, one that was scarcely dependent on the Spanish for its vocabulary or even for its syntax. This
language was the symbol of their profound identity with one another, for just
as resignation was a word insufficient to
describe the spiritual change that came
over the Marquesa de Montemayor on
that night in the inn, so *love* is inadequate to describe the tacit almost
ashamed oneness of these brothers.

But at last the first shadow fell across
this unity and the shadow was cast by
the love of women. One night the manager of the theater, foreseeing a thinning
house, gave them a free admission. Between the acts of the comedy Camila
Perichole, the greatest actress in Lima,
danced before the curtain. Esteban had
some copying to do and went home
early; but Manuel stayed on. The red
stockings and shoes of the Perichole had
made their impression.

Henceforth all Manuel's errands
seemed to lead him past the theater.
Late at night he would drift about
among the trees beneath her dressing-
room window.

ESTEBAN knew that his brother was
continually brooding over the Perichole, but he never suspected that he
saw her. From time to time during the
next two months a small boy would approach him in great haste and ask
whether he was Manuel or Esteban, and
being informed that he was only Esteban, the boy would add that Manuel
was wanted at the theatre. Esteban
assumed that the call was for copyist's
work and was therefore utterly unpre-

pared for a visit that they received o
night in their room.

It was almost midnight. Esteban ha
gone to bed, and lay gazing out fro
under the blanket at the candle besi
which his brother was working. The
was a light tap at the door and Manu
opened to admit a lady heavily veile
out of breath and nervous. She thre
back the scarf from her face and sa
hurriedly:

"Quick, ink and paper. You a
Manuel, yes? You must do a letter f
me at once."

For a moment her glance fell on t
two bright eyes that glared at her fro
the edge of the cot. She murmure
"You must excuse me. I know it is late
Then turning to Manuel, she whisper
into his ear: "Write this: *I, the Pe*
chole, am not accustomed to wait at
rendez-vous. You are only a cholo, a
there are better matadors than you, ev
in Lima. But I shall laugh the last, f
even an actress does not grow old as f
as a bull-fighter."

To Esteban in the shadows the pictu
of Camila leaning over his brothe
hand and whispering into his ear w
complete evidence that a new conge
ality had formed such as he would ne
know. He seemed to shrink away i
space, infinitely tiny, infinitely u
wanted. He took one more glance
the tableau of love, all the paradise fr
which he was shut out, and turned
face to the wall.

CAMILA seized the note the mome
it was done, pushed a coin alo
the table and in a last flurry of bla
lace, and excited whispers left the roo
Manuel turned from the door with
candle. He sat down, put his hand o
his ears, his elbows on his knees.
worshipped her. He murmured to hi
self over and over again.

He emptied his mind of everythi
but this sing-song, and it was t
vacancy that permitted him to beco

Then turning to Manuel, she (Camilla) whispered into his ear: "Write this . . . ."

Illustration for Thornton Wilder's
"THE BRIDGE OF SAN LUIS REY"

ware of Esteban's mood. He was filled with terror; for he saw that all the other ttachments in the world were shadows, or the illusions of fever, even the Perichole. He could not understand why Esteban's misery should present itself as demanding a choice between him and he Perichole, but he could understand Esteban's misery, as misery.

Esteban came back and went to bed and the matter was not mentioned again for many weeks. The very next evening Manuel had an opportunity of declaring his position. A messenger arrived from the Perichole and was told harshly to inform the actress that Manuel would write no more letters for her then or any other time.

The Separation

ONE evening Manuel tore open the flesh on his knee against a piece of metal. Neither brother had ever been ill or as much as a day in his life, and now Manuel, utterly bewildered, watched his leg swell and felt the waves of pain rise and fall in his body.

Manuel gradually became delirious and under this affliction all the thoughts he did not permit himself in his right mind would burst magnified from his mouth.

"God condemn your soul to the hottest hell there is. A thousand devils torture you forever, Esteban. She was mine, do you hear, and what right had you . . ." and he would go off into an elaborate description of the Perichole.

These outbursts recurred hourly. It was some time before Esteban was able to realize that his brother's mind was not then clear. After some moments of horror, in which his being a devout believer had its part, he would return to the room and go about his duties. Esteban took to pressing his hand firmly over his brother's mouth during the moments of greatest stress. This increased Manuel's personal rage at him and he would babble all through the night.

On the third night, Esteban sent for the priest and amidst the enormous shadows Manuel received the sacrament, and died.

ALL Lima was interested in this separation of the brothers. Housewives whispered together sympathetically about it as they unfurled their carpets.

One day a sister came running into the office of Madre María del Pilar with the news that Esteban was lingering about the door of the convent. The Abbess hurried out into the street. For months she had been asking herself what strategy could reconcile this half demented boy to living among them again.

Suddenly the thought came to her to send for Captain Alvarado. There was no stranger and more noble figure in Peru in these years than this great traveller. Three weeks later she had a ten minute conversation with him. And the next day he started for Cuzco where, it was said, Esteban was doing some copying for the University.

The brothers had always entertained a great respect for Captain Alvarado. So now when the great traveller came into the dark kitchen where Esteban was eating, the boy was glad.

They had supper together and it was arranged that they were to start for Lima the next morning.

They started for Lima. When they reached the bridge of San Luis Rey, the Captain descended to the stream below in order to supervise the passage of some merchandise, but Esteban crossed by the bridge and fell with it.

Uncle Pio

YOU should know first that Uncle Pio was Camila Perichole's maid. He was also her singing-master, her coiffeur, her masseur, her reader, her errand-

boy, her banker; rumor added: her father.

Lima was too far away from the theatres of Spain to realize that the

Perichole was the best actress in the Spanish world. Only one person knew for certain that she was a great performer and that was Uncle Pio.

He had discovered Camila Perichole. She was singing in cafés at the age of twelve and Uncle Pio had always been the very soul of cafés. Now as he sat among the guitarists and watched this awkward girl singing ballads, imitating every inflection of the more experienced singers who had preceded her, the determination entered his mind to play Pygmalion. So he bought her.

He wrote songs for her, he taught her how to listen to the quality of her tone, and bought her a new dress. At first all she noticed was that it was wonderful not to be whipped, to be offered hot soups, and to be taught something.

It was Uncle Pio who was really dazzled. His rash experiment flourished beyond all prophecy. The little twelve-year-old, silent and always a little sullen, devoured work. He set her endless exercises in acting and mimicry; he set her problems in conveying the atmosphere of a song; he took her to the theatres and made her notice all the details of a performance.

But it was from Camila as a woman that he was to receive his greatest shock. The long legs and arms were finally harmonized into a body of perfect grace. The almost grotesque and hungry face became beautiful. Her whole nature became gentle and mysterious and oddly wise; and it all turned to him. She could find no fault in him and she was sturdily loyal. They loved one another deeply but without passion.

CAMILA was passing the years in the hard-working routine of the theatre, when Don Andrés de Ribera, the Viceroy of Peru, suddenly transported her to the most delicious midnight suppers at the Palace. Contrary to all the traditions of the stage and state she adored her elderly admirer; she thought she was going to be happy forever. Don Andrés taught the Perichole a great many things

and to her bright eager mind that was one of the sweetest ingredients of love.

Uncle Pio was made anxious by Camila's invitations from the Palace. He would have preferred that she continue her little vulgarian love affairs. But when he saw that her art was gaining a new finish he was well content. She had a new way of fingering a wine-glass, or exchanging an adieu, a new way of entering a door that told everything. To Uncle Pio nothing else mattered.

Uncle Pio never ceased watching Camila because it seemed to him that she had never undergone the initiation of love. He knew that the first sign of her entrance into the true possession of the world would be the mastery of certain effects in her acting. But her treatment of such passages became more and more cursory, not to say embarrassed.

Uncle Pio held his breath for years. Camila bore the Viceroy three children, yet remained the same.

Camila's little Don Jaime, at seven years, was a rachitic little body who seemed to have inherited not only his mother's forehead and eyes, but his father's liability to convulsions. He bore his pain with the silent bewilderment of an animal, and like an animal he was mortally ashamed when any evidence of it occurred in public. Camila was never cross with Don Jaime and she was never demonstrative.

CAMILA was about thirty when she left the stage and it required five years for her to achieve her place in society. She gradually became almost stout, though her head seemed to grow more beautiful every year.

In the earliest stages of her progress upward she had intimated to Uncle Pio that he was not to be seen with her in public, but finally she became impatient even of his discreeter visits. She conducted the interviews with formality and evasion. Her eyes never crossed his and she angled for pretexts to quarrel with him. Still he ventured out once a month to try her patience and when the call ad become impossible he would climb he stairs and finish the hour among her children.

Suddenly the news was all over Lima. The lady that used to be Camila the Perichole, had the small-pox. A wild hope ran about the town that the beauty would be impaired that had enabled her to despise the class from which she sprang. The news escaped from the sickroom that Camila had became ludicrous in homeliness and the cup of the envious overflowed.

As soon as she was able she had herself carried from the city to her villa in the hills; she ordered the sale of her elegant little palace. She returned her jewels and she sold her fine clothes. Her incerest admirers besieged her door still with messages and gifts; the messages were ignored and the gifts were returned without comment. As an answer to his repeated attempts the Viceroy received a large sum of money from her with a letter compounded of all that is possible in bitterness and pride.

The assumption that she need look for no more devotion now that her beauty had passed proceeded from the fact that she had never realized any love save love as passion. Such love, though it expends itself in generosity and thoughtfulness, though it gives birth to visions and to great poetry, remains among the sharpest expression of self-interest. Not until it has passed through a long servitude, through its own self-hatred, through mockery, through great doubts, can it take its place among the loyalties. Many who have spent a lifetime in it can tell us less of love than the child that lost a dog yesterday.

CAMILA was convinced that her life was over, her life and children's. In her hysterical pride she had given back more than she owed and the approach of poverty was added to the loneliness and the gloom of her future. There was nothing left for her to do but to draw out her days in jealous solitude in the center of the little farm.

Uncle Pio did not allow himself to be discouraged. By dint of making himself useful to the children, by taking a hand in the management of the farm and by discreetly lending her some money he obtained his entrance into the house and even into the presence of its veiled mistress.

"Camila, it is I—Uncle Pio. Forgive me, but I must speak to you."

"What is it then? Hurry. I am not well."

"Camila, let me take Don Jaime for a year to live with me in Lima. Let me be his teacher. Let me teach him the Castilian. Here he is left among the servants. He is learning nothing."

"No."

"Camila, what will become of him? He has a good mind and he wants to learn."

"He is sick. He is delicate. Your house is a sty. Only the country is good for him. A mother cannot be separated from her child like that. It is impossible. Do not try to disturb me again. I do not want to see any human being."

Now it was that Uncle Pio felt obliged to use a hard measure. "Then pay me the money that you owe me," he said.

"Now I see that you are a very hard man. But it is right that I pay you what I owe you."

"No, Camila, I only said that to enforce my request. I shall take no money from you. But lend me Don Jaime for one year. I shall love him and take every care of him."

There was a silence. Then she said: "If Jaime wishes to go with you, very well. I shall talk to him in the morning. If he wishes to go with you, you will find him at the inn about noon. Good night."

THE next day the grave little boy appeared at the inn. His mother had given him a gold piece for spending money and a little stone that shone in the dark to look at in his sleepless nights.

They set off together in a cart, but soon Uncle Pio became aware that the jolting was not good for the boy. He carried him on his shoulder. As they drew near to the bridge of San Luis Rey, Jaime tried to conceal his shame, for he knew that one of those moments was coming that separated him from other people. He was especially ashamed be- cause Uncle Pio had just overtaken a friend of his, a sea-captain. And just as they got to the bridge he spoke to an old lady who was travelling with a little girl. Uncle Pio said that when they had crossed the bridge they would rest, but it turned out not to be necessary.

Camila's Comments From the Skies

CAMILA had started from the farm to attend the service. Her heart was filled with consternation and amaze- ment. Here was another comment from the skies; that was the third time she had been spoken to. She was as ashamed as though letters had appeared on her forehead. An order from the palace an- nounced that the Viceroy was sending her two daughters to a convent school in Spain. That was right. She was alone.

At a little more than half the journey, at the mud church of San Luis Rey, she slipped in and knelt against a pillar to rest. She wandered through her memory, searching for the faces of her two. She waited for some emotion to appear. "But I feel nothing," she whispered to herself. "I have no heart. I am a poor meaning- less woman, that's all."

And scarcely had she paused when a terrible incommunicable pain swept through her, the pain that could not speak once to Uncle Pio and tell him of her love and just once offer her courage to Jaime in his sufferings. She started up wildly: "I fail everybody," she cried. "They love me and I fail them."

She returned to the farm and carried for a year the mood of her self-despair. One day she heard by accident that the wonderful Abbess had lost two persons whom she loved in the same accident. Camila decided to go to Lima and speak to the Abbess. At last she found the courage to call upon her.

"Mother," she said, "I . . . I . . . was the actress, I was the Perichole."

"Oh, yes. Oh, I have wished to know you for a long while, but they told me you did not wish to be seen. You too I know, lost in the fall of the bridge of San . . ."

Camila rose and swayed. There! again that access of pain, the hands of the dead she could not reach. Her lips were white. Her head brushed the Abbess' knees.

And as the time passed the whole tide of Camila's long despair, her lonely ob- stinate despair since her girlhood, found its rest on that dusty friendly lap.

The Bridge Is Love

BUT where are sufficient books to con- tain the events that would not have been the same without the fall of the bridge? From such a number I choose one more.

"The Condesa d'Abuirre wishes to see you," said a lay-sister to the Abbess.

The tall, rather languorous beauty en- tered the room. Doña Clara, who was generally so adequate, seemed con- strained for once. "Are you busy, dear Mother, may I talk to you for a while?"

"I am quite free, my daughter. You will excuse an old woman's memory; have I known you before?"

"My mother was the Marquesa de Montemayor . . ." Doña Clara suspected that the Abbess had not admired her mother and would not let the older woman speak until she herself had made a long passionate defense of Doña María. The languor fell away.

At last the Abbess told her of Pepita and Esteban, and of Camila's visit. "All, all of us have failed. One wishes to be punished. One is willing to assume all kinds of penance, but do you know, my daughter, that in love—I scarcely dare say it—but in love our very mistakes don't seem to be able to last long."

The Condesa showed the Abbess Dona María's last letter. Madre María dared not say aloud how great her astonishment was that such words could spring in the heart of Pepita's mistress. "Now learn," she commanded herself, "learn at last that anywhere you may expect grace." And she was filled with happiness like a girl at this new proof that the traits she lived for were everywhere.

Suddenly the Abbess disappeared a moment to return with one of her helpers, one who had likewise been involved in the affair of the bridge and who had formerly been an actress. Doña Clara stood in the door as the Abbess talked to them, the lamp placed on the floor beside her.

Madre María stood with her back against a post. Even while she was talking, other thoughts were passing in the back of her mind. "Even now," she thought, "almost no one remembers Esteban and Pepita, but myself. Camila alone remembers her Uncle Pio and her son: this woman, her mother. But soon we shall die and all memory of those five will have left the earth, and we ourselves shall be loved for a while and forgotten.

"But the love will have been enough; all those impulses of love return to the love that made them. Even memory is not necessary for love. There is a land of the living and a land of the dead and the bridge is love, the only survival, the only meaning."

FLOWERS WITHOUT FRUIT

PRUNE thou thy words, the thoughts control
    That o'er thee swell and throng;
They will condense within thy soul,
    And change to purpose strong.

But he who lets his feelings run
    In soft luxurious flow,
Shrinks when hard service must be done,
    And faints at every woe.

Faith's meanest deed more favour bears,
    Where hearts and wills are weighed,
Than brightest transports, choicest prayers,
    Which bloom their hour and fade.
            —J. H. Newman

MY SERIOUS SON

MY serious son! I see thee look
First on the picture, then the book.
I catch the wish that thou couldst paint
The yearnings of the ecstatic saint.
Give it not up, my serious son!
Wish it again, and it is done.
Seldom will any fail who tries
With patient hand and steadfast eyes,
And wooes the true with such pure sighs.
            —W. S. Landor

Margaret Ayer Barnes

YEARS OF GRACE

E ACH generation handles the facts of life differently. The Victorian generation approached them gingerly. Their children who reached the "dangerous age" in 1912 were more nonchalant. "Years of Grace," published in 1930, is a romance of the nonchalant generation and of a woman who despite her love for another woman's husband couldn't be nonchalant about her own husband and children. Mrs. Barnes (1886-) has painted a vivid and unforgettable picture of a time just past—of a time that saw the automobile replace the tandem bicycle and witnessed deeper and more subtle changes in family relationships.

Just Jane

J ANE sat at the dressing-table of her mother-in-law's guest room in Nantucket. She was brushing the long straight strands of her brown hair, looking critically at her reflection in the glass as she did so. For more than a year, now, Jane had been endeavouring to think of herself as "middle-aged."

On the momentous occasion of her thirty-fifth birthday she had said firmly to Stephen, "Middle-age is from thirty-five to fifty." But curiously enough, in spite of that stoical statement, Jane had continued, incorrigibly, to think of herself as "young." In this soft light, thought Jane dispassionately, in her new pink dressing-gown, she really did not look old. And she was prettier at thirty-six than she had been at twenty. No, not that, exactly. The freshness was gone. But prettier *for* thirty-six than she had been *for* twenty.

But what difference did it make, anyway? It didn't make any difference at all, thought Jane solemnly, unless you were still unmarried, or, though married, you went on collecting infatuated young men.

What use had Jane, at home in a Chicago suburb, for youth or beauty or any other intriguing quality? Looking young didn't help you to preside over the third-grade mothers' meeting in the Lakewood Progressive School. Looking beau-

tiful didn't help you to keep your coo through a suburban winter. There wa Stephen, of course. But wasn't it St phen's most endearing quality—or wa it his most irritating?—that for ten yea or more Stephen had never reall thought about how she looked at all? T Stephen Jane looked like Jane. That wa enough for him.

The attitude was endearing, of cours when you looked a fright. But when yo had bought a snappy little hat that—c even when you were sitting in front c your dressing-table in a soft light and new pink dressing-gown, waiting fc Stephen to stop gossiping with h mother and come up to join you—it *wa* irritating to reflect that, no matter wha you did, to Stephen you would alway look exactly as you always had. That yo would look like Jane.

Jane put down her hairbrush with sigh of resignation and selected a ne pink hair-ribbon from her dressing-tabl drawer. She tied it carefully in a bo above her pompadour and, picking up hand glass, turned to admire the effe in the mirror. She wished her hair we curly. Suddenly the frivolity of that in memorial wish and the sight of the fl satin hair-ribbon and the long strands c straight hair made Jane think of Andr Of André and of being fourteen. Funn that just the sight of a hair-ribbon shoul make her feel his presence so vividl Should so recall that funny little warn happy feeling, deep down inside, tha was so integral a part of being fourteen and loving André and never feeling quite sure of how he felt about her in return.

André. André was a bridegroom now. Four months a bridegroom. Jane wished she had written to him, as she almost had, that day last spring when she had found his picture in the May copy of "Town and Country"; "Noted Sculptor Weds" had been the caption. Yes, André was a bridegroom, while she, Jane, was a settled suburban housewife and the middle-aged mother of a fourteen-year-old daughter and an eleven-year-old daughter and a nine-year-old son.

André's wife, under the floating tulle, hadn't looked a day over eighteen. Four years older than her daughter Cicily, perhaps, and bewitchingly pretty. Sixteen-year-old André, a middle-aged Frenchman with a child bride!

Jane shivered as she thought of it. Men should marry when they were young. André should have married when he loved her. But if he had he would never have become one of France's most distinguished sons. Chicago would have stifled him.

BUT *she* had married young. And Stephen had been young when she married him. They had had together those ridiculous, unthinking, heartbreaking years of almost adolescent domesticity, with two babies in the sand pile and another in the perambulator and a contagious disease sign often on the front door and a didy always on the clothesline! They'd had all that.

But had they really had romance? Romance, such as she'd known with André? Stephen had had it, perhaps, in

the first years of their marriage. But— had she? Hadn't she always been rather afraid of romance, all those young years when it might have been hers for the taking? Did a woman ever really value romance until she felt it slipping away from her? Wasn't that the surest sign of all of being middle-aged? You might be still slim and agile and not grey, but when you felt that wistful, almost desperate impulse to live your life to the full before it was over, didn't it really mean that it *was* over, that youth, at any rate, was over, that it was too late to recapture the glamour that you saw only in retrospect——

But this was ridiculous, thought Jane. Life wasn't over at thirty-six. She loved Stephen and Stephen loved her. He had never looked at another woman. Anything they wanted was theirs for the taking. Their personal relationship was only what they made it. She must say to Stephen, "Look at me, Stephen! *Really* look at me! You haven't for ten years!" And he would laugh—of course he always laughed at her—— That was Stephen's step on the stair.

As he opened the door, Jane rose from her mirror to meet him. He stood a moment on the threshold, smiling contentedly around the lamplit room. Dear old Stephen—even in the soft light he still looked white and jaded. Jane walked slowly over to him.

"I'm *very* glad you've come," she said.

Stephen turned his head abruptly. Her voice seemed to rouse him from revery. Poor old Stephen—he looked very tired. As for herself, from the nature of his smile Jane knew what *she* looked like. There was absolutely nothing to be done about it. She looked like Jane.

Agnes

IF YOU want to go to New York to see Agnes," pursued Jane's sister-in-law, Silly, still gazing at the silver cloud, "I think you ought to go. How long since you've seen Agnes?"

"Oh, mercy!" said Jane. "Ever so long! Seven years. Not since she married. The

last time I saw her was when she came West for her father's funeral."

"I think you ought to go," repeated Silly. "Mother won't care as long as you're going to meet the Furnesses."

That was probably true, thought Jane. The bond between Mrs. Carver and her brother was a very close one. Whatever Mrs. Carver might think of the folly of a headstrong daughter-in-law who deserted her husband and children to spend a week in New York for the purpose of seeing an old Bryn Mawr classmate, she would consider it a very suitable attention for Stephen's wife to meet his uncle and cousin on the dock at Hoboken. The Furnesses' arrival *did* make a plausible pretext for a trip to New York, and Jane *did* care, terribly, about being with Agnes again for a few days and seeing her five-year-old daughter and meeting the gentleman whom Jane had always privately characterized as "that dreadful husband."

In Jane's opinion, Agnes had ruined her life by marrying Jimmy Trent. She never understood how it could have happened. Level-headed Agnes, at the great age of thirty-one, with a reputation really established as a writer of short stories, with one good novel published and a better one half-finished, had succumbed to the incomprehensible charm of a ne'er-do-well journalist, hanging about the outskirts of the newspaper world of New York, three years younger than Agnes and perfectly incapable of holding down a lucrative job for more than two months at a time. When Jane considered Agnes as she had been in college, the marriage was really incredible.

One moment of romance had ruined for Agnes ten years of accomplishment. The baby had come at once, of course, and the second novel had never been finished. After a year or two of living in boarding-houses and trying to subsist on Jimmy's non-existent income, Agnes had abandoned her writing and had taken job in the advertising department Macy's. It was a good job, she had wr ten Jane very cheerfully, at the time. S liked advertising. On the whole, s liked it better than writing. They ha taken a nice little flat in Greenwich V lage and little Agnes was established a play school at the age of three a Jimmy did a little writing, now a then, mainly musical criticism, a worked with his fiddle, which amus him awfully, and took her to hear a] of good music, of which he was ve fond.

Jane's lip curled as she remember that letter. She had had another l week. It was this second letter that h determined her to go to New York.

"I wish I could see you," Agnes h written. "Jimmy may go West for a fe months. He's had a temporary positi offered him on the Chicago *Da News*. I hope he takes it. I'd like hi to see Chicago. Of course I have to sti at Macy's."

Jane read between the lines just wh Agnes really wanted. She wanted Ja to meet Jimmy and like Jimmy a make things pleasant for him in Cl cago, so that he would hold down tl new job and make life a little easier f them all, financially speaking, when returned to the Greenwich Village fl Jane didn't relish the task. She kne perfectly well what she would think Jimmy and what Stephen would thi of Jimmy. But Agnes was Agnes. A Agnes's husband was Agnes's husban Jane would do what she could for hi But she would like to go to New Yo and look over the field.

Jimmy

THREE mail-boxes met her eye and on the middle one a card, "Mr. and Mrs. James Trent." She pushed the electric bell beneath the mail-box and, after a minute or two in which absolutely nothing happened, she opened the inner door. The odour of cooking cabbage instantly assailed her nostrils. A straight steep staircase, with uncarpeted wood treads, led to the upper floors. Ja slowly ascended the stairs into compai tive darkness. At the front end of t upper corridor was a white-panell door. Jane knocked at it tentatively. T door was suddenly opened by a you man. He stood smiling at her on t hreshold. A rather charming young man, with tousled dark hair and an open collar, who looked, Jane thought from the dusk of the corridor, with his quizzical eyebrows and his pointed ears and his ironical smile, exactly like a faun.

"Come in," said the young man pleasantly. Jane stepped, a little hesitantly, over the threshold. "You must be Jane." His smile deepened into a grin of appreciation. "You don't look at all as I thought you would. Come in and sit down. Agnes will be home any minute." Then, as she continued to stare at him in perplexity, "I'm Jimmy."

Jane's eyes widened with astonishment. This boy, Jimmy—Agnes's husband? He did not look a day over twenty-five. Jane knew he was thirty-four, however.

"Oh—how do you do?" she said. "Yes —I'm Jane."

"You must have been an infant prodigy," went on Jimmy.

"Why?" asked Jane unguardedly.

"To have been Agnes's classmate," said Jimmy promptly.

Jane frowned. She didn't like that. She didn't like it at all. That was no way for Agnes's husband to speak of Agnes.

"I wish she'd come home," she said with severity.

"Do you?" smiled Jimmy. "Well, she will soon. She stops at the Play School every evening to bring home the child. It began again last week, thank God! Another day of vacation and I should have committed infanticide."

Jane did not reply to this sally. She continued to look, very seriously, at Jimmy. But he rattled on, ignoring her silence.

"A Play School is a wonderful invention. It takes children off their parents' hands for nine hours a day. I call it immoral—but very convenient. So much immorality *is* merely convenience, isn't it? Saloons and play schools and brothels —they're all cheap compromises, forced on us by civilization. In an ideal Utopia I suppose we'd all drink and love and bring up our children at home. Do it

and like it—though that seems rather a contradiction in terms. Progressive education is really only one of many symptoms of decadence. It's a sign of the fall of the empire." He paused abruptly and looked charmingly over at Jane, as if waiting for her applause. Jane felt an inexplicable impulse not to applaud him.

"That's all very clever," she said quickly. "But of course it isn't true."

Jimmy burst into amiable laughter.

"So you are a pricker of bubbles, are you, Jane?" he asked amusedly. "You certainly don't look it. Are you a defender of the truth and no lover of dialectic for dialectic's sake? Do beautiful rainbow-coloured bubbles, all made up of watery ideas and soapy vocabulary, floating airly, without foundation, in the void, mean nothing in your life?"

As he spoke, Jane heard with relief the sound of a latchkey in the outer door.

"That's Agnes!" she cried, springing to her feet.

"It must be," said Jimmy, rising reluctantly to his.

THE door opened quickly, and Agnes, hand in hand with her five-year-old daughter, stood beaming on the threshold. Just the same old Agnes, with her funny freckled face and her clever cheerful smile! It was not until the embrace was over that she noticed how grey Agnes's hair had grown.

"Come with me while I clean the child," said Agnes. She opened the door through which Jimmy had vanished in quest of his necktie. It led into a narrow dark corridor. Agnes pushed open another door and Jane found herself in a bedroom. A very dark bedroom, with one corner window opening on a dingy airshaft.

A bureau and two iron beds completely filled the room. One bed was neatly made and covered with a cotton counterpane. The other was in complete disorder.

"Jimmy never gets up until after I've gone in the morning," said Agnes apologetically, "so he never gets his bed made until I come home at night." As she spoke she picked up a pair of pajamas from the floor and hung them on a peg behind the door.

Lots of wives, of course, lay serenely in bed every morning until long after the bread-winner had departed for his day's work. But that seemed different, somehow. Why did it? If Jimmy had nothing in life to get up for, there was, of course, no real reason for his getting up. Still wasn't Jimmy acting just the way she had always wished that Stephen sometimes would? Stephen thought the world would come to an end if he did not catch the eight o'clock train every morning at the Lakewood Station. Jane had been mocking that delusion of Stephen's for the last fifteen years.

Agnes reëntered the room with a clean blue-rompered daughter at her side. Jane smoothed the counterpane over the pillow. Agnes walked over to the bureau and, still without glancing in the mirror, ran a comb casually through her low pompadour. Agnes did her hair just the way she always had since the day that she first put it up—a big figure eight twisted halfway up her head in the back. She always had run a comb through it just like that, without a thought for a looking-glass.

"Come on," said Agnes. "Tony's is just around the corner." She slipped one arm through Jane's and the other through Jimmy's. Little Agnes skipped on ahead of them. Jane threw a glance past Agnes's clever, contented face to Jimmy's faun-like countenance. It was clever, too, but it wasn't very contented, Jane thought. In the grey September twilight Jimmy looked older than he had in the softer light of the chintz-hung living-room. Suddenly he met her eyes and smiled.

"This is swell!" he said cheerfully. "But an embarrassment of riches! Taking two beautiful women out to dinner at Tony's the same night!" And suddenly he began softly, ridiculously, to sing.

"How happy could I be with either,
Were t'other dear charmer away!"

Jimmy might be irritating, thought Jane, and of course he was a worthless husband, but he *had* charm.

The Ironical Eye

THE Twentieth Century was pulling slowly into the La Salle Street Station. Jane stood in the vestibule, knee-deep in luggage, looking eagerly for Stephen beyond the little crowd of porters that lined the greasy platform. Jimmy, who had come to claim his job on the *Daily News,* was at her elbow. No Stephen was to be seen. Jimmy was watching her with his ironical smile.

"He's forgotten you," he said presently. "He isn't here."

"He always meets me," said Jane. "In fifteen years of matrimony he's met me every time I've come home."

"What an idyll!" smiled Jimmy. It didn't seem impertinent because of the smile.

Suddenly Jane saw Stephen. In a moment he was at her side. Jane cast herself into his arms. She knew Jimmy was watching them. She pressed her cheek against the rough tweed of Stephen's coat lapel, then turned her face to his. She felt a trifle histrionic, under Jimmy's ironical eye. Stephen kissed her cheek, very tranquilly.

"Hello, Jane!" he said cheerfully. "Your train's an hour late. You can get a dollar back from the railroad."

Jane wished his greeting had been a bit more idyllic. Jimmy was grinning now, quite frankly.

"Stephen," said Jane, "this is Jimmy—Jimmy Trent. He's been giving me a whirl all the way from New York."

Stephen looked over at Jimmy. He seemed a little surprised, Jane thought, at what he saw. Or perhaps it was a what she had said. She remembered her last words on Jimmy in South Station eight days before, "I know I'll hate

im." Jimmy had stepped forward and
xtended his hand.

"How do you do, sir," he said simply.
His ultimate monosyllable struck
ane's ear. She glanced from Jimmy to
tephen. Jimmy looked very casual and
ebonair. Stephen looked—well, Stephen
ooked just like what he was, the forty-
our-year-old first vice president of the
Midland Loan and Trust Company. Jane
elt again that curious little pang of
ity. Stephen had once looked quite as
asual and as debonair as Jimmy. He
vas only ten years older than Jimmy
hat minute. Yet Jimmy had called him
sir." And the worst of it was that it
had sounded quite suitable.

"Could you have lunch with me?"
immy asked. "Meet me somewhere at
ne and show me the town."

"Oh, I couldn't," said Jane. "I have to
o out to the country and have lunch
vith the children."

They all turned away from the ticket
vindow to the taxi entrance. Jane was
olemnly reflecting that Jimmy was out-
ageous. She felt very thankful that Ste-

phen had not heard him invite her to
lunch. Suddenly she heard his voice at
her ear.

"And when am I going to see you?"
said Jimmy.

"You must come out to Lakewood
sometime," she said vaguely. "For a
night or a week-end. Give me a ring
when you find a good boarding-house."

"Oh, I'll give you a ring," said Jimmy.

By this time Stephen had hailed a taxi.

"I won't go with you to the other
station," he said. "I've got to run into
the Federal Building." Jane stepped into
the cab. "Your mail's on your desk, dear.
Don't pay the painter's bill 'til I talk to
you about it."

Jane nodded very brightly. She was
once again conscious of Jimmy's ironical
eye. This time she wouldn't stoop to be
histrionic. She waved her hand casually
as the taxi started. Jimmy and Stephen,
standing bareheaded on the curbstone,
both smiled and waved cheerfully in reply. Their waves and their smiles were
very different, however, reflected Jane, as
the taxi turned into the traffic.

It Happened

IT happened just seven weeks later. It
happened Thanksgiving afternoon,
ut beneath the apple tree beyond the
ittle clump of evergreens at the foot of
he garden. Jane was very much sur-
rised when it did.

The seven weeks had been full of in-
ident. She had been seeing Jimmy quite
ften, of course. He had come out per-
aps once a week to dinner. She had
unched with him in town one day and
one with him to a concert that he had
had to review for his paper. That was
he only time, really, that they had been
lone. He usually brought his fiddle
vhen he came out to Lakewood and
hey had had lots of Debussy and a few
nore ballads. The children adored him,
f course and he had somewhat to Jane's
urprise made rather a hit with Stephen.
Her father had raised the only dissent-
ng voice. And all he had said was after
immy had spent an unusually scintil-

lating evening at the Wards' dinner-
table that Agnes deserved a better fate.
Jane knew that her father would think
almost any fate unworthy of Agnes. He
had admired her since her first days at
Miss Milgrim's School. When pressed by
his indignant daughters for further and
more flattering comment, even Mr.
Ward had admitted that Jimmy was
very clever. He fitted delightfully in
Jane's most intimate circle. That was
why she had asked him out for Thanksgiving luncheon with the family.

Thanksgiving luncheon had been like
all Thanksgiving luncheons—not very
brilliant. There had been too much turkey and too many children to make for
clever conversation around the groaning
board.

After dinner, her nephew, Jack
Bridges had sprung to his feet and asked
Cicily, rather sheepishly, to go for a
walk. She had deserted the younger chil-

dren immediately and, whistling to the cocker-spaniel puppy, had started off with him across the terrace. Jane had watched Jack help her, with adolescent gallantry, to climb over the stile that led to the open meadows. She had smiled, a trifle wistfully, over Cicily's budding coquetry. While she was smiling, Jimmy had roused himself from lethargy. He too had been watching the children.

"'The younger generation is knocking at the door,' Jane," he had smiled. "But they have the right idea. Come out and walk five miles with me before sunset."

She had gone for her hat and coat without a moment's hesitation.

They went out the terrace door and down the garden path and out into the fields in the opposite direction from the one which the children had taken. The November day was very cold and clear. It was difficult to talk in the teeth of the gale, and they had covered nearly two miles over the uneven stubble before they said much of anything.

"We must go back," said Jane, trying to tuck her wind-blown pompadour under her felt hat-brim. "I'm all out of breath. It's rough going for an old lady." She drew in a great gasp of the bracing autumn air.

"You don't look much older than Cicily this minute," said Jimmy. "Whose privilege was it, Jane, to look at you when you were Cicily's age?"

"Oh," said Jane vaguely, "he—he was —just a boy."

"A broth of a boy?" questioned Jimmy. "Did you get much of a kick out of it?"

"Yes, I did," said Jane simply. "Oh, I confessed him to Stephen."

Again Jimmy looked very much amused at her candour.

"Good girl!" he said approvingly. "You must always confess them to Stephen."

"There haven't been any others," she said severely.

"Do you expect me to believe that?" said Jimmy.

"I don't *want* any others," said Jan indignantly. "I think clandestine lov affairs would be horribly inconvenient.

"There are higher things than conven ience," said Jimmy sublimely.

Jane ignored his comment.

"Jane," said Jimmy suddenly, "are yo really as innocent as you seem?"

Jane stared at him.

"Jane," said Jimmy suddenly, "I'm g ing to kiss you." And he caught her suc denly in his arms and turned her fac to him.

"Jimmy!" cried Jane in horro "Jimmy!" His lips stopped her word He kissed her long and ardently. Jan struggled in his arms. His cheek scratched her face. She pulled herse from his embrace and stood staring a him.

"Oh, Jimmy!" she cried again. "Hov —how *could* you? I wouldn't have b lieved it of you!" He was looking dow at her, now, still breathing rathe quickly. The excited little smile sti twisted the corners of his mouth. H looked more like a faun than eve thought Jane, with an unconsciou shiver. "Will you please go back to Ch cago, now, at once?" she said with dig nity. "Will you please go back withou coming into the house?"

"Why, Jane—Jane——" he faltere "Do you really mind, so awfully?"

"I'm going in," said Jane. "And don't want you to follow me." Sh turned abruptly away from him an walked up the garden path to the te race, trying to put her face in order. Sh opened the terrace door and entered th living-room. The family were all sti lounging about the fire.

"Where's Jimmy?" asked Isabel.

"He's gone," said Jane, turning h back on them to close the terrace doo "He wasn't staying to supper. He had t get back to the *News*." Lies, she thoug contemptuously.

Her father was sitting comfortably i Stephen's armchair beside the smoulde ing fire. Behind a cloud of cigar smok he was watching his younger daught ery intently. Jane managed to achieve a mile. No one else was paying any attention to her whatever. Mr. Ward continued to watch them all from behind the cloud of cigar smoke. Jane tried to look as if she had forgotten that kiss.

The End of the Winter

THE April sunshine was slanting in Jane's open living room window. The pale, profuse sunshine of early April, flickering through the bare boughs of the oak trees. The crocuses were blooming in the garden. The daffodils nodded their yellow heads in the bed beneath the evergreens. The apple tree was an emerald mist of tiny budding leaves.

Jane sat at the window watching for Jimmy who had just been announced.

"I didn't expect you 'til four," said Jane, smiling up at Jimmy as he entered the room.

"I couldn't wait to play you my last cadenza," said Jimmy. "Jane, that concerto is finished. I couldn't wait an hour——"

"Oh, Jimmy, I can't believe—truly I can't believe—that you've really done it."

"You know who made me," said Jimmy. His eyes searched hers for a moment, before he turned to pick up his fiddle-case from the table. "It's really your concerto." It seemed to Jane, at the moment, a very solemn dedication. She looked up at Jimmy very seriously as he raised his bow. She never took her eyes off his slender, swaying figure, until the last note had sounded.

"It's beautiful, Jimmy," she said then, solemnly, "it's very beautiful."

"You know why, don't you?" said Jimmy, looking down at her from the hearthrug.

Just then Sarah came in with the tea. Jimmy's job at the News would be ended in a fortnight. They had had a lovely winter—the loveliest winter, Jane thought, that she had ever known. Jimmy had written his reviews and had finished his concerto, and she—she had never been so happy, really, with Stephen and the children, never so contented at Lakewood, never so sure and satisfied, in her secret heart, that life was worth living, that it would always, somehow, be fun to live.

And now Jimmy was going—going in two weeks—back to New York and to the Greenwich Village flat and the big and little Agneses. And Jane—Jane would be left in Lakewood to—to watch the spring come and buy the children's thin clothes and clean the house and pack up for the Nantucket summer. Jane sighed a little as she thought of the months before her. Just like all other spring months, of course. But she *would* miss Jimmy dreadfully, and she would never see him again, of course, just as she had this last lovely winter.

"A penny for your thoughts, Jane?" said Jimmy.

"I was just thinking of us," said Jane, "and of all that's happened this winter."

"Have you really liked it?" asked Jimmy.

"Oh, yes," breathed Jane. Then, after a moment, "It seems so funny, now, to think I didn't think I would, when Agnes first wrote me you were coming. I thought you'd be *terrible,* Jimmy——"

"I *am* terrible," said Jimmy; with a smile.

"Oh, no, you're not," said Jane very wisely.

"I know you can do great things if you're prodded by a little encouragement——"

"Say rather if I'm prodded by 'the endearing elegance of female friendship,'" said Jimmy, still with the smile. "It does more for a man than you know."

JIMMY spent the night. The next morning Stephen had his eighteen holes of golf with him. The April day had dawned very bright and fair. The men came home from the links just a little late for luncheon with Jane and the children.

Both men seemed silent, Jane thought, at table. Tired out, perhaps, by their morning of golf in the open air. Cicily rather monopolized the conversation. She was chattering of the educational plans of the rising generation. In particular of the educational plans of Jack Bridges, on whom the family interest was centering that spring. Cicily, herself, wanted to go to Rosemary next year with her cousin Belle. Jane had tried in vain to interest her in Bryn Mawr. She tried again, a little half-heartedly, this evening at the table.

"Why should I go to college, Mumsy?" said Cicily. "And lock myself up on a campus for four years?"

Lock herself up on a campus, thought Jane. That was what college life meant to the rising generation. For her Bryn Mawr had spelled emancipation. To Cicily it seemed ridiculous servitude.

"I don't want to go to college," said Cicily. "I want to room with Belle at boarding-school and come out when I'm eighteen. Then I want to do everything and go everywhere. I like surprises."

"Nevertheless, you want to know what you're doing and where you're going," said Jane severely.

"The child's a hedonist, Jane," said Jimmy. "Let her alone. You'll never understand a hedonist. 'Not the fruit of experience, but experience itself, is the end.' Pater said that first, but it's ver true. I learned pages of Pater by heart when I was at night school at the settle ment. I thought he had the right idea 'A counted number of pulses only i given to us of a variegated, dramati life. How shall we pass most swiftl from point to point and be presen always at the focus where the greates number of vital forces unite in thei purest energy? To burn always wit this hard, gem-like flame, to maintai this ecstasy, is success in life.' That wa my credo, Cicily, when I was not s much older than you are. Go on burn ing, my dear, burn like your golden hair and never bother about the conse quences."

Cicily was staring at him with wide non-comprehending eyes. Jane knew sh had not understood a word of the Pater

"That's very immoral doctrine," sh said.

"But didn't you think it was swell," said Jimmy, "when you first read it wit Agnes at Bryn Mawr?"

"Yes, I did," said Jane honestly. "Bu I was too young to know what it meant."

Jane rose from the table.

"Go up and do your home work Cicily," she said cheerfully. "And don' listen to Mr. Trent. You'll never learr the past participle of *moneo,* unless yo apply yourself to Latin Grammar."

In a Garden

THE children trooped upstairs to the playroom. Stephen picked up the Sunday paper. What with the golf all morning and the family all afternoon, he had not really assimilated the real estate columns. Jimmy wandered over to the glass doors that opened on the terrace.

" 'Come out in the garden, Maud,' " he said lightly to Jane.

Jane looked at Stephen a little hesitantly.

"You come, too, Stephen," she said.

Stephen looked up over the margin of the *Morning Tribune.* "Run along with Jimmy," he said.

Jane walked at Jimmy's side across the shaded terrace. The night was fresh an just a little cool.

"Sit down, Jane," he said. "Are you cold?"

"No," said Jane, sinking down on the bench beside him. "I think the air i lovely."

"I want you to be comfortable," con tinued Jimmy, ignoring her comment 'because I'm going to talk to you for a long, long time."

Jane looked quickly up at him, dis quieted by his words. Jimmy's face wa very calm. He seemed, at the moment, a very tranquil faun. In one instant, however, by one sentence, he shattered the traquillity of the moment.

"What do *you* think," he said, "is going to happen to you and me?"

Jane stared at him.

"I'm married to Agnes," said Jimmy; "you're married to Stephen. We've known each other just seven months and we're in love with each other. What's going to happen?"

Jane, in her utter astonishment. half rose from the bench.

"Jimmy! Don't talk like that!" cried Jane sharply.

"But you love Stephen," went on Jimmy imperturbably. "Which complicates everything, for of course you'll want to consider him."

"*Consider* him!" cried Jane. "Of course I want to consider him!"

"Yes," said Jimmy reasonably. "That's what I said. That's what makes it so difficult."

"Makes *what* so difficult?" cried Jane.

"My persuading you to come away with me," said Jimmy calmly.

"Have you lost your mind?" demanded Jane.

"For you *are* going to come away with me, in the end, Jane," said Jimmy. "But I'll have to do an awful lot of talking first. I want you to live, darling. I want to live with you." His eager face was very close to hers. But still he had not so much as touched her hands. They were clasped very tightly in her lap.

"Jimmy," said Jane brokenly, "please stop."

"Why?" said Jimmy eagerly.

"Because it's no use," said Jane. "I won't deceive Stephen, or betray Agnes, or leave my children."

"But you love me?" said Jimmy.

Jane's troubled eyes fell before his ardent glance.

"You love me?" he repeated a little huskily. "Oh, Jane—my darling—say it!" His shaken accents tore at her heartstrings.

"Yes," whispered Jane. "I—I love you." Her eyes were on the cloud-shadows racing across the lawn. She could hardly believe that she had uttered the sentence that rang in her ears. It had fluttered from her lips before she was aware. The words themselves gave actuality to the statement. Once said they were true. They trembled in the silent garden. Winged words, that could not be recalled.

Suddenly he took her in his arms.

Jane felt herself lost in a maze of emotion.

"Jimmy," said Jane, after a moment, "this is terrible—this is perfectly terrible. I—I can't tell even you how I feel." She slipped from his embrace.

"Even me?" smiled Jimmy. Until he repeated them, Jane had not realized the tender import of her words. He took her again in his arms.

"Jimmy—don't!" said Jane faintly. "I'm sinking, Jimmy, I'm sinking into a pit that a moment before was unthinkable! Stop kissing me, Jimmy! For God's sake, stop kissing me!"

"Coming?" smiled Jimmy.

"I—don't know," said Jane. "Don't ask me that or I'll begin thinking. Just hold me, Jimmy, hold me in your arms."

The Awakening

WHEN Jane opened her eyes next morning, the cold light of the April dawn was breaking over the garden. She had come into the house with Jimmy some four hours before. Serried ranks of thoughts, battalions of thoughts, little valiant warrior thoughts that rose up singly from the ranks and stabbed her mind before she was aware of their coming. She recalled the events of the evening with horror and incredulity. It could not have happened. If it had, she must have been mad. She was Jane Carver—Mrs. Stephen Carver—Stephen Carver's wife and the mother of his three children. She had been Stephen Carver's wife for nearly sixteen years. Yes, she must have been mad last night in the moonlit garden. Mad—to let Jimmy speak, to let him hold her in his arms. Mad to sit with him there—beneath the apple tree—how many hours? Four—five—six hours she had sat with Jimmy beneath the apple tree, deceiving Stephen and betraying Agnes and planning to abandon her children.

Had it really happened? Was it a dream? No—it had happened. It had irrevocably happened. The long path into which she had turned at the moment that she had looked into Jimmy's eyes on the threshold of the Greenwich Village flat had come to its perhaps inevitable ending. She loved Jimmy. She had, incredibly, told him so. The telling had changed everything. It had changed Jimmy. It had changed herself, most of all. It had changed everything, Jane saw clearly in the light of the April dawn, but the most essential facts of the situation. You did not deceive your husband —you did not betray your friend—you did not abandon your children.

Two hours later, Jane opened her bedroom door and walked down the staircase. She entered the living-room and saw Jimmy standing by the terrace doors.

"Jimmy—" she said, still standing in the doorway.

"Don't say it!" cried Jimmy. "I know just how you feel. I know just how you've reacted. Don't say it, Jane! Give yourself time to—to get used to it."

"I *am* used to it," said Jane pitifully. "I'm terribly used to it. I've been thinking for hours."

"I know what you've been thinking!" cried Jimmy. He walked quickly over to her and caught her hand in his. "It was inevitable, Jane, that you'd think those thoughts. Don't—don't let them trouble you, Jane. I knew how it would be."

"You knew how it would be?" faltered Jane.

"Jimmy," she said, "I'm terribly sorry —I know it's rough on you—but—but I made a dreadful mistake last night in the garden."

"And now you've discovered that you don't love me," smiled Jimmy. "Well, presently you'll discover again that you do."

"No, Jimmy." Jane's voice was shrill with conviction.

"Darling!" said Jimmy, seizing her hands in his.

"Jimmy!" cried Jane in terror. "Don't kiss me! Don't you dare to kiss me! I'm not the woman I was last night in the garden." Her earnestness held him in check. "I'm not going away with you, Jimmy. This isn't just the silly reaction of a foolish woman to a moment's indiscretion. It's something much more serious. I'm in love with you, Jimmy, but I love you, too. I love you, just as I love Stephen and the children. I love you as I love Agnes. And that's one of the reasons why I won't let you do this thing. Can't I make you understand, Jimmy, what I mean? When you love people, you've *got* to be decent. You *want* to be decent. You want to be good. Just plain good—the way you were taught to be when you were a little child. Love's the greatest safeguard in life against evil. I won't do anything, Jimmy, if I can possibly help it, that will keep me from looking any one I love in the eye." Her voice was trembling so that she could not keep it up a moment longer.

"Jane," he said, "Jane—you almost shake me. I—I don't believe—you love me."

Jane turned her white face from the April garden.

"Then you're wrong, Jimmy," she said gently. "You're very wrong. It's *killing* me to do this thing I'm doing. It's killing me to be with you, here in this room. Will you please go away—back to town, I mean—and—and don't come back until you've accepted my decision."

"I'll never accept it," said Jimmy grimly.

"Then don't come back," said Jane.

Without another word he left the room. Jane opened the terrace doors and walked out into the garden. She walked on beyond the clump of evergreens and sat down on the bench beneath the apple tree. She had been sobbing a long time before she realized that she still held

Jimmy's handkerchief in her hand. She buried her face in it until the sobs were stilled in a mute misery that Jane felt was going to last a lifetime. She sat more than an hour on that bench. When she returned to the house, Sarah told her that Mr. Trent had gone back to the city on the eleven-fifteen.

In a Prussian Helmet

JANE stood staring at the map of Europe that Stephen had tacked up on the living-room wall. She was staring at the little irregular row of red-and-blue thumbtacks that marked the battle-line in eastern France. Over the battle-fields men were fighting and dying while Jane stared at the map. She had been staring at it just like that for five days. Somewhere on that wavering battle-line, as she stood there, Jimmy was fighting in the quarrel that was not of his making, Jimmy was seeking "something else again," under a rain of shot and shell. How like Jimmy, how terribly like Jimmy, to go to war on that casual quest! To go to a war that had become a crusade in the minds of all civilized people in an attitude of ironic detachment. To become—of all things—a Prussian officer at a moment when a Prussian officer represented to the minds of his countrymen a symbol of all evil. How like Jimmy to become a Prussian officer because of a beer and a blond and a few romantic thoughts on Karl Mark and Bach and Beethoven and Wagner! Jimmy—in a Prussian helmet, looking like a caricature of the Crown Prince. That would be how Jimmy would look, if he lived to sack Paris. If he lived to sack Paris absent-mindedly, because he would be thinking of her.

The ring of the doorbell roused Jane from revery. Sarah stood a moment on the threshold, unnoticed.

"Mrs. Carver," she said. "Mrs. Carver, here's a telegram."

Jane turned from the map and stared at her in silence. No, she thought, dully, no, it would be a cable! She took the yellow envelope from Sarah's hand. She opened it without misgiving.

"Jane, dear, this may be a shock to you. Have just received letter from Prussian officer in French prison camp that Jimmy had joined the German army and was killed on the Marne. Had had no word from him since he left Chicago. Jane, dear, this seems for me the end of everything. Could you come to me?

AGNES"

The yellow papers fluttered from Jane's fingers. The chintz-hung living-room turned black before her eyes. She caught herself, however, before falling, on the back of Stephen's armchair. She closed her eyes a moment and then dully opened them. The familiar living-room had returned. She felt only the need for practical action.

"I'm all right, Sarah," she said smoothly. "I—I must talk to Mr. Carver." How strange, she thought, at such a moment to turn instinctively to Stephen!

"Stephen," she said quickly, "Stephen, I've just had a wire from Agnes. Jimmy was killed on the Marne."

"On the Marne!" cried Stephen, in stupefaction.

"Agnes wants me. Will you get me a compartment on the five-thirty, this afternoon?"

"Of course!" cried Stephen. "But Jane——"

The Hero

"HE was killed instantly," said Agnes. "He was shot in the trenches. He was shot through the head."

She was sitting beside Agnes on the battered davenport sofa of the Greenwich Village flat. Little Agnes was playing in the nursery beyond the half-open folding doors. It was Saturday afternoon and Agnes had just come home from Macy's. She was still wearing her new black serge street coat. She had not even taken off her hat. The sheer black chiffon of the widow's veil, thrown carelessly over it, shadowed her weary eyes.

"Jane," said Agnes suddenly, *"Why* did he do it? *Why* did he go to war?"

"Don't—don't think about that, Agnes," Jane said simply. "It won't do any good. You'll never know."

"No," said Agnes, "I'll never know."

"Jane," said Agnes suddenly, "isn't it dreadful to think there's nothing *left* of Jimmy? With all his cleverness and all his talent he left nothing behind him. The world is just the same as if he had never lived."

"He left you," said Jane tremulously. "He left you and little Agnes."

"Yes," said Agnes, "of course he left little Agnes. And he left me. You're right, Jane. He left me a very different woman than if he'd never loved me. You're very clever, Jane, darling, to think of that. A man *does* live in the change he made in the life of a woman who loved him——"

"Yes," said Jane.

Again there was silence.

"I haven't thanked you, Jane, for all you did for Jimmy last winter. He simply loved Chicago. He was awfully happy there. He wrote me the gayest letters."

"I'm glad he did," said Jane.

"He was always funny when he was happy. Do you know, Jane, I've always understood why he didn't come back to me? I understood it even at the time. The strongest thing in Jimmy's life was his sense of adventure. I think those months in Chicago must have seemed rather adventurous, after the years with

me and little Agnes in this flat. That seems absurd to you and me, of course, for to us Chicago is just the town we grew up in—but to Jimmy I think it must have been rather a castle in Spain. He couldn't come back to humble domesticity just after it. He had to wander. To look for other castles, you know, in other countries. But he *would* have come back, Jane——" Her voice trailed off.

"Of course he would have!" said Jane.

"The thing that kills me," said Agnes soberly, "is that if he *had,* you know, our life might have been quite different. You know I've written a play and it's doing awfully well, Jane. They're going to start a second company on the road. I'm going to take a chance, Jane, and resign from Macy's to write another. I think—I think that perhaps I can really make a lot of money. Enough to have changed everything for Jimmy——"

"Agnes," said Jane solemnly, "you're perfectly wonderful."

"No, I'm not," said Agnes. "I'm just a worker."

"You're always right," said Jane.

"But not wonderful," smiled Agnes. "Jimmy was wonderful. And always wrong. Oh, Jane!" Agnes's smile was very tremulous. "Wouldn't you *know* that Jimmy would fight with the Germans and die a hero's death on the wrong side of the Marne? Jimmy was on the wrong side of every Marne from the day he was born!"

"But always wonderful," smiled Jane. "And always the hero."

"To me," said Agnes gently.

"To me, too," said Jane.

On Loyalty to Absent Friends

He who, malignant, tears an absent friend,
Or fails, when others blame him, to defend,
Who trivial bursts of laughter strives to raise
And courts for witty cynicism praise,
Who can, what he has never seen, reveal,
And friendship's secrets knows not to conceal—
Romans beware—that man is black of soul.

—Horace

RICHARD HALLIBURTON

THE ROYAL ROAD TO ROMANCE

ALL young people want Romance with a capital R and most of them dream of vaga-bonding to the four corners of the earth. To most people, adult responsibilities come early and romantic globe trotting remains a dream. But not to Richard Halliburton (1900-1939?). The minute he got out of Princeton he put on old clothes and started bumming his way around the world. "The Royal Road to Romance," published in 1925, is the story of his amazing experiences.

MAY had come at last to Princeton. There was no mistaking it. The breeze rustling through our wide-flung dormitory windows brought in the fresh odors of blossoming apple orchards and the in-tangible sweetness of bursting tree and flower. As I slouched in the window-seat looking out upon the moon-blanched campus, eleven muffled booms came from the hour bell in Nassau Hall. Eleven o'clock!—and I had not even be-gun to read my economics assignment for tomorrow.

Economics!—how could one be ex-pected to moil over such dulness when the perfume and the moon and all the demoralizing lure of a May evening were seething in one's brain? A rebel-lion against the prosaic mold into which I was being poured, rose up inside me. I flung my book away and rushed out of the apartment on the throbbing shadowy campus.

All the afternoon of that day I had spent in the woods beside Stony Brook, lost in a volume of *Dorian Gray*. And now as I tramped down-hill to the lake, I began to recite aloud to the trees and the stars, lines from it that had burned themselves into my memory: "Realize your youth while you have it. Don't squander the gold of your days, listen-ing to the tedious, or giving your life away to the ignorant and common. These are the sickly aims, the false ideals, of our age."

A wave of exultation swept over me. Youth—nothing else worth having in the world . . . and I had youth, the transitory, the fugitive, *now*, completely and abundantly. Yet what was I going to do with it?

The *romantic*—that was what I wanted. I hungered for the romance of the sea, and foreign ports, and foreign smiles. I wanted to follow the prow of a ship, any ship, and sail away, perhaps to China, perhaps to Spain, perhaps to the South Sea Isles, there to do nothing all day long but lie on a surf-swept beach and fling monkeys at the coconuts. I wanted to realize my youth while I had it, and yield to temptation before increasing years and responsibilities robbed me of the courage.

JUNE and graduation. . . . I was at liberty now to unleash the wild im-pulses within me, and follow wherever the devil led. Away went cap and gown; on went the overalls; and off to New York I danced, determined to put out to sea as a common ordinary sea-man before the mast, to have a con-scientious, deliberate fling at all the Romance I had dreamed about as I tramped alone beside Lake Carnegie in the May moonlight.

My family, thinking it was travel I wanted, offered me a de luxe trip around the world as a graduation present. But I had gone abroad that way before, and now wanted something less prosaic. So I scorned the *Olympic* and, with only the proceeds from the sale of my dormitory room furnishings in my pocket, struck out to look for work on a freighter.

At last on a July morning I sailed out of New York harbor waving gratefully at Lady Liberty. But she did not notice me. She does not flirt with seamen.

President in Pantaloons

"MAY I see the president?" I asked the kindly faced old man in pantaloons and shawl, who had come to the door of the executive mansion in response to my knocking.

"I am the president, Monsieur," he replied. "Won't you come in?"

It took me several moments to regain my composure. Presidents of republics, not arrayed in high hats and frock coats were beyond my comprehension—and here the president of Andorra stood before me in pantaloons!

He added new fuel to my confusion by seizing my arm, leading me up a flight of steps into the "White House" kitchen (likewise the reception room, since it contained the only fireplace in the building), seating me in a big chair which he himself drew up before the crackling logs.

"And now, Monsieur," he said, "of what service can I be to you?"

"No—no special service, Monsieur. I come from New York and I wanted to meet you."

"New York! And just to see me?"

"Well not altogether. But I couldn't resist paying Andorra a visit. It's such a funny, romantic, little country. Of course the trip over the Pyrenees, in all this snow and everything, was a fright, but I didn't mind. I liked it."

And I had liked it. The entire journey had been as full of adventure as a chapter from Dumas. And then, too, the very idea of visiting Andorra, the oldest, the smallest, the most isolated republic on earth, had delighted me so that even the serious obstacles in my path were met and overcome with a sort of reckless enthusiasm.

FOR years I had not been sure whether the vaguely familiar word Andorra meant a fish or a fruit, until one day I ran across it by accident on the map, and found it was nothing edible, but an independent republic of six thousand people and one hundred seventy-five square miles, with a chief executive, a capitol building, a White House, and a congress, all lost for ten hundred years in the tops of the Pyrenees. I found that this doll democracy was perhaps the one spot left in Europe uncontaminated by the vacation flood of sightseers, for the reason that, with the exception of the capital city which communicates with the outside world by means of a sixty-mile dirt road, the entire country is inaccessible except to a sure-footed man or mule.

Owing to the difficulty of communication with the north it has been the influence of Spain that has molded the character of the country. The language is Spanish dialect, the costumes, money, customs, faces and physiques are Spanish, though strange to say their preference for France as a nation, and loyalty to their sister republic rather than Spain, is unqualified.

FROM the simple appearance of his house it was obvious that the chief dignitary was truly one of the people. The big fire on the floor was not a whit different from the fires in all other houses, nor were the cooking implements less crude.

The simplicity and gentleness of the old man charmed me at once. He was not only willing, but eager, to talk. In response to my questions concerning the origin of Andorra he chatted away for a half-hour telling me how the son of Charlemagne, having expelled the Moors from the Pyrenees in the eleventh century, proclaimed the independence of the people of these valleys in return for their valiant assistance. In 1278 the tiny country, for protection, came under the joint guardianship of both France and

Spain, and this dual responsibility has continued to exist up to the present time. Thus protected by her two great neighbors, Andorra has drifted along through the centuries, history-less. She has had no wars, no enemies, no social upheavals, no heroes, no dominating figures, no change. She has been protected by her weakness, her isolation and her poverty. No one would gain anything by gaining Andorra.

"What share do these two guardians take in the government?"

"Really very little, though disapproval of a measure from either is sufficient to block action. But that never happens," he added with a shrug. "Our government is so simple and so old, an injudicious act is most unlikely. We have nothing to legislate, you see. While our twenty-four congressmen are convoked four times a year, they sit for only two days and often there is not enough to do to occupy them that long."

"Your people seem supremely content."

"Yes, it is true. It is true because we have nothing with which to contrast what we think is happiness. There was never a greater adherent to tradition than the Andorran.

"A civil war was almost precipitated by the progressive party wishing to introduce the violin and cornet for our fête dancing in the place of the age-old musette and tambourine. We have no art, no industry, no literature. Few of us have ever seen a railroad or a moving picture. But after all, what have we to do with progress? Look at the barren rocks and arid mountains! There is only one life for us—pastoral, and from that we must get what joy we can in loving the melancholy charm of our country and in worshiping the God that speaks so clearly on such a day as this has been."

"What of your population? Has it increased through the centuries?"

"No, Monsieur, it has fluctuated not two hundred people in six hundred years. We have between fifty-eight hundred and six thousand now, always have had and always will have. There is no hope of industry to attract outsiders. We are destined never to expand. It is a struggle to live even now, compressed as we are between two mountain walls."

Our conversation then turned to America, concerning which he had a few ideas, all grossly mistaken; so that it was midnight when I felt they had all been corrected, and made ready to depart.

"Adieu, Monsieur," I said as we shook hands. *"Vive Andorra and vive son President!"*

"You are very kind," he replied, "but we are a simple people unaccustomed to any glory. I hope you have received a courteous reception in our country, and regret that you must go so soon, but if you must, adieu, *et bon voyage.*"

A native son of the mountains, he stood in the doorway as I untied my mule from the White House hitching-post, and watched us until we had crossed the square.

The Taj Mahal

IT was almost night, and the first shy breeze we had felt that day came from the Jumna. Across the river, through the twilight haze, a huge and swelling dome could be dimly distinguished from the dark sky behind. Soaring from the tree-tops into a bank of clouds, it seemed a Maxfield Parrish picture come to life.

"What's that?" I asked of Ahmed, my Punjabi companion.

"That's the Taj Mahal."

Had it been the post-office or the mission church he could not have spoken with less enthusiasm, yet it would be impossible to describe how deeply I was stirred by this casual reply. It was as if Columbus on his first voyage had asked Roderigo: "What's that dark line over there?" and Roderigo had answered: "Oh, that? That's land."

The Taj Mahal had been deified in

my mind ever since that childhood day when I had first looked upon an oil painting of the fairy tomb and read the immortal story of its creation. It had always been a dream castle to me, something so fabulous it could not have dimensions and weight and location; something so lovely it could not exist outside of picture books.

Facts and legends came to me now in a jumbled mass, as I stood in the fortress tower and watched the great dome disappear into the night. The follies of the Emperor Shah Jehan, who built the Taj, were forgotten; what mattered the number of his crimes—his genius as a builder, his fame as the greatest lover in history were more worthy of memory.

In the marble poetry of the Taj this greatest lover has immortalized the object of his passion. Arjemand, favorite among a thousand wives, is embodied in

PICTURE OF RICHARD HALLIBURTON
WITH THE TAJ MAHAL AS BACKGROUND

its stones; her chastity is carved into its spotless walls; her exquisiteness reproduced in every delicate line; her majesty reflected in the aereal grace of dome and minaret that floated and faded there above the river side.

WE HAD been silent for some moments, enjoying the coolness of the night that now had blotted out the distance. Ahmed was the first to speak:

"You know Shah Jehan?"

"Yes," I said, "I 'know' him."

"He died here in balcony."

"What Ahmed! Is this the Jasmine Tower?"

He assured me it was, and that we were treading thoughtlessly on stones numbered among the most hallowed in India, for this was the point from which the emperor last saw his beloved wife's memorial. For her shrine he had squandered the wealth of an empire, until his subjects, led by his own son, revolted and imprisoned the "King of Earth" here in his own palace, on the banks of the Jumna.

Dethroned, disgraced, held captive, for seven years he had only the memory of his lovely Arjemand to comfort him. At last when he felt his end was near, the old and broken man pleaded, not in vain, to be carried at dawn to the Jasmine Tower, where his dying eyes might rest upon the distant minarets of the mausoleum. There his heart and soul already were, there he knew his body was soon to be, beside her for whom he had created the one perfect thing. Through fading eyes he watched the eastern horizon brighten with light, watched the first beam of sunrise strike the dome. Then the heavy weary gates closed forever—and the Taj passed from view.

"YOU stay here all night, Sahib?"
The romantic possibilities of such an adventure captivated my fancy. Quickly I dismissed Ahmed and hid in a darkened grove. The watchmen, carrying their lamps, came close to me

—but passed on. Not for a kingdom would I have surrendered, with this opportunity before me to remain through the night by the side of my marble mistress.

Then from the entrance I heard the ponderous iron-bound doors groan as they were swung laboriously into place. I heard the clank of fastening chains, and their ominous echo, reverberating from wall to wall across the breathless garden, filled me with sudden dread, for I, a mortal, was now imprisoned with a pale pearl ghost—I was alone with the Taj Mahal.

Then, as I watched, the moon floated upward from the trees to commune in secret with the phantom Taj, while all earthly worshipers were far away and the union safe from the disenchanting gaze of mortals. Silvered, the mausoleum emerged from the shadow, and hypnotic in new radiance beckoned to me once more. Heedless of consequences I crept from my green grotto; there was no sound.

Higher rose the moon; fairer gleamed the Taj, a harmonious pile of masonry in the sunshine of the morning, a specter underneath the stars, now transfigured to a gleaming gossamer, an airy bubble that might evaporate into ether while one looked upon it.

Unaware of the passing moments, I watched the shadows move in the deep recesses of the façade, until, unable to resist the lure of the interior, I turned to the main portal. Stealthily I crept around the ' sleeping sentries, softly crossed the threshold, and entering stood beside the faint-lit tombs of the Shah-in-Shah and Arjemand.

The fourth hour came, and found me standing pensive beside the Empress' grave. A pilgrim to her shrine, she had blessed me with protection.

It was but an hour before dawn. The moon had reached the peak of its course and was shining with unearthly brilliance. Alone, in all this supernatural beauty, I felt myself transported to some previous existence that knew neither time nor space nor substance. I and all that I beheld was myth. The subconscious mind was master, linking me with previous incarnations to the dim past.

Caw—caw—caw came the cry of a crow from a neargy grove. I glanced up to find day streaking the east. There was a rush of wind, a rustle of leaves. . . . Suddenly I was aware of being bitterly cold. Realities began to emerge before my eyes. The gardens lay about me, stark and tangible. The Taj—had turned again—to stone.

Land of Many Husbands

THE highest inhabited region in the world—that is what Ladakh, with the neighboring portions of Tibet, claims to be.

In keeping with the rest of the country, Leh, with its ten thousand people, is a fantastic and picturesque little city, composed of a tumble-down cluster of ancient stone huts leaning at all angles and in all stages of disrepair. It boasts, however, of its Main Street, a broad straight avenue lined with poplar trees and swarming with a heterogeneous crowd from a hundred different races and sects. The city is not far from where India, Russia and China unite, and one finds evidence of this proximity in the features and costumes seen about the bazaars.

In Leh we had the opportunity to observe at close range the lives of the average Ladakhi, and found that they were very contented lives despite the abnormalities of their country. Though there is no real poverty in this rainless state, the land area that can be irrigated is unalterably limited which limits the food supply and that, in turn, the population. In the thirty-five thousand square miles of territory they have a square mile each to provide for them, and have a continual struggle to live.

As a means of checking the birthrate it became customary centuries ago to practise polyandry, and this unique custom is now a firmly established institution. A woman of Ladakh should look twice before she leaps into matrimony, for she doesn't marry the choice of her parents' heart alone but all his brothers as well. While the women have become accustomed to managing three or four husbands through generations of experience, where there are six brothers or more, it must become difficult to honor and obey so many.

There are circumstances, however, which relieve such a multiplicity of household heads, the eldest brother being really supreme, and his word law. He is the legal parent of all the children, and held responsible for their proper place in the community. The wife, in spite of her many mates, is often left entirely alone as Ladakhi men are usually engaged away from home. When a husband returns home he leaves his shoes on the doorstep as a warning for rival husbands to keep away, and only the eldest brother, whose shoes are inviolate, dares disturb them. No wonder one sees so few children. But perhaps it is best, for it's a wise child that knows his own father—in Ladakh.

NATURALLY I had a great desire to gain entrée into one of these polyandrous households. Having a few rupees' worth of supplies to buy I took a tour of the market and by means of our interpreter inquired of the salesman, before we made our purchase, if he were one of the multiple husbands. When the reply was affirmative, I offered to trade with him in return for the privilege of visiting his family. In this way I soon encountered an accommodating shop owner who was not only one of several husbands, but lord of the manor as well. He led me some distance out of the city, into the most palatial rock house we had seen, and thinking it an extremely amusing experience, presented me (not without a touch of native grace) to his wife, three other brother husbands and two common sons.

Although I am sure we were the first white guests this family had ever had from occasional association with foreigners in the capacity of multeers, etc. they had come to look upon them as a superior order of being, so that though they served us bountifully with rice and unleavened bread, no amount of persuasion could induce them to partake of their own food at the same time.

The wife, judging from the super abundance of her jewelry, commanded more than average wealth. She was a vision of gaudy glory. Added to the yards of beads and usual burden of barbaric rings and bracelets, she wore the most elaborate turquoise head-dress we had seen. This indispensable and inseparable ornament is the most important part of any Ladakhi woman's costume. Even the poorest man's daughter and wife, though they be in rags, maintain this bit of finery.

The woman, with all her turquoises, was, if possible, even less familiar with soap than the men. Her peacock headdress covered braids of unspeakably grimy hair, and the ear-flaps at the side half concealed a face which might have been fairly pretty had it not been hidden under a covering of dirt. The Ladakhi have an excuse for not bathing in winter—it's too cold; and then in the summer they are out of the habit. In consequence they never remove their clothes until they rot and fall off, which, judging from appearances, happens only once in a decade.

NEVER have I so regretted the world's confusion of tongues. There were a hundred questions I would have asked the members of this extraordinary family. With the feeble assistance of my multeer I did learn that the three younger brothers, who were usually engaged away from Leh, had all returned home because of the religious festival then taking place. A fifth brother had bolted from the flock and attached himself to a wife of his own choice. There had been six children born to the four husbands; only two survived, one, judging from marked resemblances, the son of the eldest brother, the second, of another.

From the missionary I later learned that the action of the radical brother who had reverted to monogamy, was rapidly becoming the rule, rather than the exception, for the economic and moral problems of polyandry were making it more and more unpopular with the present generation. Family ties were being dangerously loosened by the habitual infidelity of young brothers, while the large number of unmarried mothers and unsupported children was becoming a serious detriment to social order.

Each year sees fewer polyandrous families, so that the day no doubt is not far distant when this abnormal custom will be relegated to the past, and every woman in Ladakh may have a husband.

Baby God

EVEN before we reached Leh it was evident that the ruling passion of the country was religion. Being essentially a part of Tibet, Ladakh clings tenaciously to the Lama form of the Buddhist faith professed by the mother country, and there are few districts in Tibet where the population is as priest-ridden and as monastery-dominated as in this, its western end.

Leh is a religious centre and the home of the "Skushok" who, being the living incarnation of Bakola (a saintly contemporary of Buddha) is the holiest and highest lama in the district. He has died about thirty times since he first became lord of the Leh monastic area, only to be reborn of noble parentage in the neighborhood of his demise. Finding a child fulfilling all their requirements of wealth and born at the proper interval after the death of Skushok, the monastery elders choose him as the incarnation of their departed master; and to prove to the people's satisfaction that he is the true saint they place personal possessions of the former lama before him, along with unfamiliar articles. The child never fails to recognize his property, it is said; probably because the elders tutor him thoroughly.

IT WAS our good fortune to be in Leh in time to attend the inauguration of the child Skushok at the local lamasery. There was a festival connected with it, in his honor, such as occurs only once in a lifetime, and which, lasting three days, had drawn the population (including the brothers of my shopkeeper host) from long distances.

On this momentous day, previous to being carried out for public observation, the boy was placed in state within the inner temple, where the leading monks from all the subsidiary monasteries came to prostrate themselves, and in return receive a strip of colored cloth from him as his blessing. Through a secluded lattice I watched the entire ceremony.

The only fresh and beautiful thing in this room filled with depressing ornaments and evil looking priests was the silk-robed child, whose sweet face and guileless eyes gave him the expression of an infant seraph. He was not more than four years old, and, while obviously bored with this unnatural life, seemed to have resigned himself to it and to be enduring it manfully.

Finally the baby on the throne went sound asleep. As his guardian lifted him from his pile of cushions and carried him back to the terrifying, devil-infested "playroom," the child threw his arms about the old priest's neck and dropped his head on the convenient shoulder. No divinity this, no superhuman saint; only a very natural and very homesick baby boy, who, after a very strenuous day, was more interested in his crib and his porridge than in the spiritual welfare of his fold.

I could not resist an urge to follow the child into the monastery, nor did any one seem to disapprove. It was almost sundown, that memorable afternoon, when the infant abbot, the priest and I returned to the seclusion of the dormitory. Seeing how attracted I was to the baby, the old man allowed me to assist in the bed-time preparations. Holding the sleepy child on my lap I removed his yellow robes of state, and wrapped him in a voluminous woolen shawl. A bowl of warm barley porridge was brought to us, and with a big wooden spoon I fed my little charge.

Near by stood the ancient blackened cradle that had nestled previous incarnations. Into it I lifted the heavy-eyed cherub, gave him his wooden doll and covered them both with a shaggy sheep skin. Then as the wild fantastic music and the babble of the multitude came faintly from the outside world, I was allowed to stand beside his little Holiness, and with the last ray of sunlight slanting in through the latticed window from the western Himalayas, softly rock this baby god to sleep.

Greatest Mystery in History

In Cairo I met an Englishman who had seen Angkor. He spoke of it in awesome tones as if it had been a superhuman experience. Again and again in India I heard the name linked with superlative adjectives relating to its monstrous size and exquisite detail, yet always encompassed in rumor and obscurity. No one there had seen it—everyone said it was a miracle.

Angkor—the murmur of its name grew as I moved eastward. Angkor—talks of its name grew as I moved eastward. *Angkor*—tales of its reputed glories were rumbling in my ears at Bangkok. ANGKOR—the wind and the jungle and the vast gray cloud of stone roared at me now as I hurried from the bungalow toward the mile-distant mystery: "Here is the superlative of industry, here the crown of human achievement. Here, here, is Angkor, the first wonder of the world, and the greatest mystery in history."

Jungle, jungle, for mile after mile on every side it smothered the earth, dense black, consuming—and from out it, unheralded and unbelievable, rose the gigantic, the magical temple with its tier on tier of gray tapestried stone, acres of carving, hundreds of delicately-wrought windows, miles of galleries, great lace towers—all powerful and beautiful and desolate beyond imagination.

The spectacle was so amazing, stumbled on here in the forest, I would have scarcely credited my eyesight had I not been prepared by the fleeting distant glimpse of it snatched over the tree tops early that morning. To have blundered upon the Pyramids or St. Peter's suffocating in the jungle depths of this wild corner of Asia and utterly deserted but for bats and lizards would not have astonished me more—indeed not nearly so much, for Angkor, built by gods for a fabulous vanished empire, in the might of its dimensions, in artistry, in purity, in magnificence, and above all in preservation, Angkor surpasses any thing Greece or Rome or Egypt has ever seen.

Whence came this superhuman monument and the even more extraordinary dead city that surrounds it, both lost for seven hundred years in the impenetrability of an Indo-China wilderness and but recently uncovered to the amazement and admiration of the world? No one knows exactly. Whither departed the Titans that piled these stones together and deluged them with incredibly lavish carvings? No one knows that either. All trace of their beginning, all records of their destruction, have been utterly lost in these merciless jungles.

For lack of a better name, history calls the mysterious race that once dwelt here the Khymers. Conjecture founds their empire in the fourth century and obliterates it in the twelfth. Except for miles and acres of bas-relief pictures of attles and mythology and common life carved on the stones of the six hundred uined public buildings found in the pace once covered by the Khymer capital, we should not know one single thing bout this race, whose ability as artists nd architects has rarely been approached.

It seems impossible that this masterpiece could have escaped for so long the ttention it is now beginning to enjoy. However, when one sees the flood of vegetation it is buried under, and realizes in what an isolated part of the vorld it is hidden, one can understand vhy it remained unknown and unsung vhile archeological monuments of a far esser magnitude were being explored, nd made familiar to the whole world.

As far back as 1857 a Frenchman, urged on by the fabulous legends of an ngel built temple, then within the outheast borders of Siam, fought his vay through leagues of jungle to the pot, and on his return to civilization old such unbelievable stories of the size nd magnificence of the ruins he had een, obviously erected by a lost race of uperbeings, that people laughed at him nd thought his deprivations had weakned his brain. But no one laughs today.

The Siamese, who are believed to ave driven the Khymers from Angkor Vat, insist it was built by divinities, beause human beings could not have been owerful enough or inspired enough to lo it. You may not be inclined to beieve this legend from seeing pictures r reading descriptions of Angkor; you nay not believe that it took four generations of constant industry to complete, r that kings commandeered and kept ccupied five hundred thousand slaves rom their sixteen provinces; but when ou at last look upon Angkor in reality, ou believe *anything*.

THE temple is in the form of a pyramid, with five hollow squares each itting into and above the other. Each orner of the last two terraces is adorned with an elaborate tower completely covered with carvings of seven-headed cobras, medallions, deities, chains of dancers; and reaching higher and higher with each tier until the great supreme tower of lace soars two hundred feet and looks with majestic defiance over the miles of waving, waiting jungle tops that stretch unbroken on to China.

Of the many Angkor wonders, the most wonderful is the bas-relief that stretches unbroken for a half mile around the second terrace. Protected from the weather by a gallery, it has withstood the ravages of time, and is as vivid and fresh today as it was seven hundred years ago. One could spend weeks before this great stone picture and not see it all, since there are fully fifty thousand figures chiseled upon it in such inextricable confusion one's head begins to swim from examining them.

One wall, three hundred and fifty feet long, portrays the battle-scene between a Khymer king and his enemies. There are hundreds of fighters in armor with shield and sword, on foot, on horseback, hundreds more in chariots and on elephants, yet not one figure is passive. It is a battle. Each army sweeps against the other, and the clash in the center is terrific.

Men are piled on one another, struggling in groups, in pairs, with clenched teeth, in agony, in fury, in despair, in triumph, arrows and spears fly thick and fast; the officers urge on their followers; the trumpeters sound the charge; the horses and elephants rear and tremble with excitement; the dead and dying are piled on the ground to be trampled by succeeding waves. At the rear deep ranks of reenforcements, cheering and hurrying, are marched forward into the slaughter.

There is action, action, and carnage and the roar of battle. One's eyes stare at this realism; one's heart beats faster in sympathy with this mortal combat. Yet all this is in stone—cold, silent, colorless stone.

Some day the artistic world will recognize the Khymers as the greatest artists that ever lived—though perhaps they never lived. Perhaps they were angels, as the Siamese insist, descended from Heaven to carve this superhuman work.

Angkor Vat, after all, is only the greatest and best preserved of a vast array of magnificent sandstone structures once enclosed in the city of Angkor Thom, which in the days of its glory had several million people and was the luxurious capital of a mighty empire. The number and dimensions of the city's ruins are staggering—and, oh, how melancholy, how indescribably desolate!

How was it possible for such a race as the Khymers to disappear so absolutely?

Did all this happen in a day? Was this heavenly city, with its vast population, its armies, its palaces, its might and glory, surprised by its enemies and destroyed over night by the sword? What diabolical wrath was spent upon it! No sooner had the roar of tumbling battlements died away than the insatiable fiend, the jungle, rushed upon the prostrate magnificence and suffocated all but a few of the most indomitable giants.

Slowly and wonderingly I climbed about these fabulous ruins. The sun set beyond the western jungle-tops, and before I realized that day had gone twilight enveloped me. Every bird became hushed; the faintest breeze seemed to hold its breath. Not even a cricket broke the pall of silence that sank upon this mighty corpse.

From the shadows, death and oblivion crept forth to seize the city from the retreating sunshine; ghosts drifted beside me as I moved and dreamed through the gathering darkness. Loneliness—loneliness—in all this stupendous graveyard of man and monument, I stood—the only living human being.

The Garden of Eden

Bali! A thrill ran through me. At last I was on the threshold of this amazing island, this little paradise in the Dutch East Indies that I had come so far to visit. At Saigon (where I had emerged from the Angkor jungles after a two day voyage down the Mekong River) I had first heard about its lure —its beautiful people—its brilliant coloring—its unspoiled naturalness.

Drifting about the docks, looking for a ship that would take me away—anywhere—I ran across an old tropical tramp who had combed the beaches of New Guinea and Sumatra, and knew every isle and city on which the sun of the equator blazed. He had been to Bali, and when he spoke of it, he might have been Adam telling Cain about the Garden of Eden. To him it was the most idyllic spot in the Pacific, chiefly because it was almost the only one not blighted by European culture and American tin cans. He assured me it was a siren isle, enslaving by its beauty and romance every one who looked upon it.

The Saigon beachcomber was right. Here indeed was a little paradise, a south sea Eden, and the Eves whose beauty he had praised so highly. Erect as Dianas, they moved about the streets no more aware of their half nude bronze bodies than the fat yellow babies that trotted at their heels.

As I entered the outskirts of the town I heard the jargon of distant native orchestras, and realizing that the great volume of their sound indicated something beyond the ordinary, hurried in the direction, coming soon upon a magnificent procession before which I stood gazing in wonder at the passing flashes of color.

Long lines of women draped in vivid hues, marched in single file, on their heads bearing food for a banquet. The *sine-qua-non* of the procession was the rout of savage monsters and ogres made of paint and plaster, that roared and pranced through the crowded side-lines, scattering the shrieking spectators and being trailed by all the naked little urchins. This glittering, hilarious, noisy spectacle wound its way through the village's palmy lanes and on to the temple, there to gorge itself to stupefaction.

Consumed with curiosity I hurried to find the English-speaking Dutch commissioner and to ask him if this Mardi Gras Procession was just a circus parade —or what.

"It's funeral," he replied.

Seeing my astonished expression he offered more information. "I think the greatest spectacle in the Indies is one of these Balinese cremation ceremonies. The more prominent the dead person, of course the more elaborate the funeral. You are very fortunate to be here now —a rajah died a few days ago, and this is going to be the biggest cremation fête they've had for a generation."

And all this hilarity I learned was only the first day of mourning, the actual cremation not taking place till next day.

The beachcomber had been right in saying that the Balinese were a simple people; yet they have their own little vanities, one of the most peculiar of them being a love of mortuary display. When a person dies whose family is not rich enough to afford a triumphant cremation, he is embalmed and buried, and remains buried until a nobleman or plutocrat follows suit.

Then amid the trumpeting and parades that distinguish the funeral of a lord, the bourgeois corpses are disinterred, and, attached to the end of the splendid procession, get full benefit of all the music and banqueting and ostentation, none of which their own small wealth could have commanded.

Indeed, when a rajah shows signs of approaching death there are no cremations at all for a time as every one postpones the ceremony in the hopes that the rajah will die soon and allow the lesser dead to reap the great honor, and their families the greater glory, of participating in the funeral of a king. Then too, when the gates of Heaven open to receive the nobleman, who knows but that a few spirits of common clay might not slip in?

In consequence of this custom, there were over a hundred other coffins in the second day's procession, each borne in floats of various sizes all the way from the rajah's ponderous masterpiece of glass and gilt down to the crude small box of coolie's bones.

The coffins presented one of the strangest of the many strange Balinese characteristics, for in place of the conventional oblong box, the corpse was encased in a gaily spotted hobby-bull made of wood and paper, and adorned with horns, glaring teeth and upraised tail. The vicious animal is carried on top

BEAUTY AND THE BEASTS IN THE EAST INDIAN ISLAND OF BALI

of the float, which in turn rests on the shoulders of the pall-bearers, and after being placed upon the pyre is burned to ashes along with the enclosed body. I could learn neither the origin nor the significance of this custom. It had always been observed—that was all they knew.

When the towering hearse came into view I saw that it was borne along by a mob of almost naked men, those in front pulling forward, those behind holding back—a conflict that subjected the unwieldy bull to dangerous tilting and inconstant support.

This struggle represented the reluctance of the soul to leave the body. Half the pall-bearers represented the "friends of Heaven," half the "friends of Earth." The "soul" dragged the corpse to the exterminating pyre; the "body" fought against the inevitable, and strained for prolonged earthly residence. The two forces were battling over the coffin as it labored slowly and haltingly toward the flames.

The most astonishing spectacle was yet to follow. When, after a great struggle, the coffin finally reached its goal, the saddle of the rajah's bull was displaced and the corpse itself, tightly encased in bamboo, was lifted out.

THEN began the climax of the ceremony. Suddenly the "friends of Earth," marshaling their strength for one supreme effort, seized the mummy and with shouting began to carry it away from the very gates of eternity. The "friends of Heaven," taken by surprise, were at first overpowered, but they did not abandon the field, and soon succeeded in halting the escape.

The struggle was long in doubt. Scores of fresh recruits rushed to both sides and plunged into the crushing mass of fighting humanity. The corpse was lost in a sea of brown flesh. The solid acre of sweating, yelling fanatical men were trampling on one another, clawing at the mummy, falling by the wayside, gasping for breath and devoid of the last shred of clothes. The yards of

shrouding encasing the corpse became loosened and entangled a score of the fighters.

The hundreds of spectators were as excited as the participators. They cheered on the side they favored, or unable to restrain their zeal, rushed to join in. Simultaneously, in a great circle at the edge of the glade, the hundred lesser dead were being consumed by the flames which sent forth great columns of smoke that hung ominously overhead, and mingling together made a solid wall about the mad battle within.

The final dramatic touch for this incredible picture was the musical accompaniment, for twenty native orchestras outside the wall, frenzied by the general spirit of abandon, pounded wildly on their xylophones until their rolling notes could be heard even above the crackling of the hundred pyres and the shouts of the multitude. Not until both sides were utterly exhausted was the ill-used corpse dragged back to the pyre.

A wave of revulsion rushed over me. I saw instead of gentle peaceful children of Holland's island empire, mad savages stripped of their thin veneer of Dutch culture, reveling in brute instincts inherited from cannibal ancestors. To me it was desecration of the dead, the orgy of a pack of ghouls; but I realized that I had seen what so few have seen —Bali the real, the undisguised.

FOR a few days I lived with a hermit fisherman, sailing forth with him in his miniature outrigger canoe to set his nets. Ocean water was never so clear. One could look down into it for several fathoms and watch the roving school of brilliant fish.

His living quarters could scarcely have been more Spartan—two poles covered with palm-leaves, braced against a boulder. For myself I matted a bed of fronds and slept on the sand. During the day I sprawled on the rocks of a near-by wooded promontory and let the wind and the waves dictate to me a story for my American newspapers.

Becoming restless again, I moved on up the broad beachway. Fifteen miles brought me at sundown to a little cove where a family of salt collectors had built a very attractive hut of poles and matting in a dense grove of palms. They were bathing as I passed, father, mother, son and daughter, in a fresh water pool close to the house, and being half broiled myself and parched with thirst, I followed their excellent example.

They did not know whether to be frightened or amused at my spirit of fraternity, but on hearing my desperate effort to converse in Malay, decided to take it smilingly. The mother rubbed coconut oil on my blistered arms; the half grown son climbed a tree to secure for me a "fresh drink." Little by little their original timidity wore away, disappearing altogether when I offered the père a guilder and invited myself to dine on their frugal meal of rice and fish.

The night brought forth as big and round a tropical moon as I ever saw, and a desire to cling to whatever human association I could find, if only to this simple-spirited family; so I remained all night, sleeping on my usual palm bed. It was a novel sport assisting them next day in raking the salt deposits from the hollow logs they filled with water and left in the hot sun till the moisture evaporated. By the second evening I was quite captivated by this ingenuous household, and decided to pass the time until next boat-sailing on this idyllic spot with my hospitable friends.

Most of all we enjoyed the twilight hours. Then the sea was still and the beach deserted. The boy and girl of our menage had never before had so strange a companion as this curious white man, a white man who loved the water as they loved it. In consequence darkness always found the three of us still enjoying the cool calm sea.

If hunger drove us back to the sand, Taja, the daughter, would fetch a supper from her mother's table. Then these brown children and I, speaking different languages, knowing different worlds, would sit on the beach under the rising moon eating our meal and laughing as merrily as if we were of one race and one mind. Communication of thought soon ceased to hamper us. A common tongue is not vital to understanding when there is congeniality of spirit.

In these romantic hours I forgot the difficulties that had beset me in the search for them. I forgot all previous existence, since in my shell of coconut milk these gentle Balinese had pressed a lotus bloom that dimmed all recollection of the past.

We obeyed the behest of Rupert Brooke; we heard "the calling of the moon, and the whispering scents that strayed about the idle warm lagoon." We hastened "down the dark, the flowered way." "Along the whiteness of the sand and in the water's soft caress," we washed our minds, "of foolishness."

I felt deeply grateful to the island for the refreshing weeks of rare happiness it had afforded me. I had found what I had been seeking these many months. I had justified what I wished to believe. I could henceforth challenge the idea that there is no novelty left on earth, and I derived great satisfaction from the thought that if my spirit of romanticism were ever endangered by the materialism and artificiality of the Western world, I could always seek refuge and rejuvenation in this far-off land of the lotus, this Eden, this idyllic little isle, this Bali.

BEAUTY comes, we scarce know how, as an emanation from sources deeper than itself.—*Shairp.*

AFFECTATION is an awkward and forced Imitation of what should be genuine and easy, wanting the Beauty that accompanies what is natural.—*Locke.*

Booth Tarkington

THE MAGNIFICENT AMBERSONS

Tʜɪs story might have been laid in almost any town in America at the beginning of the century—for everybody knows an Amberson family. It is this "true to American life" quality in Booth Tarkington's books which won the Pulitzer Prize in 1918 for "The Magnificent Ambersons" and has made "Penrod," "Seventeen" and "The Gentleman from Indiana" such universal favorites. Tarkington celebrated his seventieth birthday last summer and his short stories still appear frequently in popular magazines.

The Princely Terror

Aᴛ ᴛʜᴇ age of nine, George Amberson Minafer was a princely terror, dreaded not only in Amberson Addition but in many other quarters through which he galloped on his white pony. "By golly, I guess you think you own this town!" an embittered labourer complained, one day, as Georgie rode the pony straight through a pile of sand the man was sieving. "I will when I grow up," the undisturbed child replied. "I guess my grandpa owns it now, you bet!" And the baffled workman, having no means to controvert what seemed a mere exaggeration of the facts, could only mutter "Oh, pull down your vest!"

There were people—grown people they were—who expressed themselves longingly: they did hope to live to see the day, they said, when that boy would get his come-upance! *Something* was bound to take him down, some day, and they only wanted to be there!

The yearners were still yearning when Georgie, at sixteen, was sent away to a great "Prep School." "Now," they said brightly, "he'll get it! He'll find himself among boys just as important in their home towns as he is, and they'll knock the stuffing out of him when he puts on airs with them! Oh, but that would be worth something to see!"

They were mistaken, it appeared, for when Georgie returned, a few months later, he still seemed to have the same stuffing. He had been deported by the authorities, the offense being stated as "insolence and profanity." But he had not got his come-upance, and those who counted upon it were embittered by his appearance upon the down-town streets driving a dog-cart at a criminal speed, making pedestrians retreat from the crossings, and behaving generally as if he "owned the earth."

There was no great change in him until he came home for the Christmas holidays when he was a sophomore in college. Then his exterior was visibly altered. The gilded youth's manner had become polite, but his politeness was of a kind which democratic people found hard to bear. In a word, M. de Duc had returned from the gay life of the capital to show himself for a week among the loyal peasants belonging to the old château, and their quaint habits and costumes afforded him a mild amusement.

Cᴀʀᴅs were out for a ball in his honour, and this pageant of the tenantry was held in the ballroom of the Amberson Mansion the night after his arrival.

George, white-gloved, with a gardenia in his buttonhole, stood with his mother and his grandfather, embowered in the big red and gold drawing room downstairs, to "receive" the guests; and, standing thus together, the trio offered a picturesque example of good looks persistent through three generations.

Isabel, standing between her fathe

"You're not wanted in this house."

Illustration for Booth Tarkington's
"THE MAGNIFICENT AMBERSONS"

and her son caused a vague amazement in the mind of the latter. He had no perception of her other than as an adjunct to himself, his mother. The woman, Isabel, was a stranger to her son; as completely a stranger as if he had never in his life seen her or heard her voice. And it was tonight, while he stood with her, "receiving," that he caught a glimpse of this stranger.

George was disturbed by a sudden impression coming upon him out of nowhere, so far as he could detect, that her eyes were brilliant, that she was graceful and youthful—in a word, that she was romantically lovely. There was nothing in either her looks or her manner to explain George's uncomfortable feeling; and yet it increased, becoming suddenly a vague resentment, as if she had done something unmotherly to him.

The fantastic moment passed. What restored him completely was a dark-eyed little beauty of nineteen, very knowing in lustrous blue and jet.

"Remember you very well indeed!" he said, his graciousness more earnest than any he heretofore displayed. Isabel heard him and laughed.

"But you don't, George!" she said. "You don't remember her yet, though of course you will! Miss Morgan is from out of town, and I'm afraid this is the first time you've ever seen her. You might take her up to the dancing; I think you've pretty well done your duty here."

"Be d'lighted," George responded formally, and offered his arm. The little beauty entrusted her gloved fingers to his coat-sleeve, and they moved away together.

Waltzing Around Again

GEORGE danced well, and Miss Morgan seemed to float as part of the music, the very dove itself of "La Paloma." George became conscious of strange feelings within him: an exaltation of soul, tender, but indefinite, and seemingly located in the upper part of his diaphragm. The stopping of the music came upon him like waking to an alarm clock; for instantly six or seven of the calculating persons about the entryways bore down upon Miss Morgan to secure dances.

"Give me the next and the one after that," George said hurriedly, recovering some presence of mind, just as the nearest applicant reached them. "And give me every third one the rest of the evening."

"It sounds as though you were just telling me to give you all those dances," she laughed.

"Well, I want 'em!" George insisted.

"Good gracious!" she laughed. "Yes!"

Here and there were to be seen couples so carried away that, ceasing to move at the decorous, even glide, considered most knowing, they pranced and whirled through the throng. George

suffered a shock of vague surprise when he perceived that his aunt, Fanny Minafer, was the lady-half of one of these wild couples. She had never been more childlike than she was tonight as she flew over the floor in the capable arms of a queer looking duck who was her partner.

The queer-looking duck had been a real dancer in his day, it appeared; and evidently his day was not yet over. In spite of the headlong, gay rapidity with which he bore Miss Fanny about the big room, he danced authoritatively, avoiding without effort the slightest collision with other couples.

What was most remarkable to George, and a little irritating, this stranger in the Amberson Mansion had no vestige of the air of deference proper to a stranger in such a place: he seemed thoroughly at home. He seemed offensively so, indeed, when, passing the entrance to the gallery stairway, he disengaged his hand from Miss Fanny's for an instant, and not pausing in the dance, waved a laughing salutation more than cordial, then capered lightly out of sight.

George gazed stonily at this manifestation, responding neither by word nor sign. "How's that for a bit of freshness?" he murmured.

"What was?" Miss Morgan asked.

"Why, I don't know that queer looking duck from Adam."

"You don't need to. He was waving at me."

THEY sat down on the stairs and a few minutes later Isabel came dancing by with the queer-looking duck; and it was to be noted that the lively gentleman's gait was more sedate than it had been with Miss Fanny Minafer, but not less dexterous and authoritative. He was talking to Isabel as gaily as he had talked to Miss Fanny, though with less laughter, and Isabel listened and answered eagerly: her colour was high and her eyes had a look of delight. She saw George and Lucy on the stairway and nodded to them.

"How lovely your mother is!" Lucy said. "She's the gracefulest woman in that ballroom."

"I think so," he agreed gently.

"How wonderfully they dance together!"

"Who?"

"Your mother and—and the queer-looking duck," said Lucy. "I'm going to dance with him pretty soon."

George feared no such rival; he laughed loudly. "I suppose he's some old widower!"

Lucy became serious at once. "Yes, he is a widower," she said. "I ought to have told you before; he's my father."

George stopped laughing abruptly. "Well, that's a horse on me. If I'd known he was your father, of course I wouldn't have made fun of him."

"Nobody could make fun of him," she said quietly.

Upon this, George had a gleam of intelligence. "Well, I'm not going to make myself silly any more then; I don't want to take chances with you."

Love and Death

"ALMOST" was Lucy's last word on the last night of George's vacation—that vital evening in which she had half consented to "settling things" between them. And George, discontented with the "almost," but contented that she seemed glad to wear a sapphire locket with a tiny photograph of George Amberson Minafer inside it, found himself wonderful in a new world at the final instant of their parting.

She wrote him a month later:

No. It must keep on being almost.

Isn't almost pretty pleasant? You know well enough that I care for you. I did from the first minute I saw you, and I'm pretty sure you knew it—I'm afraid you did. I'm afraid you always knew it.

You write that I "take the whole affair too lightly." Isn't that odd! Because to myself I seem to take it as something so much more solemn than you do. I shouldn't be a bit surprised to find myself an old lady, some day, still thinking of you—and me forgotten ages ago!

"Lucy Morgan," you'd say, when you saw my obituary. Then you'd shake your big white head and stroke your long white beard—you'd have such a distinguished long white beard! and you'd say, "No. I don't seem to remember any Lucy Morgan; I wonder what made me think I did?"

Good-bye for today. Don't work too hard—dear!

George immediately seized pen and paper, and vigorously requested Lucy not to imagine him with a beard, distinguished or otherwise, even in the extremities of age. Then he concluded his missive in a tone mollified to tenderness, and proceeded to read a letter from his mother which had reached him simultaneously with Lucy's.

I think your father looks better already, darling, though we've been here only a few hours. The doctors said they hoped that this place would build him up and if it does it will be worth the long struggle we had to get him to give up his business and come.

Poor dear man, he was so blue, not about his health but about giving up the worries down at his office and forgetting them for a time.

He is waiting for me to take a walk with him—that's a splendid sign because he hasn't felt he could walk much, at home, lately. I mustn't keep him waiting.

We plan to stay six weeks if the place agrees with him. Devotedly, your affectionate mother.
ISABEL.

But she did not keep her husband there for the six weeks she anticipated. She did not keep him anywhere that long. Four days after he had received the letter George found a telegram upon his desk.

He read it twice before he comprehended its import.

Papa left us at ten this morning, dearest.
MOTHER.

A friend saw the change in his face. "Not bad news?"

George lifted utterly dumbfounded eyes from the yellow paper.

"My father," he said weakly. "She says—she says he's dead. I've got to go home."

On the train going back to college ten days later George paused to reflect upon the sweet mournfulness of his mother's face, as she had said good-bye to him at the station, and of how lovely she looked in her mourning. He thought of Lucy, whom he had seen only twice, and he could not help feeling that in these quiet interviews he had appeared to her as tinged with heroism—she had shown, rather than said, how brave she thought him in his sorrow.

"Being Things"

THE collegian did not return to his home for the next Christmas holidays. Instead, Isabel joined him and they went South for two weeks. She was proud of her stalwart, good-looking son at the hotel where they stayed. Indeed, her vanity in him was so dominant that she was unaware of the other guests staring at her with more interest and an admiration friendlier than George evoked. Yet both of them felt constantly the difference between this Christmas-time and other Christmastimes of theirs —in all, it was a sorrowful holiday.

But when Isabel came East for George's commencement, in June, she brought Lucy with her—and things began to seem different, especially when George Amberson arrived with Lucy's father on Class Day. Eugene had been in New York, on business; Amberson easily persuaded him to this outing and they made a cheerful party of it, with the new graduate of course the hero and center of it all.

George took no conspicuous part in either the academic or the social celebrations of his class; he seemed to regard both sets of exercises with a tolerant amusement, his own "crowd" "not going in much for either of those sorts of things," as he explained to Lucy. What

his crowd had gone in for remained ambiguous; some negligent testimony indicating that, except for an astonishing reliability which they all seemed to have attained in matters relating to musical comedy, they had not gone in for anything.

George, like his "crowd," not only preferred "being things" to "doing things," but had contented himself with four years of "being things" as a preparation for going on "being things." And when Lucy rather shyly pressed him for the probable definition of the "things," George raised his eyebrows slightly, meaning that she should have understood without explanation: but he did explain: "Oh, family and all that—being a gentleman, I suppose."

Lucy gave the horizon a long look, but offered no comment.

ISABEL came to George's door one night soon after they had returned home. When she had kissed him good-night she remained in the open doorway with her hand upon his shoulder and her eyes thoughtfully lowered, so that her wish to say something more than good-night was evident. After another moment of hesitation, she came quickly in, and closed the door.

"Dear," she said, "I wish you'd tell me something. Why don't you like Lucy's father?"

"Oh, I like him well enough," George returned, with a short laugh. "I like him well enough—in his place."

"No, dear," she said hurriedly. "I've had a feeling from the very first that you didn't really like him—that you really never liked him. It seems so queer especially when you feel as you do about his daughter."

"Well, I'll tell you something," George said slowly; and a frown of concentration could be seen upon his brow, as from a profound effort of self-examination. "I haven't ever thought much on that particular point, but I admit there may be a little something in what you say. The truth is, I don't believe I've ever thought of the two together, exactly —at least, not until lately. I've always thought of Lucy just as Lucy, and of Morgan just as Morgan.

"I don't say, though, that I feel unfriendly to Mr. Morgan. I don't say that I feel friendly to him. I can't quite promise to like people I don't care about one way or another, but you can be sure I'll be careful not to let him see it. It's all right, and you'd better toddle along to bed, because I want to undress."

Thus the interview closed perforce. She kissed him again before going slowly to her own room, her perplexity evidently not dispersed; but the subject was not renewed between them either the next day or subsequently.

Enduring Charms

During this period he successfully avoided contact with Lucy's father, though Eugene came frequently to the house, and spent several evenings with Isabel and Fanny; and sometimes persuaded them to go riding.

One day when he was walking from the stable to the house he glanced toward the street, and saw his mother standing with Eugene Morgan. Evidently he had been calling upon her, and she had come from the house with him, continuing their conversation and delaying their parting.

The conversation was evidently serious; his head was bent, and Isabel's lifted hand rested against her cheek; but all the significances of their thoughtful attitude denoted companionableness and a shared understanding.

Yet, a stranger, passing, would not have thought them married: somewhere about Eugene, not quite to be located, there was a romantic gravity; and Isabel, tall and graceful with heightened colour and absorbed eyes, was visibly no wife walking down to the gate with her husband.

George stared at them. A hot dislike struck him at the sight of Eugene, and a vague revulsion like a strange, unpleasant taste in his mouth, came over him as he looked at his mother; her manner was so eloquent of so much thought about her companion and of such reliance upon him.

The two began to walk on toward the gate, where they stopped again, turning to face each other, and Isabel's glance, passing Eugene, fell upon George. Instantly she smiled and waved her hand to him; while Eugene turned and nodded. But George, standing as in some rigid trance, and staring straight at them, gave these signals of greeting no sign of recognition whatever. He turned away as if he had neither seen nor heard, and stalked into the house by the side door.

"Everybody Is Talking"

His Aunt Fanny had opened the door before he reached it and closed it behind her. Her look was that of a person who had just seen something extraordinary.

"George," she said hurriedly, "I saw what you did when you wouldn't speak to them. You did exactly right! You're behaving splendidly about the whole thing, and I want to tell you I know your father would thank you if he could see what you're doing."

"My Lord!" George broke out at her. "What are you making all the fuss about?"

"I never in the world would have said anything about it if I hadn't seen that somebody else had told you, or you'd found out for yourself some way. I—"

In despair of her intelligence, and in some doubt of his own, George struck the palms of his hands together. "Somebody else has told me what? I'd found what out by myself?"

"How people are talking about your mother."

"What?" said George, fiercely. "I thought that mother never saw him except when she was chaperoning you."

"They were alone hardly ever, before your father died. But you don't suppose that stops people talking, do you? Your father never went anywhere, and people saw Eugene with her everywhere she went—and though I was with them people just thought"—she choked—"they just thought I didn't count. 'Only old Fanny Minafer,' I suppose they'd say?

Besides, everybody knew that he'd been engaged to her—"

"What's that?" George cried.

"Well, they were engaged. Everybody knows it; and she broke it off on account of that serenade when Eugene didn't know what he was doing. He drank when he was a young man and she wouldn't stand it, but everybody in this town knows that Isabel has never really cared for any other man in her life! Poor Wilbur! He was the only soul alive that didn't know it!"

Nightmare had descended upon the unfortunate George: he gazed wildly at his aunt. "And because he comes here—and they see her with him driving—and all that—they think they were right when they said she was in—in love with him before—before my father died?"

"Why, George," she said, gently, "don't you know that's what they say? You must know that everybody in town thinks they're going to be married very soon."

George uttered an incoherent cry; and sections of him appeared to writhe. He was upon the verge of actual nausea.

Modern Hamlet

Breakfast the next morning was brought to him in his room, as usual; but he did not make his normal healthy raid upon the dainty tray: the food remained untouched, and he sustained himself upon coffee—four cups of it, which left nothing of value inside the glistening little percolator.

During this process he heard his mother being summoned to the telephone in the hall, and then her voice responding: "Yes? Oh, it's you! . . . Indeed I should! . . . Of course. . . . Then I'll expect you about three. . . . Yes. . . . Good-bye till then."

There was an air of briskness about her and she laughed gaily over something he said, and this unconcerned cheerfulness of hers was terrible to her son.

Having lunched upon more coffee, he went to a front window of the long "reception room," and sat looking out through the lace curtains. At ten minutes of three, he saw an automobile stop in front of the house and Eugene Morgan jump lightly down from it. He was a figure of the new era which was in time to be so disastrous to stiff hats and skirted coats; and his appearance afforded a debonair contrast to that queer looking duck capering at the Amberson Ball in an old dress coat. Some change might be seen in his face, too, for a successful man is seldom to be mistaken, especially if his temper is genial. Eugene had begun to look like a millionaire.

But above everything else, what was most evident about him, as he came up the path, was his confidence in the happiness promised by his present errand; the anticipation in his eyes could have been read by a stranger. His look at the door of Isabel's house was the look of a man who is quite certain that the next moment will reveal something ineffably charming, inexpressibly dear.

A SLIGHT change shadowed the face of Eugene; his look of happy anticipation gave way to something formal and polite. "How do you do, George," he said. "Mrs. Minafer expects to go driving with me, I believe—if you'll be so kind as to send her word that I'm here."

George made not the slightest movement.

"No." he said.

Eugene was incredulous, even when his second glance revealed how hot of eye was the haggard young man before him. "I beg your pardon. I said—"

"I heard you," said George. "You said you had an engagement with my mother, and I told you, No!"

Eugene gave him a steady look, and then he asked quietly: "What is the—the difficulty?"

George kept his own voice quiet enough, but that did not mitigate the vibrant fury of it. "My mother will have no interest in knowing that you came for her today," he said. "Or any other day!"

Eugene continued to look at him with a scrutiny in which began to gleam a profound anger, none the less powerful because it was so quiet. "I am afraid I do not understand you."

"I doubt if I could make it much plainer," George said, raising his voice slightly, "But I'll try. You're not wanted in this house, Mr. Morgan, now or at any other time. Perhaps you'll understand—this!"

And with the last word he closed the door in Eugene's face.

Eugene made no further attempt; the silhouette disappeared; footsteps could be heard withdrawing across the floor of the veranda; and George, returning to the window in the "reception room," was rewarded by the sight of an automobile manufacturer in baffled retreat, with all his wooing furs and fineries mocking him. Observing the heaviness of his movements as he climbed into the tonneau, George indulged in a sickish throat rumble which bore a distant cousinship to mirth.

The Honor of the Family

HE HAD not slept at all, the night before, and he had eaten nothing since the preceding day at lunch, but he felt neither drowsiness nor hunger. His set determination filled him, kept him but too wide awake, and his gaze at the grayness beyond the window was wide-eyed and bitter.

Darkness had closed in when there was a step in the room behind him. Then someone knelt beside the chair, two arms went round him with infinite compassion, a gentle head rested against his shoulder.

"You mustn't be troubled, darling," his mother whispered.

"How can I help but be?" he said.

"No, no." She soothed him. "You mustn't be troubled, no matter what happens. I want to tell you: brother George has been here, and he told me everything—about how unhappy you'd been—ah, you do look so troubled, poor dear! One thing you couldn't doubt, beloved boy: you know I could never care for anything in the world as I care for you—never, never!"

"Now, mother—"

She released him, and stepped back. "Just a moment more, dearest. I want you to read this first. We can get at things better." She pressed into his hand a sheet of paper covered with Eugene's handwriting:

I have understood for quite a long time that young George was getting to dislike me more and more. I think it may be he felt from the first that I cared a great deal about you, and he naturally resented it.

It's perfectly comprehensible to me, also, that at his age one gets excited about gossip.

Dear Isabel, what I'm trying to get at is that you and I don't care about this nonsensical gossip, ourselves, at all. Yesterday I thought the time had come when I could ask you to marry me, and you were dear enough to tell me "sometime it might come to that."

But now we're faced with—not the slander and not our own fear of it, but someone else's fear of it—your son's.

I know what your son is to you, and it frightens me! Let me explain a little: I don't think he'll change—at twenty-one or twenty-two so many things appear solid and permanent and terrible which forty sees are nothing but disappearing miasma. Forty can't tell twenty about this; that's the pity of it. . . .

And so we come to this dear: Will you live your life your way, or George's way? I'm going a little further; George will act toward you only as your long worship of him, your sacrifices, all the unseen little ones every day since he was born—will make him act. . . . Dear, it breaks my heart for you, but what you have to oppose now is the history of your own selfless and perfect motherhood.

Are you strong enough, Isabel? Can you make the fight? I promise you that if you will take heart for it, you will find so quickly that it has all amounted to nothing. You shall have happiness, and, in a little while, only happiness. The angel in your son will bring him to you; I promise. What is good in him will grow so fine, once you have beaten the turbulent Will—but it must be beaten. . . .

Don't strike my life down twice, dear—this time I've not deserved it.

EUGENE.

CONCLUDING this missive, George tossed it abruptly from him so that one sheet fell upon his bed.

"Did you read it, dear?"

"Yes, I did." George's face was pale no longer, but pink with fury.

Nervousness and an irresistible timidity possessed her. "I—I wanted to say, George," she faltered. "I was afraid you might think it would be a little queer about Lucy. Of course, she'd not be even legally related to you, and if you—if you cared for her—"

"I have already given up all idea of Lucy," he said. "Naturally, I couldn't have treated her father as I deliberately did treat him—if I had expected his daughter ever to speak to me again. Anyway, we should never have been happy; she was "superior" all the time, and critical of me—not very pleasant, that! I was disappointed in her, and I

might as well say it. I don't think she has the very deepest nature in the world, and—well, it's all over, and I don't care to speak of it again. It's settled. Don't you understand?"

"But, dear—"

"Now I want to talk to you about this letter of her father's."

"Yes, dear, that's why—"

"It's simply the most offensive piece of writing that I've ever held in my hands. How did you ever happen to bring it to me?"

"I thought it would be the simplest and more straight-forward thing."

"Very well, we'll agree that it was simple and straight-forward. You think he is trying to be fair, yet do you suppose it ever occurs to him that I'm doing my simple duty. He says he and you don't care what they say, but I know better! He may not care—probably he's that kind—but you do. There never was an Amberson yet that would let the Amberson name go trailing in the dust like that! It's the proudest name in this town and it's going to stay the proudest; and I tell you that's the deepest thing in my nature—to protect that name, and to fight for it to the last breath when danger threatens it, as it does now—through my mother! Well, what are you going to do about it?"

"I—I don't quite know, dear," she murmured. "Marrying doesn't mean so much, after all—not at my age. It's enough to know that—that people think of you—and to see them. I thought we were all—oh, pretty happy the way things were, and I don't think it would mean giving up a great deal for him or me, either, if we just went on as we have been. I—I see him almost every day, and—"

"Mother!" George's voice was loud and stern. "Do you think you could go on seeing him after this!"

She had been talking helplessly before; her tone was more broken now.

"Not—not even—see him?"

"How could you?" George cried. "Mother, it seems to me that if he ever set foot in this house again—oh! I can't speak of it!"

"Oh, this won't do!" she said. "I've

never let you see me cry before, except when your father died. I mustn't." And she ran from the room.

"No Particular Sacrifice"

HAVING finished some errands down-town, the next afternoon, George Amberson Minafer was walking up National Avenue when he saw in the distance, coming toward him, the figure of a young lady. For a panicky moment he thought of facing about in actual flight; he had little doubt that Lucy would meet him with no sign of recognition, and all at once this probability struck him as unendurable.

But the girl approaching him was unaware of his trepidation, being perhaps somewhat preoccupied with her own. Though she was the mistress of her own ways and no slave to any lamp save that of her own conscience, she had a weakness; she had fallen in love with George Amberson Minafer at first sight, and no matter how she disciplined herself, she had never been able to climb out. The thing had happened to her; that was all.

As they drew nearer, George tried to prepare himself to meet her with some remnants of aplomb. She came straight to meet him smiling, and with her hand offered to him.

"Why—you—" he stammered, as he took it. "Haven't you—"

"Haven't I what?" she asked; and he saw that Eugene had not yet told her.

"Nothing!" he gasped. "May I—may I turn and walk with you a little way?"

"Yes, indeed!" she said cordially.

Now when he must in good truth "give up all idea of Lucy," he was amazed that he could have used such words as "no particular sacrifice," and believed them when he said them! She had never looked so bewitchingly pretty as she did today.

"Lucy—this may be the last time I'll see you—ever—ever in my life. Mother and I are starting tomorrow night for a trip around the world. We have no plans for coming back."

"Your mother is going with you?" she said brightly. "And do you plan to be travelling all the time, or stay in one place the greater part of it?"

"Good heavens!" he groaned. "Lucy, doesn't it make any difference to you that I am going?"

At this her cordial smile instantly appeared again. "Yes, of course," she said. "I'm sure I'll miss you ever so much. Are you to be gone long? I think it would be lovely to—"

"Lucy!" Then he said after drawing his breath. "Well, it is quite a shock to find out at last how deeply you've cared for me. To see how much difference this makes to you!"

Her cordial smile was tempered now with good nature. "George!" She laughed indulgently. "Surely you don't want me to do pathos on a downtown corner!"

"I can't stand this any longer," he said. "I can't! Good-bye, Lucy!" He took her hand. "It's good-bye—I think it's good-bye for good, Lucy!"

"Good-bye! I do hope you'll have the most splendid trip." She gave his hand a cordial little grip, then released it lightly.

"Give my love to your mother. Good-bye!"

Lucy remained where she was until he was out of sight. Then she went slowly into a drugstore.

"Please let me have a few drops of aromatic spirits of ammonia in a glass of water," she said.

A moment later as the clerk turned from the shelves with the potion she had asked for in his hand, he uttered an exclamation: "For goshes' sake, Miss!" And, describing this adventure to his fellow-boarders, that evening, "Sagged pretty near to the counter, she was," he said. "'F I hadn't been quick she'd 'a' flummixed plum!"

"The Old Order Changeth"

New faces appeared at the dances of the winter; new faces had been appearing everywhere, for that matter, and familiar ones were disappearing, merged in the increasing crowd, or gone forever and missed a little and not long; for the town was growing and changing as it never had grown and changed before.

What was left of the patriotic old-stock generation that had fought the Civil War, and subsequently controlled politics, had become venerable and was little heeded. The descendants of the pioneers and early settlers were merging into the new crowd becoming part of it, little to be distinguished from it. What happened to Boston and to Broadway happened here; the old stock became less and less typical.

These were bad times for Amberson Addition. This quarter, already old, lay within a mile of the center of town, but business moved in other directions; and the Addition's share of Prosperity was only the smoke and dirt, with the bank credit left out. The owners of the original big houses sold them, or rented them to boarding house keepers, and the tenants of the multitude of small houses moved "farther out" (where the smoke was thinner) or into apartment houses, which were built by dozens now.

"George and Isabel will find things pretty changed, I'm afraid," Fanny said. "If they ever do come home!"

George Amberson had just returned from Paris where he had visited his sister.

"Isabel does want to come home," he told Fanny gravely. "She's wanted to for a long while—and she ought to come while she can stand the journey—" And he amplified this statement, leaving Fanny looking startled and solemn. "Of course she makes nothing of it, but it seemed rather serious to me when I noticed she had to stop and rest twice to get up the one short flight of stairs in their two floor apartment. I told her I thought she ought to make George let her come home."

The time came when it was no longer a question of George's letting his mother come home. He had to bring her, and to bring her quickly.

She was lifted from the chair into a carriage, and seemed a little stronger as they drove home; for once she took her hand from George's and waved it feebly toward the carriage window.

"Changed," she whispered. "So changed."

"You mean the town," Amberson said. "You mean the old place is changed, don't you, dear?"

She smiled and moved her lips: "Yes."

Isabel lived through the night. At eleven o'clock Fanny came timidly to George in his room. "Eugene is here," she whispered. "He's downstairs. He wants—" She gulped. "He wants to know if he can't see her. I didn't know what to say."

"The doctor said we 'must keep her peaceful,'" George said sharply. "Do you think that man's coming would be very soothing?"

Fanny acquiesced tearfully. "I'll tell him. I—I didn't know—"

An hour later the nurse appeared in George's doorway. "She wants to see you."

Isabel's eyes were closed, and she did not open them or move her head, but she smiled and edged her hand toward him as he sat on a stool beside the bed.

"I wonder if—if Eugene and Lucy know that we've come—home."

"I'm sure they do."

"Has he—asked about me?"

"Yes, he was here."

"Has he gone?"

"Yes, mother."

She sighed faintly. "I'd like—"

"What, mother?"

"I'd like to have—seen him." It was just audible, this little regretful murmur. Several minutes passed before there was another. "Just—just once," she whispered, and then was still.

Starting Over Again

WHEN the great Amberson Estate went into court for settlement, "there wasn't any."

"We'll survive, Georgie—you will, especially," said George Amberson. "For my part I'm a little too old and too accustomed to fall back on somebody else for supplies to start a big fight with life. But you—of course you've had a poor training for making your own way, but you're only a boy after all, and the stuff of the old stock is in you. I'll come out and do something. Still, you have a little tiny bit, and you'll have a little tiny salary, too; and of course your Aunt Fanny's here, and she's got something you can fall back on."

George's "little tiny bit" was six hundred dollars which had come to him from the sale of his mother's furniture.

THIS was the last "walk home." For tonight would be the last night that he and Fanny were to spend in the old house. Tomorrow they were to "move out," and George was to begin work. He had not come to this collapse without a fierce struggle—but the struggle was inward, and the rolling world was not agitated by it, and rolled calmly on. For of all the "ideals of life" which the world, in its rolling, inconsid-

erately flattens out to nothingness, the least likely to retain a profile is that ideal which depends upon inheriting money.

He entered the house and climbed up the stairs to Isabel's room and shut the door. He did not come forth again, and bade Fanny good-night through the closed door when she stopped outside it later.

She had said the one thing she should not have said just then: "I'm sure your mother's watching over you, Georgie." She had meant to be kind, but it destroyed his last chance for sleep that night.

When the space that was Isabel's room came to be made into the small bed rooms and "kitchenettes" already designed as its destiny, that space might well be haunted and the new occupants come to feel that some seemingly cause-less depression hung about it.

It may be that to this day some impressionable, overworked woman in a "kitchenette," after turning off the light, will seem to see a young man kneeling in the darkness, shaking convulsively. It may seem to her that she hears the faint cry, over and over:

"Mother, forgive me! *God,* forgive me!"

George Gets His Come-Uppance

HE FOUND a job. It needed an apprenticeship of only six weeks, during which period George was to receive fifteen dollars a week; after that he would get twenty-eight. This settled the apartment question, and Fanny was presently established in a greater contentment than she had known for a long time.

When George returned in the evening he usually denied that he was tired, though he sometimes looked tired, particularly during the first few months, and he explained to her frequently—looking bored enough with her insistence—that his work was "fairly light and fairly congenial, too." Fanny hadn't

the foggiest idea of what it was, though she noticed that it roughened his hands and stained them. "Something in those new chemical works," she explained to casual inquirers. It was not more definite in her own mind.

On Sunday mornings Fanny went to church and George took long walks. On one of these walks he made a sour pilgrimage. He tramped through the early spring slush to the dripping department store which now occupied the big plot of ground where once had stood both the Amberson Hotel and the Amberson Opera House. From there he drifted to the old "Amberson Block," but this was fallen into a back-water; business had stagnated here.

He turned away from the devastated sight, thinking bitterly that the only Amberson mark still left upon the town was the name of the boulevard—Amberson Boulevard. But he reckoned without the city council of the new order. The street sign which should have stencilled "Amberson Boulevard" exhibited the words "Tenth Street."

IT HAD begun to rain, but George stood unheeding, staring at the little sign. "Damn them!" he said finally, and turning up his coat collar, plodded back through the soggy streets toward "home."

The lobby of the apartment hotel was empty, as it always was on Sunday mornings, and having nothing better to do he stopped before a flamboyant volume reposing on the center table for the enlightenment of the guests. It was the History of the City and it contained the names of the Most Prominent Citizens and Families. George turned to the index and skipped through the A's. His eyes remained for some time fixed on the thin space between the names "Allen" and "Ambrose." Then he closed the book quietly, and went up to his own room.

The elevator boy noticed nothing unusual about him and neither did Fanny, when she came in from church. But something had happened—a thing which, years ago, had been the eagerest hope of many, many good citizens of the town. They had thought of it, longed for it, hoping acutely that they might live to see the day it would come to pass. And now it had happened at last: Georgie had got his come-upance.

Another Radiance

EUGENE's feeling about George had not been altered by a talk with his friend Kinney in the club window, though he was somewhat disturbed. He was not disturbed by Kinney's hint that Fanny Minafer might be left on the hands of her friends through her nephew's present dealings with nitroglycerin, but he was surprised that Kinney had "led up" with intentional tact to the suggestion that a position might be made for George in the Morgan factory.

Kinney had represented Georgie as a new Georgie—at least in spots—a Georgie who was proving that decent stuff had been hid in him by taking a risky job for the sake of his aunt, poor old silly Fanny Minafer. Eugene didn't care what risks Georgie took, or how much decent stuff he had in him; nothing that Georgie would ever do in this world or the next could change Eugene Morgan's feeling toward him.

His bitterness for himself might have worn away, but never his bitterness for Isabel. He took that thought to bed with him—and it was true that nothing George could do would ever change this bitterness of Eugene. Only George's mother could have changed it.

The next morning Eugene boarded the train for New York, on business. Ordinarily he would probably have overlooked this obscure item in his morning paper:

LEGS BROKEN

G. A. Minafer, an employee of the Akers Chemical Company was run down by an automobile yesterday and had both legs broken. Minafer was to blame for the accident, according to the patrolman who witnessed the affair. He was taken to the City Hospital where physicians stated later that he was suffering from internal injuries besides the fractures of his legs but might recover.

Eugene read the item twice, then tossed the paper upon the opposite seat of his compartment, and sat looking out of the window. His feeling toward Georgie was changed not a jot by his human pity for Georgie's human pain and injury. He thought of Georgie's tall and graceful figure, and he shivered, but his bitterness was untouched. He had never blamed Isabel for the weakness which had cost them the few years of happiness they might have had together; he had put the blame all on the son, and it stayed there.

He began to think poignantly of Isabel: he had seldom been able to "see" her more clearly than as he sat looking out of his compartment window, after reading the account of this accident. She might have been just on the other side of the glass, looking in at him—and then he thought of her as the pale figure of a woman, seen yet unseen, flying through the air, beside the train—pleading with him.

For a moment he had believed that Isabel was there, believed that she was close to him, entreating him—entreating him "to be kind." A strange agitation came upon him. Had not she spoken to him. Hadn't the true Isabel—oh, indeed her very soul—called to him.

A RED-CAP at the station, when he arrived home several days later, leaped for his bag. "Yessuh. You' car waitin' front the station fer you, Mist' Morgan, suh!" And people in the crowd about the gates whispered: *"That's Morgan."*

"I'll not go home now, Harry," said Eugene when he had climbed in. "Drive to the City Hospital."

"Yes, sir," the man returned. "Miss Lucy's there. She said she expected you'd come there before you went home."

"She did? I suppose Mr. Minafer must be pretty bad," he said.

"Yes, sir. I understand he's liable to get well, though sir."

Fanny met him in the upper corridor, and took him to an open door. He stopped on the threshold, startled; for, from the waxen face on the pillow, almost it seemed the eyes of Isabel herself were looking at him; never before had the resemblance between mother and son been so strong—and Eugene knew that now he had once seen it thus startling, he need divest himself of no bitterness "to be kind" to Georgie.

George was startled, too. He lifted a white hand in a queer gesture, half forbidding, half imploring, and then let his arm fall back upon the coverlet. "You must have thought my mother wanted you to come," he said, "so that I could ask you to—to forgive me."

But Lucy, who sat beside him, lifted ineffable eyes from him to her father, and shook her head. "No, just take his hand—gently."

She was radiant.

But for Eugene another radiance filled the room. He knew that he had been true at last to his one true love.

◆

SHAKESPEARE

OTHERS abide our question. Thou art free.
We ask and ask: Thou smilest and art still,
Out-topping knowledge. For the loftiest hill
That to the stars uncrowns his majesty,
Planting his steadfast footsteps in the sea,
Making the Heaven of Heavens his dwelling-place,
Spares but the cloudy border of his base
To the foiled searching of mortality:
And thou, who didst the stars and sunbeams know,
Self-schooled, self-scanned, self-honoured, self-secure,
Didst walk on Earth unguessed at. Better so!
All pains the immortal spirit must endure,
All weakness that impairs, all griefs that bow,
Find their sole voice in that victorious brow.

—*M. Arnold*

Robert W. Chambers

CARDIGAN

Tʜɪs is the story of the struggle between England and the Colonies for the adherence of the Indians preceding the Revolutionary War. More particularly it is the story of one Michael Cardigan's exploit with the Indians and the treacherous servants of the English crown. "Cardigan," published in 1901, is one of the most successful novels of Robert W. Chambers (1865-1933). He has captured the romance and drama of the Revolutionary period.

Oɴ ᴛʜᴇ first of May, 1774, I left the schoolroom, a lad of eighteen puffed up in a glow of pride. I was to be received at last as man among men!

What a change had come to me, all in ne brief May morning! A great tide f benevolent condescension for the ther children swept over me, a ripple f pity and good will for the hapless hildren whose benches lay in a row efore me.

I walked on tiptoe to Silver Heels ench. There lay her quill and inky orn and a foolscap book sewed neatly nd marked:

Felicity Warren
1774
Her Booke

Poor child, doomed for years still steep her little fingers in the ink owder while, with the powder I should quire hereafter, I expected to write ercer tales on living hides with plumets cast in bullet molds.

I know my head was all swelled with ain imaginings: I saw myself riding ith Sir William as his deputy. I heard m say, "Mr. Cardigan, the enemy are pon us! We must fly!"—and I: "Sir illiam, fear nothing. The day is our vn!" And I saw a lad of eighteen, with vord pointing upward and one hand visted into Pontiac's scalp lock, smile nignly upon Sir William, who had st himself upon my breast, protesting at I had saved the army and that the

King should hear of it. Truly I painted life in cloying colors; and always, when I accomplished gallant deeds, there stood Silver Heels to marvel.

In a sort of ecstasy I paraded the school room, the splendor of my visions dulling eyes and ears. Suddenly I observed Mr. Butler standing in the doorway. He was my schoolmaster and Sir William's secretary. It was he who was betrothed to my Silver Heels. The unwelcome sight cleared my brains like a dash of spring water on the face.

"It is one o'clock," said Mr. Butler, "and time for your carving lesson. Did you not hear the bugles from the forts?"

Sᴜᴅᴅᴇɴʟʏ all the hatred and contempt I held for my schoolmaster and rival burst out into language I now blush for.

"Measure me!" I said, venomously. "I am as tall as you, lacking an inch. I am a man! This day Sir William freed me from that spider web you tenant, and now in Heaven's name let us settle that score which every hour has added to since I first beheld you!"

"Not your blood," he said, with a stealthy glance at the dining-room door. "Not the blood of an untried boy."

"You will not meet me!" I blurted out, mortified.

Then from within the dining hall came Sir William's roar; "Body o' me! Am I to be kept here at twiddle-thumbs for lack of a carver?"

I stepped back, bowing to Mr. Butler. "I will be patient for a year, sir," I said. And so opened the door while he passed me, and into the dining-hall.

The Prophet

AFTER I had carved the juicy joint, the gillie served Sir William, then Mr. Butler, then Silver Heels.

"Your good health, Michael," said Silver Heels, sweetly.

I pledged her with a patronizing amiability that made her hazel-gray eyes open wide. I sat there, somewhat dizzied by my new dignity, yet not deaf to the talk that went on. Mr. Butler and Sir William spoke gravely of the discontent now rampant in the town of Boston, and of Captain John Johnson's mission to Albany. At first I listened greedily, sniffing for news of war, but presently understanding little of their discourse save what pertained to the Indians, I lost interest.

I was roused by Sir William's voice in solemn tones: "Now, God forbid I should live to see that, Captain Butler!" and I pricked up my ears once more, for they were talking about certain disloyal men in Massachusetts and New York who might rise against our King.

"God forbid that I, a humble loyal subject of my King, should ever bear out the work of rebels or traitors," said Sir William. "But I solemnly say to you that the rebels and traitors are not the counterfeit Indians who tossed the tea into the sea, not the men who fired the *Gaspee* aflame from spirit to topmast. But they are those who whisper evil to my King at St. James's—and may God have mercy on their souls!"

In the hush that followed, Sir William leaned forward, his heavy chin set on his fists, his eyes looking into the future which he alone saw so clearly. None durst interrupt him.

There he sat, this great Irishman, eyes on vacancy; a plain man, a baronet of the British realm, a member of the King's Council, a major-general of militia, and the superintendent of the Indian Department in North America.

A plain man, but a vast landowner, the one man in America trusted blindly by the Indians, a man whose influence was enormous; a man who was as simple as a maid, as truthful as a child, as kind as the Samaritan who passed not on the other side.

A plain man, but a prophet.

THAT night I sat alone with Sir William in the twilight. Now, for the first time in my life, I saw a trace of physical decline in my guardian.

When he spoke at last he said: "I am an old man, a tired old man. This land has drunk the sweat of my body. I have not spared myself in sickness or in health. I have journeyed far through snow, through heat, from the Canadas to the Gulf—all my life I have journeyed on business for other men—for men have never seen and shall never see—men yet to be born!"

Then came a flush of earnest color into his face. He leaned forward toward me, elbow resting on the table, hand outstretched.

"Why, look you, Michael," he said with childlike eagerness, "I found wilderness and I leave a garden! Look at the valley! Look at this fair and pretty village! The English hay smells sweet but not so sweet as the Mohawk Valley hay to me. This is my country."

Presently he roused, shaking the dream from his eyes, and slapped the table with the flat of his hand.

"Look, Michael; should war come betwixt King and colonies, neither King nor colonies should forget that our frontiers are crowded with thousands of savages who, if adroitly treated, will remain neutral and inoffensive. Yet here is this madman Cresap, on the very eve of a struggle with the greatest power in the world, turning the savages against the colonies by his crazy pranks on the Ohio!"

"But," said I, "in his blindness and folly, Colonel Cresap is throwing into our arms these very savages as allies!"

Sir William stopped short and stared at me with cold, steady eyes. "What

m striving for," he said, "is to so conduct that these Indians on our frontiers
hall take neither one side nor the other,
out remain passive while the storm
ages. To work openly for this is not
oossible. If it were possible to work
penly, I would send such a message to
ny Lord Dunmore of Virginia as would
nake his bloodless ears burn! And they
nay burn yet!

"You are to know, Michael, that Lord
Dunmore, governor of Virginia, is, in
ny opinion, at the bottom of this. He it
s who has sent the deluded Cresap to
ick a quarrel with my Cayugas, know-
ng that he is making future allies for
England. It is vile! It is a monstrous
hing! It is not loyalty; it is treason!"

He struck his pinched forehead and
trode up and down.

"Can Dunmore know what he is do-
ng? God! The horror of it!—the
orror of border war! Has Dunmore
ver seen how savages fight? Has he
een raw scalps ripped from babies? Has

he seen naked prisoners writhing at the
stake, drenched in blood, eyeless sockets
raised to the skies?"

He stood still in the middle of the
room. There was a sweat on his cheek.

"Michael," said he, presently, "when
this war comes—as surely it will come—
choose which cause you will embrace,
and then stand by it to the end. As for
me, I cannot believe that God would
let me live to see such a war; that He
would leave me to choose between the
King who had honored me and mine
own people in this dear land of mine!

"If we must fight, let us fight like
men," he muttered, "without fear or
favor, without treachery! But, Michael,
woe to the side that calls on these savages for aid! Woe to them! Woe! Woe!"

The outburst left me stunned. It had
never entered my head that there could
be any course save unquestioned loyalty
to the King in all things. Save for Sir
William, I knew not where now where
to anchor my faith.

Fateful Meeting

Now the dark pages turning in the
book of fate were flying fast. Our
ouse was now thronged with Indians.
leven hundred Mohawks, Cayugas,
enecas, Onondagas, and a few Tusca-
oras lay encamped around us. Officers
ame from the Royal American and
rom the three regiments of militia
vhich Tryon County maintained to
ut the fear of the King's authority into
he hearts of the settlers.

And now, piling confusion on con-
ision, comes from the south my Lord
Dunmore from Virginia, satin-coated,
oppish, all powder and frill, and scented
ke a French lady. But, oh, the gallant
ompany he brought to Johnson Hall—
nose courtly Virginians with their low
ows and noiseless movements, elegant
s panthers, suave as Jesuits, and proud
s heirs to kingdoms all.

For two days, however, I saw little
f the company, for by Sir William's
rders I lodged at the blockhouse.

One evening when I was feeling par-

ticularly left out of things I saw a party
of gentlemen lounging in the library of
Johnson Hall. Thinking no harm to
enter, I walked in and sat down on the
arm of a leather chair by the window.

Nobody had observed me, however,
and I was on the point of respectfully
making known my presence to Sir William, when I saw Walter Butler rise and
shut the door, taking the additional precaution to lock it. Turning to rejoin the
company around the table, his dark
golden eyes fell upon me, and he stood
still.

"If Mr. Cardigan has been here all this
time, I, for one, was not aware of it,"
observed Mr. Butler, coldly.

I began to explain to Sir William that
I had but that moment come in, when
he interrupted, querulously.

"Tush! tush! Let be, let be, Captain
Butler! My young kinsman has my confidence, and it is time he should know
something of what passes in his own
country.

"AND now, gentlemen, concerning our show of force here. It is my opinion that firstly, the disaffected classes in Boston and New York will not care a fig for our show of militia; that, secondly, if they should once entertain a suspicion that England, in the event of war, proposes to employ savages as allies to subdue rebellion, we should have tomorrow the thirteen colonies swarming like thirteen hives to sting us all to death."

As he paused, Walter Butler spoke in his passionless voice:

"It is come to the point where either the rebels are to win over the Indians, or where we must take measures to secure their services. I beg Sir William to make it clear to us what chances we have to win the support of the Six Nations—in the event of a rebel rising against the King's authority."

The tangled knot was cut; the cat had sprung from the bag. Yet nobody by glance or word or gesture appeared to be aware of it.

Sir William's manner was perfectly composed as he spoke.

"Captain Butler believes that it has come to this: that either those in authority or the disaffected must seek allies among these savage hordes along our frontiers. Gentlemen, I am not of that opinion. If war must come between England and these colonies, let it be a white man's war; in mercy, let it be a war between two civilized peoples, and not a butchery of demons!

"I do solemnly believe that it is possible to so conduct that these savages will remain neutral if war must come."

He lifted his eyes and looked straight at Lord Dunmore, raising his voice slightly but betraying no passion.

"It has come to my knowledge that certain unauthorized people are tampering with a distant tribe of my Cayuga Indians. I know not what the motives of these men may be, but I protest against it, and I shall do all in my power to protect my Cayugas from unlawful aggression!"

"Damme!" gurgled Lord Dunmore. "Damme, Sir William, d'ye mean to accuse me? Curse me! Skewer me! Claw me raw! but it is not fair," he sniveled. "No, it is not fair! Take your hands off my sleeve and be done a-twitching it, Captain Butler."

Captain Butler's shameless impudence in openly attempting to muzzle his noble partner in conspiracy passed all bounds of decency. I saw the angry light glimmer in Sir William's eyes, and I knew it boded no good to Walter Butler, as far as his hope of Silver Heels was concerned. A fierce happiness filled me. So now, at last, Sir William was discovering the fangs in his pet snake!

"I shall not require your services hereafter as my secretary, Captain Butler," said Sir William after the others had left the room. "Will you kindly hand your keys to me?"

"At your command, Sir William," replied Mr. Butler, drawing the keys from his pocket and presenting them with an ironical inclination.

"Mr. Butler," continued Sir William with reddening face, "I consider myself released from my consent to your union with my kinswoman, Miss Warren!"

"As to that, sir," observed Captain Butler, cynically, "I shall take my chances."

I heard what he said, but Sir William misunderstood him.

"It is your mischance, sir, to put no harsher interpretation on it. But my decision is irrevocable, Mr. Butler, for I have destined Miss Warren to a loyal man, my kinsman, Michael Cardigan, who stands here!"

"I'll take that chance, too," said Mr. Butler, bowing.

"What do you mean, sir?" demanded Sir William.

But Walter Butler only replied with such glare at me that Sir William involuntarily turned to find me, right behind him. The next moment Captain Butler passed noiselessly out into the starlight, wrapping his black cloak around him.

SIR WILLIAM followed him mechanically to the door, and I at his heels, burning for a quarrel with Walter Butler, and waiting only until Sir William should return to the library, and leave me free to follow the treacherous villain.

But Sir William, seeing me slinking out, laid a hand on my shoulder and spun me sharply round on my heels to look into my eyes.

"Now what the devil are *you* up to?" he broke out, half divining the truth. "Michael! Michael! Don't be a fool! Are there not fools enough here to-night? Out of all my house there is not one whom I can trust—not one!—not one!"

After a moment I plucked at his sleeve reproachfully.

"Yes— I know—I know, my boy. But I need a man now—a man of experience, a man in bodily vigor, a man in devotion."

"You need a man to go to Colonel Cresap," I whispered. For the first and only time in my life I saw that I had startled Sir William.

"Let me go, sir?" I entreated eagerly.

"I cannot," he muttered. "Tomorrow Dunmore will set his spies to see that Cresap remains undisturbed. The Ohio trails will be watched for a messenger from me. Who knows what Dunmore's and Butler's men might do?"

"But I know the woods! You, yourself, sir, say I am a very Mohawk in the woods!" I pleaded. "I fear no ambush though the highwayman Jack Mount himself were after me."

"Well, perhaps you could do it," said Sir William thoughtfully.

"Then I'm going! I'm going!" I whispered, enchanted, while he murmured brokenly that he could not spare me and that I was all he had on earth.

Together we went over the trail, mile by mile, computing the circles I should be obliged to take to avoid the carrying-places where spies were most to be feared.

"Dunmore rides South in a week," said Sir William. "But he will not wait till he reaches Virginia before he sends out his emissaries to urge Cresap on. You must beat them, lad, and go afoot at that."

"There is one thing I have thought of," said I, soberly. "It is this: if I am going out as an enemy to the King, I cannot for shame aid me by wearing the King's uniform. Therefore, with your approval, sir, I will go in my buckskins, unless you believe that I will benefit our King."

"Then," said Sir William, slowly, "you must go in your buckskins, lad. You may, for the present at least, retain your commission and your sword with honour. It is Dunmore and Butler we are fighting now, not our King."

As WE sat there, my hand in his, staring at the phantoms of that ominous future, I heard Silver Heels come running up the stairs and stop at my door, calling out to Sir William. What she whispered to him I could not hear, but he promptly shook his head in refusal, and presently it came out that she was tearing to be allowed to go with a certain fat dame, Lady Shelton, and make a month's stay with her at Pittsburg.

"I do so long to go," pleaded Silver Heels.

"Oh, go, then! Go, you little witch! And mind you take Betty with you!"

Silver Heels embraced him rapturously with a little shout of delight, and sped away to the nursery without a glance at me. I had at least the satisfaction that she was free of Walter Butler.

The Rebel Highwayman

MY FIRST three weeks in the woods were weeks of heaven. I ate and drank and slept in the dim wood stillness undisturbed. And I lived well on that swift trail where the gray grouse scuttled through the saplings, and in every mossy streamlet the cold, dusky troutlings fought for my line.

I had not met a soul on the trail, nor had I found any fresh signs save one, and that was the print of a white man's moccasin on the edge of a sandy strip near the headwaters of the Ohio, which is called the Alleghany, north of Fort Pitt.

Now a sudden instinct arose in me that I had been followed; nay, not so sudden, either, for the vague idea had been slowly taking shape.

And as I watched, I saw a man come out on the sandy bank of the stream and kneel down where my tracks crossed to the water's edge. Without a sound I sank down behind my log into a soft ball of buckskin.

The man was Walter Butler. I knew him, though he wore the shirt of a Mohawk and beaded leggings to the hips, and at that distance might easily have been taken for an Indian.

My mind was working rapidly now. What did Captain Butler mean by following me? The answer came ere the question had been fully formed, and I knew he hated me and meant to kill me.

How he had learned of my mission, whether he had actually learned of it, or only suspected it from my disappearance, concerned me little. These things were certain; he was Lord Dunmore's emissary as I was the emissary of Sir William; he was bound for Cresap's camp, as I was; and he intended to intercept me and kill me if that meant winning the race.

I must give up my visit to the Cayugas for the present. It was to be a race now to Cresap's camp.

My progress was slow because I had to travel in the wilderness without the ease of a trodden trail. Tired out before sunset I dropped my pack under a hemlock thicket, and crawled out on a heap of rocks that over hung a ravine. All over me a sweet numbness tingled. Sleep was sweet.

Then a quiver swept through me like an icy wind; with a pang I remembered my mission; my vow to Sir William. I groped for my rifle; it was gone. Panic stricken, I staggered up, drenched with dew, and saw the moon staring down at me.

Slowly I realized that death had passed me while I lay unconscious. But how far had death gone? Aye, what was that under the tree there, that shape watching me?—moving, too—a man!

"Greeting, friend," he said. "God save our country. There are some gentlemen yonder looking for you, young gentleman. I sent them south, for somehow I thought you might not be looking for them."

"If you please," I said, weakly, "give me my rifle and receive my thanks. You detain me and I have far to travel."

"Well, of all impudence!" he sneered. "Wait a bit, my young cock o' the woods. You come into camp and take supper with me, or I'll knock your head off and drag you in by the heels!"

There was nothing else I could do. Up, up, up we passed through the foggy moonlight. We finally reached a plateau, and after a minute or two I smelled the camp fire. In a moment we entered a ruddy ring of light, in the center of which great logs burned and crackled.

There sat a meager little man, weasel eyed and dingy as a summer fox. He was introduced as Cade Renard. There was another figure setaed at the base of a gigantic pine tree; a little Hebrew man, gathering his knees in his arms, Saul Shemuel!—who came every spring to Sir William for his peddling license, and sometimes sold us children gaffs and ferret muzzles. He bade me good evening in an uncertain voice, and did not appear to know me.

The darkness had obscured the face of my captor; but in the firelight his features stood out in bold relief. It was the face of Jack Mount, the highway man. I had seen a book about him with a gibbit on the cover. Everybody knew he had set fire to the King's ship *Gaspee* and started the rebels a-pitching tea overboard from Griffin's wharf. I did not doubt it was he for a moment.

Seeing my glance of amazement, Jack Mount asked me if I thought I was lucky to be there.

I managed to say that I thought I was, but my lack of enthusiasm sent the big fellow into spasms of smothered laughter. "You're supping with Jack Mount? And the Weasel's watching everything from yonder hazel bunch. And Saul Shemuel's pretending to be asleep under that pine tree? Why Mr. Cardigan, your idea of luck amazes me."

So the little Hebrew had recognized me, after all. I swallowed a lump in my throat and rose to my elbow. With Jack Mount beside me, Walter Butler prowling outside the fire ring, and I alone, stripped of every weapon, what in Heaven's sight was left for me to do?"

A Matter of Treason

CADE RENARD, the Weasel, had come up while Mount was speaking, and his bright eyes scanned me warily.

"What's his business?" he inquired o Mount. "I've searched his pack again, and I can't find anything except some Indian peace belts."

"If you are a patriot," I said, desperately, "You will leave me my belts and meddle only with your own affairs. My belts mean no harm to patriots. You think I am no patriot. But I am a better patriot than you, or I should not be in this forest today."

At the same moment I saw a dark figure step just within the outer fire ring, holding up one arm as a sign of peace.

The man was Walter Butler. I dropped back softly into the shadows.

"I am here on business of my Lord Dunmore," he said to Jack Mount. "I am here to arrest a young man named Michael Cardigan who is supposed to be hidden in your camp. I call on you, sir, whoever you are, to aid me in the execution of the law."

"The law! Gad! she's an acquaintance o' mine, the jade!" said Mount, laughing. "Pray what has this bad young man named Michael Cardigan done?"

"It is a matter of treason," retorted Butler, sharply. "Come, my good man, have done with this silly chatter and aid me to my duty in the King's name."

In a flash Mount wheeled on Butler, snarling, every tooth bared: "Blast you, sir! do you take me for your lackey or the King's handman? To hell with you, sir! To hell with your King, sir! Did you hear me? I said, to hell with your King!"

Butler's face paled in the waving firelight. Presently he said, evenly: "I shall take care that your good wishes reach the King's ears. Pray, sir, honor me with your name and quality, though I may perhaps guess both."

"No need to guess," cut in the big fellow, cheerfully. "I'm Jack Mount. I burned the *Gaspee,* I helped dump His Majesty's tea into Boston harbor, and I should be pleased to do as much for the King himself. Tell him so, Captain Butler; tell my Lord Dunmore he can have a ducking, took at his lordship's polite convenience. Now make a new trail, you Tory hangman! March!" And he gave him a prod with his rifle.

As MOUNT came up to me I rose and thanked him for the protection he had given so generously, and he laughed and laid one padded fist on my shoulder.

"Hark ye, friend," he said, "take your Indian belts and your pack and go in peace, for if Dunmore is after you, the sooner you start north the better. Go, lad. I'm not your enemy!"

"I go south to Cresap's camp," I said.

"So do we," Mount exclaimed. "Why don't you join us. It's safer than going alone.

So I decided to travel to Fort Pitt with the three highwaymen. After we had gone in silence for a space Mount grinned at me slyly and said: "Did you know that Dunmore's suite ought to be in Pittsburg tomorrow?"

I had not expected them to get there so quickly.

Mount rambled on: "Since you left Johnstown, all are talking of the new beauty who threw over Walter Butler— a certain Miss Warren, whom the Indians call Silver Heels. It is commonly reported that the dispute over the Indians and the quarrel betwixt Butler and Sir William stopped the match."

"What of it!" I broke out hoarsely.

"Only that this beautiful Miss Warren came with Lord Dunmore's suite to Pittsburg, and Walter Butler has openly boasted he will marry her in spite of Sir William or the devil himself."

To hear her name in the southern wilderness, to hear these things in this place, told with a wink and a leer, raised a black fury in me. But with the greatest effort I controlled myself.

We journeyed on, hour after hour, until the big yellow moon floated above the hills and the river faded into th blue shadows of a splendid night. Sud denly a light twinkled on the edge of clearing, then another broke out, an soon all about us cabin window gleamed brightly.

The sentry greeted Mount cheerfull and nodded and smiled at Renard als

"Friend of liberty," said Mount in low voice, "Is Colonel Cresap in th fort?"

"No," said the sentry, looking har at me. "But he'll be back tomorrow Who is this gentleman, Jack?"

Mount did not hesitate; he laid h great paw on my shoulder and said "He's a good lad, corporal. Give him bed and a bowl o' porridge, and it's kindness to Jack Mount you will do."

Then he held out his hand to me.

"Good night, lad," he said heartil "We'll meet again tomorrow at th Inn."

The Misguided Colonel

"How long do you stay here?" Mount asked me the next day after we had settled down at a table in the Inn.

"Until I deliver my peace belts to the Cayugas tomorrow," I answered.

"I thought you wished to see Colonel Cresap, too?" he said.

"I do. He will return today, they tell me."

"Hark ye, friend Michael," he said. "Colonel Cresap, three-quarters of the militia, and all save a score or so of these villagers here are patriots."

"If he is a true patriot," I said, "how can he deliberately drive the Six Nations to take up arms against the colonies? I tell you, Dunmore means to have a war started here that will forever turn the Six Nations against us."

"Against us?" said Mount, meaningly.

"Yes—us!" I exclaimed. "If it be treason to oppose such a monstrous crime at that which Lord Dunmore contemplates, then I am guilty! If to be a patriot means to resist such men as Dunmore and Butler—if to defend the land of one's birth against the plots of these

men makes me an enemy to the King why—why, then," I ended, violently, am the King's enemy to the last blood drop in my body!"

There was a silence. I sat there wit clinched fist on the table, teeth set, rea izing what I had said, glad that I ha said it.

"But Lord Dunmore is only doing h duty," urged Mount. "His Majesty nee allies."

"Do you mean to say that Lord Du more is provoking war here at th King's command?" I asked, in horror

A young man by the chimney stoo up and bent his pleasant eyes on me.

"I have here," he said, tapping th letter in his hand, "my Lord Dunmore commission as major-general of militi and his Majesty's permission to enlist thousand savages to serve under me the event of rebellion in these colonies

I had risen to my feet at the sound the stranger's voice; Mount, too, ha risen, tankard in hand.

"Pray, be seated, Mr. Cardigan Colonel Cresap said, smiling. "I kno you have a message for me from Sir William Johnson. I hold it an honour to receive commands from such an honourable and upright gentleman."

He motioned Mount and me to be seated; the tap-boy brought his tankard; he tasted it sparingly, and leaned back while I told him, with some heat, that the whole land would hold him responsible for an outbreak on the frontier.

When I had finished, he thanked me for coming and begged me to convey his cordial gratitude to Sir William. Then he began his defense, very modestly and with frankest confession that he had been trapped by Dunmore into a pitfall the existence of which he had never suspected.

"For months I have been aware that Dunmore wishes a clash with the Cayugas yonder," he said, "but until Sir William Johnson opened my eyes, I have never understood why Lord Dunmore desired war. Why, Jack, it's perfectly plain to me now! We've been tricked. This very commission in my hands, here, made out for the purpose of buying my loyalty to Dunmore. You say the whole country will hold me responsible. I cannot help that, though God must know how unjust it would be.

"Were I to counsel the abandonment of this fort and village, Lord Dunmore would arrest me and clap me into Fort Pitt. Is it not better for me to say here among these people who trust me? Is it not better that I remain and labour among my people in the cause of liberty?

"I can do nothing while a royal Governor governs Virginia. But if the time ever comes when our Boston brothers sound the call to arms, I can lead six hundred riflemen out of this forest, whose watchword will be, 'Liberty or Death!'

"Go to your Cayugas," he said, catching his breath. "Tell them the truth, or as much of the truth as Sir William's wisdom permits. I am here to watch, to watch such crafty agents as Greathouse, and young Walter Butler."

He tasted his ale once more, thoughtfully.

"When do you speak to the Cayugas with belts?" he asked.

"At dawn," I replied, soberly.

"Poor devils," said Cresap, sadly, "poor, tricked, cheated, and plundered devils! This is their land. I should never have come had not Dunmore assured me the Cayugas had been paid for the country. And there is their great sachem, Logan, called 'The Friend of the White Man.' Greathouse has made a drunken sot of Logan, and all his family down to the tiny maid of ten. Ay, sir, I have seen Logan's children lying drunk in the road there by Greathouse's tavern—poor, little babies of twelve and ten, stark-naked, lying drunk in the rain!"

As we sat there, silent, I heard the rain drumming against the window.

"You are not going to leave us after you see the Cayugas, are you, lad?"

"I have my message to deliver to Sir William," I answered, earnestly. "And," I added "truly, I do not believe there is anything on earth that can prevent my delivering my message, nor retard my returning and slaying this frightful enemy of mankind, Walter Butler."

Peace and War

The Cayuga trail was broad and plain, however, and I took it at a wolf-trot. Dark forms loomed up in the eye of the sun as I drew nigh; men who stood motionless as the pines where the council fire smoked.

"Peace!" I said, halting with upraised hand. "Peace, you wise men and sachems!"

"Peace!" repeated a low voice. "Peace, bearer of belts!"

I moved nearer, head high. And when I came to the edge of the fire I drew a white belt of wampum from my bosom and held it aloft, flashing in the sun, until every chief and sachem had sunk down into their blankets, forming a half-circle before me.

A miracle of speech came to me. I spoke as I had never dared hope I might speak. Forgotten phrases, caressing idioms, words long lost flew to aid me. My words were earnest and pitiful, for my heart was full of tenderness for Sir William and for these patient children of his.

The ceremony of condolence was more than a ceremony for me. With eager sympathy I raised up the three stricken tribes; I sweetened the ashes of the eternal fires; I cleared evil from the Cayuga trail, and laid the ghastly ghosts of those who stood in forest highways to confront the fifth nation of the great confederacy.

The last belt was passed, flashing through the smoke; the chief sachem of the Cayugas rose to receive it, a tall, withered man of the Wolf tribe, painted and draped in scarlet. His dim, wrinkled eyes peered at me through the smoke. Then the old man placed the belt at his feet, straightened up, and spoke feebly.

A frightful scream cut him short; scream after scream arose from the hidden lodges.

The assembly rose in a body, blankets falling to the ground, and stood paralyzed, silent, while the horrid screaming rose to an awful, long-drawn shriek.

Somebody was coming—somebody plodding heavily, shrieking at every step, nearer, nearer—an old woman who staggered out into the circle of the council, dragging the limp body of a young girl.

"Nine!" she gasped. "Nine slain at dawn by Greathouse! Nine of the family of Logan! Look, you wise men and sachems! Look at Logan's child! Dead! Slain by Greathouse!"

Sick with horror, I moved forward, and the stir seemed to arouse the sachems. One by one they looked down at the dead, then turned their flashing eyes on me. I strove to speak; I could not utter a sound.

The old sachem bent slowly and took a handful of ashes from the cold embers.

Then, rubbing them on his face, h flung down every belt I had given him and signed to me to do the same with the belts delivered to me.

With a gesture he bade me depart. went, stunned by the calamity that ha come as lightning to blast the work had done.

Overwhelmed, I wandered aimlessl into the forest and sat down. Long I sa there, and my shocked senses strove onl to find some way to avert the conse quences of the deed wrought by Grea house. But the awful work had bee done; the Gordian knot cut; my Lor Dunmore's war had begun at last, i deference to my Lord Dunmore's desire and in accordance with his plans. Now Cresap must fight; now, the Six Nation would rise to avenge the Cayugas on th colonies; now, the King of Englan would have the savage allies he desire so ardently, and the foul pact would b sealed with the blood of Logan's chi dren! I had failed, totally failed. A suc den insane fever overcame me and began to wander in the forest aimlessl

How I managed to get to the fort never knew. I did not remember th the savages had carried me; I had n recollection of walking.

My own memories begin with an e plosion that brought me stun bling blindly out of bed, to find Jac Mount firing through a loophole an watching me, while he reloaded, wit curious satisfaction.

Along the parapets the soldiers we firing frenziedly. I had a glimpse, belo me, of Cresap leading out a company soldiers to cover the flight of his rifl men, and at intervals I saw single I dians, kneeling to fire, then springir forward, yelping and capering.

All around us, house after house w bursting into black smoke and spouts flame. Fire leaped like lightning alor those pine walls. Faster and faster f the flaming arrows. I forgot my wea ness and fatigue, and found myse nimbly speeding after the fiery arrov

nd knocking out the sparks with an
mpty bucket.

All at once the fiery shower ceased.
'resently we saw that the savages were
alling back to the forest.

"You know," Mount observed, turn-
ıg to me, "that we abandon the fort
onight."

The day wore away in preparation for
ae march.

At nine o'clock that evening the
ostern was opened quietly; and after
couts had reported the coast clear, the
olumn started in perfect silence. We
lodded on in silence for a while. Pres-
ntly Mount asked me what I meant to
o in Pittsburg.

"I mean to see Lord Dunmore," I relied, quietly.

"What are you going to do to old
Dunmore?" urged the big fellow, curi-
usly.

"As an accredited deputy of Sir William Johnson, I am going to tell my
Lord Dunmore exactly what I think of
him," I replied.

I had been looking ahead along the
line of wagons, where a lanthorn was
glimmering. The convoy had halted, and
I walked on until I came to where the
light shone on a group of militia officers
and riflemen. Cresap was there, wrapped
in his heavy cloak. I was surprised to
see a tall Indian standing beside Cresap,
muffled to the chin in a dark blanket.

It was Logan, the father of the murdered Indian family. Cresap asked me
to find out what his business was. After
speaking to Logan, I interpreted his
words to the Colonel.

"He seeks justice at Fort Pitt from
Lord Dunmore," I explained.

"Bid him come with us," replied
Cresap, soberly. "He may not get jus-
tice at Fort Pitt, but there is a higher
Judge than the Earl of Dunmore."

Silver Heels

SOMBER thoughts oppressed me; I had
a hard rôle to act before Silver Heels,
: she were still in Pittsburg.

I found that she was there of a cer-
ain. In fact, the gossip was that she
vas going to wed my Lord Dunmore
a July. My thoughts were awhirl. That
hild thrown into the arms of a thing
ke Dunmore! What possessed all these
vitless gallants to go mad over my play
ellow? Why should this bloodless Dun-
nore seek to make her Countess of
Dunmore and the first lady in Virginia?

And Silver Heels, had she sold her
eauty for the rank that this toothless
ssassin could give her? How could she
ndure him? How could she look at him
vithout scorn and loathing?

Agitated and furious, I paced the hall-
vay, resolving to seek out my lady Silver
Ieels without loss of time, and conduct
er back to the nursery where the little
ool belonged.

I found no difficulty in discovering
1e great, white-pillared house of Lady
helton, set in an orchard.

There was a lady in the orchard. At
the craunch of my moccasins on the
gravel path she looked around. It was
Silver Heels.

"Are you a runner from Johnstown?"
she asked, sharply.

That she did not recognize me was
less to be wondered at. The dark mask
of the sun, which I now wore, had
changed me to an Indian; anxiety and
fatigue had made haggard a youthful
face.

But that I had not recognized her till
she spoke distressed me. She, too, had
grown tall; she looked shockingly frail;
and with her painted cheeks and powdered hair, and her laces and her frills,
she might have been a French noble-
woman from Quebec. It were idle to
deny her beauty, but it was the beauty
of death itself.

"Silver Heels," I said. "Do you know
why I am here?"

Her hand flew to her bosom as she
suddenly recognized me. "Why are you
here?" she said.

"I'm here to seek Lord Dunmore."
In a shamed voice I told here what I

It were idle to deny her beauty, but it
was the beauty of death itself.

had heard. She did not deny it. When
I drew for her a revealing portrait of
the Earl of Dunmore, she only smiled
and set her lips tight.

"What of it?" she asked. "I am to
marry him; you and Sir William will
not have him to endure."

"It's a disgraceful thing," I said, hotly.
"If you cannot perceive the infamy of
such a marriage, then I'll do your thinking for you and stop this shameful betrothal now!"

"I shall wed Dunmore in July."

"No, you won't!" I retorted, stung to
fury. "Sir William has betrothed you to
me. And, by Heaven! if it comes to that,
I will wed you myself, you little fool!'

Suddenly she broke down and laid
her head in her arms.

Much disturbed, I watched her. Anger
died out; I leaned on the wall beside
her, speaking gently and striving to
draw her fingers from her face.

"What is the matter, Silver Heels," I
said. "Never have I seen you like this.

Have you been ill long? What is it, littl
comrade? Are you in love?"

"Aye, sick with it," she said, slowl
with closed lids.

"Who is this fool whom you love,"
asked, harshly.

I had not thought to fright or hu
her, but she flushed and burned unt
all her face was surging scarlet to h
hair.

"Silver Heels," I stammered, catchin
her fingers.

A T THE touch a strange thrill struc
through my body and I choked, u
able to utter a word; I caught her finge
and drew them interlocked, from h
eyes. Her eyes! Their beauty amaze
me; their frightened, perilous sweetne
drew my head down to them. Breathles
her mouth touched mine. Then su
denly she had gone, and I sprang to m
feet to find her standing tearful, quive
ing, with her hands on her throbbin
throat. I leaned against a sapling, daze
my thoughts whirling rapturously.

"You must go—dear heart," she w
repeating, her eyes and lips tender
smiling at me. "My Lady Shelton an
Lord Dunmore will surely catch yo

"But will you not tell me when yo
first loved me, Silver Heels?"

"You know I—I have always love
you dearly," she said tremulously.

"But," I insisted, "you grew co
enough to wed Lord Dunmore—"

"Horror! Why must you ever har
back to him when I tell you it was n
I who did that, but a cruelly used an
foolish child, stung with the pain
your indifference—"

It was at that very instant that Lad
Shelton came out on the porch of h
house followed by my Lord Dunmor
Before they could see me, I disappeare
into the bushes. Had I raised a hand
Lord Dunmore, then, I would hav
ruined my plans. I had other means
revealing his treachery. However I di
not leave before Silver Heels had agree
to leave for Johnson Hall with me th
next evening at 11 o'clock.

Audience with the Governor

THE so-called "Governor's Hall," which stood within the limits of the fortifications, was Dunmore's temporary residence in Pittsburg. It was in this gloomy hall that my Lord Dunmore consented to receive the old Cayuga chief, Logan. I had been called to act as interpreter and to deliver my message from Sir William.

I sat in the Convention Hall with Jack Mount and the Weasel. They told me that most of the people who had come to see Logan were patriots. The others were Tories and Dunmore's spies. I caught a glimpse of the scarred, patched-up visage of one of the men whom I had seen with Butler on the trail. Startled, and realizing now the proximity of Walter Butler, I hunted the hall for him with hot, eager eyes. I could not find him.

Ah! There was the Governor. Before he was pleased to seat himself, he peered up into the balcony and kissed his finger tips, and I, following his eyes, saw Silver Heels sitting with her sad eyes fixed, not on my Lord Dunmore, but on me.

Before I met her eyes I had been sullenly frightened, dreading to speak aloud in such a company. Now, with her deep, steady eyes meeting mine, fear fell from me. I smiled gayly up at her, and she smiled back at me.

"Is the messenger from His Majesty's Superintendent for Indian Affairs present," boomed the Governor's Deputy. "Let him be assured of a warm welcome from his Lordship, the Earl of Dunmore, Governor of Virginia."

FOUND that all eyes were on me. It was now or never.

"Lord Dunmore," I said, steadily, "I am not here to tell you of that chain which links the Governor of Virginia with the corpse of Logan's youngest child—nor to count the links of that chain backward, from Greathouse to—"

"Stop!" burst out the Governor, springing to his feet. "Who are you?

What are you? How dare you address such language to the Earl of Dunmore?"

Astonished, furious, he stood shaking his fist at me. The interruption stirred up my blood to the boiling. "I am Michael Cardigan, cornet in the Border Horse, and deputy of Sir William Johnson, Baronet, His Majesty's Superintendent of Indian Affairs for North America! Who dares deny me right of speech?"

Dunmore lay in his chair, a shrunken mess of lace and ribbon.

"I am not here," I said, coolly, "to ask your lordship why this war, falsely called Cresap's war, should be known to honest men as 'Dunmore's war.' Nor do I come to ask you why England should seek the savage allies of the Six Nations, which this war, so cunningly devised, has given her—"

"Treason! Treason!" bawled a voice.

"But," I resumed, pointing my finger straight at the staring Governor, "I am here to demand an account of your stewardship! Where are those Cayugas whom you have sworn to protect from the greed of white men? Where are they? Answer, sir! Where are Sir William Johnson's wards of the Long House? Answer, sir! for this is my mission from Sir William Johnson. Answer!"

Hubbub and outcry and tumult rose around me. Dunmore got on his feet, and went shambling out of the door behind the platform, while in the hall the uproar swelled into an angry shout: "Shame on Dunmore! God save Virginia!"

An officer in the gallery leaned over the edge, waving his gold-laced hat.

"God save the King!" he roared, and many answered, "God save the King!" but that shout was drowned by a thundering outburst of cheers: "God save our country! Hurrah! Hurrah! Hurrah!"

Jack Mount and the Weasel managed to get me out of the building and to safety before Dunmore's men could take action against me.

Into Endless Night

THAT night at ten o'clock I stood waiting for Silver Heels near Lady Shelton's.

One by one I counted and discounted the dangers I ran: first, arrest at any moment as an accomplice of the notorious Jack Mount; second, assassination by Dunmore's agents; third, assassination by Butler's company; fourth, arrest and imprisonment as a suspected rebel and open advocate of sedition; fifth, danger from the Cayugas after our escape from Fort Pitt.

Should any of these things befall me, as well they might, what in the world would become of Silver Heels?

The post chaise, loaded and ready, stood with the four strong horses harnessed, and Jack Mount to their heads. It lacked an hour yet of the time appointed, and it was the suspense of that hour's waiting which set every nerve in my body aching.

Far away in the fortress the bell struck the half-hour. Suddenly the dark door opened; a heavy figure appeared in silhouette against the light. My heart stood still; it was Black Betty, Silver Heel's maid.

The negress peered out into the darkness, and looked up at the stars. Then, as though summoned from within, she turned quickly and entered the house, leaving the door wide open behind her.

Impatience was racking me now. Alarm, too. I waited until I could wait no longer; then I stole up to the porch. The hallway was empty; I stepped to the sill, crossed it. Then I saw three people enter the living room. They stood there in low-voiced consultation—Lady Shelton, my Lord Dunmore, and my mortal enemy, Walter Butler, tricked out in lace and velvet.

Suddenly, I was startled to hear a door slam and the next instant Silver Heels sprang through the portal.

Dumfounded, I looked stupidly after her. Then my heart leaped up, for there, at the foot of the garden, stood a post chaise and four. There, too, were Silver Heels and Betty, setting foot to the chaise step. Dark figures aided them, the chaise door shut. I thanked God silently. When I looked back into the living room and saw that Dunmore, insane with fury, was drawing at a window to raise it; Butler had come swiftly from the inner room and was trying the door. Finding it locked, he looked at Dunmore with a ghastly laugh.

"Give place there!" said Butler, brutally elbowing the frantic man aside. "Let me through that window, you doddering fool! You're done for; it's my turn now."

"What!" gasped Dunmore. The terror blanched his face and he began to scream: "That was *your* chaise! You mean to cheat me! You mean to steal her!"

"Drive on!" shouted Butler to the people in the chaise.

TO MY horror the chaise began to move off. Suddenly I understood that the chaise was not my own.

"Mount!" I shouted in terror. "She has taken another chaise. It's Butler's men! Ride for her! Ride!" and I ran for my horse. Soon after we began the chase, the noise of rapidly galloping horses sounded plainly; wheels striking stones rang out sharp and clear.

On, on we came, horses at a gallop, chaise lurching, right into the crossroad. Then a blinding flash and crash split the gloom, echoed by another, and then a third. I leaped into a frantic mass of struggling horses while Mount, swinging his rifle, knocked down a man who fired at him and beat him till he lay still.

As I sprang toward the chaise, the driver pitched off heavily, landing in a heap at my feet, face downward in the grass. Now the horses swung in front of me, plunging furiously in the smashed harness. Crash! went a wheel; the chaise sank forward; a horse fell.

"Look out! Look out!" shouted Mount

ehind me as I ran to the swaying ve-
icle.

"Silver Heels!" I cried, tearing at the
oor of the chaise.

For a second I saw her terrified face
t the window; her cry rang in my ears;
ien the door burst open and a man
prang out, burying his knife in my
eck.

Down we went together, down, down
into a smothering darkness that had no
end. Yet I remember, after a long, long
time, looking up at the stars—or perhaps
into her eyes.

Then my body seemed to sink again,
silently as a feather, and my soul
dropped out, falling like a lost star into
an endless night.

Home Is Not Home

KNEW afterward—long, long afterward—that I had been stabbed re-
eatedly. They had thought me already
ded when they tore my assailant from
y body and grimly dispatched him.

I appeared to be quite dead, and
hether to bury me there or in some
inder spot, none could determine, while
ie dear maid I loved lay senseless in
lack Betty's arms.

My senseless sweetheart they bore to
ie waiting chaise and, my body still
taining some warmth, they bore that,
o, because they dared not bury me
efore she had seen me dead with her
wn eyes.

Betty bared my body to the waist and
ashed it. For a corpse they do as much.
ater, without hope, Mount brought a
innikinful of blue-balsam gum, pricked
om the globules on the trunk, and
hen Betty had once more washed me,
iey filled the long gashes with the
ilsam and closed them decently, strip
i strip, with the fine cambric shift
hich my sweetheart tore from her own
ody.

What I have heard from others is
igue, and to me unreal as a painted
ene in a picture. I hear that I breathed
irough days that I never saw, that I
ened my eyes on lands that are strange
me, that my babble broke primeval
lences that God himself had sealed.

One night a new sound woke me, and
felt the presence of another person.
Ioonlight silvered the windows of a
om that I knew; but I was very quiet
id waited for the sun, lest the phan-
ms I divined should trick me.

Then came a morning when I knew

I was in a bed and very tired; and knew,
too, that I had made no mistake about
the room. It was Sir William's room at
Johnson Hall.

The next day I saw Doctor Pierson
beside me, and asked for Sir William.

"Poor lad!" he said, holding my
hands.

My eyes never left his.

"Aye," he said, softly, "his last word
was your name. He loved you dearly,
lad."

And so I knew that Sir William was
dead.

DAY after day I lay in my bed, staring
at the ceiling till night blotted it
out. Then, stunned and exhausted, I
would lie in the dark, crying in my
weakness, whimpering for those I loved
who had left me here alone. Yet my
thinned blood gradually grew warmer,
and day by day its currents flowed with
slightly increasing vigor through my
emaciated body.

The dreadful anguish of my bereavement came only at intervals, succeeded
by an apathy that served as a merciful
relief. But most I thought of Silver
Heels, and why she had left me here,
and when she might return.

They told me that she had gone to
Boston with Sir John Johnson. But no
one knew why. Sir John was returning
without her.

Long before Sir John returned I was
dressed and making hourly essays at
walking, first in the house, then through
the dooryard to the guardhouse, where
I would sit in the hot sun and breathe
the full-throated October winds. My eyes

grew clear and strong, my lean cheeks filled, my wasted limbs once more began to bear me with the old-time lightness and delight.

The first thing that Sir John did upon his return was to acquaint me with the provisions of Sir William's will.

"You know," he said, "that my father has invested your small fortune most wisely. The income is ample for a young man, and on the decease of your uncle, Sir Terence, you will come into his title and estate in Ireland. This should make you wealthy. However, Sir William has seen fit to provide you with several hundred valuable acres in this country. It is strange that Sir William thought fit to bequeath you such a vast property."

"What provision was made for Felicity?" I asked, quietly.

"Certain documents have come to my attention which indicate that she is not Sir Peter Warren's daughter and therefore not the niece of Sir William. She will therefore receive nothing from Sir William's will. I have left her with her lawyer, Thomas Foxcroft, in Boston. She would have been better off had you allowed her to wed Lord Dunmore."

Sir John's contemptuous tone as he spoke Felicity's name, his utter disregard of all I had told him about Dunmore set me trembling in every limb. I sprang up, furious.

"Dunmore is a scoundrel!" I stammered. "A black scoundrel! An infamous, treacherous murderer! I care not who hears me! And I say shame on you for your heartlessness! Shame on you for your callous, merciless judgment, you bloodless hypocrite!"

"Silence!" he said, turning livid. "You leave this house tonight for your regiment."

I walked out of the room and up the stairs to my own little chamber, there to remove from my body the livery of my King, never again to resume it. Then I dressed me once more in buckskins. I was determined to get to Boston and settle Silver Heel's affairs as soon as possible.

On the Eve of Revolution

IT was on the road to Boston that I met Jack Mount who had disappeared mysteriously after depositing me at Johnson Hall. He was bemoaning the loss of Cade Renard, *alias* the Weasel. In trying to figure out what had happened to him he explained to me that Cade had once been a Boston gentleman. Sixteen years before, his wife had run off with Sir Peter Warren, taking their baby daughter with them. This had caused Renard to take the downward path and he had finally wound up with my friend Mount on the highway.

After reaching Boston I wrote a letter to Silver Heels who replied that Sir John Johnson's investigations had shown that she was the daughter of Cade Renard and not of Sir Peter Warren. This made no difference to me and I was determined to wed her.

Unfortunately I was arrested by the Massachusetts authorities in the company of Jack Mount and we were both sentenced to be hanged as highwaymen on April 19, 1776. However, at the eleventh hour we both made our escape from the jail and I immediately sought out Silver Heels who was reported to be living with her father Cade Renard in Lexington.

Upon our arrival in Lexington with Thomas Foxcroft, Silver Heel's lawyer, we found that Cade Renard had become mentally unbalanced and could not remember his old friend Jack Mount or me. He introduced us to his "daughter."

"Silver Heels! Silver Heels!" I cried with a sob.

"Do you want me—now?" she whispered.

I caught her fiercely in my arms; she clung to me with closed eyes.

And, as we stood there, I heard the measured gallop of a horse on the highway, coming nearer, nearer. Instantly Jack Mount glided from the room; Foxcroft silently drew his pistol; I reached or my rifle and I stepped to the center of the room. The door opened gently, and there in the moonlight stood Walter Butler.

Something is dreadfully wrong, gentlemen," quavered poor Cade Renard. "This is Captain Butler, my daughter's affianced. I pray you follow no ancient quarrel under my roof, gentlemen. I cannot permit this difference between gentlemen in my daughter's presence—"

"That she-devil swore to wed me!" he broke out, hoarsely, pointing a shaking finger full at Silver Heels. "She—swore it!" His voice sank to a hiss.

"To save my father from a highwayman's death!" said Silver Heels, deathly white.

A cold fury blinded me so I could scarcely see Butler. I cocked my rifle and drew my hand across my eyes to clear them.

"This is not your quarrel!" he said, desperately. "This woman is the daughter of Cade Renard, a notorious highwayman known as the Weasel. Would you wed with the Weasel's child?"

"But she is not his child, sir!" cried Foxcroft, turning on Mount. "She is Captain Warren's own child; I journeyed to England and proved it; I have papers here to prove it! The letters supposed to have been written to Sir William by Sir Peter Warren were forged. I can prove that Walter Butler was the forger! I can prove that Sir John Johnson knew it! And Sir John and Captain Butler conspired to make Miss Warren believe herself the child of a half-crazed forest runner who had been vowing that she was his own child!"

Butler was sitting forward in his chair, his eyes on vacancy. He did not seem to hear the words that branded him; he did not appear to see us as we drew closer around him.

"In the orchard," muttered Mount; "we can hang him with his own bridle."

"Not that! No!" I stammered. "I can't do it! Give him a sword—give him something to fight with! Jack—I can't do it! I am not made that way!"

There was a touch on my arm; Silver Heels stood beside me.

"Let them deal with him," she murmured. "You cannot fight with him; there is no honor in him."

"No!—no honor in him!" I repeated.

He had risen, and now stood, staring vacantly at me.

"By the mighty!" cried Mount. "You can't let him loose on the world again!"

"I cannot slay him," I said.

War was at hand. War would come at dawn when the Grenadiers marched into Concord town. To slay him, then, would be no murder. But now?

There was no prison to hale him to; the jails o' Boston lodged no Tories. Justice? Law? The King's Governor was the law—Gage, the friend of this man. What was I to do? Once again Mount raised his rifle.

"No," I said, "I shall not kill him."

So passed Walter Butler from among us, riding slowly out into the shadowy world, under the calm moon. God witness that I conducted as my honour urged, not as my hot blood desired.

So rode forth mine enemy, Walter Butler, invulnerable for me in his armour of dishonour, unpunished for the woe that he had wrought, unmarked by justice which the dawn had not yet roused from her long sleep in chains.

Suddenly there came a far cry through the misty chill of dawn: "The British are coming! The British are coming!"

The next instant a drum was banging, and the men around us had stumbled to their feet, rifles in hand.

At that same moment our post chaise came lumbering around the corner of the tavern yard, Mount acting as postboy, and Foxcroft and the Weasel riding together in the rear.

I placed Silver Heels in the chaise, with my eyes still fixed on the foggy Boston Road.

And so, guarded by our faithful three, we started for the north, out of the bloody village where our liberty was born. Soon we were back to the inland winds and waters and the incense of our own dear forests. There in Johnstown, I left Silver Heels until, as all men know, our liberty at last was won. Then —even as we had promised—Jack Mount, Cade Renard, and I returned to long mellow years in the blue hills of Tryon.

Content, I sit at dusk with her I love tying my soft feather-flies just as I tied them for Sir William in the golden time. The trout have nothing changed, no have I.

"Listen, Micky," murmurs Silver Heels, and again I listen with her.

From above comes the babble of the children old Betty is tucking into bed and from near by comes the ripple of sweet water flowing on under the clustered stars.

SINCLAIR LEWIS

ARROWSMITH

H IS graphic pen laid bare the chicanery of small town life in "Main Street"; he created the immortal "Babbit" and now the stream of Sinclair Lewis' satire is directed at the career of a medical man and the forces that act on his private life. Its medical authenticity may be attributed to Dr. Paul De Kruif who helped plan the story and make the characters living people. The result, according to William Allen White, is "a real book, a beautiful book, a bitter gentle story, done by a master's hand."

Insubordination near Ward D

S HE was a smallish and slender probationer, muffled in a harsh blue denim dress, an enormous white apron, and a turban bound about her head with an elastic— a uniform as grubby as her pail of scrubwater. She peered up with the alert impudence of a squirrel.

"Nurse," he said, "I want to find Ward D."

Lazily, "Do you?"

"I do! If I can interrupt your work—"

"Oh! Sounds exactly like our old prof, back home."

Her indolent amusement, her manner of treating him as though they were a pair of children making tongues at each other in a railroad station, was infuriating to the earnest young assistant of Professor Gottlieb.

"I am Dr. Arrowsmith," he snorted, "and I've been informed that even probationers learn that the first duty of a nurse is to stand when addressing doctors. I wish to find Ward D, to take a strain of—it may interest you to know! —a very dangerous microbe, and if you will kindly direct me—"

"Oh, gee, I've been getting fresh again. I'll stand up." She did. Her every movement was swiftly smooth as the running of a cat. "You back, turn right, then left. Honestly, Doctor—if you are a doctor—"

"I don't see that I need to convince you!" he raged, as he stalked off.

But her image would not wilt, even

after he had found the interne who was to help him take the spinal fluid. She was before him, provocative, enduring. He had to see her again, and convince her— "Take a better man than she is, better man than I've ever met, to get away with being insulting to me!" said the modest young scientist.

He had raced back to her room and they were staring at each other before it came to him that he had not worked out the crushing things he was going to say. She had risen from her scrubbing. She had taken off her turban, and her hair was silky and honey-colored, her eyes were blue, her face was childish. There was nothing of the slavey in her. He could imagine her running down hillsides, shinning up a stack of straw.

"Oh," she said gravely. "I didn't mean to be rude then. I was just—scrubbing makes me bad-tempered. I thought you were awfully nice, and I'm sorry I hurt your feelings, but you did seem so young for a doctor."

"I'm not. I'm a medic. I was showing off."

"So was I!"

H E FELT an instant and complete comradeship with her, a relation free from fencing and posing. He knew that this girl was of her own people. If she was vulgar, jocular, unreticent, she was also gallant, she was full of laughter at humbugs, she was capable of a loyalty too casual and natural to seem heroic. His voice was lively, though her words were only: "Pretty hard, this training for nursing," she said. "But not as hard as being a medic, I guess."

"I'm not much of a medic. I like the lab side. I think I'll be a bacteriologist, and raise Cain with some of the fool theories of immunology. And I don't think much of the bedside manner."

"I'm glad you don't. You get it here. You ought to hear some of the docs that are the sweetest old pussies with their patients—the way they bawl out the nurses. But labs—they seem sort of real. I don't suppose you can bluff a bacteria —what is it:—bacterium?"

"No, they're— What do they call you?"

"Oh, it's an idiotic name—Leora."

"What's the matter with Leora? It's fine."

Sound of mating birds, sound o spring blossoms dropping in the tranqu air, the bark of sleepy dogs at midnight who is to set them down and mak them anything but hackneyed? And a natural, as conventional, as youthfull gauche, as eternally beautiful and au thentic as those ancient sounds was th talk of Martin and Leora in that pas sionate half-hour when each found i the other a part of his own self, alway vaguely missed, discovered now witl astonished joy. They rattled on like her and heroine of a sticky tale, like swea shop operatives, like bouncing rustics like prince and princess. Their word were silly and inconsequential, heard on by one, yet taken together they were a wise and important as the tides or th sounding wind.

Birds of Passage

WHEN they were married Leora had to leave the hospital. He found a room for her on the frayed northern edge of Zenith, miles nearer Mohalis and the University than her hospital had been: a square white and blue room, with blotchy but shoulderwise chairs. The landlady was a round German woman with an eye for romance. It is doubtful if she ever believed that they were married. She was a good woman.

Till Martin graduated they kept the room. No one was so domestic as these birds of passage. At least two evenings a week Martin dashed in from Mohalis and studied there. She had a genius for keeping out of his way, for not demanding to be noticed, so that, while he plunged into his books, he had ever the warm half conscious feeling of her presence. Sometimes, at midnight, just as he began to realize that he was hungry, he would find that a plate of sandwiches had by silent magic appeared

at his elbow. He was none the less affec tionate because he did not comment. Sh made him secure.

If he had given up Gottlieb-worshir and his yearning for the laboratory a for a sanctuary, if he had resolved to be a practical and wealth-mastering doctor yet something of Gottlieb's spirit re mained. He wanted to look behind de tails and impressive-sounding lists of technical terms for the causes of things for general rules which might reduce the chaos of dissimilar and contradictory symptoms to the orderliness of chemistry

If he ached a little for research and Gottlieb's divine curiosity—well, he would be such a country doctor a Robert Koch! He would not degenerate into a bridge-playing, duck-hunting drone. He would have a small labora tory of his own. So he came to the end of the year and graduated, looking rather flustered in cap and gown, and emerged as Martin L. Arrowsmith, M.D.

Country Doctor

THEY decided that they would settle in Wheatsylvania, Leora's home town.

Excitedly he ordered a steel stand, a

sterilizer, flasks, test tubes, and a white enamelled mechanism with enchanting levers and gears which transformed it from examining-chair to operating table.

"I'm not a sentimentalist; I'm a scientist!" he boasted.

Illustration for Sinclair Lewis'
"ARROWSMITH"

He yearned over the picture of a centrifuge while Leora was admiring the "stunning seven-piece Reception Room umed oak set, upholstered in genuine Barcelona Longware Leatherette, will give your office the class and distinction of any high-grade New York specialist's."

"Aw, let 'em sit on plain chairs," Martin grunted.

Whistling he sawed out racks for the glassware and turned the oven of a discarded kerosene stove into a hot-air oven for sterilizing glass ware. "But understand, Lee, I'm not going to go monkeying with any scientific research. I'm through with all that."

For ten days Martin tinkered at his hot-air oven or sat at his desk, reading and trying to look busy. Late one afternoon when he was in a melancholy way preparing to go home, into the office stamped a grizzled Swedish farmer who grumbled, "Doc, I got a fish-hook caught in my thumb and it's all swole." To Arrowsmith, interne in Zenith General Hospital with its out-patient clinics treating hundreds a day, the dressing of a hand had been less important than borrowing a match, but to Dr. Arrowsmith of Wheatsylvania it was a hectic operation, and the farmer a person remarkably charming. Martin shook his left hand violently and burbled, "Now if there's anything, you just phone me— you just phone me."

When he had practised medicine in Wheatsylvania for one year, Martin was an inconspicuous but not discouraged country doctor. When his flock turned to him for help, their need and their patient obedience made them beautiful. Once or twice he lost his temper with jovial villagers who bountifully explained to him that he was less aged than he might have been; once or twice he drank too much whisky at poker parties in the back room of the Cooperative Store; but he was known as reliable, skilful, and honest—and on the whole he was rather less distinguished than Alec Ingleblad, the barber, less prosperous than Nils Krag, the carpenter, and less interesting to his neighbors than the Finnish garageman.

Their baby was coming in five months. Martin promised to it everything he had missed.

"He's going to have a real education!" he gloated, as they sat on the porch in the spring twilight. "Here we are, stuck in this two by twice crossroads for the rest of our lives—but maybe we've gone a little beyond our dads, and he'll go way beyond us."

He was worried, for all his flamboyance. Leora had undue morning sickness. Till noon she dragged about the house, peagreen and tousled and hollow-faced. Trained now to the false cheerfulness of the doctor, he shouted, when she was racked and ghastly. "There, that's fine, old girl! Wouldn't be making a good baby if you weren't sick. Everybody is." He was lying, and he was nervous. Whenever he thought of her dying, he seemed to die with her. Barren of her companionship, there would be nothing he wanted to do, nowhere to go.

He denounced Nature for her way of tricking human beings, by every gay device of moon-light and white limbs and reaching loneliness into having babies, then making birth as cruel and clumsy and wasteful as she could. He was abrupt and jerky with patients who called him into the country. With their suffering he was sympathetic as he had never been, for his eyes had opened to the terrible beauty of pain, but he must not go far from Leora's need.

Her morning sickness turned into pernicious vomiting. Suddenly, while she was torn and inhuman with agony, he sent for Dr. Hesselink, and that horrible afternoon when the prairie spring was exuberant outside the windows of the poor iodoform reeking room, they took the baby from her dead.

Martin saw nothing. He was not a physician. He was a terrified boy, less useful to Hesselink than the dullest nurse.

When he was certain that Leora would

recover, Martin sat by her bed, coaxing, "We'll just have to make up our minds we never can have a baby now, and so I want—Oh, I'm no good! And I've got a rotten temper. But to you, I want to be everything!"

She whispered scarce to be heard: "He would have been such a sweet baby. Oh, I know! I saw him so often."

She tried to laugh. "Perhaps I wanted him because I could boss him. I've never had anybody that would let me boss him. So if I can't have a real baby, I'll have to bring you up, Make you a great man that everybody will wonder at like your Sondelius . . . Darling, I worried so about your worry—"

He kissed her, and for hours they sat together, unspeaking, eternally understanding, in the prairie twilight.

HE HAD read in the *Journal of the American Medical Association* that Gustaf Sondelius was giving a series of lectures at Harvard. He wrote asking whether he knew of a public health appointment. Sondelius answered, in a profane and blotty scrawl, that he remembered with joy their Minneapolis vacation, that he disagreed with Entwisle of Harvard about the nature of Metathrombin, that there was an excellent Italian restaurant in Boston, and that he would inquire among his health-official friends as to a position.

Two days later he wrote that Dr Almus Pickerbaugh, Director of Public Health in the city of Nautilus, Iowa was looking for a second-in-command and would send particulars.

Leora and Martin swooped on a almanac.

"Gosh! Sixty-nine thousand people in Nautilus! Against three hundred and sixty-three here. People! People that can talk. Theatres! Maybe concerts. Leora we'll be like a pair of kids let loose from school."

The mimeographed form which was sent him said that Dr. Pickerbaugh required an assistant who would be the only full-time medical officer besides Pickerbaugh himself. The assistant would be epidemiologist, bacteriologist, and manager of the office clerks, the nurses, and the lay inspectors of dairies and sanitation. The salary would be twenty-five hundred dollars a year—against the fifteen or sixteen hundred Martin was making in Wheatsylvania.

Martin wrote to Sondelius and to Max Gottlieb, now at the McGurk Institute in New York.

Dr. Pickerbaugh informed him, "I have received a very pleasant letter from Dr. Sondelius about you, but the letter from Dr. Gottlieb is quite remarkable. He says you have rare gifts as a laboratory man. I take great pleasure in offering you the appointment. Kindly wire."

Two-fisted Doc

MARTIN left Leora at the old-fashioned, second-best hotel in Nautilus, to report to Dr. Pickerbaugh, Director of the Department of Public Health.

Dr. Almus Pickerbaugh was forty-eight. He was a man who never merely talked; he either bubbled or made orations. He received Martin with four "Well's," which he gave after the manner of a college cheer; he showed him through the Department, led him into the Director's private office, gave him a cigar, and burst the dam of manly silence.

"Doctor, I'm delighted to have a man with your scientific inclinations. Not that I should consider myself entirely without them. In fact I make it a regular practice to set aside a period for scientific research, without a certain amount of which even the most ardent crusade for health methods would scarcely make much headway."

It sounded like the beginning of a long seminar. Martin settled in his chair. He was doubtful about his cigar, but he found that it helped him to look more interested.

"I assume you agree with me, or you

will when you have had an opportunity to see the effect our work has on the city, and the success we have in selling the idea of Better Health, and what the world needs is a really inspired, courageous, overtowering leader—say a Billy Sunday of the movement—a man who would know how to use sensationalism to awake the people out of their sloth.

"You went to Winnemac and had your internship in Zenith, didn't you? Well, this might interest you. It's from the *Zenith Advocate-Times* and its by Chum Frink. Dear old Chum! He wrote this poem about me.

"Zenith welcomes with high hurraw
A friend in Almus Pickerbaugh.
The two-fisted fightin' poet doc
Who stands for health like Gibraltar's rock.
He's jammed with figgers and facts and fun,
The plucky old, lucky old son-of-a-gun!"

Martin felt strongly that he would like to get away and recover. He walked back to the hotel. He realized that to a civilized man the fact that Pickerbaugh advocated any reform would be sufficient reason for ignoring it.

Martin had thought of himself, freed from tinkering over cut fingers and ear-aches, as spending ecstatic days in the laboratory, emerging only to battle with factory-owners who defied sanitation. But he found it was impossible to define his work except that he was to do a little of everything that Pickerbaugh, the press, or any stray citizen of Nautilus might think of. Which included buying paper-clips and floor wax at the lowest prices; scolding the garbage removal company, and placating voluble voters who came in to complain of everything from the smell of sewer gas to neighboring beer parties.

But there was a little laboratory work; with tests, Wassermanns for private physicians, the making of vaccines, cultures in suspected diphtheria.

"I GET it," said Leora, as they dressed for dinner at the Pickerbaugh's. "Your job will only take about twenty-eight hours a day, and the rest of the time you're perfectly welcome to spend in research unless somebody interrupts you."

Nautilus was one of the first communities in the country to develop the Weeks habit, now so richly grown that we have Correspondence School Week, Christian Science Week, Osteopathy Week, and Georgia Pine Week.

Martin was enthusiastic during Better Babies Week. Leora and he weighed babies, examined them, made out diet charts (and in each child saw the baby they could never have). But when it came to More Babies Week, then he was argumentative. He believed, he said, in birth-control. Pickerbaugh answered with theology, violence, and the example of his own eight beauties.

Martin was equally unconvinced by Anti-Tuberculosis Week. He liked his windows open at night, he disliked men who spat tobacco juice on sidewalks, but he was jarred by hearing these certainly esthetic and possibly hygienic reforms proposed with holy frenzy and bogus statistics. Pickerbaugh impressed everyone except Martin.

Whenever he hinted criticism, Pickerbaugh answered, "What if my statistics aren't always exact? What if my advertising, my jollying of the public, does strike some folks as vulgar? It all does good; it's all on the right side. No matter what methods we use, if we can get people to have more fresh air and cleaner yards and less alcohol, we're justified."

To himself, a little surprised, Martin put it, "Yes, does it really matter? Does truth matter—clean, cold, unfriendly truth, Max Gottlieb's truth? Everybody says: 'Oh, you mustn't tamper with the truth' and everybody is furious if you hint that they themselves are tampering with it. Does anything matter, except making love and sleeping and eating and being flattered?

"I think truth does matter to me, but if it does, isn't the desire for scientific precision simply my hobby, like another man's excitement about his golf? Anyway, I'm going to stick by Pickerbaugh."

The School-boy Czar

OVER the *Nautilus Cornfield's* announcement was the vigorous headline:

ALMUS PICKERBAUGH WINS
*First Scientist Ever Elected
to Congress*
SIDE-KICK OF DARWIN AND PASTEUR
GIVES NEW PUNCH TO STEERING
SHIP OF STATE.

Pickerbaugh's resignation was to take effect at once; he was, he explained, going to Washington before his term began, to study legislative methods and start his propaganda for the creation of a national Secretaryship of Health.

Martin realized that he was likely to be the next Director of the Department. Pickerbaugh had told him, "Your work is very satisfactory. There's only one thing you lack, my boy: enthusiasm for getting together with folks and giving a long pull and strong pull, all together. But perhaps that'll come to you when you have more responsibility."

Martin sought to acquire a delight in giving long strong pulls all together, but he felt like a man who has been dragooned into wearing yellow tights at a civic pageant.

"Gosh, I may be up against it when I become Director," he fretted. "I wonder if there's people who become what's called 'successful' and then hate it? Well, anyway, I'll start a decent system of vital statistics in the department before they get me. I won't lay down! I'll fight! I'll make myself succeed!"

IT CANNOT be said that Martin showed any large ability for organization, but under him the Department of Public Health changed completely. Inspection of plumbing and food was perhaps more thorough, because Martin lacked Pickerbaugh's buoyant faith in the lay inspectors. Also he gave thought to the killing of rats and fleas and he regarded the vital statistics as something more than

a recording of births and deaths. He had notions about their value which were most amusing to the health department clerk. He wanted a record of the effect of race, occupation, and a dozen other factors upon the disease rate.

The chief difference was that Martin found himself with plenty of leisure. He estimated that Pickerbaugh must have used half his time in being inspirational and eloquent.

The first to protest was His Honor the Mayor.

"Doc," he said after he had summoned Martin to his office, "I don't want to butt in on your department—my specialty is never butting in—but it certainly strikes me that after being trained by a seventy-horse-power booster like Pickerbaugh, you ought to know that it's all damn' foolishness to spend so much time in the laboratory, when you can hire an A1 laboratory fellow for thirty bucks a week. What you ought to be doing is jollying along these slobs that are always panning the administration. Get out and talk to the churches and clubs, and help me put across the ideas that we stand for."

"Maybe he's right," Martin considered. "I'm a rotten bacteriologist. Probably I never will get my experimenting together. My job here is to keep tobacco chewers from spitting. Have I the right to waste the tax-payers' money on anything else?"

But that week he read, as an announcement issued by the McGurk Institute of Biology of New York, that Dr. Max Gottlieb had synthesized antibodies *in vitro*.

He pictured the saturnine Gottlieb not at all enjoying the triumph but with locked door, abusing the papers for their exaggerated reports of his work and as the picture became sharp, Martin was like a subaltern stationed in a desert isle when he learns that his old regiment is going off to an agreeable Border war.

Then opposition began to develop.

Various physicians were against him, not only because of the enlarged clinics, but because he rarely asked their help and never their advice. The reporters disliked him for his secrecy and occasional brusqueness. Of all these forces Martin was more or less aware, and behind them he fancied that doubtful business men, sellers of impure ice cream and milk, owners of unsanitary shops and dirty tenements, men who had always hated Pickerbaugh but who had feared to attack him because of his popularity were gathering to destroy the entire Department of Health. . . . He appreciated Pickerbaugh in those days, and loved soldier-wise the Department.

There came from the Mayor a hint that he would save trouble by resigning. He would not resign. Neither would he go to the citizens begging for support. He did his work, and leaned on Leora's assurance, and tried to ignore his detractors. He could not.

News-items and three-line editorial squibs dug at his tyranny, his ignorance, his callowness. An old woman died after treatment at the clinic, and the coroner hinted that it had been the fault of "our almighty health-officer." Somewhere arose the name "the Schoolboy Czar" for Martin, and it stuck.

The Mayor then appointed over him, Dr. Bissex, the football coach and health director of Mugford College, who invited Martin to resign.

"I will like hell!" said Martin. "Come on, be honest, Bissex. If you want to fire me, do it, but let's have things straight. I won't resign, and if you fire me I think I'll take it to the courts, and maybe I can turn enough light on you and His Honor to keep you from taking all the guts out of the work here."

"Why, Doctor, what a way to talk. Certainly I won't fire you," said Bissex, in the manner of one who has talked to difficult students. "Stay with me as long as you like. Only in the interests of economy, I reduce your salary to eight hundred dollars a year!"

"All right, reduce and be damned," said Martin.

It sounded particularly fine and original when he said it, but less so when Leora and he found that, with their rent fixed by their lease, they could not by whatever mean economies live on less than a thousand a year.

"I'm licked. I'm a complete failure— at thirty-two! I'll resign. I'll wander on," said Martin.

Then he wrote to Angus Duer. He was appointed pathologist in the Rouncefield Clinic. But, Angus wrote, "They could not at the moment see their way clear to pay him forty-five hundred a year, though they were glad to go to twenty-five hundred."

Martin accepted.

"I know I am going to love Chicago," said Leora.

Loose Knots Tied

After the first daze of white tile and bustling cleverness at the Rouncefield Clinic, Martin had the desire to tie up a few loose knots of his research. He gave his spare time to it.

When Angus Duer discovered it, he hinted, "Look here, Martin, I'm glad you're keeping on with your science, but if I were you I wouldn't, I think, waste too much energy on mere curiosity. Dr. Rouncefield was speaking about it the other day. We'd be glad to have you do all the research you want, only we'd like it if you went at something practical.

Take for instance: if you could make a tabulation of the blood-counts in a couple of hundred cases of appendicitis and publish it, that'd get somewhere, and you could sort of bring in a mention of the clinic, and we'd all receive a little credit—and incidentally maybe we could raise you to three thousand a year then."

This generosity had the effect of extinguishing Martin's desire to do any research whatever.

"Angus is right. What he means is: as a scientist I'm finished. I am. I'll never do anything original again."

It was at this time, when Martin had been with the clinic for a year, that his streptolysin paper was published in the *Journal of Infectious Diseases*.

He gave reprints to Rouncefield and to Angus. They said extremely nice things which showed that they had not read the paper, and again they suggested his tabulating blood-counts.

He also sent a reprint to Max Gottlieb, at the McGurk Institute of Biology in New York.

Gottlieb wrote to him, in that dead-black spider-web script, Martin knew so well:

Dear Martin:

I have read your paper with great pleasure. The curves of the relation of hemolysin production to age of culture are illuminating. I have spoken about you to Tubbs. When are you coming to us—to me? Your laboratory and diener are waiting for you here. The last thing I want to be is a mystic, but I feel when I see your fine engraved letterhead of a clinic and a Rouncefield that you should be tired of trying to be a good citizen and ready to come back to work. We shall be glad, & Dr. Tubbs, if you can come.

Truly yours,
M. Gottlieb.

"I'm simply going to adore New York," said Leora.

Martin Comes Home

AT THE door of the laboratory he stared hungrily.

Gottlieb was thin-cheeked and dark as ever, his hawk nose bony, his fierce eyes demanding, but his hair had gone gray, the flesh round his mouth was sunken, and Martin could have wept at the feebleness with which he rose. The old man peered down at him, his hand on Martin's shoulder, but he said only:

"Ah! Dis is good. . . . Your laboratory is three doors down the hall. . . . But I object to one thing in the good paper you send me. You say, 'The regularity of the rate at which the streptolysin disappears suggests that an equation may be found—'"

"But it can, sir!"

"Then why did you not make the equation?"

"Well—I don't know. I wasn't enough of a mathematician."

"Then you should not have published till you knew your math!"

"I— Look, Dr. Gottlieb, do you really think I know enough to work here? I want terribly to succeed."

"Succeed? I have heard that word. It is English? Oh, yes, it is a word that liddle school boys use at the University of Winnemac. It means passing examinations. But there are no examinations to pass here. . . . Martin, let us be clear. You know something of laboratory technique; you have heard about dese bacillili; you are not a good chemist, and mathematics—pfue!—most terrible! But you have curiosity and you are stubborn. You do not accept rules. Therefore I t'ink you will either make a very good scientist or a very bad one, and if you are bad enough, you will be popular with the rich ladies who rule this city, New York, and you can gif lectures for a living or even become, if you get to be plausible enough, a college president. So anyway, it wil be interesting."

Martin was blissful with the certainty that he had come home. His work began fumbling. There were days when, for all the joy of it, he dreaded lest Tubbs strike in and bellow, "What are you doing here? Get out!"

He had isolated twenty strains of staphylococcus germs and he was testing them to discover which of them was most active in producing a hemolytic, a blood-disintegrating, toxin, so that he might produce an antitoxin.

When he had obtained a satisfactory toxin, Martin began his effort to find an antitoxin. He made vast experiments with no results. Sometimes he was certain that he had something, but when he rechecked his experiments he was bleakly certain that he hadn't. Once he rushed into Gottlieb's laboratory with the announcement of the antitoxin, whereupon Gottlieb showed him that he had not considered certain dilutions.

"The fact is, Martin, you can do nothing till you know a little mathematics. If you are not going to be a cookbook bacteriologist, like most of them, you must be able to handle some of the fundamental of science. All living things are physiochemical machines. Then how can you make progress if you do not know physical chemistry, and how can you know physical chemistry without much mathematics?"

For half an hour Martin defended himself, not too politely, before the gem-like Gottlieb. The man meant so much that he could be furious with him as he would have been with Leora, with his own self.

"I'm sorry you think I don't know anything," he raged, and departed with the finest dramatic violence. He slammed into his own laboratory, felt freed, then wretched. Without volition, like a drunken man, he stormed to Gottlieb's assistant's room. "I suppose he's right. My physical chemistry is nix, and my math rotten. What am I going to do—what am I going to do?"

The embarrassed barbarian grumbled,

"Well, for Pete's sake, Slim, don't worry. The old man was just egging you on. Fact is, he's tickled to death about the careful way you're starting in. My own math isn't any too good, Slim, but if you'd like to have me come around evenings and tutor you—Free, I mean!"

Thus began the friendship between Martin and Terry Wickett; thus began a change in Martin's life whereby he gave up three or four hours of wholesome sleep each night to grind over matters which every one is assumed to know, and almost everyone does not know. By the end of his first nine months at McGurk, Martin had reviewed trigonometry and analytic geometry and was finding differential calculus romantic.

It was Leora who bore the real tedium.

She sat quiet (a frail child, only up to one's shoulder, not nine minutes older than at marriage, nine years before), or she napped inoffensively, in the long living room of their flat, while he worked over his dreary digit-infested books till one, till two, and she politely awoke to let him worry at her.

The Great Experiment

Then he forgot Leora, night, weariness, success, everything, as he charged into preparations for an experiment, his first great experiment.

During the week Gottlieb occasionally peered over his shoulder, but Martin was unwilling to report until he should have proof, and one good night's sleep, and perhaps even a shave.

When he was sure that the X Principle did reproduce itself indefinitely, so that in the tenth tube it grew to have as much effect as in the first, then he solemnly called on Gottlieb and laid before him his results.

The old man tapped his thin fingers on the report, read it intently, looked up and beamed.

"You haf a big thing. Now do not let the Director know about this and get enthusiastic too soon. I am glad, Martin."

There was that in his voice which sent Martin swanking down the corridor, back to work—and to not sleeping.

He extended his investigation to the intestinal group of organisms and discovered an X Principle against the colon bacillus. At the same time he gave some of the original Principle to a doctor in the Lower Manhattan Hospital for the treatment of boils, and from him had excited reports of cures, more excited inquiries as to what this mystery might be.

With these new victories he went parading into Gottlieb and suddenly he was being trounced.

"Oh! So! Beautiful! You let a doctor try it before you finished your research. You want fake reports of cures to get into the newspapers and have everybody in the world that has a pimple come tumbling in to be cured, so you will never be able to work? You want to be a miracle man and not a scientist. Get out of my office."

Martin crept out, and when he met one of his colleagues in the corridors who said "Up to something big? Haven't seen you lately," Martin answered: "Oh —no—gee—I'm just grubbing along, I guess."

Next morning Gottlieb came slowly into Martin's room. He stood by the window; he seemed to be avoiding Martin's eyes. He sighed, "Something sort of bad—perhaps not altogether bad—has happened. It is a pity Martin, but you are not the discoverer of the Z Principle. D'Hérelle of the Pasteur Institute has just now published a report—it is your X Principle, absolute. Only he calls it 'bacteriophage.'"

"Then I'm—"

In his mind Martin finished it, "Then I'm not going to be famous or anything else. I'm back in the gutter." All strength went out of him and all purpose, and the light of creation faded to dirty gray.

"Now of course," said Gottlieb, "you could claim to be codiscoverer and spend the rest of your life fighting to get recognized. Or you could forget it, and write a nice letter congratulating D'Hérelle, and go back to work."

Martin mourned, "Oh, I'll go back to work."

Gottlieb straggled away, looking back a little sadly.

Tubbs came in to wail, "If you had only published earlier, Dr. Arrowsmith.

"So I'm not going to be rich. Leora, poor kid, she won't have her new dresses and flat and everything. We— Won't be so much fun in the lil old flat, now. Oh, quit whining! Bacteriophage, the Frenchman calls it. Better just call it *phage*. Even got to take his name for it. Well, I had a lot of fun, working all those nights—working—"

He was coming out of his trance. He plodded into Gottlieb's office to secure the journal containing D'Hérelle's report and read it minutely, avidly, enthusiastically.

"There's a man, there's a scientist!" he chuckled.

IT WAS more than a year after Martin's anticipation by D'Hérelle when Tubbs appeared in the laboratory.

"I've been thinking, Arrowsmith," said Tubbs, "that D'Hérelle's discovery hasn't aroused the popular interest I thought it would. If he'd only been here with us, I'd have seen to it that he got the proper attention. Practically no newspaper comment at all. Perhaps we might be able to do something with phage in practical healing. I want you to experiment with phage in pneumonia, plague, perhaps typhoid and when your experiments get going, make some practical tests in collaboration with the hospitals."

That day, concealing from Gottlieb his abandonment of the quest for the fundamental nature of phage, Martin set about fighting pneumonia, before attacking the Black Death.

The Stuff of Salvation

NO ONE dared speak of it. No one liked to shake hands with his oldest friend; every one fled from every one else, though the rats loyally stayed with them; and through the island of St. Hubert galloped the Panic, which is more murderous than its brother, the Plague.

But Stokes of St. Swithin's secretly wrote to Dr. Max Gottlieb of McGurk Institute, that the plague was ready to flare up and consume all the West Indies,

and would Dr. Gottlieb do something about it.

But Gottlieb did not move. He was assailed by inquiries: public health officials, one Dr. Almus Pickerbaugh, a congressman who was said to be popular in Washington, Gustaf Sondelius, and a Martin Arrowsmith who could not (whether because he was too big or too small) quite attain Gottlieb's concentrated indifference.

It was rumored that Arrowsmith of

McGurk had something which might irradicate plague. Letters demanded of Gottlieb, "Can you stand by with the stuff of salvation in your hands, and watch thousands of these unfortunate people dying in St. Hubert, and what is more, are you going to let the dreaded plague gain a foothold in the Western hemisphere?"

Whether it was the demands of the public spirited, or whether Gottlieb's own imagination aroused enough to visualize the far-off misery of the blacks in the canefields, he summoned Martin and remarked:

"It comes to me that there is bubonic plague in St. Hubert. If I could trust you, Martin, to use the phage with only half your patients and keep the others as controls, under normal hygienic conditions but without the phage, then you could make an absolute determination of its value, as complete as what we have of mosquito transmission of yellow fever, and then I would send you down to St. Hubert. What do you t'ink?"

MARTIN swore by Jacques Loeb that he would observe test conditions; he would determine forever the value of phage by the contrast between patients treated and untreated, and so, perhaps, end all plague forever; he would harden his heart and keep clear his eyes.

"We will get Sondelius to go along," said Gottlieb. "He will do the big boom-boom and so bring us the credit in the newspapers which I am told we must obtain."

When Leora received the idea that he was going off to a death-haunted isle, she took the notion secretively away with her, to look at it. Martin was glad she did not add to his qualms by worrying. Then, after three days, she spoke.

"I'm going with you."

"You are not!"

Leora seized his lapels, as comic-fierce as a boxing kitten, but her eyes were not comic, nor her wailing voice; age-old wail of the soldiers' women:

"Sandy, don't you know I haven't any life outside of you? I might've had, but honestly, I've been glad to let you absorb me. I'm a lazy, useless, ignorant scut, except as maybe I keep you comfortable. If you were off there, and I didn't know you were all right, or if you died, I'd go mad. I mean it—can't you see I mean it—I'd go mad."

Gottlieb opposed it, Sondelius roared about it, Martin worried about it, but Leora went, and—his only act of craftiness—Gottlieb made her "Secretary and Technical Assistant to the McGurk Plague and Bacteriophage Commission to the Lesser Antilles," and blandly gave her a salary.

Unmoral Soldier of the Lord

THERE were no carriages, and the hotel-runners who once had pestered tourists landing from the boat, whatever the hour, were dead now or hidden. The Commission, with Stokes and the harbor police who had manned the launch, carried the baggage (Martin weaving with a case of the phage) through the rutty balconied streets to the San Marino Hotel.

Once or twice faces, disembodied things with frightened lips, stared at them from alley-mouths. As they entered the hotel, Martin saw under a street light the first stirring of life: a crying woman and a bewildered child following an open wagon in which were heaped a dozen stiff bodies.

"And I might have saved all of them, with phage," he whispered to himself.

WHILE Martin prepared his laboratory, Sondelius was joyfully at work, finding out what was wrong with the administration, which proved to be almost everything that could possibly be wrong.

Then Sondelius, that crafty and often lying lobbyist, that unmoral soldier of the Lord, burst in and became dictator.

He terrified the Board of Health. He quoted his own experiences in Mongolia and India. He assured them that, if they did not cease being politicians, the plague might cling in St. Hubert forever, so that they would no more have the amiable dollars of the tourists and the pleasures of smuggling.

He immediately started rat-killing. His rat crew searched each warehouse before pumping in hydrocyanic acid gas, lest some one be left in the place. But in the third one a tramp had been asleep, and when the doors were anxiously opened after the fumigation, there were not only thousands of dead rats but also a dead and very stiff tramp.

"Poor fella—bury him," said Sondelius.

There was no inquest.

He was cheerful, but never with reproving and infuriating cheerfulness. He shouted and sang—and took precautions for working among rats and agile fleas. It happened that he was, without Martin or Gottlieb ever understanding it, the most brilliant as well as the least pompous and therefore least appreciated warrior against epidemics that the world has known.

Thus with Sondelius, though for Martin there were as yet but embarrassment and futility and the fear of fear.

He had seen the suffering of the plague and he had been tempted to forget experimentation, to give up the possible saving of millions for the immediate saving of thousands. He heard men shrieking in delirium; a dozen times he saw that face of terror—sunken bloody eyes, drawn face, open mouth—which marks the Black Death; and once he beheld an exquisite girl child in a coma on the edge of death, her tongue black and around her the scent of the tomb.

It came to him that Gottlieb in his secluded innocence, had not realized what it meant to gain leave to experiment amid the hysteria of an epidemic. But he swore that he would not yield to a compassion which in the end would make all compassion futile.

"I'm not a sentimentalist; I'm a scientist!" he boasted.

They snarled at him in the streets now.

People had heard that he was wilfully withholding their salvation. The panic was increasing. They who had at first kept cool could not endure the strain of wakening at night to see upon their windows the glow of the pile of logs on Admiral Knob, the emergency crematory where Gustaf Sondelius and his curly gray mop had been shoveled into the fire along with a crippled negro boy and a Hindu beggar.

The Eternal Triangle

THE plague had only begun to invade St. Swithin's, but it was unquestionably coming and Martin was able to make plans. He divided the population into two equal parts. One of them was injected with plague phage, the other half was left without.

The pest attacked the unphaged half of the parish much more heavily than those who had been treated. The unfortunate cases, he treated, giving the phage to alternate patients, in the somewhat barren almshouse of the parish.

Despite Martin's discouragement, Mrs. Lanyon, a rich American who had been stranded on the island, came there to cook. She also made beds and showed much intelligence about disinfecting herself. As she bustled about the rusty kitchen, in a gingham gown she had borrowed from a maid, she so disturbed Martin that he forgot to be gruff.

Mrs. Lanyon talked to Martin as one who had shared his work, but when she had bathed and powdered and dressed, he talked to her as one who was afraid of her.

Often Martin returned to his patients at night, but once or twice, Mrs. Lanyon and he fled to the shore of a rocky lagoon which cut far in from the sea.

They sat on a cliff, full of the sound of the healing tide and he perceived that Mrs. Lanyon's white frock was flut-

ering about her knees. He realized that
he too was strained and still. They were
silent together, and when his hand crept
to hers they sat unimpassioned, comprehending, free to talk of what they would.

He stood outside her door, when they
had returned to the house, and imagined
her soft moving within.

"No," he raged. "Can't do it. Joyce—
women like her—one of the million
things I've given up for work and for
Lee. Well, that's all there is to it then.
But if I were here two weeks— Fool!
She'd be furious if you knocked! But—"

He was aware of the dagger of light
under her door; the more aware of it
as he turned his back and tramped to
his room.

But he had triumphed. In three or
four days he would drive to Penrith
Lodge and get Leora. She and Joyce
Lanyon should become such friends that
Joyce would never again turn to him in
loneliness, he was willing, he was eager
—he was almost eager.

When Martin left her at the Lodge,
in the leafy gloom high on the
Penrith Hills, Leora felt his absence.
They had been so little apart since he
had first come on her, scrubbing a hospital room in Zenith.

She was so desperately lonely that she
thought of walking to Blackwater, finding a motor and fleeing to Martin.

Then she awoke one morning with a
fever, a headache, her limbs chilly.
When the maids discovered her in the
morning, they fled from the house.

She was bewildered; she was lonely;
she dared not start on her long journey
without his hand to comfort her. She
listened for him—listened—tense with
listening.

"You will come! I know you'll come
and help me! I know. You'll come! Martin! Sandy! Sandy!" she sobbed.

Then she slipped down into a kindly
coma. There was no more pain, and
all the shadowy house was quiet but for
her hoarse and struggling breath.

Out of the Wreck

Like Sondelius, Joyce Lanyon tried to
persuade Martin to give the phage
to everybody.

"I'm getting to be good and stern,
with all you people after me. Regular
Gottlieb. Nothing can make me do it,
not if they tried to lynch me," he
boasted.

He had explained Leora to Joyce. "I
was afraid to let her come here—didn't
know what I'd find—but now I'm going
to hustle to Penrith and bring her here
today.

He came to Penrith Lodge bawling,
"Lee! Leora! Come on! Here we are!"

His voice echoed in a desperate silence.
He was uneasy. He darted in, found no
one in the living room, the kitchen, then
hastened into their bedroom.

On the bed, across the folds of the
torn mosquito netting, was Leora's body,
very frail, quite still. He cried to her,
he shook her, he stood weeping.

He talked to her, his voice a little
insane, trying to make her understand

that he had loved her, and had left her
here only for her safety.

There was rum in the kitchen, and
he went out to gulp down raw full
glasses. They did not affect him.

By evening he strode to the garden,
the high and windy garden looking
toward the sea, and dug a ditch. He
lifted her light stiff body, kissed it, and
laid it in the pit. At night he wandered.
When he came back to the house and
saw the row of her little dresses with the
lines of soft body in them, he was
terrified.

Then he went to pieces.

Because death had for the first time
been brought to him, he gave phage to
every one who asked. Only in St.
Swithin's, since there his experiment was
so excellently begun, did some remnant
of honor keep him from distributing the
phage universally.

All day, Martin injected a line of
frightened citizens. Stokes begged him
at least to turn the work over to another

doctor and take what interest he could in St. Swithin's, but Martin had a bitter satisfaction in throwing away all his significance, in helping to wreck his own purposes. Then, after a fortnight when he was tired of the drama, he had four doctors making the injections.

He did not see Joyce Lanyon. He hated her. He swore that it was not her presence which had kept him from returning earlier to Leora, but he was aware that while he had been chattering with Joyce, Leora had been dying.

Whether from phage or rat-killing or Providence, the epidemic paused, and six months after Martin's coming, when the West Indian May was broiling and the season of hurricanes was threatened, the plague had almost vanished and the quarantine was lifted.

Martin was on the wharf when Joyc Lanyon sailed.

Strong of hand, almost as tall as h she looked at him without flutter an rejoiced: "I don't suppose I helped yo but I did try. You see, I'd never bee trained in reality. You trained m Goodby."

"Mayn't I come to see you in Nev York?"

"If you'd really like to."

She was gone, yet she had never bee so much with him as through tha tedious hour when the steamer was los beyond the horizon.

But that night, in panic, he fled up t Penrith Lodge and buried his cheek i the damp soil above the Leora wit whom he had never had to fence and ex plain, to whom he had never needed t say, "Mayn't I come to see you?"

Architecture is frozen music.—*Goethe.*

There is no good in arguing with the inevitable. The only argument availabl with an east wind is to put on your overcoat.—*Lowell.*

Ah, don't say that you agree with me. When people agree with me I alway feel that I must be wrong.—*Oscar Wilde.*

The perfection of art is to conceal art.—*Quintilian.*

Art is the right hand of Nature. The latter has only given us being, the forme has made us men.—*Schiller.*

The pen is the tongue of the mind.—*Cervantes.*

And choose an author as you choose a friend.—*Wentworth Dillon.*

The most original modern authors are not so because they advance what i new, but simply because they know how to put what they have to say, as if it had never been said before.—*Goethe.*

The chief glory of every people arises from its authors.—*Samuel Johnson.*

The ink of the scholar is more sacred than the blood of the martyr.—*Mo hammed.*

The great and good do not die even in this world. Embalmed in books, thei spirits walk abroad. The book is a living voice. It is an intellect to which one stil listens.—*Sam'l Smiles.*

Nothing is beautiful from every point of view.—*Horace.*

A pleasing countenance is no slight advantage.—*Ovid.*

Arthur Guy Empey

OVER THE TOP

Tʜɪs is a play by play description of modern warfare as it affects the private soldier. It was written by an American, Arthur Guy Empey (1883–   ) who joined up in 1915. After doing his bit he came home to tell his countrymen what it was like "over there." Horror and humor are combined so convincingly in "Over the Top" that soon after its publication in 1917 it had become one of the big best sellers of all time.

Iᴛ ᴡᴀs in an office in Jersey City. I was sitting at my desk talking to a Lieutenant of the Jersey National Guard. On the wall was a big war map decorated with variously colored little flags showing the position of the opposing armies on the Western Front in France. In front of me on the desk lay a New York paper with big flaring head lines:

LUSITANIA SUNK!
AMERICAN LIVES LOST!

The windows were open and a feeling of spring pervaded the air. Through the open windows came the strains of a hurdy-gurdy playing—*I Didn't Raise my Boy to be a Soldier.*

"*Lusitania* Sunk! American Lives Lost!" *I Didn't Raise my Boy to Be a Soldier.* To us these did not seem to jibe.

The telephone rang and I answered it. It was a business call for me requesting my services for an out-of-town assignment. Business was not very good, so this was very welcome. After listening to the proposition, I seemed to be swayed by a peculiarly strong force within me, and answered, "I am sorry that I cannot accept your offer, but I am leaving for England next week," and hung up the receiver.

The Lieutenant swung around in his chair, and stared at me in blank astonishment. I answered his look with, "Well, it's so. I'm going." And I went.

Rᴇᴄʀᴜɪᴛɪɴɢ posters were everywhere in England. The one that impressed me most was a life-size picture of Lord Kitchener with his finger pointing directly at me, under the caption of "Your King and Country Need you." No matter which way I turned, the accusing finger followed me. I was an American, in mufti, and had a little American flag in the lapel of my coat. I had no king, and my country had seen fit not to need me, but still that pointing finger made me feel small and ill at ease.

Presently I came to a recruiting office. Inside, sitting at a desk was a lonely Tommy Atkins. I decided to interview him in regard to joining the British Army.

He asked my nationality. I immediately pulled out my American passport and showed it to him. After looking at the passport, he informed me that he was sorry but could not enlist me, as it would be a breach of neutrality.

I insisted that I was not neutral, because to me it seemed that a real American could not be neutral when big things were in progress, but he still would not enlist me.

With disgust in my heart I went out in the street. I had gone about a block when a recruiting Sergeant who had followed me out of the office tapped me on the shoulder and said: "S'y, I can get you in the Army. We have a 'Lefttenant' down at the other office who doesn't know what neutrality is."

I accepted his invitation for an introduction to the Lieutenant. I entered the office and went up to him, opened up my passport and said:

"Before going further I wish to state that I am an American, not too proud to fight, and want to join your army."

He looked at me in a nonchalant manner, and answered, "That's all right, we take anything over here." He got out an enlistment blank, and placing his finger on a blank line said, "Sign here."

I explained to him that I would not sign it without first reading it. I read it over and signed for duration of war.

Then I was hustled to the quartermaster stores and received an awful shock. The Quartermaster Sergeant spread a waterproof sheet on the ground, and commenced throwing a miscellaneous assortment of straps, buckles, and other paraphernalia into it. I thought he would never stop, but when the pile reached to my knees he paused long enough to say, "Next, No. 5217, 'Arris, 'B' Company."

Struggling under the load, with frequent pauses for rest, I reached our barracks (large car barns), and my platoon leader came to the rescue. It was a marvel to me how quickly he assembled the equipment. After he had completed the task, he showed me how to adjust it on my person. Pretty soon I stood before him a proper Tommy Atkins in heavy marching order.

Somewhere in France

HAVING served as Sergeant-Major in the United States Cavalry, I tried to tell the English drill sergeants their business but it did not work. They immediately put me as batman in their mess. Many a greasy dish of stew was accidentally spilled over them.

I would sooner fight than be a waiter, so when the order came through from headquarters calling for a draft of 25 reinforcements for France, I volunteered.

We were put into troop trains and sent to Southampton, where we detrained, and had our trench rifles issued to us. Then in columns of twos we went up the gangplank of a little steamer lying alongside the dock. We were then ordered to take life belts from the racks overhead and put them on. I have crossed the ocean several times and I knew I was not seasick, but when I buckled on that life belt, I had a sensation of sickness.

After we got out into the stream all I could think of was that there were a million German submarines with a torpedo on each, across the warhead of which was inscribed my name and address.

After five hours we came alongside a pier and disembarked. I had attained one of my ambitions. I was "somewhere in France."

We slept in the open that night on the side of a road. About six the next morning we were ordered to entrain. I looked around for the passenger coaches, but all I could see on the siding were cattle cars. We climbed in these. On the side of each car was a sign reading "Hommes 40, Chevaux 8." When we got inside the cars, we thought that perhaps the sign painter had reversed the order of things. After forty-eight hours in these trucks we detrained at Rouen.

At this place we went through an intensive training for ten days. This training consisted of the rudiments of trench warfare. Trenches had been dug, with barbed-wire entanglements, bombing saps, dugouts, observation posts, and machine gun emplacements. We were given a smattering of trench cooking, sanitation, bomb throwing reconnoitering, listening posts, constructing and repairing barbed wire, "carrying in" parties, methods used in attack and defense, wiring parties, mass formation, and the procedure for poison gas attacks.

ON THE tenth day we again met our friends "Hommes 40, Chevaux 8." Thirty-six hours more of misery and we arrived at the town of F——. A dull rumbling could be heard. But the sun was shining. Coming towards us was an old grizzled Sergeant, properly fed up with the war, so I asked him what the noise was.

"Them's the guns up the line, me lad, and you'll get enough of 'em before you gets back to Blighty."

My knees seemed to wilt, and I squeaked out a weak "Oh."

Our billet was a spacious affair, a large barn on the left side of the road, which had one hundred entrances, ninety-nine for shells, rats, wind, and rain, and the hundredth one for Tommy. I was tired out, and using my shrapnel-proof helmet, (shrapnel proof until a piece of shrapnel hits it), or tin hat, for a pillow, lay down in the straw.

I must have slept about two hours, when I awoke with a prickling sensation all over me. As I thought, the straw had worked through my uniform. I woke up the fellow lying on my left, who had been up the line before, and asked him,

"Does the straw bother you, mate? It's worked through my uniform and I can't sleep."

In a sleepy voice, he answered, "That ain't straw, them's cooties."

From that time on my friends the "cooties" were constantly with me. There is no way to get rid of them permanently. No matter how often you bathe, and that is not very often, or how many times you change your underwear, your friends, the "cooties" are always in evidence. The billets are infested with them especially so, if there is straw on the floor.

The greatest shock a recruit gets when he arrives at his battalion in France is to see the men engaging in a "cootie" hunt. With an air of contempt and disgust he avoids the company of the older men, until a couple of days later, in a torment of itching, he also has to resort to a shirt hunt or spend many a sleepless night of misery. During these hunts there are lots of pertinent remarks bandied back and forth among the explorers, such as, "Say Bill, I'll swap you two little ones for a big one," or, "I've got a black one here that looks like Kaiser Bill."

Baptism by Fire

ONE morning we were informed that we were going up the line, and our march began. It took us three days to reach reserve billets—each day's march bringing the sound of the guns nearer and nearer. At night, way off in the distance we could see their flashes, which lighted up the sky with a red glare.

Just before reaching reserve billets we were marching along, laughing and singing when overhead came a "swish" through the air, rapidly followed by three others. Then about two hundred yards to our left in a large field, four columns of black earth and smoke rose into the air, and the ground trembled from the report—the explosion of four German five-nine's, or "coal-boxes."

We divided into small squads and went into the fields on the right and left of the road, and crouched on the ground. No other shells followed this salvo. It was our first baptism by shell

fire. From the waist up I was all enthusiasm, but from there down, everything was missing. I thought I should die with fright.

About five that night, we reached the ruined village of H——. Marching down the main street we came to the heart of the village, and took up quarters in shell proof cellars (shell proof until hit by a shell). Shells were constantly whistling over the village and bursting in our rear, searching for our artillery.

These cellars were cold, damp, and smelly, and overrun with large rats—big black fellows. Most of the Tommies slept with their overcoats over their faces. I did not. In the middle of the night I woke up in terror. The cold, clammy feet of a rat had passed over my face. I immediately smothered myself in my overcoat, but could not sleep for the rest of that night.

Next evening, we took over our sector of the line. In single file we wended our way through a zig zag communication trench, six inches deep with mud. This trench was called "Whiskey Street."

In about thirty minutes we reached the front line. It was dark as pitch. Every now and then a German star shell would pierce the blackness out in front with its silvery light. I was trembling all over, and felt very lonely and afraid.

The boy in front of me named Prentice crumpled up without a word. A piece of shell had gone through his shrapnel-proof helmet. I felt sick and weak.

But my ambition had been attained. I was in a front-line trench on the Western Front, and oh, how I wished I were back in Jersey City.

Front-Line Trench

Suddenly, the earth seemed to shake and a thunderclap burst in my ears. The parapet on my left toppled into the trench, completely blocking it with a wall of tossed-up earth. The man on my left lay still. I rubbed the mud from my face, and an awful sight met my gaze—his head was smashed to a pulp, and his steel helmet was full of brains and blood. A German "Minnie" (trench mortar) had exploded in the next traverse. Men were digging into the soft mass of mud in a frenzy of haste. Stretcher-bearers came up the trench on the double. After a few minutes of digging, three still, muddy forms on stretchers were carried down the communication trench to the rear. Soon they would be resting "somewhere in France," with a little wooden cross over their heads. They had done their bit for King and Country, had died without firing a shot.

Later on, I found out their names. They belonged to our draft. I was dazed and motionless. Suddenly a shovel was pushed into my hands, and a rough but kindly voice said:

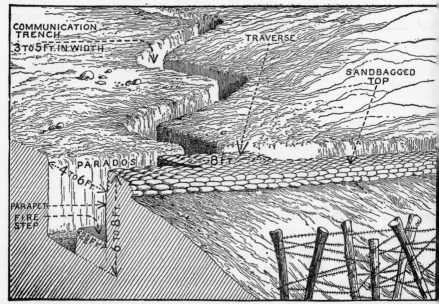

DIAGRAM SHOWING TYPICAL FRONT-LINE AND COMMUNICATION TRENCHES

"Here, my lad, lend a hand clearing the trench, but keep your head down, and look out for snipers. One of the Fritz's is a daisy, and he'll get you if you're not careful."

Lying on my belly in the bottom of the trench, I filled sandbags with the sticky mud, they were dragged to my rear by the other men, and the work of rebuilding the parapet was on. The harder I worked, the better I felt. Although the weather was cold, I was soaked with sweat.

Occasionally a bullet would crack overhead, and a machine gun would kick up the mud on the bashed-in parapet, At each crack I would duck and shield my face with my arm. One of the older men noticed this action of mine, and whispered:

"Don't duck at the crack of a bullet, Yank; the danger has passed,—you never hear the one that wings you. Always remember that if you are going to get it, you'll get it, so never worry."

This made a great impression on me at the time, and from then on, I adopted his motto, "If you're going to get it, you'll get it."

It helped me wonderfully. I used it so often afterwards that some of my mates dubbed me, "If you're going to get it, you'll get it."

After an hour's hard work, all my nervousness left me, and I was laughing and joking with the rest.

THAT night I was put on guard with an older man. We stood on the fire step with our heads over the top, peering out into No Man's Land. It was nervous work for me, but the other fellow seemed to take it as part of the night's routine.

Once, out in front of our wire, I heard a noise and saw dark forms moving. My rifle was lying across the sandbagged parapet. I reached for it, and was taking aim to fire, when my mate grasped my arm, and whispered, "Don't fire," he challenged in a low voice. The reply came back instantly from the dark forms:

"Shut your blinkin' mouth, you bloomin' idiot; do you want us to click it from the Boches?"

Later we learned that the word, "No challenging or firing, wiring party out in front," had been given to the sentry on our right, but he had failed to pass it down the trench. An officer had overheard our challenge and the reply, and immediately put the offending sentry under arrest. The sentry clicked twenty-one days on the wheel, that is, he received twenty-one days' Field Punishment No. 1, or "crucifixion," as Tommy terms it.

This consists of being spread-eagled on the wheel of a limber two hours a day for twenty-one days, regardless of the weather. During this period, your rations consist of bully beef, biscuits, and water.

A few months later I met this sentry and he confided to me that since being "crucified," he has never failed to pass the word down the trench when so ordered. In view of the offence, the above punishment was very light, in that failing to pass the word down a trench may mean the loss of many lives, and the spoiling of some important enterprise in No Man's Land.

Army Discipline

SOON after my enlistment, I had found that in the British Army discipline is very strict. One has to be very careful in order to stay on the narrow path of government virtue. There are about seven million ways of breaking the King's Regulations; to keep one you have to break another.

The worst punishment is death by a firing squad or "up against the wall" as Tommy calls it. This is for desertion, cowardice, mutiny, giving information to the enemy, destroying or willfully wasting ammunition, looting, rape, robbing the dead, forcing a safeguard, striking a superior, etc.

Then comes the punishment of sixty-four days in the front-line trench without relief. During this time you have to engage in all raids, working parties in No Man's land, and every hazardous undertaking that comes along. If you live through the sixty-four days you are indeed lucky.

This punishment is awarded where there is a doubt as to the willful guilt of a man who has committed an offence punishable by death.

Then comes the famous Field Punishment No. 1. You get crucified for repeated minor offences.

Next in order is Field Punishment No. 2. This is confinement in the "Clink," without blankets, getting water, bully beef, and biscuits for rations and doing all the dirty work that can be found. This may be for twenty-four hours or twenty days, according to the gravity of the offence.

Then comes "Pack Drill" or Defaulters' Parade. This consists of drilling, mostly at the double, for two hours with full equipment. Tommy hates this, because it is hard work. Sometimes he fills his pack with straw to lighten it, and sometimes he gets caught. If he gets caught, he grouses at everything in general for twenty-one days, from the vantage point of a limber wheel.

Next comes "C.B." meaning "Confined to Barracks." This consists of staying in billets or barracks for twenty-four hours to seven days. You also get an occasional Defaulters' Parade and dirty jobs around the quarters.

The Sergeant-Major keeps what is known as the Crime Sheet. When a man commits an offence he is "Crimed," that is, his name, number, and offence is entered on the Crime Sheet.

To gain the title of a "smart soldier," Tommy has to keep clear of the Crime Sheet, and you have to be darned smart to do it.

I have been on it a few times, mostly for "Yankee impudence."

Over the Top

ON MY second trip to the trenches our officer was making his rounds of inspection, and we received the cheerful news that at four in the morning we were to go over the top and take the German front-line trench.

Some of the Tommies, first getting permission from the Sergeant, went into the machine-gunners' dugout, and wrote letters home, saying that in the morning, they were going over the top, and also that if the letters reached their destination it would mean that the writer had been killed. These letters were turned over to the captain with instructions to mail same in the event of the writer's being killed. Some of the men made out their wills in their pay book, under the caption, "will and last testament."

Then the nerve-racking wait commenced. Every now and then I would glance at the dial of my wrist-watch and was surprised to see how fast the minutes passed by.

At ten minutes to four, word was passed down, "Ten minutes to go!" Ten minutes to live! We were shivering all over. My legs felt as if they were asleep. Then word was passed down: "First wave get on and near the scaling ladders."

Before a charge Tommy is the politest of men. There is never any pushing or crowding to be first up these ladders. We crouched around the base of the ladders waiting for the word to go over. was sick and faint, and was puffing away at an unlighted fag. Then came the word, "three minutes to go; upon the lifting of the barrage and on the blast of the whistles, 'Over the Top with the Best o' Luck and Give them Hell.'

The famous phrase of the Western Front. The Jonah phrase of the Western Front. To Tommy it means if you are lucky enough to come back, you will be minus an arm or a leg. Tommy hates to be wished the best of luck; so, when peace is declared, if it ever is, and you

neet a Tommy on the street, just wish
him the best of luck and duck the brick
that follows.

How I got up that ladder I will never
know. The first ten feet out in
front was agony. Then we passed
through the lanes of our barbed wire. I
knew I was running, but could feel no
motion below the waist. Patches on the
ground seemed to float to the rear as if
I were on a treadmill and scenery was
rushing past me. The Germans had put
a barrage of shrapnel across No Man's
Land, and you could hear the pieces
slap the ground about you.

The crossing of No Man's Land remains a blank to me. Men on my right
and left would stumble and fall. Some
would try to get up, while others remained huddled and motionless. Then
smashed-up barbed wire came into view
and seemed carried on a tide to the rear.
Suddenly, in front of me loomed a giant
form with a rifle which looked about
ten feet long, on the end of which
seemed seven bayonets.

Then through my mind flashed the
admonition of our bayonet instructor
back in Blighty. He had said, "Whenever you get in a charge and run your
bayonet up to the hilt into a German,
the Fritz will fall. Perhaps your rifle
will be wrenched from your grasp. Do
not waste time, if the bayonet is fouled
in his equipment, by putting your foot
on his stomach and tugging at the rifle
to extricate the bayonet. Simply press
the trigger and the bullet will free it."

In my present situation this was fine
logic, but for the life of me I could not
remember how he had told me to get
my bayonet into the German. To me,
this was the paramount issue. I closed
my eyes, and lunged forward. My rifle
was torn from my hands. I must have
gotten the German because he disappeared.

Then something hit me in the left
shoulder and my left side went numb.
It felt as if a hot poker was being driven
through me. I felt no pain—just a sort
of nervous shock. A bayonet had pierced
me from the rear. I fell backward on the
ground, but was not unconscious, because I could see dim objects moving
around me. Then a flash of light in front
of my eyes and unconsciousness. Something had hit me on the head. I have
never found out what it was.

I dreamed I was being tossed about in
an open boat on a heaving sea and
opened my eyes. The moon was shining.
I was on a stretcher being carried down
one of our communication trenches. At
the advanced first-aid post my wounds
were dressed, and then I was put into
an ambulance and sent to one of the base
hospitals. The wounds in my shoulder
and head were not serious and in six
weeks I had rejoined my company for
service in the front line.

Dead Men Are Better

Speaking of stretcher-bearers and
wounded, it is very hard for the
average civilian to comprehend the enormous cost of taking care of wounded
and the war in general. He or she gets
so accustomed to seeing billions of dollars in print that the significance of the
amount is passed over without a
thought.

From an official statement published
in one of the London papers, it is stated
that it costs between six and seven thousand pounds ($30,000 to $35,000) to kill
or wound a soldier. This result was attained by taking the cost of the war to
date and dividing it by the killed and
wounded.

It may sound heartless and inhuman,
but it is a fact, nevertheless, that from
a military standpoint it is better for a
man to be killed than wounded.

If a man is killed he is buried, and
the responsibility of the government
ceases, except for the fact that his people
receive a pension. But if a man is
wounded it takes three men from the
firing line, the wounded man and two
men, to carry him to the rear to the

advanced first-aid post. Here he is attended by a doctor, perhaps assisted by two R.A.M.C. men. Then he is put into a motor ambulance, manned by a crew of two or three. At the field hospital, where he generally goes under an anaesthetic, either to have his wounds cleaned or to be operated on, he requires the services of about three to five persons.

From this point another ambulance ride impresses more men in his service, and then at the ambulance train, another corps of doctors, A.R.M.C. men, Red Cross nurses, and the train's crew. From the train he enters the base hospital or Casualty Clearing Station, where a good-sized corps of doctors, nurses, etc., are kept busy. Another ambulance journey is next in order—this time to the hospital ship. He crosses the Channel, arrives in Blighty—more ambulances and perhaps a ride for five hours on an English Red Cross train with its crew of Red Cross workers, and at last he reaches the hospital. Generally he stays from two to six months, or longer, in this hospital. From here he is sent to a convalescent home for six weeks.

If by wounds he is unfitted for further service, he is discharged, given a pension, or committed to a Soldiers' Home for the rest of his life,—still the expense piles up. When you realize that all the ambulances, trains, and ships, not to mention the man-power, used in transporting a wounded man, could be used for supplies, ammunition, and reinforcements for the troops at the front, it will not appear strange that from a strictly military standpoint, a dead man is sometimes better than a live one (if wounded).

The boys in the section welcomed me back, but there were many strange faces. Several of our men had gone West in that charge, and were lying "somewhere in France" with a little wooden cross at their heads. We were in rest billets.

Staged Under Fire

TOMMY loves to be amused, and being a Yank, they turned to me for something new in this line. I taught them how to pitch horseshoes, and this game made a great hit for about ten days. Then Tommy turned to America for a new diversion. I was up in the air until a happy thought came to me. Why not write a sketch and break Tommy in as an actor? I had written a few plays for amateur performances back in the States and I thought I could write one that the boys would like.

One evening after "Lights out," when you are not supposed to talk, I imparted my scheme in whispers to the section. They eagerly accepted the idea of forming a Stock Company and could hardly wait until the morning for further details.

After eight days constant writing I completed a two-act farce comedy which I called "The Diamond Palace Saloon." Upon the suggestion of one of the boys in the section I sent a proof of the program to a printing house in London.

Notes from the program follow:

The Management requests that patrons will remove their steel helmets.

In case of an attack, keep your seats, don't interrupt the performance.

If you don't like the show, leave, don't put on your gas helmets.

Patrons will not bring live bombs into the theatre.

No one allowed past the barbed wire in front of the footlights as it is the actors' only protection. No firing at actors.

It is earnestly requested that any incivility or inattention towards patrons from the employees of this Theatre be reported at the Booking Office, so that the offender may be shot at sunrise (if he gets up in time).

Gentlemen are requested not to swear aloud at actors, the show, playwright or orchestra. It is not their fault that they are rotten, they know it as well as you do.

The whole Brigade was crazy to witness the first performance. The performance was scheduled to start at 6 p.m. At 5:15 there was a mob in front of our one entrance and it looked like a big night. We had two boxes each accommodating four people, and these were immediately sold out. Then a brilliant idea came to Ikey Cohenstein. Why not use the rafters overhead, call them boxes, and charge two francs for a seat on them? The only difficulty was how were the men to reach these boxes, but to Ikey this was a mere detail. He got long ropes and tied one end around each rafter and then tied a lot of knots in the ropes. These ropes would take the place of stairways. We figured out that the rafters would seat about forty men and sold that number of tickets accordingly.

When the ticket-holders for the boxes got a glimpse of the rafters and were informed that they had to use the rope stairway, there was a howl of indignation, but we had their money and told them that if they did not like it they could write to the management later and their money would be refunded; but under these conditions they would not be allowed to witness the performance that night.

After a little grousing they accepted the situation with the promise that if the show was rotten they certainly would let us know about it during the performance.

EVERYTHING went lovely and it was a howling success, until Alkali Ike appeared on the scene with his revolver loaded with blank cartridges. Behind the bar on a shelf was a long line of bottles. Alkali Ike was supposed to start on the left of this line and break six of the bottles by firing at them with his revolver. At each shot from Alakli's pistol a man behind the scenes would hit one of the bottles with his entrenching tool handle and smash it, to give the impression that Alkali was a good shot.

Alkali Ike started in and aimed at the right of the line of bottles instead of the left, and the poor boob behind the scenes started breaking the bottles on the left, and then the box-holders turned loose; but outside of this little fiasco the performance was a huge success.

New troops were constantly coming through, and for six performances we had the "S.R.O." sign suspended.

So you see, Mr. Atkins has his fun mixed in with his hardships, and contrary to popular belief, the rank and file of the British Army in the trenches is one big happy family.

One Big Happy Family

I FOUND Tommy to be the best of mates and a gentleman through and through. He never thinks of knocking his officers. If one makes a costly mistake and Tommy pays with his blood, there is no general condemnation of the officer. He is just pitied.

But the average English officer is a good sport, he will sit on a fire step and listen respectfully to Private Jones' theory of how the war should be conducted. This war is gradually crumbling the once unsurmountable wall of caste.

You would be convinced of this if you could see King George go among his men on an inspecting tour under fire, or pause before a little wooden cross in some shell-tossed field with tears in his eyes as he reads the inscription. And a little later perhaps bend over a wounded man on a stretcher, patting him on the head.

More than once in a hospital I have seen a titled Red Cross nurse fetching and carrying for a wounded soldier, perhaps the one who in civil life delivered the coal at her back door. Today she does not shrink from lighting his fag or even washing his grimy body.

It is amusing to notice the different characteristics of the Irish, Scotch and English soldiers. The Irish and Scotch are very impetuous, especially when it comes to bayonet fighting, while the Englishmen, though a trifle slower, thoroughly does his bit; he is more methodical and has the grip of a bulldog on a captured position. He is slower to think, that is the reason why he never knows when he is licked.

Twenty minutes before going over the top the English Tommy will sit on the fire step and thoroughly examine the mechanism of his rifle to see that it is in working order and will fire properly. After this examination he is satisfied and ready to meet the Boches.

But the Irishman or Scotchman sits on the fire step with his rifle and bayonet fixed between his knees. The butt of his rifle is sinking into the mud and the bolt couldn't be opened with a team of horses because it is so rusty. He spits on his sleeve and slowly polishes his bayonet. When this is done he also is ready to argue with Fritz.

Tommy divides the German army into three classes according to their fighting abilities. They rank as follows: Prussians, Bavarians, and Saxons.

When up against a Prussian regiment it is a case of keep your napper below the parapet and duck. A bang-bang all the time and a war is on. The Bavarians are little better, but the Saxons are fairly good sports and are willing occasionally to behave as gentlemen and take it easy, but you cannot trust any of them over long.

At one point of the line the trenches were about thirty-two yards apart. This sounds horrible, but in fact it was easy, because neither side could shell the enemy's front-line trench for fear shells would drop into their own. This eliminated artillery fire.

In these trenches when up against the Prussians and Bavarians, Tommy had a hot time of it, but when the Saxons "took over" it was a picnic, they would yell across that they were Saxons and would not fire. Both sides would sit on the parapet and carry on a conversation. This generally consisted of Tommy telling them how much he loved the Kaiser while the Saxons informed Tommy that King George was a particular friend of theirs.

When the Saxons were to be relieved by Prussians or Bavarians, they would yell this information across No Man's Land and Tommy would immediately tumble into his trench and keep his head down.

If an English regiment was to be relieved by the wild Irish, Tommy would tell the Saxons, and immediately a volley of "Donner und Blitzen's" could be heard, and it was Fritz's turn to get a crick in his back from stooping, and the people in Berlin would close their windows.

Usually when an Irishman takes over a trench he sticks his rifle over the top aimed in the direction of Berlin and engaged in what is known as the "mad minute." This consists of firing fifteen shots in a minute. He is not aiming at anything in particular,—just sending over each shot with a prayer, hoping that one of his strays will get some poor unsuspecting Fritz in the napper hundreds of yards behind the lines. It generally does; that's the reason the Boche hate the man from Erin's Isle.

Prisoners Needed

At Brigade Headquarters I happened to overhear a conversation between our G.O.C. (General Officer Commanding) and the Divisional Commander. From this conversation I learned that we were to bombard the German lines for eight days, and on the first of July the "Big Push" was to commence.

In a few days orders were issued to that effect, and it was common property all along the line. On the afternoon of the eighth day of our strafeing, an order was passed down the trench that Old Pepper, our General, requested twenty volunteers to go over on a trench raid that night to try and get a few German prisoners for information purposes. I immediately volunteered for this job and went to the rear to give my name to the officers in charge of the raiding party. I was accepted, worse luck.

At 9:40 that night we reported to the Brigade Headquarters dugout to receive instructions from Old Pepper. After reaching this dugout we lined up in semi-circle around him, and he addressed us as follows:

"All I want you boys to do is to g

over to the German lines tonight, surprise them, secure a couple of prisoners, and return immediately. Our artillery has bombarded that section of the line for two days and personally I believe that that part of the German trench is unoccupied, so just get a couple of prisoners and return as quickly as possible."

We were ordered to black our faces and hands. You do this so that the light from the star shells will not reflect on your pale face. In a trench raid there is quite sufficient reason for your face to be pale. If you don't believe me, try it just once.

Then another reason for blacking your face and hands is that, after you have entered the German trench at night, "white face" means Germans, "black face" English. Coming around a traverse you see a white face in front of you. With a prayer and wishing Fritz "the best o' luck," you introduce him to your "persuader" or knuckle knife.

A little later we arrived at the communication trench named Whiskey Street, which led to the fire trench at the point we were to go over the top.

In our rear were four stretcher bearers and a Corporal of R.A.M.C. carrying a pouch containing medicines and first-aid appliances. Kind of a grim reminder to us that our expedition was not going to be exactly a picnic.

The stretcher bearers, no doubt, were hoping that, if they did have to carry anyone to the rear, he would be small and light. Perhaps they looked at me when wishing, because I could feel an uncomfortable, boring sensation between my shoulder blades. They got their wish all right.

Going up this trench, about every sixty yards or so we would pass a lonely sentry, who in a whisper would wish us "the best o' luck, mates." We would blind at him under our breaths; that Jonah phrase to us sounded very ominous.

Without any casualties the minstrel troop arrived in Suicide Ditch, the frontline trench. Previously, a wiring party of the Royal Engineers had cut a lane through our barbed wire to enable us to get out into No Man's Land without much trouble.

In No Man's Land

CRAWLING through this lane, our party of twenty took up an extended-order formation about one yard apart. We had a tap code arranged for our movements while in No Man's Land, because for various reasons it is not safe to carry on a heated conversation a few yards in front of Fritz's lines.

The star shells from the German lines were falling in front of us, therefore we were safe. After about twenty minutes we entered the star shell zone. A star shell from the German lines fell about five yards in the rear and to the right of me; we hugged the ground and held our breath until it burned out. The smoke from the star shell travelled along the ground and crossed the middle of our line. Some Tommy sneezed. The smoke had gotten up his nose. We crouched on the ground, cursing the offender under our breath, and waited

the volley that generally ensues when the Germans have heard a noise in No Man's Land. Nothing happened.

We received two taps and crawled forward slowly five yards, no doubt the officer believed what Old Pepper had said, "Personally I believe that that part of the German trench is unoccupied." By being careful and remaining motionless when the star shells fell behind us, we reached the German barbed wire without mishap.

Then the fun began. I was scared stiff as it is ticklish work cutting your way through wire when about thirty feet in front of you there is a line of Boches looking out into No Man's Land with their rifles lying across the parapet, straining every sense to see or hear what is going on in No Man's Land.

We had cut a lane about halfway through the wire when, down the center of our line, twang! went an improperly cut wire. We crouched down, cursing under our breath, trembling all over, our knees lacerated from the strands of the but barbed wire on the ground, waiting for a challenge and the inevitable volley of rifle fire. Nothing happened. I suppose the fellow who cut the barbed wire improperly was the one who had sneezed about half an hour previously.

The officer, in my opinion, at the noise of the wire should have given the four tap signal, which meant, "On your own, get back to your trenches as quickly as possible," but again he must have relied on the spiel that Old Pepper had given us. Anyway, we got careless, but not so careless that we sang patriotic songs or made any unnecessary noise.

During the intervals of falling star shells we carried on with our wire cutting until at last we succeeded in getting through the German barbed wire. At this point we were only ten feet from the German trenches.

If we were discovered, we were like rats in a trap. Our way was cut off unless we ran along the wire to the narrow lane we had cut through. With our hearts in our mouths we waited for the three-tap signal to rush the German trench. Three taps had gotten about halfway down the line when suddenly about ten to twenty German star shells were landed in the barbed wire to the rear of us, turning night into day and silhouetting us against the wall of light made by the flares. In the glaring light we were confronted by the following unpleasant scene.

ALL ALONG the German trench, at about three-foot intervals, stood a big Prussian guardsman with his rifle at the aim, and then we found out why we had not been challenged when the man sneezed and the barbed wire had been improperly cut. About three feet in front of the trench they had constructed a single fence of barbed wire and we knew our chances were one thousand to one of returning alive. We could not rush their trench on account of this second defence. Then in front of me the challenge, "Halt," given in English rang out, and one of the finest things I have ever heard on the western front took place.

From the middle of our line some Tommy answered the challenge with, "Aw, go to hell." It must have been the man who had sneezed or who had improperly cut the barbed wire; he wanted to show Fritz that he could die game.

"All Quiet . . ."

THEN came the volley. Machine guns were turned loose and several bombs were thrown in our rear. The Boche in front of me was looking down his sight. This fellow might have, under ordinary circumstances, been handsome, but when I viewed him from the front of his rifle he had the goblins of childhood imagination relegated to the shade.

Then came a flash in front of me, the flare of his rifle—and my head seemed to burst. A bullet had hit me on the left side of my face about half an inch from my eye, smashing the cheek bones. I put my hand to my face and fell forward, biting the ground and kicking my feet. I thought I was dying, but my past life did not unfold before me.

WHEN I came to the bullets were cracking overhead. I crawled a few feet back to the German barbed wire and in a stooping position I went down the line looking for the lane we had cut through. I had just turned down this lane when something inside me seemed to say, "Look around." I did so; a bullet caught me on the left shoulder. It did not hurt much, just felt as if someone had punched me in the back, and then my left side went numb.

My arm was dangling like a rag. But all fear had left me and I was consumed with rage and cursed the German trenches. With my right hand I felt in my tunic for my first aid or shell dressing. In feeling over my tunic my hand

ame in contact with one of the bombs
vhich I carried. Gripping it, I pulled
he pin out with my teeth and blindly
hrew it toward the German trench.

I must have been out of my head beause I was only ten feet from the trench
nd took a chance of being mangled if
he bomb had failed to go into the
rench. By the flare of the explosion of
he bomb, which luckily landed in their
rench, I saw one big Boche throw up
is arms and fall backwards, while his
fle flew into the air. Another one wilted
nd fell forward across the sandbags—
en blackness.

Realizing what a foolhardy and risky
hing I had done, I was again seized
vith a horrible fear. I dragged myself
o my feet and ran madly down the
ne through the barbed wire, stumbling
ver cut wires, tearing my uniform, and
cerating my hands and legs. Just as I
vas about to reach No Man's Land
gain, that same voice seemed to say
gain, "Turn around." I did so, when,
crack," another bullet caught me, this
me in the left shoulder about one half
ch away from the other wound. Then
was taps for me. The lights went out.

When I woke up I was in an ad-
anced first-aid post. I asked the doctor
we had taken the trench. "We took
e trench and the wood beyond, all
ght," he said, "and you fellows did
our bit; but, my lad that was thirty-
x hours ago. You were lying in No
Ian's land in that bally hole for a day
nd a half. It's a wonder you are alive."

He told me that out of the twenty
at were in the raiding party, seventeen
ere killed. The officer died of wounds

AFTER THE TRENCH RAID

in crawling back to our trench and I
was severely wounded, but one fellow returned without a scratch, without any
prisoners. No doubt this chap was the
one who had sneezed and improperly
cut the barbed wire.

In the official communique our trench
raid was described as follows:

"All quiet on the Western front, excepting in the neighborhood of Gomme-
court Wood, where one of our raiding
parties penetrated the German lines."

Until I die Old Pepper's words, "Personally I don't believe that that part of
the German trench is occupied," will
always come to me when I hear some
fellow trying to get away with a fishy
statement. I will judge it accordingly.

Duty Done

CAN'T help saying that the doctors,
sisters, and nurses in the English
ospitals, are angels on earth. I love
em all and can never repay the care
nd kindness shown to me. For the rest
f my life the Red Cross will be to me
e symbol of Faith, Hope and Charity.

After four months in the hospital, I
ent before an examining board and_

was discharged from the service of his
Britannic Majesty as "physically unfit
for further war service."

After my discharge I engaged passage
on the American liner, *New York,* and
after a stormy trip across the Atlantic,
one momentous day, in the haze of early
dawn I saw the Statue of Liberty looming over the port rail, and I wondered

if ever again I would go "over the top with the best o' luck and give them hell."

AND even then, though it may seem strange, I was really sorry not to be back in the trenches with my mates. War is not a pink tea but in a worthwhile cause like ours, mud, rats, cooties, shells, wounds or death itself, are far outweighed by the deep sense of satisfaction felt by the man who does his bit.

There is one thing which my experience taught me that might help the boy who may have to go. It is this—anticipation is far worse than realization. In civil life a man stands in awe of the man above him, wonders how he could ever fill his job. When the time comes he rises to the occasion, is up and at it, and is surprised to find how much more easily than he anticipated he fills his responsibilities. It is really so "out there."

He has nerve for the hardships; the interest of the work grips him; he finds relief in the fun and comradeship of the trenches and wins that best sort of happiness that comes with duty done.

Of Adversity

IT WAS a high speech of Seneca (after the manner of the Stoics), that, "the good things which belong to prosperity are to be wished, but the good things that belong to adversity are to be admired." (*"Bona rerum secundarum optabilia, adversarum mirabilia."*) Certainly, if miracles be the command over nature, they appear most in adversity. It is yet a higher speech of his than the other (much too high for a heathen), "It is true greatness to have in one the frailty of a man, and the security of a God." (*"Vere magnum habere fragilitatem hominis, securitatem Dei."*) This would have done better in poesy, where transcendencies are more allowed; and the poets, indeed, have been busy with it; for it is in effect the thing which is figured in that strange fiction of the ancient poets, which seemeth not to be without mystery; nay, and to have some approach to the state of a Christian, "that Hercules, when he went to unbind Prometheus (by whom human nature is represented), sailed the length of the great ocean in an earthen pot or pitcher," lively describing Christian resolution, that saileth in the frail bark of the flesh through the waves of the world. But to speak in a mean, the virtue of prosperity is temperance, the virtue of adversity if fortitude, which in morals is the more heroical virtue. Prosperity is the blessing of the Old Testament, adversity is the blessing of the New, which carrieth the greater benediction, and the clearer revelation of God's favour. Yet even in the Old Testament, if you listen to David's harp, you shall hear as many hearse-like airs as carols; and the pencil of the Holy Ghost hath labored more in describing the afflictions of Job than the felicities of Solomon. Prosperity is not without many fears and distastes; and adversity is not without comforts and hopes. We see in needleworks and embroideries, it is more pleasing to have a lively work upon a sad and solemn ground, than to have a dark and melancholy work upon a lightsome ground: judge, therefore, of the pleasure of the heart by the pleasure of the eye. Certainly virtue is like precious odours, most fragrant when they are incensed, or crushed: for prosperity doth best discover vice, but adversity doth best discover virtue.

—*Francis Bacon, Viscount St. Albans*

Theodore Dreiser

AN AMERICAN TRAGEDY

WAS it an accident? Murder? Suicide? Theodore Dreiser builds the flesh and blood and tears about an actual murder trial which screamed at us through the newspaper headlines several years ago. It is a human tale of love and desire, of hope and heartbreak, of crime and punishment which has been acclaimed in Europe and America as one of the greatest American novels of our generation.

Fifteen Dollars to Begin

IT WAS near the dinner hour and by degrees the Griffiths family were assembling. On this occasion the preparations were more elaborate than usual, owing to the fact that Mr. amuel Griffiths had just returned from conference of shirt and collar manufacurers in Chicago. He had concluded everal agreements which spelled trade armony and prosperity for at least one ear and he was inclined to feel on ood terms with the world.

"I had a curious experience in Chicago is time," he observed suddenly to his ife and three children. "Something I ink you will be interested in."

"Spin the big news, Dad," said his dest son, Gilbert.

"Well, while I was in Chicago at the nion League Club, I met a young man ho is related to us, a cousin of you ree children, by the way, the eldest n of my brother Asa, who is out in enver now, I understand. I haven't en or heard from him in over thirty ars."

"Not the one who is a preacher somehere, Daddy?" inquired Bella.

"Yes, the preacher," continued Griffhs, dubiously. "Well, his son is a very teresting young man, I think,— out your own age, I should say, Gil. e hasn't much of a job; he's only a ell-hop in the Union League Club, present. But he is a very pleasant and ntlemanly sort of boy, I will say. I as quite taken with him. In fact, be-

cause he told me there wasn't much opportunity for advancement where he was, and that he would like to get into something where there was more chance to do something and be somebody. I told him that if he wanted to come on here and try his luck with us, we might do a little something for him—give him a chance to show what he could do, at least."

"Well, I think that's very kind of you, father," observed Mrs. Griffiths, pleasantly and diplomatically. "I hope he proves satisfactory."

"And there's another thing," added Griffiths wisely and sententiously. "I don't expect this young man, so long as he is in my employ and just because he's a nephew of mine, to be treated differently to any other employee in the factory. He's coming here to work—not play. And while he is here, trying, I don't expect any of you to pay him any social attention—not the slightest. He didn't impress me as the sort of a boy who would come here with any notions that he would be put on an equal footing with us anyway."

And so it was decided that Clyde might be inducted into the very bottom of the business—the basement of the Griffiths plant, where the shrinking of all fabrics used in connection with the manufacture of collars was brought about. And since he must support himself in *some form* not *absolutely incompatible* with the standing of the Griffiths family of Lycurgus, New York, it was decided to pay him fifteen dollars.

The Basement World

AT FIRST sight, and considering what his general dreams in connection with this industry were, Clyde was inclined to rebel. For the type of youth and man he saw were in his estimation rather below the type of individuals he hoped to find here—individuals neither so intelligent nor so alert as those employed by the Union League Club by a long distance. At the same time, their spare and practical manner of dressing struck dead at one blow any thought of refinement in connection with the work. How unfortunate that his lack of training would not permit his being put to office work or something like that upstairs.

In addition, not knowing just what Clyde was, or what his coming might mean to their positions, his fellow workers were inclined to be dubious and suspicious of him. After a week or two, however, coming to understand that Clyde was a nephew of the president, a cousin of the secretary of the company, and hence not likely to remain here long in any menial capacity, they were jealous and suspicious of him in another way. For after all, Clyde was not one of them and under such circumstances could not be. He might smile and be civil enough—yet he was part of the rich and superior class and every poor man knew what that meant. The poor must stand together everywhere.

In so far as his life at his boarding house went, he was not so very happily placed, there, either. For that was but a commonplace rooming and boarding house, which drew to it, at best, such conservative mill and business types as looked on work and their wages, and the notions of the middle-class religious world of Lycurgus as most essential to the order and well being of the world. From the point of view of entertainment or gayety, it was in the main a very dull place.

And so for all of five weeks Clyde was allowed to drift along in his basement world wondering what was intended for him. Then when he had finally decided that he would always be excluded from his great relatives he was invited to a Griffiths' family meal.

He decided to make the best of this opportunity, and accordingly, on the appointed evening, his nerves decidedly taut, he set out for the Griffiths' residence. And when he reached the main gate, a large, arched wrought-iron affair he was filled with a quaking sense of adventure.

The beauty! The ease! What member of his own immediate family had ever dreamed that his uncle lives thus! The grandeur! And his own parents so wretched—so poor, preaching on the streets of Denver. Conducting a mission

For consider who the Griffiths were here, as opposed to "who" the Griffiths were in Denver. The enormous difference! A thing to be as carefully concealed as possible.

HE SAW Mrs. Griffiths approaching him. "My nephew, I believe," she smiled.

"Yes," replied Clyde simply, and because of his nervousness. "I am Clyde Griffiths."

"I'm very glad to see you and to welcome you to our home," began Mrs. Griffiths with a certain amount of aplomb which years of contact with the local high world had given her at last. She arranged herself on one of the large divans before the fire and Clyde rather awkwardly seated himself at a respectful distance from her. Mrs. Griffiths was about to ask after his mother and father when they were interrupted by Samuel Griffiths who now approached.

"Well, so here you are, eh? They've placed you, I believe, without my ever seeing you."

"Yes, sir," replied Clyde, very deferentially and half bowing.

"Like it where you are now?" the older man observed condescendingly.

"Well, yes, sir, that is, I wouldn't say that I like it exactly," replied Clyde quite honestly. "But I don't mind it. It's as good as any other way to begin, I suppose." The thought in his mind at the moment was that he would like to impress on his uncle that he was cut out for something better.

"Well, that's the proper spirit," commented Samuel Griffiths, pleased.

From this Clyde wondered how long he was to be left in that dim world below stairs. At this moment a maid announced that supper was served.

Clyde was not a little troubled and embarrassed by a chain of questions which flowed rather heavily and solemnly from Samuel Griffiths or his wife about the nature of his family life. Fortunately, Bella came in soon with two other girls. One of them was introduced as Sondra Finchley, as smart and vain and sweet a girl as Clyde had ever laid his eyes upon—so different to any he had ever known and so superior. Indeed her effect on him was electric —thrilling—arousing in him a curiously tinging sense of what it was to want and not to have—to wish to win and yet to feel, almost agonizingly, that he was not destined to win even a glance from her. It tortured and flustered him.

Sondra was pleased to note that he was obviously stricken with her, which was her due, as she invariably decided in connection with youths thus smitten. But having thus decided, she concluded that she need pay no attention to him, for the present anyway. He was too easy.

Clyde, left quite to himself for the moment, was thinking what an easy, delightful world this must be—this local society. For here they were without a care, apparently, between any of them. All of their talk was of houses being built, horses they were riding, friends they had met, places they were going.

And Bella, his cousin, trifling around with these girls in the beautiful homes of this street while he was shunted away in a small third-floor room with no place to go. And with only fifteen dollars a week to live on. And in the morning he would be working in the basement again, while these girls were rising to more pleasure. And out in Denver were his parents with their small lodging house and mission, which he dared not even describe accurately here.

Up the Ladder

One Saturday in the spring several weeks after the Griffiths' supper, Samuel Griffiths decided to make a complete inspection of his factory. Reaching the shrinking department, he observed for the first time with some dismay, Clyde in his undershirt and trousers working at the feeding end of two of the shrinking racks. And recalling how very neat and generally presentable he had appeared at his house but a few weeks before, he was decidedly disturbed by the contrast. And the sight of Clyde here, looking so much like Gilbert working with these men, tended to impress upon him more sharply than at any time before the fact that Clyde was his nephew, and that he ought not to be compelled to continue at his very menial form of work any longer.

Clyde was called to Gilbert's office very soon afterwards.

"I want to discuss with you a temporary vacancy that has occurred in one of our departments upstairs," Gilbert began. "My father and I think that you may be able to fill it."

"This plant is practically operated by women from cellar to roof," Gilbert explained. "On that account every one in whom we entrust any responsibility around here must be known to us as to their moral and religious character. Don't think that because you're related to us that we won't hold you strictly to account for everything that goes on up there and for your conduct. We want to be sure that the women who are working here are going to receive civil treatment always."

And Clyde replied: "Yes, I understand. I think that's right." His present mood was that, because of his abnormal interest in girls, it would be better if he had nothing to do with them at all, never spoke to any of them, kept a very distant and cold attitude, such as Gilbert was holding toward him. It must be so, at least if he wished to keep his place here. And he was now determined to keep it and to conduct himself always as his cousin wished.

"Very good," said Gilbert. "Your salary from now on will be twenty-five dollars, and I want you to dress neat and clean so that you will be an example to the other men who have charge of departments."

He arose coldly and distantly, but Clyde, very much encouraged and enthused by the sudden jump in salary, as well as the admonition in regard to dressing well, felt very grateful toward his cousin.

He bustled out of the plant with a jaunty stride, resolved to be cool, cold, even, and if necessary severe, where these girls of this department were concerned.

Girls and a Girl

CLYDE was not so very favorably impressed with the type of girl who was working in his department. For the most part, as he saw them, they were of a heavy and rather unintelligent company. But among the extras that were brought to him during the succeeding days, finally came one who interested Clyde more than any girl whom he had seen so far. She was, as he decided on sight, more intelligent and pleasing— more spiritual—though apparently not less vigorous, if more gracefully proportioned. Her name was Roberta Alden.

The reasons why a girl of Roberta's type should be seeking employment with Griffiths and Company at this time and in this capacity are of some point. For, somewhat after the fashion of Clyde in relation to his family and his life, she too considered her life a great disappointment. She was the daughter of Titus Alden, farmer in a small town some fifty miles north.

As for the parents of Roberta, they were excellent examples of that native type of Americanism which resists facts and reveres illusion. Titus Alden was one of that vast company of individuals who are born, pass through and die out of the world without ever quite getting any one thing straight.

In so far as the daughter of these parents was concerned, and in the face of natural gifts which fitted her for something better than this world from which she derived, she was still, in part at least, a reflection of the prevailing religious and moral notions. At the same time, because of a warm, imaginative sensuous temperament, she was filled with the world-old dream of all of Eve's daughters that her beauty and charm might some day smite bewitchingly and irresistibly the soul of a given man or men.

And so it was that Roberta, after encountering Clyde and sensing the superior world in which she imagined he moved, and being so taken with the charm of his personality was seized with the very virus of ambition and unrest that afflicted him. And every day that she went to the factory now she could not help but feel that his eyes were upon her in a quiet, seeking and yet doubtful way.

DAY after day and because he was so much alone he was conscious that a strong chemic or temperamental pull was asserting itself. He could no longer keep his eyes off of her—or she, hers from him. There were evasive and yet strained and feverish eye-flashes between them.

Her pretty mouth, her lovely big eyes, her radiant and yet so often shy and evasive smile. And, oh, she had such pretty arms—such a trim, lithe, sentient, quick figure and movements. If he only dared be friendly with her—venture to lk with and then see her somewhere fterwards—if she only would and if he nly dared. Confusion. Aspiration. Hours of burning and yearning.

How unfair and ridiculous for the Griffiths to insist that a man in his posiion should not associate with a girl uch as Roberta, for instance, and just ecause she worked in the mill.

On the third Sunday afternoon in July, Clyde, as lonely and rebellious, was addling about in a dark blue canoe long the south bank of a lake about a aile and a half from Lycurgus. He ounded a point studded with a clump f trees and bushes and covering a hallow where were scores of water lilies float. And on the bank to the left was a girl standing. It wasn't Roberta! It couldn't be! Yes, it was.

"My, Miss Alden! It is you, isn't it?" he called. "I was wondering whether it was. I couldn't be sure from out there."

"Why, yes it is," she laughed, puzzled, and again just the least bit abashed by the reality of him. For in spite of her obvious pleasure at seeing him again, only thinly repressed for the first moment or two, she was on the instant beginning to be troubled by her thoughts in regard to him—the difficulties that contact with him seemed to prognosticate. For this meant contact and friendship, maybe, and she was no longer in any mood to resist him, whatever people might think.

The Fever of Youth

THE outcome of that afternoon was so wonderful for both that for days hereafter neither could cease thinking bout it or marveling that anything so omantic and charming should have rought them together so intimately rhen both were considering that it was ot wise for either to know the other ny better than employee and superior.

This meeting was but the prelude, as oth Clyde and Roberta realized, to a eries of contacts and rejoicings which vere to extend over an indefinite period. hey had found love. They were deciously happy, whatever the problems ttending this present realization might e.

But all this was preliminary to troubles nd strains and fears which took their ise from difficulties which sprang up mmediately afterwards. For once she ad come to a complete emotional understanding with Clyde, she saw no way of meeting him except clandestinely.

Both struggled in vain against the greater intimacy which each knew that the other was desirous of yielding to, and eventually, so yielding, looked forward to the approaching night with an eagerness which was as a fever embodying a fear. Yet the thing once done, a wild convulsive pleasure motivated both. Yet, not without, before all this, an exaction on the part of Roberta to the effect that never—come what might—would he desert her, since without his aid she would be helpless. Yet, with no direct statement as to marriage. And he, so completely overcome and swayed by his desire, thoughtlessly protesting that he never would—never.

And Roberta, peering nervously into the blank future, wondering what—how, in any case, by any chance, Clyde should change, or fail her. Yet the night returning, her mood once more veering, and she as well as he hurrying to meet somewhere—only later, in the silence of the middle night, to slip into this unlighted room which was proving so much more of a Paradise than either might ever know again.

Social Possibilities

AND then, one November evening as Clyde was walking home, an event ccurred which was destined to bring bout a chain of events unforeseen.

A closed car of great size and solidity stopped directly in front of him. The chauffeur stepped down and opened the door and Clyde instantly recognized

Sondra Finchley leaning forward in the car. At the same time, as she thought, she saw Gilbert Griffiths approaching along the sidewalk and so she called.

"Oh, hello. Walking tonight? Why don't you ride along with me."

However, in a moment Sondra realized that she had made a mistake. "Oh, pardon me, you're Mr. Clyde Griffiths, I see now. I thought you were Gilbert. I couldn't quite make you out in the light."

Then Sondra, seeing at once that Clyde was if anything much more attractive than his cousin and obviously greatly impressed with her charms unbent sufficiently to say with a charming smile: "But that's all right. Won't you get in, please, and let me take you where you are going. Oh, I wish you would. . . . I will be so glad to take you."

"Why, yes, of course," he said jerkily, "that is, if you want me to. I understand how it was." There was an admiring, pleading light in his eyes which now quite charmed her. What a pleasing young man. So different from Gilbert.

"Do you expect to be in Lycurgus all winter?" she asked when he had settled himself in the car.

"Oh, yes. I'm quite sure of it. I hope to be anyhow," he added, quite yearningly, his eyes expressing his meaning completely.

"Well, perhaps, then I'll see you again somewhere, some time."

She nodded and gave him her fingers.

"Good night! Good night!" she called as the car sprang away and Clyde, looking after it wondered if he would ever see her again so closely and intimately.

THE effect of this so casual contact was really disrupting in more senses than one. For now in spite of his comfort in and satisfaction with Roberta once more and in this positive and to him entrancing way, was posed the whole question of his social possibilities here. And that strangely enough by the one girl of this upper level who had most materialized and magnified for him the meaning of that upper level itself The beautiful Sondra Finchley!

Ah, to know this perfect girl more intimately! To be looked upon by her with favor, made, by reason of that favor, a part of that fine world to which she belonged. Was he not a Griffiths— as good looking as Gilbert Griffiths any day? And as attractive if he only had as much money—or a part of it even.

The devil! He would not go around to Roberta's this evening. He would trump up some excuse—tell her in the morning that he had been called upon by his uncle or cousin to do some work. He could not and would not go, feeling as he did just now.

And so it was that Clyde, returning from the factory one early December evening about two weeks after his encounter with Sondra, was surprised by the sight of a cream-colored note leaning against the mirror of his dresser. He tore it open and drew out a card which read:

"Dear Mr. Griffiths. Thought you might like to come to the Winter Dinner Dance on December 4th. It will be quite informal. And I'm sure you'll like it. If so, will you let Jill Trumbull know? Sondra Finchley."

Dark Knowledge

SOMETHING of this latest mood in him reached Roberta now, even as she listened to his words and felt his caresses. They failed to convey sincerity. His manner was too restless, his embraces too apathetic, his tone without real tenderness.

One of the things that Roberta soon found was that her intuitive notions in regard to all this were not without speedy substantiation, for there were last moment changes of plan and unannounced absences. For Clyde was now hopelessly enamored of Sondra and by no means to be changed, or moved even, by anything in connection with Roberta Sondra was too wonderful!

Subsequent to the Winter Dance he

"Why Clyde! What is it? I never saw you look like this before."

Illustration for Theodore Dreiser's
"AN AMERICAN TRAGEDY"

as all too frequently appearing at the factory of a morning with explanatory statements that because of some invitation from the Griffiths, Harriets, or others, he would not be able to keep an engagement with her that night that he had made a day or two before. And later, on three different occasions, because Sondra had called for him in her car, he had departed without a word, trusting to what might come to him the next day in the way of an excuse.

Then in addition to her own troubled conclusions in regard to Clyde, there had sprung up over night the dark and constraining knowledge that she was pregnant. And for four days preceding this Clyde had not even been near her. And

his attitude at the factory was more remote and indifferent than ever.

For the first time forsaken in this rather cold and indifferent way, in such a crisis as this, Roberta returned to her room with her thoughts and fears, more stricken and agonized than ever before she had been in all her life.

Clyde was the one who had brought her to this difficulty, and against her will, and he had so definitely assured her that nothing would happen. And now she must lie here alone and worry, not a single person to turn to, except him, and he was leaving her for others. And he had caused it all! Was that quite right?

"Oh, Clyde! Clyde!"

The Impending Disaster

Two long, dreary, terrifying months went by without hope for her. She was convinced that apart from mediating and thinking of some way to escape his responsibility, Clyde had no real intention of marrying her, still, like Clyde, she drifted, fearing to act really. For in several conferences following that in which she had indicated that she expected him to marry her, he had reiterated, if vaguely, a veiled threat that in case she appealed to his uncle he would not be compelled to marry her, after all, for he would go elsewhere.

In the very teeth of his grave dilemma Clyde continued to pursue the enticing dream in connection with Sondra—the dark situation in connection with Roberta seeming no more at moments than a dark cloud which shadowed this other. And hence nightly, or as often as the exigencies of his still unbroken connection with Roberta would permit, he was availing himself of such opportunities as his flourishing connections now afforded.

And it was the contrast presented by these two scenes which finally determined for him the fact that he would never marry Roberta—never.

One night he purchased a paper hoping via the local news of all whom he knew, to divert his mind for the time

being. There, upon the first page of the *Times-Union* of Albany, was an item which read:

ACCIDENTAL DOUBLE TRAGEDY AT PASS LAKE—UPTURNED CANOE AND FLOATING HATS REVEAL PROBABLE LOSS OF TWO LIVES AT RESORT NEAR PITTSFIELD—UNIDENTIFIED BODY OF GIRL RECOVERED—THAT OF COMPANION MISSING.

HE THREW the paper down, little concerned at first, and turned to other things. But later as he was putting out the light before getting into bed and thinking of the complicated problem which his own life presented, he was struck by the thought that if he and Roberta were in a small boat somewhere and it should capsize at the very time, say, of this dreadful complication which was so harassing him? What an escape?

On the other hand—hold—not so fast!—for could a man even think of such a solution in connection with so difficult a problem as his without committing a crime in his heart, really—a horrible crime? And yet—and yet.

And yet this loss.

This impending disaster.

How to avoid that and win Sondra after all.

How, how, how?

The solution suggested by the item in the *Times-Union* again thrust itself forward, psychogenetically, born of his own turbulent, eager and disappointed seeking. And hence persisting.

Go to the lake.

Pick a boat that will upset easily—one with a round bottom.

And if necessary strike a light blow, so as to stun her—no more—so that falling in the water, she will drown the more easily.

Assume that you will be successful.

And whisper, whisper—let your language be soft, your tone tender, loving even. It must be, if you are to win her to your will now.

So the Efrit of his own darker self.

Cataclysmic Moments

WHY was he waiting now?

What was the matter with him, anyhow?

Why was he waiting?

At this cataclysmic moment, and in the face of the utmost, the most urgent need of action, a sudden palsy of the will—of courage—of hate or rage sufficient; and with Roberta from her seat in the stern of the boat gazing at his troubled and then suddenly distorted and fulgurous, yet weak and even unbalanced face—a face of a sudden, instead of angry, ferocious, demoniac—confused and all but meaningless in its registration of a balanced combat between fear and a harried and restless and yet self-repressed desire to do—to do—to do—

And in the meantime his eyes—the pupils growing momentarily larger and more lurid; his face and body and hands tense and contracted—the stillness of his position.

And Roberta, suddenly noticing the strangeness of it all, exclaimed: "Why Clyde! Clyde! What is it? Why, I never saw you look like this before. What is it?" And suddenly rising or rather leaning forward, and by crawling along the even keel, attempting to comfort him.

As she drew near him, seeking to take his hand in hers, she flung out at her—not with any intention to do other than free himself of her—her touch—her pleading—consoling sympathy—her presence forever—God!

Yet (the camera still unconsciously held tight) pushing at her with so much vehemence as not only to strike her lips and nose and chin with it, but to throw her back sidewise which caused the boat to career to the very water's edge.

AND then he rose and reaching half to assist or recapture her, half to apologize for the unintended blow, capsized the boat. And the left wale of the boat struck Roberta on the head as she sank and then rose for the first time, her frantic, contorted face turned to Clyde, who by now had righted himself. For she was stunned, horrorstruck, unintelligible with pain and fear—her lifelong fear of water and drowning and the blow he had so accidentally and all but unconsciously administered.

"Help! Help!

"Oh, my God, I'm drowning, I'm drowning. Help! Oh, my God!

"Clyde, Clyde!"

And then the voice at his ear!

"But this—this—is not this that which you have been thinking and wishing for this while—you in your great need? And behold! For despite your fear, your cowardice, this—this—has been done for you. An accident—an accident—an unintentional blow on your part is now saving you the labor of what you sought and yet did not have the courage to do.

"Wait—wait—ignore the pity of that appeal. There! It is over. She is sinking now. You will never, never see her alive any more—never. And there is your own hat upon the water—as you wished. And upon the boat, clinging to that rowlock a veil belonging to her. Leave it. Will it not show that this was an accident?"

And apart from that, nothing—a few ripples—the peace and solemnity of this wondrous scene.

ly 9th

MYSTERY IN GIRL'S DEATH

DY FOUND YESTERDAY IN ADIRONDACK
LAKE

MAN COMPANION MISSING

ugust 6th

OY SLAYER OF WORKING-GIRL SWEETHEART
INDICATED CLYDE GRIFFITHS, NEPHEW
OF WEALTHY COLLAR MANUFACTURER OF
LYCURGUS, NEW YORK, CHARGED WITH
THE KILLING OF MISS ROBERTA ALDEN AT
BIG BITTEN LAKE IN THE ADIRONDACKS
ON JULY 8 LAST.

ETURNED INDICTMENT CHARGING MURDER
IN THE FIRST DEGREE

IN SPITE OF ALMOST OVERWHELMING CIR-
CUMSTANTIAL EVIDENCE

PLEADED NOT GUILTY.

REMANDED FOR TRIAL SET FOR OCTOBER 15

STUNNED AND DROWNED HIS WORKING-
GIRL SWEETHEART.

NO RELATIVE HAS COME FORWARD.

November 8th

PROSECUTION IN GRIFFITHS' CASE CLOSES
WITH IMPRESSIVE DELUGE OF TESTIMONY

MOTIVE AS WELL AS METHOD HAMMERED
HOME

DESTRUCTIVE MARKS ON FACE AND HEAD
SHOWN TO CORRESPOND WITH ONE SIDE
OF CAMERA.

The Verdict

FINALLY many small and dangerous and difficult points having been ridged or buttressed or fended against s well as each side could, it became Clyde's lawyer's duty to say his last word. And to this he gave an entire day, most carefully retracing and emphasizing very point which tended to show how, almost unconsciously, if not quite innocently, Clyde had fallen into the relationship with Roberta which had ended o disastrously for both. Mental and moral cowardice, as he now reiterated, inflamed or at least operated on by various lacks in Clyde's early life, plus new opportunities such as previously had never appeared to be within his grasp, had affected his *"perhaps too pliable and sensual and impractical and dreaming mind."*

No doubt he had not been fair to Miss Alden. He had not. But on the other hand he had not proved ultimately so cruel or vile as the prosecution would have the public and this honorable jury believe. Many men were far more cruel in their love life than this young boy had ever dreamed of being, and, of course, they were not necessarily hung for that.

And in passing technically on whether this boy had actually committed the crime charged, it was incumbent upon this jury to see that no generous impulse relating to what this poor girl might

have suffered be permitted to sway them to the decision that this youth committed the crime stated in the indictment.

AND then the District Attorney, blazing with his conviction that Clyde was a murderer of the coldest and blackest type, and spending an entire day in riddling the "spider's tissue of lies and unsupported statements" with which the defense was hoping to divert the minds of the jury from the unbroken and unbreakable chain of amply substantiated evidence wherewith the prosecution had proved this "bearded man" to be the "red-handed murderer" that he was. And with hours spent in retracing the statements of the various witnesses. And other hours in denouncing Clyde, or re-telling the bitter miseries of Roberta —so much so that the jury, as well as the audience, was on the verge of tears.

And then the judge finally instructing the jury: "Gentlemen—all evidence is in a strict sense, more or less circumstantial, whether consisting of facts which permit the inference of guilt or whether given by an eyewitness. It must be remembered that evidence is not to be discredited or decried because it is circumstantial. It may often be more reliable evidence than direct evidence.

"If the jury finds that Roberta Alden accidentally or involuntarily fell out of the boat and that the defendant made no attempt to rescue her, that does not make the defendant guilty and the jury must find the defendant 'not guilty.' On the other hand, if the jury finds that the defendant in any way, intentionally, there and then brought about or contributed to that fatal accident, either by a blow or otherwise, it must find the defendant guilty."

And then, that point having been reached, the jury rose and filed from the room.

When the jury door swung open again a few hours later, Clyde knew the verdict at once because not one of the twelve looked at him.

"Gentlemen of the jury, have yo agreed on a verdict?" asked the clerk.

And the foreman announced: "W have. We find the defendant guilty murder in the first degree."

"Convicted! Convicted!" And tha meant that he must die. In that larg crowd out there there was not one wh did not believe him totally and con pletely guilty—Roberta—her determina tion to make him marry her—her gian fear of exposure—had dragged hir down to this. To conviction. To deatl Away from all he had longed for—awa from all he had dreamed he migh possess. And Sondra! Sondra! Not word! Not a word!

A Thousand Deaths

THE "death house" in Auburn prison was one of those crass maintenances of human insensitiveness and stupidity for which no one was really responsible. And to the end that a man, once condemned by a jury would be compelled to suffer not alone the death for which his sentence called, but a thousand others before that. The arrangement of the death house as well as the rules governing the lives and actions of the inmates, was sufficient to bring about this torture, willy-nilly.

It was a room thirty by fifty feet, of stone and concrete and steel, and surmounted some thirty feet from the floor by a skylight. Presumably an improvement over an older and worse death house, with which it was still connected by a door, it was divided lengthwise by a broad passage, along which, on the ground floor, were twelve cells, six on a side and eight by ten each and facing each other. And above again a second tier of what were known as balcony cells—five on a side.

Besides, by housing all together in two such tiers as were here, it placed upon each convict the compulsion of enduring all the horrors of all the vicious, morbid or completely collapsed and despairing temperaments about him. No true privacy of any kind. By day—a

blaze of light pouring through the over arching skylight above the walls. B night—glistening incandescents of larg size and power which flooded each noo and cranny of the various cells.

Worse yet, and productive of perhap the most grinding and destroying of al the miseries here—the transverse passag leading between the old death house an the execution chamber. For this was th scene of the tragedy that was so regu larly enacted—the final business of exe cution.

When the fatal hour for any one ha at last arrived, every prisoner was actu ally if not intentionally compelled t hear the final preparations—the remova of the condemned man and the fina and perhaps weeping visit of a mother son, daughter, father.

AT FIRST, of course, Clyde sensed littl if anything of all this. In so far a his first day was concerned, he had bu tasted the veriest spoonful of it all.

Then came the executions, one by one, and he found to his invariable horror, no one ever became used to such things there; farmhand Mowrer for the slaying of his former employer; office Riordan for the slaying of his wife— and a fine upstanding officer too but a minute before his death. And after him

Larry Donahue, the overseas soldier—with a grand call—just before the door closed behind: "Good-by, boys. Good luck."

And after him again—but, oh—that was so hard; so much closer to Clyde—so depleting to his strength to think of bearing this deadly life here without Miller Nicholson. For after five months in which they had been able to walk and talk and call to each other from time to time from their cells—and Nicholson had begun to advise him as to books to read.

And Clyde thereafter—lonely—terribly so. Now there was no one here —no one—in whom he was interested. He could only sit and read—and think —or pretend to be interested in what these others said, for he could not really be interested in what they said.

And so after a long and dreary summer had passed (soon a year since he had entered here) a note was passed into his cell. Although it was typewritten with no date nor place save on the envelope, which was postmarked New York—yet he sensed it might be from Sondra. His hand trembled slightly as he opened it. And then reading—over and over and over—during many days thereafter: "Clyde—This is so that you will not think that some one once dear to you has utterly forgotten you. She has suffered much, too. And though she can never understand how you could have done what you did, still, even now, although she is never to see you again, she is not without sorrow and sympathy and wishes you freedom and happiness."

But no signature—no trace of her own handwriting. She was afraid to sign her name and she was too remote from him in her mood now to let him know where she was.

His last hope—the last trace of his dream vanished. Forever! It was at that moment, as when night at last falls upon the faintest remaining gleam of dusk in the west. A dim, weakening tinge of pink—and then the dark.

He seated himself on his cot. The wretched stripes of his uniform and his gray felt shoes took his eye. A felon. These stripes. These shoes. This cell.

And for this he had sought so desperately to disengage himself from Roberta—even to the point of deciding to slay her. This! This! He toyed with the letter, then held it quite still.

And then in the dark of a midwinter morning with the guards coming, first to slit his right trouser leg for the metal plate and then going to draw the curtains before the cells: "It is time, I fear. Courage, my son." It was the chaplain who was addressing Clyde.

Now he was getting up from his cot. He had been listening to the reading of the Bible. "Let not your heart be troubled. Yet believe in God—believe also in me." And then the final walk.

But various voices—as Clyde entered the first door to cross to the chair room calling: "Good-by, Clyde." And Clyde, with enough earthly thought and strength to reply: "Good-by, all." His feet were walking, but automatically, it seemed. And he was conscious of that familiar shuffle—shuffle—as they pushed him on and on toward that door.

Now it was here; now it was being opened. There it was—at last—the chair he had so often seen in his dreams—to which he was compelled to go. He was being pushed toward it—into that—on —on—through the door which was opened to receive him—but which was as quickly closed again on all the earthly life he had ever known.

EVERYBODY has his own theatre, in which he is manager, actor, prompter, playwright, scene-shifter, boxkeeper, doorkeeper, all in one, and audience into the bargain.—*J. C. and A. W. Hare.*

HERMANN RAUSCHNING

THE VOICE OF DESTRUCTION

UNTIL recently everyone thought that "Mein Kampf" was a clear statement of Hitler's aims. But current events and this book indicate that he was holding back much. "The Voice of Destruction" is practically a verbatim report of the author's private conversations with Hitler between 1932 and 1935. Eight years ago Hitler explained the tactics of the "New War" which astonished the Allies and mapped out his designs on America. Former confidants of Der Führer don't get out of Germany alive, but Rauschning did. Thus his revelations of Hitler's personality and ideas are probably the most authentic on record.

Eight Years Before

"THE next war will be quite different from the last world war. Infantry attacks and mass formations are obsolete. Interlocked frontal struggles lasting for years on petrified fronts will not return. I guarantee that. They were a degenerate form of war."

Hitler gazed fixedly across from the little glass veranda of his mountain eyrie to the precipitous wall opposite. It was an August morning in 1932.

"Is it true, Herr Hitler, that Germany has prepared secret inventions which will break down every resistance, inventions against which even the French Maginot Line will be defenseless?" The Danzig *Gauleiter* (district leader) Albert Forster indicated by a sign to me that he had now led Hitler into his favorite subject.

"All armies have secret inventions. I am skeptical as to their value," Hitler returned.

"But the penetrative power of our new S-munitions. Isn't it true that electrical warfare yields entirely new possibilities of attack?" Forster persisted. "And the new poison gases and bacterial warfare? Will bacteria be used as a weapon in the next war?"

"A nation denied its rights may use any weapon, even bacterial warfare." Hitler's voice rose. "I have no scruples, and I will use whatever weapon I require. The new poison gases are horrible.

But there is no difference between a slow death in barbed-wire entanglements and the agonized death of a gassed man or one poisoned by bacteria. In the future, whole nations will stand against each other, not merely hostile armies. We shall undermine the physical health of our enemies as we shall break down their moral resistance. I can well imagine that there is a future for bacterial warfare. We have not quite perfected it yet, but experiments are being made. I hear that they are very promising. But the use of this weapon is limited. Its significance lies in wearing down the enemy *before* the war. Our real wars will in fact all be fought before military operations begin. I can quite imagine that we might control Britain in this way. Or America."

"Do you believe, my Führer, that America will again interfere in European affairs?" asked the third of the company, the young leader of the then Danzig S.A.

"Certainly we shall prevent it from trying again," was the reply. "There are new weapons which are effective in such cases. America is permanently on the brink of revolution. It will be a simple matter for me to produce unrest and revolts in the United States, so that these gentry will have their hands full with their own affairs. We have no use for them in Europe.

"You said that we should poison the enemy with bacteria even before the war starts. How can that be done in peacetime?" Forster asked.

"Through agents, harmless commercial travelers. That is the surest method—at the moment the only effective one," Hitler replied. "The results would not be immediate. It would take several weeks, if not longer, for an epidemic to appear. Perhaps we shall introduce bacteria at the height of the war, at the moment when the powers of resistance of the enemy are beginning to fail."

OUR conversation then dealt with some details of a future gas and bacterial war. We sat in the rather narrow veranda of Wachenfeld House in the Obersalzberg. Hitler seemed to me preoccupied and moody. From having been communicative, he fell suddenly into a dry silence. The political moment was full of danger. National Socialism was approaching one of its crises. The Party was in a well-nigh desperate position. But Hitler's every word rang with the firm conviction that he would soon be in power, and able to lead the German people to a new destiny. We spoke of the result of the war, and the tragical turn of all German victories.

"We shall not capitulate—no, never," Hitler exclaimed. "We may be destroyed, but if we are, we shall drag a world with us—a world in flames."

He hummed a characteristic *motif* from the *Götterdämmerung*. Our young friend of the S.A. broke the silence by saying that it was the superior armament of our enemies that had brought about the unhappy conclusion of the last war.

"It is not arms that decide, but the men behind them—always," Hitler rebuked him. "Who says I'm going to start a war like those fools in 1914? Are not all our efforts bent towards preventing this? Most people have no imagination." Here his face twisted into an expression of contempt. "They can imagine the future only in terms of their own petty experience. They are blind to the new, the surprising things. Even the generals are sterile. They are imprisoned in the coils of their technical knowledge.

The creative genius stands always outside the circle of the experts.

"I," he went on, "have the gift of reducing all problems to their simplest foundations. War has been erected into a secret science and surrounded with momentous solemnity. But war is the most natural, the most every-day matter. War is eternal, war is universal. There is no beginning and there is no peace. War is life. Any struggle is war. War is the origin of all things.

"Let us go back to primitive life, the life of the savages. What is war but cunning, deception, delusion, attack and surprise? People have killed only when they could not achieve their aim in other ways. Merchants, robbers, warriors—at one time, all these were one. There is a broadened strategy, a war with intellectual weapons. What is the object of war, Forster? To make the enemy capitulate. If he does, I have the prospect of wiping him out. Why should I demoralize him by military means if I can do so better and more cheaply in other ways?"

Linsmayer, our S.A. leader, now asked to be allowed to photograph Hitler in a group with the rest of us. We went outside and took up our position beneath a steep cliff. Hess took the picture with Hitler in the center.

THEN Hitler went on to develop the outlines of his war as he has since widely tested it. At that time it seemed a novel and not very convincing doctrine. It was evident, however, that he had given much thought to these matters.

"When I wage war, Forster," he declared, "in the midst of peace, troops will suddenly appear, let us say, in Paris. They will wear French uniforms. They will march through the streets in broad daylight. No one will stop them. Everything has been thought out, prepared to the last detail. They will march to the headquarters of the General Staff. They will occupy the ministries, the Chamber of Deputies. Within a few minutes, France, Poland, Austria, Czechoslovakia, will be robbed of their leading men. An army without a general staff! All political leaders out of the way! The confusion will be beyond belief. But I shall long have had relations with the men who will form a new government—a government to suit me.

"We shall find such men, we shall find them in every country. We shall not need to bribe them. They will come of their own accord. Ambition and delusion, party squabbles and self-seeking arrogance will drive them. Peace will be negotiated before the war has begun. I promise you, gentlemen, that the impossible is always successful. The most unlikely thing is the surest.

"Today you don't believe me, gentlemen. But I will accomplish it, move by move.

"Perhaps we shall land at their flying-fields. We shall be capable of transporting, not only men, but arms, by air. No Maginot Line will stop us. Our strategy, Forster, is to destroy the enemy from within, to conquer him through himself."

He went on with growing enthusiasm: "How to achieve the moral break-down of the enemy before the war has started —that is the problem that interests me. Whoever has experienced war at the front will want to refrain from all avoidable bloodshed. Anything that helps preserve the precious German blood is good. We shall not shrink from the plotting of revolutions. Remember Sir Roger Casement and the Irish in the last war. We shall have friends who will help us in all the enemy countries. We shall know how to obtain such friends. Mental confusion, contradiction of feeling, indecisiveness, panic: these are our weapons. Of course you know," here Hitler turned to me, "the history of revolutions. It is always the same: the ruling classes capitulate. Why? Defeatism; they have no longer the will to conquer. The lessons of revolution, these are the secret of the new strategy. I have learnt from the Bolsheviks. I do not hesitate to say so. One always learns most from one's enemies. Do you know the doctrine of the *coup*

d'état? Study it. Then you will know our task."

WE LISTENED, none of us guessing how close we were to the realization of these ideas.

"I shall never start a war without the certainty that a demoralized enemy will succumb to the first stroke of a single gigantic attack." Hitler's eyes took on a fixed stare, and he began to shout "When the enemy is demoralized from within, when he stands on the brink of revolution, when social unrest threatens —that is the right moment. A single blow must destroy him. Aerial attacks, stupendous in their mass effect, surprise, terror, sabotage, assassination from within, the murder of leading men, overwhelming attacks on all weak points in the enemy's defense, sudden attacks, all in the same second, without regard for reserves or losses: that is the war of the future. A gigantic, all-destroying blow. I do not consider consequences; I think only of this one thing."

He paused as if to give us time to take in this terrific program and some at least of its fearful implications. His next words were spoken with impressive calmness.

"I do not play at war. I shall not allow myself to be ordered about by 'commanders-in-chief.' *I* shall make war. *I* shall determine the correct moment for attack. There is only one most favorable moment. I shall await it—with iron determination. I shall not miss it. I shall bend all my energies towards bringing it about. That is my mission. If I succeed in that, then I have the right to send youth to its death. I shall have saved as many lives then as could be saved. Gentlemen, let us not play at being heroes, but let us destroy the enemy. Generals, in spite of the lessons of the war, want to behave like chivalrous knights. They think war should be waged like the tourneys of the Middle Ages. I have no use for knights. I need revolutions. I have made the doctrines of revolution the basis of my policy."

Hitler paused again. His next words came like a peroration:

"I shall shrink from nothing. No so-called international law, no agreements will prevent me from making use of any advantage that offers. The next war will be unbelievably bloody and grim. But the most inhuman war, one which makes no distinction between military and civilian combatants, will at the same time be the kindest, because it will be the shortest. And together with the fullest use of our arms, we shall grind down our enemy with a war of nerves.

We shall provoke a revolution in France as certainly as we shall *not* have one in Germany. Take my word for it. The French will hail me as their deliverer. The little man of the middle class will acclaim us as the bearers of a just social order and eternal peace. None of these people any longer want war and greatness. But *I* want war. To me all means will be right.

"My motto is not: 'Don't, whatever you do, annoy the enemy!' My motto is: 'Destroy him by all and any means.' *I* am the one who will wage the war!"

Dining with Hitler

In the summer of 1933 I frequently dined with Hitler in his flat. He lived at that time on the second floor of the new Reich Chancellory. His home was good middle-class, one might almost say *petit bourgeois*. The rooms were smallish, the furnishing simple and without refinement. There was not a single piece that revealed anything of good personal taste or artistic value.

Whenever Hitler was in Berlin, he asked people to dine with him. It was considered a high honor to eat at Hitler's table, and there were usually ten to twenty people, at most. The food was simple. In this, too, the party Führer liked to give an impression of modest living on proletarian lines. He frequently expressed his intention of changing none of his previous habits, either in his clothing or in his style of living. As a matter of fact, this did form an agreeable contrast to the extravagant behavior of some of the new bosses. Hitler retained his old habit of sitting beside the chauffeur in his car; his clothes consisted of his familiar raincoat seldom surmounted by a hat, while under it he usually wore a civilian jacket with the party uniform trousers, or an ordinary lounge suit.

At dinner, there was soup, followed by a meat course, vegetables and a sweet. Hitler himself ate no meat, but he devoured astonishing portions of the sweet, and his personal cook, an old party member, prepared special vegetable dishes for him. But Hitler placed no vegetarian compulsion on his guests, nor did he refuse them alcohol in the shape of beer. There was a choice between beer and lemonade, and it was amusing to watch newcomers, especially enthusiastic party members, choosing lemonade, with a side-glance at the temperate Führer, in order to make a good impression.

There was always a mixed and varied company at the table. Invariably some outstanding person was present, a film star, an artist or a leading member of the party. There were ladies, too, but usually in the minority. On one occasion I met two strikingly pretty blondes; Hitler asked one of them to sit beside him, and kept putting his hand on her arm.

The tone was informal. Often Hitler was silent, or made only desultory remarks. Again, he would pontificate in a booming voice, and everyone would listen in silence. It was interesting to watch Hitler talking himself into a fury, and to note how necessary to his eloquence were shouting and a feverish *tempo*. A quiet conversation with him was impossible. Either he was silent or he took complete charge of the discussion. Hitler's eloquence is plainly no natural gift, but the result of a conquest of certain inhibitions which, in intimate conversation, still make him awkward. The convulsive artificiality of his character is specially noticeable in such intimate circles; particularly notable in his lack of any sense of humor. Hitler's laugh is hardly more than an expression of scorn and contempt. There is no relaxation about it. His pleasures have no repose.

At one of these dinners I had, in fact, the opportunity of hearing his views on humor. I was sitting opposite Goebbels, who was on Hitler's left. The two were discussing the National Socialist humorous papers and the significance of wit as a weapon. In humor, too, or what he called humor, Hitler saw only a weapon. It was at this time that, in connection with the *Stürmer* and its Jewish caricatures, he gave utterance to the remark later much quoted in the party, that this was "the form of pornography permitted in the Third Reich." Evidently Hitler took pleasure in these filthy stories.

After dinner, coffee and liqueurs were served in Hitler's small study. There was some smoking too, but not much. Occasionally the coffee would be served on a large terrace rather like a roof-garden, which overlooked the treetops in the gardens of the old Reich Chancellery. Hitler's entire entourage, especially his stepsister, Frau Raubal, who at that time lent his home a housewifely character, were continually worried about his safety. Attempts at assassination were already feared, particularly within the Chancellery gardens, and Hitler had been warned against walking in them. He took little exercise.

Hitler's Foot in South America

IT was on this terrace that, after dinner one evening in the early summer of 1933, I was present at a conversation that was most revealing of Hitler's political opinions about America, and showed how far-reaching were his plans even then, and how mistaken was the belief that National Socialism had political aims only in the east and southeast of Europe. A trusted, leading member of the S.A. had just returned from South America, and Hitler had engaged him in conversation, and asked him many questions. Over the coffee, he took up the thread of the discourse again. Evidently his information was not detailed, and he was merely repeating various notions—highly popular at the time—concerning the land of the future that he had gleaned from certain publications. He was specially interested in Brazil.

"We shall create a new Germany there," he cried. "We shall find everything we need there."

He then outlined broadly all that a hard-working and energetic government could do to create order. All the preconditions for a revolution were there, a revolution which in a few decades, or even years, would transform a corrupt mestizo state into a German dominion.

"Besides, we have a right to this continent, for the Fuggers and Welsers had possessions there. We have got to repair what our German disunity has destroyed; we must see to it that it is no longer true that we have lost all that we once occupied. The time has passed for us to give place to Spain and Portugal, and be everywhere at a disadvantage."

Von P., his guest, agreed as to the special opportunities of Germany in Brazil.

"THESE people will need us if they are going to make anything of their country," Hitler remarked. They had less use, he said, for investment capital than for the spirit of enterprise and for organizing ability. And they were fed up with the United States. They knew they were being exploited by them, and had nothing to expect from them for the development of their country.

"We shall give them both: capital and the spirit of enterprise. We shall make them a third gift: our philosophy," said Hitler. "If ever there is a place where democracy is senseless and suicidal, it is in South America. We must strengthen these people's clear conscience, so that they may be enabled to throw both their liberalism and their democracy overboard. They are actually ashamed of their good instincts! They think they must still give lip-service to democracy. Let us wait a few years, and in the meantime do what we can to help them. But we must send our people out to them. Our youth must learn to colonize. For this, we have no need of formal officials and governors. Audacious youth is what we want. They need not go into the jungle, either, to clear the ground. What we want are people in good society. What do you know about the German colony? Can anything be done along these lines?"

He turned to von P., who replied that it was very doubtful whether we ought to keep in touch with good society. In his opinion we should attain our purpose more quickly by making use of other classes, such as the *Indios* and the mestizos.

"Both, my dear P.," Hitler interrupted impatiently. "We require two movements abroad, a loyal and a revolutionary one. Do you think that's so difficult? I think we have proved that we are capable of it. We should not be here otherwise. We shall not land troops like William the Conqueror and gain Brazil by the strength of arms. Our weapons are not visible ones. Our conquistadores, my dear P., have a more difficult task than the original ones, and for this reason they have more difficult weapons."

Hitler asked further questions about German possibilities in South America. The Argentine and Bolivia were in the first line of interest, and it appeared that there were many points where National Socialist influence might make itself felt. Hitler propounded ideas which were much later realized by Bohle on the one hand and Ribbentrop on the other, and took shape in two mutually antagonistic onslaughts of propaganda. Essentially it was a question of personnel. The task of getting a firm foothold in Latin America and squeezing out North American and Hispano-Portuguese influ-

ence could only be carried out by new, energetic, unscrupulous representatives of overseas Germanhood.

I turned to Hanfstängel with the suggestion that this seemed to me a most alarming repetition in an aggravated form of the whole pre-war policy. Would it not be wiser not to challenge Britain and America, at least until Germany's position was unassailable? Moreover, this proposed policy was in contradiction to the fundamental rules laid down by *Mein Kampf*. But now for the first time I heard derogatory mention made of this book in Hitler's presence, and concluded from this that it was by no means regarded in the inner circles as the binding pronouncement it was given out to be for the masses.

It was Hanfstängel's opinion that sooner or later we should in any case have to face the hostility of the United States and Britain. Germany was ready. Was I still cherishing, he contemptuously asked, illusions about Britain? As for the United States, they would certainly never interfere in Europe again; he knew that better than anyone, for he knew these gentry and their weaknesses. Britain, he proclaimed, was dead. Where else, he added, should Germany get the elements of her future world empire if not from the disintegrating empires of Britain and France? The final struggle with Britain could not be evaded.

"And if you look closer," concluded Hanfstängel, "you will find that everything about Britain in *Mein Kampf* is of purely tactical value. Hitler had good reason to write as he did."

That night I heard mentioned for the first time the general outlines of the future great German overseas Reich. I was amazed to hear that Hitler was reaching out to the Pacific. Above all, he was interested in the former great German island empire, embracing the Dutch possessions and the whole of New Guinea. Japan must not be allowed to grow too big, Hitler remarked. It must be deflected against China and Russia.

But Hitler also anticipated a Central African Dominion of Germany as well as a complete revolutionary transformation of the U. S. A. With the breakdown of the British Empire, Hitler believed he could also break Anglo-Saxon influence in North America, and substitute for it the German language and culture as a preliminary step towards incorporating the United States.

The United States According to Hitler

ABOUT the United States, Hitler had his firm, preconceived opinion which no argument could shake. This opinion was that North America would never take part in a European war again, and that, with her millions of unemployed, the United States was on the brink of a revolution from the outbreak of which only Hitler could save her.

In June, 1933, I was present at a dinner-table conversation in Hitler's flat in which he gave expression to this view. Later, however, I had frequent occasions to hear the same view expressed. One of the guests suggested that it might be of decisive importance for Germany to win the friendship of North America. Certain members of the German government at that time had publicly emphasized the unique value of friendly relations with the United States, and for this reason had some misgivings about the anti-Semitic policy of the Reich.

"Whose friendship?" Hitler brusquely interposed. "The friendship of the Jewish jobbers and moneybags or that of the American people?"

He expressed his contempt of the present government of the United States.

"This is the last disgusting death-rattle of a corrupt and outworn system which is a blot on the history of this people. Since the Civil War, in which the Southern States were conquered, against all historical logic and sound sense, the Americans have been in a condition of political and popular decay. In that war, it was not the Southern States, but the American people themselves who were conquered. In the spurious blossoming of economic progress and power politics, America has ever since been drawn deeper into the mire of progressive self-destruction. A moneyed clique, which presumes to be good so-ciety and to represent the old families, rules the country under the fiction of a democracy which has never before been so nakedly exposed as a mass of corruption and legal venality. The beginnings of a great new social order based on the principle of slavery and inequality were destroyed by that war, and with them also the embryo of a future truly great America that would not have been ruled by a corrupt caste of tradesmen, but by a real *Herren*-class that would have swept away all the falsities of liberty."

THAT word "equality" seemed to lash him into a fury. "Equality of whom?" he shouted. "Of the descendants of old Spanish ruling families and of Swedish settlers with the degenerate masses from Poland, Bohemia, Hungary, with all the scum of East Baltic and Balkan Jewry? But I am firmly convinced that in a certain section of the American middle class and the farmers, the sound fighting spirit of colonial days has not been extinguished. We must awaken that spirit. It has not yet been destroyed. The wholesome aversion for the Negroes and the colored races in general, including the Jews, the existence of popular justice, the *naïveté* of the average American, but also the skepticism of certain intellectual circles who have found their wisdom vain; scholars who have studied immigration and gained an insight, by means of intelligence tests, into the inequality of the races—all these strains are an assurance that the sound elements of the United States will one day awaken as they have awakened in Germany. National Socialism alone is destined to liberate the American people from their ruling clique and give them back the means of becoming a great nation."

Hitler had grown animated. All other conversation died away.

"I shall," he continued, "undertake this task simultaneously with the restoration of Germany to her leading position in America."

"In what sense, my Führer?" asked Goebbels.

"Have you forgotten that the declaration of German as the national language was lost by only one voice in Congress? The German component of the American people will be the source of its political and mental resurrection. The American people is not yet a nation in the ethnographical sense; it is a conglomerate of disparate elements. But it is the raw material of a nation. And the Yankees have failed to create a nation from it! They have instead kept their noses in their moneybags. Today this is being avenged. Their difficulties will become insuperable."

"Do you mean," I asked, "that the German-American, rejuvenated by National Socialism, will be called to lead a new America?"

"That is exactly what I mean," Hitler returned. "We shall soon have an S.A. in America. We shall train our youth. And we shall have men whom degenerate Yankeedom will not be able to challenge. Into the hands of our youth will be given the great statesmanlike mission of Washington which this corrupt democracy has trodden under foot."

"Shall we not very greatly complicate our own struggle in Europe if we do this?" interposed Hitler's guest. "Will not the powerful families become our bitterest enemies? My Führer, I am apprehensive that your great plans will be shattered before they have time to ripen."

Hitler became excited.

"Will you understand, sir, that our struggle against Versailles and our struggle for a new world order is one and the same; we cannot set limits here or there as we please. We shall succeed in making the new political and social order the universal basis of life in the world. Or else we shall be destroyed in our struggle against a peace-treaty which has in reality never existed, and proved on the very first day of its ratification that the conquerors had accidentally been taken for the conquered, and vice versa."

"Nothing will be easier than to produce a bloody revolution in North America," Goebbels interposed. "No other country has so many social and racial tensions. We shall be able to play on many strings there."

Hitler's guest, with whom I was not intimately acquainted, remained silent, visibly confounded. Hitler observed this and seemed irritated by it.

"North America is a medley of races," Goebbels said. "The ferment goes on under a cover of democracy, but it will not lead to a new form of freedom and leadership, but to a process of decay containing all the disintegrating forces of Europe. The America of today will never again be a danger to us."

"IT is a mistake to assume that it was a danger to us in the last war," Hitler remarked crossly. "Compared with the British and French, the Americans behaved like clumsy boys. They ran straight into the line of fire, like young rabbits. The American is no soldier. The inferiority and decadence of this allegedly new world is evident in its military inefficiency."

"Nevertheless," Hitler's guest repeated, "I should like to be allowed to express a most humble warning that the Americans ought not to be underestimated as an enemy."

"Who says anything of underestimation?" Hitler exclaimed angrily, as he rose to lead the way from the table. "I guarantee, gentlemen, that at the right moment a new America will exist as our strongest supporter when we are ready to take the stride into overseas space.

"We have the means of awakening this nation in good time," he added after a pause. "There will be no new Wilson arising to stir up America against us."

World-Embracing Secret Service

THE various German organizations in different parts of the world are all in the same position. Largely without their knowledge, their functions are all being terribly distorted. Only history will show how great an accumulation of trust and belief has been wantonly destroyed. All these overseas German communities have become the breeding-ground of a mushroom growth of propaganda, flourishing in the dark, which has run through all the stages up to effective espionage.

Every German, whether still a German national or a citizen of the country in which he was living, was impressed into the service of this enormous machine. Every organization that did not explicitly state its aims as being anti-Nazi was more or less the agent of a system of political propaganda and espionage center that far exceeded all legal and legitimate limits. They were all committed to the task of making Germandom abroad the instrument of a gigantic, world-embracing system of secret service.

EARLY in the summer of 1934, Hitler addressed a group of foreign agents thus:

"It is a good idea," he said emphatically, "to have at least two German societies in every country. One of them can then always call attention to its loyalty to the country in question, and will have the function of fostering social and economic connections. The other one may be radical and revolutionary. It will have to be prepared to be frequently repudiated by myself and other German authorities. I want to make it quite clear, too, that I make no distinction between German nationals and Germans by birth who are citizens of a foreign country. Superficially we shall have to make allowances for such citizenship. But it will be your special task to train all Germans, without distinction, unconditionally to place their loyalty to Germandom before their loyalty to the foreign state. Only in this way will you be able to fulfill the difficult tasks I shall give you. I must leave to your discretion the means by which you train your fellow-Germans to this new discipline. It will not always be possible without friction. For me, success is the only criterion. The means are of no interest to me. But whoever opposes you should know that he has nothing more to expect from the German Reich. He will be outlawed for all time. And in due course he will reap the fruits of his treacherous attitude."

Hitler concluded his address as follows:

"It will depend on you, gentlemen, whether we reach our goal with comparative ease and without bloodshed. You must prepare the ground. Germany will spread its might far beyond its borders in the east as well as in the southeast. You, too, gentlemen, will have the same duties overseas. Forget all you have learned hitherto. We do not seek equality, but mastery. We shall not waste time over minority rights and other such ideological abortions of sterile democracy. When Germany is great and victorious no one will dare to give any of you the cold shoulder. It is your mission to win this leading role for Germany.

"If you succeed, then you too will be called to leadership, unhampered by agreements and legal red tape. It will be your task to lead these conquered countries in the name of the German people. You shall be my viceroys in the countries and among the people who today persecute and oppress you. What has been our handicap—the splitting, the century-long impotence of the German Reich, leaving millions of the best Germans to emigrate and become the natural fertilizer for other countries—this is now our pride. Just as the Jews became the all-embracing world power they are today only in their dispersal, so shall we today, as the true chosen people of God become in our dispersal the omnipresent power, the masters of the earth."

Nazi Morality

Hitler once conferred on me the privilege of learning his views on morality and the things of the spirit. They were a mixture of misunderstood Nietzsche and popularized ideas of a certain tendency in current philosophy. All this stuff he poured forth with the air of a prophet and a creative genius. He seemed to take it for granted that the ideas were his own. He had no notion of their actual origin, and considered that he had worked them out himself, and that they were inspirations, the product of his solitude in the mountains. I give here some of these dicta, noted down at the time, but not all of them now in their original context. They are fragments from various talks.

"We are now at the end of the Age of Reason. The intellect has grown autocratic, and has become a disease of life."

"Our revolution is not merely a political and social revolution; we are at the outset of a tremendous revolution in moral ideas and in men's spiritual orientation."

"Conscience is a Jewish invention. It is a blemish, like circumcision."

"A new age of magic interpretation of the world is coming, of interpretation in terms of the will and not of the intelligence."

"There is no such thing as truth, either in the moral or in the scientific sense."

"Every deed has its place, even crime."

"All passivity, all inertia, on the other hand, is senseless, inimical to life. From this proceeds the divine right of destroying all who are inert."

"The word 'crime' comes from a world of the past. There are positive and negative activities. Every crime in the old sense towers above respectable inactivity. Action may be negative from the viewpoint of the community, and must then be prevented. But it is at least action."

"We must distrust the intelligence and the conscience, and must place our trust in our instincts. We have to regain a new simplicity."

"People set us down as enemies of the intelligence. We are. But in a much deeper sense than these conceited dolts of *bourgeois* scientists ever dream of."

"Providence has ordained that I should be the greatest liberator of humanity. I am freeing men from the restraints of an intelligence that has taken charge; from the dirty and degrading self-mortifications of a chimera called conscience and morality, and from the demands of a freedom and personal independence which only a very few can bear."

"To the Christian doctrine of the infinite significance of the individual human soul and of personal responsibility, I oppose with icy clarity the saving doctrine of the nothingness and insignificance of the individual human being, and of his continued existence in the visible immortality of the nation. The dogma of vicarious suffering and death through a divine savior gives place to that of the representative living and acting of the new Leader-legislator, which liberates the mass of the faithful from the burden of free will."

Pronounced with the authority of the recognized leader in the presence of his entourage, such *dicta,* studding a conversation, gave the impression of deep revelations. Hitler, moreover, was offended if anyone gave expression to his feelings that they had been said before or were being said by others who shared his opinions.

It is true that no one else drew the same revolutionary conclusions from these ideas, combining cultural and social, political and moral elements in a single general conception of a vast world change. This was his original contribution. What this world change amounted to in his idea was a point that he left unexplained. He spoke of it only in pictures, of doubtful originality. But we had the feeling that in his exaggeration of his own importance he came dangerously near to the limit beyond which Neitzsche passed when he announced that he was the Dionysus-God, the Anti-Christ become flesh. He believes his influence will be greatest after his death.

Hitler Himself

Is HITLER MAD? I think everyone who has met the Führer two or three times must have asked himself this question. Anyone who has seen this man face to face, has met his uncertain glance, without depth or warmth, from eyes that seem hard and remote, and has then seen that gaze grow rigid, will certainly have experienced the uncanny feeling: "That man is not normal."

I cannot judge whether Hitler is near madness in the clinical sense. My own experience of him and what I have learned from others indicate a lack of control amounting to total demoralization. His shrieking and frenzied shouting, his stamping, his tempests of rage— all this was grotesque and unpleasant, but it was not madness. When a grown-up man lashes out against the walls like a horse in its stall, or throws himself on the ground his conduct may be morbid, but it is more certainly rude and undisciplined.

Hitler, however, has states that approach persecution mania and dual personality. His sleeplessness is more than the mere result of excessive nervous strain. He often wakes up in the middle of the night and wanders restlessly to and fro.

Then he must have light everywhere. Lately he has sent at these times for young men who have to keep him company during his hours of manifest anguish. At times these conditions must have become dreadful.

A man in the closest daily association with him gave me this account: Hitler woke up one night with convulsive shrieks. "He! He! He's been here!" he gasped. His lips were blue. Sweat streamed down his face. Suddenly he began to reel off figures, and odd words and broken phrases, entirely devoid of sense. It sounded horrible. He used strangely composed and entirely un-German word-formations. Then he stood quite still, only his lips moving. He was massaged and offered something to drink. Then he suddenly broke out—

"There, there! In the corner! Who's that?"

He stamped and shrieked in the familiar way. He was shown that there was nothing out of the ordinary in the room, and then he gradually grew calmer. After that he lay asleep for many hours, and then for some time things were endurable.

It is terrible to think that a madman may be ruling Germany and driving the entire world to war. And hysteria is infectious. Anyone who has seen splendid youngsters, entirely normal, slowly but steadily become demoralized through association with hysterical women, will not wonder that hysteria should be extending to high dignitaries of the Reich, *Gauleiter,* officials, officers, and a whole nation.

But how comes it that so many visitors are charmed to the point of ecstasy over this man, and consider him an outstanding genius? Not only very young people, but men of knowledge and experience and critical judgment, are unable to speak of their experience without emotion. What is the magic that has captured them?

This man, awkward and ill at ease, and always at a loss for words when he cannot be rhetorical, has not even the irritating attractiveness of the wayward. What, then, is it in him that so powerfully affects his visitors?

There is an instructive parallel— mediums. Most of these are ordinary, undistinguished persons; yet suddenly they acquire gifts that carry them far above the common crowd. These qualities have nothing to do with the medium's own personality. They are conveyed to him from without. The medium is possessed by them. He, himself, however, is uninfluenced by them. In the same way undeniable powers enter into Hitler, genuinely daemonic powers, which make men his instruments.

I have often had the opportunity of examining my own experience, and I must admit that in Hitler's company I have again and again come under a spell which I was only later able to shake off, a sort of hypnosis. He is, indeed, a remarkable man. It leads nowhere to depreciate him and speak mockingly of him. He is simply a sort of great medicine-man. He is literally that, in the full sense of the term. We have gone back so far toward the savage state that the medicine man has become king among us.

Hitler is exacting, spoiled, avaricious, greedy. He does not know how to work steadily. Indeed, he is incapable of working. He gets ideas, impulses, the realization of which must be feverishly achieved and immediately got rid of. He does not know what it is to work continuously and unremittingly. Everything about him is "spasm," to use a favorite word of his. Nothing about him is natural. His professed love of children and animals is a mere pose.

He loves solitary walks. These walks are his divine service, his prayers. Then he hears voices. I have met him when he is in this mood. Hitler not only looks and acts strange; he recognizes nobody. For everything he needs to be worked up. He must prepare beforehand for the smallest decision, the simplest action: he must screw himself up to it. In the past he used to complain for weeks at a time, blaming the ingratitude of his followers or the unkindness of fate for his own inactivity. He was fond of posing as a martyr and dwelling on the idea of pre-mature death. At such times he would seem to be giving up. He was then full of compassion, but only for himself.

All the more astonishing are the explosions of his "determined will," his sudden activity. Then he neither tires nor hungers; he lives with a morbid energy that enables him to do almost miraculous things.

Everything is done then, in his own words, "with determination," "without tolerating" (whatever obstacle may be in question), "fanatically." But everything about him is jerky and abrupt. He is entirely without balance. And in this respect he shows not the slightest improvement as he grows older. He has no natural greatness, even in the vastest of his new and most palatial rooms.

Hitler used to like to be seen with a riding whip in his hand; he has given up this habit. But the qualities it revealed remain—contemptuousness, arrogance, brutality, vanity. Hitler has never mounted a horse; but the tall riding boots and the riding whip bore witness to his resentment at past years of submission to his officers.

Brutal and vindictive, he is also sentimental—a familiar mixture. He loved his canaries, and could cry when one of them sickened and died. But he would have men against whom he had a grudge tortured to death in the most horrible way. He eats incredible quantities of sweetmeats and whipped cream; and he has the instinct of the sadist, finding sexual excitement in inflicting torture on others. In Roman history he gloats over such a figure as Sulla, with his proscriptions and mass executions. Once he recommended to me as instructive reading a banal novel of which Sulla was the hero.

Most loathsome of all is the reeking miasma of furtive, unnatural sexuality that fills and fouls the whole atmosphere round him, like an evil emanation. Nothing in this environment is straightforward. Surreptitious relationships, substitutes and symbols, false sentiment and secret lusts—nothing in this man's surroundings is natural and genuine, nothing has the openness of a natural instinct.

Hitler and Women

HITLER has a room with obscene nudes on the wall, concealing nothing. Such pictures have no artistic intention. He revels in this style of painting.

"Oh!" said Forster once to me—"Forster Boy," one of Hitler's closest intimates, the *enfant terrible* among the *Gauleiter*—"Oh, if Hitler only knew how it does one good to have a fresh, natural girl!" Forster had just begun "courting." "Poor Hitler!" he said. I did not pursue the subject.

But it is to women's encouragement that he owes his self-assurance. It is absurd that he of all men should always be surrounded by a crowd of women, most of them rather over-blown—that women, indeed, launched him on his career.

Hitler was discovered by society ladies, who pushed him forward, when still a young man, after the Great War. It was the wives of some of the great industrialists, before their husbands, who gave him financial support, surreptitiously supplying him with money, and in the inflation period with valuables. It was in the company of a clique of educated women that the paid propagandist developed into a political prophet. How much they contributed to his stock of ideas may be doubtful. But it was they who pampered him and ministered to his conceit with extravagant advance laurels.

In the struggle for power it was the woman's vote that brought Hitler to triumph. In the mass meetings in every town the front rows were always filled with elderly women of a certain type, married and single. Anyone looking down from the platform on those front seat women and watching their expressions of rapturous self-surrender, their moist and gleaming eyes, could not doubt the character of their enthusiasm. The S.S. men who guarded the hall at these meetings soon had a coarse phrase for these women enthusiasts: they were the "varicose vein squad."

Eroticism is an important political factor in modern mass propaganda, the erotic effect of a speaker's voice, of tonality and speaking melody. These are much more important elements of a speech than its content. Hitler has taken factors of this sort into account, and owes not a little of his political success to their cynical exploitation. How much of his relations with women has been a genuine sublimation of erotic intensity and how much cold calculation, I do not know. Hitler, as I see him, is a personality so exclusively wrapped up in himself that he is incapable of genuine devotion. And thus the more or less morbid women who swarm around him and pay him homage, women with more than a touch of hysteria, are a deliberately selected company.

Later I frequently found with him strikingly pretty young blondes. They sat beside him at meals. He stroked their hands. He permitted himself little intimacies. The whole thing was play-acting. The whole conceit and unnaturalness of this man shows itself even in the most elementary relations in human life. He has shaken off nothing of his past. He still carries it with him, and with its insincerity and uncleanness and monstrousness it burdens the whole German people.

IT IS TRUE that Hitler is no longer the young man of 1923. In 1933, when he came into power, he was already more realistic, more calculating, more cynical. Since then he has further changed. The Byzantines of the New German court speak of a process of ripening to greatness. They praise Hitler's rise to be the most eminent of statesmen and predict that some day he will also prove himself the greatest of army commanders. But the essential Hitler is unchanged. He has remained the same hopelessly immature man, with the same morbid lusts. His technique, his routine, may have ripened. Otherwise he is tragically identical with the Hitler of twenty years ago. He may well claim that he laid the foundations of his philosophy of life in his Vienna days, and since then has added nothing to his mental and spiritual stature.

Hitler cannot shake off his past. In everything that he does he remains true to type. But can anyone shake off his past? Only by spiritual development; and of this Hitler is incapable. This man of the unending revolution, of unending movement and change, is confined in his own tragic nature that shuts out every creative influence that ripens a man. He remains unchanged.

To this day he is the hireling of whoever offers the best terms. To this day he is the vain and touchy person of his boyhood. To this day he is the excitable, theatrical revolutionary of the years of inflation, his hand on his heart as he swears tremendous oaths; and then, when he breaks them, tearfully entreating forgiveness and comprehension of his claim that he had to obey the higher call of the Fatherland.

How Long?

AT THE TIME of the conversations just recorded, it was still possible to hope that our nation would withstand the temptation of this grotesque doctrine of violence. But that would be possible only if Hitler could be forced to abdicate, and his place taken by a statesman who would bring reconciliation and a new constitutionalism. But could Hitler be overthrown?

His horoscope spoke of a sensational progress, of victory after victory. Then it became confused and ambiguous. A prophecy spoke of an unparalleled downfall.

The Middle Ages had been resuscitated. Comets and dark prophecies were expected to bring the truth to light, where other sources were banned or restricted to the political struggle. The whole nation was affected.

The sect of Bible Searchers searched the Scripture, and came in the Book of Daniel to the vision of the tyrant. "He," they whispered to one another, "is he of whom it is written (Dan. xi. 37): 'Neither shall he regard the God of his fathers, nor the desire of women, nor regard any good: for he shall magnify himself above all. But in his estate shall he honor the god of forces.'"

For their prophecy they were condemned to concentration camps and death. But the masses ask, "How long?"

HITLER'S CARD INDEX

The Nazi Dictator, as quoted by Rauschning:

"I AM not going to wait until these gentlemen [the statesmen and diplomats of all countries] wake up to the fact that they have got to start learning over again. I am building up a great organization of my own. It costs a lot of money, but it gets things moving for me. I have drawn up a *questionnaire* covering details of the persons I am interested in. I am having a comprehensive card index compiled of every influential person in the world. The cards contain every detail of importance. Will he take money? Can he be bought in any other way? Is he vain? Is he sexual? In what way? Is he homosexual? That is of the utmost value, because it provides close associations than can never be escaped from. Has he anything in his past to conceal? Can he be subjected to pressure? What is his business? His hobby, his favorite sport, his likes and dislikes? Does he like travel? And so on. It is on the strength of these reports that I choose my men. That really is politics. I get men who will work for me. I create a force of my own in every country."

Elizabeth Robins

THE MAGNETIC NORTH

Mrs. george richmond parks, *née* Elizabeth Robins, was an author and actress who was born in Louisville, Kentucky in 1865. She and her husband, also an actor, spent much of their life in London. When Ibsen's plays were under English interdict, Mrs. Parks championed the Norwegian dramatist and gave several brilliant performances in Ibsen rôles. Under the pseudonym C. E. Raimond, she published her first book "George Mandeville's Husband" in 1894. The best of her novels, both in construction and characterization, is her tale of Alaska called "The Magnetic North," which was published in 1904.

Months of Silence

This is the story of five men, as different in character as in previous occupation, who, after many adventures, arrive at last at the Klondike goldfields.

Only two of them knew anything about "roughing it." These were Jimmie O'Flynn, "of Frisco," an Irish-American lawyer, and MacCann, a Nova Scotian schoolmaster, who was also an amateur naturalist. The others were a Kentucky "colonel" who had never smelt powder; Potts, a bank clerk from Denver, and the Boy.

Four hundred miles from the mouth of the Yukon River, in Alaska, one of their boats had gone to the bottom; the other wasn't much of a boat by the time she was moored in quiet water away from the cannonading of the ice.

After eight weeks of travel they were still 1,300 miles away from the Klondike. They were 2,500 miles from railroad or telegraph, and now that winter was at their heels they were eight months from anywhere in the civilized world.

The three "pardners," "Mac," Potts and O'Flynn, were so discouraged by the outlook that they built a ramshackle little cabin that proved to be too cold to sit in. So they messed and spent all their waking time in the quarters made by the Colonel and the Boy. The cabin of these two ultimately became famous up and down the river for hundreds of miles, not only because it was bigger and better built than other cabins, not only because the chinks between the logs were so well caulked with moss and mud-mortar that no draughts came whistling in, but chiefly because of the great outside chimney built of rough stone, and because of the generous atmosphere that reigned over the mud hearth inside.

Provisions and equipment were pooled, and stored in the Big Chimney cabin. Mac set traps and went shooting now and then, and though he didn't get much game, he got specimens of sub arctic fauna to add to the "collection."

One bitter grey day, after the great river had frozen, the Boy went off with his gun, and came back in wild excitement to announce the approach of a party of natives. These turn out to be four Esquimaux, headed by Nicholas of Pymeut, a native village ten miles up the river.

The Big Chimney men were immensely pleased to find they had neighbours. Nicholas told of the Esquimau practice of cutting a hole in the river ice and spearing fish, or of putting down a long wicker trap to catch them. Nicholas was a steamboat pilot in summer and a hunter. He said moose is to be found and caribou, and spoke of snaring ermine, otter, fox and wolverine. A valuable ally! He and the Boy became great friends.

The next visitor was a Jesuit priest

with a native servant and a dog team. Father Wills belonged to the Catholic mission forty miles above on the river. He was returning from an expedition to a provision steamer, frozen in some miles away. The suffering among the stranded Klondikers all along the lower river was very great. Even greater was the misery in the native villages. The few men who had supplies meant to make a fortune out of others' necessities, and credit was dead.

A Tragedy in Syrup

For five dissimilar men to eat and live in a single room on short and dwindling rations through the gloom of the long Arctic night is to make heavy drafts on human nature.

Under these conditions a much-needed diversion came to the Big Chimney Camp in the guise of a little Esquimau. The priest discovered the child in one of the underground huts, bound, with dried grass stuffed in his mouth to drown his cries.

Mac, who had a little boy of his own at home, took a tremendous fancy to Kaviak, as the child was called, named after his tribe. The little Esquimau became an amusing addition to the circle round the Big Chimney. Kaviak had an awful moment when his new friends stripped off his single garment (a filthy fur parki), and also when they took away the precious amulet he wore in a birdskin pouch.

But these reverses paled before the awful disaster (as it seemed to the Esquimau) of being put in a pail of water and washed with soap. In this last adventure Kaviak plainly saw the awful fate that overtakes a young gentleman deprived of his amulet. Kaviak adores golden syrup, and the instant he has finished one helping he holds out his dish, and says "maw." When he is told he's had enough and there is no more, he says firmly, "Yeh. Maw in the plenty pot," and stands waiting.

There is a tragic sequel to Potts's secret abstraction of some of the syrup. Suspicion falls on Kaviak. He denies all knowledge of the empty tin, and Mac, who is a disciplinarian and, above all, a worshipper of truth, takes Kaviak away from his dinner down to the Little Cabin, and thrashes him. After this pain-ful business is over, Kaviak escapes, runs down to the river and falls into the fish hole.

Potts, who has been wretched about Kaviak's punishment, but isn't man enough to own up, risks his life to save the child. He and Kaviak are both pulled out of the hole, and the other men realize presently that Potts was the real culprit.

The Boy goes to Pymeut to visit Nicholas, and has some curious adventures. His eyes are opened as to Esquimau marriage customs, and he is present at an incantation made by the Shaman —a powerful medicine man. The purpose of this ceremony is to cure Nicholas's aged father, who seems to be at death's very door.

During the performance of the heathen rite one of the mission priests appears unexpectedly on the scene. He is unspeakably horrified by the idolatry and blasphemy of these natives, whom he and his brethren have devoted their lives to convert. The outraged priest leaves the village in great wrath. The Pymeuts are dreadfully agitated. These Jesuits are their best friends, and the most powerful people in the country. Everybody agrees that a penitential journey must be made to the mission for the purpose of obtaining absolution for this back-sliding.

At the special request of Nicholas's sister, Muckluck, the Boy says he will go and help to explain the somewhat delicate situation to the priests. For the fact seems to be that whereas Ol' Chief under Christian ministration was dying, he is so mightily invigorated by the Shaman's howling and incantation that he is not only saved from death, but ready to go in the sled the thirty miles to the mission, and add an Ol' Chief's prayers and gifts to those of less distinguished persons.

When the powers are appeased, the father superior pronounces a few simple sentences about the gentleness of Christ with the ignorant, but how offended the Heavenly Father is when those who know the true God descend to idolatrous practices, and how entirely he can be depended upon to punish wicked people.

Ol' Chief nodded vigorously and with sudden excitement. "Me jus' like God," he said.

"Hein?" exclaimed the priest.

"Oh, yes. Me no stan' wicked people. When me young me kill two ol' squaws —witches."

A sudden change passed over the tired face of the father. "Go, go!" he said. "Go to the schoolhouse and get fed, for it's all you seem able to get there." In spite of his companion's tactlessness, the Boy lays the foundation of a friendship with these mission people, a friendship which affects all his life. He also comes to know a little nun in the native school and she gives the Boy a silver cross.

He goes home to the Big Chimney and finds things in a bad way. Bad, ill-cooked food, and not nearly enough of that. The food supply is so low by Christmas that there is very little hope of much cheer.

But unexpected gifts come pouring in; the best—a haunch of moose—is marked, "To Kaviak's friends by the Big Chimney, from Kaviak's friends at Holy Cross." This meat is, of course, frozen solid, and cannot be cut. The men try chopping it, and bits fly about as though the moose were an uncommonly tough and brittle kind of wood. The proper way, they find, is to saw steaks off the haunch. They have a Christmas-tree for Kaviak, and the general jollity is added to by the arrival of two travellers with a dog team. They are from Minook, a mining camp more than half as near again as the Klondike, and at Minook they've struck it rich.

THESE new arrivals have made their fortunes. "Seein's believin'," said they, and out of long buckskin pouches they poured a stream of nuggets and coarse, bright gold.

The crowd about the table drew audible breath. Nobody actually spoke at first, except O'Flynn, who said reverently, "Be—the siven howly pipers— that danced at me—gran'mother's weddin'!" Low exclamations, hands thrust out to feel, and drawn back in a sort of superstitious awe.

Here it was, this wonderful stuff they'd come for. Each one knew how in secret he had been brought to doubt it being there. But here it was, on the cabin table.

If only the Big Chimney men could get to Minook before the river opened and the new camp should be overrun!

The Lone Trail

A FEW weeks after this there is a scene in the cabin about the shortness of rations and the certainty of there not being enough to support life "till the ice goes out."

That night the Colonel hears a noise, gets up, and finds the Boy gone. He rushes out, and in the dimness sees a shadow moving towards the river. The Colonel calls out "Stop, or I'll shoot." The grey shape halts—it is the Boy, who was going off alone to Minook, partly to be early in the field, but still more to relieve the strain at the camp. The Boy must wait till the next day, says the Colonel, and he will go too.

Hurrying by Pymeut they very nearly leave the Boy there, at the bottom of the river. For he had put up a sail, using his sled for an ice boat, when he fell into one of the river blowholes.

At Holy Cross everyone tried to make the travellers abandon their enterprise.

"My son," said Father Richmond to the Boy, "you must not go on this mad journey."

"I must, you know."

"You must *not*. Sit there." He pushed him to a chair. "Let me tell you. I do not speak as the ignorant. I have in my day travelled many hundreds of miles on the ice; but I've done it in the season when the trail's at its best, *with dogs*, my son, and with tried native servants."

"I know it is pleasanter that way, but——"

"I assure you, my son, it is madness, this thing you are trying to do. The chances of either of you coming out alive are one in fifty. In fifty, did I say? In five hundred."

"I don't think so, father. We don't mean to travel when——"

"But you'll have to travel. To stay in such places as you'll find yourself in will be to starve. Or if by any miracle you escape the worst effects of cold and hunger, you'll get caught in the ice in the spring break-up, and go down to destruction on a floe. You've no conception what it's like. If you were six weeks earlier, or six weeks later, I would hold my peace."

The Boy looked at the priest and then away. *Was* it going to be so bad? Would they leave their bones on the ice? Would they go washing by the mission in the great spring flood, that all men spoke of with the same grave look? He had a sudden vision of the torrent as would be in June.

Dimly the Boy knew he was even now borne along upon a current equally irresistible, this one setting northward, as that other back to the south. He found himself shaking his head under the Jesuit's remonstrant eyes.

YET not all that was said at the mission had fallen on deaf ears. Ever since the two men had left their homes in the south, they had looked on at the spectacle of people "hustling" for a fortune. In a gold rush you see the accepted commonplace of human selfishness magnified and multiplied a thousandfold. You get the quintessential poison of competition. Alaska was a

place no one had come to in order to live there; only to get something, and with all possible speed to take it away. No one had brought anything to give— except these priests. In spite of prejudice, they made an impression that endured. Still, although the Boy was told "with all your journeying, my son, you will come to no continuing city"—the two go on their way. They have many adventures, and grow familiar with the face of death —and with an even grimmer visage.

They think the worst is over when they are able at an Indian village to buy dogs. Nig, the leader, becomes a much-loved friend, and there is a horrible moment when, in spite of all the Boy can do or say, it seems as if Nig is going to be shot to keep his masters from starving. The Boy runs away so that he may be out of hearing.

"That's the kind of world it is," he says bitterly. "Do your level best, drag other fellas' packs hundreds o' miles over the ice with a hungry belly and bloody feet, and then—Poor old Nig!— 'cause you're lame—poor old Nig!" With a tightened throat and hot water in his eyes, he kept on repeating the dog's name as he stumbled forward in the snow. "Nev' mind, old boy; it's a lonely kind of world, and the right trail's hard to find."

Suddenly he stood still. His stumbling feet were on a track. He had reached the dip in the saddle-back of the hill, and—Yes, this was the *right* trail; for down on the other side below him were faint lights—huts—an Indian village!— with fish and food for everybody!

They exchange tea and tobacco for food, and Nig goes on to Minook with his friends. Here at the gold camp they find the good claims already staked, and everybody absorbed in drinking, gambling and "waiting for the ice to go out."

The Colonel is swindled about the purchase of a mine, and would have come out worse than he did but for the friendly warning of Maudie, a girl of the camp and a very rough diamond. Later there is a great stampede to jump some claims, and the Boy wins a prize in the race. He comes in for a promising claim, and the Colonel for one less desirable, and then they, like all the rest of the camp, sit down and wait for the first steamer.

While they wait, Maudie's store of gold dust and nuggets is stolen. Suspicion falls on the wrong man, and while the mob is getting ready to hang him, the Boy discovers the real thief. He and the Colonel make him disgorge, and then help him to escape.

Down to Klondike

SPRING comes at last. The vast ice sheet over the river cracks, is shattered and hurled away on the mighty floods. Any hour now a steamer may appear. All Minook is agog, and more than half of Minook is packed and ready to depart.

The Colonel, having no more money this side of Kentucky, wanted to sell his dogs soon after his arrival. With the last thirty dollars he had in the world, the Boy bought Nig from the Colonel, and then, in order to live, he hired the dog out. When he went to recover Nig, the man, who was using him as a draft-dog, refused to give him up, and carried him down the river.

The Boy took a boat and a gun, and went in pursuit. He got Nig back, and while trying to restrain the dog's dripping caresses, he looked up and saw something queer off there above the tops of the cottonwoods—a narrow cloud wavering along the sky. The grey pennon was going round the other side of the island, and the Boy was losing the boat to the Klondike!

He caught up his gun and fired. Nig howled, and the Boy waved his arms like a madman, and, as luck would have it, the steamer had just then to "hunt easier water"—the flood had altered the channel—and an order had been given to reverse engines. When Nig and his friend came alongside in the canoe, the Boy looked so wild with his long hair and ragged buckskin trousers, that even if the steamer had not been full, he would hardly have been allowed to board her. But he begged to be taken "as far as Minook, anyway," and was over the ship's side with Nig and the canoe while the captain was giving

orders. Among the motley horde of passengers were O'Flynn, Potts and Mac. The ship was loaded to the guards. All along the river the captain had been refusing large sums from men praying to be taken on board.

As soon as the new channel was found the Boy went and harangued the captain, told him about Minook and, in particular, about his claim. When he had got the captain interested, the Boy offered to make over one-third of his Minook property if the captain would take him and the Colonel to the Klondike. The captain absolutely refused, but ultimately he was brought round. As the steamer neared Minook, all the inhabitants lined the shore, packed and ready to depart. The only one of all that eager company allowed on board is the Boy's partner.

So the five men of Big Chimney Camp share together the memorable moment of arriving at the journey's end and the unprecedented spectacle of Dawson during the gold craze. The Colonel and the Boy leave the hurly-burly, and go out to see the mines. It was June now, and the short, fierce summer heat made travelling through mud and morass nearly as difficult as "hitting the winter trail." At last they came to Bonanza Creek.

"Well, here we are."

"Yes, this is what we came for."

On from claim to claim the newcomers went, till they were at the head of the richest placer mining district the world has seen. But they knew well enough now that every inch was owned, and that the best they could look for was work as unskilled laborers, day shift or night, on the claims of luckier men; for the "property in Minook" is far away, and no one wants to buy.

The Colonel, who is ill, but won't give in, gets work on the claim belonging to Scoville Austin, a hard and insolent man. They have high words one day, and the Boy takes the Colonel's part. The next day Austin is found lying face down among the cottonwoods above the gold-shotted gravel, a bullet wound in his back. He is carried back to Bonanza, and revived sufficiently to say he had not seen the man who shot him, but he guessed he knew him all the same. Then he swore feebly at the lawlessness of the south, and gave up the ghost. Not a man on the creek but understood whom Scoville Austin meant.

The Grand Forks constable had a watch put on the Colonel's tent, but the Colonel was not likely to escape. He was down with typhoid. They came to arrest his partner, the Boy. The constable touched him on the shoulder. "We have a warrant for you."

"Look here," the boy whispered, "I— don't know what you mean, but I'll go along with you, of course; only don't talk before this man. And just give me a second, will you?" he said to the North-West Mounted Police. "Just till I hear what the doctor fella says about my pardner."

They agreed, and the Boy goes back into the tent. Maudie, who has followed the Colonel from Minook on one of the later steamers, has installed herself as nurse. The Boy gives her money to use for the sick man. "Look here, pull the Colonel through, Maudie. Pull him through."

"I'll do my darnedest," she said. For the first time the Boy shook hands with Maudie. Then he went out, and gave himself up.

Nicholas of Pymeut's sister, Muckluck, who, like all the rest of the world, had also come up the river, had been hanging about in company with a native man. When she heard what had happened she rushed to Dawson and made an explanation.

Her companion had shot Austin. Yes, he admitted it. He was one of the few people on Bonanza Creek who had no cause to hate Austin. But another native had killed a white man, and been taken away in a ship and had "the time of his life," being tried and acquitted, since it was found he had acted in self-defence. He had travelled on a railroad, seen a white man's city, and lived like a lord. He came home to find himself the most famous man of his tribe.

His example fired Muckluck's rejected lover. He, too, would kill one of these white men, and get himself taken away from the hard-hearted Pymeut maiden and be shown all the wonders of the earth. So he put a bullet into Austin's back.

Now, Muckluck knew better than to believe things would turn out as her suitor thought, and she made him hold his tongue till she heard the Boy was going to suffer. She couldn't stand that. She had a soft place in her heart for the Boy. So she made the native own up and the Boy was saved.

He got back to Bonanza to find Maudie had nursed the Colonel faithfully, but, all the same, he was dying. O'Flynn and Mac and Potts came out from Dawson to see the Colonel before he went "over the Great Divide."

He was buried in the old moose pasture, with people standing by who knew the world had worn a friendlier face because he had been in it.

When the ice began to run in the Yukon, the gold-seekers, lucky and unlucky—Potts, O'Flynn, Mac, Maudie, and hundreds more—made ready to go home by the shorter, better route by sea, along the coast of British Columbia.

On the last boat to go down the river, amongst a motley crowd, was the Boy's friend, the little sister of St. Ann, who had been sent from the Yukon Mission to nurse the typhoid patients in the

Catholic hospital at Dawson. The purser refused to allow her on board the steamer because she had no ticket. The Boy explained that a nun was forbidden to carry money, and finally he paid for her. As the boat moved off down the great river, it was seen that the Boy and Nig were on board. O'Flynn rushed to the wharf's edge, and screamed at the captain to "Stop, be the Siven!" Mac issued orders, and Muckluck wept excitedly. Potts drawled, "Guess he means to go that way."

"Well," said a bystander, "I never seen any feller as calm as that who was bein' took the way he didn't want to go."

"D'ye mean there's a new strike?"

The suggestion flashed electric through the crowd.

"*He* knows what he's about!"

"Lord! I wish I'd a' froze to him!"

As O'Flynn, back from his chase, hoarse and puffing, stopped suddenly. "Be the Siven! Father Brachet *said* the little divil'd be coming back to Howly Cross!"

"Where's that?"

"Lower River Camp."

"Gold there?"

"No."

"Then you're talking through your hat!"

"Say, Potts, where in hell *is* he goin'?"

THE ROSEBUD

QUEEN of fragrance, lovely Rose,
The beauties of thy leaves disclose!
—But thou, fair Nymph, thyself survey
In this sweet offspring of a day.
That miracle of face must fail,
Thy charms are sweet, but charms are frail:
Swift as the short-lived flower they fly,
At morn they bloom, at evening die:
Though Sickness yet a while forbears,
Yet Time destroys what Sickness spares:
Now Helen lives alone in fame,
And Cleopatra's but a name:
Time must indent that heavenly brow,
And thou must be what they are now.
                    —*William Broome*

PRAISE AND PRAYER

PRAISE is devotion fit for mighty minds,
    The diff'ring world's agreeing sacrifice;
Where Heaven divided faiths united finds:
    But Prayer in various discord upward flies.

For Prayer the ocean is where diversely
    Men steer their course, each to a sev'ral coast;
Where all our interest so discordant be
    That half beg winds by which the rest are lost.

By Penitence when we ourselves forsake,
    'Tis but in wise design on piteous Heaven;
In Praise we nobly give what God may take,
    And are, without a beggar's blush, forgiven.
                    —*Sir William Davenant*

J. B. PRIESTLEY

ANGEL PAVEMENT

ANGEL PAVEMENT is a typical London sidestreet, except that it is shorter, narrower and dingier than most. Into one of its dingier and narrower offices the author has chosen to put individuals who represent various aspects of city life today, whether it be London, New York or Singapore. How romance, success, and excitement were brought for a time to their drab existences is refreshingly told by J. B. Priestley, whose wisdom, humor, and broad observation of life make him universally recognized as one of the outstanding authors of our day.

A Mine of Glittering Material

MR. GOLSPIE took the typewritten sheets from Miss Matfield and then spread them out on her table. "All six letters alike, eh? That's the style, Miss Matfield. Hello, is this exactly what I said?"

"As a matter of fact, it isn't." And Miss Matfield raised her eyes and gave him a steady level glance. "I've changed *was* into *were* twice, simply for the sake of making it more grammatical. That's all."

"Half a minute, half a minute," Mr. Golspie boomed at her. "Not more grammatical. Just grammatical. Either it's grammatical or it isn't, d'you see?" He guffawed, suddenly, dreadfully. "Well, I'll take these nice grammatical letters away with me. You've addressed the envelopes, have you? Right." He turned his broad back on her, gave Mr. Smeeth a wink, whistled softly, and departed for the private office.

Miss Matfield drew her full lower lip between her teeth and frowned at her typewriter. As usual, she was left with a vague sense of defeat. It was, of course, the man's insentiveness that made him so difficult to snub.

She could not make up her mind about him, had no label or pigeon-hole ready for him, and this annoyed her, for she liked to know exactly what she felt and thought about people; to be able to dismiss them in a phrase. The fact that

Mr. Golspie spoke to her every day, if only for a few minutes, gave her work to do, was sufficient to make her anxious to determine her attitude towards him.

In the talk among the girls at the Club, all the men who dictated letters to them became immense characters, comic, grotesquely villainous, or heroic and adorable. Their feminity, frozen for a few hours every day at the keyboard of their machines, thawed and gushed out in these perfervid personalities. Behind their lowered eyes, their demure expressions, as they sat with their notebooks on hard little office chairs, these comic and romantic legends buzzed and sang, to be released later in the dining room, the lounge, the tiny bedrooms of the Club.

THUS something had to be done about Mr. Golspie, who would have appeared to most of the girls, as Miss Matfield knew only too well, a gigantic find, a mine of glittering material. So far he had merely passed as "weird," but that would not do. It had not sufficed in Miss Matfield's private thoughts since the first two days.

She knew exactly what she thought about the others at the office. Mr. Dersingham she neither liked nor disliked; she merely tolerated him with a sort of easy contempt; he was "sloppy and a bit feeble," and a familiar type with nothing at all weird about *him*. Smeeth seemed to her a vaguely pathetic creature who lived a grey life in some grey suburb; the pleasure he got from what seemed to her his drudgery sometimes irritated her, but at other times it roused something like pity; and when she was not despising him, she liked him.

Turgis she despised and occasionally resented. She resented his shabbiness and dinginess, his unhealthy skin and open mouth, his whole forlorn air, simply because these things, which were always there in the office beside her, hurt her own pride by indicating the indignity of her situation. Occasionally, perhaps

after a week-end in the country, when the thought of going back to Angel Pavement almost made her feel sick, there flashed through her mind an image of Turgis. There had been moments when she had felt sorry for him, but they were very rare.

But not Mr. Golspie, the mysterious, large, jocular, brutal man, who always contrived—and for the life of her she could not discover how he did it—to get the best of her in any talk between them, who irritated one half of her, the sensible half by making the other half feel fluttered and foolish, all girlish—ugh!

New Year's Eve

MANY a time afterwards Miss Matfield wondered if Mr. Golspie deliberately engineered that staying late on New Year's Eve. She never asked him and never made up her own mind about it. At the time, it seemed accidental enough.

"Do you know why I came to your place?" said Mr. Golspie, as they walked along. "I looked up the names of the firms in this line of business, and Twigg and Dersingham took my fancy not because of their name, but because of the address. Angel Pavement did it. I was so tickled by that name, I said to myself, I must have a look at that lot, first of all. And if I hadn't said that, I shouldn't have been here, and you wouldn't have been trotting along here with me, would you?"

"Didn't you know anything about this business before?" she asked.

"Not a thing. But I've picked up a good many different sorts of business in my time, and I haven't finished yet, not by a long chalk. But I don't call this veneer trade a proper business. It's a side line. There's no size to it. You might as well be selling sets o' chessmen or rocking-horses. No size to it, no chance of real growth, you see? It's all right for Dersingham—it's about his mark—but then he's not really in business. He's only got one leg in it instead of being up to his neck in it. He thinks he's a gentle-

man amusing himself. Too many of his sort in the City here. That's how the Jews get on, and the Americans. None of that nonsense about them."

A taxi came jogging along at that moment, and Mr. Golspie at once claimed it, shouted "Bundle's" to the driver, and then sat very close to Miss Matfield.

Mr. Bundle, whoever he was, had remembered one simple fact when he first established his tradition of catering, and that was that Man is one of the larger *carnivora*. Whole beeves and droves must have been slaughtered daily in its name. If you asked for beef at Bundle's, they took you at your word and promptly wheeled up to you the red dripping half of a roasted ox and the waiter would cut off a pound or two here and a pound or two there. A request for mutton was not treated perhaps with the same high seriousness, but even that meant that legs and shoulders came trundling up from all directions, and you found yourself facing a few assorted pounds of it on your plate.

MUTTON was wheeled at Miss Matfield and beef was wheeled at Mr Golspie, and, while acolytes brought vegetables, the high priests gravely pointed to fat and lean and under-done and over-done, and then sliced away Mr. Golspie, after consulting briefly with her, ordered a good rich burgundy.

"Only about half a glass, please. It's lovely rich sunshiny stuff. I feel as if I'd have about fifteen of my Club dinners rolled into one. I don't believe I shall ever be hungry again."

"You look well on it," said Mr. Golspie, who perhaps looked a shade too well on it himself. "You've a fine colour, Miss Matfield, and your eyes are sparkling, and altogether you look full of fight and fun, too good for Angel Pavement, I can tell you. I said that to myself the first time I set eyes on you. That's why I kept my eye on you. Did you notice me keeping my eye on you?"

"Mnnn, ye-es," looking at him and hoping that her eyes were still sparkling. "Sometimes I thought you seemed quite human."

"Human!" he roared, so that a waiter jumped forward. "I'm human enough, I can tell you. I'm a dam' sight too human."

"If you're in the City, you can't be too human for me, Mr. Golspie. I've spent months there sometimes and never spoken to anyone who seemed to me really human. Awful creatures. Then people like Mr. Smeeth, all grey and withered and not bad really, but just—pathetic."

"No, Smeeth's not a bad feller. But he's not pathetic. He doesn't make me weep, anyhow. All he wants is to be safe, that's what's the matter with him. But he's better than that dreary youngster you have in there—what's his name—Turgis?"

"Oh, he's hopeless, I agree."

"He's a typical specimen of what they're breeding here now—no sense, no guts, no anything. I can't even remember the look of the lad, although I see him nearly every day. That shows you what impression he makes."

"I know. And yet that funny little Cockney girl, Poppy Sellers, thinks he's marvellous. I've watched her worshipping him at a distance. Isn't it strange—I mean, the way everybody amounts to something different to everybody else?"

"Well, a lad like that 'ull never mean anything to me, never amount to anything to anybody, I should think, no more than a bit of straw or paper blowing about the streets," said Mr. Golspie.

He lit a cigar and then, over coffee and liqueurs rumbled on about his experiences in Baltic countries and in other places still more mysterious and romantic to her. He talked in the way she had always felt a man should talk. And he was interested in her; he was not merely filling in an idle hour; she attracted him, had attracted him, she felt now, for some time; and—oh!—it was all amusing and exciting.

WHEN they were safely in a taxi and on the way home he swept her to him and kissed her several times. "I'm just wishing you a proper Happy New Year," he said, and held her close, so close that she could hardly breathe.

She could not have described it as being either pleasant or unpleasant. It was not an experience that could fall into such easy categories. If it belonged anywhere, it belonged to the fire, flood and earthquake department. Her quickening blood faced and replied to this huge masculine onslaught, but the rest of her was simply dazed and shaken.

She suddenly felt very tired and quite disinclined to talk. She drooped, leaned against him and could only repeat to herself that it was all quite absurd, though all the time she knew very well that whatever else it might be, it was not absurd. Mr. Golspie was quiet too, although in that little enclosed space he seemed now a gigantically vital creature, a being essentially different from herself, a huge throbbing engine of a man.

"We'll have some more nights out together, shall we? Just the two of us, roaming round a bit, going to a show or two, and so on. What d'you say?"

"Yes, I'd like to. In fact—I'd love it." She glanced out of the window, then rapped on it. "We're just outside now. Please don't come out. No, no more. All right then—there! Good-bye—and—and thank you for my nice big dinner."

Flying Rumors of Disaster

WHEN he asked her, two days later, to spend another evening with him she gladly accepted, although she had told herself several times before that she would refuse; and after that they spent a good deal of time together. They would have dinner somewhere, and then amuse themselves by visiting some show of his choice.

She never learned a great deal about him; he would talk about odd experiences he had had by the hour, but he remained mysterious; she never discovered what his plans were, and at times she suspected that he did not intend to stay in England much longer, but this suspicion was only based on casual vague remarks; she never went near his flat, never met his daughter, and never heard a single word from him about his dead wife, if indeed she was dead; and yet she felt she knew him as she had never known a man before.

Sometimes he was simply friendly or uncle-ish, dismissing her with a pat on the shoulder; sometimes he turned cynically and grossly amorous, and when he tried to paw her and she repulsed him, he jeered at her and said things that were all the more brutal because there was in them a hard core of truth, and then she saw him as a gross, middle-aged toper, loathed him, and despised herself for having anything to do with him.

But at other times, after a happy exciting evening, he would reach out to her in a sudden passion and her own mood would flare up to match with his, and in some little patch of darkness or in the taxi going home, they would kiss and clutch and strain to one another, without a single word of love passing between them, and she would be left shaken and gasping, unable to decide whether she was a woman who was falling in love with this strangely unlikely man or a crazy little fool who had just had too much excitement and wine, who ought to go and have a good hot bath and learn some sense and decency.

Then, one night, as he took her back to the Club, he said, quite casually: "I see they're having a nice fine spell on the South Coast. What about a trip down there next week-end, Lilian? Might get hold of a car."

"Oh, yes," she cried at once, without thinking, for week-ends out of London were her dream, even in January. "Let's do that."

"Is it a bargain?" he said quickly, triumphantly.

And then she realised what it meant. "No, no. I'm sorry. I spoke without thinking."

"Ah, she spoke without thinking, did she? You do far too much thinking. Girls shouldn't think too much, not good-looking ones, anyhow. When I first met you, you'd done nothing but think for a long time, and you weren't looking too cheerful on it. Well I'm disappointed in you. Still, I'll try again. Otherwise, y'know, you might regret saying that, some day. You think it over."

"I won't."

But she did think it over, and unfortunately she began that very night, so that it was hours and hours before she got to sleep. Her angry taut body refused to relax; her head was a huge hot ring round which her thoughts went galloping dustily; and as she turned in the uneasy darkness she heard the late taxis and cars go hooting far away, melancholy hateful sounds in the deep night, like flying rumors of disaster.

He Touched Wood

MR. SMEETH among his little figures was as busy and happy as a monk at his manuscript. Turgis, whose duty it was to see that goods were duly forwarded to and from Twigg & Dersingham's became both hoarse and haughty down the telephone to all manner of forwarding agents, and spoke to railway goods clerks as if they were strange and unwelcome dogs. Miss Matfield rattled off her letters with slightly less contempt and disgust, rather as if they were no longer the effusions of complete lunatics.

Mr. Smeeth was happier than he had been for a long time. The shadow of dismissal unemployment, degradation, ruin, had gone, except in occasional dreams, when, after a bit of fried liver or toasted cheese had refused to be digested, he had found himself out of a job for ever and walking down vague dark streets with nothing on but his vest and pants. It had vanished from his waking hours.

There had been times when he had almost hated going to the bank, for he felt that even the cashiers were telling one another that Twigg & Dersingham were looking pretty rocky, but it had been a pleasure to work there since the advent of Mr. Golspie. Smeeth remembered graphically the afternoon several weeks before when the tide turned. Dersingham had called him into his private office.

"The position is this, Smeeth," Mr. Dersingham had explained. "Golspie's got the sole agency for all this new Baltic stuff. They won't sell it to anybody here but him. It's good wood, all of it, quite up to standard, and he can get it at prices, thirty, forty and fifty percent lower than we've been paying. I don't mind telling you that when he first explained what he was after, I wasn't keen at all. It sounded fishy to me."

"Does seem a bit queer he should come along like that, doesn't it, sir?"

"That's what I thought. But we've been going round with some of his samples at prices we could sell the stuff at on his figures, and they've been absolutely leaping at them. We can cut everybody out, absolutely clean cut. We can do

more business, Smeeth, with this new stuff in a fortnight than the firm's ever done, even in its best days, in a month. And you know what business we've been doing lately? Awful!

"Now then, this is what's happening. Golspie came along here to see me quite by chance. He'd got this contract, but he wanted some firm already in the trade to join up with. All this is—er—in—y'know—between ourselves, Smeeth."

"I understand, sir" said Mr. Smeeth, flattered and delighted.

"Golspie—Mr. Golpsie—is coming in here as a sort of general manager, working on a jolly good commission. But then he's bringing all the business really, and he'll be responsible for getting the wood over and all that side of it.

"This next week or two, Smeeth," and here Mr. Dersingham sprang up and clenched his fists, just as if he had never seen a decent public school, "we've got to drive it hard, go all out, and I'm depending on you for the office side of it. You people have got to stand behind me in this. It's a great chance for all of us, and, of course, a tremendous stroke of luck, Golspie's coming here. He's going all out himself on this—he's that sort of chap, very keen and all that—and we've got to keep pace."

To Mr. Smeeth—though he did not say so—life was a journey, unarmed and without guide or compass, through a jungle where poisonous snakes were lurking and man-eating tigers might spring out of every thicket. Only when he saw a little clear space in front of him could he be easy in mind.

Thus he lived, this man who went so cosily from his little house to his little office, more apprehensively, more dangerously, than one of Edward Third's bowmen. He touched wood, and desperately hoped for the best.

Chap in the Crowd

Turgis' father took no interest in him, hadn't for years, and he had no other near relations. They didn't care much about him at the office. He had no friends. He was just a chap in the crowd. Nearly all his time away from the office was spent in a crowd somewhere, getting back to his lodgings in the packed tube, returning to the thronged streets afterwards, perhaps eating in some crowded place, then waiting in a queue to get in a picture theatre, making one of a huge audience, wandering along the lamp-lit pavements, and he was for ever surrounded by strange, indifferent or hostile faces, looking into millions of eyes that never lit up with any gleam of recognition, and spending hour after hour in the very thick of packed humanity without exchanging a single word with anybody.

What he wanted was Love, Romance, a Wonderful Girl of His Own. And these had lately all been assuming the same shape in his mind, that of Miss Lena Golspie. He had never spoken to her, had never seen her except once, at a distance, since the day she appeared at the office, but he had thought a great deal about her.

He had seen the very house, or rather the upper half of the house, in which she and her father lived. He had, in fact, seen it several times, and had actually been watching when lights were being turned on and off there. He had been tempted to walk boldly up to 4a and offer some wild excuse for trying to see Miss Golspie. But he could think of nothing that did not sound insane, and realising that this crazy step might spoil everything and get him into trouble at the office, he dismissed the notion.

Then one afternoon Mr. Smeeth came out, looking fussy, as he always did when he had something special to do. "Let's see," he said, looking round the office, "does anybody here live Maida Vale way?"

What was this? Turgis' heart jumped and knocked. "Is there anything I ca do, Mr. Smeeth. I know somebody i Maida Vale, often go there."

"Yes, I think you'd better have th job, Turgis," said the unconscious M Smeeth. "You see, Mr. Golspie's got daughter living with him—well, yo know that, because she came here on day, didn't she? Her father has ar ranged with us to let her have som money from his account here. She want it at once and we've just telephone to see if she'll be in, and she will trust her!"

"Well, I'll take it, Mr. Smeeth." Oh wouldn't he just!

"I say, listen," cried Poppy Sellers "If you get a chance of going in, go in and then tell us what it's like tomor row. I'd like to know what sort of place Mr. Golspie lives in. Wouldn't you, Mis Matfield?"

Miss Matfield, to Turgis's surprise, for he expected her to be disdainful of such idle curiosity, admitted at once that she would. "I'm rather sorry I didn't ask for the job," she added. "It would be amusing to see what the daughter's like. I have just seen her but that's all. And I can't imagine what sort of place Mr. Golspie lives in, though it's probably some furnished maisonette they're camping in. Maida Vale's stiff with them."

"I'll say 'Good afternoon,'" cried Tur gis loudly and cheerfully and off he went, the money and the receipt form snugly tucked away in the inside pocket of his coat, the best coat he had and all brushed and as natty as you like.

Dreams Come True

It was Miss Lena herself who came to the door. She was dressed in shimmering greenish-blue, and she was prettier than ever. At the sight of her standing there, solid and real again at last, his heart bumped and his mouth went suddenly dry.

"I've come from Twigg and Dersingham's, Miss Golspie," he announced, stammering a little.

Her face lit up at once. "Oh, have you brought that money?" she cried, in that same queer fascinating voice he remembered so well. "How much is it? Come in, though. This way. You're the one I spoke to that day when I called

Mr. Golspie pounced on him at once
clapping a heavy hand on his shoulder.

Illustration for J. B. Priestley's
"ANGEL PAVEMENT"

t the office, aren't you? Do you remem-
er me?"

Turgis assured her fervently that he
id. He was still standing, awkwardly,
vith his hat in his hand and his over-
oat hanging loose from his shoulders,
nd he felt rather hot and uncomfortable.

"You seem jolly sure about it," she said
ightly. "How did you remember so
vell?"

"Well, I remembered you," he replied,
asping a little, "because I thought you
vere the prettiest girl I'd ever spoken
o in all my life."

"You didn't, did you? Are you seri-
us?" She shrieked with laughter. "What
marvellous thing to say! Is that why
ou brought the money?"

"Yes, it is," he said earnestly.

When they had concluded their little
ransaction, she said suddenly, "Have
ou had any tea?"

"No, I haven't," said Turgis promptly.

"Well, I haven't, either. Let's have
ome."

After they had finished tea and were
alling each other by their first names
ne leaned back in her chair and said:
What shall we do now? You haven't to
o home or anything, have you?"

Turgis, looking his devotion, said at
nce that he hadn't to go home or any-
vhere.

"Let's go to the movies. We can go
o the place near here. It's not bad. Just

wait; I shan't be long. Or, look here,
you could take these tea things back
into the kitchen."

It was better still when they were sitting, close, cosier than ever, in the
scented and deep rose-shaded dimness of
the balcony in the picture theatre. (Turgis had paid for these best seats, and was
left with exactly three-and-threepence.

They were both enthusiastic and
knowing patrons of the films, so that
they had a good deal to talk about, and
frequently as they whispered, her head
came close to his and her hair even
brushed his cheek. He was content to sit
there, to whisper, to be so near to this
fragrant dim loveliness, with his hunger,
which he had taken into so many picture theatres, momentarily appeased.

He took her home and when they
were standing by the door he took her
hand, as if he were about to shake it,
but was at the moment too busy trying
to stammer out a few adequate phrases.

"I don't know what on earth you're
trying to say," she told him, "so don't
bother. And you might as well go now
before Dad gets back. And I'll see you
tomorrow night. Oh, don't dither so
much, silly. There!" And with that she
leaned against him, putting a hand on
each shoulder, kissed him swiftly on the
mouth, drew back, laughed, and then
shut the door on him.

Girls Are Famous For It

T was only half-past seven the next evening when he arrived at the Sov-
reign; but he did not mind that, for
would be pleasant just standing there,
atching the crowd, and knowing that
ery minute brought Lena nearer to
im.

At five minutes to eight, he pointed
ut to himself that girls always kept a
nap waiting. They were famous for it.
t eight o'clock he began to be anxious.
Ie wondered if he was waiting in the
rong place, and he hastily searched the
hole breadth of the entrance. At quar-
r past eight, his eyes began to smart.

Time, which had passed so slowly at
first, was now rushing away.

The next half hour was nothing but
a dismal farce, for he knew that she
could not be coming now, yet somehow
his feet refused to move more than a
yard or two away. It was nine o'clock
when he finally left the place, with two
useless tickets in his pocket.

Once he had made up his mind, he
did not hesitate at all, but marched
straight up to the door and rang the bell.

The door opened a few inches. "Yes,"
said a voice, "what is it?"

"Is Miss Golspie in, please?"

The girl, obviously the maid who had been out on the previous night, now opened the door properly and came forward to have a look at him. "Oh no, she isn't. I think she went out with a friend, because she got all dressed up just after seven and she told me she wouldn't be back till very late, and then about half-past seven a young gentleman called for her in a motor car. And that's all I can tell you. Would you like to leave a message?"

"No, no message." He walked slowly down the garden, out of the gate, across the road. He had to stop at the corner, because he was biting his handkerchief, which he had screwed into a ball. When at last he was quiet and had put his handkerchief away, he walked on and on through a blank misery of a night.

The outward changes in Turgis, already noticed by Miss Matfield and Mr. Smeeth, were only tiny scattered hints and clues, and by no means in proportion to the changes within, for during the last seven weeks, ever since the night when Lena Golspie had failed to keep her appointment with him, his life had been like a bad dream.

He had been able to call again at the flat but she had only spent half an hour with him and had been vague and shifty in her excuses. She had been cold, had criticized his appearance, his manners, and had made him jealous. When he had tried to kiss her, she had laughed at him and evaded him.

After that, he never bothered going again, living entirely in his thought of Lena and in the memory of that first rapturous night. He was ready, was eager, to see in everything she had done a queenly wilfulness that would gradually be consumed in the mounting fires of passion. He knew that this was what happened with these wonderful creatures: he had seen it happen many a time in the pictures.

Then he decided that he must see her just once again. The door was opened by the enormous woman in the apron.

"Do you know if Miss Golspie's in please?"

"I'll see. I'll give her a shout." And the woman went down the hall and climbed a few steps: "Miss Golspie there's a young man here. He wants to know if you're alone up there and can he come up to see you?"

"Yes, I'm all on my lonesome tonight," Turgis heard Lena cry. "Tell him to come up, please, and I won't be a minute." She sounded as if she was pleased. It was wonderful to hear her like that.

"Hel-lo!" cried Lena gaily in the doorway. Then the sound was cut short. "Oh!" she cried, staring at him. "It's you." And her face fell, her voice dropped. "Do you want to see my father about something?" she demanded.

"No, I want to see you—Lena—about Everything."

"I told you as plainly as I could I didn't want to see you any more. Why can't you go away and stay away? Just because I felt sorry for you once and hadn't anything much to do and was nice to you, do you think I've got to spend all my time trailing round to the pictures with you?"

"Lena, please, please, just listen a minute—"

"Oh, go away, can't you! Fool!"

"You'll have to listen," he screamed. He sprang forward, dropping his hat, and seized both her wrists and held them tight.

"You damned rotten, rotten—"

Then she flared up into a shriek: "Keep your filthy hands off me," and she flung her own hands up into his face, pushing him away.

He looked at her and there came, like a flash of lightning, the conviction that she was hateful, and something broke, and a great blinding tide of anger swept over him. Her scream was cut short, for his hands were round her soft white throat, pressing and pressing it as he shook her savagely. A horrible rusty noise came from her open mouth. She suddenly went limp and, as his hands eleased their grip, her eyes closed and he slipped backwards, striking her head against the corner of the divan. She made no movement at all, not a twitch, not a tremor. No, that wasn't Lena any more; that was a body. You couldn't lie there like that unless you were dead. Lena was dead.

Turgis Is Sacked

THE office door was slightly open, so that a thin pencil of light pointed across the landing. Turgis waited a minute, staring at it from the shadow. Then, summoning all the courage left him in the world, he blundered in, almost flinging himself into the private office beyond.

"Now who the hell are you?" roared Mr. Golspie, jumping up from his chair at the table. Somebody gave a scream. It was Miss Matfield, in the corner.

"Lena," said Turgis, choking over the name. "I think—I've killed her."

Mr. Golspie pounced on him at once, clapping a heavy hand on his shoulder. "Come on, then. What happened? Get it out, quick."

Turgis blurted out a few sentences, broken and confused, but they were quite enough.

"My God, if she is, I'll kill you. Come on, get up, you—you bloody little rat— we're going straight into the taxi and we're going to see, and you're coming with us."

It was a long, long journey. For the first five minutes or so, nothing was said, but after that Mr. Golspie, out of sheer impatience, began to ask questions, and piece by piece, he dragged the whole miserable story out of Turgis, who sat facing him, on one of the little seats. Miss Matfield hardly spoke a word the whole time, and when she did it was in a very soft shaky voice. But she stared at Turgis, and when lights flashed in he saw that her face was pale.

TURGIS had not been in the Golspie house more than a minute before he knew that Lena was not dead.

"Little monkey!" Mr. Golspie rumbled. "Good job you thought something was up and came in. I'm much obliged. Very grateful. Just take Miss Matfield in to her, will you, and I'll be back in a minute or two." He must be talking to the landlady.

"Is she all right?" cried Turgis, as Mr. Golspie came into the room.

"I don't know about that," he replied grimly, "but she's a damned sight better than she was when you left her lying here, you crazy little skunk. Come here."

"Oh!—thank God!"

"Come here. You can do your thanking afterwards." And he grabbed Turgis by the lapel of his coat and yanked him nearer. "You don't go back to that office, understand. Keep right away from it. Keep away from me altogether, see? The very sight of you turns my stomach, see? So get out and bloody well stay out. There!" And Mr. Golspie put his hand in the small of his back and with a short run and a tremendous heave sent him sprawling down the stairs. He pitched forward, badly banged his nose so hard that it bled, and was bruised, but he managed to pick himself up at the bottom and go blindly along the hall to the front door.

He waited a minute outside, leaning dizzily against one of the pillars. The cool darkness rocked round him. In the garden he was violently sick.

Done In

IT was wearing away like any other Friday afternoon. There was nothing to suggest that it might blow up any minute, unless the unusual activities of Mr. Dersingham, who appeared to be moving uneasily now in the private office, were considered to be fantastically significant.

"Smeeth, Smeeth."

"Yes, Mr. Dersingham." Mr. Smeeth did not like being summoned in this fashion; it was not dignified. He hurried in, however, for Mr. Dersingham sounded as if he had something important he wanted to say.

"Shut the door, Smeeth," said Mr. Dersingham, who did not look so pink and cheerful as usual.

"Everything's wrong, Smeeth, every damned thing, unless you can see a way out. Golspie's cleared out and he's done us in, absolutely done us in. I ought to have known."

"But what's happened, Mr. Dersingham? I thought you knew he might leave us. You told me so a week or two ago, and you said you were getting him to sign an agreement, when he drew all the forward commission, so that you would have the agency."

"Oh, we've got the agency all right," cried Mr. Dersingham, with great bitterness. "Only it's not worth having now, that's all. Mikorsky's have raised all their prices. They're all up fifty and sixty and even seventy per cent."

"As much as that? Good Lord, Mr. Dersingham, that's a ridiculous advance. It makes them as dear as the most expensive of the old firms we were dealing with before, doesn't it? I see, now."

"No, you don't see, you don't see at all, yet," Mr. Dersingham yelled at him. "It's a lot worse than that. I got a letter from Golspie this morning. Here, you can read it for yourself."

M R. SMEETH read it through twice. It pretended to be an ordinary business letter, but there was a good deal of unpleasant irony in it. One phrase, which practically said that Mr. Dersingham had tried to sneak the agency for himself and had not succeeded, made Smeeth look up and ask a question.

"Did you really write to those people and try to get the agency yourself, sir?" he asked.

Mr. Dersingham nodded.

Mr. Smeeth hesitated a moment. "I don't think you ought to have done that, sir," he said finally, respectful but reproachful.

"Oh, well," cried Mr. Dersingham, struggling with his embarrassment, "perhaps I oughtn't to. As it's turned out, it was a bad move. But I wasn't really trying anything underhand, you know, Smeeth. I never liked the look of Golspie and I didn't know what tricks he might be up to. So I just wrote a confidential letter to Mikorsky's, saying it would pay them to have the agency properly in the hands of a wholesale firm here like ours, and that the—er—present arrangement wasn't really satisfactory to them or to us either and that they ought to consider it. I didn't know they were friends of his. I thought they had an ordinary business agreement, and I considered I was entitled to suggest another business agreement, leaving Golspie out."

"Yes, I see that," said Mr. Smeeth, still a little doubtful. "And I suppose they told him then, and that's what put his back up?"

"Oh, they did that, but I think he'd been ready to play any dirty little trick right from the first. You see he encloses a little document that had—what is it?—escaped his memory. Well, there's the little document, that—that statement of Mikorsky's, dated over a month ago, raising all the prices."

"But—but," Mr. Smeeth stammered, as he looked at this list, "we can't be expected to pay these prices. We've already bought heavily on the old prices."

"Have we? Golspie did the buying, and I can't find any acknowledgment from them. The point is, Smeeth—don't you see?—whether we've bought the stuff or not, we've *sold it.* We've sold stacks and stacks of it, thousands of square feet, big orders, all those orders we paid Golspie that commission on."

"But Mr. Dersingham—it's—it's ruination, sheer ruination."

" A ND it's damnably, damnably unfair, Smeeth. We've simply been swindled. And the worst of it is that we have nothing that we can sue him for. All he's done is to collect some commission and keep a letter back. You can't go to the police about that. Swine!

"Where I made the mistake though, Smeeth, was not trusting to what's it—instinct, intuition; you know, I was trying to be a smart City bounder, with an eye for a tricky bit of business and nothing else—y'know. Not my style at all, really. I didn't like the chap and I ought to have known he'd do me down. Never mind, he'll come to a sticky finish.

"That was a queer business, y'know, Smeeth, about Turgis and that girl, when Golspie came and said Turgis would have to be sacked because he's been up to some mysterious games with the daughter. I never really understood what it was all about—though I'd like to bet that Golspie's daughter was up to her tricks there—she looked that sort. Thinking it over now, though I feel a bit sorry for the poor devil. Have you heard anything about him, Smeeth?"

"Miss Sellers has seen him once or twice, I believe. I fancy she's a bit sweet on him. He's not got another job yet, of course, and it's not likely he will for some time." He breathed hard, like a man who wants to sigh but has forgotten how to do it.

"Well, I'd better be getting along," said Mr. Dersingham. "I'll stop at the club and see if I can get a bite. I might see a fellow there who could give me one or two tips about this miserable business. Then I'll go home, and that's the part I'm not looking forward to, I can tell you. Are you going home now?"

"Yes," said Mr. Smeeth slowly, buttoning his overcoat. "I'm going home."

Imitation Wedding Ring

As HER bus turned into that hive of buses in front of Victoria station, Miss Matfield shivered a little. She was nervous; she was excited and her mind was facing two different ways. She went to the place where she had arranged to meet Mr. Golspie, which was on the departure side. Mr. Golspie was not to be seen. This did not surprise her, for she was rather early. She was somewhat relieved to find that he was not there. It left her with a welcome breathing space. She was by no means single-minded about this adventure.

Last Tuesday, just before they parted, he had asked her once again to go away for the week-end with him, and this time, moved obscurely by many different feelings and forces, something genuinely eager and passionate in the man's voice, a sudden desire to clutch at experience, to throw herself upon life, a contempt for her qualms and misgivings and timidities, she had agreed to go.

Yet there was a creature in her that had some of her rich blood flowing through it, that very blood which this coarse, middle-aged man could so inspire that it dazzled and inflamed her, a shrinking and fastidious creature that cried to run away, to run away and hide. It protested against the shabbiness and furtiveness of this adventure, and pounced upon the sinister lack of fairness in it. It loathed the cheap imitation wedding ring that was now tucked away in her bag, a ring that was part of the adventure, and that had seemed rather a joke when it first had been mentioned last Tuesday.

IF GOLSPIE had asked her to marry him, no matter if he had told her that they would have to settle in the most outlandish place, she would have agreed; but he had not asked her to marry him. Yet he wanted her, not idly either, and when all was said and done, that was a heartening and exciting fact; and after this, he might want her still more, and then—well, everything might be different.

Only two minutes now. She hurried over to the entrance to No. 17 platform and looked over the barrier down the waiting train. Then she returned, even more hastily, to her place near the clock. From there she heard the train go out. When the train had gone, she stood quite still for a minute or two longer, then walked away.

She had to wait again before she could

get a telephone call put through to his flat. There was a reply and it obviously came from a maid.

"Is Mr. Golspie there, please?"

"No, he's not. He's gone. So has Miss Golspie. They've both gone to South Africa or South America or one of them places. In a boat, I do know."

He had gone, left the country, without even telling her he was going, without even telling her he could not keep this appointment at the station. He had simply tossed the week-end away, and her with it, as if it had been a crumpled bit of paper. If he had not forgotten all about it, then he had not cared enough to see her for the last time or even to send a message. And this was the man—oh, the humiliation of it all!

Once in the Club, she hurried upstairs, as if she had stolen the suitcase she carried. Hastily, mechanically, she washed, tidied her hair, powdered her face and then went down to the dining room. She did not really want food, but something impelled her to throw herself back into the routine of the Club. When she got back to her room after dinner, she began examining all her clothes and grimly set aside some stockings to be mended. Then she remembered something.

"Yes, he's gone, and that means there'll be an awful lot to do and they'll have to get new people. Well, I'm going down to Angel Pavement in the morning and I shall tell Mr. Dersingham that I believe I can do anything that any man could do—and that he ought to give me a chance. I believe he will too, particularly now. Very soon, I might have a real job, with a decent salary and proper responsibility and everything."

During the next hour Messrs. Twigg & Dersingham grew more and more prosperous and she, a real member of the firm, grew more and more prosperous with it. Before she finally got to sleep, she had furnished not only her tiny flat in town, but also her little week-end cottage, which was the delightful admiration of her mother and other occasional guests. "Lilian, you are *lucky*." This wa the last dream of the day, and it was ver pleasant.

The dreams that followed in the night the dreams that came without being asked, were curiously different, all dark and troubled, like the dreams of a child who has been hurried away to a strange place.

Mr. golspie and his new acquaint ance leaned over the rail, and de cided that they were ready for lunch Meanwhile they talked idly.

"I don't blame you," said Mr. Sugden "I don't like London myself—never did I had a year there once. Didn't like i at all. I couldn't get on with the Lon doners—too much of this haw-haw-haw stuff and the striped trousers and black coat and white spat business. Didn't sui me, I can tell you. They thought the were smart, too."

"They're not—most of 'em," said Mr Golspie. "I soon found that out. I ha about four or five months of them an that was quite enough for me. They're half dead, most of 'em—half dead. N dash. No guts. I want a place where everybody's alive, where there's some thing doing."

"Where were you in London?"

"Down in the City. I wonder if yo know the place. I'd never heard of i before. Angel Pavement."

"Angel Pavement? No, I never hear of that. Meet any angels there?"

"Well, I met somebody who nearl turned into one, but not quite. No, the were all just human, and they hadn't go too damn much of that. I was sorry fo the poor devils—some of them."

A string of barges passed them, mov ing slowly on to the very heart of th city. A gull dropped, wheeled, flashed was gone, and with it went the sun.

"Well, the sun's gone in," said Mr Golspie, "so I'll go in, too." Somewhere a steamer hooted twice out of the ghostli ness. He gave a last look toward Lon don, then turned away. "And that' that."

GENE STRATTON-PORTER

MICHAEL O'HALLORAN

THE appeal of "Michael O'Halloran," as of all Gene Stratton-Porter's novels, is on the plus side of life because it is a story of persons who do credit to human nature. "Mickey" is only an orphaned street waif who manages to support himself by selling papers. But through sheer wit and grit he manages to straighten out not only his own life but the lives of his more fortunately placed friends. Mrs. Porter (1868-1924) wrote many deservedly popular stories about the people of her native State, Indiana.

"Aw KID, *come on! Be square!*"

"*You look out what you say to me.*"

"*But ain't you going to keep your word?*"

"*Mickey, do you want your head busted?*"

"*Naw! But I did your work so you could loaf; now I want the pay you promised me.*"

"*Let's see you get it! Better take it from me, hadn't you?*"

"*You're twice my size; you know I can't, Jimmy! Besides that ain't business! I did what I promised fair and square; I was giving you a chance to be square too.*"

"*Oh! Well next time you won't be such a fool!*"

Jimmy turned to step from the gutter to the sidewalk. Two things happened to him simultaneously: Mickey became a projectile. He smashed with the force of a wiry fist on the larger boy's head, while above both, an athletic arm gripped him by the collar.

Douglas Bruce was hurrying to see a client before he should leave his office and heard Mickey's admonition: "Be square!"

He sent one hasty glance toward the gutter. He saw a sullen-faced newsboy of a size that precluded longer success at paper selling, because public sympathy goes to the little fellows. Before him stood one of these same little fellows, lean, tow-haired, and blue-eyed, clean of face, neat in dress; with a pecu-liar modulation in his voice that caught Douglas squarely in the heart.

Mickey, well aware that his first blow would be all the satisfaction coming to him, put the force of his being into his punch. At the same instant Douglas thrust forth a hand that had pulled for Oxford and was yet in condition.

"What did he promise you for selling his papers?" demanded a deep voice.

"Twen—ty-*five*," answered Mickey, with all the force of inflection in his power. "And if you heard us, Mister, you heard him own up he was owing it."

"I did," answered Douglas Bruce tersely. Then to Jimmy: "Hand him over twenty-five cents."

Jimmy glared upward, but what he saw and the tightening of the hand on his collar were convincing. He drew from his pocket five nickels, dropping them into the outstretched hand of Douglas, who passed them to Mickey, the soiled fingers of whose left hand closed over them, while his right snatched off his cap. Fear was on his face, excitement was in his eyes, triumph was in his voice, while a grin of comradeship curved his lips.

"Many thanks, Boss," he said. "And would you add to them by keeping that strangle hold 'til you give me just two seconds the start of him?" He wheeled, darting through the crowd.

"Mickey!" cried Douglas Bruce. "Mickey, wait!"

But Mickey was half a block away turning into an alley.

Happy Home

FINALLY he entered a last alley. He began climbing interminable stairs. At the top of the last flight he unlocked his door to enter his happy home; for Mickey had a home, and it was a happy one. No one else lived in it, while all it contained was his.

Mickey knew three things about his father: he had had one, he was not square, and he drank himself to death. He could not remember his father, but he knew many men engaged in the occupation of his passing, so he well understood why his mother never expressed any regrets.

Vivid in his mind was her face, anxious and pale, but twinkling; her body frail and overtaxed, but hitting back at life uncomplainingly. Bad things happened, but she explained how they might have been worse; so fed on this sop, and watching her example, Mickey grew like her. The difficult time was while she sat over a sewing machine to be with him. When he grew stout-legged and self-reliant, he could be sent after the food, to carry the rent, and to sell papers, then she could work by the day, earn more, have better health, while what both brought home paid the rent of the top room back, of as bad a shamble as a self-respecting city would allow; kept them fed satisfyingly if not nourishingly, and allowed them to slip away many a nickel for the rainy day that she always explained would come. And it did.

One morning she could not get up; the following Mickey gave all their savings to a man with a wagon to take her to a nice place to rest. The man was sure about it being a nice place. She had told Mickey so often what to do if this ever happened, that when it did, all that was necessary was to remember what he had been told. After it was over and the nice place had been paid for, with the nickels and the sewing machine, with enough left for the first month's rent, Mickey faced life alone. But he knew exactly what to do, because she had told him. She had even written it down lest he forget. It was so simple that only a boy who did not mind his mother could have failed. The formula worked perfectly.

> *Morning: Get up early. Wash your face, brush your clothes. Eat what was left from supper for breakfast. Put your bed to air, then go out with your papers. Don't be afraid to offer them, or to do work of any sort you have strength for; but be deathly afraid to beg, to lie, or to steal, while if you starve, freeze, or die, never, never touch any kind of drink.*

Any fellow could do that; Mickey told dozens of them so.

He got along so well he could pay the rent each month, dress in whole clothing, have enough to eat, often cooked food on the little gasoline stove, if he were not too tired to cook it, and hide nickels in the old place daily. He had a bed and enough cover; he could get water in the hall at the foot of the flight of stairs leading to his room for his bath, to scrub the floor, and wash the dishes. From two years on, he had helped his mother with every detail of her housekeeping; he knew exactly what must be done.

It was much more dreadful than he thought it would be to come home alone, and eat supper by himself, but if he sold papers until he was almost asleep where he stood, he found he went to sleep as soon as he reached home and had supper. He did not awaken until morning; then he could hurry his work and get ahead of the other boys, and maybe sell to their customers. It might be bad to be alone, but always he could remember her, and make her seem present by doing every day exactly what she told him. Then, after all, being alone was a very wonderful thing compared with having parents who might beat and starve him.

He could dure cold, hunger, and loneliness, but he felt that he had no talent for being robbed, beaten, and starved; while lately he had fully decided upon a dog for company, when he could find the right one.

The Abandoned Child

MICKEY unlocked his door, entering for his water bucket. Such was his faith in his environment that he relocked the door while he went to the water tap.

At the foot of the fire-escape that he used in preference to the stairs, he met a boy he knew tugging a heavy basket.

"Take an end for a nickel," said the boy.

"Sure!" said Mickey. "Cross my palm with the silver."

The nickel changed hands. The place where they delivered the wash made Mickey feel almost prosperous. When he stepped from the door a long, low wail that made him shudder, reached his ear.

"What's that?" he asked the woman.

"A stiff was carried past to-day. Mebby they ain't took the kids yet."

Mickey went slowly down the stairs, his face sober. That was what his mother had feared for him. That was why she had trained him to care for himself, to save the pennies, so that when she was taken away, he still would have a home. Sounded like a child! He was halfway up the long flight of stairs before he realized that he was going. He found the door at last, then, stood listening. He heard long-drawn, heartbreaking moaning. Presently he knocked. A child's shriek was the answer. Mickey straightway opened the door. The voice guided him to a heap of misery in a corner.

"What's the matter kid?" inquired Mickey huskily.

The bundle stirred, while a cry issued. He glanced around the room. What he saw reassured him. He laid hold of the tatters, beginning to uncover what was under them. He dropped his hands, stepping back, when a tangled yellow mop and a weazened, bloated girl-child face peered at him.

"Did you come to 'get' me?" she quavered.

"No," said Mickey. "I heard you from below so I came to see what hurt you. Ain't you got folks?"

She shook her head: "They took granny in a box and they said they'd come right back and 'get' me. Oh, please, please don't let them!"

"Why they'd be good to you," said Mickey largely. "They'd give you"—he glanced at all the things the room lacked, then enumerated—"a clean bed, lots to eat, a window you could be seeing from, a doll, maybe."

"No! No!" she cried. "Granny always said some day she'd go and leave me; then they'd 'get' me. She's gone! The big man said they'd come right back. Oh don't let them! Oh hide me quick!"

"Well—well——! If you're so afraid, why don't you cut and hide yourself then?" he asked.

"My back's bad. I can't walk," the child answered.

"Oh Lord!" said Mickey. "Wher did you get hurt?"

"It's always been bad. I ain't ever walked," she said.

MICKEY took both the small bony hands reaching for him. He was so frightened with their hot, tremulous clutch, that he tried to pull away, dragging the tiny figure half to light and bringing from it moans of pain.

"Oh my back! Oh you're hurting me! Oh don't leave me! Oh boy, oh *dear* boy, please don't leave me!"

When she said "Oh dear boy," Mickey heard the voice of his mother in an hourly phrase. He crept closer.

"My name's Mickey," he said. "What's yours?"

"Lily Peaches," she answered. "Mickey, hide me. Oh hide me! Don't let them *get* me!" she begged.

She burrowed in the covers, screeching again.

"Wonder if I could keep them from getting you?" said Mickey. "There's nothing of you. If I could move you there, I bet I could feed you more than your granny did, while I know I could keep you cleaner. You could have my bed, a window to look from, and clean covers." Mickey was thinking aloud. "Having you to come home to would be lots nicer than nothing. You'd beat a dog all hollow, 'cause you can talk. If I could get you there, I believe I could be making it. Yes, I believe I could do a lot better than this, and I believe I'd like you, Lily Peaches, you are such a game little kid."

"She could lift me with one hand," she panted. "Oh Mickey, take me! Hurry!"

Mickey went back to the room where he helped deliver the clothes basket. "How much can you earn the rest of the night?" he asked the woman.

"Mebby ten cents," she said.

"Well, if you will loan me that basket and ten cents, and come with me an hour, there's that back and just a dollar in it for you, lady," he offered.

She turned from him with a sneering laugh.

"Honest, lady, I got the money," said Mickey, "and 'sides, I got a surprise party for you. When you get back you may go to that room and take every scrap that's in it. Now come on; you're going to be enough of a sporting lady to try a chance like that, ain't you? May be a gold mine up there, for all I know. Put something soft in the bottom of the basket while I fetch the kid."

WHEN Mickey got Lily Peaches home, there were strange and peculiar stirrings in his lonely little heart. She was so grimy he scarcely could tell what she looked like, but the grip of her tiny hot hands was on him.

Mickey set the washtub on the floor near the sleeping child, and filling the dishpan with water, put it over the gasoline burner. Then he produced soap, a towel, and comb. He looked at the child again, and going to the box that contained his mother's clothing he hunted out a nightdress. Then he sat down to wait for the water to heat.

"I ain't going to be washed," she said. "It'll hurt me. Put me on the bed."

"Put you on my bed, dirty like you are?" cried Mickey. "I guess not! You are going to be a soaped lady. If it hurts, you can be consoling yourself thinking it will be the last time, 'cause after this you'll be washed every day so you won't need skinning alive but once."

"I won't! I won't!" she cried.

"Now looky here!" said Mickey. "I'm the boss of this place. If I say wash, it's *wash!* See! I ain't going to have a dirty girl with mats in her hair living with me. You begged me and begged me to bring you, now you'll be cleaned up or you'll go back. Which is it, back or soap?"

The child stared at him, then around the room.

"Soap," she conceded.

"That's a lady," said Mickey. "Course it's soap! All clean and sweet smelling like a flower. See my mammy's nice white nightie for you? How bad is your back, Lily Peaches? Can you sit up?"

"A little while," she answered. "My legs won't go."

"Never you mind," said Mickey. "I'll work hard and get a doctor, so some day they will."

"They won't ever," insisted Peaches. "Granny carried me to the big doctors once, an' my backbone is weak, an' I won't ever walk, they all said so."

"Poot! Doctors don't know everything," scorned Mickey. "That was *long* ago, maybe. By the time I can earn enough to get you a dress and shoes, a doctor will come along who's found out how to make backs over. There's a Dr. Carrel that put different legs on a dog. I read about it in the papers I sold. We'll save our money and get him to put another back on you. Just a bully back."

"Oh Mickey, will you?" she cried.

"Sure!" said Mickey. "Now you sit up and I'll wash you."

Peaches obeyed. Mickey soaped a cloth, knelt beside her; then he paused. "Say Peaches, when was your hair combed last?"

"I don't know, Mickey," she answered.

"There's more dirt in it than there is on your face."

"If you got shears, just cut it off," she suggested.

"Sure!" said Mickey.

He produced shears and lifting string after string cut all of them the same distance from her head. Then Mickey soaped and scoured until the last tangle was gone, then rinsed and partly dried the hair, which felt soft and fine to his fingers.

"B'lieve it's going to curl," he said.

"Always did," she answered.

"Now you scour yourself while I get supper," he said.

Peaches did her best. Mickey locked her in and went after more milk. He wanted to add several extras, but remembering the awful hole the dollar had made in his finances, he said grimly: "No-sir-ee! With a family to keep, and likely to need a doctor at any time and a Carrel back to buy, there's no frills for Mickey. Seeing what she ain't had, she ought to be thankful for just milk."

So her supper consisted of a cup of milk with half the bread broken in, and a banana. Peaches was too tired to eat, so she drank the milk while Mickey finished the remainder. Then he threw her rags from the window, and spread his winter covers on the floor for his bed. Soon both of them were asleep.

"Little Brother" Mickey

Douglas Bruce was telling his fiancée, Leslie Winton, about his encounter with the mysterious Mickey.

"Such a little chap, with an appealing voice, while his inflection was the smallest part of what he was saying. 'Aw kid, come on. Be square!'"

"Why Douglas!" the girl cried. "Tell me!"

"I heard a little lad saying the things that are in the blood and bone of the men money can't buy and corruption can't break. I heard him plead like a lawyer and argue his case straight. I lent a hand when his eloquence failed, got him his deserts, then let him go! I did have an impulse to keep him. I did call after him. But he disappeared."

"Douglas, we can find him!" she comforted. "Perhaps he will be at the Salvation Army banquet for newsies at Thanksgiving."

"Mickey didn't have a Salvation Army face," he said. "I am sure he is a free lance, and a rare one. He was a little chap, a white, clean, threadbare little chap, with such a big voice, so wonderfully intoned, and such a bigger prin-

ciple, for which he was fighting. I certainly would like to take him on as a Little Brother."

Mickey knew that washing, better air, enough food, and oil rubbing were improving Peaches. What he did not know was that adding the interest of her presence to his life, even though it made his work heavier, was showing on him. He actually seemed bigger, stronger, and his face brighter and fuller.

He swung down the street thrusting his papers right and left, crossed and went up the other side, watching closely for a customer. It was ten o'clock and opportunities with the men were almost over. Mickey turned to scan the street for anything even suggesting a sale. He saw none and started with his old cry, watching as he went: "I *like* to sell papers! *Sometimes* I sell them! Sometimes I *don't*——*!*"

Then he saw Leslie Winton, but he did not know it was she. Straight toward her went Mickey.

The girl's eyes betokened interest; her smiling lips encouraged Mickey. He laid his chin over her arm, leaned his head against it and fell in step with her.

"*Sometimes* I sell them! Sometimes I *don't!* If I *sell* them, I'm happy! If I don't, I'm *hungry!* If you *buy* them, you're happy! Pa—per?—lady."

"Not to-day, thank you," she said. "I'm shopping, so I don't wish to carry it."

His face sobered, his voice changed, taking on unexpected modulations.

"Aw lady! I thought *you'd* buy my paper! Far down the street I saw you *coming.* Lady, I like your gentle *voice.* I like your pleasant *smile!* You don't want a nice *sterilized* paper?—lady."

The lady stopped short; she lifted Mickey's chin in a firm grip, looking intently into his face.

"Just by the merest chance, could your name be Mickey?" she asked.

"Sure, lady! Mickey! Michael O'Halloran!"

Her smile became even more attractive.

"I really don't want to be bothered with a paper," she said; "but I do wish a note delivered. If you'll carry it, I'll pay you the price of half a dozen papers."

"Sure I will!" cried Mickey.

"One minute!" she said. She stepped to the inside of the walk, opened her purse, wrote a line on a card, slipped it in an envelope, addressed it and handed it to Mickey.

Mickey took a last glimpse at the laughing face, then wheeling ran. Presently he went into a big building, studied the address board, then entered the elevator and following a corridor reached the number.

He stepped inside the open door before him, crossed the room and laid the note near a man who was bending over some papers on a desk. The man reached a groping hand, tore open the envelope, taking therefrom a card on which was pencilled: "Could this by any chance be your Little Brother?"

He turned hastily, glanced at Mickey, then in a continuous movement arose with outstretched hand.

"Why Little Brother," he cried, "I'm so glad to see you!"

Mickey's smile slowly vanished as he whipped his hands behind him, stepping back.

"Nothin' doing, Boss," he said. "You're off your trolley. I've no brother. My mother had only me."

"Don't you remember me, Mickey?" inquired Douglas Bruce.

"Sure!" said Mickey. "You made Jimmy pay up!"

"Has he bothered you again?" asked the lawyer.

"Nope!" answered Mickey.

"Sit down, Mickey, I want to talk with you."

"I'm much obliged for helping me out," said Mickey, "but I guess you got other business, and I know I have."

"What is your business?" was the next question.

"Selling papers. What's yours?" was the answer.

"Trying to be a corporation lawyer," explained Douglas. "I've been here only two years, and it is slow getting a start. I often have more time to spare than I wish I had, while I'm lonesome no end. You could help me with my work and share my play, while possibly I could be of benefit to you."

"I just wondered if you wasn't getting to that," commented Mickey.

"Getting to what?" inquired Douglas.

"Going to do me good!" explained Mickey. "The swell stiffs are always going to do us fellows good. Mostly they do! They do us good and brown! They pick us up a while and make lap dogs of us, then when we've lost our appetites for our jobs and got to have a hankerin' for the fetch and carry business away they go and forget us, so we're a lot worse off than we were before. Some of the fellows come out of it knowing more ways to be mean than they ever learned on the street," explained Mickey. "If it's that Big Brother bee you got in your bonnet, pull its stinger and let it die an unnatural death! Good-bye!"

"Mickey, wait!" cried Douglas.

"Me business calls, an' I must go—
'way to my ranch in Idaho!" gaily sang
Mickey.

"I'd like to shake you!" said Bruce.

"Well, go on," said Mickey. "I'm here
and you're big enough."

"If I thought it would jolt out your
fool notions and shake some sense in,
I would," said Douglas indignantly.

"Now look here, Kitchener," said
Mickey. "Did I say one word that ain't
so, and that you don't know is so?"

"So you are going to refuse education,
employment and a respectable position?"
demanded Douglas.

"No day is long enough for the work
I do right now," said Mickey. "You can
take my word for it that I'm respectable,
same as I'm taking yours that you are."

"All right!" said Douglas. "We will
let it go then. Maybe you are right. At
least you are not worth the bother it
requires to wake you up. Will you take
an answer to the note you brought me?"

"Now the returns are coming in," said
Mickey. "Sure I will."

Providing for the Family

Mickey returned to the street shortly
after noon, with more in his
pocket than he usually earned in a day,
where by expert work he soon disposed
of his last paper. He bought a slate for
Peaches, then hurried home carrying it
and the box. At the grocery he carefully
selected food again. Then he threw open
his door and achieved this:

*"Once a little kid named Peaches,
Swelled my heart until it eatches.
If you think I'd trade her for a dog,
Your think-tank has slipped a cog!"*

Peaches laughed, stretching her hands
as usual. Mickey stooped for her caress,
scattering some ribbons Leslie Winton
had given him over her as he arose. She
gasped in delighted amazement, catching both hands full.

"Let me wash you," said Mickey, "and
rub your back to rest you from all this
day, then I'll comb your hair and you
pick the prettiest one. I'll put it on the
way she showed me, so you'll be a
fash'nable lady."

"Who showed you Mickey, and gave
you such pretties?"

"A girl I carried a letter to. After
you're bathed and have had supper I'll
tell you."

Then Mickey began work. He
sponged Peaches, rubbed her back, laid
her on his pallet, putting fresh sheets
on her bed and carefully preparing her

supper. After she had eaten he again
ran the comb through her ringlets, telling her to select the ribbon he should
use.

A soft warm pink pleased her, so
Mickey folded it into the bands in which
it had been creased before, binding it
around Peaches' head, then with awkward fingers did his best on a big bow.

Then as had become her custom, she
demanded that Mickey write his last
verse on the slate, so she might learn
and copy it on the morrow. She was
asleep before he finished. Mickey walked
softly, cleared the table, placed it before
the window. Then he took from his
pocket an envelope and a sheet of
folded paper, on which he wrote long
and laboriously. Then locking Peaches
in, he slipped down to the mail-box and
posted this letter:

Dear Mister Carrel:

I saw in papers I sold how you put different
legs on a dog. I have a little white flowersy-
girl that hasn't ever walked. It's her back.
The next time you come here, I guess I will
let you see my little girl; and maybe I'll have
you fix her back. When you see her you will
know that to fix her back would be the biggest
thing you ever did or ever could do. I can pay
her way and mine, and save two dollars a
week for you. I couldn't pay all at once, but
I could pay steady; and if you'd lose all you
have in any way, it would come in real handy
to have that much skating in steady as the
clock every week for as long as you say, and
soon as I can, I'll make it more. I'd give all I
got, or ever can get, to cure Lily's back, and

because you fixed the dog, I'd like you to fix her. I do hope you will come soon, but of course I don't wish anybody else would get sick so you'd have to. You can ask if I am square of Mr. Douglas Bruce, Iriquois Building, Multiopolis, Indiana, or of Mr. Chaffner, editor of the *Herald*, whose papers I've sold since I was big enough.

MICHAEL O'HALLORAN.

THERE's one feature of the Big Brother business that I was a little too fast on," thought Mickey. "Mebby I'll investigate that business a little fur-

ther, 'cause hereafter I provide for my own family, and I guess it's going to be pretty expensive. There ain't any lapdog business in a job, and being paid for it. I'm going to ask him more about the job he offered me, and if we can agree, I'm going to take it. I'll know every day exactly what I'll have, and when the rent is counted out, and for the papers, all the rest will be for eating, and what you need, and to save for the new back."

Just Friends

I'VE no time to talk," said Douglas Bruce, as Mickey appeared the following day; "my work seems too much for one man. Can you help me?"

"Sure!" said Mickey, wadding his cap into his back pocket. Then he rolled his sleeves a turn higher, lifted his chin a trifle and stepped forward. "Say what!"

It caught Douglas so suddenly there was no time for concealment. He laughed heartily.

"That's good!" he cried. Mickey grinned in comradeship. "First, these letters to the box in the hall."

"Next?" Mickey queried as he came through the door.

"This package to the room of the Clerk in the City Hall, and bring back a receipt bearing his signature."

Mickey saluted, laid the note inside the cover of a book, put it in the middle of the package, and a second later his gay whistle receded down the hall.

In one-half the time the trip had taken the messenger boys Douglas was accustomed to employing, Mickey was back like the Gulf in the Forum, demanding "more."

"See what you can do for these rooms, until the next errand is ready," suggested Douglas.

Mickey began gathering up the morning papers, straightening the rugs, curtains and arranging the furniture.

"Hand this check to the janitor," said Douglas. "And Mickey, kindly ask him if two dollars was what I agreed to pay him for my extras this week."

"Sure!" said Mickey.

Douglas would have preferred "Yes sir," but "Sure!" was a permanent ejaculation decorating the tip of Mickey's tongue. The man watching closely did not fail to catch the flash of interest and the lifting of the boy figure as he paused for instructions. When he returned Douglas said casually: "While I am at it, I'll pay off my messenger service. Take this check to the address and bring a receipt for the amount."

Next he carried a requisition for books to another city official and telephoned a café to deliver a pitcher of lemonade and some small cakes, and handed the boy a dime.

"Why didn't you send me and save your silver?"

"I did not think," answered Bruce. "Some one gets the tip, you might as well have had it."

"I didn't mean me *have* it, I meant you *save* it."

"Mickey," said Douglas, "you know perfectly I can't take your time unless you accept from me what I am accustomed to paying other boys."

"Letting others bleed you, you mean," said Mickey indignantly. "Why I'd abeen glad to brought the juice for five! You never ought to paid more."

"Should have paid more," corrected Douglas.

"'Should have paid more,'" repeated Mickey. "Thanks!"

He retired to a window seat, enjoyed the cool drink and nibbled the cake, his eyes deeply thoughtful. When offered a second glass Mickey did not hesitate.

"Nope!" he said conclusively. "A fellow's head and heels work better when his stomach is running light. I can earn more not to load up with a lot of stuff. I eat at home when my work is finished. What next, sir?"

"Call 9-40-X, and order my car here," said Douglas.

H E BENT over his papers to hide his face when from an adjoining room drifted Mickey's voice in clear enunciation and suave intonation: "Mr. Douglas Bruce desires his car to be sent immediately to the Iriquois Building."

His mental comment was: "The little camp has drifted to street lingo when he lacked his mother to restrain him. He can speak a fairly clean grade of English now if he chooses."

"Next?" briskly inquired Mickey.

"Now I am driving to the golf grounds for an hour's play," said Douglas. "Will you go and caddy for me?"

"I never did. I don't know how," answered Mickey.

"You can learn, can't you?" suggested Douglas.

"Sure!" said Mickey. "I've seen boys carrying golf clubs that hadn't enough sense to break stone right. I can learn, but my learning might spoil your day's sport."

"It would be no big price to pay for an intelligent caddy," replied Douglas.

"I'd go to the *country* in the car with you, every day you play, and carry your clubs?" asked Mickey wonderingly.

"Yes," answered Douglas.

"Over real hills, where there's trees, grass, cows and water?" questioned Mickey.

"Yes," repeated Douglas.

"Then before we begin to play we ought to finish business," said Mickey. "If your door ain't shut I guess I'd like to stick around here. Gimme a few days to sell my route to the best advantage I can, and I'll come all day. I'll come for about a half what you are paying now."

"But you admit you need money urgently."

"Well not so urgently as to skin a friend to get it. I've seen you pay out over seven to-day. I'll come for six. Is it a bargain?"

"No," said Douglas, "it isn't! The janitor bill was for a week of half-done work. The messenger bill was for two days, no carrying at all. If you come you will come for not less than eight and what you earn extra over that. I don't agree to better service for less pay. If you will have things between us on a commercial basis, so will I."

"Oh the Big Brother business would be all right—with you," conceded Mickey, "but I don't just like the way it's managed, mostly. God didn't make us brothers no more than he did all men, so we better not butt in and try to fix things over for Him. Looks to me like we might cut the brother business and just be *friends*."

"And I to you Mickey," said Douglas Bruce, holding out his hand. "Have it as you will. Friends, then! Look for you at noon to-morrow. Now we play. Hop in and we'll run to my rooms and get my clubs."

A Real Home

B RUCE had played three holes that afternoon when he overtook a man who said a word that arrested his attention, so both of them stopped, and with notebooks and pencils under the shade of a big tree began discussing the investigation of city politics which Bruce was engaged in at the moment. He dismissed Mickey for the afternoon, telling him to be ready at six to drive back to town.

Telling the driver that if he were not back by six, he would be waiting down the road, Mickey started on foot, in thought so deep he scarcely appreciated the grasses he trod, the perfume in his nostrils, the concert in his ears. What did at last arouse him was the fact that he was very thirsty.

He walked slowly along, intending to stop at the nearest farmhouse to ask for water. But the first home was not to Mickey's liking. He went on, passing another and another. Then he came to one that attracted him.

He scarcely could realize that there were places in the world where families lived alone like this. He tried to think how he would feel if he belonged there. Then the screen to the front door swung back as a smiling woman in a tidy gingham dress came through and stood awaiting Mickey.

"I just told Peter when he came back alone, I bet a penny you'd go off at the wrong stop!" she cried.

For one second Mickey was dazed. "'Most breaks my heart to tell you," he said, "but I ain't the boy you're expecting. I'm just taking a walk and I thought maybe you'd let me have a drink. I've wanted one past the last three houses, but none looked as if they'd have half such good, cool water as this."

"Now don't that beat the nation!" exclaimed the woman. "The Multiopolis papers are just oozing sympathy for the poor city children who are wild for woods and water; and when I'd got myself nerved up to try one and thought it over till I was really anxious about it, and got my children all worked up too, here my husband, Peter, knocks off plowing and goes to the trolley to meet one, and he doesn't come. But you wanted water, come this way."

Mickey followed a footpath white with pear petals around the big house and standing beside a pump waited while the woman stepped to the back porch for a cup. He took it, drinking slowly.

"Thank you ma'am," he said as he handed it back, turning to the path. He felt like crying. The woman was beside him, her hand on his shoulder.

"WAIT a minute," she said. "Sit on this bench under the pear tree and tell me right straight what's the matter!"

Mickey tried but no sound came. The woman patted his shoulder. "Now doesn't it beat the band?" she said, to the backyard in general. "Just a little fellow not in long trousers yet, and bearing such a burden he can't talk. I guess maybe God has a hand in this; I'm not so sure my boy hasn't come after all. Who are you, and where are you going? Don't you want to send your ma word you will stay here a week with me?"

Mickey lifted a bewildered face.

"Why, I couldn't, lady," he said brokenly, but gaining control as he went on. "I must work. Mr. Bruce needs me. I'm a regular plute compared with most of the 'newsies'; you wouldn't want to do anything for me who has so much, but if you're honestly thinking about taking a boy and he hasn't come, how would you like to have a little girl in his place? A little girl about so long, and so wide, with a face like Easter church flowers, and rings of gold on her head and who wouldn't be half the trouble a boy would, because she hasn't ever walked, so she couldn't get into things."

"Oh my goodness! A crippled little girl?"

"She isn't crippled," said Mickey. "She's as straight as you are, what there is of her. She had so little food, and care, her back didn't seem to stiffen, so her legs won't walk. She wouldn't be half so much trouble as a boy. Honest dearest lady, she wouldn't!"

"Who are you?" asked the woman.

Mickey produced a satisfactory pedigree, and gave unquestionable references which she recognized, for she slowly nodded at the names of Chaffner and Bruce.

"And who is the little girl you are asking me to take?"

Mickey studied the woman and then began to talk, cautiously at first. Ashamed to admit the squalor and the awful truth of how he had found the thing he loved, then gathering courage he began what ended in an outpouring of everything about himself.

No MATTER how much bother she was, I guess I could stand it for a week, if she's such a little girl, and can't walk," said the woman. "The difficulty is this: I promised my son Junior a boy and his heart is so set. But I'll talk this over with Peter. If we decided to try the little girl she couldn't be much trouble. I should think we could manage her, and a boy too. I wish you could be the boy. I'd like to have *you*."

"A big boy that can run and play doesn't need you, dearest lady, half so much as my little girl. Do you think he does?" Mickey asked.

"No, I think the Lord sent you straight here. If you don't stop I'll be so worked up I can't rest. I may come and get you to-morrow."

Mickey arose, holding out his hand. "Thank you dearest lady," he said. "I must be getting out where the car won't pass without my seeing it."

The woman made supper an hour late standing beside the gate watching for a green car. Many whirled past, then at last one with the right look came gliding along; so she stepped out and raised her hand for a parley. The car stopped.

"Mr. Douglas Bruce?" she asked.

"At your service, Madam!" he answered.

"Just a word with you," she said.

He arose instantly, swung open the car door, and stepping down walked with her to the shade of a big widely branching maple. The woman looked at him, and said flushing and half confused: "Please to excuse me for halting you, but I'd like to find out something about Mickey."

"I see," said Douglas Bruce. "I haven't known Mickey so long, but owing to the circumstances in which I met him, and the association with him since, I feel that I know him better than I could most boys in a longer time. The strongest thing I can say to you is this: had I a boy of my own, I should be proud if Mickey liked him and would consider being friends with him. He is absolutely trustworthy, that I know."

"Then I won't detain you further," she said.

Peaches Improves

THAT night the nice lady and her husband decided to ask Mickey and Peaches to visit them for a week. The next day they drove to town to pick them up.

Because she had expected the trip to result in the bringing home of the child, Mrs. Harding (for that was her name) had made ready a low folding davenport in her first-floor bedroom, beside a window where grass, birds and trees were almost in touch, and where it would be convenient to watch and care for her visitor. There in the light, pretty room, Mickey gently laid Peaches down and said: "Now if you'll just give me time to get her rested and settled a little, you can see her a peep; but there ain't going to be *much* seeing or talking to-night. If she has such a lot she ain't used to and gets sick, it will be a bad thing for her, and all of us, so we better just go slow and easy."

"Right you are, young man," said Peter. "Come out of here you kids! Come to the back yard and play quietly. When Little White Butterfly gets rested and fed, we'll come one at a time and kiss her hand, and wish her pleasant dreams with us, and then we'll every one of us get down on our knees and ask God to help us take such good care of her that she will get well at our house. Nothing would make me prouder."

Having been with Peaches every day Mickey could not accurately mark improvements, but he could see that her bones did not protrude so far, that her skin was not the yellow, glisteny horror it had been, that the calloused spots were going under the steady rubbing of nightly oil massage, so lately he had added the same treatment to her feet; if they were not less bony, if the skin were not soft and taking on a pinkish colour, Mickey felt that his eyes were unreliable.

Surely she was better! Of course she was better! She had to be! She ate more, she sat up longer, she moved her feet where first they had hung helpless. She was better, much better, and for that especial reason, now was the time to watch closer than before. Since he had written Dr. Carrel, Mickey had rubbed in desperation, not only nights but mornings also, lest he had asked help before he was ready for it; for the sick back could not be operated until the child was stronger.

Mickey watched. Any one could have seen the delicate flush on Peaches' cheek, the hint of red on her lips, the clearing whites of her lovely eyes.

Peter explained to Mickey the circulatory system and why all the years of lying, with no movement, had made her so helpless. He told her why scarce and wrong food had not made good blood to push down and strengthen her feet so they would walk. He told her the friction of the sand-rubbing would pull it down, while the sun, water, and earth would help. Peaches with wide eyes listened, her breath coming faster and faster, until suddenly she leaned forward and cried: "Rub, Mickey! Rub 'til the blood flies! Rub 'em hot as hell!"

Mickey suddenly bent to kiss the bony little foot he was chafing.

"Yes darling, I'll rub 'til it a-most bleeds," he said.

When the feet were glowing with alternate sand-rubbing and splashing in cold water, Peter looked at his wife.

"I think that's the ticket!" he said. "Nancy, don't you? That pulls down the blood with rubbing, and drives it back with the cold water, and pulls it down, to be pushed back again—ain't that helping the heart get in its work? Now if we strengthen her with right food, and make lots of pure blood to run in these little blue canals on her temples and hands and feet, ain't we gaining ground? Ain't we making headway?"

"We've just got to be," said Mrs. Harding. "There's no other way to figure it. But this is enough for a start."

Peaches leaned toward her and asked: "May we do this again to-morrow, nicest lady?"

"Well I'm a busy woman, and my spare time is scarce; and even light as you are, you'd be a load for me; but I guess every few hours we can take a little time off for rubbing and splashing."

An hour before supper time Mickey appeared and without a word began watching Mrs. Harding. Suddenly her work lightened. When she was ready for water, the bucket was filled, saving her a trip to the pump. When she lifted thed ishpan and started toward the back door, Mickey met her with the potato basket. When she glanced questioningly at the stove, he put in more wood. He went to the dining-room and set the table. He made the trip to the cellar with her and brought up bread and milk, while she carried butter and preserves. As she told Peter that night, no strange woman ever had helped her as quickly and understandingly.

With dishwashing he was on hand for he knew that Peaches' fate hung on how much additional work was made for Mrs. Harding.

Establishing Protectorates

"I'M SORRY no end!" said Mickey to Bruce a few weeks later. "First time I ever been late. I was helping Peter; we were so busy that the first thing I knew I heard the hum of the trolley gliding past the clover field, so I was left. I know how hard you're working. It won't happen again."

Mickey studied his friend closely.

Douglas Bruce was pale and restless he spent long periods in frowning thought. He aroused from one of these and asked: "What were you and Peter doing that was so very absorbing?"

"Well about the most interesting thing that ever happened," said Mickey. "You see Peter is one of the grandest men who ever lived; he's so fine and doing so many *big* things, in a way he kind of fell behind in the *little* ones."

"I've heard of men doing that before," commented Douglas. "Can't you tell me a new one?"

"Sure!" said Mickey. "You know the place and how good it seems on the outside—well it didn't look so good inside, in the part that counted most. You've noticed the big barns, sheds and outbuildings, all the modern conveniences for a man, from an electric lantern to a stump puller; everything I'm telling you—and for the nice lady, nix.

"When I pointed all this out, Peter didn't do a thing but figure up the price he'd paid for every labor-saver he ever bought for himself, and he came out a little over six thousand. He said he wouldn't have wanted Ma in a hardware store selecting his implements, so he guessed he wouldn't choose hers. He just drew a check for what he said was her due, with interest, and put it in her name in the bank, and told her to cut loose and spend it exactly as she pleased."

"What did she do?" marvelled Douglas.

"Well she was tickled silly, but she didn't lose her head; she began investigating what had been put on the market to meet her requirements. At present we are living on the threshing floor mostly, and the whole house is packed up; when it is unpacked, there'll be a bathroom on the second floor, and a lavatory on the first. There'll be a furnace in one room of the basement, and a coal bin big enough for a winter's supply. We can hitch on to the trolley line for electric lights all over the house, and barn, and outbuildings, and fireless cooker, iron, and vacuum cleaner, and a whole bunch of conveniences for Ma, including a washing machine, and stationary tubs in the basement. Gee! Get the picture?"

"What does the lady say about it?"

"*Mighty little!*" said Mickey. "She just stands and wipes the shiny places with her apron or handkerchief, and laughs and cries, 'cause *she's so glad.*"

"Mickey, this is so interesting it has given my head quite a rest. Maybe now I can see my way clearly. But one thing more: how long are you planning to stay there? You talk as if——"

"'Stay there?'" said Mickey. "Didn't you hear me say there was a horse and saddle and a room for me, and a room for Lily? 'Stay there!' Why for ever and ever more! That's *home!* When I got into trouble and called on Peter to throw a lifeline, he did it up browner than his job for Ma. A line. was all I asked; *but Peter established a regular Pertectorate —nobody can 'get' us now——*"

"You mean Peter adopted both of you?" cried Douglas.

"Of course," said Mickey. "He said *sure* Lily was *mine,* and I had a perfect *right* to *keep* her; but the law *might* butt in, 'cause there *was* a law we couldn't evade that *could* step in and take her any day. He said too, that if she had to go to the hospital, sudden, first question a surgeon would ask was who were her parents, and if she had none, who in their place could give him a right to operate. He said while she was *mine,* and it was my *right,* and *my job,* the law and the surgeon would say *no,* 'cause we were not related, and I was not of age. He said there were times when the law got its paddle in, and went to fooling with red tape, it let a sick person lay and die while it decided what to do. He said he'd known a few just exactly such cases; so to keep the law from making a fool of itself, as it often did, we'd better step in and fix things to suit us before it ever got a showdown."

"What did he do?" asked Douglas Bruce eagerly.

"Well, after we'd talked it over we moved up to the back porch and Peter explained to Ma, who is the boss of that family, only she doesn't *know* it, and she said: 'You go first thing in the morning and adopt them, and adopt them *both.* Lily will make Mary just as good a sister as she could ever have,' said she, and then she reached over and put her arms right around me and she said, 'And if you think I'm going to keep on trying to run this house without Mickey, you're mistaken.' I began to cry, 'cause I had had a big day, and I was shaking on my feet anyway.

"Then Peter said, 'Have you figured it out to the end? Is it to be 'til they are of age, or forever?' She just gripped tighter and said fast as words can come, 'I say make it forever, and share and share alike. I'm willing if you are.' Peter, he said, 'I'm willing. They'll pay their way any place.'"

"Mickey, why didn't you tell me?" asked Douglas. "Why didn't you want me to adopt you?"

"Well so far as 'adopting' is concerned," said Mickey, "I ain't *crazy* about it, with anybody. I don't love him any more than I do you; but I've just this minute discovered that it ain't in my skin to love any man more than I do Peter. Say, she and Peter will adopt you too, if you say so, and between us, just as man to man, Peter is a regular lifesaver! If you got a chance you better catch on! No telling what you might want of him!"

"Mickey, you do say the most poignant things!" cried Douglas. "I'd give all I'm worth to catch on to Peter right now, and cling for much *more* than life; but what I started, I must finish, and Peter isn't here."

An Ugly Situation

"WELL what's the matter with me?" asked Mickey.

"Think you are big enough to serve as a straw for a drowning man, Mickey?" inquired Douglas.

"Sure! I'm big enough to establish a *Pertectorate* over you, this minute. The weight of my body, hasn't anything to do with the size of my heart, or how fast I can work my brains and feet, if I must."

"Mickey," said Douglas despairingly, "it's my candid opinion that no one can save me, right now."

Suddenly Douglas Bruce's long arms stretched across the table before him, his head fell on them, and shuddering sobs shook him.

"Aw come on now!" Mickey begged. "Cut that out! That won't help none! What shall I *do?* Shall I call Mr. Minturn? Shall I get Miss Leslie on the wire?"

Bruce arose and began walking the floor.

"Yes," he said. "Yes! call her!"

Mickey ran to the telephone. In a minute, "Here she is," he announced. "Shall I go?"

"No! Stay right where you are."

"Hello Leslie! Are you all right? I'm sorry to say I am not. I'm up against a proposition I don't know how to handle. Why just this: remember your father told me in your presence that if in the course of my investigations I reached his office, I was to wait until he got back? Yes. I thought you'd remember. You know the order of the court gave me access to the records, but the officials whose books I have gone over haven't been pleased about it, although reflection would have told them if it hadn't been I, it would have been some other man. But the point is this: I'm almost at the finish and I haven't found what obviously exists somewhere. I'm now up to the last office, which is your father's. The shortage either has to be there, or in other departments outside those I was delegated to search; so that further pursuit will be necessary.

Two or three times officials have suggested to me that I go over your father's records first, as an evidence that there was no favouritism; now I have reached them, and this proposition: if I go ahead in his, as I have in other offices, I disobey his express order. If I do not, the gang will set up a howl in to-morrow morning's paper, and they will start an investigation of their own. Did you get anything from him this morning Leslie? Not for four days? And he's a week ast the time he thought he would be ack? I see! Leslie, what shall I do? In my morning's mail there is a letter from he men whose records I have been over, giving me this ultimatum: 'begin on Vinton's office immediately, or we will.'

"Tell them to go ahead? But Leslie! Yes I know, but Leslie—— Yes! You are ordering me to tell them that I propose o conduct the search in his department as I did theirs, and if they will not await his return from this business trip, they are perfectly free to go ahead—— You are *sure* that is the thing you want said? But Leslie—— Yes, I know, but Leslie t is *disobeying* him, and it's barely possible there might be a traitor there; better men than he have been betrayed by their employees. I admit I'm all in. I wish you would come and bring your ast letter from him. We'll see if we can't locate him by wire. It's an ugly situation. Of course I didn't think it would come to this. Yes I wish you would! If you say so, I will, but—— All right then. Come at once! Good-bye!"

Douglas turned to his desk, wrote a few hasty lines and said to Mickey: "Deliver that to Muller at the City Hall."

Mickey took the envelope and went acing. In half the time he would have used in going to the City Hall he was n the office of James Minturn, Bruce's best friend.

After Minturn understood the situation, he called up Mr. Winton's bank.

"Hello, Mr. Freeland. This is Minturn talking—James Minturn. You will remember some securities I deposited with you not long ago? I wish to use a part of them to pay a debt I owe Mr. Winton. Kindly credit his account with— oh, he's there in the bank? Well never mind then. I didn't know he was back yet. Let it go! I'll see him in person."

"Now where am I at?" demanded Mickey.

"I don't think you know, Mickey," said Mr. Minturn, "and I am sure I don't, but I have a strong suspicion that

Mr. Winton will be here in a few minutes, and if his mission has been successful, his face will tell it; and if he's in trouble, that will show; and then we will know what to do. Mr. Bruce would like to know he is here, and at the bank I think."

"I'll go tell him right away," said Mickey.

Douglas was walking the floor as Mickey entered.

"You delivered the letter?" he cried.

Mickey shook his head, producing the envelope.

"You didn't!" shouted Bruce. "You didn't! Thank God! Oh, thank God you *didn't!*"

"Aw-w-ah!" protested Mickey. "Did you know that Mr. Winton's down at his desk right now?"

"What?" cried Douglas.

"Sure!" said Mickey. "Back on time! At the bank fixing things so you can investigate all you want to. Go on and write your letter over, and tell them anxious, irritated gents, that you'll investigate 'til the basement and cupola are finished, just as soon as you make out the reports you are figuring up *now*. That will give you time to act independent, and it will give Daddy time to be ready for you——"

"Mickey, what if he didn't get the land sold?" wavered Douglas. "What if his trip was a failure?"

"Well that's fixed," said Mickey. "Mr. Minturn will furnish the money. Mr. Minturn said we could tell the minute we saw him——"

"Well young man, can you?" inquired a voice behind them.

With the same impulse Douglas and Mickey turned to find Mr. Winton and Leslie standing far enough inside the door to have heard all that had been said. A slow red crept over Mickey's fair face. Douglas sprang to his feet, his hand outstretched, words of welcome on his lips. Mr. Winton put him aside with a gesture.

"I asked this youngster a question,"

he said, "and I'm deeply interested in the answer. *Can you?*"

Mickey stepped forward, taking one long, straight look into the face of the man before him; then his exultant laugh trilled as the notes of Peter's old bobolink bird on the meadow fence.

"Surest thing you know!" he cried in ringing joy. "Gee, you made it! I should say I *could* tell!"

Mr. Winton caught Mickey, lifting him from his feet. "God made a jewel after my heart when he made you lad," he said. "If you haven't got a father, I'm an insistent candidate for the place."

"Gee, you're the nicest man!" said Mickey. "If I was out with a telescope searching for a father, I'd make a hom run for you; but you see I'm fairly wel fixed. Here's my boss, too fine to tall about, that I work for to earn money t keep me and my family; there's Peter better than gold, who's annexed both m and my child; I'd *like* you for a father only I'm crazy about Peter. Just yo come and see *Peter,* and you'll under stand——"

"I'll be there soon," said Mr. Winton "I have reasons for wanting to know him thoroughly. And by the way, how do you do, Douglas? How is the grea investigation coming on? 'Fine!' I'n glad to hear it. Push it with all you: might."

The Miracle

MICKEY came home from the office early one afternoon, his face anxious. He saw the Harding car at the gate, and wondered at Peter sitting dressed for leisure on the veranda.

"Got anxious about Lily," Mickey explained. "I thought I heard her call me, then I had the notion she was crying for me. Mr. Bruce laughed at me, but I couldn't stand it. Is she asleep, as they said she'd be?"

Peter opened his lips, but no word came. Mickey slowly turned a ghastly white. Peter reached in his side pocket, drew out a letter, and handed it to the boy. Mickey pulled the sheet from the envelope, still staring at Peter, then glanced at what he held and collapsed on the step. Peter moved beside him, laid a steadying arm across his shoulders and proved his fear was as great as Mickey's by being unable to speak. At last the boy produced articulate words.

"*He came?*" he marvelled.

'About ten this morning," said Peter.

'He took her to the hospital?" panted Mickey.

"Yes," said Peter.

"Why did you let him?" demanded Mickey.

That helped Peter. He indicated the letter.

"There's your call for him!" he said,

emphatically. "You asked me to adop her so I could give him orders to g ahead when he came."

"Why didn't you telephone me?" asked Mickey.

"I did," said Peter. "The woman who answered didn't know where you were but she said their car had gone to town so I thought maybe they'd find you there. I was just going to call them again."

"Was she afraid?" wavered Mickey.

"Yes, I think she was," said Peter.

"Did she cry for me?" asked Mickey.

"Yes she did," admitted Peter, who hadn't a social lie in his being, "but when he offered to put off the examination till he might come again, she climbed from the cot and made him take her. Ma went with her."

"She may be on that glass table right now," gulped Mickey. "What time is it? When's the next car? Run me to the station will you, and if you've got any money, let me have it 'til I get to mine."

"Of course!" said Peter.

"Hurry!" begged Mickey.

Peter took hold of the gear and faced straight ahead.

"She's oiled, the tank full, the engine purring like a kitten," he said. "Mickey, I always wanted to beat that trolley just once, to show it I *could,* if I wasn't

aded with women and children. Awful
ice road——"

"Go on!" said Mickey.

ETER was miles ahead of all regulations as he stopped before the hos-
ital entrance.

"Take me to her quick!" begged
Mickey of a nurse.

Mickey had a glimpse of Mrs. Hard-
ng, and three men, one of whom he
ecognized from reproductions of his
eatures in the papers. A very white,
red-looking Peaches stretched both
ands and uttered a shrill cry as Mickey
ppeared in the doorway. His answer
was inarticulate while his arms spread
widely. Then Peaches arose, and in a
ew shuffling but sustained steps fell on
is breast.

"Oh darling, you'll kill yourself,"
ailed Mickey.

He laid her on the davenport and
nelt clasping her. Peaches regained self-
ontrol first; she sat up, shamelessly wip-
ng Mickey's eyes and her own alter-
ately.

Mickey appealed to Dr. Carrel. "How
bout this?" he demanded.

"She's going to walk," said the great
man assuringly.

"It's all over? You've performed your
miracle?" asked Mickey.

"Yes," said Dr. Carrel. "It's all over
Mickey; but you had the miracle per-
ormed before I saw her, lad."

Again Mickey turned to the surgeons.
"*Are you sure?* Will it hurt her? Will
t last?"

"Very sure," said Dr. Carrel. "Calm
ourself, lad. Her case is not so unusual;
only more aggravated than usual. I've
examined her from crown to sole, and
she's straight and sound. You have
started her permanent cure; all you need
is to keep on exactly as you are going,
and limit her activities so that in her
joy she doesn't overdo and tire herself.
You are her doctor. I congratulate you!"

Dr. Carrel came forward, holding out
his hand, and Mickey took it with the
one of his that was not gripping Peaches
and said, "Aw-a-ah!" but he was a
radiant boy.

"Thank you sir," he said. "Thank
everybody. But thank you especial, over
and over. I don't know how I'll ever
square up with you, but I'll pay you all
I have to start on. I've some money
I've saved from my wages, and I'll be
working harder and earning more all
the time."

"But Mickey," protested the surgeon,
"you don't owe me anything. I didn't
operate! You had the work done before
I arrived. I would have come sooner,
but I knew she couldn't be operated
upon, even if her case demanded it,
until she had gained more strength——"

He was watching Mickey's face and
he read aright, so he continued: "I liked
that suggestion you made in your letter
very much. Something 'coming in steadily' is a good thing for any man to
have. For the next three months, suppose you send me that two dollars a
week you offered me if I'd come."

Mickey gathered Peaches in his arms
and looked over his shoulder as he
started on the homeward trip.

"Thank you sir," he said tersely.
"That would be square."

PROUD WORD YOU NEVER SPOKE

PROUD word you never spoke, but you will speak
  Four not exempt from pride some future day.
Resting on one white hand a warm wet cheek,
  Over my open volume you will say,
  "This man loved *me!*" then rise and trip away.
                                    —*W. S. Landor*

Gertrude Atherton

BLACK OXEN

"The years like Black Oxen tread the world
And God the herdsman goads them on behind."

This couplet, by W. B. Yetes, was the inspiration for one of the most successful postwar novels. Thousands who are seeking to ward off old age will find the theme of "Black Oxen" and its famous author sources of great inspiration. Mrs. Atherton was sixty-six when this book appeared in 1923, and now considerably past eighty she is still adding to her long list of successful novels.

The Ghost of Mary Ogden

THE actors bowed en masse, in threes, in twos, singly. The curtain descended, the lights rose, the audience heaved. Men climbed over patient women and hurried up the aisle.

People began to visit. And then the woman two seats ahead of Lee Clavering did a singular thing. She rose slowly to her feet, turned her back to the stage, raised her opera glasses and leisurely surveyed the audience.

"I knew it!" Clavering's tongue clicked. "European. No American woman ever did that—unless, to be sure, she has lived too long abroad to remember our customs."

He had not been able to see her face, but her graceful figure had attracted his attention, and the peculiar shade of her hair: the color of warm ashes. There was no woman of his acquaintance with that rare shade of blonde hair. Profiles were out of date, but in an old-fashioned corner of his soul he admired them, and he was idly convinced that a woman with so perfectly shaped a head, long and narrow, but not too narrow, must have a profile.

He was now gazing at her eagerly, and felt a slight sensation of annoyance that the entire house was following his example. The opera glasses concealed her eyes, but they rested upon the bridge of an indubitably straight nose. In spite of its smooth white skin and rounde contours above an undamaged throat, was, subtly, not a young face. The figu was very slight, but as subtly mature the face, possibly because she held uncompromisingly erect; apparently sh had made no concession to the dem cratic absence of "carriage."

She lowered the opera glasses an glanced over the rows of upturned fac immediately before her, scrutinizin them casually, as if they were fish in a aquarium. She had dropped her li slightly before her eyes came to rest o Clavering. He was leaning forward, d ing his best to compel her notice. H glance did linger on his for a momer before it moved on indifferently, but i that brief interval he experienced a cu ious ripple along his nerves . . . almo a note of warning. . . . They were ver dark gray eyes, and inconceivably wis cold, and disillusioned.

She did not look a day over twent eight. There were no marks of dissipa tion on her face. But for its cold regu larity she would have looked younger with her eyes closed. The eyes seeme to gaze down out of an infinitely remo past.

Suddenly she seemed to sense the co centrated attention of the audience, co ored slightly and sat down. But her r pose was absolute. She made no litt embarrassed gestures as another woma would have done. She did not even affe to read her program.

CLAVERING left his chair and wandered up the aisle. His gaze paused abruptly on the face of Mr. Charles Dinwiddie. Mr. Dinwiddie's countenance as a rule was as formal and politely expressionless as became his dignified status, but tonight it was not. It was pallid. The other prominent eyes were staring, the mouth was relaxed. Clavering hastened toward him in alarm.

"Ill, old chap?" he asked. "Better come out."

Mr. Dinwiddie focussed his eyes, then stumbled to his feet and caught Clavering by the arm. "Yes," he muttered. "Get me out of this and take me where I can get a drink. Seen a ghost. That woman was there, wasn't she?"

"She was there, all right." Clavering's face was no longer cynical and mysterious; it was alive with curiosity. "D'you know who she is?"

"Thirty-odd years ago any one of us old chaps would have told you she was Mary Ogden, and like as not raised his hat. She was the beauty and the belle of our day. But she married a Hungarian diplomat, Count Zattiany, when she was twenty-four, and deserted us. Never been in the country since. I never wanted to see her again. Too hard hit. But I caught a glimpse of her at the opera in Paris about ten years ago—faded! Always striking of course with that style, but withered, changed, skinny where she had been slim, her throat concealed by a dog collar a yard long—her expression sad and apathetic—the dethroned idol of men. God! Mary Ogden! I left the house."

"It is her daughter, of course—"

"Never had a child—positive of it. Zattiany's title went to a nephew who was killed in the war . . . No . . . it must be . . . must . . ." His eyes began to glitter. "There were stories about Mary Ogden—Mary Zattiany. She had a reputation for getting herself compromised. She must have had a daughter and stowed her away somewhere. Wonder where she kept her? That girl has been educated and has all the air of the best society. Must have got friends to adopt her. Gad! What a secret chapter. But why on earth does she let the girl run round loose?"

"I shouldn't say she was a day under twenty-eight. No doubt she looked younger from where you were sitting."

"Twenty-eight! Mary must have begun sooner that we heard. But—well, we never felt that we knew Mary—that was one of her charms. Wonder if she's here now. She must be a wreck, poor thing. She ran a hospital during the war and was in Buda-Pesth for some time after the revolution broke out.

"Perhaps she sent the girl over to look after her affairs."

"That's it. Beyond a doubt. And I'll find out. Trent is Mary's attorney and trustee. I'll make him open up. I'll see Trent in the morning. Dine with me at the club at eight?"

"Rather!"

THE next evening when he arrived at the club he found Mr. Dinwiddie fuming.

"What do you think!" he exclaimed as he led his guest to his favorite table in the corner. "That old rascal bluffed me! Said there was no relative of Countess Zattiany in the country that he knew of. Looked blank as a post when I told him of the extraordinary resemblance of that girl to Mary Ogden. Said he never heard of her But he was lying and he knew that I knew he was lying.

"Go ahead. I know that you haven't finished."

"You're right, I haven't. I've done a little prospecting on my own account. Mary inherited the old Ogden house over on Murray Hill. I happen to know that the lease ran out last year and that it hasn't been rented since. Well, I walked past there today, and some one is living in it. She's there, mark my words."

"Not a doubt of it. Why didn't you walk boldly up and send in your card?"

"Hadn't the courage. Besides, that girl never heard of me. I hadn't the ghost of an excuse."

Rendez-vous at Midnight

THREE weeks passed. There were almost twice as many first-nights which Clavering covered for his daily newspaper column. "Mary Ogden," as Clavering called her for want of the truth, was at each. She never rose in her seat again, and, indeed, seemed to seek inconspicuousness, but she was always in the second row in the orchestra, and she wore a different gown on each occasion. As she entered after the curtain rose and stole out before it went down for the last time, few but those in the adjacent seats and boxes were edified by any details of those charming creations, although it was noticeable that the visiting of both sexes was most active in her neighborhood.

For by this time she was "the talk of the town," or of that important and excessively active-minded section of Greater New York represented at first-nights. But there seemed to be not the remotest prospect of meeting her, nor even of solving the mystery.

On the sixth of these first-nights, when the unknown slipped quietly from her seat at the end of the last act, she saw the aisle in front of her almost blocked. One after another the rows of seats were hurriedly deserted. Clavering, as usual, was directly behind her. When she reached the foyer she found herself surrounded by men and women whose frank interest was of the same well-bred but artless essence as that afforded a famous actress or prima donna exhibiting herself before the footlights.

The crowd made way for her and she crossed the pavement to wait for her car. Clavering, always hoping that some drunken brute would give him the opportunity to succor her, followed and stood as close as he dared. Her car drove up and she entered. As it started she turned her head and looked straight at him. And then Clavering was sure that she laughed outright.

He started recklessly after the car, plunging between automobiles going in four different directions, and jumpi_ on the running board of a taxi, told t_ man to drive like hell toward Park A_ nue.

He dismissed the taxi at the corner _ her street and walked rapidly toward t_ house. He had no definite object, b_ with the blood of romantic anceste_ who had serenaded beneath magno_ trees pounding in his veins, he thoug_ it likely he would take up his sta_ under the opposite lamp-post and rema_ there all night.

Suddenly, to his amazement, he sa_ her run down the steps of her house a_ disappear into the area. She was on_ more at the gate when he hurried up_ her.

"May I—am I—" he stammered. '_ anything the matter?"

FOR a moment she had shrunk back _ alarm, but the narrow silent str_ between its ramparts of brown stone w_ bright with moonlight and she reco_ nized him.

"Oh, it is you," she said with a fai_ smile. "I forgot my key and I cann_ make anyone hear the bell. Yes, you c_ do something. Are you willing to bre_ a window, crawl in, and find your w_ up to the front door?"

"Watch me!" Clavering forgot that _ was saturnine and remote and turni_ thirty-four. He lifted his foot, kicked o_ a pane, found the catch, opened the wi_ dow and ran up the dark narrow sta_ and opened the door. He expected to _ dismissed with a word of lofty thank_ but she said in a tone of casual hos_ tality:

"There are sandwiches in the libra_ and I can give you a whiskey and soda_ She took a key from a drawer a_ handed it to him. "You will find wh_ key and a syphon in that cabinet, M_ Clavering. I keep them for Jud_ Trent."

"Mr. Cla—" He came out of his daz_ "You know who I am then?"

'But certainly. I am not as reckless as that. I was driving one day with dge Trent and saw you walking with r. Dinwiddie."

"Trent—ah!" And then after a pause asked bluntly, "Will you tell me who u are? This is hardly fair, you know."

"I am the Countess Zattiany."

"The Countess Zattiany!"

"The Countess Josef Zattiany, to be act. I went to Europe when I was a ild, and when I finished school, vis-d my cousin, Mary Zattiany—I belong the Virginia branch of her mother's mily—at her palace in Vienna and arried her cousin's nephew."

"Ah! That accounts for the resem-ance!" exclaimed Clavering who did t believe a word of it.

"Ah, yes," she said meeting his eyes lmly. "Cousin Mary always said that e likeness of herself as a young woman as rather remarkable, that we might be other and daughter instead of only ird cousins."

"Ah—yes—exactly. Is—is she with u?"

"No, alas! She is in a sanitarium in ienna and likely to remain there for a ng time. When Judge Trent wrote at it would be well for her interests if e came to New York she asked me to me instead and gave me her power attorney. Judge Trent is growing old d says that women nowadays take an terest in their investments. I certainly d it highly diverting."

"No doubt. But surely you will not ntinue to shut yourself up? Surely a oman as young and beautiful—"

"Oh, men!" Clavering had never heard profound disillusion in any woman's nes. Fear flitted through her eyes.

"What has some brute of a man done to her?" thought Clavering with furious indignation, and feeling more romantic than ever.

"You are too young to hate men," he stammered. And then he went on with complete banality, "You have never met the right man."

"I am older than you perhaps think," she said drily. "And I have known a great many men—and of a variety! But," she added graciously, "I shall be glad if you will come and see me sometimes. I enjoy your column, and I am sure we shall find a great deal to talk about. Perhaps you will dine with me tomorrow night if you have nothing better to do. And—" She hesitated a moment, then added with a curious smile, "Bring Mr. Dinwiddie. It is always charitable to lay a ghost. At half after eight?"

"WELL?" he asked, as he and Din-widdie were walking away from the house the next evening. "Do you still think her a base impostor?"

"Don't know what I think and don't much care. She can pack me in her trunk, as we boys used to say. She's a great lady and a charming one; as little doubt about the first as the last. She's like Mary Ogden and she isn't. She can't be the usual rank impostor, that's posi-tive. She has the same blood as Mary in her veins, and if she's Mary's daugh-ter and wishes to keep it dark, that's her business. I'll never give her away."

"Well, good luck. Glad it went off so well."

They parted at the door of Mr. Din-widdie's rooms and Clavering walked slowly home in an extremely thoughtful mood.

The Awakening

MADAME ZATTIANY adjusted the chain on the front door and returned ery slowly to the library. Suddenly she egan to laugh, a laugh of intense and onic amusement; but it stopped in mid-ourse and her eyes expanded with an xpression almost of panic.

She had realized that this young man, so unlike any she had ever known in her European experience, had been more or less in her thoughts since the night he had followed her out of the theatre and stood covertly observing her as she waited for her car. But she had felt merely amusement at the time, possibly a thrill of gratified vanity, accustomed as she was to admiration and homage.

It was only tonight that she had been conscious of a certain youthful eagerness as she paced up and down the hall waiting to hear him run up the steps. She had paused once and laughed at herself as she realized that she was acting like a girl expecting her lover, when she was merely a coldly—no longer even bitterly—disillusioned woman, bored with this enforced inaction in New York, welcoming a little adventure to distract her mind from its brooding on the misery she had left behind her in Europe, and on the future to which she had committed herself.

But she knew now, and her hands clenched and her face distorted as she admitted it, that if he had suddenly snatched her in his arms she would have flamed into passion and felt herself the incarnation of youth and love.

Incredible. Unthinkable. She!

What should she do? Flee? She had come to New York for one purpose only, to settle her financial affairs in the briefest possible time and return to th country where her work lay. But sh had been detained beyond expectation.

Business. She hated the word. Wh did it matter— But she knew that it di matter, and supremely. She might hav the beauty, the brains, and the sex dom nation to win men to her way of thin ing when she launched herself into th maelstrom of politics, but she was we aware that her large fortune would l half the battle. It furnished the halo an the sinews, and it gave her the power buy men who could not be persuade She had vowed that Austria should l saved at any cost.

But her mind drifted back to the pa month. Senses? And if it were not th alone, but merely the inevitable accom paniment of far stranger processes .. if it were what she had once so lon sought and with such disastrous resul . . . She had believed for so many yea that it existed somewhere, in some ma . . . that it was every woman's rig . . . even if it could not last for eve She sank back and closed her eyes, su cumbing to an ineffable languor.

Tête-à-Tête by the Fire

A PILE of letters lay on his newspapers, and the topmost one, in a large envelope, addressed in a flowing meticulously fine hand, he knew, without speculation, to be from Madame Zattiany. "Dear Mr. Clavering:

"I have been in Atlantic City for a few days getting rid of a cold. I hope you have not called. Will you dine with me tomorrow night at half after eight? I shall not ask any one else.

Sincerely
        Marie Zattiany."

So her name was Marie. It had struck him once or twice as humorous that he didn't know the first name of the woman who was demanding his every waking thought. And she had been out of town and unaware that he had deliberately avoided her.

Feeling as normal and unromantic as a man generally does when digesting a meal and the news, he concluded that refuse her invitation, to attempt to avoi her, in short, would not only be futil as he was bound to respond to that ma net sooner or later, but would be further confession of cowardice.

And so he ascended her steps at exact half-past eight with the blood poundin in his ears and his heart acting like schoolboy's in his first attack of ca love.

"Dinner will be served in the librar sir," said the footman. "Madame will l down in a moment."

A tête-à-tête by the fire! Worse an worse. He hoped she had a cold in h head.

But she had not. As she entere dressed in a white tea gown of chiffo and lace, she looked like a moonbean and as if no mortal indisposition ha ever brushed her in passing. When sh

t down by the fire only one narrow foot
its silvery slipper moved occasionally,
nd her white and beautiful hands,
hose suggestion of ruthless power
lavering appreciated apprehensively,
emed, although they were quiet, subtly
lack the repose of her body.

"Now I know what you look like!"
e exclaimed, and was surprised to find
hat his voice was not quite steady. "A
Nordic princess."

"Oh! That is the very most charming
ompliment ever paid me. Do you think
hat romance is impossible in New
ork?"

"Are you waiting for romance, then?
Have you come to this more primitive
ivilization to find it?"

She raised her head and looked him
ull in the eyes. "No, I did not believe
the possibility then."

"May I have a high-ball?"

"Certainly."

H E TOOK his drink on the other side
of the room. It was several minutes
efore he returned to the hearth. Then
e asked without looking at her: "How
o you expect to find romance if you
hut yourself up. Who *are* you?"

"Nothing that you have imagined. It
far stranger—I fancy it would cure
ou."

"Cure me?"

"Yes. Do you deny that you love me?"

"No, by God! I don't! But you take
a devilish advantage. Of course, you are
playing with me—with your cursed
technique . . . Unless . . ." He reached
her in a stride and stood over her. "Is it
possible—do you—*you*—"

She pushed back her chair, and stood
behind it. Her cheeks were very pink,
her eyes startled, but very soft. "I do not
admit that yet—I have been too astounded—I went away to think by myself—where I was sure not to see you—
but—my mind seemed to revolve in circles. I don't know! I don't know!"

"You do know! You are not the
woman to mistake a passing interest for
the real thing."

"I—I want to be sure. I have dreamed
. . . I—I have leisure, you see. This old
house shuts out the world—Europe—the
past. Please let me be sure and go now."

"Will you marry me?"

"I can't tell. Not yet. Are you content
to wait?"

"I am not! You may have ten thousand strange reasons—they count for
nothing with me. And I intend to see
you every day. I'll call you up in the
morning. Now I will go, and as quickly
as I can get out."

Then he was gone.

Stark Revelation

W HEN he awoke at two o'clock in
the afternoon his brain felt like
he ashes of a bonfire and his spirits
ere a leaden weight. He'd see her to-
ay and force some sort of understand-
g.

But when he opened his door and
ound a letter in her handwriting he
ade no attempt at the farce of self-dis-
pline; he opened it at once.

"I am not going to see you until Sat-
rday," it read. "I wish to tell you about
yself and for that reason I ask that
ou will not discuss me with Mr. Din-
iddie or any one else, beforehand. It
ill probably be the last time I shall
e you, but I am prepared for that

"After Saturday night, *mon ami*, matters will be entirely in your hands. You
will realize whether you have merely
been dazzled and fascinated or whether
there is really between us that mysterious
bond that no circumstances can alter.
Such things have happened to men and
women if we may believe history, but
I have too good reason to believe that
it is not for me.

"However—at least for a brief time
you have given me back something of
the hopes and illusions of youth. This in
itself is so astonishing that whatever the
result I shall never be able to forget you.

"Until Saturday.

"M."

As he took her hand and drew her gently into the house on Saturday evening he felt that she was trembling.

"Come," he said, his own voice shaking. "Remember that you need tell me nothing unless you wish. This idea of confession before marriage is infernal rot. I have not the least intention of making one of my own."

"Oh!" She gave a short harsh laugh. "I should never dream of asking for any man's confession. They are all alike. And I must tell you. I cannot leave you to hear it from others."

As she had chosen the large high-backed chair, Clavering, knowing her love of comfort, hoped that her discourse would be brief.

"When I finish," she said in her low vital voice, "I shall leave the room immediately and I must have your word that you will make no attempt to detain me, and that you will go at once and not return until Monday afternoon. I shall not wish to see you again until you have had time to deliberate calmly on what I shall tell you."

"Oh!" He ground his teeth. "Very well—my dear."

"It is the most difficult of all—the beginning." Her hands were clenched and her voice shook slightly.

"Let me remind you that to begin anywhere you've got to begin somewhere." And then as she continued silent, he burst out: "For God's sake, say it!"

"Is—is—it possible that the suspicion has never crossed your mind that I am Mary Ogden?"

"Wh-a-at!"

"Mary Ogden, who married Count Zattiany thirty-four years ago. I was twenty-four at the time. You may do your own arithmetic."

But Clavering made no answer. His cigarette was burning a hole in the carpet. He mechanically set his foot on it, but his faculties felt suspended, his body immersed in ice-water. And yet something in his unconscious rose and laughed . . . and tossed up a key . . .

If he had not fallen in love with he he would have found that key long since. His news sense rarely failed him

"I've told a good many lies, I'm afraid," she went on, and her voice wa even and cool. The worst was over "You'll have to forgive me that at least I had no intention of being forced t tell you or any one the truth until chose to tell it. Be sure that I never en tertained the thought that I could eve love any man again. But I have made u my mind to disenchant you as far a possible, not only for your sake but m own. I wish you to know exactly whom you have fallen in love with."

"You grow more interesting every mo ment," said Clavering politely, "and have never been one-half as intereste in my life."

"I met Otto Zattiany in Paris, wher he was attached to the Embassy of th Dual Empire. He was an impetuou wooer and very handsome. I did not lov him, but I was fascinated. I was tired o American men and American life. Di plomacy appealed to my ambition, m love of power and intrigue. He followe me back to New York, and although m parents were opposed to all foreigners, had my way; there was the usual wed ding in Saint Thomas's, and we saile immediately for Europe.

"I hated him at once. I shall not g into the details of that marriage. For tunately he soon tired of me and re turned to his mistresses. But he was ver proud of me and keenly aware of m value as the wife of an ambitious diplo mat. He treated me with courtesy an concerned himself not at all with m private life.

"Of course the time came when ugl memories faded, my buoyant youth as serted itself and I wanted love. I mad my choice and was happy for a time. soon discovered that I had not foun happiness. Men want. They rarely love I realized that I had demanded in lov far more than passion, and I receive nothing else. Those whom I tried to lov would soon have tired of me had I no played the game as adroitly as themselves, and if I had permitted them to feel sure of me. The last thing any of them wanted was depth of feeling, tragic passion.

"My most desperate affair was my last. The awakening was violent. He was an Austrian with an important place in the Government. He was a very great person in many ways, and I think I really loved him, for he seemed to me entirely worthy of it. He certainly was mad enough about me for a time—for a year, to be exact.

"I shall always remember this man with a certain pleasure and respect, for he is the only man who ever made me suffer. (He married a young girl, out of duty to his House, and unexpectedly fell in love with her.) Therefore, although I recovered, and completely, still do I sometimes dwell with a certain cynical pleasure on the memory of him—

"I DETERMINED to put love definitely out of my life. I believed then and finally that I had not the gift of inspiring love: nor would I ever risk humiliation and suffering again. Unfortunately women who have wasted so much time on love never realize the tragic futility until Time himself disposes of temptation, and then it is too late for anything but regret of another sort. The war solved the problem for me and for many a desperate spirit.

"I turned the Zattiany palace in Buda-Pesth into a hospital. And then for four years I was an automaton. When I thought about myself at all, it seemed to me that this selfless and strenuous interval was the final severance from my old life.

"After the revolution broke out I was forced to leave in secret to escape being murdered. As my husband had died, I naturally went to Vienna. I was too tired and nervous to struggle with any new problems and so instead of opening up the Zattiany Palace I went to a sanitarium.

"The doctor in charge soon began to pay me something more than perfunctory visits when he found that intelligent conversation after my long dearth did me more good than harm. Finally he told me of a method of treatment that might restore my youth, and begged me to undertake it.

"I must tell you that the explanation of my condition, as of others of my age, was that the endocrines or the ductless glands had undergone a natural process of exhaustion. The idea involved is that the stimulation of these exhausted cells would cause the other glands to function once more at full strength and a certain rejuvenation ensues as a matter of course; unless, of course, they had withered beyond the power of science. I was a promising subject, for examination proved that my organs were healthy, my arteries soft; and I was not yet sixty. The upshot was that I consented to the treatment. It consisted of the concentration of powerful Röntgen—what you call X-Rays—on that portion of the body covering the ovaries.

"Almost suddenly at the end of the fourth or fifth week, it seemed to me that an actual physical weight that had depressed my brain lifted, and I experienced a decided activity of both mind and body, foreign to both for many years. Nevertheless, the complete re-energizing of both was very slow, the rejuvenation of appearance slower still.

"The time came when I knew that youth was returning to my face as well as to the hidden processes of my body; and I can assure you that it excited me far more than the renewed functioning of my brain. Eminent biologists who have given profound study to the subject estimate that it will last ten years at least, when it can be renewed once at all events. Of course the end must come. It was not intended that man should live forever.

"Science has defeated nature at many points. The triumph over diseases that once wasted whole nations, the arrest of infant mortality, the marvels of vivisection and surgery—the list is endless. It is entirely logical, and no more marvellous, that science should be able to arrest senescence. The wonder is that it has not been done before."

She rose, still looking down at the fire, which Clavering had replenished twice. "I am going now. And I have no fear that you will not keep your promise! But remember this when thinking it over: I do not merely *look* young agai﹇ *I am* young. I am not the years I hav﹇ passed in this world, I am the age of t﹇ rejuvenated glands in my body.

"Of course I cannot have childre﹇ The treatment is identical with that f﹇ sterilization. This consideration may i﹇ fluence you. You will have decided upo﹇ all that before we meet again. Goo﹇ night." And she was gone.

The Last of His Doubts

It seemed to Clavering that he had run the gamut of the emotions while listening to that brief biography, so sterilely told, but there had also been times when he had felt as if suspended in a void even while visited by flashes of acute consciousness that he was being called upon to know himself for the first time in his life. And in such fashion as no man had ever been called upon to know himself before.

His own room, where he was nearly always alone, with its warm red curtains and rug and several family portraits on the wall, restored his equilibrium and his brain was abnormally clear.

For an hour he excoriated her, hated her, feared her, dissociating her from the vast army of womanhood, but congratulating himself upon having known her. She was a unique if crucifying study.

But nothing could alter the fact that she was the most beautiful and the most wholly desirable woman he had ever known, the one woman who had focussed every aspiration of his mind, his soul, and his body. He knew he must ask himself the inevitable question and face it without blinking. Was he appalled by her real age; could he ever get away from the indubious fact that whatever miracle science may have effected, her literal age was verging on sixty?

And he doubted if any man could look at Mary Zattiany for three consecutive minutes and recall that she had ever been old, or imagine that she ever could be old again. He doubted if any man would weigh anything against his ego's demand to mate with a woman lik﹇ Mary Zattiany. He certainly would no﹇ That was final.

Did he love her? Comprehensively an﹇ utterly? Clear thinking fled with the la﹇ of his doubts . . . And when a man d﹇ taches himself from the gross materi﹇ surface of life and wings to the realr﹇ of the imagination, where he glimpse﹇ immortality, what matter the penalty﹇ Any penalty? Few had the thric﹇ blessed opportunity. If he were one ﹇ the chosen, the very demi-gods, jeerin﹇ at mortals, would hate him.

And then abruptly he fell asleep.

As Clavering entered the library sh﹇ was standing by the hearth, on﹇ hand on the mantelshelf. Her repose wa﹇ absolute as she turned her head. In he﹇ eyes was an insolent expression, a littl﹇ mocking, a little challenging.

"What have you been through?" h﹇ asked abruptly. "I've been through hell﹇

"So I imagined," she said drily. "﹇ can't say I've been through hell. I'v﹇ grown too philosophical for that! I le﹇ it on the knees of the gods."

"I don't believe you had a moment ﹇ misgiving. You were too sure of me."

"Oh, no, I was not! I know life to﹇ well to be sure of anything, *mon am﹇* Poor boy, I'm afraid you've been chokin﹇ ever since—"

"Don't 'poor boy' me. I won't have i﹇ I feel a thousand years old. You ar﹇ sure of me now—and quite right. I'﹇ more in love with you than ever, if yo﹇ want to know. When will you marr﹇ me?"

She lowered the opera glasses and glanced over the rows.

Illustration for Gertrude Atherton's
"BLACK OXEN"

"Shall we say two months from to-day?"

"Two months! Why not tomorrow?"

"Oh, hardly. In the first place I'd like all to be quite perfect, and I'd dreamed f spending our honeymoon in the Dolo-ites. I've a shooting box there on the hore of a wonderful lake. But we'll ave to live in New York more or less —I suppose?"

"More or less? Altogether. My work is ere."

"I believe there is more work for both f us in Europe."

"And do you imagine I'd live on your noney? I've nothing but what I make. Besides I've every intention of being a laywright."

"But playwriting isn't—not really—quite as important as poor Europe. And know of several ways in which we ould be of the greatest possible use. Not nly Austria—"

"Perhaps. But you'll have to wait until 've made money on at least one play.

I'll be only to glad to spend the honey-moon in the Dolomites, but then I re-turn and go to work. You'll have to make up your mind to live here for a year or two at least. And the sooner you marry me, the sooner we can go to Eu-rope to live—for a time. So you better marry me tomorrow."

"I can't get away for at least two months—possibly not then. And a honey-moon in New York would be too flat.

"Better than nothing . . . however—here's an idea. I'll get to work on my play at once and maybe I can finish it before I leave. If it went over big I could stay longer. Besides, it'll be some-thing to boil over into."

"Very well . . ."

"Well, that's that. We'll marry two months from today. I can finish my play in that time, and I won't wait a day longer. And now I want to kiss you."

And as Mary Zattiany never did any-thing by halves she was completely happy, and completely young.

A Nameless Fear

CLAVERING stood on his high balcony and looked down upon Madison Square. He was jubilant over his play nd the enthusiasm of his friends. They alked of nothing else: his play, his bril-iant future, his sure place in the crack egiment "if he hung on," and they in-isted that he must also express himself t least once through the medium of the novel. The great New York novel had et to be written. They fairly dinned his gifts into his ears, until he was almost ick of them.

He sat down to read his newspapers: e had merely glanced at the headlines nd his column. His eye was arrested by he picture of a man at the top of the irst page of his own newspaper. Claver-ng studied it for a moment before read-ng the news text, wondering faintly at nis interest. It was unmistakably the face f a statesman who was the complete naster of himself and accustomed to the nastery of men.

Clavering read the story.

PRINCE HOHENHAUER ARRIVES
IN NEW YORK

GOES AT ONCE TO WASHINGTON.

"Prince Hohenhauer, a distinguished political factor under the old Austrian Empire, arrived yesterday morning on the *Noordam*. He has recently returned to Vienna to accept a position in the Cabinet. As it is well known that Aus-tria desires the backing of the American Government to enable her to overcome the opposition of France to her alliance with Germany, or, it is whispered, with a kingdom farther south, it is not unrea-sonable to infer that he has come to the United States on a special, if secret, mis-sion."

Clavering dropped the newspaper. There could be little doubt as to who the man was. And yet there was as little doubt that Mary Zattiany had long since ceased to care for him. That was over fifteen or sixteen years ago.

Clavering had too much of the arro-

gance of youth and he was too sure of
Mary Zattiany's love for himself, to be
apprehensive of the charms of a man of
sixty, but he was invaded by a nameless
and almost sickening fear. He had very

swift and often very sure intuitions, a
he was shaken by a premonition that
some manner, which, in his ignoran
of the facts he was unable to define, th
man's presence boded no good.

The Rarest Thing in Life

Mary's "headache" had continued for
two days, but Clavering came to
her house by appointment the next afternoon at five o'clock.

He would never suspect the black turmoil of these past two days, nor its cause,
but it would be equally disconcerting if
he attributed her low spirits to the arrival of Hohenhauer. What a fool she
had been to have made more than a
glancing reference to that last old love-
affair, almost forgotten until that night
of stark revelation. It didn't matter, and
he must have "placed" Hohenhauer at
once this morning, and would imagine
that she was depressed at the thought of
meeting him.

She looked up at him, smilingly from
her deep chair as he stood above her on
the hearthrug.

"The rest has done you good," he
said, smiling also. "But I've already
made up my mind that you need a
change and dropped Din a hint to open
his camp in the Adirondacks and give
you a farewell house party. He jumped
at the chance and its all arranged."

"Really, Lee, you are high-handed.
You might have consulted me first."

Her faint resentment vanished and she
felt a languid sense of well-being in this
enveloping atmosphere of the tactless imperious male, so foreign to her experience; and the prospect was certainly enchanting. Moreover, she would be able to
avoid seeing Hohenhauer in surroundings where this strange love affair of hers
had obliterated the past (for the most
part) and she had found, for a time at
least, happiness and peace.

Clavering had tied the boat to a tree
in a little inlet far down the lake,
and they were walking through a wood
of spruce trees and balsam.

He sighed, finally, and said, "Y
must understand that in spite of t
erratic creature you have known sin
you refused to marry me at once a
left me with no resource but to let th
play boil out, I am man first and
writer incidentally. I also have a strong
ambition to be your husband than
write plays. But I must have the mon
to be independent of newspaper wor
Otherwise I should have neither peace
mind nor be able to live abroad wi
you. I'll write my plays in New Yo
and rush production. The greater pa
of the year I shall spend with you
Europe."

"But, are you sure? You seem so muc
a part of New York, of this strange hig
pitched civilization. If you are not su
—if you are only tired of New York f
the moment. I—yes, I will. I'll give it a
up and live here. No doubt my dream
doing great things in Europe was me
vanity—"

"Do you believe that?"

"Perhaps not. But, after all, what
tried to do might be so easily frustrate
in that cauldron—why should I risk pe
sonal happiness—the most precious an
the rarest thing in life, for what may k
a chimera—wasted years and a waste
life."

"I don't know that I shall ask th
sacrifice of you. A part of your brain
asleep now, but it is a very active an
insistent part when awake. In time yo
might revert—and resentment is a fat
canker; but let's leave it open."

He put both arms about her. The pa
was blank to both. Their pulsing li
met in the wonder and the ecstasy of th
first kiss of youth, of profound and pe
fect and imperishable love. They clun
together exalted and exulting and for th
moment at least they were one.

Stern Duty

s THEY walked up the steep path
to the camp a sense of coming dis-
er drove into her mind and banished
e memory of the past hour. She had
rely taken off her coat and scarf when
e heard a tap on her door. Mr. Din-
ddie entered and closed the door bend him.

"I had this telegram an hour ago from
ent."

Mary snatched the paper from his
nd and was reading it aloud.

"Hohenhauer took morning train for
untersville stop must see M.Z. stop
n't let anything prevent."

"Hohenhauer!" exclaimed Mary, and
w, oddly enough, she felt only aston-
ment and annoyance. "Why should
come all this way to see me? He
uld have written if he had anything
say. But I suppose I shall have to see
m."

wo tall dignified bodies adjusted
themselves to chairs both slippery
d bumpy. He had closed the door bend him.

"Now that the amenities are over,
xcellenz," she said with the briskness
e had picked up from her American
iends, "let us come to the point. I in-
r you did not take a day's journey and
ut up with this abominable hotel to tell
e that you are forming a Federation of
ustria and the South German States.
ou were sometimes kind enough to ask
y help in the past, but I have no in-
uence in Washington."

"No, dear Gräfin. I do not need your
ssistance in Washington. But I do need
in Austria, and that is why I am here.
shall not waste the little time at our
isposal in diplomacy. I have been told
at you intend to marry a young Amer-
an."

Mary was annoyed to feel herself
ushing, but she answered coldly, "It is
uite true that I intend to marry Mr.
lavering."

"And I have come here to ask you to

renounce that intention and to marry me
instead."

"You!" Mary almost rose from her
chair. "What on earth do you mean?"

"If what I say sounds brutal, it is
merely to remind you that love—the intense passionate love, I have no doubt,
you have for this young man who helps
you to realize your renewed youth—
never lasts. And when this new love of
yours burns itself out—You never had
the reputation of being constant, dear
Marie. You will have an alien young
man on your hands, while that remarkable brain of yours will be demanding
its field of action.

"Do you imagine for a moment that
you could play the great role in Austrian
affairs you have set yourself, handicapped by an American name—and an
American husband? Not with all your
gifts, your wealth, your genius for playing on that complex instrument called
human nature. Austria may be a Republic of sorts, but it is still Austria.
You would be an American and an outsider—a presumptuous interloper."

She stared at him aghast. "I—oh!—I
had not thought of that. It seems incomprehensible—but I had never thought of
myself as Mrs. Clavering. I have been
Gräfin Zattiany so long!"

"And your plans were well-defined,
and your ambition to play a great role
on the modern European stage possessed
you utterly until you met this young
man—is it not so?"

"Oh, yes, but—"

"I understand. It must have been a
quite marvellous experience, after those
barren years, to feel yourself glowing
with all the vitalities of youth once more;
to bring young men to your feet with a
glance and to fancy yourself in love—"

"Fancy!" She interrupted him passionately. "I am in love—and more—more
than I ever was with you."

"You and I have sterner duties. Do
you suppose that I would sacrifice Austria for some brief wild hope of human

happiness? And you are only two years younger than I am. Nothing can alter the march of years. Moreover, you owe to Austria this wonderful rejuvenescence of yours. Remember, Marie, that under that miracle of science, the body may go back but never the mind. You, your ego, your mind, your self, are no younger than your fifty-eight hardlived years.

"If you marry this young man you will marry him as Marie Zattiany, without an illusion left in that clear brain of yours—from which the mists have been blown by the cold wind of truth. And in a year—if you can stand self-contempt and ineffable ennui so long—you will leave him, resume your present name—and return to us. But it may be too late. Vienna would still be laughing. Are you quite indifferent to this, Marie?"

She shrugged and rose. "It must be time for luncheon," she said. "It will no doubt be horrible, but at least we can have it here. I will find Mr. Dinwiddie and ask him to order it."

"I Have Had My Dream"

CLAVERING forced himself to eat a good breakfast and read his newspapers. He was determined to show her that he was completely master of himself. She should be able to draw no unfavorable comparisons with Hohenhauer whose composure had probably not been ruffled in forty years.

It was ten o'clock when he presented himself at Madame Zattiany's door. The footman who answered his ring informed him that Madame was in her car and begged him to join her.

She was completely at her ease, and she was the Madame Zattiany of the night he had met her. But she did not elaborate the role, and asked him how he had left his friends at the camp and if he had enjoyed his fishing trip.

"Enough of this," he interrupted. "I know that you went down to Huntersville to meet Hohenhauer, and that the result of that interview was an abrupt flight from me—possibly from him. I want the truth. Do you still intend to marry me?"

"I have promised to marry you, remember; and I do not lightly go back on my word . . . But . . . I had intended to ask if you would be willing to let me go alone to Vienna for six months—and then join me—"

"After I had lost you completely! I shall marry you here, today, or not at all. I love you but I'll not let you play with me. I'll go to Austria with you, and you may do as you choose when you get there. You'll belong to me and I'll make the best of it."

"If I married you now it would not be worth my while to return to Austria . . . You see, I'd be an American. I'd no longer be Gräfin Zattiany . . . I could accomplish nothing . . . It is the strangest thing in the world, but I never had thought of changing my name—"

"Until Hohenhauer reminded you, I suppose. Well, I could have told you that myself."

"You have acknowledged there is no place for me here, and there would be no place for me in Europe if I married you." She said apparently without hearing his remark. "Do you wonder that I came away to think, after Prince Hohenhauer—who, remember, knows me far better than you do—pointed out the inexorable truth? What would you do with me?"

"I don't know," he said miserably. "I only know that I love you."

"There is a long generation, Lee. And it is I who have lived it, not you. Hohenhauer told me many cruel truths and every word he said was true. I must go forward. I cannot—cannot go back. I love you and I believe that I shall always love you—but I don't see any way out. Love is a very old story to me. It could never be to me again the significant thing it is even to a woman of middle age, much less to the young. Oh, no, my friend. Oh, no. Let those women who have it in their power to repeople the earth which has lost so many millions of its sons, cherish that delusion of the supreme importance of love; but not I! I have had my dream, but it is over.

"You have not the courage to marry me—here—today."

"Courage! I could contemplate going back to certain death at the hands of an assassin, or in another revolution; to stand on the edge of the abyss, the last human being alive in Europe, and look down upon her expiring throes before I went over the brink myself. But I have not the courage to marry you."

Clavering picked up the tube and told the driver to stop.

He closed the door and lifted his hat. "Good-bye, Madame Zattiany," he said. And as the driver was listening, he added: "A pleasant journey."

On the Death of Mr. Robert Levet, a Practiser in Physic

Condemned to Hope's delusive mine,
    As on we toil from day to day,
By sudden blasts or slow decline
    Our social comforts drop away.

Well tried through many a varying year,
    See Levet to the grave descend,
Officious, innocent, sincere,
    Of every friendless name the friend.

Yet still he fills affection's eye,
    Obscurely wise and coarsely kind;
Nor, lettered Arrogance, deny
    Thy praise to merit unrefined.

When fainting nature called for aid,
    And hovering death prepared the blow,
His vigorous remedy displayed
    The power of art without the show.

In Misery's darkest cavern known,
    His useful care was ever nigh,
Where hopeless Anguish poured his groan,
    And lonely Want retired to die.

The busy day, the peaceful night,
    Unfelt, uncounted, glided by:
His frame was firm—his powers were bright,
    Though now his eightieth year was nigh.

Then with no fiery throbbing pain,
    No cold gradations of decay,
Death broke at once the vital chain,
    And freed his soul the nearest way.
          —*Samuel Johnson* (1709-1784).

Irvin S. Cobb

OLD JUDGE PRIEST

Irvin S. Cobb was born (1876) and brought up in Paducah, Kentucky, whose local color and odd characters form the background against which Old Judge Priest plays his wily part. Irvin Cobb's books, plays, and movie scenarios have been brightening our lives for the past forty years but he never created a character more beloved than the Old Judge. Here is a collection of stories about him which inspired the famous movie, starring Will Rogers.

The Lord Provides

This story begins with Judge Priest sitting at his desk at his chambers at the old courthouse. He strains to reach an especially itchy spot between his shoulder blades and addresses words to Jeff Poindexter, coloured, his body servant and house boy.

"They ain't so very purty to look at—red flannels ain't," said the judge. "But, Jeff, I've noticed this—they certainly are mighty lively company till you git used to 'em. I never am the least bit lonely fur the first few days after I put on my heavy underwear."

There was no answer from Jeff except a deep, soft breath. He slept. At a customary hour he had come with Mittie May, the white mare, and the buggy to take Judge Priest home to supper, and had found the judge engaged beyond his normal quitting time.

That, however, had not discommoded Jeff. Jeff always knew what to do with his spare moments. Jeff always had a way of spending the long winter evenings. He leaned now against a book-rack, with his elbow on the top shelf, napping lightly. Jeff preferred to sleep lying down or sitting down, but he could sleep upon his feet too—and frequently did.

Having, by brisk scratching movements, assuaged the irritation between his shoulder blades, the judge picked up his pen and shoved it across a sheet of legal cap that already was half

covered with his fine, close writing. He never dictated his decisions, but always wrote them out by hand. The pen nib travelled along steadily for awhile. Eventually words in a typewritten petition that rested on the desk at his left caught the judge's eye.

"Huh!" he grunted, and read the quoted phrase, " 'True Believers' Afro-American Church of Zion, sometimes called ——' " Without turning his head he again hailed his slumbering servitor: "Jeff, why do you-all call that there little church-house down by the river Possum Trot?"

Mightily well Jeff understood the how and the why and the wherefore of the True Believers. He could have traced out step by step, with circumstantial detail, the progress of the internal feud within the despised congregation that led to the upspringing of rival sets of claimants to the church property, and to the litigation that had thrown the whole tangled business into the courts for final adjudication. But except in company of his own choosing and his own colour, wild horses could not have drawn that knowledge from Jeff, although it would have pained him to think any white person who had a claim upon his friendship suspected him of concealment of any detail whatsoever.

"He-he," chuckled Jeff. "I reckin that's jes' nigger foolishness. Me, I don' know no reason why they sh'd call a church by no sech a name as that. I ain't never had no truck wid 'em ole True Believers, myse'f. I knows some calls 'em the Do-Righters, and some calls 'em the Possum Trotters." His tone subtly altered to one of innocent bewilderment: "Whut you doin', Jedge, pesterin' yo'se'f wid sech low-down trash as them darkies is?"

Further discussion of the affairs of the strange faith that was divided against itself might have ensued but that an interruption came.

Judge Priest swung about to find a woman in his doorway. She was a big, upstanding woman, overfleshed and overdressed, and upon her face she bore the sign of her profession as plainly and indubitably as though it had been branded there in scarlet letters.

The old man's eyes narrowed as he recognised her. But up he got on the instant and bowed before her. No being created in the image of a woman ever had reason to complain that in her presence Judge Priest forgot his manners.

"Howdy do, ma'am," he said ceremoniously. "Will you walk in? And mout I enquire the purpose of this here call?"

"Yes, sir, I'm a-goin' to tell you what brought me here without wastin' any more words than I can help," said the woman. "No, thank you, Judge," she went on as he motioned her toward a seat; "I guess I can say what I've got to say, standing up."

Her voice was coarsened and flat; it was more like a man's voice than a woman's, and she spoke with a masculine directness.

"There was a girl died at my house early this mornin'," she told him. "Viola St. Claire was the name she went by here. I don't know what her real name was—she never told anybody what it was. She wasn't much of a hand to talk about herself. She must have been nice people though, because she was always nice and ladylike, no matter what happened. From what I gathered off and on, she came here from some little town down near Memphis. I certainly liked that girl. She'd been with me nearly

ten months. She wasn't more than nineteen years old.

"Well, all day yestiddy she was out of her head with a high fever. But just before she died she come to and her mind cleared up.

"She called me, and I leaned over her and asked her what it was she wanted, and she told me. She knew she was dyin'. She told me she'd been raised right, which I knew already without her tellin' me, and she said she'd been a Christian girl before she made her big mistake. And she told me she wanted to be buried like a Christian, from a regular church, with a sermon and flowers and music and all that.

"She made me promise that I'd see it was done just that way. She made me put my hand in her hand and promise her. She shut her eyes then, like she was satisfied, and in a minute or two after that she died, still holdin' on tight to my hand."

"Well, ma'am, I'm very sorry for that poor child. I am so," said Judge Priest, and his tone showed he meant it; "yit still I don't understand your purpose in comin' to me, without you need money to bury her."

"It's something else I wanted to speak with you about. I've rid miles on the street cars, and I've walked afoot until the bottoms of my feet both feel like boils right this minute, tryin' to find somebody that was fitten to preach a sermon over that dead girl. But every last one of them preachers said no."

"Do you mean to tell me that not a single minister in this whole city is willin' to hold a service over that dead girl?" Judge Priest shrilled at her with vehement astonishment—and something else—in his voice.

"No, no, not that," the woman made haste to explain. "There wasn't a single one of 'em but said he'd come to my house and conduct the exercises. They was all willin' enough to go to the grave too. But you see that wouldn't do. I explained to 'em, until I almost lost my voice, that it had to be a funeral in a regular church, with flowers and music and all. That poor girl got it into her mind somehow, I think, that she'd have a better chance in the next world if she went out of this one like a Christian should ought to go. I explained all that to 'em, and from explainin' I took to arguin' with 'em, and then to pleadin' and beggin'. I bemeaned myself before them preachers. I was actually ready to go down on my knees before 'em.

"So finally, when I was about to give up, I thought about you and I come here as straight as I could walk."

"But, ma'am," he said, "I'm not a regular church member myself. I reckin' I oughter be, but I aint. And I still fail to understand why you should think I could serve you, though I don't mind tellin' you I'd be mighty glad to ef I could."

"Maybe you don't remember it, Judge, but two years ago this comin' December that there Law and Order League fixed up to run me out of this town. They didn't succeed, but they did have me indicted by the Grand Jury, and I come up before you and pleaded guilty—they had the evidence on me all right. You fined me, you fined me the limit, and I guess if I hadn't 'a' had the money to pay the fine I'd 'a' gone to jail. But the main point with me was that you treated me like a lady.

"I ain't forgot that. I ain't ever goin' to forget it. And awhile ago, when I was all beat out and discouraged, I said to myself that if there was one man left in this town who could maybe help me to keep my promise to that dead girl, Judge William Priest was that man."

"Was it stated—was it specified that a preacher must hold the funeral service over that dead girl?" he inquired.

THE woman caught eagerly at the inflection that had come into his voice.

"No, sir," she answered; "all she said was that it must be in a church and with some flowers and some music. But I never heard of anybody preachin' a regular sermon without it was a regular preacher. Did you ever, Judge?" Doubt and renewed disappointment battered at her just-born hopes.

"I reckin mebbe there have been extryordinary occasions where an amateur stepped in and done the best he could," said the judge. "Mebbe some folks here on earth couldn't excuse sech presumption as that, but I reckin they'd understand how it was up yonder."

He stood up, facing her, and spoke as one making a solemn promise:

"Ma'am, you needn't worry yourself any longer. You kin go on back to your home. That dead child is goin' to have whut she asked for. I give you my word on it."

She strove to put a question, but he kept on:

"I ain't prepared to give you the full details yit. You see I don't know myself jest exactly whut they'll be. But inside of an hour from now I'll be seein' the undertaker and he'll notify you in regards to the hour and the place and the rest of it. Kin you rest satisfied with that?"

She nodded, trying to utter words and not succeeding. Emotion shook her gross shape until the big gold bands on her arms jangled together.

"So, ef you'll kindly excuse me, I've got quite a number of things to do betwixt now and suppertime. I kind of figger I'm goin' to be right busy."

For a fact the judge was a busy man during the hour which followed upon all this, the hour between twilight and night. Over the telephone he first called up M. Jansen, our leading undertaker; indeed at that time our only one, excusing the coloured undertaker on Locust Street. He had converse at length with M. Jansen. Then he called up Doctor Lake, a most dependable person in sickness, and when you were in good health too. Then last of all he called up a certain widow who lived in those days, Mrs. Matilda Weeks by name; and this lady was what is commonly called a character. Mrs. Weeks was daily guilty of acts that scandalised all proper people. But the improper ones worshipped the ground her feet touched as she walked. She was much like that disciple of Joppa named Tabitha, which by interpretation is called Dorcas, of whom it is written that she was full of good works and almsdeeds which she did. Yes, you might safely call Mrs. Weeks a character.

With her, back and forth across the telephone wire, Judge Priest had extended speech. Then he hung up the receiver and went home alone to a late and badly burnt supper.

The Procession

OH, we've had funerals and funerals down our way. But the funeral that took place on an October day that I have in mind will long be talked about.

It came as a surprise to most people, for in the daily papers of that morning no customary black-bordered announcement had appeared. Others had heard of it by word of mouth. In dubious quarters, and in some quarters not quite so dubious, the news had travelled, although details in advance of the event were only to be guessed at.

Anyhow, the reading and talking public knew this much: That a girl, calling herself Viola St. Claire and aged nineteen, had died. It was an accepted fact, naturally, that even the likes of her must be laid away after some fashion or other. If she were put under ground by stealth, clandestinely as it were, so much the better for the atmosphere of civic morality. That I am sure would have been disclosed as the opinion of a majority, had there been inquiry among those who were presumed to have and who admitted they had the best interests of the community at heart.

So you see a great many people were entirely unprepared against the coming of the pitiably short procession that at eleven o'clock, or thereabout, turned out of the little street running down back of the freight depot into Franklin Street, which was one of our main thoroughfares. First came the hearse, drawn by M. Jansen's pair of dappled white horses and driven by M. Jansen himself, he wearing his official high hat and the span having black plumes in their head stalls, thus betokening a burial cere-

mony of the top cost. Likewise the hearse was M. Jansen's best hearse—not his third best, nor yet his second best.

The coffin, showing through the glass sides, was of white cloth and it looked very small, almost like a coffin for a child. However, it may have looked so because there was little of its shape to be seen. It was covered and piled and banked up with flowers. These were such flowers as, in our kindly climate, grew out of doors until well on into November: late roses and early chrysanthemums, marigolds and gladioluses, and such. They lay there loosely, with their stems upon them, just as Mrs. Weeks had sheared them, denuding every plant and shrub and bush that grew in her garden, so a girl whom Mrs. Weeks had never seen might go to her grave with an abundance of the blossoms she had coveted about her.

Behind the hearse came a closed coach. We used to call them coaches when they figured in funerals, carriages when used for lodge turnouts, and plain hacks when they met the trains and boats. In the coach rode four women. The world at large had a way of calling them painted women; but this day their faces were not painted nor were they garishly clad. For the time they were merely women—neither painted women nor fallen women—but just women.

AND that was nearly all, but not quite. At one side of the hearse, opposite the slowly turning front wheels, trudged Judge Priest, carrying in the crook of one bent arm a book. It wouldn't be a law book, for they commonly are large books, bound in buff leather, and this book was small and flat and black in colour. On the other side of the hearse, with head very erect and eyes fixed straight ahead and Sunday's best coat buttoned tightly about his sparse frame, walked another old man, Doctor Lake.

And that was all. At least that was all at first. But as the procession—if you could call it that—swung into Franklin Street I know that some men stood along the curbstones and stared and that other men, having first bared their heads, broke away to tail in at the end of the marching figures. And I know that of those who did this there were more than of those who merely stood and stared. The padding of shoe soles upon the gravel of the street became a steadily increasing, steadily rising thump-thump-thump; the rhythm of it rose above the creak and the clatter of the hearse wheels and the hoofs of the horses.

Heralded by the sound of its own thumping tread and leaving in its wake a stupefaction of astonishment, the procession kept straight on down Franklin Street, until it reached the very foot of the street. There it swung off at right angles into a dingy, ill-kempt little street that coursed crookedly along the water front, with poor houses rising upon one side and the raw mud banks of the river falling steeply away upon the other.

It followed this street until the head of it came opposite a little squat box-and-barn of a structure, built out of up-and-down planking; unpainted, too, with a slatted belfry, like an overgrown chicken coop, perched midway of the peak of its steeply pitched tin roof.

Now this structure, as all knew who remembered the history of contemporary litigation as recorded in the local prints, was the True Believers' Afro-American Church of Zion, sometimes termed in derision Possum Trot, being until recently the place of worship of that newest and most turbulent of local negro sects, but now closed on an injunction secured by one of the warring factions within its membership.

Technically it was still closed. Actually and physically it was at this moment open—wide open. The double doors were drawn back, the windows shone clean, and at the threshold of the swept and garnished interior stood Judge Priest's Jeff, with his broom in his hand and his mop and bucket at his side. Jeff had concluded his share of the labors barely in time.

As M. Jansen steered his dappled span close up alongside the pavement and brought them to a standstill, Judge Priest looked back and with what he saw was well content. He knew that morbid curiosity might account for the presence of some among this multitude who had come following after him, but not for all, and perhaps not for very many. He nodded to himself with the air of one who is amply satisfied by the results of an accomplished experiment.

"Suffer the Little Children . . ."

WHEN the crowd was in and seated —all of it that could get in and get seated—a tall, white-haired woman in a plain black frock came silently and swiftly through a door at the back and sat herself down upon a red plush stool before a golden-oak melodeon. But Mrs. Matilda Weeks' finger ends fell with such sanctifying gentleness upon the warped keys, and as she sang her sweet soprano rose so clearly and yet so softly, filling this place whose walls so often had resounded to the lusty hallelujahs of shouting black converts, that to those who listened now it seemed almost as though a Saint Cecilia had descended from on high to make this music.

When she finished singing, Judge Priest got up from a front pew where he had been sitting and went and stood alongside the flower-piled coffin, with his back to the little yellow-pine pulpit and his prayer book in his hands, a homely, ungraceful figure, facing an assemblage that packed the darky meeting house until it could hold no more.

I deem it to have been characteristic of the old judge that he made no explanation for his presence before them and no apology for his assumption of a rôle so unusual. He opened his black-bound volume at a place where his plump forefinger had been thrust between the leaves to mark the place for him, and in his high, thin voice he read through the service for the dead, with its promise of the divine forgiveness. When he had reached the end of it he put the book aside, and spoke to them in the fair and grammatical English that usually he reserved for his utterances from the bench in open court:

"Our sister who lies here asked with almost her last conscious breath that at her funeral a sermon should be preached. Upon me, who never before attempted such an undertaking, devolves the privilege of speaking a few words above her. I had thought to take for my text the words: 'He that is without sin among you, let him first cast a stone at her.'

"But I have changed my mind. I changed it only a little while ago. For I recalled that once on a time the Master said: 'Suffer little children to come unto Me, and forbid them not: for of such is the kingdom of Heaven.' And I believe, in the scheme of everlasting mercy and everlasting pity, that before the eyes of our common Creator we are all of us as little children whose feet stumble in the dark. So I shall take that saying of the Saviour for my text."

Perhaps it would be unjust to those whose business is the preaching of sermons to call this a sermon. I, for one, never heard any other sermon in any other church that did not last longer than five minutes. And certainly Judge Priest, having made his beginning, did not speak for more than five minutes; the caressing fingers of the sunlight had not perceptibly shifted upon the flower-strewn coffin top when he finished what he had to say and stood with his head bowed. After that, except for a rustle of close-packed body and a clearing of men's huskened throats, there was silence for a little time.

THEN Judge Priest's eyes looked about him and three pews away he saw Ashby Corwin. It may have been he remembered that as a young man Ashby Corwin had been destined for holy orders until another thing—some said it was a woman and some said it was whisky, and some said it was first the woman and then the whisky—came into his life and wrecked it so that until the end of his days Ashby Corwin trod the rocky downhill road of the profligate and the waster. Or it may have been the look he read upon the face of the other that moved Judge Priest to say:

"I will ask Mr. Corwin to pray."

At that Ashby Corwin stood up in his place and threw back his prematurely whitened head, and he lifted his face that was all scarified with the blighting flames of dissipation, and he shut his eyes that long since had wearied of looking upon a trivial world, and Ashby Corwin prayed.

There are prayers that seem to circle round and round in futile rings, going nowhere; and then again there are prayers that are like sparks struck off from the wheels of the prophet's chariot of fire, coursing their way upward in spiritual splendour to blaze on the sills of the Judgment Seat. This prayer was one of those prayers.

After that Judge Priest bowed his head again and spoke the benediction.

The Collection

ON THE morning of the day following the day of this funeral Judge Priest sat putting the last words to his decision touching upon the merits of the existing controversy in the congregation of the True Believers' Afro-American Church of Zion. The door opened and in walked Beck Giltner, saloon keeper, sure-thing gambler, handy-man-with-a-gun, and, according to the language of a resolution unanimously adopted at a mass meeting of the Law and Order League, force-for-evil.

"Good mornin', Beck," said the judge. "Well?"

"Judge Priest," said Giltner, "as a rule I don't come to this courthouse except when I have to come. But to-day I've come to tell you something. You made a mistake yesterday!"

"A mistake, suh?" The judge's tone was sharp and quick.

"Yes, suh, that's what you did," returned the tall gambler. "I don't mean in regards to that funeral you held for that dead girl. You probably don't care what I think one way or the other, but I want to tell you I was strong for that, all the way through. But you made a mistake just the same, Judge; you didn't take up a collection.

"So last night I took it on myself to get up a collection for you. I started it with a bill or so off my own roll. Then I passed the hat round at several places where you wouldn't scarcely care to go yourself. And I didn't run across a single fellow that failed to contribute. Some of 'em don't move in the best society, and there's some more of 'em that you'd only know of by reputation. But every last one of 'em put in something. There was one man that didn't have only seven cents to his name—he put that in. So here it is—four hundred and seventy-five dollars and forty-two cents, accordin' to my count."

From one pocket he fetched forth a rumpled packet of paper money and from the other a small cloth sack, which gave off metallic clinking sounds. He put them down together on the desk in front of Judge Priest.

"I appreciate this, ef I am right in

my assumption of the motives which actuated you and the purposes to which you natchally assumed this here money would be applied," said Judge Priest as the other man waited for his response. "But, son, I can't take your money. It ain't needed. Why, I wouldn't know whut to do with it. There ain't no outstandin' bills connected with that there funeral. All the expense entailed was met—privately. So you see——"

"Wait just a minute before you say no!" interrupted Giltner. "Here's my idea and it's the idea of all the others that contributed: We-all want you to take this money and keep it—keep it in a safe, or in your pocket, or in the bank to your credit, or anywheres you please, but just keep it. And if any girl that's gone wrong should die and not have any friends to help bury her, they can come to you and get the cash out of this fund to pay for puttin' her away. And if any other girl should want to go back to her people and start in all over again and try to lead a better life, why you can advance her the railroad fare out of that money too.

"You see, Judge, we are aimin' to make a kind of a trust fund out of it, with you as the trustee. And when the four seventy-five forty-two is all used up, if you'll just let me know I'll guarantee to rustle up a fresh bank roll so you'll always have enough on hand to meet the demands. Now then, Judge, will you take it?"

Judge Priest took it. He stretched out and scooped in currency and coin sack, using therefor his left hand only. The right was engaged in reaching for Beck Giltner's right hand, the purpose being to shake it.

.   .   .   .   .   .

FORREST'S LAST CHARGE

JUDGE PRIEST's way took him to Soule's Drug Store, the gathering place of his set in fair weather and in foul. He was almost there before he heard of the trouble. It was Dave Baum who brought the first word of it. Seeing him

pass, Dave came running, bareheaded, out of his notions store.

"Judge Priest, did you know what's just happened?" Dave was highly excited. "Why, Beaver Yancy's been cut all to pieces with a dirk knife by one of those Dagos that was brought on here to work on the new extension—that's what just happened! It happened just a little bit ago, down there where they've got those Dagos a-keepin' 'em. Beave, he must've said somethin' out of the way to him, and he just up with his dirk knife and cut Beave to ribbons. Judge, what do you think ought to be done about this business?"

"Well, son," said Judge Priest, "to begin with, ef I was you I'd run back inside of my store and put my hat on before I ketched a bad cold. And ef I was the chief of police of this city I'd find the accused party and lock him up good and tight. And ef I was everybody else I'd remain ez ca'm ez I could till I'd heared both sides of the case. There's nearly always two sides to every case, and sometimes there's likely to be three or four sides. I expect to impanel a new grand jury along in January and I wouldn't be surprised ef they looked into the matter purty thoroughly.

"It's too bad, though, about Beaver Yancy!" added the judge; "I certainly trust he pulls through. Maybe he will —he's powerful husky. There's one consolation—he hasn't got any family, has he?"

And, with that, Judge Priest left them and went on down the snow-piled street and turned into Soule's Drug Store.

Labor Trouble

I T WOULD seem Beaver Yancy had more friends than any unprejudiced observer would have credited him with having. Mainly they were the type of friends who would not have lent him so much as fifty cents under any conceivable circumstance, but stood ready to shed human blood on his account. Likewise, as the day wore on, and the snow, under the melting influence of the sun, began to run off the eaves and turn to slush in the streets, a strong prejudice against the presence of alien day laborers developed with marvellous and sinister rapidity.

Yet, had those who cavilled but stopped long enough to take stock of things, they might have read this importation as merely one of the changes that was coming over our neck of the woods with the advent of the railroad. When, after many false alarms, the P. A. & O. V. got its Boaz Ridge Extension under way the contractors started with Negro hands; but the gang bosses came from up North, whence the capital had likewise come, and they did not understand the Negroes and the Negroes did not understand them, and there was trouble from the go-off.

Having a time limit ever before their pestered eyes, it sorely irked the contractors that, whereas five hundred black, brown and yellow men might drop their tools Saturday night at six o'clock, a scant two hundred or so answered when the seven-o'clock whistle blew on Monday morning. The others came straggling back on Tuesday or Wednesday, or even on Thursday, depending on how long their wages held out.

Then the contractors just fired the whole outfit bodily; and they suspended operations, leaving the fills half-filled and the cuts half-dug until they could fetch new shifts of laborers from the North. They fetched them—a trainload of overalled Latins, and some of these were tall and swarthy men, and more were short, fair men; but all were capable of doing a full day's work.

Speedily enough, the town lost its first curious interest in the newcomers. Indeed, there was about them nothing calculated to hold the public interest long. They played no guitars, wore no handkerchief headdresses, offered to kidnap no small children, and were in no respect a picturesque race of beings. They talked their own outlandish language dined on their own mysterious messes, slept in their bunks in the long barracks the company knocked together for them in the hollow down by the Old Fort, hived their savings, dealt with their employers through a paid translator, and beautifully minded their own business, which was the putting through of the Boaz Ridge Extension.

Tony Palassi, who ran the biggest fruit stand in town, paid them one brief visit—and one only—and came away, spitting his disgust on the earth. It appeared that they were not his kind of people at all, these being but despised Sicilians and he by birth a haughty Roman, and by virtue of naturalisation processes a stalwart American. Nobody ever thought of calling Tony a Dago, and nobody ever had—more than once; but these other fellows, plainly, were Dagos and to be regarded as such. For upward of a month now their presence in the community had meant little or nothing to the community, one way or the other, until one of them so far forgot himself as to carve up Beaver Yancy.

The Crime

THE railroad made a big mistake when it hired Northern bosses to handle black natives; it made another when it continued to retain Beaver Yancy, of our town, in its employ after the Sicilians came, he being a person long of the arm and short of the temper. Even so, things might have gone forward to a conclusion without misadventure had it not been that on the day before the snow fell the official padrone of the force, who was likewise the official interpreter, went North on some private business of his own, leaving his countrymen without an intermediary during his absence.

It came to pass, therefore, that on the December morning when this account properly begins, Beaver Yancy found himself in sole command of a battalion whose tongue he did not speak and whose ways he did not know.

At starting time he ploughed his way through the drifts to the long plank shanty in the bottoms and threw open a door. Instead of being up and stirring, his charges lay in their bunks against the walls, all of them stretched out comfortably there, except a half dozen or so who brewed garlicky mixtures on the big stoves that stood at intervals in a row down the middle of the barracks. Employing the only language he knew, which was a profanely emphatic language, he ordered them to get up, get out and get to work. By shakes of the head, by words of smiling dissent and by gestures they made it plain to his understanding that for this one day at least they meant to do no labour in the open.

One more tolerant than Beaver Yancy, or perhaps one more skilled at translating signs, would have divined their reasons readily enough. They had come South expecting temperate weather. They did not like snow. They were not clad for exposure to snow. Their garments were thin and their shoes leaked. Therefore would they abide where they were until the snow had melted and the cold had moderated. Then they would work twice as hard to make up for this holiday.

The burly, big, overbearing man in the doorway was of a different frame of mind. In the absence of his superior officers and the padrone, his duty was to see that they pushed that job to a conclusion. He'd show 'em! He would make an example of one and the others would heed the lesson. He laid violent grasp on a little man who appeared to be a leader of opinion among his fellows and, with a big, mittened hand in the neckband of the other's shirt, dragged him, sputtering and expostulating, across the threshold and, with hard kicks of a heavy foot, heavily booted, propelled him out into the open.

The little man fell face forward into the snow. He bounced up like a chunk of new rubber. He had been wounded most grievously in his honour, bruised most painfully and ignominiously elsewhere. He jumped for the man who had mishandled him, his knifeblade licking out like a snake's tongue. He jabbed three times, hard and quick—then fled back indoors; and for a while, until help came in the guise of two children of a shanty-boater's family on their way to the railroad yards to pick up bits of coal, Beaver Yancy lay in the snow where he had dropped, bleeding like a stuck pig.

He was not exactly cut to ribbons. First accounts had been exaggerated as first accounts so frequently are. But he had two holes in his right lung and one in the right side of his neck, and it was strongly presumptive that he would never again kick a Sicilian day laborer —or, for that matter, anybody else.

JUDGE PRIEST, speaking dispassionately from the aloof heights of the judicial temperament, had said it would be carrying out an excellent and timely idea if the chief of police found the knife-using individual and confined him in a place that was safe and sound; which, on being apprised of the occurrence, was exactly what the chief of police undertook to do. Accompanied by two dependable members of his day shift, he very promptly set out to make an arrest and an investigation; but serious obstacles confronted him.

To begin with, he had not the faintest notion of the criminal's identity or the criminal's appearance. The man he wanted was one among two hundred; but which one was he? Beaver Yancy, having been treated in Doctor Lake's office, was now at the city hospital in no condition to tell the name of his assailant even had he known it, or to describe him either, seeing that loss of blood, pain, shock and drugs had put him beyond the power of coherent speech. Nevertheless, the chief felt it a duty incumbent on him to lose no time in visiting what the *Daily Evening News* with a touch of originality, called "the scene of the crime." This he did.

Had the big-hatted chief been wise in the ways of these men, he might peacefully have attained his object by opening his topcoat and showing his blue uniform, his brass buttons and his gold star;

but naturally he did not think of that, and as he stood there before them, demanding of them, in a language they did not know, to surrender the guilty one, he was ulstered, like any civilian, from his throat to the tops of his rubber boots.

In him the foreigners, bewildered by the sudden turn in events, saw only a menacing enemy coming, with no outward show of authority about him, to threaten them. They went right on at their task of barricading the windows with strips of planking torn from their bunks. They had food and they had fuel, and they had arms. They would stand a siege, and if they were attacked they would fight back. In all they did, in all their movements, in their seadfast stare, he read their intent plainly enough.

Gabriel Henley was no coward, else he would not have been serving his second term as our chief of police; but likewise and furthermore he was no fool.

Under the circumstances, with the padrone away, with Tony Palassi away, with the sheriff away, and with the refuge of the culprit under close watch, Chief of Police Henley decided just to sit down and wait—wait for developments; wait for guidance; perhaps wait for popular sentiment to crystallize and, in process of its crystallization, give him a hint as to the steps proper to be taken next. So he sat him down at his roll-top desk in the old City Hall, with his feet on the stove, and he waited.

Maybe if people just turned in and mobbed a few of these bloodthirsty Dagos it would give the rest of them a little respect for law and order? What if they didn't get the one that did the cutting? They could get a few of his friends, couldn't they—and chase all the others out of the country, and out of the state? Well, then, what more could a fair-minded citizen ask? And if the police force could not or would not do its duty in the premises, was it not up to the people themselves to act?—or words to that general effect.

The Man for the Emergency

Serenely unaware of these things, Judge Priest spent his day at Soule's Drug Store, beat Squire Roundtree at checkers, went trudging home at dusk for supper and, when supper was eaten, came trudging back downtown again, still happily ignorant of the feeling that was in the icy air. Eight o'clock found him in the seat of honour on the platform at Kamleiter's Hall, presiding over the regular semi-monthly meeting of Gideon K. Irons Camp.

Considering weather conditions, the judge, as commandant, felt a throb of pride at the size of the attendance. Twenty-two elderly gentlemen answered to their names when the adjutant, old Professor Reese, of the graded school, called the roll. Two or three more straggled in, bundled up out of all their proper proportions, in time to take part in the subsequent discussion of new business. Under that elastic heading the Camp agreed to co-operate with the Daughters in a campaign to raise funds for a monument to the memory of General Meriwether Grider, dead these many years; voted fifty dollars out of the Camp treasury for the relief of a dead comrade's widow; and listened to a reminiscence of the retreat from Atlanta by Sergeant Jimmy Bagby.

Old Press Harper, from three miles out in the county, was sitting well back toward the rear of the little hall. It is possible that his attention wandered from the subject in hand. He chanced to glance over his shoulder and, through the frosted panes of a back window, he caught a suffused reflection. Instantly he was on his feet.

"Hey, boys!" called out Mr. Harper. "Somethin's on fire—looky yander!"

It surely was. There was a thud of booted feet on the creaking boards. Somebody was coming three stairs at a jump. The door flew open and Circuit Clerk Elisha Milam staggered in, gasping for breath.

"It's that construction camp down below town burning up," he said between pants.

"How did it get started?"

"It didn't get started—somebody started it. Gentlemen, there's trouble beginning down yonder. Where's Judge Priest? . . . Oh, yes, there he is!"

Mr. Milam, essentially a man of peace, hastened hotfoot to Kamleiter's Hall for the one man to whom, in times of emergency, he always looked—his circuit-court judge.

As for Judge Priest, he, for a space of seconds after Mr. Milam had concluded, said nothing at all. And then he made a speech to them—a short, quick speech, but the best speech, so his audience afterward agreed, that ever they heard him make.

"Boys," he cried, lifting his high, shrill voice yet higher and yet shriller, "I'm about to put a motion to you and I want a vote on it purty dam' quick! They've been sayin' in this town that us old soldiers was gittin' too old to take an active hand in the affairs of this community any longer; and at the last election, ez you all know, they tried fur to prove it by retirin' most of the veterans that offered themselves ez candidates fur re-election back to private life.

"I ain't sayin' they wasn't partly right neither; fur here we've been sittin' this night, like a passel of old moo-cows, chewin' the cud of things that happened forty-odd year' ago, and never suspicionin' nothin' of what was goin' on, whilst all round us men, carried away by passion and race prejudice, have been plottin' to break the laws and shed blood and bring an everlastin' disgrace on the reppitation fur peace and good order of this fair little city of ourn. But maybe it ain't too late yit fur us to do our duty ez citizens and ez veterans. Oncet on a time—a mighty long while ago—we turned out to pertect our people ag'inst an armed invader. Let's show 'em we ain't too old or too feeble to turn out oncet more to pertect them ag'inst themselves."

He reared back, and visibly, before their eyes, his short fat figure seemed to lengthen by cubits.

"I move that Gideon K. Irons Camp of United Confederate Veterans, here assembled, march in a body right now to save—ef we can—these poor Eyetalians who are strangers in a strange and hosstil land from bein' mistreated, and to save —ef we can—our misguided fellow townsmen from sufferin' the consequences of their own folly and their own foolishness. Do I hear a second to that motion?"

Did he hear a second to his motion? He heard twenty-five seconds to it, all heaved at him together, with all the blaring strength of twenty-five pairs of elderly lungs.

"Will we go?" whooped Sergeant Bagby, waving his pudgy arms aloft so that his mittened hands described whizzing red circles in the air. "You betcher sweet life we'll go! We'll go through hell and high water—with you as our commandin' officer, Billy Priest."

As the little column of old men swung round the first corner below Kamleiter's Hall, the lights coming through the windows of Tony Palassi's fruit shop made bright yellow patches on the white path they trod.

"Halt!" ordered Judge Priest suddenly; and he quit his place in the lead and made for the doorway.

"If you're looking for Tony to go along and translate you're wasting time, Judge," sang out Mr. Crump. "He's out of town."

Within might be seen Mrs. Delia Callahan Palassi, wife of the proprietor, putting the place to rights before locking it up for the night; and at her skirts tagged Master Antonio Wolfe Tone Palassi, aged seven, only son and sole heir of the same, a round-bellied, red-cheeked little Italian-Irish-American. The judge put his hand on the latch and jiggled it.

Whatever Judge Priest said to Mrs. Palassi didn't take long for the saying of it; yet it must have been an argument powerfully persuading and powerfully potent. For in less than no time at all, when Judge Priest reissued from the fruit shop, there rode pack-fashion on his back a little figure so well bundled up against the cold that only a pair of big brown Italian eyes and a small, tip-tilted Irish nose showed themselves, to prove that Judge Priest's burden was not a woolly Teddy-bear, but a veritable small boy.

The "Charge"

The flimsy framework of resiny pine burned fast, considering that much snow had lain on the roof and much snow had melted and run down the sides all day, to freeze again with the coming of night-time.

Against the nearermost bank, the foreigners were clinging in a tight, compact black huddle, all scared but not so badly scared that they would not fight. Yonder, across the snow, through the gap where a side street debouched at a gentle slope into the hollow, the mob advanced —men and half-grown boys—to the number of perhaps four hundred, coming to get the man who had stabbed Beaver Yancy and string him up on the spot—and maybe to get a few of his friends and string them up as an added warning to all Dagos. They came on and came on until a space of not more than seventy-five yards separated the mob and the mob's prospective victims. From the advancing mass a growling of many voices rose. Rampant, unloosed mischief was in the sound.

A man who appeared to hold some manner of leadership over the Italians advanced a step from the front row of them. In his hand he held an old-fashioned cap-and-ball pistol at full cock. He raised his right arm and sighted along the levelled barrel at a spot midway between him and the oncoming crowd. Plainly he meant to fire when the first of his foes crossed an imaginary line. He squinted up his eye, taking a careful aim; and he let his trigger finger slip gently inside the trigger guard—but he never fired.

On top of the hill, almost above his head, a bugle blared out. A fife and a drum cut in, playing something jiggy and brisk; and over the crest and down into the flat, two by two, marched a little column of old men, following after a small silken flag which flicked and whispered in the wind, and led by a short, round-bodied commander, who held by the hand a little briskly trotting figure of a child. Tony Wolfe Tone had grown too heavy for the judge to carry.

Out across the narrow space between the closing-in mob and the closed-in foreigners the marchers passed, their feet sinking ankle-deep into the crusted snow. Their leader gave a command; the music broke off and they spread out in single file, taking station, five feet apart from one another, so that between the two hostile groups a living hedge was interposed. And so they stood, with their hands down at their sides, some facing to the west, where the Italians were herded together, some facing toward the east, where the would-be lynchers, stricken with a great amazement, had come to a dead stand.

"In Eyetalian—Quick and Loud"

JUDGE PRIEST, still holding little Tony Wolfe Tone's small mittened hand fast in his, spoke up, addressing the mob. His familiar figure was outlined against the burning barracks beyond him and behind him. His familiar whiny voice he lifted to so high a pitch that every man and boy there heard him.

"Fellow citizens," he stated, "this is part of Forrest's Cavalry you see here. We done soldierin' oncet and we've turned soldiers ag'in; but we ain't armed—none of us. We've only got our bare hands. Ef you come on we can't stop you with guns; but we ain't agoin' to budge, and ef you start shootin' you'll shorely git some of us. So ez a personal favour to me and these other gentlemen, I'd like to ast you jest to stand still where you are and not to shoot till after you see what we're fixin' to try to do. That's agreeable to you-all, ain't it? You've got the whole night ahead of you—there's no hurry, is there, boys?"

He did not wait for any answer from anyone. By name he knew a good half of them; by sight he knew the other half. And they all knew him; and they knew Tony Palassi's boy; and they knew Father Minor, who stood at his right hand. They would not shoot yet; and, as though fully convinced in his own mind they would bide where they were until he was done, and relying completely on them to keep their unspoken promise, Judge Priest half-turned his back on the members of the mob and bent over little Tony.

"You see all them men yonder, don't you, boy?" he prompted. "Well, now you speak up ez loud ez you can, and you tell 'em whut I've been tellin' you to say all the way down the street ever since we left your mammy. You tell 'em I'm the big judge of the big court. Tell 'em there's one man among 'em who must come on and go with me. He'll know and they'll know which man I mean. Tell 'em that man ain't goin' to be hurt ef he comes now. Tell 'em that they ain't none of 'em goin' to be hurt ef they all do whut I say. Tell 'em Father Minor is here to show 'em to a safe, warm place where they kin spend the night. Kin you remember all that, sonny-boy? Then tell 'em in Eyetalian—quick and loud."

And Tony Wolfe Tone told them. Unmindful of the hundreds of eyes that were upon him—even forgetting for a minute to watch the fire—Tony opened wide his small mouth and in the tongue of his father's people, richened perhaps by the sweet brogue of his mother's land, and spiced here and there with a word or two of savoury good American slang, he gave the message a piping utterance.

In the sheltering crotch of little Tony's two plump bestraddling legs, which encircled his neck, the old judge chuckled to himself. A wave of laughter ran through the ranks of the halted mob—Tony's voice had carried so far as that, and Tony's mode of speech apparently had met with favour. Mob psychology, according to some students, is hard to fathom; according to others, easy.

From the midst of the knot of Sicilians a man stepped forth—not the tall man with the gun, but a little stumpy man who moved with a limp. Alone, he walked through the crispened snow until he came up to where the veterans stood, waiting and watching. The mob, all intently quiet once more, waited and watched too.

With a touch of the dramatic instinct that belongs to his race, he flung down a dirk knife at Judge Priest's feet and held out both his hands in token of surrender. To the men who came there to take his life he gave no heed—not so much as a sidewise glance over his shoulder did he give them. He looked into the judge's face and into the face of little Tony, and into the earnest face of the old priest alongside these two.

"Boys"—the judge lifted Tony down and, with a gesture, was invoking the attention of his townsmen—"boys, here's the man who did the knifin' this mornin', givin' himself up to my pertection—and yours. He's goin' along with me now to the county jail, to be locked up ez a prisoner. I've passed my word and the word of this whole town that he shan't be teched nor molested whilst he's on his way there, nor after he gits there. I know there ain't a single one of you but stands ready to help me keep that promise. I'm right, ain't I, boys?"

"Oh, hell, judge—you win!" sang out a member of the mob, afterward identified as one of Beaver Yancy's close friends, in a humorously creditable imitation of the judge's own earnest whine. And at that everybody laughed again and somebody started a cheer.

"I THOUGHT so," replied the judge. "And now, boys, I've got an idea. I reckin, after trampin' all the way down here in the snow, none of us want to tramp back home ag'in without doin' somethin'—we don't feel like ez ef we want to waste the whole evenin', do we? See that shack burnin' down? Well, it's railroad property; and we don't want the railroad to suffer. Let's put her out—let's put her out with snowballs!"

Illustrating his suggestion, he stooped, scooped up a double handful of snow, squeezed it into a pellet and awkwardly tossed it in the general direction of the blazing barracks. It flew wide of the mark and fell short of it; but his intention was good, that being conceded. Whooping joyously, four hundred men and half-grown boys, or thereabouts such a number, pouched their weapons and dug into the drifted whiteness.

"Hold on a minute—we'll do it to soldier music!" shouted the judge, and he gave a signal. The drum beat then; and old Mr. Harrison Treese buried the fife in his white whiskers and ripped loose on the air the first bars of Yankee Doodle.

. . . . . .

Judge Priest Comes Back

FROM time to time persons of an inquiring turn of mind have been moved audibly to speculate—I might even say to ponder—regarding the enigma underlying the continued presence in the halls of our National Congress of the Honourable Dabney Prentiss. All were as one in agreeing that he had a magnificent delivery, but in this same connection it has repeatedly been pointed out that he so rarely had anything to deliver. It was an editorial writer upon a metropolitan daily, who once referred to Representative Prentiss as The Human Voice. The title stuck, a fact patently testifying to its aptness.

That which follows here in this chapter is an attempt to explain the mystery of this gentleman's elevation to the high places which he recently adorned.

To go back to the very start of things we must first review briefly the case of old Mr. Lysander John Curd, even though he be but an incidental figure in the narrative. He was born to be incidental, I reckon, heredity, breeding and the chance of life all conspiring together to fit him for that inconsequential rôle.

Considering him in all his aspects—as a volunteer soldier in the Great War, as a district school-teacher, as a merchant in our town, as a bachelor of long standing, as a husband for a fleeting space, and as a grass widower for the rest of his days—I have gleaned that he never did anything ignoble or anything conspicuous. Indeed, I myself, who knew him as a half-grown boy may know a middle-aged man, find it hard after the lapse of years to describe him physically for you. He abides merely as a blur in my memory.

On a certain morning of a certain year, the month being April, Judge Priest sat at his desk in his chamber, so-called, when there came a mild rap at the outer door.

"Come right on in, whoever 'tis," he called out.

The door opened and old Mr. Ly-sander John Curd entered, in his over-coat, with his head upon his chest.

"Good morning, Judge Priest," he said in his gentle halting drawl; "could I speak with you in private a minute? It's sort of a personal matter and I wouldn't care to have anybody maybe overhearing."

"You most certainly could," said Judge Priest.

"Set down here, Lysandy," he said in that high whiny voice of his, "and let's hear whut's on your mind. Nice weather, ain't it?"

There was in the judge's words an intangible inflection of understanding, say, or sympathy; no, call it compassion—that would be nearer to it. The two old men—neither of them would ever see sixty-five again—lowered themselves into the two chairs and sat facing each other across the top of the judge's piled and dusty desk.

Through his steel-rimmed glasses the judge fixed a pair of kindly, but none-the-less keen, blue eyes on Mr. Lysander Curd's sagged and slumped figure. There was despondency and there was embarrassment in all the drooping lines of that elderly frame. Judge Priest's lips drew up tightly, and unconsciously he nodded—the brief nod that a surgeon might employ on privately confirming a private diagnosis.

The Trouble

OLD Mr. Curd raised his face and in his faded eyes there was at once a bewildered appeal and a fixed and definite resolution. He spoke on very slowly and carefully, choosing his words as he went, but without faltering:

"I don't know as you know about it, Judge Priest—the chances are you naturally wouldn't—but in a domestic way things haven't been going very smoothly with me—with us, I should say—for quite a spell back. I reckon after all it's a mistake on the part of a man after he's reached middle age and got set in his ways to be taking a young wife, more especially if he can't take care of

her in the way she's been used to, anyhow in the way she'd like to be taken care of. I suppose it's only human nature for a young woman to hanker after considerable many things that a man like me can't always give her—jewelry and pretty things, and social life and running round and seeing people and such as that. And Luella—well Luella really ain't much more than a girl herself yet, is she?"

The question remained unanswered. It was plain, too, that Mr. Curd had expected no answer to it, for he went straight on:

"Judge Priest, I've never been a

iever in divorce as a general thing. It eemed to me there was too much of hat sort of thing going on round this ountry. That's always been my own private doctrine, more or less. But in my own case I've changed my mind. We've been talking it over back and forth and we've decided—Luella and me have—hat under the circumstances a divorce is the best thing for both of us; in fact we've decided that it's the only thing. I want that Luella should be happy and I think maybe I'll feel easier in my own mind when it's all over and done with and settled up according to the law. I'm aiming to do what's best for both parties —and I want that Luella should be happy."

He paused and with his tongue he moistened his lips, which seemed dry.

"I don't mind telling you I didn't feel this way about it first-off. It was a pretty tolerably hard jolt to me—the way the proposition first came up. I've spent a good many sleepless nights thinking it over. At least I couldn't sleep very much for thinking of it," he amended with the literal impulse of a literal mind to state things exactly and without exaggeration. "And then finally I saw my way clear to come to this decision. And so——"

"Lysandy Curd," broke in Judge Priest, "I don't aim to give you any advice. In the first place, you ain't asked fur it; and in the second place, even ef you had asked, I'd hesitate a monstrous long time before I'd undertake to advise any man about his own private family affairs. But I jest want to ask you one thing right here: It wasn't you, was it, that first proposed the idea of this here divorce?"

"Well, no, Judge, I don't believe 'twas," confessed the old man whose misery-reddened eyes looked into Judge Priest's from across the littered desk. "I can't say as it was me that first suggested it. But that's neither here nor there. The point I'm trying to get at is just this:

"The papers have all been drawn up and they'll be bringing them in here sometime to-day to be filed—the lawyers in the case will, Bigger & Quigley. Naturally, with me and Luella agreeing as to everything, there's not going to be any fight made in your court.

"And now that everything's been made clear to you, I want to ask you, Judge, to do all in your power to make things as easy as you can for Luella. I'd a heap rather there wouldn't be any fuss made over this case in the newspapers. It's just a straight, simple divorce suit, and after all it's just between me and my present wife, and it's more our business than 'tis anybody else's. So, seeing as the case is not going to be defended, I'd take it as a mighty big favour on your part if you'd shove it up on the docket for the coming term of court, starting next Monday, so as we could get it done and over with just as soon as possible. That's my personal wish, and I know it's Luella's wish too. In fact she's right anxious on that particular point. Do you reckon you could do that much for me, Judge Priest—for old times' sake?"

"AH-HAH," assented Judge Priest. "I reckin part of it kin be arranged anyway. I kin have Lishy Milam set the case forward on the docket at the head of the list of uncontested actions. Speaking personally, I should think jest a line or two ought to satisfy the readers of the *Daily Evenin' News*. I jedge you've got no call to feel uneasy about whut's goin' to be said in print. You was sayin' jest now that the papers would be filed sometime to-day?"

"They'll be filed to-day sure."

"And no defence is to be made?" continued Judge Priest, tallying off the points on his fingers. "And you've retained Bigger & Quigley to represent you—that's right, ain't it?"

"Hold on a minute, Judge," Mr. Curd was shaking his whitey-grey head in dissent. "I've taken up a lot of your valuable time already, and still it would seem like I haven't succeeded in getting this affair all straight in your mind. Bigger

& Quigley are not going to represent me. They're going to represent Luella."

He spoke as one stating an accepted and easily understood fact, yet at the words Judge Priest reared back as far as his chair would let him go and his ruddy cheeks swelled out with the breath of amazement.

"Do you mean to tell me," he demanded, "that you ain't the plaintiff here?"

"Why, Judge Priest," answered Mr. Curd, "you didn't think for a minute, did you, that I'd come into court seeking to blacken my wife's good name? She's been thoughtless, maybe, but I know she don't mean any harm by it, and besides look how young she is. It's her, of course, that's asking for this divorce—I thought you understood about that from the beginning."

Still in his posture of astonishment, Judge Priest put another question and put it briskly: "Might it be proper fur me to ask on what grounds this lady is suin' you fur a divorce?"

A wave of dull red ran up old Mr. Curd's throat and flooded his shamed face to the hair line.

"On two grounds," he said—"non-support and drunkenness."

"Non-support?"

"Yes; I haven't been able to take care of her lately as I should like to, on account of my business difficulties and all."

"But look here at me, Lysandy Curd—you ain't no drunkard. You never was one. Don't tell me that!"

"Well, now, Judge Priest," argued Mr. Curd, "you don't know about my private habits, and even if I haven't been

drinking in public up to now, that's n[o] sign I'm not fixing to start in doing s[o] Besides which my keeping silent show[s] that I admit to everything, don't it Well, then?" He stood up. "Well, [I] reckon that's all. I won't be detainin[g] you any longer. I'm much obliged t[o] you, Judge, and I wish you good-day sir."

For once Judge Priest forgot hi[s] manners. He uttered not a syllable, bu[t] only stared through his spectacles i[n] stunned and stricken silence while M[r] Curd passed out into the hallway, gentl[y] closing the door behind him. The[n] Judge Priest vented his emotions in [a] series of snorts.

In modern drama what is technicall[y] known as the stage aside has gone ou[t] of vogue; it is called old-fashioned. Ha[d] a latter-day playwright been there the[n] he would have resented the judge' thoughtlessness in addressing empt[y] space. Nevertheless that was exactly wha[t] the judge did.

"Under the strict letter of the law [I] ought to throw that case out of court, [I] s'pose. But I'm teetotally dam' ef I d[o] any sech thing! . . . That old man' heart is broke now, and there ain't n[o] earthly reason that I kin think of wh[y] that she-devil should be allowed to tromp on the pieces. And that's just exactl[y] whut she'll do, shore ez shootin', unles[s] she's let free mighty soon to go her ow[n] gait. . . . Their feet take hold on hell . . . I'll bet in the Kingdom there'll b[e] many a man that was called a simple minded fool on this earth that'll wea[r] the biggest, shiniest halo old Peter ki[n] find in stock."

Fuel to the Flame

THE *Daily Evening News* carried merely the barest of bare statements, coupled with the style of the action and the names of the attorneys for the plaintiff; but with spicy added details, pieced out from surmise and common rumour, the amazing tidings percolated across narrow roads and through the panels of partition fences with a rapidity which

went far toward proving that the tongu[e] is mightier than the printed line, or a[t] least is speedier.

Hard upon the heels of the first joltin[g] disclosure correlated incidents eventu ated, and these, as the saying goes, sup plied fuel to the flames. Just befor[e] suppertime old Mr. Lysander Curd wen[t] with dragging feet and downcast hea[d]

Mrs. Teenie Morrill's boarding house, rrying in one hand a rusty valise, and om Mrs. Morrill he straightway en- ged board and lodging for an indefi- te period.

And in the early dusk of the evening rs. Lysander Curd drove out in the nart top-phaeton that her husband had ven her on her most recent birthday— e sitting very erect and handling the obons on her little spirited bay mare ry prettily, and seemingly all oblivious the hostile eyes which stared at her om sidewalks and porch fronts. About rk she halted at the corner of Clay d Contest, where a row of maples, w fledged with young leaves, made a ick shadow across the road.

Exactly there, as it so chanced, State nator Horace K. Maydew happened to loitering about, enjoying the cooling eezes of the spring night, and he ted his somewhat bulky but athletic rty-year-old form into the phaeton ongside of the lady. In close conversa- on they were seen to drive out Contest and to turn into the Towhead Road; and—if we may believe what that will- ing witness, old Mrs. Whitridge, who lived at the corner of Clay and Contest, had to say upon the subject—it was eleven o'clock before they got back.

Mrs. Whitridge knew the exact hour, because she stayed up in her front room to watch, with one eye out of the bay window and the other on the mantel clock. To be sure, this had happened probably a hundred times before—this meeting of the pair in the shadows of the water maples, this riding in company over quiet country roads until all hours —but by reason of the day's sensational developments it now took on an en- hanced significance. Mrs. Whitridge could hardly wait until morning to call up, one by one, the members of her cir- cle of intimate friends. I judge the tele- phone company never made much money off of Mrs. Whitridge even in ordinary times; she rented her tele- phone by the month and she used it by the hour.

An Up-and-Coming Man

N LESS than no time at all following this—in less than two weeks there- ter, to be exact—the coils which united r. Lysander Curd and Luella his wife the bonds of matrimony were by due rocess of the statutory law unloosed d slackened off. Being free, the ex- usband promptly gathered together ich meagre belongings as he might call is own and betook himself to that little nortgage-covered farm of his out Lone lm way. Being free also, the ex-wife ith equal celerity became the bride of tate Senator Horace K. Maydew, with handy justice of the peace to officiate the ceremony. It was characteristic of tate Senator Maydew that he should iove briskly in consummating this, the aramount romance of his life. For he as certainly an up-and-coming man.

He had been mayor; at this time he as state senator; presently it was to anspire that he would admire to be iore than that.

When a vacancy occurred in the dis- trict chairmanship it seemed quite in keeping with the trend of the political impulses of the times that Senator May- dew should slip into the hole. Always a clever organiser, he excelled his past record in building up and strengthening the district organisation. It wasn't long before he had his fences as they should be—hog-tight, horse-high and bull- strong.

It was just about a year after the Senator's marriage, in response to the demands of a host of friends and ad- mirers—so ran the language of his column-long paid-for card in the *Daily Evening News* and other papers—an- nounced himself as a candidate for the Democratic nomination for congress- man. Considering conditions and every- thing, the occasion appeared to be propitious for such action on his part.

The incumbent, old Major J. C. C. Guest, had been congressman a long,

long time—entirely too long a time, some were beginning to say. His principal asset and his heaviest claim upon the support of his fellow-citizens had been an empty trouser-leg. In eighty-four, a cross-roads wag had said he didn't believe Major Guest ever lost that leg in battle—it was his private opinion that he wore it off running for office.

Nevertheless, Major Guest was by no means ready to give up and quit. With those who considered him ripe for retirement he disagreed violently. As between resting on his laurels and dying in the harness he infinitely preferred the chafe of the leather to the questionable softness of the laurel-bed. So the campaign shaped itself to be a regular campaign. Except for these two—Maydew and Guest—there were no openly avowed candidates, though Dabney Prentiss, who dearly loved a flirtation with reluctant Destiny, was known to have his ear to the ground, ready to qualify as the dark horse in the event a deadlock should develop.

Possibly it was because Dabney Prentiss generally kept his ear to the ground that he had several times been most painfully trampled upon. From head to foot he was one big mental bruise.

Since he held the levers of the distri machinery in the hollows of his tw itching hands, Senator Maydew ve naturally and very properly elected direct his own canvass. Judge Pries quitting the bench temporarily, cam forth to act as manager for his frien Major Guest.

At this there was rejoicing in th camp of the clan of Maydew. To Ma dew and his lieutenants it appeared th providence had dealt the good cards in their laps. Undeniably the judge w old and, moreover, he was avowed old-fashioned. It stood to reason h would conduct the affairs of his cand date along old-fashioned lines. To b sure, he had his following; so much w admitted. Nobody could beat Judg Priest for his own job; at least nobod ever had. But controlling his own jo and his own county was one thing. E gineering a district-wide canvass i behalf of an aging and uninspiring ir cumbent was another. And if over th bent shoulders of Major Guest the might strike a blow at Judge Pries why, so much the better for Maydev now, and so much the worse for Pries hereafter. Thus to their own satisfactio the Maydew men figured it out.

Where All Roads Ran

COUNTY conventions to name delegates to the district conventions which, in turn, would name the congressional nominee were held simultaneously in the nine counties composing the district at two P.M. of the first Tuesday after the first Monday in August.

Late in the afternoon of the first Tuesday after the first Monday, when the smoke cleared away and the shouting and the tumult died, the complete returns showed that of the nine counties, totalling one hundred and twenty delegate votes, Maydew had four counties and fifty-seven votes.

Guest had carried four counties also, with fifty-one votes, while Bryce County, the lowermost county of the district, had failed to instruct its twelve delegates for

either Maydew or Guest, which, to any body who knew anything at all abou politics, was proof positive that in th main convention Bryce County woul hold the balance of power. It wouldn' be a walkover; that much was certain anyhow.

Maydew's jaunty smile lost some of it jauntiness, and anxious puckers mad little seams at the corners of those greed eyes of his, when the news from Bryc County came.

As for Judge Priest, he displaye every outward sign of being well con tent as he ran over the completed fig ures. Bryce was an old-fashioned county mainly populated by a people who clun to old-fashioned notions. Old soldier were notably thick in Bryce, too. Ther as a good chance yet for his man. It all depended on those twelve votes of Bryce County.

To Marshallville, second largest town in the district, befell the honour that year of having the district convention held in its hospitable midst; and, as the *Daily Evening News* smartly phrased it, to Marshallville on a Thursday All Roads Ran.

A Heaven-Sent Freshet

As THE delegates gathered that very warm August afternoon, a lady sat in solitary state. She seemed fairly well pleased with herself as she sat there. Certainly she had no cause to complain of a lack of public interest in her and her costume. To begin with, there was a much beplumed hat, indubitably a thing of great cost and of augmented size, which effectively shaded and set off her plump face. No such hat had been seen in Marshallville before that day.

The lady, plainly, was not exactly displeased with herself. Even a rear view of her revealed this. There was assurance in the poise of her head; assuredly there was a beaming as of confidence in her eyes. Indeed, she had reasons other than the satisfaction inspired by the possession of a modish and becoming garb for feeling happy. Things promised to go well with her and what was hers that afternoon. Perhaps I should have stated sooner that the lady in question was Mrs. Senator Maydew, present to witness and to glorify the triumph of her distinguished husband.

For a fact, triumph did seem near at hand now—nearer than it had been any time these past forty-eight hours. A quarter of an hour earlier an exultant messenger had come from her husband to bring to her most splendid and aus-picious tidings. Luck had swung his way, and no mistake about it: of the doubtful delegates from Bryce County only two had arrived.

The other ten had not arrived. Moreover there was no apparent possibility that they would arrive before the following day, and by then it would be all over but the shouting. A Heaven-sent freshet in Little River was the cause. For it had washed out the only bridge which the ten Bryce County men could cross. Sitting there now in her stage box, Mrs. Senator Maydew silently blessed the name of Little River.

Two of Bryce County's delegates, who chanced to live in the upper corner of the county, had driven through hub-deep mud to the junction and there caught the train for Marshallville; but their ten compatriots were even now somewhere on the far bank, cut off absolutely from all prospect of attending the convention.

Senator Maydew, always fertile in expedient, meant to ride to victory, as it were, on the providential high tide in Little River. For our purposes it is sufficient, I think, to say that the Maydew machine, operating after the fashion of a well-lubricated, well-steered and high-powered steam roller, ran over all obstacles with the utmost despatch.

Judge Priest Curls Up

DRIPPING with perspiration, his broad old face one big pinky-red flare, his nasal whine rising to heights of incredible whininess under the stress of his earnestness, Judge Priest led the fight for the minority. The steam roller went out of its way to flatten him. Not once, but twice and thrice it jounced over him, each time leaving him figuratively squashed but entirely undismayed. He was fighting a losing but a valiant fight for time.

To him in this dire emergency the Guest forces, now neck-deep in the last ditch, looked hopefully for a counter-fire that might yet save them from the defeat looming so imminent. There and then, for once in his life the judge failed to justify the hopes and the faith of his followers. He seemed strangely unable to find language in which effectively to combat the proposition before the house. He floundered about, making no headway, pushing no points home. He practically admitted he knew of nothing in party usage or in parliamentary law that might prevent voting that day.

The Mims County man, with a contemptuous flirt of his thumb, indicated the broad back of Judge Priest as the judge ambled deliberately along toward the door.

"I knowed it," he said in the tones of bitter recapitulation; "I knowed it frum the start and I told 'em so; but no, they wouldn't listen to me. I knowed old Priest yonder was too old to be tryin' to run a campaign ag'inst a smart feller like Maydew, dern his slick hide! When the real test come, whut did your Jedge Priest do? Why, he jest natchelly curled up and laid flat down—that's whut he done. I reckin they'll listen to me next time."

For once in his life, and once only, Sergeant Jimmy Bagby teetered just the least bit in his unquestioning allegiance to his life-long friend.

"Well, I don't know," he said, shaking his head; "I don't know. You might be right in what you say, and then ag'in you might be wrong. It shore did look like he slipped a little, awhile ago, but you can't jest always tell whut's on Jedge Priest's mind," he added, pluckily renewing his loyalty.

The Mims County man grunted his disgust.

"Don't be foolin' yourself," he stated morosely. "You take it frum me—when old men start goin' they don't never come back. And your old Jedge is plumb gone. A baby could 'a' seen that frum the way he acted jest now."

THE object of this criticism plough his slow way outdoors, all the wh shaking his head with the air of o who has abandoned hope. In the stre he gently but firmly disengaged himse from those who would have speech wi' him, and with obvious gloom in h manner made a way across the squa to the Mansard House, where he ar Major Guest had adjoining rooms c the second floor.

From the privacy of his room he se out for certain men. They went awa saying nothing to any one, for the gi of silence was an attribute that these tw shared in common. Then the judge ha brief audience with Major Guest, wh emerged from the conference a crushe and diminished figure. Finally he aske to speak with Sergeant Bagby. The se geant found him sitting in his shir sleeves, with his feet on a window ledg looking out into the square and gentl agitating a palm-leaf fan.

"Jimmy," he said, "I want you to ru an errand fur me. Will you go fin Dabney Prentiss—I seen him down ther on the street a minute ago—and tell hir I say to git a speech ready?"

"Whut kind of a speech?" inquire Sergeant Bagby.

"Jimmy Bagby," reproved Judg Priest, "ain't you knowed Dab Prentis long enough to know that you don' have to tell him whut kind of a speecl he's to make? He's got all kinds o speeches in stock at all times. I'll con fide this much to you though—it'll be the kind of a speech that he woulc 'specially prefer to make. Jest tell him l say be ready to speak out and utter a few burnin' words when the proper time comes, ef it does come, which I certainly hope and trust it may."

A Bolt from the Blue

NO SOONER had the convention reassembled than the chairman mounted to the stage and took his place alongside a small table behind the footlights and called the meeting to order.

Then Judge Priest got slowly up from

where he sat and took an action which was not entirely unexpected, inasmuch as rumours of it had been in active circulation for half an hour or more. In twenty words he withdrew the name of the Honourable J. C. C. Guest.

Only a rustle of bodies succeeded this announcement—that and an exhalation f breath from a few delegations, which tained to the volume of a deep joint gh.

The chairman glanced over the house ith a brightening eye. It was almost me to begin the jubilation. As a mat- r of fact several ardent souls among e Maydewites could hardly hold them- lves in until the few remaining for- alities had been complied with. They oised themselves upon the edges of eir chairs, with throats tuned to lead the yelling.

"Are there any other nominations?" sked the chairman, turning this way nd that. He asked it as a matter of orm merely. "If not, the nominations ill be closed and the secretary will——"

"Mister Cheerman, one minute, ef you lease."

The interrupting voice was the high- iped voice of Judge Priest, and the hairman straightened on his heels to nd Judge Priest still upon his feet.

"It was my painful duty a minute ago o withdraw the candidate that I had een privileged to foller in this cam- aign," said Judge Priest in his weedy otes. "It is now my pleasure to offer n his stead the name of another man as suitable and a fittin' representative of his district in the National Halls of Congress.

"The man whom I would nominate as never so fur as I know been active in olitics. So fur as I know he has never spired to or sought fur public office t the hands of his feller-citizens; in act, he does not now seek this office. n presentin' his name for your consid- ration I am doin' so solely upon my wn responsibility and without con- ultin' any one on this earth.

"My present candidate is not an orator. He is not a mixer or an organiser. I am constrained to admit that, meas- ured by the standards of commerce, he is not even a successful man. He is poor in this world's goods. He is leadin' at this moment a life of retirement upon a little barren hillside farm, where the gulleys furrow his tobacco patch and the sassafras sprouts are takin' his cornfield, and the shadder of a mortgage rests heavy upon his lonely roof tree.

"But he is an honest man and a God- fearin' man. Ez a soldier under the stars and bars he done his duty to the sor- rowful end. Ez a citizen he has never wilfully harmed his feller-man. He never invaded the sanctity of any man's home, and he never brought sorrow to any hearthstone. Ef he has his faults—and who amongst us is without them?—he has been the sole sufferer by them. I believe it has been charged that he drank some, but I never seen him under the influence of licker, and I don't believe anybody else ever did either.

"I nominate——" His voice took on the shrillness of a fife and his right fist, pudgy and clenched, came up at arm's length above his head—"I nominate— and on that nomination, in accordance with a rule but newly framed by this body, I call here and now fur an alpha- betical roll call of each and every dele- gate—I offer as a candidate fur Congress ag'inst the Honourable Horace K. May- dew the name of my friend, my neigh- bour and my former comrade, Lysandy John Curd, of the voting precinct of Lone Ellum."

There was no applause. Not a ripple of approbation went up, nor a ripple of hostility either. But a gasp went up—a mighty gasp, deep and sincere and tre- mendously significant.

The Dark Horse

DAUNTED and bewildered, the chair- man hesitated, his gavel trembling n his temporarily palsied hand. In that ame moment Sheriff Giles Birdsong ad got upon the stage, too; only he deemed his proper place to be directly alongside the desk of the secretary, and into the startled ear of the secretary he now spoke.

"Start your roll call, buddy," was

what Mr. Birdsong said, saying it softly, in lullaby tones, yet imparting a profound meaning to his crooning and gentle accents. "And be shore to call off the names in alphabetical order—don't furgit that part!"

Inward voices of prudence dictated the value of prompt obedience in the brain of that secretary. Quaveringly he called the first name on the list of the first county, and the county was Bland and the name was Homer H. Agnew.

Down in the Bland County delegation, seated directly in front of the stage, an old man stood up—the Rev. Homer H. Agnew, an itinerant Baptist preacher.

"My county convention," he explained, "instructed us for Maydew. But under the law of this convention I vote now as an individual. As between the two candidates presented I can vote only one way. I vote for Curd."

Having voted, he remained standing. There were no cheers and no hisses. Everybody waited. In a silence so heavy that it hurt, they waited. And the secretary was constrained to call the second name on the Bland County list: "Patrick J. Burke!"

"I vote for Curd," said Patrick J. Burke, and likewise he stood up, a belligerent, defiant, stumpy, red-haired man.

There were eleven names on the Bland County list. The secretary had reached the eighth and had heard eight voices speak the same word, when an interruption occurred—perhaps I should say two interruptions occurred.

A gentleman by the name of Maydew darted out from the wings, bounded over the footlights and split a path for himself to the seat of Judge Priest. For once he forgot to be oratorical. "We'll quit, Judge," he panted, "we're ready to quit. I'll withdraw if you'll take Curd's name down too. Any compromise candidate will do."

"All right, son," said Judge Priest, raising his voice to be heard, for by now the secretary had called the ninth name and the cheering was increasing in

volume; "that suits me first rate. But you withdraw your man first."

Turning, he put a hand upon Sergeant Bagby's arm and shook him until the sergeant broke a whoop in two and hearkened.

"Jimmy," said Judge Priest with little chuckle, "step down the aisle, will you, and tell Dabney Prentiss to uncork himse'f and git his speech of acceptance all ready. He don't know it yit, but he's goin' to move up to Washington, D. C., after the next general election."

Just as the sergeant started on his mission the other interruption occurred. A lady fainted. She was conspicuously established in the stage box on the right-hand side, and under the circumstances and with so many harshly appraising eyes fixed upon her there was really nothing else for her to do, as Mrs. Senator Maydew, except faint.

Although I may have wandered far from the main path and taken the patient reader into devious byways, I feel I have accomplished what I set out to do in the beginning: I have explained how Dabney Prentiss came to be our representative in the Lower House of the National Congress. The task is done, yet I feel that I should not conclude the chapter until I have repeated a short passage of words between Sergeant Jimmy Bagby and that delegate from Mims County who was a distant kinsman of Major Guest. It happened just after the convention, having finished its work, had adjourned, and while the delegates and the spectators were emerging from the Marshallville opera house.

All jubilant and excited now, the Mims County man came charging up and slapped Sergeant Bagby upon the shoulder.

"Well, suh," he clarioned, "the old Jedge did come back, didn't he?"

"Buddy," said Sergeant Bagby, "you was wrong before and you're wrong ag'in. He didn't have to come back, because he ain't never been gone nowheres."

Noel Coward

CAVALCADE

Noel coward (1899-   ) insists that people read profound meanings into "Cavalcade" which he never dreamed were there. Actually it was conceived from his somewhat selfish desire to write a play on a big scale. The fact that it mirrored authentically the heartbreaks of war and the changing social conditions of the first thirty years of this century and wrung tears from the most sophisticated movie- and play-going audiences in England and America came as a complete surprise. While Mr. Coward never appeared in "Cavalcade" he usually directs and has an important part in his plays, which include "Private Lives," "Design for Living" and "Tonight at 8:30."

Part I

SCENE I

Scene: *The drawing-room of a London house. The room is charmingly furnished in the taste of the period.*
Time: *About 11:45 p.m. Sunday, December 31st, 1899.*

When the curtain rises, Ellen, *the parlormaid, is discovered setting the table with a light supper consisting of sandwiches and cake. She is a pleasant-looking woman of twenty-five.*

Enter Bridges, *the butler, with a bottle of champagne in a bucket of ice. He is older than* Ellen, *about forty, with iron-grey hair.*

Ellen: How was Cook when you come up?

Bridges: Running round that kitchen like a cat on a griddle; New Year's Eve's gone to 'er 'ead, and no mistake.

Ellen: She's been queer all day, she says she feels like as if it was the end of everything. So do I, for that matter.

Bridges: Don't start all that over again.

Ellen: Oh, Alfred!

Bridges: What?

Ellen: I can't bear to think what it's going to be like when you've gone.

Bridges: Well, don't.

Ellen: What's the war for, anyhow? Nobody wanted to 'ave a war.

Bridges: We've got to 'ave wars every now and then to prove we're top-dog——

Ellen: This one don't seem to be proving much.

Bridges: 'Ow can you tell sitting at 'ome 'ere safe and sound? 'Ow can you tell what our brave boys are suffering out there in darkest Africa, giving their life's blood for their Queen and country?

Ellen: Africa looks very sunny and nice in the *Illustrated London News*.

Bridges: If this wasn't New Year's Eve, I'd lose my temper, and that's a fact.

Ellen: Well, it wouldn't be the first time. You better go and get the 'ot punch, they'll be in in a minute.

Bridges: You mark my words, Ellen, if we didn't go out and give them Boers wot for, they'd be over 'ere wreakin' 'avoc and carnage before you could say Jack Robinson.

Ellen: Oh, get along with you.

Bridges *goes out.* Ellen *puts the finishing touches to the table and then, going to the windows, she pulls back the curtains.*

Enter Jane Marryot. *She is a handsome woman of about thirty-one. She is wearing an evening gown and cloak. Enter* Robert, Jane's *husband, following her. He is older, about thirty-five, also in evening dress.*

Jane (*throwing off her cloak*): I thought we should never get here in time. I'm sure that cabby was tipsy, Robert. How nice the table looks, Ellen. Where did those flowers come from?

Ellen: They're from Bridges and me, ma'am, with our very best wishes, I'm sure.

JANE: Thank you, Ellen, very much indeed.

ROBERT: A charming thought, Ellen. Thank you both.

ELLEN: Not at all, sir—it's—it's a pleasure indeed.

ELLEN *withdraws from the room covered with respectful embarrassment.*

JANE *smiles at* ROBERT.

JANE: Small things are so infinitely touching, aren't they? I feel I want to cry. Just a few gentle tears to usher in the new century.

ROBERT: Do, by all means, dearest: this evening was planned sentimentally.

JANE (*suddenly running into his arms*): Oh, my darling, my darling, why must you leave me? I shall miss you so.

ROBERT (*smiling and holding her tenderly*): The Bugle Call, dear, the Red, White and Blue——

Britons never, never, never shall be slaves.

JANE: Don't tease me—not about that. What does it matter about the Boers— it can't matter, really. Thank heaven for one thing. The boys are too young. They won't have to fight; Peace and Happiness for them. Oh, please God, Peace and Happiness for them, always. (*She leans against the window and looks out.*)

Enter BRIDGES *with a bowl of punch, followed by* ELLEN, *carrying a tray of punch glasses and almonds and raisins.*

BRIDGES: It's started, sir. Just twelve o'clock now.

ROBERT: Open the windows quick.

ROBERT *takes the punch from* BRIDGES *and fills two glasses. Bridges opens the windows wide. Outside can be heard the growing noise of sirens and chimes of bells.* ELLEN *and* BRIDGES *are about to go.*

JANE (*suddenly*): Stay and drink with us, won't you? Robert, two more glasses.

BRIDGES: Thank you very much, ma'am.

ELLEN: Thank you, ma'am.

ROBERT (*pouring them two glasses of punch*): Here you are, Jane, Ellen, Bridges. 1900—1900.

JANE: 1900.

ELLEN and BRIDGES (*together*): 1900.

Suddenly JANE *hears a sound upstairs. She puts down her glass hurriedly and runs out of the room.*

ELLEN: It sounded like Master Joe.

ROBERT (*going to the door and calling after* JANE): Dearest, bring them down here. Bring them both down. (*Coming slowly back into the room, smiling* How very impolite of the twentieth century to waken the children.

The lights fade as the noise of chimes and sirens grows louder.

SCENE II

SCENE: *The same as* SCENE I.

TIME: *About five o'clock on the afternoon of Friday, May 18th, 1900.*

When the lights go up EDWARD *and* JOE MARRYOT *and* EDITH HARRIS *are discovered playing soldiers on the floor.* EDWARD *is aged twelve,* JOE *eight and* EDITH HARRIS *about ten.*

JOE (*shooting off a cannon*): Bang— bang, bang, bang.

EDITH (*giving a little squeak*): Oh— oh, dear!

EDWARD: How many?

EDITH: Seven.

EDWARD (*curtly*): Good! You'd better retreat.

EDITH: I don't know how. Need always be the Boers?

EDWARD: Yes.

EDITH: Why?

JOE: Because you're a girl—only a girl. Bang, bang, bang!

EDITH (*struggling with her cannon and ammunition*): I'll teach you, you mean little pig! Bang, bang, bang! There. Bang——

The cannon sticks, so EDITH *throws it at* JOE's *battalion, annihilating about fifty soldiers.*

JOE (*yelling*): It's not fair.

EDWARD: Be quiet, Edith, that was cheating.

EDITH (*in tears*): I'm sick of being the Boers—I'll never be the Boers again, never as long as I live!

The door opens. Enter JANE, *looking obviously worried and nervy. Enter*

ᴀʀɢᴀʀᴇᴛ Hᴀʀʀɪs, *following* Jᴀɴᴇ. *She is*
ʌicely dressed woman of about thirty.

Jᴀɴᴇ: Children, why on earth are you
ᴋking such an awful noise? I heard
ʌ right down in the hall. Edith, what's
ᴇ matter? Joe, be quiet. Can't you play
ʏ other games but soldiers, soldiers—
ᴅiers hurting each other—killing each
ᴇr? Go away from me—go away—go
ᴀy—go away——

Mᴀʀɢᴀʀᴇᴛ, *seeing that* Jᴀɴᴇ *is in a bad*
ʈe *of nerves, bustles all three children*
ʈ *of the room.*

Mᴀʀɢᴀʀᴇᴛ: Go along, all of you. Edith,
ʌ ashamed of you, making such a fuss.
• along, now, all of you.

Exeunt Eᴅɪᴛʜ, Eᴅᴡᴀʀᴅ *and* Joᴇ. Mᴀʀ-
ʀᴇᴛ *shuts the door after the children*
d comes back to Jᴀɴᴇ. Jᴀɴᴇ *is wearily*
ʌoving her hat in front of a mirror.
barrel organ in the street strikes up
ʌldiers of the Queen."

Jᴀɴᴇ: There's no escape anywhere, is
ʈre? (*sitting down*): Will these days
ʋer end?

Mᴀʀɢᴀʀᴇᴛ: News will come soon.

Jᴀɴᴇ: I don't believe I shall see him
ʈr again.

Mᴀʀɢᴀʀᴇᴛ: Don't give way to despair,
ʌe. It's foolish. You must have courage.

Jᴀɴᴇ: It's much easier to be brave
ʌen there's something to hear, some-
ʌg definite; this long suspense, these
ʌgging, dragging weeks of waiting are
ʀrible. The one person I love best in
ᴇ world, so remote from me, beyond
ᴄh of my love, probably suffering—it's
ᴇadful, dreadful——

Enter Eʟʟᴇɴ *with tea. She places it on*
• *table and looks enquiringly at* Mᴀʀ-
ʀᴇᴛ. Mᴀʀɢᴀʀᴇᴛ *shakes her head.*

Mᴀʀɢᴀʀᴇᴛ: No news yet, Ellen. We've
ᴇn standing outside the Mansion
ᴏuse for hours, and then we went to
ᴇet Street to the newspaper offices.

Eʟʟᴇɴ (*to* Jᴀɴᴇ): Have a nice cup of
ʌ, ma'am, it'll make you feel better.

Jᴀɴᴇ: Thank you, Ellen.

Eʟʟᴇɴ: There ain't no cause to worry
ʌut the master, ma'am; he's all right.
ᴇel it in me bones. You see, he's got
• Alfred with 'im, and if anything

'appened to either of them we'd be
bound to 'ear from one of them, if you
know what I mean.

Jᴀɴᴇ: You must be fearfully worried,
too, Ellen.

Eʟʟᴇɴ: Well, on and off, I am, but I
say to myself—no news is good news,
and what must be must be, and you'd
never believe how it cheers me up.

Eʟʟᴇɴ *goes out.*

Mᴀʀɢᴀʀᴇᴛ: Poor Ellen!

A newsboy runs by, shouting.

Jᴀɴᴇ (*jumping up*): Quick! Quick!
Give me a halfpenny.

Jᴀɴᴇ *rushes on to the balcony and*
leans over.

What is it, Ellen—what is it?

Eʟʟᴇɴ *apparently answers "nothing*
much," and Jᴀɴᴇ *returns wearily.*

Ellen's up those area steps like lightning
every time a paper boy passes. No news
is good news. What must be must be.
Oh, God!

Mᴀʀɢᴀʀᴇᴛ *gets up with an air of de-*
termination.

Mᴀʀɢᴀʀᴇᴛ: Now, look here, Jane. I'm
going now, and I shall be back at a
quarter to seven.

Jᴀɴᴇ: A quarter to seven—why?

Mᴀʀɢᴀʀᴇᴛ: We're going out to dine at
a restaurant and we're going to a theatre.

Jᴀɴᴇ: Margaret—no, really, I——

Mᴀʀɢᴀʀᴇᴛ (*kissing Jane*): Don't argue
—just do what you're told.

Jᴀɴᴇ: Margaret, don't be so silly.

Mᴀʀɢᴀʀᴇᴛ: I mean it—it's a gesture.
Robert and Jim would hate to think of
you weeping and wailing. They're being
gallant enough. We'd better try and be
gallant, too. We'll dine at the Café
Royal.

Jᴀɴᴇ: Margaret!

Mᴀʀɢᴀʀᴇᴛ: Be ready at a quarter to
seven.

Mᴀʀɢᴀʀᴇᴛ *goes out.* Jᴀɴᴇ *makes a*
movement to call her back and then sub-
sides into her chair. Suddenly directly
under the window another barrel organ
strikes up "Soldiers of the Queen." Jᴀɴᴇ
jumps up and runs to the window.

Jᴀɴᴇ (*on balcony*): Go on, then—play
louder—play louder! Soldiers of the

Queen—wounded and dying and suffering for the Queen! Play louder, play
louder!

She comes back into the room laugh-
ing hysterically and proceeds to kick the
children's toy soldiers all over the room;
finally collapsing on to the sofa in a
storm of tears as the lights fade.

SCENE III

Principals: Mrs. Snapper, Cook, Annie,

Ellen, Bridges, Cabby.

Scene: *The kitchen of a London house.*
Time: *About 5 p.m. Monday, January*
21st, 1901.

When the lights go up Cook *is mak-*
ing toast in front of the range.

Mrs. Snapper (Ellen's *mother*) *is*
sitting on a chair beside a mailcart in
which reposes (mercifully invisible to
the audience) the Bridges' *infant*
Fanny.

Annie, *a scullery-maid, stands about*
with her mouth open, obviously in a
state of considerable excitement, occa-
sionally putting ineffective finishing
touches to the table.

Mrs. S.: I do 'ope Ellen didn't cry at
the station, it does make her nose so red.

Cook: Alfred will be so pleased to see
'er 'e won't mind if it's red or blue.
Come on, Annie, 'urry.

Annie: 'Ere they are.

Cook: 'Ere, quick! The rosette for
baby. (*She rushes to the dresser and*
snatches up a red, white and blue ro-
sette.) You pin it on 'er, Mrs. Snapper,
while I tidy me 'air.

Annie (*at window*): They've come in
a cab. Oo-er!

There is a great air of tension and ex-
citement in the kitchen, while Ellen's
and Bridges' *legs appear down the area*
steps.

The Cabby *follows with* Bridges' *kit-*
bag, which is dumped in the passage.

Bridges *enters first, looking very hale*
and hearty.

Bridges (*entering*): You settle the cab,
Ellen, I want to see my love-a-duck.
'Allo, Cook—'allo, Ma—where's my girl?

(*He kisses* Cook *and* Mrs. Snapper, *an*
then puts his head inside the pram
'Allo, Fanny. Coo, 'aven't you grow
Ma' you 'aven't 'arf bin feedin' 'er u
(*He makes delighted gurgling noises an*
prods the baby with his finger.) See '
laugh—she knows 'er dad. (*Then r*
turns and puts his arm around Mr
Snapper.) Well, Ma, 'ow's everything

Mrs. S.: I mustn't grumble.

Bridges: So I should just think not.
got a surprise for you.

Mrs. S.: What is it?

Bridges: Well, 'Erbert Smart's got
pub, see, and he's staying out in Afric
and I've bought it from 'im cheap, se
So much a year until it's paid off. V
always wanted to 'ave somewhere of o
own, and you can come and live with v
Ma—'ow's that suit?

Mrs. S.: A pub—is it a respectal
pub?

Bridges: All depends on 'ow you t
have, Ma, you know what you are wh
you've 'ad a couple.

Mrs. S. (*sniggering*): Oh, Alfred, 'c
can you?

Bridges: Well, what d'you think abo
it?

Mrs. S.: It sounds lovely—but 'c
about them upstairs?

Bridges: That's all right. I took t
master into me confidence. He wish
me luck.

Mrs. S. (*breaking down*): Oh, dear
can 'ardly believe it, not 'aving to li
alone any more—oh, dear!

Bridges: 'Ere, cheer up, Ma. Come o
'ave a cup of tea. There ain't nothing
cry about. Let's all 'ave tea, for Go
sake. Come on, Cook, me old girl
'ow'd you like to be a barmaid, eh?

They all sit down to tea, a grand
with eggs and shrimps. Everybody
talking at once.

Suddenly the cry of a Newsboy o
side cuts through their conversati
Annie *comes clattering in with the*
per. Bridges *snatches paper from An*
and reads it.

Bridges (*reading*): Whew! The Que
—it says she's sinking!

Soldiers march uphill . . . . out of darkness into darkness

Illustration for Noel Coward's
"CAVALCADE"

MRS. S.: There now—I told you so.

COOK (*taking paper*): Let's 'ave a ook.

ANNIE: She's very old, ain't she?

COOK: Be quiet, Annie. What's that ot to do with it?

ANNIE: Well, I never seen 'er.

BRIDGES: I 'ave—driving along Birdcage Walk once—years ago. Coo! England won't 'arf seem funny without the Queen!

The lights fade out.

Part II

SCENE I

cene: *The Bar Parlour of a London pub.*

ime: *About 5 p.m. Saturday, June 16th, 1906.*

When the curtain rises High Tea is just over. Seated round the table are JANE, EDWARD, MRS. SNAPPER, FLO *and* GEORGE GRANGER. FLO *and* GEORGE *are very smartly got up.* ELLEN *is seated at the piano with her back to the room.* FANNY (*aged 7*) *is dancing. When the dance is finished everyone applauds.*

JANE: She dances beautifully, Ellen. ome here, dear. (FANNY *goes to her.*) knew you when you were a little tiny aby.

FLO: She's a born dancer, if you ask e—haighly talented, haighly.

ELLEN (*leaving the piano*): She cerinly does love it. On the go all day she jigging about.

MRS. S.: Can I press you to another p, your ladyship?

JANE: No, thank you, we really must going in a moment.

FLO (*to* EDWARD): 'Ow was Hoxford hen you left it, Mr. Marryot?

EDWARD: Awfully nice.

GEORGE: Oh, yes, nice place, Oxford. ry antique—if you know what I mean.

ELLEN: I'm so glad to 'ear the master, r Robert, is well.

JANE: He was so sorry not to be able come down, but as you know, he's a ry busy man these days. He wished ry specially to be remembered to you d your husband. He'll be sorry to hear at he's ill.

ELLEN: It was so kind of you, ma'am, come all this way to see us and to ng Fanny that lovely doll, and every-thing. Fanny, come and say good-bye to 'er ladyship. (FANNY *makes an abortive effort at a curtsey.* JANE *bends down and kisses* FANNY.)

JANE (*to* ELLEN): Good-bye Ellen, it's been delightful seeing you again, and to find you so well and happy. Don't fail to remember me to Bridges; my husband and I miss you both still, it seems only yesterday that you were with us.

ELLEN: We miss you, too, ma'am.

JANE: Time changes many things, but it can't change old friends, can it?

ELLEN (*emotionally*): No, ma'am. Oh, no, ma'am.

JANE *and* EDWARD *are about to leave when the street door bursts open and* BRIDGES *staggers into the room. He looks unkempt and unshaven, and is obviously drunk. There is a moment of horrible silence.* BRIDGES *sees* JANE *and* EDWARD *and pulls up short.*

ELLEN (*in agonised tones*): Oh, Alfred!

BRIDGES: Ow! So that's why you wash trying to get me out of the way——

MRS. S.: Alfred Bridges, be'ave yourself and take yer 'at orf.

BRIDGES (*bowing to* JANE): Pleashed to see you again, milady, I' shure—welcome to our 'ovel.

He lurches toward JANE. *Jane makes an instinctive movement away from* BRIDGES, *who draws himself up unsteadily.*

Ow! I shee—proud and 'aughty, are we——

ELLEN (*wildly*): Alfred, stop it! Stop it!

JANE (*suddenly coming forward and taking both* ELLEN'S *hands in hers*): Ellen—dear Ellen—I'm so very, very sorry, and I quite understand. Please don't be upset and let me come and see you again soon.

JANE *goes out with* EDWARD. *Again there is silence.* ELLEN *bursts into hopeless sobbing.*

ELLEN (*wailing*): Oh, oh, oh! I'll never be able to raise me 'ead again—never—never——

BRIDGES: 'Oo give Fanny that doll? 'Er noble ladyship?

MRS. S. (*stepping forward*): You let the child alone.

BRIDGES (*pushing* MRS. SNAPPER *so hard that she falls against the table*): I can buy me own child a doll, can't I? Don't want any bloody charity 'ere. (*He snatches the doll from* FANNY *and pitches it into the fire.*)

ELLEN *goes for* BRIDGES. BRIDGES *hits* ELLEN. FLO *and* GEORGE *grab* BRIDGES *and push him out of the room.* ELLEN, *sobbing, takes* FANNY *in her arms.* MRS. SNAPPER *sinks into a chair.*

ELLEN: She was right—she was right. Time changes many things——

The lights fade.

SCENE II

SCENE: *The beach of a popular seaside resort.*

TIME: *About 6 p.m. Monday, July 25th, 1910.*

UNCLE GEORGE: Ladies, Gentlemen and kiddies. I am very happy to announce the winner of this week's Song and Dance Competition is little Miss Fanny Bridges.

Everyone applauds.

And it gives me great pleasure to present her with this handsome prize as a souvenir of Uncle George and his merry men. Come on up, my dear.

ELLEN (*in black*) *hoists* FANNY *up from the front row.* FANNY *is hoisted up by* ELLEN. *She is wearing a white dress with a black sash.* UNCLE GEORGE *kisses* FANNY *and presents her with a box of chocolates.* ELLEN *and* FANNY *walk across the beach with* MRS. SNAPPER, FLO *and* GEORGE. *They meet* MARGARET HARRIS, JANE *and* JOE.

JANE: Why, it can't be—Ellen—what a surprise!

They shake hands.

ELLEN: Oh, Ma'am—I'd no idea—fancy you being here!

JANE: Margaret, Joe, you remember Ellen, don't you?

MARGARET (*shaking hands*): Of course yes—how do you do, Ellen?

JOE: Hullo, Ellen.

Everyone shakes hands and talks politely.

ELLEN: Well, Master Joe, 'ow you 'ave grown. Quite the young man about town! How's Master Edward?

JOE: He's here. He and Edith have been to a concert on the pier. They'll be along soon.

ELLEN (*to* JANE): I got your letter, ma'am, when my Alfred died; it was kind of you to write.

JANE: How is your business going?

ELLEN: Oh, very well, really. I've managed to save quite a bit one way and another, and now I've closed the 'ole place for a month so as to give Fanny a holiday. She goes to dancing school now. She's going on the stage.

MARGARET: Surely she's very young.

MRS. S.: She's set on it—plain set on it.

ROBERT *comes down on to the beach. He has grey hair now and looks very distinguished.*

ROBERT: Jane—there you are—why, Ellen! (*He shakes hands.*)

All the introductions start over again.

ELLEN: It's been lovely seeing you again, ma'am, and you, too, Mrs. Harris. I expect your Edith has grown into a great big girl by now. I remember her when she was so small. (*To* ROBERT) Good-bye, sir—good-bye, Master Joe.

ROBERT: Good-bye, Ellen.

JOE: Good-bye.

JANE: You must come and see us one day—bring Fanny to tea.

ELLEN: Thank you, ma'am—I'd like to see the 'ouse again. I was very 'appy there——

The Marryots and Margaret go off. Mrs. Snapper, Ellen and Fanny rejoin Flo and George, who have been standing waiting for them a little way off. A man walks along with a tray of pink rock, yelling. Suddenly there is the noise of an aeroplane. Everyone screams and surges down to the beach, staring upwards. People half dressed rush out of bathing machines. Somebody starts cheering—then everyone takes it up. The aeroplane noise grows fainter. The lights fade.

SCENE III

SCENE: *The deck of an Atlantic liner.*
TIME: *About 7 p.m. Sunday, April 14, 1912.*

EDWARD *and* EDITH, *he in dinner-jacket, she in evening dress, are leaning on the rail.*

EDITH: It's too big, the Atlantic, isn't it?

EDWARD: Far too big.

EDITH: Wouldn't it be awful if a magician came to us and said: "Unless you count accurately every single fish in the Atlantic you die to-night?"

EDWARD: We should die to-night.

EDITH: How much would you mind —dying, I mean?

EDWARD: I don't know really—a good deal, I expect.

EDITH: I don't believe I should mind so very much now. You see, we could never in our whole lives be happier than we are now, could we?

EDWARD: Darling, there *are* different sorts of happiness.

EDITH: This is the best sort.

EDWARD (*kissing her*): Sweetheart!

EDITH: Did you ever think when we were children, going to the pantomime, and going to the Zoo, and playing soldiers, that we should ever be married?

EDWARD: Of course I didn't.

EDITH: Was I nice as a child?

EDWARD: Horrible!

EDITH: So were you, and so was Joe—vile. You always used to take sides against me.

EDWARD: And yet we all liked one another really.

EDITH: I think I liked Joe better than

you, but then he was younger and easier to manage. Dear Joe, he was awfully funny at the wedding, wasn't he?

EDWARD: Ribald little beast!

EDITH: He has no reverence, I'm afraid.

EDWARD: Absolutely none.

EDITH: He's passing gallantly through the chorus-girl phase now, isn't he?

EDWARD: Gallantly, but not quickly.

EDITH: Well, darling, you took your time over it.

EDWARD: Now then, Edith——

EDITH: Perhaps I should have learnt some tricks to hold you with when you begin to get tired of me.

EDWARD: I never shall, tricks or no tricks.

EDITH: Yes, you will one day. You're bound to; people always do. This complete loveliness that we feel together now will fade.

EDWARD: Look at father and mother; they're perfectly happy and devoted, and they always have been.

EDITH: They had a better chance at the beginning. Things weren't changing so swiftly; life wasn't so restless.

EDWARD: How long do you give us?

EDITH: I don't know—and Edward—(*she turns to him*) I don't care. This is our moment—complete and heavenly. I'm not afraid of anything. This is our own, for ever.

Edward takes Edith in his arms and kisses her.

EDWARD: Do you think a nice warming glass of sherry would make it any more heavenly?

EDITH: You have no soul, darling, but I'm very attached to you. Come on——

Edith takes up her cloak which has been hanging over the rail, and they walk away. The cloak has been covering a life-belt, and when it is withdrawn the words "S. S. Titanic" can be seen in black letters on the white. The lights fade into complete darkness, but the letters remain glowing as the orchestra plays very softly and tragically "Nearer, My God, to Thee."

SCENE IV

SCENE: *The drawing-room of a London house. The room is dark; the blinds are down over the windows.*

TIME: *About 11:16 p.m. Tuesday, August 4th, 1914.*

There is the sound of voices outside. Enter Jane and Margaret, both in travelling clothes. Jane turns on the lights and the room is soon to be enshrouded in dust-sheets.

JANE: Help me with these dust-sheets, Margaret. Put them anywhere. We'll get a char in to-morrow to clean up.

They proceed to pull the dust-sheets off the furniture.

I shall never go on a holiday again, ever. It's horrid when you're there, and much worse when you come back.

MARGARET: Still it's better to be here in London if anything's going to happen.

JANE: It's going to happen all right. I'm afraid there's no doubt about it, now.

JOE *comes in.*

JANE: Where's father?

JOE: Groping about in the wine cellar like an angry old beetle. He says strong drink is essential in a crisis.

ROBERT, *who is entering with two bottles and some glasses.*

ROBERT: I could only find hock and port, and port's far too heavy at this time of night; so we'll have to drink to the downfall of Germany in their own damned wine.

JOE: I rather like Germans, don't you, Father?

ROBERT: Enormously. Move these things off the table, and help me open the bottles.

JOE (*wrestling with a bottle*): If there is a war, how long do you think it will last?

ROBERT: Three months, at the outside.

JOE: I suppose we shall win, shan't we?

ROBERT: Yes—we shall win.

JOE (*hopefully*): Maybe it will last six months.

ROBERT: Leaving everything else aside,

that would be economically quite impossible. Have you any idea of what a war costs, Joe, in actual money?

JOE: Hell of a lot, I should think.

ROBERT: You're quite right. And the Germans can afford it even less than we can.

JOE: I wish Edward hadn't been drowned, we could have started off together.

ROBERT (*after a slight pause*): Don't be too impulsive and patriotic and dashing, Joey. Think of your mother. Think of me, too, you're all we've got left. *Robert abruptly puts down the bottle he is holding and goes out on to the balcony. Jane enters carrying a tray. A newsboy runs by outside, shouting. Robert shouts from the balcony and goes hurriedly from the room. Joe, Jane and Margaret stand stock still, waiting. Robert returns with the paper.*

ROBERT: We're at war, my dears.

JOE (*grabbing the paper*): Let me see —let me see——

MARGARET: Listen—listen!

From far away comes the sound of cheering. Jane sinks down on a chair.

JANE: Edward missed this, anyhow. At least he died when he was happy, before the world broke over his head.

ROBERT: Don't take that view, dearest, it's foolish. We've had wars before without the world breaking.

JANE: My world isn't very big.

A group of people pass along under the balcony laughing and cheering. Some of them start singing the "Marseillaise" and the others drown them with "Rule Britannia." JANE gets up suddenly.

JANE: Drink to the war, then, if you want to. I'm not going to. I can't! Rule Britannia! Send us victorious, happy and glorious! Drink, Joey, you're only a baby, still, but you're old enough for war. Drink like the Germans are drinking, to Victory and Defeat, and stupid, tragic sorrow. But leave me out of it, please!

JANE *goes abruptly from the room. The lights fade.*

SCENE V

Above the proscenium 1914 glows in lights. It changes to 1915-1916, 1917 and 1918. Meanwhile, soldiers march uphill endlessly. Out of darkness into darkness. Sometimes they sing gay songs, sometimes they whistle, sometimes they march silently, but the sound of their tramping feet is unceasing. Below the vision of them, brightly dressed, energetic women appear in pools of light, singing stirring recruiting songs. With 1918 they fade away, as also does the vision of the soldiers, although the soldiers can still be heard very far off, marching and singing their songs.

SCENE VI

SCENE: *A restaurant.*

TIME: *About 7.30 p.m. Tuesday, October 22nd, 1918.*

JOE *and* FANNY *are seated at a table; they have just finished dinner.* JOE *is in officer's uniform.* FANNY *is in very charming day clothes. She is now nineteen and extremely attractive.*

JOE (*pouring some champagne into* FANNY's *glass*): Have some more.

FANNY: Darling, I shall be tight. You don't want me to fall down during my first number, do you?

JOE: How much do you love me?

FANNY: Now, then, dear, we've had all this out before. (*Pauses*)

FANNY: Are you coming down to talk to me while I make up?

JOE: No, I promised to go home. Mother's waiting for me.

FANNY: I shall have to give it to you now, then.

JOE: What?

FANNY: Just a little something I had made for you.

JOE: Oh, Fanny—what is it?

FANNY: Hold on a minute, dear. It's in my bag. (*She searches in her bag and produces a small packet*). Here—with my love.

JOE (*opening it*): Oh, it's lovely.

FANNY: It's nothing really. Just a little souvenir of all the fun we've had.

JOE: You are a darling——

FANNY (*grabbing it from* JOE): Here, silly, you've missed the whole point. It opens—there. (*Fanny opens the little locket and discloses a minute photograph of herself.*)

JOE (*taking it*): It will be with me always, to the end of my days.

FANNY: You won't want it that long.

JOE: I almost wish I didn't love you quite so awfully. It makes going back much worse.

FANNY: I shall miss you dreadfully.

JOE: It has been fun, hasn't it?

FANNY: Lovely.

JOE: You don't regret it—any of it?

FANNY: Not a moment of it.

JOE: How wonderful you are. Do you really love me, I wonder, deep down inside, I mean?

FANNY: Yes, I think so.

JOE: Enough to marry me?

FANNY: Yes, but I wouldn't.

JOE: Why not?

FANNY: It would be too difficult. We shouldn't be happy married. Your Mother wouldn't like it.

JOE: She'd be all right.

FANNY: Don't let's talk about it now. Let's wait until you come back.

JOE: Very well.

There is silence for a moment. FANNY *puts her hand on* JOE's *across the table.*

FANNY: Listen, dear. I love you and you love me, and I've got to go now or I shall be late; and you've got to go, too, but I'm not going to say good-bye. We've had fun, grand fun, and I don't want you to forget me, that's why I gave you the locket. Please keep it close to you, Joey—darling Joey.

FANNY *goes as the lights fade.*

SCENE VII

Principals: JANE, ELLEN, GLADYS (*a parlourmaid*)

SCENE: *The drawing-room of a London house. The decoration of the room has changed slightly with the years, but not to any marked extent. It looks very much the same as it has always looked.*

Time: *About 11 a.m. Monday, November 11th, 1918.*

As the lights go up on the scene, a parlourmaid shows Ellen into the room. Ellen has certainly changed with the years. She is very well dressed, almost smart.

GLADYS: Her Ladyship will be down in a moment, madam.

ELLEN: Thanks.

Gladys goes out. Ellen wanders about the room. There is a photograph of Edward on the table, and also one of Joe. She looks at them both and sighs. Jane enters. She is dressed in street clothes.

JANE: Ellen! Gladys said Mrs. Bridges, but I couldn't believe it was you.

ELLEN: I just thought I'd call. It's rather important, as a matter of fact.

JANE: What is it? What on earth is the matter?

ELLEN: About Fanny and Master—her and Joe.

JANE: Joe?

ELLEN: Yes. They've been—well—er —to put it frankly, if you know what I mean, they've been having an affair.

JANE: My Joe?

ELLEN: Yes—your Joe. His last two leaves he spent a lot of time with Fanny.

JANE (*slowly*): Oh, I see.

ELLEN: I wouldn't have come to see you about it at all, only I think Fanny's very upset about it, and now that the war's over—or almost over, that is—and he'll be coming home—I thought——

JANE (*coldly*): What did you think?

ELLEN: Well, I thought they ought to get married.

JANE: Does Fanny want to marry him?

ELLEN: No—er—not exactly. That is— I haven't talked about it to her. She doesn't know I know.

JANE: How do you know?

ELLEN: I found a letter from him——

JANE: And you read it?

ELLEN: Yes—it's here. I've brought it with me. (*She fumbles in her bag.*)

JANE: I don't wish to see it, thank you.

ELLEN: I only brought it because——

JANE (*cutting ELLEN short*): Is Fanny in any sort of trouble?

ELLEN: Oh, no. Nothing like that.

JANE (*rising*): Then I think we'd better leave it until Joe comes home. Then he and Fanny can decide what they wish to do.

ELLEN (*also rising*): I—I didn't mean to upset you.

JANE: I'm not in the least upset.

ELLEN: It's been on my mind—it's been worrying me to death.

JANE: I think you should have spoken to Fanny before you came to me. I never interfere with my son's affairs.

ELLEN: Well, I'm sure I'm very sorry.

JANE: Please don't let's discuss it any further. Good-bye, Ellen.

ELLEN: I suppose you imagine my daughter isn't good enough to marry your son; if that's the case I can assure you you're very much mistaken. Fanny's received everywhere; she knows all the best people.

JANE: How nice for her; I wish I did.

ELLEN: Things aren't what they used to be, you know—it's all changing.

JANE: Yes, I see it is.

ELLEN: Fanny's at the top of the tree now; she's having the most wonderful offers.

JANE: Oh, Ellen!

ELLEN: What is it?

JANE: I'm so very, very sorry.

ELLEN: I don't know what you mean.

JANE: Yes, you do—inside, you must. Something seems to have gone out of all of us, and I'm not sure I like what's left. Good-bye, Ellen.

Gladys enters with a telegram. Jane takes telegram.

Excuse me, will you. (*She opens it and reads it, and then says in a dead voice.*) There's no answer, Gladys.

GLADYS (*excitedly*): It's all over, milady—it's eleven o'clock—the maroons are going off.

JANE: Thank you, Gladys, that will do.

GLADYS: Yes, milady. (*Gladys goes out.*)

(*Jane stands holding the telegram. She sways slightly.*)

ELLEN: What is it? What's happened? Oh, my God!

JANE: You need'nt worry about Fanny and Joe any more, Ellen. He won't be able to come back after all because he's dead. (*She crumples up and falls to the ground.*)

Maroons can be heard in the distance and people cheering. The lights fade.

SCENE VIII

SCENE: *Trafalgar Square.*

TIME: 11 *p.m. Monday, November 11th, 1918.*

Before the scene begins JANE *appears far up stage in a pool of light. Her hat has been pushed on to one side, her clothes look dishevelled, and her handbag hangs on her arm wide open. Twined round her neck and over her hat are coloured paper streamers. She holds in her left hand a large painted wooden* rattle, in her right hand a red, white and blue paper squeaker. Her face is dead white and quite devoid of expression.

The lights go up.

JANE *can be seen threading her way like a sleep-walker through dense crowds of cheering, yelling people. They push her and jostle her. One man blows a long squeaking paper tongue into her face. There is a motor bus festooned with people and a Rolls Royce and one or two taxis and a hansom cab, all equally burdened with screaming humanity. They move at a snail's pace.* JANE *finally arrives down stage under a lamp-post in the centre. She stands there cheering wildly, with the tears rolling down her face. The lights dim and the yelling crowds fade away.* JANE *is left, still cheering and occasionally brandishing the rattle and blowing the squeaker. But she can't be heard at all because the full strength of the orchestra is playing "Land of Hope and Glory."*

Part III

SCENE I

SCENE: *Drawing-room of a London house.*

TIME: 11.45 *p.m. Tuesday, December 31st, 1929.*

MARGARET *and* JANE, *both old women, are sitting by the fire.* MARGARET *is made up, with dyed hair.* JANE's *hair is white.* MARGARET *is wearing a coloured evening gown.* JANE *is in black.* ROBERT *enters. His hair is also white, but he is otherwise hale and hearty.*

ROBERT: It's nearly time.

MARGARET: Good heavens, I must fly. I wouldn't interfere with your little ritual for the world.

JANE: You wouldn't interfere—you're an old friend.

MARGARET (*kissing* JANE): That's very sweet, Jane, but all the same I must go. I promised I'd be at the Embassy at eleven-thirty. Happy New Year to you both. Remember you're both dining with me on Thursday.

ROBERT: Good night, Margaret—same to you.

MARGARET *goes out.* ROBERT *goes over to* JANE.

Did Franklin bring the champagne up?

JANE: Yes, it's by the table.

ROBERT: Good!

JANE: Well, Robert—here we go again.

ROBERT: I believe you laugh at me inside—for my annual sentimental outburst.

JANE: No dear, I don't laugh at you.

ROBERT: One more year behind us.

JANE: One more year before us.

ROBERT: Do you mind?

JANE: Oh, no—everything passes—even time.

ROBERT: It seems incredible, doesn't it? Here we are in this same room!

JANE: Yes. I've hated it for years.

ROBERT: Do you want to move?

JANE: Of course not. Dear Robert. (*She pats* ROBERT's *hand.*) What toast have you in mind for to-night—something gay and original, I hope?

ROBERT: Just our old friend—the future. The Future of England.

JANE: It's starting—the champagne, quick!

ROBERT *gets a champagne bottle out of the bucket and struggles with it.* JANE *opens the window.*

ROBERT: I can't get the damned thing open.

JANE: Let me try.

ROBERT (*doing it*): There!

JANE *holds the glasses.* ROBERT *fills the glasses. Meanwhile the chimes and sirens are beginning outside.*

JANE (*holding up her glass*): First of all, my dear, I drink to you. Loyal and loving always. (*She drinks.*) Now, then, let's couple the Future of England with the past of England. The glories and victories and triumphs that are over, and the sorrows that are over, too. Let's drink to our sons who made part of the pattern and to our hearts that died with them. Let's drink to the spirit of gallantry and courage that made a strange Heaven out of unbelievable Hell, and let's drink to the hope that one day this country of ours, which we love so much, will find dignity and greatness and peace again.

They both lift their glasses and drink as the lights fade.

CENSORSHIP OF THE PRESS

THAT there should be a restraint upon the press seems a matter of necessity: but the manner of it a matter of debate.

The use and intent of printing is (the same with that of preaching) for communicating our thought to others.

And there is equal reason (in itself) for suppressing the one as the other.

But this communication being the natural right of mankind (as sociable creatures, and all embarked in one common salvation) the suppressing of either of these is *taking away the children's bread.*

And in this communication, printing is more diffusive than speaking.

In the beginning of the Gospel, for calling the Gentiles, the Spirit of God interpreted the first preaching of it to every auditor in his own language.

And since that miraculous communication of it hath ceased,

It pleased God in His own time to have dictated to man the invention of printing to supply the place of it.

By which what is at first published in one language only is made intelligible to all others by translations.

And though several errors have and will be vented by the occasion of this invention, this is no more an argument against the invention itself than the growing of tares among wheat is an argument against sowing of corn.

Nor any more a reason for suppressing it by a law than it would be for shutting up the church doors because hypocrites crowd into the church with true worshippers.

Whenever the sons of God came to present themselves before the Lord, Satan would jostle in among them, and present himself before the Lord also.

And yet we don't hear that they quitted their devotion upon it.

And as Satan used our Saviour Himself so:

Have not I chosen you twelve, and one of you is a devil?

So it will be to the end of the world.

—J. Asgill.—An Essay for the Press

Emerson Hough

THE COVERED WAGON

Oh, then, Susannah, don't you cry fer me!
I'm goin' out to Oregon, with my banjo on my knee.

From Kansas City, the jumping off place of the West, across the great, broad prairies to Oregon, the front of American Civilization in 1848, leads the trail of the Covered Wagon—a trail of romance, glamour and hardship. Here is the great adventure told by Emerson Hough (1857-1923) in this thrilling novel which was first published in 1922.

Spring: 1848

More than two thousand men, women and children waited on the .Missouri for the green fully to tinge the grasses of the prairies farther west. Wagons came daily and neighbors waited for neighbors, tardy at the great rendezvous.

The encampment, scattered up and down the river front, had become more and more congested. Men began to know one another, families became acquainted, the gradual sifting and shifting in social values began. Knots and groups began to talk of some sort of accepted government for the common good. For they were now at the edge of the law.

Amid much bickering of petty politics, Jesse Wingate was chosen for the thankless task of train captain. He stood, a strong and tall man of perhaps forty-five years, of keen blue eye and short, close-matted, tawny beard. His garb was the loose dress of the outlying settler of the western lands. A farmer he must have been back home.

"It's time," said the campmaster to his wife. "The grass is up and we can't lie here much longer waiting for Molly to end her spring term, teaching in Clay School, in Liberty."

"She'll be here today," asserted his wife. "Besides, I think that's her riding a little one side the road now. Not that I know who all is with her. One young man—two. Well"—with maternal pride

—"Molly ain't never lacked for beaus! Yes, that's Sam Woodhull, of course. He hung around all winter, telling how him and Colonel Doniphan whipped all Mexico and won the war. I'll rest assured it's account Molly's going out to Oregon that he's going too!"

"Who's the other fellow, though?" demanded her husband.

To their surprise, they were not able to identify the rider who now set spur to his horse and came toward them at a gallop. He swung easily out of saddle as though rising from a chair in the presence of a lady, and removed his beaver to the frontier woman before he accosted her husband.

"Good morning, madam," said he in a pleasant quiet voice. "Good morning, sir. You are Mr. and Mrs. Jesse Wingate, I believe. Your daughter yonder told me so."

"That's my name," said Jess Wingate. "You're from the Liberty train?"

"Yes, sir. My name is Banion—William Banion. I'm leading a bunch of Missouri wagons. I was a major under Doniphan in Mexico. Knew Sam Woodhull there. But I'm not a major now." A change, a shadow came over the stranger's face. "They tell me you've been elected captain of the Oregon train. I wanted to throw in with you if I might, sir."

"You certainly can, Major Banion," said Jesse Wingate heartily. "The water and the grass is free. Drive in and light down. You said you saw our daughter, Molly—here she is now."

A LOVELY lass of eighteen years or so, was Molly, blue of eye and of abundant red-brown hair of that tint which has ever turned the eyes and heads of men. Above the middle height of woman's stature, she had none of the lank irregularity of the typical frontier woman but was round and well developed. Her conquests had been many since the time, when, fulfilling her parents' desire to educate their daughter, she had come all the way from the Sangamon country of Illinois to the best school then existent so far west—Clay Seminary, of quaint old Liberty.

Education, betterment, progress, advance—those things perhaps lay in the vague ambitions of the twice two hundred men who now lay in camp at the border of our unknown empire. They were all Americans—second, third, fourth generation Americans.

Surely American also were these two young men whose eyes now unconsciously followed Molly Wingate in hot craving.

Of the two, young Woodhull, planter and man of means, mentioned by Molly's mother as open suitor, had not seemed so ill a figure. Townsmen accorded him first place with Molly Wingate, until Will Banion came back from the wars.

About a Gal

MOLLY advanced to where Banion's horse stood. "What a pretty horse you have, major," she said. "May I ride him?"

"No woman ever rode that horse and not many men. I'd rather you wouldn't," replied Banion. "It might be dangerous."

She turned to Woodhull. "Help me up, sir," she said imperiously. "I can ride him, man saddle and all."

Woodhull caught her up under the arms and lifted her to the saddle. In terror at his unusual burden the animal reared and broke away from them all.

With a leap, Banion was in the saddle of Woodhull's horse, which had been left at hand. He drove in the spurs and headed across the flat at top speed. But this horse was no match for his.

Molly had not uttered a word or cry, either to her mount or in appeal for aid. In sooth, she was too frightened to do so. But she heard the rush of hoofs and the high call of Banion's voice back of her:

"Ho, Pronto! Pronto! *Vien' aqui!*"

Something of a marvel it was, and showing companionship of man and horse on the trail; for suddenly the mad black ceased his plunging. An instant and Banion had his cheek strap. Another and he was off, with Molly Wingate, in a white dead faint, in his arms.

By that time Woodhull had joined him, in advance of the other people.

"What do you mean, you damned fool you, by riding my horse off without my consent!" he broke out. "If she ain't dead—that damned wild horse—you had the gall—"

Will Banion's self-restraint at last was gone. He made one answer, voicing all his acquaintance with Sam Woodhull, all his opinion of him, all his future attitude in regard to him.

He dropped his hat to the ground, caught off one wet glove, and with a long back-handed sweep struck the cuff of it full and hard across Sam Woodhull's face.

THERE were dragoon revolvers in the holsters at Woodhull's saddle. He made a rush for a weapon. But the long, lean hand of the Missourian gripped his wrist even as he caught at a pistol grip. He turned a livid face to gaze into a cold and small blue eye.

By now the crowd surged between the two men, voices rose.

"He struck me!" broke out Woodhull "Let me go! He struck me!"

"I know he did," said the intervener "I heard it. I don't know why. But whether it was over the girl or not, we ain't goin' to see this other feller shot down till we know more about hit. Ye can meet—"

"I'll fight him any way he likes, or any way you say," said Banion. "It's not my seeking. I only slapped him because he abused me for doing what he ought to have done. Yes, I rode his horse. If I hadn't that girl would have been killed. It's not his fault she wasn't. I didn't want her to ride that horse."

"I don't reckon hit's so much a matter about a hoss as hit is about a gal," remarked Bill Jackson sagely. "Ye'll hatter fight."

From the opposite sides the two antagonists stepped forward. There was no ring, there was no timekeeper, no single umpire. There were no rounds, no duration set. It was man to man, for cause the most ancient and most bitter of all causes—sex.

Banion caught his antagonist by the wrist, and swift as a flash stooped, turning his own back and drawing the arm of his enemy over his own shoulder, slightly turned, so that the elbow joint was in peril and so that the pain must be intense. It was one of the jiu jitsu holds, discovered independently perhaps at that instant; certainly a new hold for the wrestling school of the frontier. Woodhull's friends saw a look of pain come on his face, saw him wince, saw him writhe, saw his rise on his toes. Then, with a sudden squatting heave,

Banion cast him full length in front of him, upon his back! Before he had time to move he was upon him, pinning him down. A growl came from the observers. Nobody raised a hand when they saw the balls of Will Banion's thumbs pressed against the upper orbit edge of his enemy's eyes.

"Do you say enough?" panted the victor.

A groan from the helpless man beneath.

"Am I the best man? Can I whip you?" demanded the voice above him.

"Go on—do it! Pull out his eye!" commanded Bill Jackson savagely. "He called it free to you! But don't wait!"

But the victor sprang free, stood, dashed the blood from his own eyes, wavered on his feet.

The hands of his fallen foe were across his eyes. But even as his men ran in, stooped and drew them away the conqueror exclaimed.

"I'll not! I tell you I won't maim you, free or no free! Get up!"

So Woodhull knew his eyes were spared, whatever might be the pain of the sore nerves along the socket bone.

"You fool!" said old Bill Jackson, drawing Banion to one side. "Do ye know what ye're a-sayin'? Whiles he was a-layin' thar I seen the bottoms o' his boots. Right fancy they was, with smallish heels! That skunk'll kill ye in the dark, Will. Ye'd orto hev put out'n both his two eyes!"

Worse than Indians

With the first thin line of pink the coyotes, hanging on the flanks of the great encampment, raised their immemorial salutation to the dawn. Their clamorings were stilled by a new and sterner voice—the notes of the bugle summoning sleepers of the last night to the duties of the first day. Down the line from watch to watch passed the Plains command, "Catch up! Catch up!" It was morning of the jump-off.

The first dust cut by an ox hoof was set in motion by the whip crack of a

barefooted boy in jeans who had no dream that he, one day, would rank high in the councils of his state, at the edge of an ocean which no prairie boy ever had envisioned.

The opulent, inviting land lay in a ceaseless succession of easy undulations, stretching away illimitably to far horizons, "in such exchanging pictures of grace and charm as raised the admiration of even these simple folk to a pitch bordering upon exaltation."

Here lay the West, barbaric, abound-

The Oregon Trail stretched 2000 miles from Kansas City to Portland. First traced by Indians and trappers, it was definitely routed by Lewis and Clark in 1804.

ing, beautiful. Surely it could mean no harm to any man.

Molly was rapidly becoming a good frontierswoman and thoughtful of her locomotive power. One day when the caravan was held up she resolved to find better pasturage for her wagon mules. The quest took her several miles from the covered wagons.

How long she sat alone, miles apart, an unnoticed figure, she herself could not have said—surely the sun was past zenith—when, moved by some vague feeling of her own, she noticed the uneasiness of her feeding charges.

Far off, low lying like a pale blue cloud, was a faint line of something that seemed to alter in look, to move, to rise and fall, to advance—down the wind. She never had seen it, but knew what it must be—the prairie fire! The lack of fall burning had left it fuel even now.

DANGER? Yes! Worse than Indians, for yonder were the cattle; there lay the parked train, two hundred wagons, with the household goods that meant their life savings and their future hope in far-off Oregon. Women were there, and children—women with babes that could no walk. True, the water lay close, but it was narrow and deep and offered no salvation against the terror coming on the wings of the wind.

A swift, absurd memory came to her. She could build an Indian fire signifying danger to warn them. Yes, it was three short puffs of smoke and a long pillar.

It worked! The column cut off by her shawl bent over in a little detached cloud. Again, with a quick flirt, eager eyed, and again the detached irregular ball. A third time—Molly rose, and now cast on dry grass till a tall and moving pillar of cloud by day arose.

At least she had warned them. She could do no more.

The world went black, with many points of red. Everywhere was the odor and feel of smoke. She fell and gasped, and knew little, cared little what might come. The elemental terror at last had caught its prey—soft, young, beautiful prey, this huddled form, a bit of brown and gray, edged with white of wind-blown skirt.

Dully, Molly heard the lowing, heard the far shouts of human voices. Then, it seemed to her, she heard the rush of other hoofs coming toward her. Yes, something was pounding down the slope toward her wagon, toward her.

Out of the smoke curtain broke a rider, his horse flat; a black horse with flying frontlet—she knew what horse. She knew what man rode him, too, black with smoke as he was now.

An arm reached down to hers, swept up—and she was going onward, the horn of a saddle under her, her body held to that of the rider, swung side-wise. The horse was guided not down but across the wind.

Twice and three times, silent, Will Banion flung her off and was down, kindling his little back fires—the only defense against a wildfire. He breathed thickly, making sounds of rage. And now the horse swerved, and headed him not away from the fire but straight into it!

Molly felt a rush of hot air; surging, actual flame singed the ends of her hair. She felt his hand again and again sweep over her skirts, wiping out the fire as it caught. It was blackly hot, stifling—and then it was past!

Before her lay a wide black world. Her wagon stood, even its white top spared by miracle of the back fire.

One Mad Instant

HE HEARD her voice at last:
"It's the second time you have saved me—saved my life, I think. Why did you come?"

"I saw your signal!" he said shortly. "Incidentally, have you anything in your wagon that we can use on burns?"

Molly climbed up to the seat, and rummaging about found a jar of butter.

"Come up on the seat," said she. "This is better medicine than nothing."

Gently, without asking his consent, she began to coat his burned skin as best she might with her makeshift of allevia-tion. His hand trembled under hers. And then all in one mad, unpremeditated in-stant it was done!

His hand caught hers, regardless of the pain to either. His arm went about her, his lips would have sought hers.

It was done! Now he might repent.

He came to his senses as she thrust him away; saw her cheeks whiten, her eyes grow wide.

"Oh!" she said. "Oh! Oh! Oh!"

"Oh!" whispered Will Banion to himself, hoarsely.

"It had to be sometime," he went on, since she still drew away from him. "What chance have I had to ask you before now? It's little I have to offer but my love."

"What do you mean? It will never be at any time!" said Molly Wingate slowly, her hand touching his no more.

"What do you mean?" He turned to her in agony of soul. "You will not let me repent? You will not give some sort of chance?"

"No," she said coldly. "You have had

chance enough to be a gentleman—as much as you had when you were in Mexico with other women. But Major William Banion falsified the regimental accounts. I know that too. I didn't—I couldn't believe it—till now."

He remained dumb under this. She went on mercilessly.

"Oh, yes, Captain Woodhull told us. Yes, he showed us the very vouchers. My father believed it of you, but I didn't. Now I do."

He could not speak. The fire marks showed livid against a paling cheek.

"Yes, I know you saved me—twice, this time at much risk," resumed the girl. "Did you want pay so soon? You'd —you'd—"

"Did he tell you that about me?" demanded Will Banion savagely. "Woodhull—did he say that?"

"I have told you, yes. My father knows."

She moved now as though to leave the wagon, but he raised a hand.

"Wait!" said he. "Look yonder! You'd not have time now to reach camp."

In the high country a great prairie fire usually or quite often was followed by a heavy rainstorm. What Banion now indicated was the approach of yet another of the epic phenomena of the prairies, as rapid, as colossal and as merciless as the fire itself.

THERE was no interval at all between the rip of the lightning and the crash of thunder as it rolled down on the clustered wagons. The electricity at times came not in a sheet or a ragged bolt, but in a ball of fire, low down, close to the ground, exploding with giant detonations.

Then came the rain, with a blanketing rush of level wind, sweeping away the last vestige of the wastrel fires.

Banion and Molly sat it out in the light wagon, the girl wrapped in blankets. Banion spent much of the time out in the storm, swinging on the ropes to keep the wagon from overturning. He had no apparent fear. His calm assuaged her own new terrors. In spite of her bitter arraignment, she was glad that he was here, though he hardly spoke to her at all.

"Look!" he exclaimed at last, drawing back the flap of the wagon cover. "Look at the rainbow!"

Over the cloud banks of the rain-wet sky there indeed now was flung the bow of promise. The entire clouded sky, miles on untold miles, was afire. All the opals of the universe were melted and cast into a tremendous picture painted by the Great Spirit of the Plains.

"Oh, wonderful!" exclaimed the girl. "It might be the celestial city in the desert, promised by the Mormon prophet!"

"It may be so to them. May it be so to us. Blessed be the name of the Lord God of Hosts!" said Will Banion.

She looked at him suddenly, strangely. What sort of man was he, after all, so full of strange contradictions—a savage, a criminal, yet reverent and devout?

"Come," he said, "we can get back now, and you must go. They will think you are lost."

He was no more than guide. But as she approached safety Molly Wingate began to reflect how much she really owed this man. He had been a pillar of strength, elementally fit to combat all the elements, else she had perished.

Two Who Loved

"I OUGHT to thank you," she said. "I do thank you."

His utter silence made it hard for her. He could see her hesitation, which made it hard for him, coveting sight of her always, loath to leave her.

Now a sudden wave of something, a directness and frankness born in some way in this new world apart from civilization, like a wind-blown flame, irresponsible and irresistible, swept over Molly Wingate's soul as swiftly, as unpremeditatedly as it had over his.

"If it had not been for what happened

in Mexico, I suppose after a time I wouldn't have minded what you did back there. I might have kissed you," she said hesitatingly.

"It was criminal!" he broke out. "But even criminals are loved by women. They follow them to jail, to the gallows. They don't mind what the man is—they love him, they forgive him. They stand by him to the very end!"

"Yes, I suppose many a girl loves a man she knows she never can marry."

The great and wistful regret of her voice was a thing not to be escaped. She spread her hands just apart and looked at him in what she herself felt was to be the last meeting of their lives; in which she could afford to reveal all her soul for once to a man, and then go about a woman's business of living a life fed on the husks of love given her by some other man.

"Oh, Will Banion, how could you take away a girl's heart and leave her miserable all her life?"

The cry literally broke from her. It seemed in her own ears the sudden voice of some other woman speaking—some unaccountable, strange woman.

"Your—heart?" he whispered, now close to her in the dusk. "You were not —you did not—you—"

But he choked. She nodded, not brazenly or crudely or coarsely, not even bravely, but in utter simplicity. For the time she was wholly free of woman coquetry. It was as though the elements had left her also elemental. Her words now were of the earth, the air, the fire, the floods of life.

"Yes," she said, "I will tell you now, because of what you have done for me.

"Yes! I believe I love you, although I am promised to—you know—Captain Woodhull. I believe I could follow a man to the gallows. Now I will not, because you didn't tell me you were a thief. I can't trust you. But I'll kiss you once for good-by. I'm sorry. I'm so sorry."

Being a man, he never fathomed her mind at all. But being a man, slowly, gently, he took her in his arms, drew her tight. Long, long it was till their lips met —and long then. But he heard her whisper "Good-by," saw her frank tears, felt her slowly, a little by little, draw away from him.

That night Molly turned on a sodden pallet which she had made down beside her mother in the great wagon. But she slept ill. Over and over to her lips rose the same question: "Oh, Will Banion, Will Banion, why did you take away my heart?"

Dire Forebodings

Two things troubled Banion: The possibility of grass exhaustion near the trail and the menace of the Indians. Squaw men in from the north and west said that the Arapahoes were hunting on the Sweetwater, and sure to make trouble; that the Blackfeet were planning war; that the Bannacks were east of the Pass; that even the Crows were far down below their normal range and certain to harass the trains.

These stories, not counting the hostility of the Sioux and Cheyennes of the Platte country, made it appear that there was a tacit suspense of intertribal hostility, and a general and joint uprising against the migrating whites.

These facts Banion did not hesitate to make plain to all his men; but, descendants of pioneers, with blood of the wilderness in their veins, and each tempted by adventure as much as by gain, they laughed long and loud at the thought of danger from all Indians of the Rockies. Had not their fathers worked with rifle lashed to the plow beam? Indians? Let them come!

The entire caravan now had passed in turn the Prairies and the Plains. In the vestibule of the mountains they had arrived in the most splendid out-of-doors country the world has ever offered. The climate was superb, the scenery was a constant succession of changing beauties new to the eyes of all. Game was at hand in such lavish abundance as none of them had dreamed possible. The buffalo ranged always within touch, great bands of elk now appeared, antelope always were in sight. The streams abounded in noble game fish, and the lesser life of the open was threaded across continually by the presence of the great predatory animals—the grizzly, the gray wolf, even an occasional mountain lion.

WATE's wagons which had traveled several miles ahead of Banion's since the breach with Woodhull, kept well apace with the average schedule of a dozen miles a day. At times they spurted to fifteen or twenty miles, and made the leap over the heights of land between the North Platte and the Sweetwater, which latter stream, often winding among defiles as well as pleasant meadows, was to lead them to the summit of the Rockies at the South Pass, beyond which they set foot on the soil of Oregon, reaching thence to the Pacific. Before them now lay the entry mark of the Sweetwater Valley, that strange oblong upthrust of rock, rising high above the surrounding plain, known for two thousand miles as Independence Rock.

At this point, more than eight hundred miles out from the Missouri, a custom of unknown age seemed to have decreed a pause. It become known as a resting place; indeed, many rested there forever, and never saw the soil of Oregon. Weddings, as well as burials, were postponed till the train got to Independence Rock.

Here then, a sad-faced girl, true to her promise and true to some strange philosophy of her own devising, was to become the wife of a suitor whose persistency had brought him little comfort beyond the wedding date. All the train knew that Molly Wingate was to be married there to Sam Woodhull. Some said it was a good match, others shook their heads, liking well to see a maid either blush or smile in such case as Molly's, whereas she did neither.

At all events, Mrs. Wingate was two days baking cakes at the train stops.

Friends got together little presents for the bride. Jed, Molly's brother, himself a fiddler of parts, organized an orchestra of a dozen pieces.

THEN approached the very hour—ten of the night, after duties of the day were done. A canopy was spread for the ceremony. A central camp fire set the place for the wedding feast. Within a half hour the bride would emerge from the secrecy of her wagon to meet at the canopy under the Rock the impatient groom, already clad in his best, already giving largess to the riotous musicians, who now attuned instruments, now broke out into rude jests.

But Molly Wingate did not appear, nor her father, nor her mother. A hush fell on the rude assemblage. The minister of the gospel departed to the Wingate encampment to learn the cause of the delay. He found Jesse Wingate irate to open wrath, the girl's mother stony calm, the girl herself white but resolute.

"She insists on seeing the marriage license, Mr. Doak," began Jesse Wingate. "As though we could have one! As though she should care more for that than her parents!"

The voice of the bride was not low and diffident, but high pitched, insistent.

"Provisional? Provisional? What is it you are saying, sir? Are you asking me to be married in a provisional wedding? Am I to give all I have provisionally? Is my oath provisional, or his?"

"Now, now, my dear!" began the minister.

"Like images, you are!" she went on hysterically, her physical craving for one man, her physical loathing of another, driving her well-nigh mad. "You wouldn't protect your own daughter!"—to her stupefied parents. "Must I think for you at this hour of my life? How near—oh, how near! But not now—not this way! No! No!"

Then, without a word, with no plan or purpose, Molly Wingate turned, sprang away from them and fled out into a night that was black indeed.

She was gone, a white ghost in her wedding gown, her little slippers stumbling over the stones, her breath coming sobbingly as she ran.

They followed her.

Back to them, at the great fire whose illumination deepened the shadows here, rose a murmur, a rising of curious people, a pressing forward to the Wingate station.

Molly Wingate ran for some moments, to some distance—she knew of neither. Then suddenly all her ghastly nightmare of terror found climax in a world of demons. Voices of the damned rose around her. There came a sudden shock, a blow. Before she could understand, before she could determine the shadowy form that rose before her in the dark, she fell forward like the stricken creature.

The Indians!

There was no wedding that night at the Independence Rock. The Arapahoes saw to that. But there were burials the day following, six of them—two women, a child, three men. The night attack had caught the company wholly off guard, and the bright fire gave good illumination for shaft and ball.

"Put out the fires! Corral! Corral!"

Voices of command arose. The wedding guests rushed for the shelter of their own wagons. Men caught up their weapons and a steady fire at the unseen foe held the latter at bay after the first attack.

Indeed, a sort of panic seized the savages. A warrior ran back exclaiming that he had seen a spirit, all in white, not running away from the attack, but toward them as they lay in cover. He had shot an arrow at the spirit, which then had vanished. It would be better to fall back and take no more like chances.

For this reason the family of Molly Wingate, pursuing her closely as they could, found her at last, lying face down in the grass, her arms outspread, her white wedding gown red with blood. An arrow, its shaft cracked by her fall, was imbedded in her shoulder, driven deep by the savage bowman who had fired in fear at an object he did not recognize. So they found her, still alive, still unmutilated, still no prisoner. They carried the girl back to her mother, who reached out her arms and laid her child down behind the barricaded wagon wheels.

At sunrise the train moved on, grim, grave, dignified and silent in its very suffering. There was no time for reprisal or revenge. The one idea as to safety was to move forward in hope of shaking off pursuit.

But all that morning and all that day the mounted Arapahoes harassed them. At many bends of the Sweetwater they paused and made sorties; but the savages fell back, later to close in, sometimes under cover so near that their tauntings could be heard.

All the tribes were in league to stop the great invasion of the white nation, who now were bringing their women and children and this thing with which they buried the buffalo. They meant extermination now. They were taking their time and would take their revenge for the dead who lay piled before the white man's barricade.

Soon the savage strategy became plain. The fight was to be a siege.

Banion's wagons had trailed several miles in their rear ever since his fight with Woodhull. But now even Woodhull admitted that Banion and his Missourians were the Wingate train's only hope.

Two days later the emigrants, now half mad of thirst, and half ready to despair of succor or success, heard the Indian drums sound and the shrilling of the eagle-bone whistles. The Crows were chanting again. Whoops arose along the river bank.

"My God! they're coming!" called out a voice. Then the savage hosts broke from their cover, more than a thousand men, ready to take some loss in their hope that the whites were now more helpless.

But before the three ranks of the Crows had cleared the cover the last line began to yell, to whip, to break away. Scattering but continuous rifle fire followed them, war cries arose, not from savages, but white men. A line of riders emerged, coming straight through to the second rank of the Crow advance. Then the beleaguered knew that the Missourians were up.

The Crows swerved under the enfilading fire of the men who now crossed the ford. Caught between three fires, and meeting for their first time the use of the revolver, they lost heart and left their dead, breaking away into a mad flight west and north which did not end till they had forded the upper tributaries of the Green and Snake, and found their way back west of the Tetons to their own country far east and north of the Two-go-tee crossing of the Wind River Mountains; whence for many a year they did not emerge again to battle with the white nation on the Medicine Road.

What many men had not been able to do of their own resources, less than a

fourth their number now had done Side by side, Banion, Jackson, a ha dozen others, rode up to the wagon gap now opened. They were met by a surg of the rescued. Women, girls threv themselves upon them kissing them, em bracing them hysterically. Where ha been gloom, now was rejoicing.

Woodhull made way with the other Most men of both parties now knew c the feud between Banion and Wood hull, and the cause underlying i Woman gossip did what it might. A ha dozen determined men quietly watche Woodhull. As many continually wer near Banion, although for quite a di ferent reason.

Banion came to the place under wagon where they had made a hospita cot for Molly Wingate. She held out he arms and he bent above her, kissing he forehead gently and shyly as a boy.

"Please get well, Molly Wingate," sai he. "You are Molly Wingate?"

"Yes. At the end—I couldn't! I ra away, all in my wedding clothes, Wil In the dark. Someone shot me. I've bee sick, awfully sick, Will."

"Please get well, Molly Wingate! An I'll come back to you. Wait for me, m dear."

Gold

Now they had the news! This was the greatest news that ever came to old Fort Hall—the greatest news America knew for many a year, or the world— the news of the great gold strikes in California.

Wealth, success, ease, luxury was at hand for the taking. What a man had dreamed for himself he now could have. In California, just yonder, was gold, gold, gold!

Go to Oregon and plow? Why not go to California and dig in a day what a plow would earn in a year? Had it not been foreordained that they should get the news before anyone else?

Molly had a letter from Will Banion saying that he was taking the trail for California and would come back to her

a rich man. And one day the carava missed Sam Woodhull. The story wer around that he too was bound for Cal fornia, not for gold but to wreak h deadly vengeance on Banion.

At first almost alone, Jesse Winga stayed the stampede by holding out f Oregon in the council with his captain "Did you ever see pick or shovel bui a country? Oregon's ours because v went out five years ago with wagons ar plows—we all know that. To hold country you need wheels, you need plow. I'm for Oregon!"

Imperiously as though he were I zarro's self he drew a line in the dust the trail.

"Who's for Oregon?" he demanded Wingate, his three friends; a litt group, augmenting, crossed for Oregon. The women and the children stood aloof, —sunbonneted women, brown, some with new-born trail babies in arms, silent as they always stood. Across from the Oregon band stood almost as many men, for the most part unmarried, who had not given hostages to fortune, and were resolved for California. A cheer arose from these.

Parting of Ways

THREE days later the vanguard of the remnant of the train, less than a fourth of the original number, saw leaning against a gnarled sagebrush a box lid which had scrawled upon it in straggling letters one word—"California." Here now were to part the pick and the plow.

"Last chance for Californy, men," said old Jim Bridger calmly. "Do-ee see the tracks? Yan's where Woodhull's wagons left the road. Below that, one side, is the tracks o' Banion's mules."

"I wonder," he added, "why thar hain't ary letter left fer none o' us here at the forks o' the road."

He did not know that, left in a tin at the foot of the board sign certain days earlier, there had rested a letter addressed to Miss Molly Wingate. It never was to reach her. Sam Woodhull knew the reason why. Having opened it and read it, he had possessed himself of exacter knowledge than ever before of the relations of Banion and Molly Wingate.

Bitter as had been his hatred before, it now was venomous.

The decision for or against California was something for serious weighing now at the last hour, and it affected the fortune and the future of every man, woman and child in all the train. Never a furrow was plowed in early Oregon but ran in bones and blood; and never a dollar was dug in gold in California— or ever gained in gold by any man— which did not cost two in something else but gold.

Twelve wagons pulled out of the trail silently, one after another, and took the winding trail that led to the left, to the west and south to California.

Molly Wingate, in the Oregon train, sat with a letter clasped in her hand, frank tears standing in her eyes. It was no new letter, but an old one. She pressed the pages to her heart.

"Oh, God keep you, Will!" she said almost audibly. "Oh, God give you fortune, Will, and bring you back to me!"

The Killer Killed

A ROUGH low cabin of logs, hastily thrown together, housed through the winter months of the Sierra foothills the two men who now, in the warm days of early June, sat by the primitive fireplace cooking a midday meal. The older man was the mountain man, Bill Jackson, as anyone might tell who ever had seen him, for he had changed but little.

That his companion was Will Banion it would have taken closer scrutiny even of a friend to determine, so much had the passing of these few months altered him in appearance and in manner. Once light of mien, now he smiled never at all. For hours he would seem to go about his duties as an automaton.

Here he and his partner had in a few months of strenuous labor taken from a narrow and unimportant rivulet more wealth than most could save in a lifetime of patient and thrifty toil. Yes, fortune had been kind. And it all had been so easy, so simple, so unagitating, so matter-of-fact! Banion could not realize that now, young though he was, he was a rich man.

As he sat, half musing, Will Banion heard, on the ravine side around the bend, the tinkle of a falling stone, lazily rolling from one impediment to another. It might be some deer or other animal, he thought. He hastened to get view of the cause, whatever it might be.

He turned the corner. Almost level with his own, he looked into the eyes of a crawling man who—stooped, one hand steadying himself against the slant of the ravine, the other below, carrying a rifle—was peering frowningly ahead.

It was an evil face, bearded, aquiline, not unhandsome; but evil in its plain meaning now. The eyes were narrowed, the full lips drawn close, as though some tense emotion now approached its climax.

For months most men had avoided Woodhull. It was known that he was on a man hunt. His questions, his movements, his changes of locality showed that. Well, he was not alone among men whose depths were loosed. Some time his hour might come.

It had come! He stared now full into the face of his enemy! He at last had found him. Here stood his enemy, unarmed, delivered into his hands.

For one instant the two stood, staring into one another's eyes. Banion's advance had been silent. Woodhull was taken as much unawares as he.

The report came; and Banion fell. But even as he wheeled and fell, stumbling down the hillside, his arm apparently had gained a weapon. It was not more than the piece of rotten quartz he had picked up and planned to examine later. He flung it straight at Woodhull's face —an act of chance, of instinct. By a hair it saved him.

Firing and missing at a distance of fifty feet, Woodhull remained not yet a murderer in deed. The rifle carried but the one shot. He flung it down, reached for his heavy knife, raising an arm against the second piece of rock which Banion flung as he closed. He felt his wrist caught in an iron grip, felt the blood gush where his temple was cut by the last missile.

Banion fought fast and furiously, striving to throw, to bend, to beat back the body of a man almost as strong as himself, and now a maniac in rage and fear.

The sound of the rifle brought Jackson to the scene with a gun. Another dry report cut the confined air of the valley and the body of Sam Woodhull dropped. The small blue hole an inch above the eyes showed the murderer's man hunt done. Jackson had saved his friend.

Fulfillment

At the new farm of Jesse Wingate, in Oregon, the wheat was in stack and ready for the flail.

It was evening. Wingate and his wife sat on their little stoop, gazing down the path that led to the valley road. A mounted man was opening the gate, someone they did not recognize.

Molly Wingate sat in her own little room, looking through her window at the far forest and the mountains. She was no longer the tattered emigrant girl in fringed frock and mended moccasins. Ships from the world's great ports served the new market of the Columbia Valley. It was a trim and trig young woman in the habiliments of sophisticated lands who sat here now, her heavy hair, piled high, lighted warmly in the illumination of the window.

Quiet, reticent, reserved—cold, some said; but all said Molly Wingate, teacher at the mission school, was beautiful, the most beautiful young woman in all the great Willamette settlements. Her hand were in her lap now, and her face as usual was grave. A sad young woman her Oregon lovers all said of her.

She heard a footfall on the gallery floor, then on the floor of the hall. Her heart almost stopped with it. Some undiscovered sense warned her, cried aloud to her. She faced the door wide-eyed as it was flung open.

"Molly!"

Will Banion's deep-toned voice told her all the rest. At first he could only push back her hair, stroke her cheek until at last the rush of life and youth came back to them both, and their lips met in the sealing kiss of years. They both were young again.

"Will! Oh, Will! It can't be!" she whispered again and again.

"But it is! It had to be! Now I've found my real fortune."

Suddenly he pulled an envelope from his pocket. "My pardon!" he said, "From the President of the United States! Not guilty—oh, not guilty! And I never was!"

"Oh, Will, Will! That makes you happy?"

"Doesn't it you?"

"Why, yes, yes! But I knew that always! And I know now that I'd have followed you to the gallows if that had had to be. I would have stood by you to the very end."

He said no more. In the sweetness of the silence he kissed her tenderly again and again.

ADDRESS TO THE OCEAN

O thou vast Ocean! ever-sounding sea!
Thou symbol of a drear immensity!
Thou thing that windest round the solid world
Like a huge animal, which, downward hurled
From the black clouds, lies weltering and alone,
Lashing and writhing till its strength be gone.
Thy voice is like the thunder, and thy sleep
Is as a giant's slumber, loud and deep.
Thou speakest in the east and in the west
At once, and on thy heavily-laden breast
Fleets come and go, and shapes that have no life
Or motion, yet are moved and meet in strife.
The earth hath naught of this: no chance or change
Ruffles its surface, and no spirits dare
Give answer to the tempest-wakened air;
But o'er its wastes the weakly tenants range
At will, and wound its bosom as they go:
Ever the same, it hath no ebb, no flow;
But in their stated rounds the seasons come,
And pass like visions to their wonted home;
And come again, and vanish; the young Spring
Looks ever bright with leaves and blossoming;
And Winter always winds his sullen horn,
When the wild Autumn, with a look forlorn,
Dies in his stormy manhood; and the skies
Weep, and flowers sicken, when the summer flies.

. . . .

Oh! wonderful thou art, great element:
And fearful in thy spleeny humours bent,
And lovely in repose; thy summer form
Is beautiful, and when thy silver waves
Make music in earth's dark and winding caves,
I love to wander on thy pebbled beach,
Marking the sunlight at the evening hour,
And hearken to the thoughts thy waters teach—
Eternity—Eternity—and Power.

—*B. W. Procter*

Élie Metchnikoff

THE PROLONGATION OF LIFE

"THE PROLONGATION OF LIFE: STUDIES IN OPTIMISTIC PHILOSOPHY," was published in 1907. In it Professor Élie Metchnikoff (1845-1916) lays down certain principles for the prolongation of life. These principles have been put into practice by many people since the publication of Metchnikoff's book. Senile changes, largely due to auto-intoxication, have supposedly been arrested by a diet including sour milk. Professor Metchnikoff received the Nobel prize for medicine in 1908.

Senile Debility

WHEN we study old age in man and the lower animals, we observe certain features common to both. But often among vertebrates there are found animals whose bodies withstand the ravages of time much better than that of man. I think it a fair inference that senility, that precocious senescence which is one of the greatest sorrows of humanity, is not so profoundly seated in the constitution of the higher animals as has generally been supposed. The first facts which we must accept are that human beings who reach extreme old age may preserve their mental qualities, notwithstanding serious physical decay, and that certain of the higher animals can resist the influence of time much longer than is the case with man under present conditions.

Many theories have been advanced regarding the cause of senility. It is certain that many parts of the body continue to thrive and grow even in old age, as, for instance, the nails and hair. But I believe that I have proved that in many parts of the body, especially the higher elements, such as nervous and muscular cells, there is a destruction due to the activity of the white cells of the blood. I have shown also that the blanching of the hair in old age is due to the activity of these white cells, which destroy the hair pigment. Progressive muscular debility is an accompaniment of old age;

physical work is seldom given to men over sixty years of age, as it is notorious that they are less capable of it. Their muscular movements are feebler, and soon bring on fatigue; their actions are slow and painful. Even old men whose mental vigour is unimpaired admit their muscular weakness. The physical correlate of this condition is an actual atrophy of the muscles, and has for long been known to observers. I have found that the cause of this atrophy is the consumption of the muscle fibres by what I call phagocytes, or eating cells, a certain kind of white blood cells.

IN THE case of certain diseases we find symptoms, which look like precocious senility, due to the poison of the disease. It is no mere analogy to suppose that human senescence is the result of a slow but chronic poisoning of the organism. Such poisons, if not completely destroyed or got rid of, weaken the tissues, the functions of which become altered or enfeebled in which the latter have the advantage. But we must make further studies before we can answer the question whether our senescence can be ameliorated.

The duration of the life of animals varies within very wide limits. As a general rule, small animals do not live as long as large ones, but there is no absolute relation between size and longevity, since parrots, ravens, and geese live much longer than many mammals, and han some much larger birds. Buffon long ago argued that the total duration of life bore some definite relation to the length of the period of growth, but further inquiry shows that such a relation cannot be established. Nevertheless, there is something intrinsic in each kind of animal which sets a definite limit to the length of years it can attain. The purely physiological conditions which determine this limit leave room for a considerable amount of variation in longevity. Duration of life, therefore, is a character influenced by environment.

The duration of life in mammals is relatively shorter than in birds, and in the so-called cold-blooded vertebrates. No indication as to the cause of this difference can be found elsewhere than in the organs of digestion. Mammals are the only group of vertebrate animals in which the large intestine is much developed. This part of the alimentary canal is not important, for it fulfils no notable digestive function. On the other hand, it accommodates among the intestinal flora many microbes which damage health by poisoning the body with their products. Among the intestinal flora there are many microbes which are inoffensive, but others are known to have pernicious properties, and auto-intoxication, or self-poisoning, is the cause of the ill-health which may be traced to their activity. It is indubitable that the intestinal microbes or their poisons may reach the system generally, and bring harm to it. I infer from the facts that the more the digestive tract is charged with microbes, the more it is a source of harm capable of shortening life. As the large intestine not only is that part of the digestive tube most richly charged with microbes, but is relatively more capacious in mammals than in any other vertebrates, it is a just inference that the duration of life of mammals has been notably shortened as the result of chronic poisoning from an abundant intestinal flora.

WHEN we come to study the duration of human life, it is impossible to accept the view that the high mortality between the ages of seventy and seventy-five indicates a natural limit to human life. The fact that many men from seventy to seventy-five years old are well preserved, both physically and intellectually, makes it impossible to regard that age as the natural limit of human life. Philosophers such as Plato, poets such as Goethe and Victor Hugo, artists such as Michaelangelo, Titian, and Franz Hals, produced some of their most important works when they had passed what some regard as the limit of life. Moreover, deaths of people at that age are rarely due to senile debility. Centenarians are really not rare. In France, for instance, nearly 150 centenarians die every year, and extreme longevity is not limited to the white races. Women more frequently become centenarians than men—a fact which supports the general proposition that male mortality is always greater than that of the other sex.

It has been noticed that most centenarians have been people who were poor or in humble circumstances, and whose life has been extremely simple. It may well be said that great riches do not bring a very long life. Poverty generally brings with it sobriety, especially in old age, and sobriety is certainly favourable to long life.

The Study of Natural Death

IT is surprising to find how little science really knows about death. By natural death I mean to denote death due to the nature of the organism, and not to disease. We may ask whether natural death really occurs, since death so frequently comes by accident or by disease; and certainly the longevity of many plants is amazing. Such ages as three, four, and five thousand years are attributed to the baobab at Cape Verde, certain cypresses, and the sequoias of California. It is plain that among the lower and higher plants there are cases where natural death does not exist; and, further, so far as I can ascertain, it looks as if poisons produced by their own bodies were the cause of natural death among the higher plants where it does occur.

In the human race cases of what may be called natural death are extremely rare; the death of old people is usually due to infectious disease, particularly pneumonia, or to apoplexy. The close analogy between natural death and sleep supports my view that it is due to an auto-intoxication of the organism, since it is very probable that sleep is due to "poisoning" by the products of organic activity.

Although the duration of the life of man is one of the longest amongst mammals, men find it too short. Ought we to listen to the cry of humanity that life is too short, and that it will be well to prolong it? If the question were merely one of prolonging the life of old people, without modifying old age itself, the answer would be doubtful. It must be understood, however, that the prolongation of life will be associated with the preservation of intelligence and of the power to work. When we have reduced or abolished such causes of precocious senility as intemperance and disease, it

will no longer be necessary to give pensions at the age of sixty or seventy eyars. The cost of supporting the old, instead of increasing, will diminish progressively. We must use all our endeavors to allow men to complete their normal course of life, and to make it possible for old men to play their parts as advisers and judges, endowed with their long experience.

FROM time immemorial suggestions have been made for the prolongation of life. Many elixirs have been sought and supposed to have been found, but general hygienic measures have been the most successful in prolonging life and in lessening the ills of old age. That is the teaching of Sir Herman Weber, himself of very great age, who advises general hygienic principles, and especially moderation in all respects. He advises us to avoid alcohol and other stimulants, as well as narcotics and soothing drugs. Certainly the prolongation of life which has come to pass in recent centuries must be attributed to the advance of hygiene; and if hygiene was able to prolong life when little developed, as was the case until recently, we may well believe that with our greater knowledge a much better result will be obtained.

The Use of Lactic Acid

THE general measures of hygiene directed against infectious diseases play a part in prolonging the lives of old people; but, in addition to the microbes which invade the body from outside, there is a rich source of harm in microbes which inhabit the body. The most important of these belong to the intestinal flora which is abundant and varied. Now the attempt to destroy the intestinal microbes by the use of chemical agents has little chance of success, and the intestine itself may be harmed more than the microbes. If, however, we observe the new-born child we find that, when suckled by its mother, its intestinal microbes are very different and much fewer than if it be fed with cows' milk. I am strongly convinced that it is advan-

tageous to protect ourselves by cooking all kinds of food which, like cows' milk, are exposed to the air. It is well-known that other means—as, for instance, the use of lactic acid—will prevent food outside the body from going bad. Now as lactic fermentation serves so well to arrest putrefaction in general, why should it not be used for the same purpose within the digestive tube? It has been clearly proved that the microbes which produce lactic acid can, and do, control the growth of other microbes within the body, and that the lactic microbe is so much at home in the human body that it is to be found there several weeks after it has been swallowed.

From time immemorial human beings have absorbed quantities of lactic mi-robes by consuming in the uncooked condition substances such as soured milk, kephir, sauerkraut, or salted cucumbers, which have undergone lactic fermentation. By these means they have unknowingly lessened the evil consequences of intestinal putrefaction. The fact that so many races make soured milk and use it copiously is an excellent testimony to its usefulness, and critical inquiry shows that longevity, with few traces of senility, is conspicuous amongst these peoples.

A reader who has little knowledge of such matters may be surprised by my recommendation to absorb large quantities of microbes, as the general belief is that microbes are all harmful. This belief, however, is erroneous. There are many useful microbes, amongst which the lactic bacilli have an honourable place. If it be true that our precocious and unhappy old age is due to poisoning of the tissues, the greater part of the poison coming from the large intestine, inhabited by numberless microbes, it is clear that agents which arrest intestinal putrefaction must at the same time postpone and ameliorate old age. This theoretical view is confirmed by the collection of facts regarding races which live chiefly on soured milk, and amongst which great ages are common.

An Ideal Old Age

As I have shown in the "Nature of Man," the human constitution as it exists to-day, being the result of a long evolution and containing a large animal element, cannot furnish the basis of rational morality. The conception which has come down from antiquity to modern times, of a harmonious activity of all the organs, is no longer appropriate to mankind. Organs which are in course of atrophy must not be re-awakened, and many natural characters which, perhaps, were useful in the case of animals, must be made to disappear in men.

Human nature which, like the constitutions of other organisms, is subject to evolution, must be modified according to a definite ideal. Just as a gardener or stockraiser is not content with the existing nature of the plants and animals with which he is occupied, but modifies them to suit his purposes, so also the scientific philosopher must not think of existing human nature as immutable, but must try to modify it for the advantage of mankind. As bread is the chief article in the human food, attempts to improve cereals have been made for a very long time, but in order to obtain results much knowledge is necessary. To modify the nature of plants, it is necessary to understand them well, and it is necessary to have an ideal to be aimed at. In the case of mankind the ideal of human nature, towards which we ought to press, may be formed. In my opinion this ideal is "orthobiosis"—that is to say, the development of human life, so that it passes through a long period of old age in active and vigorous health, leading to a final period in which there shall be present a sense of satiety of life, and a wish for death.

Just as we must study the nature of plants before trying to realise our ideal, so also varied and profound knowledge is the first requisite for the ideal of moral conduct. It is necessary not only to know the structure and functions of the human organism, but to have exact ideas on human life as it is in society. Scientific knowledge is so indispensable for moral conduct that ignorance must be placed among the most immoral acts. A mother who rears her child in defiance of good hygiene, from want of knowledge, is acting immorally towards her offspring, notwithstanding her feeling of sympathy. And this also is true of a government which remains in ignorance of the laws which regulate human life and human society.

If the human race come to adopt the principles of orthobiosis, a considerable change in the qualities of men of different ages will follow. Old age will be postponed so much that men of from sixty to seventy years of age will retain their vigour, and will not require to ask assistance in the fashion now necessary. On the other hand, young men of twenty-one years of age will no longer be thought mature or ready to fulfil functions so difficult as taking a share in public affairs. The view which I set forth in the "Nature of Man" (to appear in a subsequent issue), regarding the danger which comes from the present interference of young men in political affairs has since then been strikingly confirmed.

It is easily intelligible that in the new conditions such modern idols as universal suffrage, public opinion, and the referendum, in which the ignorant masses are called on to decide questions which de-mand varied and profound knowledge, will last no longer than the old idols. The progress of human knowledge will bring about the replacement of such institutions by others, in which applied morality will be controlled by the really competent persons. I permit myself to suppose that in these times scientific training will be much more general than it is just now, and that it will occupy the place which it deserves in education and in life.

Our intelligence informs us that man is capable of much, and, therefore, we hope that he may be able to modify his own nature and transform his disharmonies into harmonies. It is only human will that can attain this ideal.

◆

Blow High, Blow Low

Blow high, blow low, let tempests tear
   The mainmast by the board;
My heart with thoughts of thee, my dear,
   And love, well stored,
Shall brave all danger, scorn all fear,
   The roaring winds, the raging sea,
     In hopes on shore
     To be once more
   Safe moor'd with thee!

Aloft, while mountains high we go,
   The whistling winds that scud along,
And the surge roaring from below,
    Shall my signal be,
    To think on thee,
   And this shall be my song:
    Blow high, blow low, &c.

And on that night when all the crew
   The mem'ry of their former lives
O'er flowing cans of flip renew,
    And drink their sweethearts and their wives,
     I'll heave a sigh, and think on thee;
    And, as the ship rolls through the sea,
    The burthen of my song shall be—
    Blow high, blow low, &c.

—*Charles Dibdin (1745-1814)*

J. M. Barrie

PETER PAN

OR THE BOY WHO WOULDN'T GROW UP

Sir James M. barrie's "Peter Pan," a play in three acts, was first produced at the Duke of York's Theatre, London, December 27, 1904, and has been re-staged annually ever since. No other work of the theatre in our time has won so enduring a place in the affections of the English-speaking race; Maude Adams' portrayal of Peter endeared her to countless thousands.

I—How Peter Found His Shadow

Once upon a time there was a little girl named Wendy Moira Angela Darling. She lived in a house with her brothers, John Napoleon Darling and Michael Nicholas Darling. This house was an ordinary house of brick and slates, but one thing about it was quite extraordinary. It contained a Newfoundland dog whose name was Nana, and this dog acted as nurse to the three children.

Nana was so clever that he never allowed the children to put on a flannel nightdress before it was aired at the fire; and he knew how to turn on the hot water when it was bath-time; and no matter how strongly the children insisted that they would *not* be bathed, or that they would *not* go to bed, Nana always saw that they should. Now, Mrs. Darling loved Nana, and she had a particular reason for keeping this brave and powerful dog as the children's nurse. One night, on visiting the nursery, she had seen a strange flitting Shape moving quickly to and fro in the dim glow of the nightlight. At sight of Mrs. Darling this Shape rushed to the window. Mrs. Darling darted towards it. Just as it sprang into the night, Mrs. Darling pulled down the window with a bang. The Shape escaped; but something fell on the floor at Mrs. Darling's feet. *It was the shadow of this strange, flitting creature.* Mrs. Darling put the shadow in a drawer; but she felt very nervous for the safety of the children. She feared that the Shape might come back and do them some dreadful harm. The only comfort she had was the presence of Nana in the nursery. The big dog, she thought, would protect her children from all danger. But one night Mr. Darling was rather cross, and he said it was ridiculous to have a dog for a nurse; he got so cross at last that he said Nana must sleep in a kennel in the yard. Mrs. Darling pleaded; the children cried; Nana barked. Mr. Darling, however, was extremely cross, and Nana was led away to the yard, moaning and growling.

That night the window was thrust open, and into the room glided and skipped the mysterious Shape.

"Where is my shadow?" it cried; while Nana barked furiously outside. "I can't be happy without my shadow. Tinker Bell, Tinker Bell, where is my dear little shadow?"

Instantly a spot of light flicked into the room, and sprang round the walls, and over the ceiling, and down the beds, and across the carpet, making a tinkling sound wherever it flitted and whenever it settled for a moment. This was Tinker Bell, a little girl fairy. She told the Shape where the shadow lay, and soon the drawer was open, the shadow pulled forth, and the Shape skipped round the room with delight, singing, dancing, laughing in its joy, while Tinker Bell flashed round the room like a luminous butterfly. But, alas! when the Shape tried to make the shadow stick on, it refused, and all the delight went, and the Shape burst into passionate tears.

Just at this moment Wendy awoke. She was not frightened, and asked the little Shape why it was crying. Then she asked it its name, and the Shape told her that it was Peter Pan. Wendy got needle and thread and stitched the shadow on to Peter Pan, and then Peten Pan danced with joy, for wherever he went the shadow followed him on the floor.

Peter Pan then told Wendy his story. He said that he lived in a place called Never-Never-Land, with a lot of little boys who had all been dropped out of their perambulators by careless nurses; and that they lived with fairies and would never grow up, but for always and always would remain happy boys in this enchanting Never-Never-Land.

He told her that when the first baby laughed, the laughter broke into little pieces, and each little piece became a fairy, and went dancing about the world. But whenever a child says that it does not believe in fairies, then one of the fairies dies. Peter Pan said it was dreadful for a child to say it did not believe in fairies. There was only one other thing that made fairies sad, he said, and this was the want of a mother; all the boys in Never-Never-Land wanted to have a mother very much indeed. Wendy asked if there was not a little girl among them who could pretend to be their mother, but Peter Pan shook his head and answered that *girls* never dropped out of their perambulators, they were far too clever. This pleased Wendy, and she loved Peter Pan.

"Oh, Wendy," cried Peter, "come and live with us and be our mother!"

The two boys woke up. Peter Pan said he would teach them all to fly if Wendy would only come and be their mother.

When the children heard that they could learn to fly, they were quite excited, and immediately began to spring in the air. But every time they fell and sprawled on the ground, or bumped flat on the beds.

"You must think beautiful thoughts," cried Peter Pan; and, so saying, soared up gracefully into the air, and sailed noiselessly round the room.

Soon the children learned, and all began to fly round the room with cries of delight. Then the windows opened wide, and Peter Pan led the way into the night; and while Tinker Bell tinkled loudly and Nana barked warningly, the children soared towards the stars.

II—The Lost Boys in Never-Never-Land

THE boys in Never-Never-Land were beginning to get anxious about Peter Pan, who was their captain. He seemed to be a long time away, and they were afraid of wolves and pirates. While they were wondering what had happened to Peter, they saw what looked to them like a large white bird flying gracefully in the sky.

As they gazed at it, Tinker Bell suddenly shone on the trees, and tinkling very loudly, told them that Peter Pan wanted them to shoot this bird at once. So they ran and got bows and arrows, and shot them into the air. Suddenly down fell—what do you think?—poor Wendy with an arrow in her breast.

Little Tinker Bell, who was very jealous of Wendy, was responsible for this awful deed.

But Wendy was not killed. Soon she revived, and then with her brothers round her, and Peter Pan holding her hand, she promised all the boys to be their mother. Then they went to work and built Wendy a funny little house with the silk hat of John Napoleon Darling for its chimney-pot; and everybody was wonderfully happy, except Tinker Bell, who was more and more jealous of Wendy.

Now, while they were so happy in their house, through the wood came the terrible pirates. The captain of the rightful gang was named Captain James Hook, and a more horrible villain never froze the blood in a child's veins. All his crew feared him and cowered before him. His long black hair was enough to make you shiver; his yellow skin made you go white; his coal-black eyes struck daggers of fear into your heart; but, far worse than all these, more awful even than his cackling laugh and his way of rolling his *r's* so that they sounded like pistols, was his right hand. His right hand wasn't a hand at all, *it was an iron hook*. How he came to have that hook is part of the story.

Peter Pan had tripped the terrible pirate into the sea, and a crocodile, a tremendous c-r-r-r-rocodile, had snapped off his hand and part of his wrist. The crocodile enjoyed the captain's hand and wrist so much that it wanted more; and so it haunted the captain wherever he went, longing to eat another bit of him, and dreaming of the happy days when it would gobble him all up. The captain always knew when his ferocious enemy was near, because on one occasion it had swallowed an alarm clock, and the ticking of this clock could plainly be heard through its skin. But the captain was nervous, because he knew the clock would one day run down, and then the crocodile would be able to steal upon him unawares.

You can imagine how this pirate hated Peter, the cause of all his troubles, and how he longed to slay him.

ONE day, when some friendly Indians were guarding the boys, up came the pirates and made a great slaughter of the poor redskins. The boys did not hear the battle, for they were listening to something Wendy was telling them underground.

Wendy, you must know, had become the mother of these boys, and they all did exactly what she told them, and all adored her, because it was delightful to have a mother after having lived so long without one. After she had seen mermaids and a bird that gave up its nest for Peter Pan to use as a boat, she settled down to be a real practical mother, giving the boys their medicine, teaching them how to behave nicely, and tucking them all up snugly in their beds. For a girl nine years old, Wendy made a splendid mother.

Well, on this night, Wendy was telling them a story about her own father and mother—a beautiful story which showed how that mother and father must be weeping for their lost children. As she was finishing, John Napoleon and Michael Nicholas sprang up in their beds, and said: "Wendy, we must go back!"

"Yes," answered Wendy, "we must go back."

You can imagine how dreadfully sad all the motherless boys were when they heard that Wendy was going home. They cried so hard that at last she told them they might come back with her and her brothers, and live in their house, and have Mr. and Mrs. Darling for their father and mother. All the boys accepted this offer with delight except Peter Pan. Peter Pan said he did not want to grow up. He did not want to live in a real house and go to school. He wanted to live always in Never-Never-Land, with the fairies and birds and mermaids. In his heart he was terribly sad at losing Wendy, whom he loved very much indeed; but he refused to go away and grow up like an ordinary boy. So they all said good-bye to Peter Pan, and one by one went up the narrow tunnel which led from their underground home to the forest and the night. Wendy was the last to go, and before she went she poured out some medicine for Peter and made him promise her that he would take it when he woke up in the morning.

But instead of kind redskins keeping guard, the pirates were there. The boys were seized one by one as they stepped on ground; a rough hand was clasped over their mouths to prevent them from crying out, and they were carried away prisoners to the pirate ship and Wendy and her brothers were taken too.

III—How the Children Went Home Again

PETER PAN lay asleep in his bed. The rest of the boys were on board the pirate ship. Peter Pan was alone. Captain Hook was creeping to the hole above. Now was his chance to slay his enemy.

Noiselessly the pirate chief crept down the hole. He arrived at the door, and peeped over the top. Peter Pan was fast asleep. He tried to open the door, and failed. Again and again his hook fumbled at the latch. Peter Pan was safe. But no! The terrible captain spied the glass of medicine left by Wendy on a shelf; he reached towards it, and then, taking a bottle of poison from his pocket, poured the contents into the glass.

Peter Pan woke up. He remembered his promise to Wendy, and went to drink the poison. At that moment Tinker Bell rushed in, crying: "Don't drink! Don't drink!"

But her warning was useless.

"I have promised Wendy," answered Peter, and walked towards the glass with his hands outstretched.

In vain did Tinker Bell warn him; but, just as Peter was about to drink, the little Shining Light popped into the glass and drained all its deadly contents. Then it flickered and paled and drooped towards its bed, dying.

Peter knew there was only one way in which he could possibly save it.

"Do you believe in fairies? Oh, please say you believe in fairies!" he cried to all the world. And back from the world, which was so sorry for poor little Tinker Bell, came the answer: "We believe in fairies."

So Tinker Bell revived and was saved, and she told Peter Pan how the pirates had carried off the lost boys, with Wendy and her brothers, to their ship, and of the danger in which they stood.

Peter immediately started out. He arrived at the ship as the captain was going to flog his prisoners before making them walk the plank. Peter Pan had an alarm clock in his pocket; he took it out, and at the first sound of that *tick-tick* the captain gave a great cry of horror, thinking that the cr-r-r-rocodile was near.

During the panic, Peter stole on board ship and hid himself in the cabin where the cat-o'-nine-tails was hidden.

The clock ran down. The captain grew brave again.

"Go and get the cat-o'-nine-tails!" he ordered.

One of the ruffians went to obey. As he entered the cabin, a terrible shriek resounded all over the ship. Another pirate was ordered to go and see what had happened. He, too, uttered a ghastly shriek, and did not come out. The rest of the crew were now wild with terror. They refused to enter the cabin; one threw himself into the sea.

Suddenly Peter Pan rushed out, sword in hand, and a terrible fight followed. Captain Hook was flung overboard, where the crocodile was waiting for him; and all the rest of the wicked pirates were killed.

THEN Wendy and all the boys went home, and you can imagine how glad Mrs. Darling and Mr. Darling and Nana were to see their lost children. Mr. Darling, we must tell you, had been so repentant for his crossness that he had made Nana live indoors and dine at the table while he himself slept in a kennel outside, and ate in the dog's trough. Mrs. Darling had always kept the window open, hoping that the children would return; and used to play and sing "Home Sweet Home," thinking that they might hear her and come back.

But Peter Pan, all alone in Never-Never-Land, longed for little Wendy; and Mrs. Darling allowed Wendy to go every now and then to visit Peter, and see that his house was nice and tidy. Peter Pan always refused to grow up, and Wendy never forgot the fairies.

IT IS not children only that one feeds with fairy tales.—*Lessing.*

Ralph Barton Perry

THE THOUGHT AND CHARACTER OF WILLIAM JAMES

Wᴵᴸᴸᴵᴀᴹ JAMES (1842-1910) had the double distinction of founding a philosophical system and of helping to found the science of psychology. He is one of the few scholars whose books have been aimed at and appreciated by the man-in-the-street. Himself typically American, he uses such expressions as "cash-value" and "results" to "sell" *pragmatism;* which is a philosophical foundation for the practical spirit of present day America.

Unconventional Upbringing

Tʜᴇ birth of William James coincides almost precisely with the beginning of the acquaintance between his father and Emerson. On March 18, 1842, Emerson wrote in his diary: "In New York I became acquainted with Henry James." James had gone to hear Emerson lecture, was attracted to him, and invited him to his house, where he arrived just in time to be taken upstairs to admire "the lately-born babe."

The schooling of William and his younger brother Henry, who was to become a well-known writer, bears a significant relation to their father's domestic philosophy. He was both restless and radical. It was not to be expected that he would be satisfied with the ordinary institutionalized routine, in education or anything else. He had apparently acquired an antipathy to college from his own experience, so that his sons were never definitely "headed" in that direction.

He believed furthermore, in the liberty of his children, for what were to him the best of reasons. "I desire my children to become upright men, men in whom goodness shall be induced not by mercenary motives but by love for it or a sympathetic delight in it. And inasmuch as I know that this disposition cannot be forcibly imposed upon them,

but must be freely assumed, I surround them as far as possible with an atmosphere of freedom." Parental affection is a dangerous passion, he thought, tending to become possessive. Parents would ideally have no claim upon their children, but would share them with others and recognize their belonging to society as a whole.

Henry James tells us that his father checked the vocational ardor of his sons, and prevented an abrupt decision in favor of this or that alternative, by asking whether it were not too "narrowing." He subordinated doing to being, having the philosopher's idea of vocation, that men's first calling is to be men. This father of a great writer and of a great scientist was an outspoken opponent both of letters and of science, because he regarded both of these vocations as belittling.

Despite their careers the sons unconsciously obeyed his injunction. Both William and Henry became men before they became anything else, and there is always a peculiar inadequacy in referring to one as a "psychologist" and to the other as a "novelist," as though to name them by what they did revealed to us what they were.

Wᴵᴸᴸᴵᴀᴹ JAMES began at a very early age, to find and appropriate the food which his characteristic appetites required. William was more "vividly bright," more daring, and prompter to respond than his brother. When the children and their friends played comedies in the attic, it was William who first composed them and then played the leading rôle. This he did not through self-assertion, but rather through quickness of wit. When William once put off his brother with the words, "I play with boys who curse and swear!" he was using, quite unconsciously, words that symbolized his greater capacity to meet the world on its own terms, his habit of always being equal to the occasion.

Henry engaged in literary and dramatic compositions from childhood, just as William engaged in juvenile forms of science and art. But William's characteristic genius showed itself boldly, Henry's furtively. William's educational career was a series of raids, from which he returned sometimes laden with spoils, sometimes empty-handed; but, in any case, he took the initiative.

Travel was a fundamental fact in the history of the James family. It was habitually resorted to as a means of education for the young and as a remedy for the old, whatever their affliction, whether of body or of mind. The incidents of travel ceased to be incidental. The comparison of the several types of European civilizations, and above all the comparison of Europe with America, became almost an obsession. A facility in the reading and speaking of European languages was acquired early enough to fructify the whole cycle of development Books were read, books of every description, because books can be read whereve one may be, or even while one is on the way.

A brief residence at Bonn in the summer of 1860 was chiefly notable as the occasion of William's decision to study painting. It was not a surprising decision since he had sketched and painted from early boyhood. But though his interes and aptitude had long since been proved even now it was not an unqualified decision. It had been hoped that through travel he might forget art's fatal attractions—and thus avoid a *mésalliance*.

That he had talent and interest is unquestionable; but he found the interest te be less compelling than he had thought and he judged the talent to be less distinguished than his standards required Thus he rejected painting and rarely looked back; never with profound regrets.

But he retained the painter's sensibility and something of the artist's detachment He cultivated style in his scientific and philosophical writing, and was offended by its absence in others. He had the artist's imagination and acute perception of sensory qualities, as when he paused in his writing to remark that "the light is shrieking away, outside." But the gifts which qualified him to be an artist were from this crucial period of his life unreservedly dedicated to scientific and speculative ends.

A Vagrant Mind at Harvard

From 1861 William James's range of vocational alternatives was narrowed to science which like his interest in painting dated from boyhood. Whether it should be science in the stricter sense of natural science, or in the broader sense of philosophy; and whether his intellectual vocation should assume the form of research, or of teaching, or of the practice of medicine—all of these questions lay ahead, to be answered only after twelve years of trial and doubt, during which the state of his health played as decisive a role as the self-revelation of interest and aptitude.

The autumn of 1861 found him a student of chemistry in the Lawrence Scientific School at Harvard. His teacher of chemistry in this school was Charles William Eliot who later became a great president of Harvard. Eliot was an acute observer of men and one who weighed his words. This is what he afterwards said of his famous pupil:—

"James was a very interesting and agreeable pupil, but was not wholly de-

Pragmatism's primary interest is in its doctrine of truth. No one doubts our ultimate ability to penetrate theoretically into the very core of reality.

Illustration for Ralph Barton Perry's
"THE THOUGHT AND CHARACTER OF WILLIAM JAMES"

voted to the study of chemistry. . . . His excursions into other sciences and realms of thought were not infrequent; his mind was excursive, and he liked experimenting, particularly novel experimenting. In 1863-4 he changed from the Department of Chemistry to that of Comparative Anatomy and Physiology in the Lawrence Scientific School. His tendency to the subject of physiology had appeared clearly during his two years in the Department of Chemistry; so that I enlisted him, in the second year of his study of chemistry, in an inquiry into the effects on the kidneys of eating bread made with Liebig-Horsford baking powder, whose chief constituent was an acid phosphate. But James did not like the bread, and found accurate determination of its effects, three times a day, tiresome and unpromising; so that after three weeks he requested me to transfer that inquiry to some other person.

WILLIAM JAMES

"The two interesting points about his education are: first, its irregularity—it did not conform to the Boston and Cambridge traditional method; and secondly, it was in large proportion observational, particularly in the biological sciences. The systematic part of his education did not foretell his subsequent devotion to philosophical studies; but his unsystematic excursions did."

JAMES was perpetually grazing and ruminating, wandering wherever the pasturage was good. Fortunately two notebooks of the year 1862-1863 have been preserved, in which appear—along with items extracted from the lectures of Agassiz on "Geology and the Structure and Classification of the Animal Kingdom," and Joseph Lovering on "Electrostatics, Electrodynamics and Acoustics"—pencil drawings, historical and literary chronologies, sayings of Charles Peirce, an outline of the French Revolution, and abstracts of Buchner's "Kraft und Stoff,"

Max Müller's "History of Ancient Sanskrit Literature," Farrar's "Origins of Language" and Jonathan Edward's "Original Sin." The entries in these books, and an index begun in 1864, ranged over the whole field of literature, history, science, and philosophy. They indicate a mind as energetic and acquisitive as it was voracious and incorrigibly vagrant.

Although in September of 1863 he again registered in the Lawrence Scientific School, the focus of his interest had shifted from chemistry to biology, and in the same month he began his studies in the Medical School.

It is clear that the *practice* of medicine did not attract him. "I embraced the medical profession a couple of months ago," he wrote on February 21, 1863. "My first impressions are that there is much hum-bug therein, and that, with the exception of surgery, in which something positive is sometimes accomplished, a doctor does more by the moral effect of his presence on the patient and family, than by anything else. He also extracts money from them."

James continued his medical studies until the end of March, 1865, when he joined the Thayer Expedition to Brazil. This promised a period of close association with Agassiz, and a trial of the career of biology, which was still a live alternative. The interruption of his studies induced a general examination of prospects and possibilities. The long voyage and the ensuing period of illness gave him leisure to reflect, while absence from his family provided an occasion for putting his reflections on record. Behind his playful manner there is evidence of a brooding preoccupation with philosophy.

AFTER a year's absence James returned to Boston, in March 1866, resuming his studies at the Harvard Medical School and at the Massachusetts General Hospital, where he held a brief internship.

The following spring brought a new interruption of his medical studies and another period devoted to searching life and considering the alternatives it offered. He sailed for Europe in April 1867, not to return until November 1868. Several causes combined to bring him to this decision. The first was a condition of ill-health from which he had been suffering since the previous autumn. He was now entering upon a period of partial incapacity, physical suffering, and depression, which lasted for nearly five years.

It is impossible in the case of James to regard the state of his health as an incident. Since he could not endure standing for hours in a laboratory, it provided a decisive reason against experimental research. It limited the amount of his reading, and no doubt was partially responsible for his extraordinary capacity to seize quickly the nourishment which his mind required. In any case it turned him from passive and cumulative erudition toward active rumination. He became essentially a thinking and observing, rather than a learning man.

James had a more specific reason for going to Europe. At the Medical School he had acquired an interest in experimental physiology, and he believed that by going to Germany at this time he could both satisfy his scientific needs and perfect his knowledge of the language.

The Birth of Psychology

WHETHER or not James is regarded as one of the founders of modern psychology, in any case he was present while it was being founded, and experienced in himself the motives which led to its founding. Writing from Berlin to Thomas W. Ward in the autumn of 1867, he said:—

"It seems to me that perhaps the time has come for psychology to begin to be a science—some measurements have already been made in the region lying between the physical changes in the nerves and the appearance of 'consciousness-at' (in the shape of sense perceptions), and more may come of it. I am going on to study what is already known, and perhaps may be able to do some work at it. Helmholtz and a man named Wundt at Heidelberg are working at it, and I hope I live through this winter to go to them in the summer."

James here alludes to the most important signs of the new "experimental psychology." In 1860 Fechner had published his "Elemente der Psychophysik," in which he had formulated the law which had been envisaged by E. H. Weber as early as 1846, and which became known as the Weber-Fechner Law. This law stated the relations between intensities of stimulus and intensities of sensation, and promised to qualify psychology (as "psycho-physics") for membership in the quantitative and experimental sciences.

Helmholtz, on the other hand, continuing the work of Johannes Müller, had approached psychology by way of the physiology of the senses. The first complete edition of his great "Handbuch der physiologischen Optik" appeared in 1867, while he was a professor of philosophy at Heidelberg.

Wilhelm Wundt was the man by whom experimental psychology was weaned from its physical and physiological parentage. He had been trained in physiology under Müller and he had already, in 1862, published a volume of experimental studies on sense perception and begun to lecture on "psychology as a natural science."

JAMES underwent in the development of his own interests a change similar to that represented by the emergence of Wundt from Müller and Helmholtz. There was in James, as in Wundt, that breadth of interest or concern with the whole of life which distinguishes the philosopher, so that if he was to be scientific it must be from a new centre. Man, for him, could not constitute a mere chapter of physics or physiology. Thus in

1868 James described himself as "wading his way" towards psychology.

This new enthusiasm reminded him sharply of his limitations: "Too late! Too late! If I had been drilled further in mathematics, physics, chemistry, logic, and the history of metaphysics, and had established, even if only in my memory, a firm and thoroughly familiar basis of knowledge in all these sciences (like the basis of human anatomy one gets in studying medicine), to which I should involuntarily refer all subsequently acquired facts and thoughts . . . I might be steadily advancing.

"I shall continue to study, or rather *begin* to, in a general psychological direction, hoping that soon I may get into a particular channel. Perhaps a practical application may present itself sometime—the only thing I can now think of is a professorship of "moral philosophy" in some western academy, but I have no idea how such things are attainable, nor if they are attainable at all to men of a non-spiritualistic mould."

R ETURNING to Cambridge in November 1868, James was able to continue his medical studies with sufficient continuity to present himself for the degree in the following spring.

The passing of his medical examination "with no difficulty" on June 21, 1869, brought James relief in two senses: it was the removal of a burden, and at the same time a prop to his self-confidence. He had long since abandoned any intention of practising medicine.

During that summer he summed up this "epoch" as follows: "So there is one epoch of my life closed, and a pretty important one, I feel it, both in its scientific 'yield' and in its general educational value as enabling me to see a little the inside workings of an important profession, and to learn from it, as an average example, how all the work of human society is performed. I feel a good deal of intellectual hunger nowadays, and if my health would allow, I think there is little doubt that I should make a creditable use of my freedom, in pretty hard study. I hope, even as it is, not to remain absolutely idle—and shall try to make whatever reading I can do bear on psychological subjects."

Though James was now looking toward biological science or psychology, a depression and inward brooding brought a perpetual deepening of his philosophical interest. He was groping for some fundamental attitude by which to orient his life.

Groping for Reality

D URING the autumn and winter of 1869 James's spirits had steadily declined. April, 1870, marked the low point of his depression and the beginnings of a permanent improvement. Three forward steps are clearly defined, despite many lesser oscillations: the spiritual crisis of 1870; the commencement of his teaching in 1872; his marriage in 1878.

His desperate neurasthenic condition during these years had contributed to his understanding of religious mysticism and morbid mentality. But it was a pathological seizure rather than a spiritual crisis. The spiritual crisis was the ebbing of the will to live, for lack of a philosophy to live by—a paralysis of action occasioned by a sense of moral impotence.

That he should have experienced such a crisis at all furnishes the best possible proof of James's philosophical cast of mind. He had for many years brooded upon the nature of the universe and the destiny of man. Although the problem stimulated his curiosity and fascinated his intellect, it was at the same time a vital problem. He was looking for a solution that should be not merely tenable as judged by scientific standards, but at the same time propitious enough to live by.

No philosophy could possibly suit him that did not candidly recognize the dubious fortunes of mankind, and encourage him as a moral individual to buckle on his armor and go forth to battle. In other words, to cure him from his weakness he needed the strong man's medicine. He was a strong man, overtaken by weakness —a man of action cut off from action by bodily incapacity, a man to whom no teaching of acquiescence or evasion could be either palatable or nutritive.

What is the strong man's medicine, diluted to suit his disabled condition? *The gospel of belief.* For belief is action, and yet a sort that may be demanded even of a sick man; and belief may have action as its object. To believe *by* an act of will *in* the efficacy of will—that is a gospel which fits the temper of action, and which may be used to bring the invalid warrior back to fighting trim.

The crisis of April 1870 was a turning point but not a cure. For several years to come the road was hard, with only a very gradual upward incline.

Evolution of Psychology

DURING the year 1871 James gradually resumed his scientific studies, and in the winter of 1872-1873 he began his career as a teacher at Harvard.

That he was to be a teacher and scholar was now settled, but what he should teach and investigate was still subject to change. Physiology, psychology, and philosophy all attracted him, and he ended by teaching them all; physiology coming first, not because his interest was greatest but because the first opportunity came to him in that field. Philosophy and psychology were to have their day, and it was not far distant. Furthermore, the three subjects all interpenetrated. Comparative anatomy and physiology led through the conception of evolution to philosophy of nature, and human physiology led to psychology; while psychology, as James knew it, looked for its causal explanation to physiology and for its deeper implications to the theory of knowledge and metaphysics.

Speaking in later years of this period of his life, James said: "I originally studied medicine in order to be a physiologist, but I drifted into psychology and philosophy from a sort of fatality. I never had any philosophic instruction, the first lecture on psychology I ever heard being the first I ever gave."

Having imbibed the newer tendencies in Europe and having followed them up with physiological and empirical studies of his own, James became one of the first American teachers to recognize the existence of psychology as an independent science.

The early history of James's teaching of psychology is briefly as follows. Beginning in 1872 and for the next few years, he gave courses in anatomy and physiology in Harvard College. In these courses James devoted considerable attention to the physiology of the nervous system and some to psychophysics. In 1875 he announced a course for graduates on "The Relations between Physiology and Psychology," and thereafter this course or some equivalent course of advanced grade was given regularly. James began his undergraduate instruction in psychology in 1876-1877 with a course announced as "Natural History 2" and described as "Physiological Psychology— Herbert Spencer's Principles of Psychology." In the following year his psychological teaching was transferred to the department of philosophy, though he remained until 1880 assistant professor of physiology.

James was clearly advocating the recognition of the new psychology—"new" in the sense of allying itself with science as well as with philosophy, and in combining the methods of observation and experiment with those of speculation and reflection. This was a distinct innovation and it is not surprising that James's early teaching of physiological psychology at Harvard attracted considerable attention.

Psychology as then taught in other colleges in the United States was indistinguishable from the philosophy of the soul, embracing a brief account of the senses and of association, but devoted mainly to the higher moral and logical processes. In doctrine it was usually a blend of common-sense realism of the Scottish school with traces of Kantian influence and such drafts upon the major philosophers as might serve the purpose of protecting religion and morals against the menace of materialism.

Early Experimental Research

JAMES's undergraduate teaching was in the main from texts, such as Spencer, Bain, and Taine, but he made use of apparatus for classroom demonstrations, gave his advanced students experimental problems, and carried on a certain amount of experimental research of his own.

One of his assistants, referring apparently to the middle '70s, wrote: "In a tiny room under the stairway of the Agassiz Museum, James had a metronome, a device for whirling a frog, a horopter chart and one or two bits of apparatus."

There was also the physiological laboratory of Dr. H. P. Bowditch at the Medical School, in Boston, of which James made frequent use as early as 1872. It is said to have been the first laboratory for experimental medicine in the United States, and, under the liberal policy of its director, border problems, such as those of physiological psychology, readily found a place.

James's work in psychical research may be said to be altogether experimental. He had a large correspondence, and in this way collected a great deal of material from amateur observers. He also made use of the questionnaire, as, for example,

in the study of consciousness of lost limbs. This method he distrusted, unless the questionnaire was filled out by an expert.

The latter was the case with the observations on "The Sense of Dizziness in Deaf Mutes," compiled by James chiefly from reports of trained physicians and attendants; and the information which he collected from ophthalmologists, on the effects of paralysis of the muscles of the eye. In order to obtain a basis of comparison for these cases, nearly two hundred students and instructors in Harvard College were also examined, which meant being "whirled around with the head in different positions." Even earlier than this James had performed similar experiments on frogs, experiments which were never published, and "which others with better eye-sight may be able to complete."

But when such scanty data as these have been compiled, the fact remains, and it is only the more striking, that James did not himself contribute experimental results of importance. Not more than a fifth of his great "Principles of Psychology" can be said to relate even to the experimental work of others.

"Principles of Psychology"

"PRINCIPLES OF PSYCHOLOGY," James's first book, was epoch-making. No one who reads it can fail to be impressed by the number and variety of principles. The plenitude of tributary streams was not an accident, nor does it imply any lack of originality on the part of the author.

He was interested in man in the round. He was willing to learn about man from any source, however disesteemed by orthodox scientists. His more or less shady excursions in psychical research are well known. He "believed there was much truth in phrenology."

He had a strong interest in physiognomy, and made a large collection of photographs both of friends and of strangers. Thus a letter from Oliver Wendel Holmes written in 1888 advises him to examine Edmund Calamy's "Nonconformist's Memorial" for portraits suggestive of "pious and painful preachers of the orthodox persuasion"—"faces worth looking over to verify or dispute the resemblances of type."

As soon as James became known he received a flood of letters from obscure or queer people, relating incidents that had come under their observation. He invited such letters and replied to them. He had the old-fashioned attitude of the "naturalist" who collects facts out of doors instead of in a laboratory. He did not scorn even the literary psychologists —when they were not too "scientific"! James quite consciously intended to draw into his psychology not only information gathered from miscellaneous and extra-scientific sources, but also from the several schools of psychological inquiry which flourished in his day. In 1900 he consented with much reluctance to write a preface to the Italian translation of the "Principles." It contains a statement of the purpose of the book, and especially emphasizes the diversity of the streams:

"We live at a time of transition and confusion in psychology as in many other things. The classic spiritualistic psychology using the soul and a definite number of distinct ready-made faculties as its principles of explanation, was long ago superseded by the school of association. But it still lingers. . . . The older associationism itself retained a half-scholastic character. Recognizing no general evolution of the human species, it took the mind too statically, as something whose peculiarities were absolute and not to be explained. Moreover, it was purely intellectualist, and did justice neither to our impulses and passions nor to the cooperation of our will with our intellectual life.

"Within our generation Darwinism has come and added its new insights to these older tendencies. It has cast a flood of light upon our instinctive and passional constitution, and has brought innumerable attempts at explaining psychological facts genetically, in its train.

"Later still, exact and ingenious studies of sense-perception and illusion began to be made in physiological laboratories, higher intellectual operations themselves were compared experimentally and their duration measured, the modern physiology of the brain fêted its triumphs, and finally the study of mental defects and aberrations and other abnormal states of consciousness began to be carried on in an intelligent and psychological way.

"All these different tendencies—the classic tradition, the associationist analysis, the psychogenetic speculations, the experimental methods, the biological conceptions, and the pathological extensions of the field, have introduced a period of chaotic fermentation from which some writers have profited by developing one-sided crudities in a very confident way.

"Such being the general condition of the time in which my book has been written, I fear that it may bear some traces of the prevalent confusion. I confess, however, that my aim in writing it, was to help to make the confusion less. I thought that by frankly putting psychology in the position of a natural science, eliminating certain metaphysical questions from its scope altogether and confining myself to what could be immediately verified by everyone's own consciousness, a central mass of experience could be described which everyone might accept as certain, no matter what the differing ulterior philosophic interpretations of it might be. On this basis I tried to reach a harmony by giving to each of the different tendencies of which I have spoken its just voice in the result. The harmony involves some compromise, and possibly no one will be absolutely contented.

"I have expressly avoided the outward appearance of doctrine and system, the definitions, classifications, subdivisions and multiplication of technical terms, because I knew that these things tend to substitute an artificial schematism for the living reality with which I wished to bring my reader into direct concrete acquaintance, whether he should have technical names to call its parts by or not. So instead of starting with the mind's supposed elements (which are always abstractions) and gradually building up, I have tried to keep the reader in contact throughout as many chapters as possible, with the actual conscious unity which each of us at all times feels himself to be.

"In sum, then, my effort has been to offer in a 'natural science' of the mind a *modus vivendi* in which the most various schools may meet harmoniously on the common basis of fact."

But it must not be supposed, that James's promiscuousness implied any neglect of "scientific psychology." He was an omnivorous reader and diligent student of the "authorities" of his day. The psychologists of whose writings James made the largest use, as judged by the citations and references in the "Principles," were Spencer, Helmholtz, Wundt, and Bain. Spencer and Wundt he both used and rejected—using them as reservoirs of facts and as texts for discussion, rejecting their characteristic and dominating ideas.

JAMES's "Principles of Psychology" was successful in a sense that is unusual for a book of science—it was widely read, not only by other psychologists, or by students of psychology, but by people who were under no professional obligation to read it. It was read because it was readable, and it was read by people of all sorts because of the very qualities which condemned it in the eyes of some professional psychologists. Because it did not substitute the artifacts of analysis for the concrete, living mind, the reader constantly recognized *himself* in its pages.

It was a tolerant, curious book; and because its author saw so wide a range of possibilities, and was so promiscuously hospitable to them, almost any recent development in psychology can trace a line of ancestry to it. His chapter on instinct gave a great impetus to social psychology, and his medical approach and emphasis on "exceptional mental states" gave him a place in the development of abnormal psychology and psychopathology.

The result is that the "Principles" was acclaimed by laymen and beginners, by students of other subjects who looked for some special application of psychology to their own problems, and by philosophical or nonsectarian students of psychology who had not yet become addicted to any special method of investigation; while at the same time it was viewed with some shade of disapproval by laboratory experimentalists and by systematizers.

The New Philosophy

UPON the publication of the "Principles" James undoubtedly experienced a profound sense of relief and a desire to disport himself in other pastures. It is also true that he never afterwards produced any considerable article or book on the standard problems of psychology. To this extent he bore out his own judgment, written in 1894: "There isn't a page more of psychological literature in this child's mental organism. Our reputation first begins as our talent commences to decay."

Although James never ceased to be a psychologist and was apt to exaggerate the fluctuations of his interest, there was on the whole a veering towards philosophy during the decade of the '90s. He wrote in 1894: "I am at present trying to dig some rational truth out of myself, but it comes hard and has to be blasted, and I fear it will result in shapeless debris."

On August 26, 1898, James gave his address on "Philosophical Conceptions and Practical Results" at the University of California. This was the lecture in which he launched the philosophical movement to which he gave the name of "practicalism" or "pragmatism"; for which he gave the credit to Charles Peirce; and which he identified with "the great English way of investigating a conception." The movement did not gather headway at once.

In the address of 1898, James credits Peirce with giving his thought "the most likely 'direction' in which to start up the trail of truth," and defines this "direction" as the idea that "the effective meaning of any philosophic proposition can always be brought down to some particular consequence, in our future practical experience, whether active or passive; the point lying rather in the fact that the experience must be particular, than in the fact that it must be active."

In this address and in an allusion of 1902 James identifies pragmatism with "the great English way of investigating a conception," namely, to look for its "cash-value in terms of particular experience"; and credits Peirce with singling out and naming the principle by which English and Scotch philosophers "were instinctively guided." In 1904 he credits Peirce with the word "pragmatism," and says that he (James) uses it to indicate "a method of carrying on abstract discussion," according to which "the serious meaning of a concept lies in the concrete difference to someone which its being true will make."

It appears from these passages that Peirce made James acutely conscious of an idea which he had already imbibed, and continued to imbibe, from many sources; and that this idea was to the effect that the meaning of a concept lay in its putting a particular face on a situation and thereby proving a particular action. James assumes that when perceived facts are altered, something is done about it, and that the meaning of a concept consists in perceptual (and therefore practical) expectations. If these expectations are the same; two concepts mean the same; if there are none, a concept is meaningless.

The Success of Pragmatism

"PRAGMATISM" occupied the centre of the philosophical stage in England and America only after the appearance in 1907 of James's book bearing that title. To the title, James appended the subtitle: "A New Name for Some Old Ways of Thinking."

James meant, no doubt, that he had not himself invented these ways of thinking; not only could their roots be traced far into the past, but they represented a broad contemporary tendency which James shared with others. This tendency embraced the newer logic of Mill, Lotze, and Sigwart, with its emphasis on the instrumental as distinguished from the representative function of ideas; the doctrines of evolution and historical relativism, stressing change, plasticity, and adaptation in human knowledge; the vogue of probability and hypothesis in scientific method. James also meant that he had himself been familiar with these "ways of thinking" and had espoused them from the beginning of his own philosophical career.

There are two of them which transcend the rest in importance, and may fairly be called the cardinal principles of pragmatism. The first, the pragmatic method, proposes to interpret concepts in terms of their consequences for experience or practice.

The second is the pragmatic theory of truth: to the effect, namely, that truth is an attribute of ideas rather than of reality; that it attaches to ideas in proportion as these prove useful for the purpose for which they are invoked. But when these two cardinal principles are stated, it is at once evident that they coincide broadly with the two doctrines which constitute James's "empiricism," and which constituted it from the beginning of his philosophical maturity: namely, experientialism and experimentalism.

The following note was written by James in 1873: "Religion in its most abstract expression may be defined as the affirmation that all is *not* vanity. The empiricist can easily sneer at such a formula as being empty through its universality, and ask you to cash it by its concrete filling,—which you may not be able to do, for nothing can well be harder. Yet as a practical fact its meaning is so distinct, that when used as a premise in a life a whole character may be imparted to the life by it. It, like so many other universal concepts, is a truth of orientation, serving not to *define* an end, but to determine a direction."

This cannot be said to be a pronouncement in favor of pragmatism, but it indicates clearly that James was already disposed to recognize that if a concept cannot be translated into terms of experience or practice, it is meaningless.

Defense of Pragmatism

James attributed the success of *Pragmatism* in part to its historic timeliness. With humanism, its *alter ego,* it was "like one of these secular changes that come upon public opinion overnight, as it were, borne upon tides 'too deep for sound or foam.'" But at the same time he felt that his own style would ensure the book's receiving public attention. Thus he wrote:—

"I have just finished the proofs of a little book called 'Pragmatism' which even you *may* enjoy reading. It is a very 'sincere' and, from the point of view of ordinary philosophy-professorial manners, very unconventional utterance, not particularly original at any one point, yet, in the midst of the literature of the way of thinking which it represents, with just that amount of squeak or shrillness in the voice that enables one book to *tell,* when others don't, to supersede its brethren, and be treated later as 'representative.' I shouldn't be surprised if ten years hence it should be rated as 'epoch-making,' for of the definitive triumph of that general way of thinking I can entertain no doubt whatever—I believe it to be something quite like the protestant reformation."

In the autumn of 1907 James was "interviewed" in his study in Cambridge, and after an informal conversation he went to his desk and wrote down this "statement." It is interesting both as an example of extemporization and as an expression of James's earnest desire to make pragmatism both intelligible and acceptable. After complaining that certain of his critics had construed pragmatism as a resort to practice in default of theory, he proceeded as follows:—

"It is true that pragmatist writers have laid more stress than any previous philosophers on human action. But nothing could be more ludicrous than to call this their primary interest, or to explain it by their belief that purely theoretical knowledge of reality, and truth as such, are unattainable.

"Pragmatism's primary interest is in its doctrine of truth. All pragmatist writers make this the center of their speculations; not one of them is sceptical, not one doubts our ultimate ability to penetrate theoretically into the very core of reality. . . .

"Instead of being a practical substitute for philosophy, good for engineers, doctors, sewage experts, and vigorous untaught minds in general to feed upon, pragmatism has proved so over-subtle that even academic critics have failed to catch its question, to say nothing of their misunderstanding of its answer. Whatever propositions or beliefs may, in point of fact prove true, it says, the truth of them consists in certain definable *relations between them and the reality* of which they make report. . . .

"Philosophers have generally been satisfied with the word 'agreement' here, but pragmatists have seen that this word covers many different concrete possibilities. . . . There are all sorts of ways of having to do with a thing. To know it, we must mean *that* thing, and not another thing; we must be able to portray or copy its inherent nature; and we must know innumerable things *about* it and its relations to other things.

"To know it rightly, moreover, we must not go astray among all these many ways of knowing it, but select the way that fits in with our momentary interest, be the latter practical or theoretical, and select the way that will work.

"Thus the first vague notion of 'agreement' with reality becomes specified into that of innumerable ways in which our thoughts may *fit* reality, ways in which the mind's activities cooperate on equal terms with the reality in producing the fit resultant truth.

"Mind *engenders* truth *upon* reality. . . . Our minds are not here simply to copy a reality that is already complete. They are here to complete it, to add to its importance by their own remodeling of it, to decant its contents over, so to speak, into a more significant shape. In point of fact, the *use* of most of our thinking is to help us to *change* the world. We must for this know definitely *what* we have to change, and thus the theoretic truth must at all times come before practical application.

"But the pragmatist writers have shown that what we call theoretic truth will be irrelevant unless it fits the purpose in hand. And, moreover, it turns out that the theoretic truth upon which men base their practice today is itself a result of previous human practice, based in turn upon still previous truth so that we may think of all truth whatever as containing so much human practice funded.

"Thus we seem set free to use our theoretical as well as our practical faculties—the practical here in the narrower sense—to get the world into better shape, and all with a good conscience. The only restriction is that the world resists some lines of attack on our part and opens itself to others, so that we must go on with the grain of her willingness. . . . Hence the *sursum corda* of pragmatism's message."

THE "angel of death" struck James down before he had said all that he had to say. Not only was much left unsaid, but there were many problems that he had neither thought out nor worked out. When death brought him down h◦ was in full flight. But the nature o◦ James's latest preoccupations and th◦ direction of his latest efforts bear out hi◦ own statement: "I think the center of m◦ whole outlook has been the belief tha◦ something is doing in the universe, an◦ that *novelty* is real."

His philosophy being so interpreted there is even a certain propriety in th◦ fact that James's task was unfinished Writing in 1908, he said, "I've grow◦ fearfully old in the past year, excep◦ 'philosophically,' where I still kee◦ young."

Philosophically he did not merely *kee◦* young—he seemed to grow younger. Ce◦ tainly at no period of his life was he s◦ curious, so receptive, so ardently specula◦ tive, as in his last years. While his phil◦ sophical powers grew,—his fertility an◦ his self-confidence,—his universe gre◦ more complex and more interesting.

But he knew that he had found n◦ solution for the old questions; he frankl◦ admitted that he expressed only anothe◦ guess, another faith. On his desk, whe◦ he died, there lay a paper on which h◦ had written his last, and perhaps hi◦ most characteristic, sentences:

"There is no conclusion. What ha◦ concluded that we might conclude in r◦ gard to it? There are no fortunes to b◦ told and there is no advice to be give◦ Farewell."

ORPHEUS

ORPHEUS with his lute made trees
And the mountain tops that freeze
  Bow themselves when he did sing:
To his music plants and flowers
Ever sprung; as sun and showers
  There had made a lasting spring.

Every thing that heard him play,
Even the billows of the sea,
  Hung their heads and then lay by.
In sweet music is such art,
  Killing care and grief of heart
  Fall asleep, or hearing, die.
         —William Shakespeare?

Frank Norris

THE PIT

"**T**HE GRAPES OF WRATH" by John Steinbeck and "The American Tragedy" by Theodore Dreiser (page 687) are two outstanding examples of modern American novels which are dedicated to the correction of social abuses. At the turn of the century this was a new school of writing and one of its leading exponents was a young man named Frank Norris. It was he who saw how the world's food supply was being gambled with on the Chicago wheat exchanges and resolved to bring the situation home to as many people as possible by writing three novels about it. "The Octopus" and "The Pit" were finished but "The Wolf" was cut short by the author's untimely death at the age of 32. But his work was not in vain for laws were subsequently passed which corrected the abuses against which he fought.

Curtis Jadwin and His Wife

LAURA DEARBORN'S native town was Barrington, in Massachusetts. Both she and her younger sister Page had lived there until the death of their father. The mother had died long before, and of all their relations, Aunt Wess', who lived at Chicago, alone remained. It was at the entreaties of Aunt Wess' and of their nearest friends, the Cresslers, that the two girls decided to live with their aunt in Chicago. Both Laura and Page had inherited money, and when they faced the world they had the assurance that, at least, they were independent.

Chicago, the great grey city, interested Laura at every instant and under every condition. The life was tremendous. All around, on every side, in every direction, the vast machinery of commonwealth clashed and thundered from dawn to dark, and from dark to dawn. For thousands of miles beyond its confines the influence of the city was felt. At times Laura felt a little frightened of the city's life, and of the men for whom all the crash of conflict and commerce had no terrors. Those who could subdue this life to their purposes, must they not be themselves terrible, pitiless, brutal? What could women ever know of the life of men, after all?

Her friend, Mr. Cressler, who had been almost a second father to her, was in business, and had once lost a fortune by a gamble in wheat; and there was Mr. Curtis Jadwin, whom she had met at the opera with the Cresslers.

Mrs. Cressler had told Laura, very soon after her arrival in Chicago, that Mr. Jadwin wanted to marry her.

"I've known Curtis Jadwin now for fifteen years—nobody better," said Mrs. Cressler. "He's as old a family friend as Charlie and I have. And I tell you the man is in love with you. He told me you had more sense and intelligence than any girl he had ever known, and that he never remembered to have seen a more beautiful woman. What do you think of him, Laura—of Mr. Jadwin?"

"I don't know," Laura answered. "I thought he was a *strong* man—mentally, and that he would be kindly and generous. But I saw very little of him."

"Jadwin struck you as being a kindly man, a generous man? He's just that, and charitable. You know, he has a Sunday-school over on the West Side—a Sunday-school for mission children—and I do believe he's more interested in that than in his business. He wants to make it the biggest Sunday-school in Chicago. It's an ambition of his. Laura," she exclaimed, "he's a *fine man*. No one knows Curtis Jadwin better than Charlie and I, and we just *love* him.

The kindliest, biggest-hearted fellow. Oh, well, you'll know him for yourself, and then you'll see!"

"I don't know anything about him," Laura had remarked in answer to this. "I never heard of him before the theatre party."

Bᴜᴛ Mrs. Cressler promptly supplied information. Curtis Jadwin was a man about thirty-five, who had begun life without a *sou* in his pockets. His people were farmers in Michigan, hardy, honest fellows, who ploughed and sowed for a living. Curtis had only a rudimentary schooling, and had gone into business with a livery-stable keeper. Someone in Chicago owed him money, and, in default of payment, had offered him a couple of lots of ground on Wabash Avenue. That was how he hap-

pened to come to Chicago. Naturall enough, as the city grew the Wabas Avenue property increased in value. H sold the lots, and bought other rea estate; sold that, and bought somewher else, and so on till he owned some of th best business sites in the city, and wa now one of the largest real-estate owner in Chicago. But he no longer bough and sold. His property had grown s large, that just the management of alone took up most of his time. As rule, he deplored speculation. He had n fixed principles about it, and occasionall he hazarded small operations.

It was after this that Laura's firs aversion to the great grey city fast disa peared, and she saw it in a kindlie aspect.

Soon it was impossible to deny th Curtis Jadwin—"J" as he was called i

THE CHICAGO WHEAT PIT
Pictures, Inc.

usiness—was in love with her. The
ousiness man, accustomed to deal with
ituations with unswerving directness,
vas not in the least afraid of Laura.
He was aggressive, assertive, and his addresses had all the persistence and
vehemence of veritable attack. He con-
rived to meet her everywhere, and
ven had the Cresslers and Laura over
o his mission Sunday-school for the
Easter festival, an occasion of which
Laura carried away a confused recollec-
ion of enormous canvas mottoes,
heaves of lilies, imitation bells of tin-
oil, revival hymns vociferated from
even hundred distended mouths, and
through it all the smell of poverty.

Somehow Laura found that with Jadwin all the serious, all the sincere, earn-
st side of her character was apt to come
o the front.

Yet for a long time Laura could not
make up her mind that she loved him,
but "J" refused to be dismissed.

"I told him I did not love him. Only
last week I told him so," Laura explained
to Mrs. Cressler.

"Well, then, why did you promise to
marry him?"

"My goodness! You don't realise what
it's been. Do you suppose you can say
'no' to that man?"

"Of course not—of course not!" declared Mrs. Cressler joyfully. "That's 'J'
all over. I might have known he'd have
you if he set out to do it."

They were married on the last day of
June of that summer in the Episcopalian
church. Immediately after the wedding
the couple took the train for Geneva
Lake, where Jadwin had built a house
for his bride.

A Corner in Wheat

THE months passed. Soon three years
had gone by since the ceremony in
St. James's Church, and all that time the
price of wheat had been steadily going
down. Heavy crops the world over had
helped the decline.

Jadwin had been drawn into the
troubled waters of the Pit, and was by
now "blooded to the game." It was in
April that he decided that better times
and higher prices were coming for wheat,
and announced his intentions to Sam
Gretry, his broker.

"Sam," he said, "the time is come for
great big chance. We've been hammering wheat down and down and down till
we've got it below the cost of production,
and now she won't go any further with
all the hammering in the world. The
other fellows, the rest of the bear crowd,
don't seem to see it; but I see it. Before
all we're going to have higher prices.
Wheat is going up, and when it does I
mean to be right there. I'm going to
buy. I'm going to buy September wheat,
and I'm going to buy it to-morrow—
,00,000 bushels of it; and if the market
goes as I think it will later on, I'm going to buy more. I'm going to boost this

market right through till the last bell
rings, and from now on Curtis Jadwin
spells b-u-double l—bull."

"They'll slaughter you," said Gretry;
"slaughter you in cold blood. You're just
one man against a gang—a gang of cutthroats. Those bears have got millions
and millions back of them. 'J,' you are
either Napoleonic, or—or a colossal
idiot!"

All through the three years that had
passed Jadwin had grown continually
richer. His real estate appreciated in
value; rents went up. Every time he
speculated in wheat it was upon a larger
scale, and every time he won. Hitherto
he had been a bear; now, after the talk
with Gretry, he had secretly "turned
bull" with the suddenness of an experienced strategist.

A marvellous golden luck followed
Jadwin all that summer. The crops were
poor, the yield moderate.

Jadwin sold out in September, having made a fortune, and then, in a single
vast clutch, bought 3,000,000 bushels
of the December option.

Never before had he ventured so
deeply into the Pit.

ONE morning in November, at breakfast, Laura said to her husband, "Curtis, dear, when is it all going to end —your speculating? You never used to be this way. It seems as though, nowadays, I never have you to myself. Even when you are not going over papers and reports, or talking by the hour to Mr. Gretry in the library, your mind seems to be away from me. I—I am lonesome, dearest, sometimes. And, Curtis, what is the use? We're so rich now we can't spend our money."

"Oh, it's not the money!" he answered. "It's the fun of the thing—the excitement."

That very week Jadwin made 500,000 dollars.

"I don't own a grain of wheat now," he assured his wife. "I've got to be out of it."

But try as he would, the echoes of the rumbling of the Pit reached Jadwin at every hour of the day and night. He stayed at home over Christmas. Inactive, he sat there idle, while the clamour of the Pit swelled daily louder, and the price of wheat went up.

Jadwin chafed and fretted at his inaction and his impatience harried him like a gadfly. Would no one step into the place of high command.

Very soon the papers began to speak of an unknown "bull" clique who were rapidly coming into control of the market, and it was no longer a secret to Laura that her husband had gone back to the market, and that, too, with such an impetuosity that his rush had carried him to the heart of the turmoil.

He was now deeply involved; his influence began to be felt. Not an important move on the part of the "unknown bull," the nameless, mysterious stranger that was not noted and discussed.

IT WAS very late in the afternoon of a lugubrious March day when Jadwin and Gretry, in the broker's private room, sat studying the latest Government reports as to the supply of wheat, and Jadwin observed, "Why, Sam, there's less than 100,000,000 bushels in the farmers' hands. That's awfully small."

"It ain't, as you might say, colossal," admitted Gretry.

"Sam," said Jadwin again, "the shipments have been about 5,000,000 a week, 20,000,000 a month, and it's four months before a new crop. Europe will take 80,000,000 out of the country. I own 10,000,000 now. Why, there ain't going to be any wheat left in Chicago by May! If I get in now, and buy a long line of cash wheat, where are all these fellows going to get it to deliver to me? Say, where are they going to get it? Come on now, tell me, where are they going to get it?"

Gretry laid down his pencil, and stared at Jadwin.

"'J.'" he faltered, "'J,' I'm blest if I know."

And then, all in the same moment the two men were on their feet.

Jadwin sprang forward, gripping the broker by the shoulder.

"Sam," he shouted, "do you know—— Great God! Do you know what this means? Sam, we can corner the market!"

The Corner Breaks

THE high prices meant a great increase of wheat acreage. In June the preliminary returns showed 4,000,000 more acres under wheat in the two states of Dakota alone, and in spite of all Gretry's remonstrances, Jadwin still held on, determined to keep up prices to July.

But now it had become vitally necessary for Jadwin to sell out his holdings.

His "long line" was a fearful expense; insurance and storage charges were eating rapidly into the profits. He *must* get rid of the load he was carrying little by little.

A month ago, and the foreign demand was a thing almost insensate. There was no question as to the price. It was, "Give us the wheat, at whatever figure, at whatever expense."

At home in Chicago Jadwin was completely master of the market. His wealth increased with such rapidity that at no time was he able even to approximate the gains. It was more than twenty million, and less than fifty million. That was all he knew.

It was then that he told Gretry he was going to buy in the July crops.

"'J,' listen to me," said Gretry. "Wheat is worth a dollar and a half to-day, and not one cent more. If you run it up to two dollars——"

"It will go there of itself, I tell you."

"If you run it up to two dollars it will be that top-heavy that the littlest kick in the world will knock it over. Be satisfied now with what you've got. Suppose the price does break a little, you'd still make your pile. But swing this deal over into July, and it's ruin. The farmers all over the country are planting wheat as they've never planted it before. Great Scott, 'J,' you're fighting against the earth itself."

"Well, we'll fight it then."

"Here's another point," went on Gretry. "You ought to be in bed this very minute. You haven't got any nerves left at all. You acknowledge you don't sleep. You ought to see a doctor."

"Fiddlesticks!" exclaimed Jadwin. "I'm all right. Haven't time to see a doctor."

So the month of May drew to its close, and as Jadwin beheld more and more the broken speculators, with their abject humility, a vast contempt for human nature grew within him. The business hardened his heart, and he took his profits as if by right of birth.

His wife he saw but seldom. Occasionally they breakfasted together; more often they met at dinner. But that was all.

And now by June 11 the position was critical.

"The price broke to a dollar and twenty yesterday," said Gretry. "Just think, we were at a dollar and a half a little while ago."

"And we'll be at two dollars in another ten days, I tell you."

"Do you know how we stand, 'J'?" said the broker gravely. "Do you know how we stand financially? It's taken pretty nearly every cent of our ready money to support this July market. Oh, we can figure out our paper profits into the millions. We've got thirty, forty, fifty million bushels of wheat that's worth over a dollar a bushel; but if we can't sell it we're none the better off—and that wheat is costing us six thousand dollars a day. Where's the money going to come from, old man? You don't seem to realize that we are in a precarious condition. The moment we can't give our boys buying orders, the moment we admit that we can't buy all the wheat that's offered, there's the moment we bust."

"Well, we'll buy it," cried Jadwin. "I'll show those brutes. I'll mortgage all my real estate, and I'll run up wheat so high before the next two days that the Bank of England can't pull it down; then I'll sell our long line, and with the profits of that I'll run it up again. Two dollars! Why, it will be two-fifty before you know how it happened."

That day Jadwin placed as heavy a mortgage as the place would stand upon every piece of real estate that he owned. He floated a number of promissory notes, and taxed his credit to its farthest stretch. But sure as he was of winning, Jadwin could not bring himself to involve his wife's money in the hazard, though his entire personal fortune swung in the balance.

Jadwin knew the danger. The new harvest was coming in—the new harvest of wheat—huge beyond all possibility of control; so vast that no money could buy it. And from Liverpool and Paris cables had come in to Gretry declining to buy wheat, though he had offered it cheaper than he had ever done before.

On the morning of June 13, Gretry gave his orders to young Landry Court and his other agents in the Pit, to do their best to keep the market up. "You can buy each of you up to half a million bushels apiece. If that don't keep the price up—well, I'll let you know what to do. Look here, keep your heads cool. I guess to-day will decide things."

In the Pit roar succeeded roar. It seemed that a support long thought to be secure was giving way. Not a man knew what he or his neighbour was doing. The bids leaped to and fro, and the price of July wheat could not so much as be approximated.

Landry caught one of the Gretry traders by the arm.

"What shall we do?" he shouted. "I've bought up to my limit. No more orders have come in. What's to be done?"

"I don't know," the other shouted back—"I don't know! Looks like a smash; something's gone wrong."

In Gretry's office Jadwin stood hatless and pale. Around him were one of the heads of a great banking house and a couple of other men, confidential agents, who had helped to manipulate the great corner.

"It's the end of the game," Gretry exclaimed. "You've got no more money! Not another order goes up to that floor."

"It's a lie!" Jadwin cried, "keep on buying, I tell you! Take all they'll offer. I tell you we'll touch the two dollar mark before noon."

"It's useless, Mr. Jadwin," said the banker quietly. "You were practically beaten two days ago."

But Jadwin was beyond all appeal. He threw off Gretry's hand.

"Get out of my way!" he shouted. "Do you hear? I'll play my hand alone from now on."

" 'J,' old man—why, see here!" Gretry implored, still holding him by the arm. "Here, where are you going?"

Jadwin's voice rang like a trumpet-call:

"*Into the Pit!* If you won't execute my orders I'll act myself. I'm going into the Pit, I tell you!"

" 'J,' you're mad, old fellow! You're ruined—don't you understand?—you're ruined!"

"Then God curse you, Sam Gretry, for the man who failed me in a crisis!" And, as he spoke, Curtis Jadwin struck the broker full in the face.

Gretry staggered back from the blow. His pale face flashed to crimson for an instant, his fists clenched; then his hand fell to his sides.

"No," he said, "let him go—let him go. The man is merely mad!"

Jadwin thrust the men who tried to hold him to one side, and rushed from the room.

"It's the end," Gretry said simply. He wrote a couple of lines, and handed the note to the senior clerk. "Take that to the secretary of the board at once."

STRAIGHT into the turmoil and confusion of the Pit, into the scene of so many of his victories, came the "Great Bull." The news went flashing and flying from lip to lip. The wheat Pit, torn and tossed and rent asunder, stood dismayed, so great had been his power. What was about to happen? Jadwin himself, the great man, in the Pit! Had his enemies been too premature in their hope of his defeat? For a second they hesitated, then moved by a common impulse, feeling the push of the wonderful new harvest behind them, gathered themselves together for the final assault, and again offered the wheat for sale—offered it by thousands upon thousands of bushels.

Blind and insensate, Jadwin strove against the torrent of wheat. Under the stress and violence of the hour, something snapped in his brain; but he stood erect there in the middle of the Pit, iron to the end, proclaiming over the din of his enemies, like a bugle sounding to the charge of a forlorn hope.

"Give a dollar for July—give a dollar for July!"

Then little by little the tumult of the Pit subsided. There were sudden lapses in the shouting, and again the clamour would break out.

All at once the Pit, the entire floor of the Board of Trade, was struck dumb. In the midst of the profound silence the secretary announced: "All trades with Gretry & Co. must be closed at once!"

The words were greeted with a wild yell of exultation. Beaten—beaten at last, the Great Bull! Smashed! The great corner smashed! Jadwin busted! Cheer followed cheer, hats went into the air. Men danced and leaped in delight.

Young Landry Court, who had stood by Jadwin in the Pit, led his defeated captain out. Jadwin was in a daze—he saw nothing, heard nothing, but submitted to Landry's guidance.

From the Pit came the sound of dying cheers.

"They can cheer now all they want. *They didn't do it,*" said a man at the door. "It was the wheat itself that beat him; no combination of men could have done it."

A Fresh Start

THE evening had closed in wet and misty, and when Laura Jadwin came down to the dismantled library a heavy rain was falling.

"There, dear," Laura said, "now sit down on the packing-box there. You had better put your hat on. It is full of draughts now that the furniture and curtains are out. You've had a pretty bad siege of it, you know, and this is only the first week you've been up."

"I've had too good a nurse," he answered, stroking her hand, "not to be as fit as a fiddle by now. You must be tired yourself, Laura. Why, for whole days there—and nights, too, they tell me —you never left the room."

Laura shook her head, and said:

"I wonder what the West will be like. Do you know I think I am going to like it, Curtis?"

"It will be starting in all over again, old girl. Pretty hard at first, I'm afraid."

"Hard—now?" She took his hand and laid it to her cheek.

"By all the rules you ought to hate me," he began. "What have I done for you but hurt you, and at last bring you to——"

But she shut her gloved hand over his mouth.

"The world is all before us where to choose, now, isn't it?" she answered. "And this big house and all the life we have led in it was just an incident in our lives—an incident that is closed."

"We're starting all over again, honey. . . . Well, there's the carriage, I guess."

They rose, gathering up their valises.

"Ho!" said Jadwin. "No servants now, Laura, to carry our things down for us and open the door; and it's a hack, old girl, instead of the victoria."

"What if it is?" she cried. "What do servants, money, and all amount to now?"

As Jadwin laid his hand upon the knob of the front door, he all at once put down his valise and put his arm about his wife. She caught him about the neck, and looked deep into his eyes a long moment. They kissed each other.

WHEREVER GOD ERECTS A HOUSE OF PRAYER

WHEREVER God erects a house of prayer,
The Devil always builds a chapel there:
And 'twill be found upon examination
The latter has the largest congregation:
For ever since he first debauched the mind,
He made a perfect conquest of mankind.
—*D. Defoe (The True-born Englishman)*

PAUL BOURGET

THE DISCIPLE

P AUL BOURGET was one of the founders of the school of idealistic fiction that Romain
Rolland carried to heights in "Jean-Christophe" (page 935). "The Disciple" which
is striking for its psychological analysis is a warning against absolute reliance on
the brain, as opposed to the heart. It is not enough to be clever, advanced and scientific
if all this involves the sacrifice of the virtues of honesty and simplicity. This poignant
story which was written under stress of a real feeling of responsibility was designed to
preserve his younger brethren from the error into which he himself had all but fallen.

The Modern Philosopher

M. ADRIEN SIXTE, sometimes styled by English critics "the French Spencer," lived alone, save for a respectable, solid old housekeeper, in a remote corner of Paris—to be exact, in the Rue Guy-de-la-Brosse, hard by the Jardin des Plantes. He lived the life of an ascetic, almost a saint, in an atmosphere of abstract speculation, famous already by his philosophic works, notably his much-debated "Psychology of God," his "Anatomy of The Will," and his "Theory of the Passions." By many these works were held to be noxious and abominable; by others they were deemed to raise their author to a height almost level with that of the greatest of the philosophers, past or present. In any case, M. Adrien Sixte was celebrated throughout the world of thought, and each succeeding volume from his pen was sure to arouse a storm of controversy.

Soon after the war of 1870 Adrien Sixte, both his parents being dead, left Nancy, his native town, and came to Paris to settle down. He was left more than enough to satisfy his very modest requirements; so, with no pecuniary or other cares, with no desire for reward or for fame, "the French Spencer" quietly resumed the business of his life which was—to think.

So regular were his habits that his neighbours in the quiet backwater where he lived might have set their clocks by his going out and his coming in. His daily movements were the same, year in, year out, summer and winter. Neither drinking nor smoking, eating barely enough to keep himself in health, M. Adrien Sixte only thought and wrote.

The calm of this mechanically regular existence was doubly broken one morning. The first shock was a summons addressed to M. Adrien Sixte requiring him to appear before M. Valette, *juge d'instruction,* and by him be questioned "on certain matters of which he would be informed"; and the second was a written request from a Madame Greslou that M. Sixte would let her call on him the following afternoon "in connection with the crime of which her unhappy son had been falsely accused."

One of M. Sixte's many peculiarities was his complete ignorance of the events of the day. Such was his indifference to current affairs that he never read a newspaper. But, puzzled as he was, he came to the right conclusion; that there was some close connection between the communication received from the examining magistrate and that of Madame Greslou. That name at first conveyed nothing to his mind; but by degrees the philosopher recalled sundry visits and letters he had had during the past two years from a young man of the name of Robert Greslou, a student at the Clermont-Ferrand *lycée,* who had submitted for his criticism a remarkable essay on a psychological subject. M. Greslou had declared himself a fervent admirer of "The Psychology of God" and the other books signed Adrien Sixte, and in more than one of his letters had styled himself "his devoted disciple and follower." The last M. Sixte had heard of the young man was that he had accepted a post as tutor in a noble family at Aydat, in Auvergne.

M. SIXTE was at the Law Courts five minutes before the time appointed to meet M. Valette, an agreeable, keen-witted man of the world, whose astonishment at the strange appearance of the celebrated writer knew no bounds. At first the magistrate was inclined to think the grave, detached manner in which the philosopher answered the questions put to him, concealed more knowledge of the matter than he desired to show; but soon it was patent to M. Valette that he had before him an absolutely unworldly character, one quite ignorant of that which all Paris, if not all France, was talking about at the moment—the extraordinary "Greslou Case," in which a young tutor, Robert Greslou—under arrest at Riom—was accused of poisoning the beautiful daughter of his employer, the Marquis de Jussat-Randon.

M. Sixte heard the news with amazement. He told M. Valette exactly what had been his relations with Robert Greslou, and expressed surprise when the magistrate informed him that among the accused tutor's books were "The Psychology of God" and the others written by the philosopher, all of them bearing copious marginal notes, indicating the most careful study. He did not understand what connection there could be between his writings and the crime, nor what testimony he could possibly be asked to give on the matter. In vain M. Valette tried to enlighten him, and the interview soon ended.

When M. Sixte got back to his rooms, he found a lady in deep mourning waiting for him. It was Madame Greslou, mother of the arrested tutor.

To M. Sixte's bewilderment, Madame Greslou told him that she held him responsible for her son's loss of faith—him and his books. "Eh, how I hated you," she exclaimed, "when I discovered who and what had made Robert forsake the Christian religion in which I had so carefully brought him up!"

But soon she grew calmer, begging the philosopher—whose *sang-froid* had well-nigh deserted him in the presence of a mother's overwhelming agitation—to forgive her if her words had wounded him. "You will do all you can for my innocent boy, I know," she stammered, through her tears. "He told me you were kind, so kind. If I knew you I should venerate you. You were a saint, he said."

When M. Sixte had done his best to comfort the widow she handed him, before leaving, a roll of paper which she had kept in her lap all the time. Her son had written an important scientific article while in prison, since his arrest, and he had entrusted it to her to give to M. Sixte. On the first sheet was the inscription, "Modern Psychology," and the second bore the words "Memorandum on Myself." Below was a request that his "dear master" would regard himself as in honor bound to keep strictly to himself the pages that followed. If M. Sixte was not willing to bind himself in this way he was begged to destroy the manuscript, and not to place it in any other hands, "even to save my life." The initials "R. G." were appended.

FOR a long time after Madame Greslou's departure the philosopher could not make up his mind to read Robert Greslou's story. On the one hand was a great curiosity to see what this very human document might contain; on the other was the possibility that the manuscript might contain evidence of the young man's innocence, which he, the depository of the secret, could not use; or, still worse, it might turn out to be a confession of guilt.

At length, psychology triumphed over all scruples. When his housekeeper came in to say M. Sixte's bed was ready she found her master seated by the fire, deep in the "Memorandum of Myself," which the author should rightly have called "Confession of a Young Man of To-day."

The Disciple's Story

ROBERT GRESLOU's narrative was dated "Riom Jail, January 1887." It opened with a succinct but clear description of his childhood and early youth, spent in his birthplace at Clermont.

His ideas, his belief, his innermost thoughts and feelings were detailed with extreme minuteness, as being necessary to explain his outlook on life, his state of mind of a little later, until at last he came to the period when the teachings and aspirations inculcated by his confessor, Father Martel, came to be definitely rejected.

Robert Greslou was seventeen, and just entering the philosophy class at the École Normale, when one day he came across "The Psychology of God," by M. Adrien Sixte. This made so profound an impression on him that immediately he procured and read the "Theory of the Passions" and the "Anatomy of the Will." These, following on the effect produced recently by the writings of Musset, Balzac, Baudelaire, Heine, Stendhal and others, served to lift the veil from what had before been a mystery. That which the literary romantics had begun, in the direction of idealism in sensations, the clear, detached, mathematically logical philosophy of Adrien Sixte completed. "The darkness shrouding the world inside and out was removed," declared the writer. "I had found my road. I was your pupil."

"In November, 1885, having failed in my philosophy examination, I accepted the post of tutor in the family of the Marquis de Jussat-Randon. The five thousand francs I was offered for about a year's tuition of the second son, a boy of twelve, tempted me to give up my independence for a time, since I was anxious that my mother should not be put to further expense on my account.

"The marquis, to whom I had been strongly recommended, took me from Clermont to Aydat in his landau, talking nearly all the time of his family and his ailments—for the most part imaginary. Already I had made up my mind to study this family closely, each member of it, and for that purpose I had provided myself with a diary, fastened by lock and key, in which I was to record my impressions of all that happened during my exile. Another resolve of mine was to have nothing to do with love. Sensuality in itself revolted me and, further, I had a profound contempt for the stupidity of women in general. Like the sage of old, I determined to 'keep all my sex in my brain.'

"When the marquis and I arrived, on a bright frosty November evening, we found all the family awaiting us in the drawing-room. The marquise and her daughter were doing crochet-work for the poor; my future pupil was looking at a picture-book; the eldest son, Comte André, an officer in the dragoons, was reading a newspaper; Mlle. Charlotte's companion and a nun were seated sewing. Madame de Jussat, big, imposing, with perfect manners, looked the model *ménagère*. The boy had nothing remarkable about him except his fat, lazy cheeks; in the daughter I was conscious of a slim figure in a light frock, with soft, grey eyes and chestnut brown hair. The charm of her low voice impressed me.

"NEVER before had I been really in touch with so male a person as this Comte André; therefore his physical perfection filled me with surprise and admiration. A little over thirty, of middle height, built like an athlete, with his broad shoulders and slim figure, he produced a sense of combined strength and suppleness that was quite new to me. And all this apart, his black hair and moustache, his firm mouth and chin and keen brown eyes, together with a high, aquiline nose, indicated not only courage, determination, will, but, above all, race, blood. One glance sufficed to show that Comte André had sprung from a line of conquerors. For the first time, I became conscious of the difference between myself, whose forebears had been mere modest tillers of the soil, and this direct descendant of their masters.

"There was no real envy or jealousy in all this; but I was acutely conscious of the enormous *difference;* and this aroused an involuntary hostility towards the proud young soldier which never left me.

"To-day, as I write, I am filled with horror at the thought that I could ever have deliberately, coldly, set out to win the love of Comte André's true, pure sister, Charlotte, without loving her, but simply to study the psychology of the passion I aroused. Yet such is the fact. I think there was at first some sort of satisfaction in my mind at getting more or less on terms with the haughty soldier by bringing his sister under my influence; it seemed to lessen the distance between us. But it was all mingled with a very genuine admiration for the girl

herself, which grew steadily day by day as I came to know her better and discover the rare charm of her proud, sensitive nature.

"Almost daily Lucien and I were accompanied on our walks by Charlotte and her middle-aged companion, Mlle. Largeyx. On one occasion, feeling depressed and morose, I was so dull and taciturn while the others were all quite merry, that at last, when we were alone for a moment, Charlotte enquired anxiously if I was ill, or if anything had upset me. Rather curtly I replied that I was perfectly well; and then it occurred to me to play on her sympathies by inventing some secret sorrow.

"Many little attentions—trivial in themselves, but of real significance to me, the analyst, the observer—revealed the interest taken by Mlle. de Jussat in me as time went on; but to my surprise and disappointment she did not appear to be much impressed when, having found a convenient opportunity, I related to her the mock story of an unhappy love experience. All she remarked was that it was strange I should have had confidence in my sweetheart, seeing that she allowed me to make love to her without her parents' knowledge; my elaborate invention had missed fire. Nevertheless, a sort of sympathy had grown up between us, and it grew into what was certainly love, on my part.

In the Wood

"I DETERMINED to reveal my feelings, and thus discover hers. Winter was passed and we were in May, which was at its loveliest. One morning—I remember the date, the 12th—we set out, the usual four of us, to go to the village of Saint-Saturnin—a longish journey through the woods. Lest Charlotte or Mlle. Largeyx should find the walk too fatiguing we took with us the little governess cart, which the second coachman drove. The companion was the first to feel tired, and presently Lucien thought he would like to rest his legs. Charlotte and I walked on alone. Every now and

then she would stop to pick a few lilies-of-the-valley. In this way we got some distance into the wood, while the carriage, of course, followed the road.

"Suddenly Charlotte came to a standstill, and, after listening a moment, exclaimed gaily: 'We're lost! Never mind, wait till I've arranged my flowers, and then we can find the others.' So saying, she sat down on a big stone, with the Spring sunshine filtering through the trees on to her fair head.

"I knew the time had come. Suddenly I seized her hand, which trembled at my touch. All pale, she strove to rise, but

I gently forced her to remain seated; and then I told my love, in a torrent of words, the eloquence of which astonished me. When I put my arm around her waist, she succeeded in freeing herself and getting up and, with tears streaming down her cheeks, begged me to leave her. All I could think of saying was: 'Forgive me!'

"Presently we heard voices calling. The blood came back to Charlotte's cheeks; without another word, gathering up her posy and her gloves, she ran as hard as she could go, in the direction of the sounds, with me behind her. In a few minutes we had rejoined the party. Saying she did not feel very well, Charlotte got into the carriage, and we all made our way homewards, I walking alone.

"Not only was I furious at what appeared to me to be my defeat, but for the next two or three days I was in constant dread of being turned ignominiously out of the house. Charlotte would tell her parents what had happened—and that would be the end of everything. But no; everyone was just as kind as before; nothing had been said; she had kept our secret.

"About a week later M. de Jussat told me his daughter had not been herself lately, and he was going to take her to Paris to consult a physician. They were to start the next morning. I had by this time resolved to abandon my enterprise, since it was quite evident that Charlotte, though anxious not to harm me, had determined to keep me at a distance. I wrote her a letter, again begging forgiveness, and telling her she would not find me there on her return. When no one was about I slipped into her room, intending to put my missive inside her blotting-case. When I opened it I saw an envelope on which was written: '12th of May, 1886.' Hastily looking inside, I saw two or three faded lilies-of-the-valley, which I remembered having given her on that last walk. So she had kept them, despite all that had happened. So she loved me, after all. I

must wait. She loved me! My letter I destroyed at once.

"Life at the château with Charlotte absent was strangely, almost delightfully, tranquil. But when, at the end of a few weeks, the Marquis wrote that he was returning, without his daughter, who preferred to stay longer in Paris, with an aunt, my mind became uneasy again, and I began to feel resentment against her. Then we heard that her holiday—if such it could be called—was to be still further prolonged, and my wounded vanity made me angrier than ever. I ventured to write to her. No answer came, but I wrote again and again—letters full of contrition, passion, despair. Later I learnt that Charlotte had kept those effusions, and only destroyed them on the night of her death.

"M. de Jussat returned, with what he described to me as 'good news.' In the first place, Charlotte's health was much improved; and, better still, she had promised to marry M. de Plane, a brother-officer of André.

"You, master, who have written in such masterly terms on the terrible thing which is jealousy, will understand my feelings. Charlotte had been out of my sight nearly five months, yet I longed for her more than ever; time only increased my malady, and every day I grew more miserable.

"Then, about the end of September, Lucien developed scarlet fever. M. de Jussat, himself in dread of infection, consulted me as to whether he ought to send for the Marquise. Much as I longed to see Charlotte, I had enough courage to dissuade him from telling them in Paris of what was happening at the château knowing full well that, if she knew, the invalid's sister would return at once, at any cost.

"But the very next day came a telegram saying the Marquise and her daughter were coming back immediately.

"I resolved to leave at once, before

their return, if M. de Jussat would let me, my engagement terminating a few days hence. This seemed to be the best solution of the difficulty: it would save the feelings of both Charlotte and myself. But M. de Jussat was so excited at the coming arrival of his wife and daughter that he could not spare time to discuss the matter. 'Not now, not now,' he said, irritably; 'wait till they're back. I can't think of anything else at the moment!'

"Who knows but my very destiny hung on the refusal of the selfish old man to listen to me? Had I gone home then and there all would have been well. But one glance at Charlotte as, pale and trembling, she met my eye on stepping from the carriage, revealed to me that she loved me as much as ever—more.

"My feelings at this time defy analysis. At last came a despairing desire to end it all. Yes, I made up my mind that for *her* sake, as well as for mine, I would bring my wretched life to a close. A chemist in the village, who knew me, let me have a small bottle of *nux vomica*. I gave him a false reason for wanting it. I felt I must see Charlotte once more before I died, and tell her again how I loved her. I wrote, saying what I had resolved to do. If she did not come to my room before midnight I would drink the poison on the stroke of the hour.

The Midnight Visit

"All that day I was in a sort of a dream, hardly conscious of what was going on around me; and when night came, and I retired to my room I watched the hours go by with a strange serenity of indifference. But when half-past eleven came my heart began to beat violently, though my will remained firm and cold.

"It wanted only a minute to the hour when I heard light footsteps approaching. They stopped at my door, and the next moment Charlotte stood before me.

"'Ah!' she exclaimed, in a voice she could scarcely control. 'Thank God, I'm not too late! Dead—I thought you would be dead! Horrible! horrible! But that's all over, is it not? Swear to me you won't kill yourself—'

"She took my hand in hers, which was icy cold, and looked at me imploringly. Then, weeping like herself, I took her in my arms and our lips met.

"'I must go!' she cried. 'Let me go! Don't come near me again—'

"'Then I must die,' said I. 'You don't love me, or you would not be going to marry another man.' And I took the black phial from the table. 'In five minutes it will all be over. Go, and thank you for coming. Go; good-bye; don't rob me of my courage—'

"'No, no!' she cried, in a voice that had grown almost hard. 'I will die too. I have suffered too much. I can stand no more. Let us die together!'

"She stretched out her hand to seize the bottle, but I prevented her; and she went on: 'Ah, yes, let me die here, with you! I've loved you so long, so long. I can tell you now. I have the right, because I'm going to die. You'll take me with you; we'll go away together—we two—!'

"'Yes,' I said, 'we'll die together. I swear it. But not at once. Ah! let me feel that you love me!' And I took her, unresisting, in my arms once more.

"Hours later, in the dim light of the lamp, I watched her as she lay sleeping beside me.

"But while she slept I was thinking. The exultation of the night had passed away. What had seemed so simple, so right, so natural only a few hours before now became monstrous, impossible. Why should we die, both of us so young, with such possibilities of happiness before us? No. I was determined we should not fulfil our compact.

"Then she woke and kissed me, and the clock struck four.

"'Come,' said Charlotte, 'give me the poison. I will drink first. Good-bye, my own love!'

"Then I had to tell her; and as I spoke, on my knees beside the bed, she stared at me with amazement, horror, in her eyes.

"'So you will not give me the poison?' she said at last. 'Well, if *you* are afraid, I am not. I will die alone!'

"When I refused, she got up, and without so much as looking at me, went straight from the room. As she got to the door she cried 'Coward! Coward!'

"Once or twice during the day I tried to speak to her, but she put me aside with so patrician a gesture that I could not find a word to say. I wrote to her. My letter was on my table unopened.

"The night before I left the château I wrote demanding a final interview. I found her standing in her room, fully dressed. It was eleven o'clock. Then coldly, as though I had been a servant, she told me how, in order to know me fully, she had forced the lock of my diary and read it. Also, she had written to her brother, telling him the whole story.

"'Now go!' she said, 'or I'll call the servants!' I went, and at six o'clock I had left the house.

"You know the rest. At Clermont I heard of the suicide of Mlle. de Jussat, and almost at the same time I was placed under arrest. From what the *juge d'instruction* said, it was clear that Charlotte had found the poison in my room, drunk it, and thrown the bottle out of the window into the garden, where someone found it next morning. They think I put the *nux vomica* into a sleeping draught and so murdered her!

"Since my arrest I have said not a word, nor will I say one even though I die for it. Comte André knows I am innocent of murder. If he, like myself, remains silent, and lets me die, we are quits. This time my pride is equal to his!

"Now I have told you all, master, send me, I beg, a word of comfort. Tell me I am not a monster, and you will have the eternal blessing of your faithful

ROBERT GRESLOU."

Justice is Done

A MONTH had passed since M. Adrien Sixte first read this astonishing document. He read it again and again, fascinated by its revelations, horrified to think that his life work, his beloved science, could possibly be intermingled with so much that was shameful and abominable. Could he really be responsible in any degree for what had happened? The thought shocked and distressed the poor philosopher deeply.

On the eve of the trial he resolved to go to Riom. If Robert should be condemned he would lay the young man's memorandum before the President. Meanwhile, he sent unsigned, to Comte André a letter inquiring if he could allow an innocent man to be condemned, and reminding him that he had in his possession a letter from his sister proving that suicide, and not murder, was the cause of her death.

This letter, sent to Lunéville, did not come into Captain de Jussat's hands at Riom until the trial of Robert Greslou was nearing its close. He was thunderstruck, for it proved that someone other than the prisoner himself knew the truth. After long and anxious deliberation Comte André had destroyed Charlotte's farewell letter, and it had appeared that unless he himself spoke, Greslou's fate was sealed, since he obstinately refused to defend his life. But this anonymous letter altered everything. How could he, André de Jussat, allow himself to be shamed by this despicable *roturier,* who, now that the test had come, was showing himself brave even unto death? He resolved to face the ordeal.

Next morning dressed in full uniform, Comte André made his way to the Court of Justice, where, after the President had explained that it was not permissible for him to testify *in camera,* he told the true story of the tragedy in open court. Among the amazed listeners was the marquis, who, on learning of his daughter's shame, fell from his seat and was carried out unconscious.

ROBERT GRESLOU, released at once, went to the hotel where his mother and M. Adrien Sixte were staying. At the door a waiter told him that Captain de Jussat had called to enquire for him.

"Where is he?" exclaimed Greslou, rushing into the street, unheeding his mother's cries to him to come back.

Outside, he found André de Jussat on the other side of the road.

"You have something to say to me, sir?" enquired Robert haughtily. "I am at your disposal."

"No, sir," replied André de Jussat. "One does not fight men of your sort. They are executed."

And, taking a revolver from his pocket, while the tutor calmly faced him, he shot him through the forehead.

When people ran up, alarmed at the report, they found the officer, who had thrown away his weapon, standing with folded arms. As he was led away, unresisting, quietly, he said: "Justice is done!"

Auf Wiedersehen

Summer

THE little gate was reached at last,
 Half hid in lilacs down the lane;
She pushed it wide, and, as she past,
A wistful look she backward cast,
 And said,—"*Auf wiedersehen!*"

With hand on latch, a vision white
 Lingered reluctant, and again
Half doubting if she did aright,
Soft as the dews that fell that night,
 She said,—"*Auf wiedersehen!*"

The lamp's clear gleam flits up the stair;
 I linger in delicious pain;
Ah, in that chamber, whose rich air
To breathe in thought I scarcely dare,
 Thinks she,—"*Auf wiedersehen!*"

'Tis thirteen years; once more I press
 The turf that silences the lane;
I hear the rustle of her dress,
I smell the lilacs, and—ah, yes,
 I hear "*Auf wiedersehen!*"

Sweet piece of bashful maiden art!
 The English words had seemed too fain,
But these—they drew us heart to heart,
Yet held us tenderly apart;
 She said, "*Auf wiedersehen!*"

—J. R. *Lowell*

Margaret Wilson

THE ABLE MC LAUGHLINS

"The able mc laughlins" was chosen from among 739 competitors as the Pulitzer Prize novel of 1923. It is a story of Scotch settlers in a pioneer Iowa community which, though realistically treated, contains the ideals and beauty of the most romantic type of fiction. Its author (1882-) considers herself the "most middle-western of all middle westerners" despite the fact that she lives in London, having married an Englishman. While the middle west is her favorite subject, she also writes of India where she spent several years as a missionary.

A Soldier's Welcome

The children's shouts had not at all disturbed the mother in the kitchen, where she sat sewing, until—could she believe her ears?— they were shouting, " 'Tis Wully, mother! 'Tis Wully!"

"It never is!" she says, unsteadily. But she can see someone in blue, someone standing up, waving a cap now. She can see his white face. The children bolt down the road. She can see him, her black-bearded first-born. The driver is whipping up the horses. Home from battles, pale to the lips, he is in her arms. But she is paler.

The strange driver is patting his horses, his back to the family reunited. Hugged, and kissed, and patted and loved, the bearded Wully turns to the stranger.

"This is Mr. Knight, of Tyler, mother. He brought me all the way."

" 'Tis a kind thing you have done!" she exclaims, shaking his hand devoutly.

"Oh, he was a soldier. And he didn't look able to walk so far."

"We'll never forget this, neither us nor our children!" It was that promise choked back in her voice that gave the Knight's grandson his work with the firm of Andrew McLaughlin, in the fall of 1920.

If the boy had a lesser mother, if he had been well, he would have gone on through four miles to Chirstie. But here was shelter, and rest for his feebleness, a fire, food, light, a mother, and children, caresses sprung from the warmest places in human hearts—all things in short, that a man needs, except one.

It seemed that the very kitchen breathed in great, deep sighs of thankfulness and content, this great night of its life, the night Wully got home from the army. The younger children sat watching him till they sank down from their chairs asleep.

Finally they were put to bed and Wully, too, with only his father and mother beside him in the kitchen.

"Your father told you about Chirstie's mother's death, Wully?" His father had told him briefly about it. He didn't say that the news had thrilled him with the certainty that now his plans could have no opposition, since Chirstie was left quite unprotected, and must be needing him.

His mother went on to say that Chirstie with her small brother and sister were living alone with no company but occasionally a neighboring girl. Isobel McLaughlin had gone to her, and begged her to come and stay with her. Other faithful friends had invited her to their home, but they had begged and pleaded in vain. Chirstie would listen to no one. It was a most unfitting and dangerous thing, a young girl like that.

Wully, the ardent, jumped instantly

to the hope that Chirstie had known he was coming, and had stayed on in the cabin to be there alone to receive him. That was the explanation of her "stubbornness" and indeed it was a brave thing for a girl to do for her lover. Alone there she would be this rainy night, grieving for her mother and waiting for him! Of course she would marry him at once. Tomorrow, not later than the next day, at most, they would be married! He slept but excitedly that night. . . .

In the morning it was still raining. The path which Wully took required caution, but the cause demanded speed. The way seemed to have stretched out incredibly since he had last gone over it. After riding what seemed a hundred miles or so, he got to the little shanty of a barn on the McNair place.

The door of the house opened, and— Oh, damn, and all other oaths!

Chirstie's aunt stood there in it. Libby Keith. She was Wully's aunt, too, that sister of his father who had married Jeannie McNair's brother John Keith! This was the first time that Wully had wanted really to curse an aunt, though he liked this one but dutifully. She saw him, and her voice fell in dismay.

"Lawsie me!" she bewailed. "I thought it was my Peter!"

Bad enough to be taken for her Peter at any time. Where was the girl? Was his aunt a permanent blockade. There she was! There was Chirstie! She had seen him. He went towards her—

And she shrank away from him!

Not only had she not an impulse of welcome, she shrank away from him! She gave him her hand because she couldn't help herself.

"Chirstie!" he faltered.

"Are you back?" she asked. She pulled her hand away in a panic. "It's a fine day," he heard her murmur.

It was the bitterest day of his life! He sat down weakly. Men stagger down helplessly that way when bullets go through them. The damnable aunt began now welcoming him fondly. He didn't know what he was answering her. It couldn't be possible, could it, that Chirstie didn't want to see him?

His eagerness, her refusal, became apparent at length to even the stupid aunt. She understood that Wully had got home only the night before, and in the morning, rain, and all, had ridden over to see the girl who didn't want to see him. He really was looking very ill. Well, well! Isobel McLaughlin would have been mightily "set up" by such a match. If Chirstie had not been Peter's own cousin, Libby Keith would have liked nothing better than the girl for her son. She had fancied at times her son had thought of it, too. Her sympathy was with the soldier. She rose heavily after really only a few minutes, put a shawl over her head, and went to the door, and closed it after her. Wully jumped to his feet, and went to bend down over his sweetheart.

"What's the matter, Chirstie? What's the matter? What have I done?"

"Sit down in your chair!" she commanded. "Don't."

He didn't. He couldn't. He stood absolutely dazed, looking at her hard face. Then she said:

"It's near dinner time. You'll be going back."

"I *will* not!" he cried, outraged. "I came for you Chirstie! I thought we could be married right away. That's what I meant. You knew that!" He bent over her again, and she struggled away angrily. She went to the door, and called:

"Auntie! Wully's going! Do you want to see him?"

Aunt Libby came heavily in. She urged him to stay for dinner. At least she would make him something hot. Why, he was all wet from the ride!

"Don't bother about me!" he said angrily, hardly knowing his own voice. "I just rode over to see a calf of Stevenson's. I'll be on my way!" Out of the house he rushed, leaving his aunt to meditate upon her theories.

A Lover's Reaction

His mother's curiosity about the lassie disappeared at the first glimpse she got of his face. She put him to bed, with hot drinks and heated stones, with quilt after quilt wrapped about him. But still he chilled and shivered. He was so wretched that she had no heart to reprove him for that rash outing.

For a long time he remained fevershaken and low-spirited. Day after day he lay contrasting in his mind those two hours with Chirstie, contrasting his dreams with the reality, while the rain continued to sweep across the prairies.

One day his brother returned dripping from the post office with the news of Lee's surrender. Wully celebrated the event with an unusually hard chill. The tidings of Lincoln's death sickened him desperately. He got to thinking he was never again to be a strong man. And he could see no reason for wanting to be.

He tried hard enough, as he grew stronger, to shake off his depression. There were plenty of girls in the world whom he might marry, weren't there? The trouble was, he hated other girls. Still, he couldn't let merely one woman make him unhappy, could he? Not much! He used to be happy all the time, before he got to thinking about her so much. He would brace up, he vowed, and forget her.

The next Sunday he walked with his brothers to the church. The man of God read the Scriptures, and then at last came that welcomed long prayer, good for fifteen minutes at least.

Wully, sitting determinedly in a certain well-considered place in the pew, bowing his head devoutly and bending just a bit to one side, could watch Chirstie through his fingers, where she sat on the other side of the church. Her eyes were closed, but his did a week's duty. There was no doubt about it. She was getting thinner and thinner. It wasn't just his imagination. She was paler. She was unhappy. He had noticed that week by week. Surely she was not happy!

The minister was an indecent man, cutting that prayer short in so unceremonious a fashion. But after the sermon there would be another prayer, just a glimpse long. He had that to look forward to.

Finally the last prayer came. He turned his head, and there—oh, Chirstie was looking at him! With head bowed, but eyes wide open, she was looking at him! Hungrily, tenderly, pitifully, just as he wanted her to look. Their eyes met, and her face blossomed red. She turned her head hastily away. Let her turn away! Let her pray! He *knew,* now.

For some reason she didn't mean him to understand. But he had found out! It was all right. He could wait. He could wait any length of time, if only she would look at him again in that way! The congregation had risen, and had began the Psalm. He would tell her, then and there, how glad he was, how he understood! He lifted up his voice and sang, sang louder than anyone else.

Waiting With a Gun

After dinner, he said he was going down to the swimming hole. But instead he rushed eagerly and cautiously over to Chirstie. He left his horse some distance away, intending, if he saw others there, to come back and wait. He hesitated as he drew nearer the house. Then he saw her. She was sitting in the little plot of shade the cabin made, on the doorstep, and her head

was bowed on her arms. She was crying! He stood still, watching her carefully. She was shaken with sobbing.

Presently she looked up and saw him. She gave a little cry and, jumping up, ran into the cabin, and slammed the door behind her. As if he were a robber. She needn't barricade the door against him, need she? Wully thought, angrily. Then he remembered her face in church.

He would sit down and wait a while. When he looked again towards the house, there she was, sitting inside the door, and in her hands she had her father's old gun!

Waiting for him with a gun! Could it be that the girl was losing her mind? Could Chirstie have been unbalanced by her mother's death! Who could tell what a girl might do with a gun! One thing he knew, he wasn't going away and leave her there alone, so madly armed, and weeping.

After a while her younger brother came home, a red-faced sweating little lad, and sat down contentedly with the soldier in the shade of the barn.

"What's happened, Dod?" Wully began at once. "When I came up, Chirstie was sitting on the door-step crying."

"She cries all the time," Dod said carelessly. "She cries when she's eating. She gets up in the morning crying. She's daft!"

"You mustn't say that, Dod!" said Wully sharply. "Can't a girl grieve for her mother without being called daft? That's no way for a man to speak!"

"She's not grieving for mother," he answered, defending himself. "She's grieving for herself. She told me so."

Wully had no longer any scruples about finding out everything he could from the boy.

"What's she sitting with that gun in her hands for, Dod? Does she shoot many chickens?"

"Her? She couldn't hit a barn. She's afraid. That's what's the matter with her."

"What's she afraid of?"

"Nothing. What's there to be afraid of here?"

"You must treat Chirstie like a man, Dod. You mustn't blame her for crying. It's the way women do, sometimes. You say to her when you go in that my mother is always waiting to do for her. She's the one that can help her. She don't need to cry any more. We can fix things right. You say that to her, Dod, and tomorrow I'll ride over and see what it is. You tell her we'll fix everything for her."

He went away in uncertainty and distress.

The Terrible Secret

As HE rode away he saw a horseman coming towards him. He smiled when he saw who it was. Peter Keith was a cousin of both Chirstie's and his, and the only remaining child of their Aunt Libby's and Uncle John Keith's, the smallest adult of Wully's seventy-one cousins, being not more than five feet seven. And he was by far the most worthless of them.

Of course Peter would be riding leisurely over after the mail in the middle of the morning, while the haying was to be finished, and the wheat was white and heavy for harvest. His excuse this summer for not working was that he had a disabled foot. He said that he had accidentally discharged his gun into it. Peter Keith was such a man that when he told that story, his hearers' faces grew shrewd and thoughtful, trying to decide whether or not he really

was lazy enough to hurt his own foot in order to get out of work.

Wully had always been more tolerant of him than some of his cousins were, because he could never imagine a man feigning so shameful a thing as physical weakness. If Peter didn't want to farm, why insist, he argued.

The two of them made themselves a shade in the grass, and talked away intimately. Wully was more affable than usual, having resolved upon first sight of Peter to learn something from him. Peter was always full of neighborhood news. Peter was the last man with whom he cared to discuss Chirstie. But he was exactly the one who might know something valuable. He delayed the question at the tip of his tongue, till even the lazy Peter thought it was time to be riding on, and rose to go. It was then or never with Wully, so he said.

"I was riding by McNairs' yesterday, and I saw Chirstie sitting there crying. What do you suppose she would be crying about, Peter?"

Peter gave him a sharp look, and grew red in one moment.

"How the devil should I know what girls cry about?" he asked angrily. "It's none of my business! Nor yours, either."

A cry of frightened anger like that sent a wave excitement through Wully.

"You know very well what it is," he cried. "You've got to tell me! It's some of your doings!"

Peter was jumping into his saddle.

"I'll tell you like hell!" he shouted.

His face told terrible secrets that Wully never till that moment imagined suspecting. Now he was pulling him down from his horse.

"Let me alone. It's not my fault! Take your hands off me! I never meant to hurt her!" Peter was fighting desperately for his freedom. Wully was trying, with all his might, to control his insane rage.

"Stand still and tell me what it is. I'm not going to hurt you!" he cried scornfully. But his grasp never relaxed. The boy was afraid he would be shaken to death.

"Let me alone! Take your hands off me. It's none of your business, anyway!" He was free now, and trembling. "I didn't mean to get her into trouble. I wish I'd never seen her! I offered to marry her once—"

He dodged Wully's blinded blow.

"*You* marry her!" he cried murderously. "*You* marry her!" The first realization of his meaning had filled Wully with a lust to kill. Peter had sprung away. He gained his horse. Wully ran after him. He called after him ragingly.

He threw himself down, too shocked to think plainly. So that was Chirstie's sickening secret! That was why she was afraid of him! That was why she was defending herself with that poor old gun! Chirstie, betrayed and— Oh, it was well he was trained in killing.

A HIDEOUS situation had been forced upon him, a thing which had to be faced out, like the war, from which there was no escape but victory. If he got rid of Peter, why should he not have her? Possession of her was worth letting the betrayer go scot free for, wasn't it? If he killed Peter, what good would that do her? It would make her notorious. Forcing him to go away and stay away, on pain of death, was better.

By supper time his mind was perfectly clear about the course he would take. He rose and ate something, excitedly, reassuring his mother that the sun had not prostrated him. He felt all right. He had only to settle with Peter, and then—!

Finally he came to Chirstie's. She was sitting there in the dusk, her head bowed in that despairing way. He gave his horse to Dod with a command, and strode over to where she sat. She needn't try to resist him now. It was useless.

"I know the whole thing!" he whispered. "I've got it all settled." He took her in his arms. She needn't struggle. "It's all right. He'll never frighten you again. You can't get away. I've come for you!"

Dawn found them sitting there together. Indeed, Wully had to urge his horse along to get home in time for breakfast.

The McLaughlins were assembled for their unexciting morning cornmeal, all at the table together, when Wully announced, in a fine loud voice:

"I'm going to be married today, mother!"

"Wully!" she gasped.

"Well, you needn't be so surprised."

"Is it Chirstie?"

Could they ask that!

"I'm *that* pleased!" his mother cried. Oh, she wouldn't have liked anything else as well! She looked at him narrowly, with delight. "But you canna just be married today, and the harvesting coming on!"

"You bet I can!" replied her American.

The News Is Broken

IT WAS growingly inevitable that the news, the determined news, must be broken. Wully, with his whole heart shrinking from the task, made light of it to Chirstie. Wasn't having her better than anything he had ever imagined! He hadn't really known at the time they were married how greatly he was enriching himself. If he had been ready then to shoulder whatever blame there might be, he was ready now to do it a dozen times over. He didn't mind in the least telling his parents about it.

It was his mother she thought most about! What would his mother ever do when she heard it? That was nothing! Wully would go and explain it all to her, after his fashion—falsely—his wife insisted on saying wretchedly. His mother would be angry, of course, at first, and give him the scolding of his life. But she'd soon get over it, and come over bringing Chirstie a lot of baby clothes. Chirstie would see if she wouldn't!

His mother kissed him fondly when he came to her, saying it was a lonely house with him away so much.

"I have something to tell you, mother," he stammered.

"I'm listening," she said encouragingly, her eyes studying him tenderly.

"We're going to have a baby! In December, mother!"

Over her face there spread swiftly a smile of soft amusement. She had always looked that way when one of her children said something especially innocent and lovable.

"You don't mean December, Wully! Dinna ye ken that? The wee'uns cann'na just hurry so!"

He couldn't look at her. "I know what I mean!" he said, doggedly. "I mean December. I understand." The silence became so ominous that at length he had to steal a look at her. Her incredulous face was flushed red with shame and anger. He rose to defend his love from her.

"You aren't to say a word against her. It wasn't *her* fault!"

Then the storm broke. "Do you think I'm likely to say a word against her— poor, greetin' bairn!" she cried. "Her sitting there alone among the wolves and snakes, and a son of mine to bring her to shame! I'll never lift my head again. You did well, now, to choose a lassie alone, with neither father nor mother to defend her from you!"

WRETCHEDLY ashamed of his deceit as he was, he was not able to take more of her reproof without trying to defend himself.

"I didn't mean any harm!" he mumbled. "I didn't think."

"And *why* did you not think!" she demanded, furiously. "Have you no mind of your own! You didn't know what you were doing, I suppose! Oh, that I should have a son who is a fool!"

Fool was a word she hated so greatly that she never allowed her children to pronounce it. It was her ultimate condemnation. He had never heard her use it before. And now she used it on him! He wasn't going to stand any more of that tone. He got up.

"I'll be going," he exclaimed. "There's no place for me here!"

"Don't go!" she answered, unrelenting. "There is always a place for you, whatever you elect to do. This is a sore stroke, Wully!"

Then she added, wearily and passionately: "When I was a girl, I wanted to be some great person. And when you all were born, I wanted only to have you great men. And when you grew up, I prayed you might be at least honest. And I'm not to have even that, it seems."

He had heard her say that before. He was so sorry for her pain that he hardly knew what to do. He rushed away, damning Peter Keith into the nethermost hell. The open air was some relief. If only women wouldn't take these things so hard. Well, that was over. The worst part. Any taunt would be easy to take after that.

After her unkissed son had gone, Isobel McLaughlin, reeling from the blow he had dealt her, sat with her hands covering her face. Nothing but Wully's own recital could ever have made her believe such a story!

That afternoon, the small McLaughlins coming home from school found a state of affairs new in their experience. There was absolutely no sign of a baby in the house, and yet their mother was in bed! Once she said, when they asked her anxiously, that her head ached. And once she said that her heart was troubling her.

A Secret is Shared

MRS. MC LAUGHLIN had come at once to see Chirstie after Wully's revelation, apparently utterly pleased over the prospect of a grandchild, never intimating by a syllable that she saw anything deplorable in the unchristian haste of his advent. Her kindness had naturally humbled the girl more than any reproof could have done, and after a long cry the two had been friends, both relieved that estrangement was a thing of the past.

Chirstie sat beside her sewing, an awe-filled pupil in the things of maternity. It was comforting, when one was feeling daily more wretched, to be assured by the mother of thirteen huskies that a baby is just nothing whatever but a joy, no trouble worth speaking of.

The more she grew to appreciate Wully's mother, the more intolerable his deception of her seemed to her. Every time a visitor came into the kitchen, and Isobel McLaughlin stood like a high wall between Chirstie and the possibility of even a slighting insinuation, Chirstie hated more the part Wully had forced upon her. It was the only thing about which she dreamed then of disagreeing with him. She begged him, she entreated him, she really prayed him to let her tell the truth. But he would not.

Her only comfort was that some time it would all come out. And then he would have to say to his mother that every day she had begged him to tell her the truth. He would have to take all the blame of this unkindness, this cruelty. . . .

It was only a few days before her confinement that one afternoon she sat knitting. She had been talking with her mother-in-law about Aunt Libby, whom they were expecting almost any moment. All the neighbors were talking about Libby Keith. She had been away again searching for Peter—in Chicago, this time, on a clue so slender, so foolish, that even the most malicious tongues wagged with a sigh.

And now she was futilely home again. And was coming to Isobel McLaughlin to pour out her restlessness. Even winter weather could not keep her at home. She went from house to house seeking reassurance from those who could have none to give.

When she came into the McLaughlin kitchen, she bent over and patted Chirstie on the shoulder commiseratingly, sighing a sigh that recalled to the girl all the agony of her daughter Flora's death in labor.

"So you're back, Libby!" Isobel was constrained to speak to her softly, as one speaks to a mourner.

"I'm back."

"You've no word of him?"

"No word." Each of her answers was accompanied by a sigh most long and deep.

Chirstie bestirred herself guiltily to offer her a bit of hope. She felt always in a way responsible for Peter's departure, however much Wully scouted the idea. It was Chirstie's opinion that Peter had written home, maybe many times, and the letters had miscarried. Maybe he had written what a good place he had to work, and how much wages he was getting. They considered this probability from all sides.

. . . there she was, sitting inside the door, and in her hands she had her father's old gun!

Illustration for Margaret Wilson's
"THE ABLE McLAUGHLINS"

Libby's attention was diverted to the girl. She began to dwell patheticlly upon the details of her daughter's eath, upon the symptoms of her abormal pregnancy. She kept at it, in spite f all Isobel's attempts to divert her until he was about to go. She rose then, and ave a sigh that surpassed all her other ghs, adequate to one oppressed by the hole scheme of life. She said:

"It oughtn't to be. There should be ome other way of them being born, ithout such suffering and pain. With e danger divided between the two. I ink—"

But that she thought was too much r Isobel, who had no patience with ose who fussed about the natural things f life.

"Havers, Libby!" she exclaimed. "How an you say such things!" And thinkg only of herself and the woman bere her, she cried passionately.

"How can you say that it's the *bearing* f them that hurts! It's the evil they do hen they're grown that's the great pain! Ve want them to be something great, nd they won't even be decent! Can you are that with anyone?"

Her words, so poorly aimed, missed eir mark, and struck Chirstie. She owed her head on the back of the chair front of her. Isobel, returning from eing Libby away, found her sitting that ay, sobbing.

She began comforting her. Chirstie asn't to listen to what the poor daft ody said! No fear of Chirstie dying. She as doing fine! But Chirstie couldn't op crying. Finally she lifted her red face om her arms, and sat erect, trying to eak.

"I don't care! I *might* die! I'm going tell you something!" And she fell to ying again.

Isobel came and stood over her. "What you going to tell me, Christie?" she asked kindly. "You needn't fear I'll tell. I don't go about telling secrets!"

"Oh, it would never be the same between us again if he finds out I told you!"

"He'll never find out from me!"

Then Chirstie sat up and said: "You needn't *say* Wully's doing evil! He isn't! This isn't any fault of his! I mean—it isn't *his!* It isn't *his* baby!"

Years might have been seen falling away from Isobel McLaughlin. She sat down slowly on the chair against which Chirstie was leaning. Bewildered she asked: "Whose is it?"

"I can't tell you that. It's not *his.*"

"And you let us think it was!"

"Oh, mother, I couldn't help it! Oh, I didn't know what to do. Every day I've told him he ought to tell you. But he wouldn't, mother. And if he finds out I have told you, he might even—"

Isobel began kissing her.

"Oh, Chirstie! You did well to tell me. You needn't fear I'll ever let him know. This is the best day of my life, Chirstie." She rose, and began walking about the house in her excitement, unable to contain her delight. "He never was an ill child, Chirstie! He wanted to help you out, I see. There never was one of the boys as good as Wully."

She went to the door presently, and called in the children who were playing outside, and when they came in, she took little Sarah passionately up in her arms. "Your mother's *young* again." she cried to the surprised child. "Young again!" She comforted Chirstie, stopping in her turns about the room to stroke her hair. She sang snatches of Psalms. She clasped and unclasped her hands excitedly. She shone.

A Happy "Shame"

The infamy of Chirstie's condition, becoming known, had been scarcely ss interesting than the scandal of Isobel cLaughlin's attitude toward it. She herlf had told her sister and her sisters-

in-law what was soon to be expected from the girl, and all her cousins and friends. She had informed them of it casually, without the flutter of an eyelid, as if, to be sure, a little less haste might have been from some points of view desirable, but, after all, Wully's marriage was the one she would have chosen for him if she had had her choice, and the young pair would be happier with a baby. The neighbors had certainly never expected Isobel McLaughlin to "take on" in such a fashion.

It had been bad enough in the beginning, but after the child was born it grew out of all bounds. Her husband's younger sister, Janet, came to remonstrate with her. For the sake of the other young people in the community, to say nothing of her own family of half-grown boys and girls she really ought to moderate her raptures somewhat. She was just encouraging them in wrongdoing!

But Isobel replied simply that since she had always had to be painfully modest in praising her own children, she was going to say exactly what she thought about this grandchild. She philosophized shamelessly about the privileges of grandmothers. And, after all, if she was his own grandmother who was saying it, Janet would have to acknowledge that the baby was an unusually fine child.

Janet did have to grant that. She was the first one, too, to notice the remarkable resemblance the child bore to his father. Isobel was grateful to her for that hint, and after that day no visitor departed without agreeing that wee Johnnie was a living picture of great Wully. Isobel would recall her son's infant features. Wully's nose had been just like that. And his eyes. She minded it well, now.

Wully had rejoiced beyond measure at the child's birth, not for the reason some supposed, but solely because Chirstie was safely through her ordeal. So gay he had become, so light-hearted, after that burden of anxiety for her had

been taken from him, that he seemed quite like a rejoicing young father.

It had been terrible for him to see her time unescapably approaching. Those days seemed to him now like a nightmare. He had planned what he would say to his wife when he adopted her baby for his own. He would go blithely in, and cry to her gayly, "Where's my son, Chirstie?" And the child would be his.

He had planned that. But it had been different. That one irrepressible moan he had heard from her before his mother had sent him for the doctor had driven him through the night cursing. Cursing that man, whose very name he hated.

AFTERWARDS he had gone in to see her, not blithely, but otherwise. He had found her lying there, hollow-eyes, exhausted, all her strength taken from her and her roundness, leaving her reduced it seemed to her essential womanhood.

When she had shown him the child— well he remembered that she had never asked him for pity for herself. But now her eyes were praying, "My baby! Love my baby, Wully."

With her lying there, even her familiar hands looking frail, her hair lying wearily against her pillow, if she had asked him to love a puppy, would he not have bent down to kiss it!

So the terrible days passed away. His wife became altogether his. And wee Johnnie slept and thrived, his tiny hand doubled against his little red face, in the cradle that had served the five younger McLaughlins. When he opened his bonnie blue eyes, he saw only adoration bending over him. He felt only delighted and reverent hands lifting him. If Johnnie was a shame to the household he was certainly an entertaining and well-fed shame; if he was a disgrace, he was surely an amusing and a hungry one.

The Torn Sleeve

IT WAS one hot day during the summer after the baby was born. Wully was working in the fields some distance away from his house when suddenly he heard

a cry. Chirstie was running towards him. She was crying out to him, too far away to be heard. He gave a look toward the house. There seemed to be no sign of fire. He tore towards her. It must be the baby. She stumbled against him gasping.

"It's Peter! Peter Keith! He's back! You said he wouldn't come back! Wully he took hold of me! He—" She was weeping with rage and terror. "Look here!" Her sleeve was torn half off. "You said he wouldn't come back!" she cried, shaking.

The sight of that torn sleeve made him suddenly blind with anger. He couldn't believe it. It wasn't possible that man had dared to come back and lay violent hands on his wife. It simply couldn't be. He lusted for his gun. He felt her trembling against him. By God, his wife wouldn't have to tremble much longer.

It seemed to him long before they came to their house—very long. He seized his gun. He went to the east door, and looked out. He went to the west door. He stood looking. He searched the house. He searched the barn. No sign of a man. No one hiding about the haystack. Beyond the wheat fields—what might be there, to the east, to the west, to the north and the south, in those wild man-high grasses. There a thousand men might hide and laugh at pursuers. Looking at those baffling stretches, Wully choked. He was helpless.

In his excitement details came rushing back to his mind to which he had long and obstinately refused entrance. He remembered all the bits of confession that Chirstie had made to him the first night that, knowing her trouble, he had gone to claim her. Peter had loved her, he had wanted her for his, she had told him. But she wouldn't listen to him because she thought of Wully. She thought of herself as his.

One night, when there was no help within a mile, she had run out of the house, undressed, barefooted across the snow—till Peter caught her, and brought her back. Wully hadn't often thought of that, because he couldn't think of it and live. But it had no mercy on him now. That story cried aloud to him shrieking

through his mind. He would kill that man, and go to the sheriff and give himself up. He would stand up and tell any twelve men in the county that story, and come home acquitted. If only he could find the man! He went beating through the grasses nearest him, maddened by the feeling that it was in vain. To the west the treacherous grasses jeered at him wavingly, and to the east. North and south they mocked him.

THE year's calendar of color was almost at an end; only white was left for it now. The fields had been black. They had grown green, shy, softly. They had given themselves up to bold greenness. They had achieved their golden maturity. They had reveled in gold, and dazzled by it. They had faded into dullness and browns. They died and lay withered. Snows would come soon for their burial. The morning's white frosts were the promise of it.

Chirstie must keep the doors shut now, for the baby's sake. With doors shut the house seemed a trap, a trap from whose windows she had often to be looking to reassure herself. Out of doors she felt safer, freer. The baby looked so blooming that Chirstie said she just had to take him visiting, to show him to the neighbors. That was an excuse for not staying home alone which Wully pretended to be deceived by.

It happened that one morning Squire McLaughlin, riding past, saw a flock of wild turkeys alight in her dooryard, and leaving his horse, he crept toward the house, to borrow Wully's gun, and bring down a bird for dinner. He had all but gained the house when out of the door shot Chirstie, crying out unintelligibly.

He didn't know what terrible thing might have happened. He started after her. He called to her questioningly. She never lessened her pace. He said later that he had never seen a woman run as fast as she did. Wully heard him and began calling to his wife.

"It's only Uncle Wully!" he called to her. She stumbled against him, panting and white, and the Squire hurried on to them, in consternation. There the three of them stood, breathless, excited, looking blankly from one to the other. Chirstie had grown red with relief and humiliation.

"Oh!" she stammered, confusedly. "Oh! I just thought—I thought you were—a tramp! You came up so quietly —I didn't know—" She paused, and looked at her husband beseechingly. "I got a fright," she murmured.

Wully knew what she thought. Pitiful, she was. Just pitiful. Standing there trembling, ashamed, trying to cover her folly.

THAT hour Wully came to a great decision. He had been considering for some time a proposition that a cousin of his had made to him. Next spring the railroad would have completed its track to its next western terminal and the new station which would become a town, was to be but three miles from Wully's farm.

From that town, all the supplies that settlers must have would be hauled a hundred miles west. What they would need first and always would be lumber

The proposition was to set up a lumber business. Wully would have a little money, and the cousin had some, and they knew where they could borrow more.

Wully had thought before the bomb of Peter's return that farming was no life for Chirstie. She was no tireless woman like his mother. Wully had often wished that in some way he might make her necessary work lighter. And now that this intolerable menace of violence hung over their home, it seemed best altogether to leave it. He knew what his father would say to the idea that a man getting a dollar and seventy cents from wheat should leave his land. But after Chirstie's flight from her uncle, Wully didn't care what he advised. He wouldn't have his wife trembling. He would give his answer to his cousin at once. They would move to town.

The Good Samaritan

THE corn was husked. The year's work in the fields was over. Wully had sold from sixty of the acres for which his father had paid two hundred and ten dollars in '64, wheat worth three thousand and sixty dollars. He had his house all paid for now. He owned three hundred acres of land, some of it a bit farther west, where a bushel of wheat still bought an acre of the faithful soil.

Everything prospered with him. Everything, except for that shadow of evil that clouded their lives hatefully. Every day Wully's mind dwelt futilely upon the problem of Peter Keith's fate. And Chirstie's eyes, he observed, still shifted apprehensively under their tender lids.

He finished the corn on a Wednesday, and on Thursday they were to have a great lark. They were to go to town together for the first time. For one day they would put aside all their misgivings, and be happy together.

Thursday turned out to be a second Indian summer, a bland day for riding

across the country. And there was a spring seat for Chirstie's and the baby's comfort.

When they got to the town Chirstie was rather overcome by her husband's grandness. He had such a worldly air— commanding people about. He kept getting more imperious, more happy all the time though he was entirely sober. After a while, when it was growing dusk, he spied a friend on the street, just going into his office.

"That's Mr. Knight, Chirstie! You remember! The man that drove me home that time! I'll take you to see him!"

"I'm McLaughlin," Wully explained to the older man. "The soldier you drove out to Harmony, two years ago. I was sick, you remember."

Mr. Knight's face lighted up with recognition "Come in, McLaughlin!" he said heartily. "Your wife? Your baby? Why, it doesn't seem possible! How the time gets away! And where did you find her?" he asked, so frankly pleased with

er appearance that she blushed more
eeply than she had at his first remark.

WULLY was delighted, Knight was a
man whose opinion was valu-
ble, a prosperous man, a man dressed
s men dress in cities, whose interest
e felt was not merely assumed for polit-
cal ends.

Mr. Knight said. "Well you certainly
on't look much like you did that morn-
ng. You were sick. Skin and bones. Do
ou remember?"

"Do I remember!" exclaimed Wully.
"Will I ever forget!" He turned to his
vife. "Chirstie, I was sitting right down
here by the elevator. I wasn't sitting,
ither. I was lying stretched out, to try
o keep from throwing up. And I was
ying there when Mr. Knight came along,
nd began asking me what was the mater of me. He said he would take me
ome 'How far is it?' you asked, and
vhen I said twenty-six miles, you said,
Oh! Twenty-six miles!' My heart sank
s they say. Anyway, I had a pang of
ome kind. And you said, 'You wait
ere!' And pretty soon along you came
vith those grays! I tell you I felt better
ven then. I got better all the way home.
Every step."

"Naturally!" remarked Mr. Knight,
ooking again with a smile, at Chirstie.

"I'll tell you another thing I remem-
er!" he began. "I got in on that night
rain, that time, you know, and I went
to the hotel where we had always
stayed. Sick, I was, you know! I told the
man—he'd seen me a dozen times before—that I hadn't the price of a room.
He never even looked to see who I was.
Just saw my uniform and began swearing! Wasn't going to be eaten out of
house and home by a lot of begging soldiers, he said.

"I went out on the street, and I
couldn't get up face enough to go some
place else and ask for a bed, at first.
Then finally I went into the Great West.
And Pierson there almost began swearing at me because I said I'd pay him
later. He didn't take a soldiers' last cent
away from them, he said. He saw how
I felt, and he went and got some milk
toast made for me. And soft boiled eggs.
And then, do you know what he did?
He went to a room with me, and when
he saw the pillows on the bed, he went
and got me a pair of good pillows from
some place. I hadn't slept on a pillow
for I don't know how long! A man notices those things when he's most dead,
I tell you. Milk toast, and pillows, by
Jiminy!"

Mr. Knight made him go on talking.
They sat there till the street was dark.
And then Wully led his wife away,
right up to the hotel. And then into the
dining room. It seemed lordly to her, that
dining room—an amazing day—and
Wully most lordly and amazing of all.
It was like a fine wedding trip.

The Tables Turn

THEY had breakfasted together before
daylight, and he had gone to load
he lumber he was taking home for his
ather, so that they might have a very
early start.

Presently she saw her husband drive
up, and get out to tie his horses. But
before he had started for the hotel door,
a stranger accosted him, and with the
stranger Wully turned and went down
the street. So she waited on.

Then, before she had expected him,
Wully was standing over her, reaching
down for the baby. She scarcely knew
him. His face was white. His eyes were
shining strangely. He bundled her and
the baby into the wagon and whipped
the horses toward home.

After a few perplexed moments, her
face darkened with terror.

"Oh, I know! You're—you've seen
him! You were like that when he came
last summer!"

He turned toward her, trying to speak.
"Yes!" he broke forth. "I saw him
dying."

"Oh, dying!" She tried to realize it.
"Oh, if he's *dying,* then we'll be happy!"

But after a minute she stirred uncomfortably.

"Where was it you saw him, Wully?"

"In a livery stable!"

"In a livery stable!" she repeated. "Dying in such a place!" Dying seemed not so sweet a word now.

"But why didn't he send word home before? Think of Aunt Libby, Wully!"

"He came in on the train last night. He was looking for someone to take him out home."

"Oh!" she exclaimed, enlightened. "He wanted to get home alive! What's the matter with him?"

"Hemmorrhage," said Wully, as shortly as it was possible to speak. He wouldn't tell her how he had seen that snake lying bloody, dirty, sunken, helpless on a bed of straw. He urged his horses on.

She looked at him. He turned away from her troubled eyes. He knew what was coming.

"Aunt Libby was always kind to me, Wully. We can't tell her that we went away and left him there to die. We ought to go back and get him. We can't treat Auntie this way!"

"Can't we!" he exclaimed bitterly. "Giddup!" he cried to the horses.

When she spoke again, it was to warn him. "If you don't go back, I will!"

"No you won't!" he cried.

Before he realized what she was doing she was over the side of the wagon. Ignoring him, defying him, she was calling to him over her shoulder:

"He made me do evil once. You made me do evil once. But nobody can make me do it again!" Down the road she ran. "I'm going back to him!"

HE DROVE on, raging against her, trying to justify himself. He went so far that he could scarcely see her now. He might have gone on home, if there had not appeared on the horizon a team, coming towards him. Somebody who might know them was coming nearer. Somebody would see Wully McLaughlin riding westward, and presently overtake his wife running east. He turned around abruptly.

Facing east he could just see her. As he came nearer she did a strange thing, for she suddenly began running toward him. He saw that she was crying softly.

"I doubt he's not dying," she wept. "I can't do it. He's too strong, Wully. He's tricky!"

"Don't cry!" he had to say.

"I won't look at him!" she sobbed. "You know I don't want to go back to him. You know I don't like him. If you don't know how much I hate him, I'll tell you. It was me that shot him that time. It wasn't his foot I was aiming at either!"

She had shot him. She had been as desperate as that. He was horrified anew. Yet she managed to urge the horses eastward.

"I'll never look at him!" she cried passionately. "You needn't think I like him."

"I know it, Chirstie. But you oughtn't to have jumped out and run away that way."

"Yes, I ought!" she retorted. "I couldn't help it. It wasn't my place to do it. But my husband wouldn't do his part. Wully, if you hurry now, hurry enough, they'll just think you've been unloading. You won't need to explain!"

The Sharpest Sword

THEY had passed the bridge on their burdened way home. They had come to the place at which Chirstie had so astonishingly defied him. They were riding together in a silence broken only by wee Johnnie's cooing, as he bounced back and forth in his mother's lap.

Never once had she turned her face towards what was in the wagon-box to see if it was indeed dying.

And now, when Wully looked at her from the corner of his eyes, his own anger, his bitter hatred seemed a small thing before hers. Her face was as white as marble, and as hard, one might have thought. Her mouth was screwed tight

loathing. She sat perfectly still, look-
ng straight ahead now. Wully was
lmost afraid of her . . . afraid certainly
o offer her comfort.

The baby grew restless. He complained
etfully of his mother's lack of attention.
Vully gave him, almost mechanically,
ae ends of the lines to play with. They
ame then to a low place. The horses
ould go only very slowly. The baby
djusted himself to the new motion of
ae wagon. There was a splashing of
aud that made him giggle delightedly.

would have been a choice morning
or any baby whose mother wasn't sit-
ng frozen. Wee Johnnie made the best
f it. He kicked, and giggled, and
quirmed about.

The horses failed to take their proper
ace again. Wully had to speak to them.
le slapped them lightly with the lines.
"Get up Nellie!" he exclaimed.
What's the matter of you?"

Wee Johnnie moved his arms exactly
Wully had done.

"Get up, Nellie!" he said. "What's the
atter of you?"

He said all that, plainly, if not per-
ctly, and before he knew what was
appening, his mother had seized him
ad was hugging him up against her,
the good old way, kissing him. She
ad been so surprised, so delighted with
er son's first sentence that she had
rned, even kissing him, to Wully, no
y complete unless he shared it.

"Did you hear that!" she cried triumphantly, her face blossoming towards
him. "Say it again, Lammie!"

AND almost before Wully could smile
in return, he stopped. He turned
around. He thought he heard a groan
from his load. He couldn't even smile
at her with that man possibly spying
upon them.

He looked—and from the end of the
wagon that man had lifted his head a
little, like a snake, and had seen the
smile that Chirstie had turned upon her
husband. At the terrible sight of that
face, Wully pitied his enemy. That
coward, in his damned way had loved
Chirstie. And in his tormented sunken
dying he had seen all the sweet intimacy
from which he had been shut out and
had sunk back, felled by the blow of that
revelation.

Wully had foregone revenge. He had
forborne running a sword less sharp
through his fallen enemy than Chirstie's
wifely smile had been. In a flash Wully
saw himself sitting there by the woman,
loved, living, not dying, full of strength
and generations, while that man, loathed
and rejected, was already burning in
hell.

The poor devil!

He pulled the horses up suddenly, and
gave his wife the lines. He climbed back
to lift his cousin into a position less painful.

"I'll stop and buy him a pillow,"
Wully resolved.

CHLOE DIVINE

CHLOE's a Nymph in flowery groves,
    A Nereid in the streams;
Saint-like she in the temple moves,
    A woman in my dreams.

Love steals artillery from her eyes,
    The Graces point her charms;
Orpheus is rivall'd in her voice,
    And Venus in her arms.

Never so happily in one
    Did heaven and earth combine:
And yet 'tis flesh and blood alone
    That makes her so divine.
            —*Thomas D'Urfey*

Sir Nevile Henderson

FAILURE OF A MISSION

MOST of us will never forget the last weeks of August, 1939, when by radio and newspaper we followed Sir Nevile Henderson's tragic efforts to keep peace in Europe. We know that war was declared, but not until now have we had a full explanation of *why*. Probably no one is in a better position to give adequate answers to our questions than Sir Nevile Henderson. In "Failure of a Mission" he dramatically describes his experiences in Germany between May 1937 and September 1939, during which time he turned from friend to foe of the Nazi regime. With Rauschning's "Voice of Destruction" (condensed in this volume) this historic document is indispensable to the understanding of pre-war Germany and its leader, Adolf Hitler.

THE first commandment of a diplomatist is faithfully to interpret the views of his own government to the government to which he is accredited; and the second is like unto it: namely, to explain no less accurately the views and standpoint of the government of the country in which he is stationed to the government of his own country.

The first commandment is much easier to keep than the second; and its fulfilment can, or should, be taken for granted. The second is sometimes far more difficult of performance. I went to Berlin resolved, in spite of my own doubts and apprehensions and in spite of many of its detestable aspects, to do my utmost to see the good side of the Nazi regime as well as the bad, and to explain as objectively as I could its aspirations and viewpoint to His Majesty's Government. Hitler and the Nazi party governed Germany, and with them it was my duty to work. But above all, I was determined to labor for an honorable peace and to follow the example of the Prime Minister in never wearying of that labor.

For two years I hoped against hope that the Nazi revolution, having run its course, would revert to a normal and civilized conduct of internal and international life, that there was a limit to Hitler's ambitions and a word of truth in some at least of his assurances a statements. Many may regard my p sistence as convicting me of the lack any intellectual understanding of Na or even German mentality. That m be true; but even today I do not reg having tried.

Whatever happens, I shall always p sist in thinking that it was right to ma the attempt, that nothing was lost making it, but that, on the contrary, should never have entered upon this w as a united Empire and nation, wi the moral support of neutral opinion hind us, if the attempt had not be made. Anyway, the fact remains th up to the fifteenth of March, 1939, a in spite of the shocks of Godesberg a Munich in 1938, I refused to aband that hope. After the occupation Prague on the Ides of last March I st struggled on, though all hope, exce in a miracle, was dead.

No miracle occurred, and on Septe ber 1st the German armies and A Force invaded Poland. There was declaration of war, and a clearer case unprovoked aggression there can ne be. Indeed, in spite of all my hopes a efforts, it is possible now to say that a year and a half before that date I h been obsessed with the idea that were moving remorselessly through t pages of a Greek tragedy to its inevital disastrous and sinister end. Those w take the trouble to read this book w realize what I mean.

Hitler never intended the ultimate ⸱d to be other than war. It seems in⸱nceivable that the will and lust for ⸱wer of one man should plunge an ⸱willing Europe into war. But so it is, ⸱d hundreds of thousands of men, omen, and children have to suffer and die for it. So long as Germany, the ⸱me of the most numerous, disciplined, ⸱d hard-working race in Europe, is ⸱verned by Hitler and his secret police ⸱estapo) and by all that Hitlerism ⸱nds for, there can be no confidence in ⸱ternational agreements and no civil⸱ed conduct in national and inter⸱tional life.

That is my profound conviction after living in the Germany of Hitler for over two years. I like and admire the German people; I feel myself very much at home among them and find them less strangers than almost any other foreign people. A prosperous, contented, and happy Germany is a vital British interest. But today the Germans are serving a false god, and their many good and great qualities are being debauched for ends which are evil. Germany can neither be prosperous nor happy till she recovers her individual and personal freedom of life and thought and has learned that the true responsibility of strength is to protect and not to oppress the weak.

Dangerous Ideological Hatreds

T WOULD be utterly unjust not to real⸱ize that great numbers of those who ⸱hered to and worked for Hitler and ⸱e Nazi regime were honest idealists, ⸱ose sole aim was to serve Germany, ⸱ improve the lot of her people, and ⸱ add to their happiness. Hitler himself ⸱ay well have been such an idealist at ⸱e start. Later he undoubtedly used this ⸱ealism as a cloak to justify the con⸱ued existence of the regime and of ⸱ leaders.

But there were others who were true ⸱ their principles, and I left Germany ⸱th feelings of high regard for men ⸱e Dr. Gurtner, the Minister of Jus⸱e; Graf Schwerin von Krosigk, the ⸱inister of Finance; Dr. Lammers, the ⸱ad of the Reichschancery; as well as ⸱ many others in various walks of ⸱cial life in Germany.

Of all the qualities of the German ⸱e its capacity for organization is out⸱nding, and Germany owes much to ⸱ astounding organizing ability of ⸱n like Field Marshal Goering; Dr. ⸱ick, the Minister of the Interior; Dr. ⸱dt, the Director of Roads and Con⸱uction; Herr Hierl, the head of the ⸱bor Service Administration; as well ⸱ to the soldiers, sailors, and airmen ⸱o built up the machine and restored ⸱rmany to her present formidable posi⸱tion. Most of us would have been proud to do for our own country what these and others like them did for theirs. It is not the machine which one must blame, but the uses to which it was put and the mind behind it.

Far be it from me to criticize those I have mentioned and many others like them. The mistake which was too easily made abroad was to condemn everything that was Nazi just because its ideology was contrary to ours and because some of its principles and many of its practices were utterly and inexcusably cruel and horrible. Ideological hatreds can be as dangerous to the peace of mankind as the ambitions of a dictator. Both involve the loss of sanity of judgment and of sense of proportion. The result at home was too much criticism and too little constructiveness in respect to Nazi Germany. If Central Europe were to settle down to peace, something more than criticism was essential.

It is probably true to say that, whatever attitude we had adopted toward Hitler and the Nazi gangsters, the result today would have been the same. Nevertheless, throughout those years from 1933 to 1938 we were not, in my opinion, always fair to Germany; and by being unfair we weakened our own case and merely strengthened that of the Nazis. The British tendency to self-righteousness played too big a part in our judgments, and Nazi methods blinded us sometimes to the arguable aspects of some of their contentions. We were too apt to make realities out of wishes and facts out of phrases. There can be no change of heart in Germany unless it comes from within; and we shall never inculcate true democratic ideas in the German people or persuade them to realize the higher responsibilities attached to force and strength unless and until we ourselves treat Germany with strict impartiality and fairness.

Two Germanies

ONE has heard much since the beginning of the war about there being or not being two Germanys: one, kindly, studious, and pacific; and the other, cruel, militarist, and aggressive. In wartime there can only be one Germany, which has to be fought and defeated. The innocent and the guilty have to suffer alike. Yet that does not alter the fact that there are two Germanys, and the outlook for the future would indeed be sad and hopeless if it were not so. Granted that the passive majority of decent Germans allow themselves today to be governed by a brutal and unscrupulous minority. Granted also that German history tends to show that this has generally been the case. Granted that Hitler is merely a typical example of an attitude of mind which has caused war after war.

For it is, of course, the case that, in the last seventy years or so, Germany has initiated or been principally responsible for five wars; against Denmark and Austria in the eighteen sixties, against France in 1870, the war of 1914, and the present one. It is consequently argued that the passive majority always joyfully and willingly follows whither the aggressive minority leads and that it will always be the same. To my mind this argument is erroneous. It is equivalent to asserting that, because the Germans are sheep (and Hitler in *Mein Kampf* himself so describes the masses of the German people), therefore, they are goats.

The wars of the last eighty years may yet prove to have been the evolutionary birth pains of German unity. Fearful thinkers may regard German unity as a consummation to be resisted to the last. A grave danger it certainly is, since no one can deny the German's tendency to be a bully when he is strong. Yet can evolution ever be more than retarded and will not the price be too high if we persist in opposing that unity just because it is a hypothetical danger? Should not our object rather be to educate Germany politically up to a true conception of civilization? We cannot do this unless there are in fact two Germanys. We have to help the sheep, if they are not always to follow the goat. Maybe this will never be possible unless we can first prove to the sheep, by the completeness of their defeat, that butting does not pay.

The Blame for the War

IF I were entitled to apportion the blame for the tragic and ghastly war we have now entered, I should do so as follows: firstly, the overweening ambition and ever growing megalomania of Hitler; secondly, the self-interested and pernicious advice of Herr von Ribbentrop and of the small clique of Nazi veterans and gangsters, of whose names the world has never heard, who fought with Hitler in the streets and on the barricades and to whom, for their services in the struggle for power, were given many of the plums of victory such as the jobs of Reichstag Deputies, Gauleiters, etc.; and thirdly, Himmler and his blackshirted S.S. and secret police.

The vicious oppression of the Gestapo, the bestialities of the prisons and concentration camps, the degradation of the system of spying and denunciation not only constituted for me by far the most repugnant feature of the Nazi regime, but also represented for me one of the most unaccountable sides of the German character. The German individual in normal life is as kindly as the Englishman, and his love for children and animals no less natural and sincere. But, put him in any abnormal position of authority, and in the majority of cases he will at once abuse it. Even in the old Germany Army, the N.C.O. bullied the private and the lieutenant the N.C.O. and so on. Perhaps it is the only language which the German thoroughly understands.

A Gestapo would be inconceivable in England; why should the German nation, accustomed to submission and amenable to discipline though it is, have endured its methods and its cruelties if it did not itself accept such methods as natural, and consequently regard them with an indifference almost amounting to tolerance, if not approval?

The Gestapo will pass away in time; but what, having regard to the future, saddened me still more, as well as filled me with apprehension, was the education of the German youth. I am no educational expert, but roughly the education of the average German boy proceeds along the following course: At six he goes to the elementary, or day school and at seven he joins the Jungvolk, or junior branch of the Hitler Jugend Youth). Much of the training in the Jungvolk corresponds to that of our boy scouts, but he also gets there political lectures on National-Socialist lines (i.e. in the doctrines of racial superiority and national self-sufficiency) as well as training in target shooting. The musket is, a fact, put on his shoulder at the age of seven.

At the age of fourteen and until eighteen it is compulsory for boys to join the Hitler Jugend itself, in which his politico-military education is intensified. At eighteen he does his six months'

labor service, and between the ages of eighteen and twenty (i.e. after his labor service) he does his two years' military service. Only after the latter does he go to the university and while there is obliged to belong to the National-Socialist student organization. There are, of course, various arrangements for specialized training which need not be mentioned here, since I am restricting myself to the life of the average German boy. Whatever his subsequent occupation in life and if he is not already in permanent military employment, he then joins one of the para-military formations such as the S.S. or the S.A.

As a member of either S.S. or S.A. every German male is liable to be called up at any moment for special military service or any other duty and undergoes, till he is well past the age of fifty, refresher or other courses. That is what I mean when I described Germany, on my arrival at Berlin, as being militarized from the cradle to the grave.

But even worse than this dangerous infusion of militaristic spirit, which has at least the redeeming virtues of discipline and obedience, so undeniably salutary to the young, is the politico-ideological poison which has no redeeming feature and with which the youth of the nation is being infected at its most malleable and impressionable stage. It is taught by means of a suppression of all real freedom and independence of thoughts, unparalleled in the history of the civilized world. "Brute force" as Hitler writes in *Mein Kampf* "can alone insure the survival of the race," and the educational values of Germany today are rated in the following order:

1. Race, i.e. the superiority of the Germanic, with its mission to dominate the world.
2. Character, i.e. political reliability in strict accordance with Nazi doctrines.
3. Body, i.e. physical fitness.
4. Knowledge.

Along these few rigidly prescribed lines the mind of German youth since 1933 has been and is being intensively trained, and the reflection was one which made me wonder whether in Germany's own, as well as Europe's ultimate interests, it were not better that war should have come after six years of it rather than after perhaps twenty-six. Even so, maybe it will take a whole generation to eradicate the evil which has been wrought in this respect by Hitler, himself childless.

But, however deplorable these aspects of Nazism might be, internal oppression, which was the German nation's own affair, was distinct for me from external aggression, which was a British concern; and, when I first went to Berlin, I felt that it was unjust and impolitic finally to condemn a whole system because of certain of its more obvious vices. Moreover, I believed that there was no real prospect of stability either in Germany or in Europe generally until the grievances arising out of the Versailles Treaty—which had created Hitler—had been rectified so far as the Germans were concerned. This done, I trusted that Hitler and the reasons for his existence and the method of his regime would disappear in the not too distant future.

But in the meantime I thought that the right policy was to carry conciliation to its utmost point before abandoning hope of agreement. That has always been the traditional policy of England and, if Hitler had had better advisers, he would have realized that its basis was strength and moral justice and not national decadence and weakness, which Ribbentrop persuaded him to believe that it was. Therefore, I was resolved to err, if anything, on the side of impartiality, to try to see the good side of the Nazi regime, if there was one, and to believe in Hitler's word until he proved himself by his deeds to be a perjurer and a breaker of faith.

The Undisputed Leader

It was impossible, indeed, not to wonder on that first occasion and up to the last wherein the greatness of Hitler lay, by what means he had succeeded in imposing himself as the undisputed leader of a great people, and what was —to me—the hidden source of his influence over his followers and of their complete subservience to him. To convince oneself of his greatness, one had to remember his actual deeds and judge by facts.

Of the facts themselves there was no doubt. He had restored to Germany her self-respect and re-created orderliness out of the chaos and distress which had followed her defeat in 1918. It is true that the price that the Germans had had to pay was a heavy one; namely, complete loss of personal liberty, of independent thought, and of free speech. All were obliged to think, speak, and act as they were told to do or suffer exile or persecution.

Nor can it be denied that the rebirth of that nation was due to Hitler's own personal inspiration. For the fact remains that he is the living example of one of those almost incomprehensible leaders who appear from time to time on earth "to fashion the destiny of a race for its weal or its woe, or to crucify the world by a sudden revelation of violence and power." He was abnormal, but so after 1918 was the whole German nation.

National Socialism is a revolution and, if, apart from his demagogic faculties, Hitler had one quality which placed him in an unassailable position above the rest of his fellow revolutionaries, it was his faith. Faith in Germany, faith in his mission for Germany, and, alas, increasingly arrogant faith in himself and in his own greatness. Faith and will power.

I once watched Hitler review his black- and brown-shirted army. The march past lasted for four hours, and practically throughout he remained with

s right arm stretched out at the Nazi
lute. I asked him afterward how he
anaged to do it. His reply was "will
·wer"—and I wondered how much of
was artificially cultivated.

He was no such administrator as is
gnor Mussolini—I doubt if he either
red or knew very much about the
tails of the machine which functioned
his name. But he set its course, put it
motion, or stopped it according to
s own plan.

During my first year in Germany I
nstantly asked those in closest touch
ith Hitler of what his chief quality
nsisted. I was told almost unani-
ously, in his *fingerspitzgefühl* (tip of
e finger feeling), that is to say, his
nse of opportunity, allied with clear-
ss of mind and decision of purpose.
The typical example which was
oted of this was his decision to re-
cupy the Rhineland in 1936, which
as taken contrary to the warning of
s general staff and of all his closest
visers. Germany was at that time not
ilitarily strong enough to disregard a
ench veto; and his followers shrank
om an act which would, they believed,
forcibly opposed by the Western
·wers. Hitler's instinct told him that
e latter would accept an accomplished
t, and he disregarded all warnings to
e contrary. The event proved him
ht and greatly reinforced his prestige,
t only among his own immediate sup-
rters but throughout Germany as a
ole. Incidentally, it was probably the
t opportunity when it would still
ve been possible for Britain and
ance to have said "no" to the Dictator
thout being obliged to go to war to
force that "no."

WAS once asked by a German acquaintance who must, in view of his
mer official position, have had many
ks with him whether I ever managed
ring my interviews with Hitler to
t a word in edgeways. It was a curious
servation, suggesting as it did that he
nself never had. That was, however,

not my experience. He may not have
heeded what I said; and he may, like
Ribbentrop, only have been thinking
what he himself was going to say next;
but he always seemed ready to listen,
nor did he speechify to any unendurable
extent.

Hitler always wore a simple brown
tunic without any decorations except the
Iron Cross of the second class, which
he had won in the great war. He was
very unlike Goering in this respect; yet,
in a sense, both extremes appealed to
the Germans. They might make fun of
but they liked Goering's unabashed display of show and medals. At the same
time Hitler's simplicity was one of the
sheet anchors of his hold on the people.
His followers built themselves villas and
gardens and acquired estates and other
private belongings by means which were
suspected of being of doubtful honesty;
and, except in Goering's case, the people
were indignant and resentful.

The comparison between the other
Nazi leaders and Hitler in this respect
was all the more flattering to the latter
and was appreciated by the mass of the
nation accordingly. The others may have
provided for themselves nest eggs
abroad, but Hitler would certainly not
have done so.

Many Germans, women in particular,
used to descant to me upon the radiance
of his expression and his remarkable
eyes. When I looked into the latter, they
were generally hot and angry. That was
possibly my misfortune, since I only
saw him on official occasions; but I must
confess that, in spite of his achievements, which no one could belittle, he
never on that first occasion or later gave
me any impression of greatness. He was
a spellbinder for his own people. That
is self-evident, nor was there any doubt
about his capacity to charm, if he set
himself out to do so. It was part of his
stock in trade, and I was more than
once the spectator of its efficiency. But
he never exerted it in my case, and I
consequently never experienced it.

In his reasonable moods I was often

disconcerted by the sanity and logic of his arguments; but, when he became excitable, which was the mood which most influenced his countrymen, I had but one inclination, which was to beg him to calm down. He had considerable natural dignity and was invariably courteous; but to the last I continued to ask myself how he had risen to what

he was and how he maintained h ascendance over the German peopl The answer to the second question lie in my opinion, in the fact that, firstl the Germans like to be governed by a autocratic ruler and that, secondly, tl party, having got its leader, cann change him. To avoid its own destru tion it is obliged to keep him there.

May: 1937

THE position in May, 1937, when I reached Berlin, was as follows: All power was concentrated in the hands of Hitler. There was control of the press but not of the budget; no rival parties were tolerated, and every official was his nominee, removable at his will. While the economic and financial position of Germany was showing signs of deterioration, her military strength in material and man power was vastly and rapidly increasing; and her foreign alliances were being consolidated and exploited. Europe was being soothed by repeated assertions that nothing was further from Hitler's mind than any thought of revolutionary or territorial conquests. Respect for other nationalities was still the declared principle of Nazism, which was sometimes euphemistically described as the form of democracy most appropriate to Germany. It was a period of calm; but, as far as Germany was concerned, of concentrated preparation.

The two main political questions were the civil war in Spain and the future of Austria. Germany was still being rep-

resented abroad as the barrier to Bo shevism, and communism was st serving as the justification for much i ternal oppression. But Britain, to judg from the German press, was publ enemy No. 1. The campaign for the turn of the German colonies had be revived in 1936 and was still interm tently but consistently prominent; b the chief grievance was Britain's do in-the-manger attitude toward Ge many's rightful place in the sun and h claims to *Lebensraum,* or living spac in Central and Eastern Europe. As Goe ing said to me on the occasion of n first visit to him, "Germany cannot pi one flower without England's saying her, *'Es ist verboten'* (It is forbidden) It was useless to discuss that misus word *Lebensraum* with the Nazis. Th could or would not see that "livi room" was only justifiable, if it impli the strengthening of economic relatio by legitimate means, but was unjusti able if it signified political dominati by means of military or economic pr sure. To them it only meant the latter

Attempts to Improve Anglo-German Relations

I HAD been just one month at Berlin when I was instructed by His Majesty's Government to make the first of what was destined to be a series of definite and considered attempts by Mr. Chamberlain (who had now succeeded Lord Baldwin as Prime Minister) to improve Anglo-German relations. It consisted in an invitation to Baron von Neurath to come to London at an early date to discuss, primarily, naval control in Spain, in which Germany had ceased

to participate after the attack on t pocket battleship *Deutschland* by Spa ish Government bombers at Iviza, b also in general to review the whole ternal political situation. The invitati was eventually accepted, and announc to take place between the twenty-thi and twenty-eighth of June.

My satisfaction at this apparent su cess was short-lived, and was typical the malignant fate which seemed to d all our efforts to open the door to Ang

German discussions. At first I was inclined to attribute this to ill chance, and
it was not until later that I realized it
was by design.

On June 19th it was officially announced in Berlin that following the
bombing of the *Deutschland* an unsuccessful torpedo attack had been made
on the German cruiser *Leipzig* off Oran;
and on the following day I received a
brief private letter from Neurath telling
me that his visit to London could not
now take place.

The twentieth of June was a Sunday,
and I spent all the morning and the
afternoon in trying to find the Minister
for Foreign Affairs. He had, I think,
regarded discretion as the better part of
valor and disappeared into the country,
destination unknown. I managed, however, to get hold of him late in the evening and went to see him at his private
house in the garden of the Ministry for
Foreign Affairs. I told him that the
Leipzig incident in itself only rendered
his visit to London still more desirable,
that I could not take his refusal to go
there as a final answer without having
first seen the Chancellor myself and put
the case to him. Baron von Neurath was
good enough to arrange this for me,
and I had an interview with him and
Hitler on the following morning.

Hitler had just come back from Wil-
helmshaven, whither the *Deutschland*
had returned to bury the thirty-odd
sailors who had been killed. Hitler refused to listen to any of my very logical
arguments and persisted in the standpoint that he could not at such a moment permit his Foreign Minister to
leave Germany. His attitude was so
utterly unreasonable that I was at a loss
to explain it even to myself.

In the light of a better acquaintance
later with the inner facts, I derived the
conclusion that the *Leipzig* incident—
the truth of which was never even
verified—had merely served as a pretext
for going back on an acceptance which
had never really appealed to Hitler himself, but still less to his Ambassador in

London, Herr von Ribbentrop. The
latter, in addition to his London post,
was Ambassador at Large, and felt that
Neurath's visit was detrimental to his
own prestige and wounding to his personal vanity. He had the fatal defect of
always looking for offense, and of
having, in consequence, a perpetual
"chip on his shoulder." I feel sure that
he did his utmost from the outset to
dissuade his master from agreeing to the
course proposed by His Majesty's Government, and the *Leipzig* story enabled
him to win his case. The notorious
failure of his mission to London was
already rankling, and it was intolerable
that another should come and show up
the personal cause of that failure.

History will assuredly attribute a large
share of the blame for September, 1939,
to Ribbentrop; and his successful intrigue against Neurath's visit to London
was neither the first nor unfortunately
the last instance of his sinister influence
on the policy of his Führer. It was a disheartening beginning for myself, and
the abrupt manner in which the visit
was cancelled by the German Government was not encouraging for His
Majesty's Government. In accordance
with the rules of ordinary civility, it
would have been proper for the German
Government, as soon as the excitement
over the *Leipzig* incident had died
down, themselves to suggest a later date
for the visit. They did not, however, do
so; and it was left to Mr. Chamberlain
to take the initiative again and to make
a second attempt, later in the year, to
establish contact by sending Lord Halifax
to Berlin.

HITLER cannot but have been—and in
fact, so I heard, was—impressed by
the obvious sincerity, high principles,
and straightforward honesty of a man
like Lord Halifax. The general German
public regarded the visit as a proof of
British good will toward Germany and
was clearly appreciative. Nevertheless,
the official German tendency was to sit
back and wait. As Goering said to me

after the visit, "Does the Prime Minister really mean business, and will he be able to impose his will upon those circles in England which seek to negative everything which is Nazi, or is not run on the old lines of the League of Nations, French encirclement, collective security, and Russia as the counterpoise to Germany in Europe?" That was the orthodox German view of British policy then; but the fact was that, in spite of all his professions of a desire for an understanding with Britain, Hitler was himself in no hurry. He was astute enough to realize that he had first to cross the Austrian and other brooks.

The clouds were unmistakably gathering over Austria, and the star of Henlein was already rising in the Sudeten firmament. The Spanish war was still the major preoccupation of the democratic governments, and behind that smoke screen Hitler was steadily and skillfully consolidating his position. Russia had been weakened by her military purges;

while, on the other hand, the Rome-Berlin Axis had become a world triangle through the signature by Italy and Japan of the Anti-Comintern Pact. The three countries constituted a new, powerful, and aggressive bloc; and the smaller states were already beginning to wonder whether comparative immunity under the aegis of Germany was not safer than the theoretical collective security offered to them at Geneva.

Generally speaking, 1937 was for Hitler a year of intensive preparation, both diplomatic and military.

I have alluded to my mission to Berlin as a drama. The year 1937 constituted its orchestral overture, of which the Wagnerian leitmotivs were the disciplined tramp of armed men, ever louder and more multitudinous, and the ceaseless clank of heavy machinery forging guns and yet bigger guns, tanks and ever heavier tanks, bombers and still more powerful and destructive bombers. It was a somber introduction.

The Third Attempt

BETWEEN, however, the prelude and the first act, there was an interlude, in the course of which Mr. Chamberlain made his third effort in eight months to initiate with Hitler discussions, the object of which was to lead to those serious negotiations, with a view to the settlement by pacific methods of all outstanding problems, which was the settled policy of Mr. Chamberlain's Government vis-à-vis Germany.

Goering had said after Lord Halifax's visit, "Does Mr. Chamberlain really mean business?" To prove that he did so I was recalled to London at the end of January, 1938, and given instructions to seek an interview with Hitler and to discuss the possibilities of a general settlement. If we judged by the German press, as well as Hitler's own statements to casual British visitors, the twin obstacles to a better understanding between our two countries were our constant opposition to Germany in Europe and our refusal to hand back the colonies of

which we had "robbed" her. I was consequently told to inform Hitler that His Majesty's Government would be ready, in principle, to discuss all outstanding questions.

I returned to Berlin on February 4th, but in view of the unsettled atmosphere caused by the reorganization following on the Blomberg marriage incident, my actual audience with Hitler was deferred until March 3rd. By that time Mr. Eden had left the Government, and Lord Halifax had succeeded him as Foreign Secretary. Unfortunately—and it seemed fated that it should always be so for my meetings with Hitler—the moment was an ill-chosen one. Dr. Schuschnigg had been summoned to Berchtesgaden on February 12th, and the Austrian kettle was boiling hard and on the point of boiling over. Hitler was consequently in a vile temper and made no effort to conceal it.

He listened, nevertheless, till I had finished and then let himself go. Nothing ng, he said, could be done until the press campaign against him in England ceased. (He never ceased harping on this subject in every conversation which I ever had with him.) Nor was he going to tolerate the interference of third parties in Central Europe. Injustice was being done to millions of Germans, and self-determination and democratic rights must be applied to Germans as well as others. Only 15 per cent of the Austrian population supported the Schuschnigg regime; if Britain opposed a just settlement, Germany would have to fight. If Germans were oppressed there, he must and would intervene; and, if he did intervene, he would act like lightning (*Blitzschnell*). Austria must be allowed to vote, and in Czechoslovakia the Germans must have autonomy in cultural and other matters.

As for colonies he did not seem the least interested in them, and the sum of his reply was that the colonial problem could wait for 4, 6, 8, or even 10 years. He promised, however, to give me a written reply on the subject, and I left Berlin a year and a half later without having ever received it.

Mr. Chamberlain's third attempt to initiate those discussions with Germany which might have been calculated to insure peace in Europe had thus failed, as it was foredoomed that it should, since at that juncture it was only Austria and Central Europe in which Hitler was interested. The episode is, however, important and should be borne in mind. It constitutes evidence of the fact that, except as a means to an end, it was not an understanding with Great Britain but the end itself, namely, dominion in Central and Eastern Europe, that Hitler alone really wanted.

What Does Hitler Want?

IN THE years between 1933 and 1938 it was a common question to hear, "What does Hitler really want?" It had always been answered—and notably by my predecessor, Sir Eric Phipps, in his valedictory dispatch of 1937—in the same sense: first, Austria, then the Sudeten Lands; and after that, the liquidation of Memel, the Corridor, and Danzig; and finally the lost colonies. From the beginning of my mission I had never found any reason to disagree with the accuracy of a judgment which I entirely indorsed.

Czechoslovakia was the keystone of the French alliance system, and the potential bulwark against German expansion southeastward. But after Hitler's bloodless conquest of Austria she was left—vis-à-vis Germany—in a completely helpless position both strategically and economically, and it was clear that the integrity of her Versailles frontiers could only be upheld if France and England were prepared either to negotiate or to fight for their maintenance. War or peaceful negotiations were, in fact, the issues at stake.

One realistic glance at the map of Europe would have sufficed to prove, namely, the indefensibility of Czechoslovakia's strategic and economic position, once Austria had become an integral part of Germany. Though heavily fortified in the north, she had now become highly vulnerable to attack from the south. Quite apart from the national artificiality of this creation of Versailles, which contained in miniature all the diverse racial problems of the old Austro-Hungarian Empire, Czechoslovakia suffered from one fatal defect: her minorities, Polish and Hungarian no less than German, were situated on her very frontiers, and contiguous to the nations which claimed them.

On the broadest moral grounds it was thus difficult to justify offhand the refusal of the right of self-determination to the 2,750,000 Sudetens living in solid blocks just across Germany's border. Its flat denial would have been contrary to a principle on which the British Empire itself was founded, and would, consequently, never have rallied to us the whole-hearted support either of the British people or of that Empire.

Only one solution had any real prospect of success, and that was the conversion of Czechoslovakia from a national state, governed solely by the Czechs, into a state of nationalities, where all, and especially the Sudetens as the biggest minority, had equal and autonomous rights. It had been understood at Versailles that that would be the case. But Dr. Benes undoubtedly felt that such a new creation could not long survive as an entity; and rather than submit to it, he resolved to shelter himself behind the optimistic belief that, in the last resort, France, England, and Russia would save him from the necessity of what he regarded as excessive and dangerous concessions to the German minority.

I have today no hesitation in stigmatizing as completely erroneous the belief held in some quarters that it was possible, with so little material force behind us and on such uncertain moral ground as the refusal of the right of self-determination to the Sudetens, to call by mere words what was alleged to have been, but certainly was not, Hitler's bluff in September, 1938. It is not enough merely to be guided by the facilely popular argument that the only thing in principle to say to a dictator is "No," and to say it as publicly as possible. As I wrote at the time, "If ever we aspire to call Hitler's bluff, let us first be quite prepared to face the consequences." France and England were not prepared in September, 1938.

Munich

IN THESE circumstances the Prime Minister set into operation his plan for personal contact with Hitler, and shortly after my return to Berlin I received instructions to arrange it accordingly.

By the terms of the subsequent Munich Pact, Germany incorporated the Sudeten Lands in the Reich without bloodshed and without firing a shot. But she had not got all that Hitler wanted and which she would have got if the arbitrament had been left to war, namely, the strategical frontier which so many Germans desired and which would have included Prague, the seat of the first German university. Czechoslovakia had lost—and a bit more—territories which it would probably have been wiser not to have included at Versailles in the Czech state and which could never, except on the basis of federation, have remained permanently therein. The humiliation of the Czechs was a tragedy, but it was solely thanks to Mr. Chamberlain's courage and pertinacity that a futile and senseless war was averted.

As I wrote at the time, "The day may come when we may be forced to fight Germany again. If we have to do so, I trust that the cause may be one in which the morality of our case is so unimpeachable, the honor and vital interests of Britain so clearly at stake, as to insure us the full support of the united British people, of the Empire and of world public opinion." This would not have been the case in September, 1938.

The Munich settlement thus deprived Hitler of the great satisfaction—to which he was ardently looking forward—of giving his army a little experience, of appearing himself in the role of a conquering hero, and of wreaking vengeance on Benes and the Czechs. In one sense he may have been not ungrateful to Mr. Chamberlain for having prevented a world war to which his army and people were opposed; in another, any gratitude which he may have felt was far outweighed by resentment at having been compelled to change his mind.

In yet another sense, too, Hitler felt irritated with himself. A section of his followers were always egging him on to fight England while the latter was still militarily unprepared. They reproached him for having accepted the Munich settlement and thus having missed the most favorable opportunity. An uneasy feeling lest they might have been right contributed to Hitler's ill humor.

Nor was Munich in itself an agreeable experience for him. He found himself there for once in the company of three men who were his equals, instead of being surrounded by sycophants obedient to his slightest gesture. The experience confirmed his dislike for settlement by negotiation.

Moreover, the evident popularity of Mr. Chamberlain with the German people not only detracted from his own personal prestige but also gave him food for uneasy reflection. He could dragoon his people, and they would always follow him; but could he count on their willing devotion in all circumstances? It was the first unpleasant rift between him and his people, and it was the peace efforts of Mr. Chamberlain which had started it.

It is certainly a fact that, after Munich, he showed considerable ill will toward those who had argued with him against pushing things to extremes. His Voice had told him that there would be no general war, or that, even if there were, there could be no more propitious moment for it than that October; and for once he had been obliged to disregard that Voice and to listen to counsels of prudence. After Munich, those whom he regarded as the faint hearts in Germany, beginning with Goering and passing through many strata of the party and of the Government officials, fell from grace. On the other hand, this uneasy reflection was the main cause of the rise to favor of the Ribbentrops and Himmlers, and of his subsequent measures for the reinforcement, by means of the S.A., of the party vis-à-vis the Army, which had also been antiwar. But it was his own faint-heartedness which probably infuriated him most; for the first time he had failed to obey his Voice.

Dr. Jekyll and Mr. Hyde

ONE is obliged to theorize to a certain extent in endeavoring to arrive at an accurate estimate of these underlying forces, since the world problem today starts with individuals. In the final report on events leading up to the declaration of war, which I wrote on my return to England, I remarked that Hitler would prove a fascinating study for historians with psychological leanings in the future. His critics today describe him by many strange names: he may be any or all of them, but I prefer to leave it to the professional psychiatrist to pronounce the verdict. For me he was a sort of Dr. Jekyll and Mr. Hyde.

To begin with, he may not have been more than a visionary of genius or a practical dreamer with a sublime faith in himself and in his mission to reinstate Germany in her former position among the nations. *Mein Kampf* shows that he was naturally endowed with a highly developed political sense, but it is unlikely that his original ambitions were as wide as they subsequently became. His initial aspiration may well have been to become Chancellor of Germany, to complete her unity by means of the incorporation of Austria, his own motherland, as a first objective, and to restore to Germany her self-respect and prosperity.

The interesting point to elucidate would be when he ceased to be Jekyll and became Hyde. It was probably a matter of gradual evolution. Dictators, having achieved absolutism, lose their sense of proportion. Each success leads to ever expanding aims, while their insatiable desire for their own permanence drives them in the end to put self before their country, and to adventure as the sole means of maintaining their hold. So it was with Napoleon and so it seems to me to have been with Hitler. The Chancellorship, the unity and prosperity of Germany were, in the end, not enough. His flatterers described him as the successor of Frederick the Great and Bismarck; and, as time went on, he felt himself called upon to emulate their military victories as well as their other constructive achievements.

Thus, to himself, he became something far greater, conceivably a sort of

Mahomet with a "sword in one hand and *Mein Kampf* in the other." And with such a sword there need be no longer any limit to his ambitions except his own death. His habit of constantly hinting, in public as well as in private, that his life would not be a long one gave rise to rumors about some incurable disease from which he was suffering; but I often wondered whether he did not merely use the idea as an excuse to justify his own restless impatience. He was a skillful mixer of fraud with force, and was always seeking to find for everything excuses which would hoodwink his people into submitting to anything which he might order for them.

But I must return to the reactions of Hitler after Munich. It must always be borne in mind that Hitler was no administrative leader, and that his power over his people was mystical rather than executive. He owed his success in the struggle for power to the fact that he was the reflection of their subconscious mind and to his ability to express in words what that subconscious mind felt that it wanted. Once he achieved power, he impressed the people most by his opportunistic or instinctive judgments as to what could or could not be done and as to the right moment to do it.

I do not know what the feelings of the German people are today, but nothing in 1938 shook their confidence in their leader more than the realization that they had been led to the brink of war to satisfy the personal resentment of their dictator. Every German approved in principle of the incorporation of their Sudeten fellow countrymen in the Reich, but they did not see the point of going to war for something which could so easily be got without war.

Was the case very different in 1939 in respect to Danzig and the Corridor?

Two Alternatives

There were, generally speaking, two obvious alternatives for Hitler after Munich: either to misuse Germany's great military strength for the purposes of political domination and for the satisfaction of his own restless and ever increasing ambitions, or to abandon jungle law in its cruder forms and to return to peaceful collaboration in conjunction with other countries.

To the ordinary observer every argument of common sense seemed, in Germany's own interests, to indicate that the latter would be not only the happiest for his people, but also the most prudent course for Hitler himself to follow. Leaving the desires of the mass of the German people out of account, even Hitler himself, after his great but exhausting successes during the past six years, should have been yearning for a period of more tranquil existence, during which he would be able not only to consolidate the unity which he had accomplished, but also to give scope to his much advertised and already partially commenced artistic and constructive plans for the beautification of Greater Germany. Moreover, Germany would be all the more powerful later if she were given time to digest the extensive additions of territory which she had just acquired.

Admittedly, if he had wished to follow the road to normalcy, he would have been obliged to break with his extremist minority, with the Ribbentrops and Himmlers, Hesses and Leys, and rabble of his street-fighting days. Possibly also with the youth of the country, which he had spent the last six years in perverting to his own revolutionary uses.

The Germans are notorious for their lack not only of balance but also of any understanding of the mentality and reactions of others. The successes of Nazism had been so great that its devotees, and especially the German youth, felt that nothing and nobody could stop them anywhere. After the postwar humiliations, their desire to prove their recuperated strength and importance to the world was a consuming one; nor did they regard anyone in continental Europe as capable of standing up to their bullying. Her postwar experiences had unfortunately taught Nazi Germany that nothing could be achieved except by force or the display of force; and in such a frame of mind any compromise or reversion to static conditions was difficult and would only have been regarded as a sign of weakness.

To ALL such elements as those just mentioned above, the road to adventure was clearly the most attractive and the most profitable. It is true that they constituted but a small minority; and, as a demagogue, Hitler's natural inclination should have been to please the majority of his people. But minorities, especially in revolutionary times, exercise an influence entirely disproportionate to their actual numbers.

Apart from these active careerists, another dangerous aspect of the situation was Germany's increasing financial and economic difficulties. The strain, both mental and material, under which the German people had been working since 1933 was immense, and required an increasingly violent psychological stimulus to keep it working. It was estimated in 1938 that 60 per cent or more of the sum of her efforts in human beings, labor, and materials was destined for war. No people, even though disciplined and hard working as are the Germans, would put up indefinitely with guns instead of butter or endure an economic policy based solely on *Wehrwirtschaft,* namely, the control of the whole of a nation's economic output in the interests of military preparedness.

There was always the question, therefore, whether Hitler would not feel obliged to seek to conquer by force the markets which Germany had lost by over-concentration on armaments, or, in other words, be compelled to follow the road of further adventure, either in order to forestall economic collapse or as the result of it.

Economic disaster spelt unpopularity for Hitler and for Nazism; and to many thinking Germans the real problem was whether Hitler could change his economic policy and revert to normalcy without another internal revolution. It had so long been organized on a purely military-autarchic basis, that it would certainly have been difficult to reverse the process and reknit the fabric of free commerce with the outside world without incurring severe dislocation and unemployment.

Yet, even in this respect I was always disinclined to accept the oversimplified theory that Hitler would necessarily be obliged to seek further adventure in order to avoid economic collapse. I had too high a respect for the capacity of German organization to regard such a theory as the whole truth. Moreover, a prosperous and peaceful Germany was a British interest. Therefore we were prepared to help her to overcome her financial and economic difficulties to the best of our ability.

From the long view, it was clear that Europe could never be stable and peaceful until Germany was once more settled and prosperous. Her prosperity would facilitate her economic rivalry with ourselves but in the end would have benefited both. There was no constructive value in standing aloof and keeping Germany, one of our best customers, permanently lean. The theory that, if Hitler were treated as a pariah, the German nation would itself overturn him and his regime had no foundation in fact and was merely the outcome of wishful thinking. The reverse was actually the case, and the denial of help and the refusal of all sympathetic understanding merely drove the nation to despair and to cling closer to him as the sole defender of German interests in all spheres of activity.

Be that as it may, I would give much to know what was at the back of Hitler's mind during those fateful six months after Munich when he stood at the parting of the ways.

"Beware the Ides of March"

THOUGH the possibility of an armed coup on Czechoslovakia in view of Germany's position and her power to foment trouble in that country could never be discarded, I must confess that almost up to the last moment I found it difficult to believe that Hitler would go quite as far as he did.

As in the case of Austria just a year earlier, events moved with startling rapidity and the German press was full of wild tales of Czech atrocities and of Germans flying for refuge. The year before, Hitler had finally made up his mind to march into Austria on March 11th, and this year the decision to occupy Czechoslovakia was taken on March 12th. Large numbers of troops were already in Vienna with a view to a review being held there, at which Hitler was to be present, to celebrate the anniversary of the *Anschluss:* others had been concentrated in South Germany with the alleged object of supporting Italian claims, which were at that time being pressed against France. The position on the chessboard was propitious, and Hitler resolved to strike once again at the exact moment most favorable to his designs.

The tales of Czech atrocities grew, Germans were reported as being illtreated and massacred, refugees from the German area of Brünn were described as streaming in thousands toward the Austrian frontier, and so on and so forth *ad nauseam.* It was these stories which served as the pretext for Hitler to change his mind, to cancel the ultimatum, and to substitute in its place a full military occupation and the establishments of the Protectorate. He was a genius at finding or creating plausible excuses for all his actions, however iniquitous!

It is difficult to believe that these machinations were not an intrinsic part of Hitler's own schemes; yet it seems but fair to relate that I heard some months later a story which seemed to indicate that they were not. On his arrival at Prague on March 15th, one of the first things which Hitler expressed a wish to do was to visit the hospitals. His entourage, probably soldiers and consequently less well informed than Himmler's blackshirts, asked him for what purpose. "To visit the German wounded victims of Czech ill treatment," was Hitler's answer. As there were none, his followers had some difficulty in persuading him that such a visit would be useless. Possibly they induced him to believe that they existed everywhere except in Prague itself; but, if the story is true—and my source was both a Czech and a good one—it would seem to indicate that some of the party were even more impatient than Hitler himself or even that the Führer was to some extent at least the tool of his extremists.

As a coup it was a brilliant success, but in every other respect it constituted an irreparable political blunder. By the occupation of Prague, Hitler put himself once for all morally and unquestionably in the wrong and destroyed the entire arguable validity of the German case as regards the Treaty of Versailles. After Prague, Nazism ceased to be national and racial and became purely dynamic and felonious. By his callous destruction of the hard and newly won liberty of a free and independent people, Hitler deliberately violated the Munich Agreement, which he had signed not quite six months before; and his undertaking to Mr. Chamberlain, once the Sudeten had been incorporated in the Reich, to respect the independence and integrity of the Czech people. Thereafter Hitler's word could never more be trusted nor could the most pacifically minded disregard the rape of Prague.

It was a repetition of Belgium, 1914, in another form; and it is no exaggeration to say that in 1939, also, the war has been caused by the deliberate tearing up by Germany of a scrap of paper.

Up till that March, as I wrote in my final report, the German ship of state had flown the German national flag. On those Ides of March, its captain defiantly hoisted the skull and crossbones of the pirate, and appeared under his true colors as an unprincipled menace to European peace and liberty.

Until then the world, passionately anxious for peace as an end in itself and fully conscious of the horrors of the next war, had watched Hitler proceed from success to success and had appeared to forgive or to be taken in by the hateful methods and technique which he invariably employed. But Prague was the limit. There was no sense of security left anywhere in Europe, nothing but an atmosphere of complete lack of confidence in Hitler's good faith or in his readiness to abide by any undertaking which he might in future give.

His Majesty's Government took the only course open to them at that moment, by recalling me for an indefinite period to London. My mission to Berlin was already a failure, and from that moment I had no real hopes of peace except in a miracle. Though the ship was sinking, to that precarious hope I clung for another five and a half weary and anxious months.

The Russo-German Alliance

THE ostensible motive of my recall to London was to report, but I left Berlin feeling that I might well never return there. But after five weeks' absence from my post I was eventually instructed by His Majesty's Government to return to Berlin. I got back there on April 24th.

If peace were to be preserved, it was essential that it should be made crystal clear beyond what limit Germany could not go without provoking England to war. In 1914 His Majesty's Government had been accused of not making this plain enough. There may have been some justification for this reproach, and Mr. Chamberlain's Government were determined that the risk should not be incurred again.

The danger signal, which all who ran might read, was accordingly hoisted, in respect to Poland. His Majesty's Government made a reciprocal agreement with Poland. And then, since Germany's designs appeared to be limitless, unilateral undertakings were similarly given a few weeks later in respect to Rumania and Greece.

Britain thus made her position unmistakably plain. Yet the upshot only shows how difficult it is to please Germans. In 1914 we were accused of having caused the war because we had not said beforehand what we intended to do. In 1939, because we did make our position crystal clear, we are equally being accused of having provoked the war by intimidating Germany.

From the outset, however, it was quite obvious that, in spite of the Anglo-Polish Agreement and whatever might be the ultimate outcome of war, neither Britain nor France was in a position to render any effective immediate aid to Poland if she were attacked by Germany's overwhelmingly powerful Air Force and highly mechanized Army. No physical courage would avail against the superiority afforded by these technical and material advantages. It could only be a question of at most a few months before Poland would be overwhelmed, *i.e.*, long before any blockade or pressure on the Siegfried Line from the west would be available to help her in her one-sided struggle. Immediate support if she were to have any, must come from the east, and Russia alone was capable of giving it.

WITH this consideration in mind, and with a view to the necessary inclusion of Russia in the peace front against further German aggression, the British and French Governments began the negotiations with the U.S.S.R. which were to drag on throughout those precious four months, only to end in

Russia's abrupt *volte-face* toward the end of August.

Persistent rumors of German counter negotiations reached us in Berlin; and, indeed, the effort thus to break the peace front was only to be expected. Nevertheless, after the actual dispatch in August of the French and our own military missions to Moscow, I no longer thought that they would be successful. I could not imagine that Russian perfidy was as great as all that. I must add that I had, and with better justification as the event proved, equally little confidence that our own negotiations would be more so, particularly after the inexplicable dismissal of Litvinov in the early stages of our negotiations.

For my part in Berlin I was preaching patience and giving solemn warnings to all and sundry. I made it quite clear that, while nobody desired more than we did an amicable arrangement between Germany and Poland in respect to Danzig and the Corridor, we were determined to oppose in the future force by force.

Though Ribbentrop was at that time making great play with his own special brand of propaganda, to the effect that Britain would never fight over Danzig, Field Marshal Goering did not appear to doubt that such was our fixed resolve. He rather seemed or pretended to believe that Britain contemplated a preventive war in any case against Germany. He probably took his cue from Hitler, who with his phenomenal capacity both for self-delusion and misrepresentation is still arguing that his justification for war was that belief.

Goering was accordingly at pains to explain to me at length why no power or combination of powers could prevail against Germany in Europe. He expatiated on the inability of France to stand a long war, on the military unpreparedness of the Poles and of their lack of real unity, on the unwillingness of the U.S.S.R. to give Poland any effective assistance, on the harm which a war would cause to the British Empire, and on Germany's invincible might.

My conversations with Goering led consequently nowhere in particular, as was, I fear, the fate of all my conversations, however stimulating, with him. But, whatever may have been in Hitler's mind, war did not appear at that time to be either the desire or an immediate preoccupation of Goering.

By July the Russian negotiations had ceased to have for me even the superficial appearance of any reality, and I still believe that from the outset Moscow never meant them to terminate in agreement with us. Moscow had become the seat of an oriental despotism, and the ideological basis of the Soviet regime was now nothing but a sham and a delusion. Stalin's sole objective was to embroil Germany with the Western Powers and to make one or the other pull the chestnuts out of the fire for himself.

It is to be hoped that someday light will be thrown on the question as to whether Stalin from the beginning was in collusion with Hitler with a view to spinning out his negotiations with us until Germany was ready to strike or whether both Germany and ourselves were merely his catspaws. I incline to the latter view myself, but it is mere guess work, and I am prejudiced.

The most that I hoped was that, if the U.S.S.R., however half-heartedly, joined the peace front, Hitler would regard discretion as the better part of valor and come down on the side of peaceful discussion. But I always believed that Moscow's chief aim was to embroil Germany and the Western Powers in a common ruin and to emerge as the *tertius gaudens* of the conflict between them. This was, up to August, similarly the professed view of all Germans from Hitler downward who commented on our Russian negotiations.

I raised this point with Hitler himself when I saw him at Berchtesgaden on August 23rd. Ribbentrop was at Moscow on that day engaged in signing the

Russo-German Treaty, and Hitler expatiated to me triumphantly on the value and great advantages of the new alliance, which he said was definite and permanent. I reminded him of his previous attitude toward the Soviets, expressed the opinion that he might find Russia's friendship even more dangerous than her enmity; and added, speaking quite personally and on purely moral grounds, that, if an agreement had to be made with Moscow, for whom communism was now merely the cloak for intense nationalism and whose ulterior motives seemed to me highly suspicious, I had rather Germany made it than ourselves. Hitler was for a moment confused and taken aback. He retorted, however, that it was all our fault: it was we who had driven him into Russia's arms. But it was the answer of a man who was seeking to excuse himself.

Last Efforts to Prevent War

At my first interview with him on that day Hitler was in a mood of extreme excitability. His language as regards the Poles and British responsibility for the Polish attitude was violent, recriminatory, and exaggerated. He referred, for instance, to 100,000 German refugees from Poland, a figure which was at least five times greater than the reality. Again I cannot say whether he was persuaded or persuaded himself of the reality of these figures.

At my second interview he had recovered his calm but was not less obdurate. Everything was England's fault. She had encouraged the Czechs last year, and she was now giving a blank check to Poland. No longer, he told me, did he trust Mr. Chamberlain. He preferred war, he said, when he was fifty to when he was fifty-five or sixty. He had himself always sought and believed in the possibility of friendship with England. He now realized, he said, that those who had argued to the contrary had been right and nothing short of a complete change in British policy toward Germany could ever convince him of any sincere British desire for good relations.

My last remark to him was that I could only deduce from his language that my mission to Germany had failed and that I bitterly regretted it.

I flew back from Berchtesgaden to Berlin the same evening. I had, in fact, little hope that either the Prime Minister's letter or my own language to Hitler, however direct and straightforward, would give him pause. The Russian Pact had, I felt, created in his opinion a situation which was favorable to his designs; and I believed his mind to be definitely made up. Though he spoke in a Neronic vein of his artistic tastes and of his longing to satisfy them, I derived the impression that the corporal of the last war was even more anxious to prove what he could do as a conquering generalissimo in the next. What the world or Germany might suffer was of no consequence so long as his lust to show what he as leader of Germany could do was satisfied. More than once he repeated to me that, if he had been Chancellor of Germany in 1914, she would never have lost that war in 1918.

Nevertheless, the visit to Berchtesgaden may after all have postponed the disaster for a week. Ribbentrop flew back to Germany with the signed Russo-German Agreement; and Hitler returned to Berlin the night of August 24th.

I have, as I have mentioned earlier, some reason to believe—though I cannot confirm it—that the order for the German Army to advance into Poland was actually issued for the night of August 25th-26th. It is difficult otherwise to find justification for the various orders and arrangements which came into force on August 26th and 27th. In the afternoon of August 27th itself all telephone communication between Berlin and London and Paris was unexpectedly cut off for several hours. The celebrations at Tannenberg were cancelled on the 26th and the party rally at Nuremberg on

August 27th; all naval, military, and air attachés at Berlin were refused permission to leave the city without prior authority's being obtained from the Ministry of War. All German airports were closed from August 26th, and the whole of Germany became a prohibited zone for all aircraft except the regular civil lines. All internal German air services were also suspended. Moreover, as from the 27th a system for the rationing of foodstuffs and other commodities throughout Germany came into force. That this latter and—for the public—depressing measure should have been adopted prior to the outbreak of war can scarcely be explained except on the assumption that war should actually have broken out on August 26th.

It was not the horrors of war or the thought of dead Germans which deterred him. He had unlimited confidence in the magnificent army and air force which he had re-created, and he was certainly not averse to putting them to the test so far as Poland was concerned. In two months, he told me, the war in the east would be ended; and he would then, he said, hurl 160 divisions against the Western Front, if England were so unwise as to oppose his plans. His hesitation was due rather to one final effort to detach Britain from Poland. Be that as it may, at about 12:45 on August 25th I received a message to the effect that Hitler wished to receive me at the Chancellery at 1:30 P.M.

Briefly put, Hitler's proposals therein dealt with two groups of questions: (a) the immediate necessity of a settlement of the dispute between Germany and Poland, and (b) an eventual offer of friendship or alliance between Germany and Great Britain.

My interview with Hitler, at which Herr von Ribbentrop and Dr. Schmidt were also present, lasted on this occasion over an hour. The Chancellor spoke with calm and apparent sincerity. He described his proposals as a last effort, for conscience' sake, to secure good relations with Great Britain; and he suggested that I should fly to London myself with them. I told His Excellency that, while I was fully prepared to consider this course, I felt it my duty to tell him quite clearly that my country could not possibly go back on its word to Poland and that, however anxious we were for a better understanding with Germany, we could never reach one except on the basis of a negotiated settlement with Poland.

Whatever may have been the underlying motive of this final gesture on the part of the Chancellor, it was one which could not be ignored; and with Lord Halifax's consent, I flew to London early the following morning (August 26th), on a German plane which was courteously put at my disposal.

Two days were spent by His Majesty's Government in giving the fullest and most careful consideration to Hitler's message, and on the afternoon of August 28th I flew back to Berlin with their reply. Therein, while the obligations of His Majesty's Government to Poland were reaffirmed, it was stated that the Polish Government were ready to enter into negotiations with the German Government for a reasonable solution of the matter in dispute on the basis of the safeguarding of Poland's essential interests and of an international guarantee for the settlement eventually arrived at. His Majesty's Government accordingly proposed that the next step should be the initiation of direct discussions between the Polish and German Governments on that basis and the adoption of immediate steps to relieve the tension in the matter of the treatment of minorities.

Furthermore, His Majesty's Government undertook to use all their influence with a view to contributing toward a solution which might be satisfactory to both parties and which would, they hoped, prepare the way for the negotiation of that wider and more complete understanding between Great Britain and Germany which both countries desired.

Finally, after a reference to a limitation of armaments, His Majesty's Government pointed out that, whereas a just settlement of the Polish question might open the way to world peace, failure to do so would finally ruin the hopes of a better understanding between our countries and might well plunge the whole world into war.

I left London at 5 P.M. on August 28th, and at 10:30 P.M. that evening I was received by Herr Hitler at the Reichschancery and handed to him the British reply, together with a German translation. Hitler was once again friendly and reasonable and appeared to be not dissatisfied with the answer which I had brought to him. He observed, however, that he must study it carefully and would give me a written reply the next day. Our conversation lasted for well over an hour, and it was nearly midnight before I arrived back at the Embassy. It was, I think, the only one of my interviews with Hitler at which it was I who did most of the talking. Possibly for this reason there is no account of it in the German White Paper which was published after the outbreak of war. I used every argument which I could think of to induce him to see reason and to come down on the side of peace. The choice, I pointed out, lay with him. Peaceful negotiation would mean the friendship of Britain, which he was always telling me that he desired: on the other hand an aggression against Poland meant war.

The Ultimatum

THE information which reached me during the course of the following day tended to represent the atmosphere as well disposed and to foreshadow readiness on Hitler's part to open direct negotiations with the Poles. I was consequently all the less prepared for the reception which I got on being summoned to the Reichschancery again at 7:15 on the evening of August 29th. Perhaps I should have been, as the German midday press had reported the alleged murder of six German nationals in Poland; and this story, which was probably fabricated by the extremists in fear lest Hitler was weakening, together with the news of the Polish general mobilization, was just the kind of thing which was most calculated to upset him. I immediately sensed in any case a distinctly more uncompromising attitude than the previous evening on Hitler's part when he handed me the answer which he had promised me.

Therein Germany's demands were declared to be the revision of the Versailles Treaty by means of the return of Danzig and the Corridor to Germany and the security for the lives of German national minorities in the rest of Poland. In reply to the British proposals for direct German-Polish negotiations and for an international guarantee of any settlement, it was stated, firstly, that the German Government, in spite of skepticism as to the prospect of their success, accepted direct negotiations with Poland, solely out of a desire to insure lasting friendship with Britain; but, secondly, that, in the event of any modifications of territory, the German Government could neither undertake nor participate in any guarantee without first consulting the U.S.S.R.

I read the note through carefully, while Hitler and Ribbentrop watched me; and, in spite of the ominous reference to Moscow, I made no comment till I reached the phrase at the end of it in which it was stated that "the German Government counted upon the arrival in Berlin of a Polish Emissary with full powers on the following day, Wednesday, the 30th August." I pointed out to His Excellency that this phrase sounded very much like an ultimatum.

This was strenuously and heatedly denied by Hitler himself, supported by Ribbentrop. It was a case of the "dictate" and "memorandum" of Godesberg over again. According to Hitler this sentence merely emphasized the urgency of the moment, not only on account of the risk of incidents when two mobilized armies were standing opposite one another but also when Germans were being massacred in Poland.

In this latter connection His Excellency asserted that "I did not care how many Germans were being slaughtered in Poland." This gratuitous impugnment of the humanity of His Majesty's Government and of myself provoked a heated retort on my part; and the remainder of the interview was of a somewhat stormy character. It was closed, however, by a brief and, in my opinion, quite honest—since it represented his feelings at the moment—harangue on Hitler's part in regard to the genuineness of his constant endeavor to win Britain's friendship, of his respect for the British Empire, and of his liking for Englishmen generally.

I left the Reichschancery that evening filled with the gloomiest forebodings. Hitler, while reiterating his desire for British friendship, had asserted that he did not intend to sacrifice therefor what he called vital German interests. When I had protested against the time limit for the arrival of a Polish plenipotentiary, he had clearly indicated that his general staff were pressing for a decision. "My soldiers," he said, "are asking me 'Yes' or 'No.'" His army and his air force were ready to strike and had been since August 25th. They were telling him that one week had already been lost, and that they could not afford to lose another, lest the rainy season in Poland be added to their enemies. (When I passed through the anteroom on my way back to my car, it was full of Army officers, Keitel and Brauschitsch among them. Meeting them there did not tend to dispel my apprehensions.)

I had asked Hitler what he meant by "vital German interests." He had referred me to his reply, which stated that the German Government would immediately draw up proposals acceptable to themselves for a solution of the Polish question and would place these at the disposal of the British Government before the arrival of the Polish negotiator.

Everything seemed, therefore, to depend on two things: the nature of those proposals and the immediate consent of the Polish Government to the dispatch of a negotiator, or plenipotentiary, to Berlin. The first did not depend on me, but I endeavored to insure the latter by asking the Polish Ambassador that evening to call on me while I was drafting my telegrams to London, by giving him an account of the German reply and of my conversation with Hitler, and by impressing upon him the need for immediate action.

Last Chance

I HAD arranged to see the Minister for Foreign Affairs at 11:30 P.M. the next evening. Shortly before the appointed time I received in code the considered reply of His Majesty's Government to the German note of August 29th. I was accordingly obliged to ask that my meeting with Ribbentrop should be postponed for half an hour in order to give me the time to have this last message deciphered.

I saw Ribbentrop at exactly midnight, before which hour the German Government had ostensibly counted on the arrival of a Polish emissary at Berlin. I say "ostensibly" since it seems hardly possible that it cannot have occurred either to Hitler or his Minister for Foreign Affairs that it was utterly unreasonable to expect a Polish plenipotentiary to present himself at Berlin without even knowing in advance the basis of the proposals about which he was expected to negotiate.

Be that as it may, it is probable that Hitler's mood in the hour when he had to decide between peace or war was not an amiable one. It was reflected in Ribbentrop, whose reception of me that evening was from the outset one of intense hostility, which increased in violence as I made each communication in turn. He kept jumping to his feet in a state of great excitement, folding his arms across his chest and asking if I had anything more to say. I kept replying that I had; and, if my own attitude was no less unfriendly than his own, I cannot but say in all sincerity that I had every justification for it. When I told him that I would not fail to report his comments and remarks to my Government, he calmed down a little and said that they were his own and that it was for Herr Hitler to decide. As for inviting the Polish Ambassador to come to see him, such a course would, he indignantly said, be utterly unthinkable and intolerable.

After I had finished making my various communications to him, he produced a lengthy document which he read out to me in German or rather gabbled through to me as fast as he could, in a tone of the utmost scorn and annoyance. Of the sixteen articles in it I was able to gather the gist of six or seven, but it would have been quite impossible to guarantee even the comparative accuracy of these without a careful study of the text itself.

When he had finished, I accordingly asked him to let me read it for myself. Herr von Ribbentrop, who always mistook rudeness for strength, refused categorically; threw the document with a contemptuous gesture on the table; and said that it was now out of date, since no Polish emissary had arrived at Berlin by midnight. I observed that in that case the sentence in the German note of August 29th to which I had drawn his and his Führer's attention on the preceding evening had, in fact, constituted an ultimatum in spite of their categorical denials. Ribbentrop's answer to that was that the idea of an ultimatum was a figment of my own imagination.

I do not desire to stress the unpleasant nature of this interview. The hour was a critical one and Ribbentrop's excitability at such a moment was understandable. It seemed to me, however, that he was willfully throwing away the last chance of a peaceful solution; and it was difficult to remain indifferent when faced with such a calamity. I still believe, as I did at the time, that Ribbentrop's exhibition of irascibility and bad manners that evening was partly due to the fact that he suspected that I had purposely postponed calling on him till midnight, *i.e.,* until the hour by which the ultimatum, which he and Hitler had assured me was no ultimatum, for the arrival of a Polish plenipotentiary had expired.

"Precise Information"

Yet in the German note of August 29th it had been stated that their proposals would, if possible, be placed at the disposal of the British Government before the arrival of that plenipotentiary. Why then should Ribbentrop have himself waited till after midnight before making the pretense of reading them to me? But, above all, why did he refuse even then to hand them to me? Not even Hitler could honestly have expected the Polish Government to appoint a plenipotentiary to discuss proposals in regard to which it was completely in the dark. Did Ribbentrop and his master not wish them to be communicated to the Polish Government lest the latter might in fact agree to negotiate? It is the only conclusion which one can draw from this episode, since it might have made all the difference to the instructions given to M. Lipski on the following day if the Polish Government had been cognizant of the official text of the German proposals.

In themselves and taken at their face value, they were not unreasonable and might well have served as a basis for negotiation. That is why one can only assume that Ribbentrop did not wish them to be discussed, and his attitude that night was not only one of ill manners, but also of ill faith. He endeavored to conceal this later by a deliberate distortion of the truth.

In the note which was handed to me

by Weizsäcker the next evening and which contained at last the text of those proposals it was stated that Herr von Ribbentrop had given the British Ambassador on the occasion of the presentation of the last British note precise information as to the text of the German proposals which would be regarded as a basis of negotiation, etc. The German White Paper on the origins of the war repeats this complete perversion of the actual facts. None of the points at issue in the memorandum were discussed at all.

Let those who wish to form their own opinion as to what Ribbentrop euphemistically describes as "precise information," read for themselves the English translation of the text of those proposals. Let them imagine that text being read to them in German, so fast as literally to be unintelligible in any language.

Did Ribbentrop have such a high opinion of my memorizing faculty as to think that, after listening to his jabber of words, I could be in a position to give either His Majesty's Government or the Polish Government an authoritative account of the exact sense of a long and complicated text? Yet that apparently was what Ribbentrop was pleased to call "precise information" about a document of vital importance, upon which peace or war depended and which consequently needed to be not only read but studied with the utmost care and circumspection.

I RETURNED to His Majesty's Embassy that night convinced that the last hope for peace had vanished. I nevertheless saw the Polish Ambassador at 2 A.M., gave him an objective and studiously moderate account of my conversation with Ribbentrop, mentioned the cession of Danzig and the plebiscite in the Corridor as the two main points in the German proposals, stated that, so far as I could gather, they were not on the whole too unreasonable, and suggested to him that he might recommend to his Government that they should propose at once a meeting between Field Marshals Smigly-Rydz and Goering. I felt obliged to add that I could not conceive of the success of any negotiations if they were conducted with Ribbentrop.

Though M. Lipski undertook to make this suggestion to his Government, it would by then probably have been in any case too late. There was, in fact, for Herr Hitler only one conceivable alternative to brute force, and that was that a Polish plenipotentiary should humbly come to him and sign on the dotted line to the greater glory of Adolf Hitler. And even that must happen at once, since his army was impatiently asking "Yes" or "No."

Early the next morning I obtained from another source in touch with Goering more definite, if unauthorized, details of the German proposals; and these I at once communicated through the Counselor of His Majesty's Embassy to the Polish Ambassador, who spent that morning on the telephone to Warsaw. It was M. Lipski's last chance to telephone; when evening came, the German Government saw to it that all methods of communication with the Polish Government were denied to him.

There was, however, a further delay of some twelve hours. The Polish Government had, it was announced, authorized their Ambassador to establish contact with Ribbentrop; and Hitler waited to learn what message M. Lipski would bring. The question, in fact, was whether his qualifications would be those of a plenipotentiary empowered by the Polish Government, in spite of its ignorance of the exact terms of the German proposals, to conduct and conclude negotiations or not. On no other terms was Hitler prepared to postpone action. His army was ready, and Poland must be taught a lesson. She must crawl or get her whipping.

I had never been under any illusion as to Poland's capacity to resist for more than a brief period Germany's highly mechanized army and overwhelmingly superior air force.

The Zero Hour

DURING the day there had been much activity on the part of Field Marshal Goering. I think that Goering himself would have preferred a peaceful solution, but in matters such as these it was Hitler's decision which alone counted; and, whatever Goering might feel, he was merely the loyal and submissive servant of his master. Moreover he had come down definitely on the side of peace a year before; and it might have been difficult for him to adopt this course a second time. He invited me, however, to come to see him that afternoon; and I did so at 5 P.M. in the company of Sir G. Ogilvie-Forbes. Inasmuch as I had heard that the text of the proposals which Ribbentrop had refused to give me was to be broadcast on the radio that evening, my first remark was to point out to the Field Marshal that this procedure would probably and finally wreck the last prospect of peace and to beg him to do his utmost to prevent their publication. Goering's reply was that he could not intervene and that the German Government felt obliged to broadcast their proposals to the world to prove their "good faith."

Goering talked for the best part of two hours on the iniquities of the Poles and of Hitler's and his own desire for friendship with England and of the benefit to the world in general and the advantage to England in particular of such a friendship. It was a conversation which led nowhere; and I could not help feeling that his remarks, which from his point of view were perfectly genuine but which I had heard often before, were chiefly intended for the edification of his listeners. I argued the worst from the fact that he was in a position at such a moment to give me so much of his time. He had a few days before been made president of the new German Defense Council for the Reich (or War Cabinet); and he could scarcely have afforded at such a moment to spare time in conversation, if it did not mean that everything, down to the last detail, was now ready for action.

My general impression of this last talk with Goering was, in fact, that it constituted a final but forlorn effort on his part to detach Britain from the Poles. Nevertheless, the Field Marshal seemed sincere when, having been called to the telephone, he returned to tell us that M. Lipski was on his way to see Ribbentrop. He seemed relieved and to hope that, provided contact was only established, war might after all prove unnecessary.

The meeting between the Polish Ambassador proved, however, quite futile. M. Lipski stated that he was acting solely in his capacity as an ambassador without plenary powers to discuss or to negotiate and handed to the Minister for Foreign Affairs a brief communication to the effect that the Polish Government were weighing favorably the proposal of His Majesty's Government for direct discussion and that a formal answer in this matter would be communicated to the German Government in the immediate future. He did not ask for the German proposals, and Ribbentrop did not offer to give them to him. Their meeting lasted but a few minutes. When, after his interview, the Polish Ambassador attempted once more to telephone to his Government, he found that it was no longer possible for him to do so. Hitler had, in fact, chosen his moment to precipitate the conflict. He did not want direct negotiations with the Poles. It was zero hour.

Declaration of War

FINALLY Hitler met the Reichstag, which had been summoned for that hour, and similarly announced to the assembled members that he had been "forced to take up arms in defense of the Reich." It was a deliberate travesty of the facts, and never can there be a case of more premeditated aggression.

In the early hours (4 A.M.) of September 3rd I was accordingly instructed by His Majesty's Government to arrange for a meeting with the Minister for Foreign Affairs at 9 A.M.

THE final ultimatum from His Majesty's Government, pointed out that unless satisfactory assurances were received by His Majesty's Government before 11 A.M., British summer time, of the suspension of all aggressive action against Poland and of the withdrawal of the German forces from that country, a state of war would exist between our two countries as from that hour. Dr. Schmidt received this communication and undertook to deliver it immediately to his chief. As no reply from the German Government was vouchsafed by 11 A.M., the German Representative in London was informed in due course at that hour that a state of war existed between Britain and Germany. By ten minutes past 11 A.M. every British consular officer in Germany had been advised by the staff of His Majesty's Embassy at Berlin that this was the case.

Shortly after 11 A.M. I received a final message from Ribbentrop asking me to call upon him at once. I did so at 11:30; and he lost no time in giving me on this occasion a lengthy document to read beginning with a refusal on the part of the German people to accept any demands in the nature of an ultimatum made by the British Government and stating that any aggressive action by England would be answered with the same weapons and the same form. The rest of the document was pure propaganda, destined presumably for home and neutral consumption, with a view to attempting to prove to the German people and the world generally that it was Britain alone who was to blame for everything which had happened.

My only comment on reading this completely false representation of events was: "It would be left to history to judge where the blame really lay." Ribbentrop's answer was to the effect that history had already proved the facts and that nobody had striven harder for peace and good relations with England than Herr Hitler had done. His last remark to me was that he wished me well personally, to which I could only reply that I deeply regretted the failure of all my efforts for peace but that I bore no grudge against the German people. Thereafter I saw no further German official except the member of the Protocol who accompanied our special train as far as Rotterdam.

AFTER returning from my interview with Ribbentrop at midday, I did not leave the Embassy again until Mr. Kirk of the United States Embassy rendered me one last service by driving me in his own car to the station the next morning.

My impression was that the mass of the German people, that other Germany, were horror-struck at the whole idea of the war which was being thus thrust upon them. It is true that I could only judge of Berlin itself and that I was not in a position to witness the reaction of German youth or of the soldiers in the troop trains which were leaving for the Polish front. It is true also that the trial black-outs, the bread cards, and the strict system of rationing, which were already in force, were not exactly cheerful beginnings to a war. But what I can say is that the whole general atmosphere in Berlin itself was one of utter gloom and depression.

Every country has the government which it deserves, and the German people must share the responsibility for the present war with those to whose authority they so meekly and readily submitted. But they have a share also of the immense pity which I feel for all those who have got to suffer because the Nazi war party, which had been foiled in September, 1938, won the day in Germany in August, 1939, and because one man was ready to sacrifice their united happiness to the satisfaction of his individual lust for military glory.

Lawrence Pearsall Jacks

EDUCATION THROUGH RECREATION

THE machine has forced the mixed blessing of leisure on millions of men and women, rich and poor, but with a few exceptions, no one seems to be able to make the most of it. Lawrence Pearsall Jacks (1860-   ) has devoted the last nine years since his retirement as Principal of Manchester College, Oxford, in writing and lecturing to enthusiastic English and American audiences on a new kind of leisure. "Education Through Recreation," published in 1932, is a summary of his revolutionary ideas on how our educational systems can be reformed so that people can get more out of life.

THE art of living is one and indivisible. It is not a composite art made up by adding the art of play to the art of work, or the art of leisure to the art of labor, or the art of the body to the art of the mind, or the art of recreation to the art of education. When life is divided into these or any other compartments it can never become an art, but at best a medley or at worst a mess. It becomes an art when work and play, labor and leisure, mind and body, education and recreation, are governed by a single vision of excellence and a continuous passion for achieving it.

A master in the art of living draws no sharp distinction between his work and his play, his labor and his leisure, his mind and his body, his education and his recreation. He hardly knows which is which. He simply pursues his vision of excellence through whatever he is doing and leaves others to determine whether he is working or playing. To himself he always seems to be doing both. Enough for him that he does it well.

THE recreation movement, represented in this country by the National Recreation Association of America, aims at uniting two things which have become separated in the modern world—recreation and education. We want to make the recreations of the people, both children and grown-ups, more educational

than they now are; and we want to give education some of the interest and the joy that belong to recreation. If we can do that two results will follow: first, recreation will become far more enjoyable than it now is; and second, education will become far more effective in building up a fine and noble race of citizenry.

I will give you a motto which explains in a sentence what we are aiming at—"Education and recreation, united they stand; divided they fall." Or a shorter motto still—"Let us have more joy in life."

We think that a vast increase of human joy can be brought about by uniting education and recreation. And if we get more joy we shall get more of other things that are sadly wanted; more music, more clean conduct; more good fellowship; more community spirit; more beautiful cities; and more value in our social life. I think that if we could get more joy into life we should soon see a great revival of all the fine arts, and perhaps a revival of trade as well. I feel sure that will happen if we succeed in uniting recreation and education.

We should never forget that recreation includes something more than the playing of games. It includes the skills, the crafts, the arts, like music, the drama and many others, which all human beings are capable of acquiring in one form or another, if they were rightly educated. These arts and crafts and skills provide the most enjoyable kinds of recreation.

All human beings are hungry for skill, for some kind of creative activity in which they can express themselves, and are never happy and contented till that hunger is appeased. I think our educational systems are much to blame for having neglected that side of human nature, spending too much time in loading young people with book knowledge, and too little in awakening the creative side of them.

THE recreation movement is trying to remedy that great defect. We want to reform education so as to give a much larger place to creative activity in the training of both children and adults. There is a vast amount of undeveloped skill waiting for the education to bring it into action with an immense increase in the joy and value of life to follow.

I have seen it done in many progressive schools. And a few weeks ago I saw in one of your great cities a crowd of unemployed, some thousands of them, who have been turned into a contented community by the skilful work of one man who had got them interested in worth while recreational activities.

They had previously given a lot of trouble and broken out into a riot. But the leader had changed all that by finding something for them to do which satisfied their hunger for skill, and by getting them to do it altogether. He saw that providing them with food and shelter was not enough. You must provide them also with something to do, something they feel to be worth while, as a means to occupy the enforced leisure in which they find themselves.

Many of our social troubles could be cured in the same way if we had leaders who understood the art of turning recreation into education. The problem of

leisure largely turns on that. The reason so many people don't know what to do with their leisure time, and spend it in all kinds of dull folly, is that the creative part of them was never awakened when they were young.

Another result that will surely follow from uniting recreation with education is the diminution of crime. All criminologists are now agreed that crime is largely the result of thwarting the natural play instincts of the young human being. It begins as juvenile delinquency and develops later into adult crime.

Here is an interesting fact that has been brought to my notice in many cities of the United States. I find that the figures for juvenile delinquency tend to be lowest in those parts of the city which are nearest to a well-organized playground, or where opportunities are given young people for practising the arts and crafts; and the figures tend to be highest in those other parts of the city which are so far away from the playgrounds and the craft schools that the young people can't get to them. If juvenile crime can be prevented in that way, all sorts of crime will be diminished.

I wonder if the public is wise enough to see the significance of that. Does it see that by spending a few millions on educational recreation it can save uncounted millions which it is now spending on courts, jails, hospitals, and asylums for the insane? This recreation movement, as I understand it, is a great work of preventive social medicine. The social evils it prevents are disease, crime, vice, folly, and bad citizenship in general. Prevention is better than cure and vastly cheaper in the long run. I believe the recreation movement will become in a few years one of the outstanding movements of the time.

Recreation is Re-creation

THE synthesis of education and recreation which is perfectly obvious to any intelligent person who will reflect upon the matter for an hour, is obscured in the minds of the thoughtless multi-

tude by the absurd associations that have gathered around the two words.

Mention the word education and nine out of ten of the hearers will immediately recall their school days. They will reember the "grind" of it all, and the edley of images—textbooks, class-ooms, blackboards, courses of lectures, xaminations—suffused with memories f boredom, recalcitration, and confinement between walls will rise before the ind. That is what they will understand y "education."

Mention recreation and immediately hey will think of joyful escape from all hat education means. It will remind hem of the happy moment when their ducation was suddenly stopped at the inging of the bell and they were sent ut to kick up their heels in the play-round during the interval of recreation. Or of the yet happier moment when the erm came to an end and the vacation which means, I suppose, a period of acancy) gave them an opportunity of drowning their education.

Nor are these unfortunate misconceptions confined to the thoughtless multitude. There are eminent pedagogues, not a few, who seem precluded, as by a law of nature, from conceiving that anything can possibly be education unless it is mediated by a book, accepted in a sitting posture, and tested by an examination; or that the function of recreation can be anything else than that of helping the pupil to stretch his limbs, "wholesomely digest his pudding" and so be in better shape for sustaining the persecutions of the classroom. But recreation is not an escape from the toil of education into the emptiness of a vacation, but a vitalizing element in the process of education itself.

The problem of leisure exists only so long as we think of leisure as a vacation or vacuum separated from the rest of life and needing to be filled with activities specially designed for filling it. In the life of a rightly educated man there is no such vacuum.

YET, so deeply engrained is our habit of putting recreation into one compartment and education into another, that some difficulties are sure to be encountered in presenting the idea of their indissoluble unity. Perhaps the situation would be eased if people would make a practice of saying re-creation instead of recreation.

For what is recreation? Four our present purpose it means what it says. It is the re-creation of something that gets damaged in human beings—the repair of human damage where it is repairable, and the prevention of it in the rising generation. Of this human damage, and this threat of further damage, there is abundance in the modern world. I need only remind you of that enormous class in our massed populations which is known to medical examiners as C.

What does the C class consist of? It consists of damaged humanity, and is said to include 60 per cent of the urban population, some putting it even higher. It is the most numerous class, and it breeds faster than any other—the damaged class. I would ask this question of those of my readers who are engaged in business—how long would you be able to keep out of the bankruptcy court if 60 per cent of the goods you produce had to be marked "damaged"? Obviously we are here in presence of a great danger, especially when the breeding phenomena are taken into account. That way lies the bankruptcy of civilization.

If now you ask what has done the damage, I am afraid the answer must be that modern civilization has done it. I am no enemy of civilization; I hope I am one of its friends. But who can shut his eyes to the fact that our civilization, along with the benefits it confers, has done an enormous amount of damage to mankind?

The New Slavery

SOME of us who have been studying the way the unemployed are spending the blank months when they are out of work have come to the conclusion that our educational system, with its three R's, its system of credits, and all the rest of it, has done very little to prepare those unfortunate millions for the deplorable condition in which they now find themselves. The majority of them are not spending their time either in the cultivation of the soul, or in the cultivation of the body.

With some exceptions, for which God be praised, they are spending their time in one of two ways; they are either simply *stagnating,* a term which defines itself, or they are letting themselves be led by the nose into spending both time and money (if they have any of the latter) on ready-made pleasures, of a cheap and sometimes vicious kind. The mental interests which would lead to the cultivation of the soul, the skilled aptitudes which would lead to the cultivation of the body, have not been created or developed by their education.

Broadly speaking, their time of unemployment is a time of degeneration. Broadly speaking, the unemployed are as sheep without a shepherd, a multitude at a loose end; with no initiative or faculty of invention to fill the empty days; with no skill beyond that which began to decay when employment ceased.

Whoever created man, whether you call the creator nature or God, intended him for a busy life of skilful activity and equipped him with faculties for that purpose. For a life of reckless leisure, in the sense of being unemployed, of being at a loose end, of stagnating, of blindly following people who lead you by the nose—for that kind of life man is naturally unfitted and begins to degenerate biologically the moment he falls into it. Four hours' work a day and twenty hours idle, which high authorities are now predicting, sounds rather attractive; but nature is against it; biology forbids it; the laws of the universe say flatly "it cannot be." Rest and refreshment have, indeed, to be provided for; but *not on that scale* for either rich or poor. The evils of enforced labor—the labor of slaves—we all know. But the evils of enforced leisure which leaves the masses of the people at a loose end and with nothing worth while to do, are almost as bad, and might be defined as a new form of slavery—slavery to those who lead them by the nose.

Frontiers for Pioneers

I BELIEVE that a beginning toward a wiser use of leisure might be made if employers, whenever it is possible, would establish schools of physical culture in connexion with their works. In the one or two instances of this that I have seen and studied, the results have been remarkable, psychologically and otherwise.

By physical culture I mean something far more significant than the ordinary procedure of jumping over parallel bars and climbing up ropes; I mean something which has now become a very beautiful and enjoyable art, founded on a profound understanding of both mind and body, and furnished with a scientific technique of its own.

Competent teachers of it are not easily found in my own country, though they are more abundant on the continent of Europe. But, seeing how many of our beautiful arts and crafts have been taught us by foreigners, I see no objection to the importation of foreigners for the purpose I have named. We should soon pick it up—as we soon picked up many other things from foreigners. There is in the Anglo-Saxon races a vast reservoir of latent skill, skill in endless variety, as yet unborn or unused, but waiting to be developed by anybody who has the wit and the courage to make the attempt, waiting, in fact, for just that type of recreational leadership which I am pleading for. What I now suggest is a beginning.

Wherever experiments of this kind have been tried, their effect might be summed up as a general rise in the level of self-respect, with distinct repercussions all round on work and on play, and especially on sex relations. With this there goes a release of vitality, which becomes available for all sorts of things outside the range of physical culture nd leads to spontaneous demands for hose higher cultures which are usually alled spiritual. Any employer who finds t possible to act on these lines will be giving a lead in the right direction.

And to give a lead is to be a leader—nd the only way of being one. The people who merely talk about these hings, as I am doing now, are not the eal leaders. The real leaders are the men who *do* them—and I know two or three. We have too much leadership of the alking kind and too little of the leader-hip that really leads. What we need in hese things is pioneers—and pioneers very time.

I will now direct your attention to the phrase I have just used—"recreational leadership." No type of leadership demands higher gifts—gifts of intellect, of imagination, of human sympathy and understanding. Your recreational leader is more than a games expert, a professional gymnast, or an athletic trainer—though he knows something about all that. Great men, gifted men, bold men, devoted men—and women of the same quality—are needed for the part of recreational leaders. A high university degree is not incompatible with their other qualifications, but their gifts must be higher and more various than those which are indicated by the highest university degree.

Colleges for Recreation

Every country ought to have its own College of Recreational Culture—you might call it a school of leisure-craft—like the one they have had for many years in Sweden, where young men and women of good ability can get hemselves thoroughly trained and go out as recreational educators into every chool, college, and civic community in he land. A new profession is waiting in hat field for the best type of young men nd woman to take up, and I am glad to ay that in my own country, Great Britain, not a few are beginning to do so.

Yes, education is the method—but ot the kind of education that now goes by the name. I respect that education for what it is worth, and it is worth a good deal, but a new kind of education is called for, which will include what is good in the old, but include many other hings now overlooked and neglected. n the new recreational universities and chools all the highest qualities of human beings, the qualities that make the whole man or the whole woman, would be studied, challenged, and developed, from he time the pupils were able to stand on heir feet till the time when their arteries began to ossify.

Here would be taught and learnt the 'threefold reverence" which Goethe proclaimed as the foundation of human cul-ture—reverence for what is above us, reverence for what is around us, reverence for what is below us—everything included as worthy of reverence from the stars over our heads to the graves beneath our feet. Here the body would be given its rights along with the mind; its beautiful aptitudes would be developed, its creative functions directed, its reservoirs of latent skill released, and led onwards to excellent performance on a thousand lines.

The greatest service education can render to any human being, child or adult, is *to lead him to the discovery of his own powers*. And in order to accomplish that you must do two things: first you must manage somehow to liberate his energies, of which an immense reservoir lies hidden in every human being; and next you must help him to discover the wonderful means nature has furnished him with for bringing those energies under beautiful control. If you think of education as a work of *liberation* and *vitalization* you have got to the essence of what it can do for human beings.

Our college would cover a wide range of studies and promote research in many directions that would challenge the ability of the student. Both study and research would be, in part, sociological. In this department particular attention would be devoted to the art—perhaps the most precious art in the world—*by which crowds can be turned into communities.* All the means of doing this would be reviewed from their simplest forms, such as community singing or community games, to their more difficult forms in the discipline of an orchestra or a rhythmic dance; all games being reckoned good which promote the community spirit, and all evil which destroy or debase it.

Instead of lecturing people on "the relation of the individual to the social whole," or exhorting them to change their anti-social hearts into social ones which no son of man ever succeeded in doing merely because he had been exhorted to do it—in place of these futile methods of promoting the community spirit, the students of our college would set about it in the only way in which it can be done, by getting people together in the joyous coöperation of beautiful activity and by making a full use of every type of recreation which offered an opportunity for turning a crowd into a community.

A Glance at the Future

IN this way, if a glance into the future may be permitted, a real foundation might be laid for that far-off divine event, dreamed of by many, when the nations of the world, now a mob in their mutual relations, will become a community of nations; an event never to be brought about by mere preachings of the community ideal.

Something short of this—far short of it, indeed, but yet pointing towards it—has already been accomplished in the recreational field. No greater educational discovery was ever made than when Baden Powell, founder of the Boy Scouts, conceived the idea of utilizing the play instinct of boys, their love of adventure, their devilry, and their aptitude for getting into mischief as a means of training them in courage, competence, self-control, self-respect, loyalty, discipline, responsibility, and welding them on that basis into a world-wide community. The art of turning a crowd into a community by use of the recreational method, and so converting recreation into the finest education imaginable, has no more telling example than the Scout movement. And this is the art which our National College would study, acquire, foster, and apply. The international values of recreation remain to be explored. Our college would explore them.

Involved in this art and essential to its practice on the recreational field, would be the devising of methods of *competition* more conducive to the team spirit (which, of course, is only another name for the community spirit).

ATTENTION would be given to the evil tendency, now prevalent in schools and colleges and athletic circles in general, to concentrate the interest of sport on the performance of star teams of expert players, the aristocracy of the game, and to make competition consist in gladiatorial combats between these groups of specialists, presented as public spectacles and often conducted on a commercial basis for the sake of the gate money they produce.

The new method of competition would aim at what I have elsewhere called the "democratization of sport"—*i.e.,* at converting it from a public spectacle performed by the aristocrats of the game, with a crowd, possibly of physical illiterates, looking on from the side lines and yelling for the victors, into a community occupation based upon *participation* rather than spectatorship.

Into the technique of the new methods I have here no space to enter. Suffice it to say that their general principle would be to give credit for *effort* rather than for success, thereby providing the weakest player with a motive for doing his best and a chance of rising into the higher ranks, so that every player, like

TAKING A PEEP AT THE WORLD FROM THE SUMMIT OF MOUNT WASHINGTON

he common soldier in Napoleon's army,
might think of himself as "carrying a
marshal's bâton in his knapsack."

In connexion with all this the students
of our college would be largely occupied
in the great and fundamental question
of correlating the culture of the body
with the culture of the mind—a correla-
tion which may be summarily described
as the "coeducation of mind and body."
In place of the one-sided or, rather, lop-
sided athletic culture which trains the
body for temporary occasions or exceptional feats and is often followed by relapse, the effort would now be to provide
the body with a *liberal education* for its
normal activities, teaching it to perform
all these with the minimum of effort,
strain, and fatigue, and the maximum
of dignity, self-control, and power of
adaptation to changing conditions, which
is precisely parallel to what a liberal
education of the mind should aim
at in the intellectual field. The two
cultures would thus be brought into a
relation of mutual support, and a basis
laid in the culture of the body for that
creative thinking which is the highest

mark of an educated mind. To effect
this object, games of physical skill
would be freely made use of in connexion
with corrective or positive disciplines.

At all points of their training the
students of our college—our future
recreational leaders—would be occupied
with the practice of these things as well
as with the theory of them. They would
graduate in physical culture, not on the
ground of their book knowledge of its
technique, but by demonstrating that
they were masters of their own bodies,
Masters of Art in that sense.

Our women graduates, for the recreational leaders of the future will be
women as often as men, will "satisfy
the examiners" by their actual skill in
bodily self-management; for example by
the degree of resemblance they show to
Virgil's goddess, who revealed her divinity to the startled eyes of Æneas by the
majesty of her walk. The men will
comply with similar tests.

Both will be masters of poise, balance,
rhythm, economy. None will be asked
to run a mile in record time, but all will

be required *to think with their whole bodies,* to use their bodies as instruments of intelligence, and to show the staying power which comes from command over themselves. And, in addition to all these fundamental things, none will receive his diploma until he has acquired proficiency in one, at least, of the specialized arts—and there are scores of them—which constitute the higher recreation or world of skill. A master of some craft our graduate must be, from the manual crafts of the potter, weaver, carpenter, gardener, to the finer arts of the imagination—music, drama, painting, sculpture, and the rest. So equipped, our graduate will go forth to play his part as a recreational leader in the new education which leads on stage by stage, from the making of mud pies to creative thinking and the art of life. What finer profession has the world to offer to men and women of good ability and wholesome ideals? I can imagine that our college, would be besieged by applicants.

The social value of such a profession, and of interfusing its work with the general system of education, would be far-reaching. There is no type of "leadership" more vitally needed at the present day than that which our college would train and equip.

It remains to be pointed out that a National Recreation School, founded and supported by the National Recreation Association of America, already exists in New York. The dream outlined above would be fulfilled by the development of this admirable beginning into a fully equipped institution, independent of existing universities, but not antagonistic to them, supported on a nation-wide basis and free of all political influences.

Rhythmic Human Companionship

MAN is naturally coöperative—a born coöperator, a fact often overlooked, though needing to be greatly stressed whenever education, either of children or of adults, is in question. Whether you study the constitution of his mind or of his body, you find at every point that the activity his structure demands, and is fitted for, is not isolated activity, but concerted activity.

There is in man an instinct for coöperation akin to that which guides the flight of a flock of birds—an instinct greatly atrophied in these days, but ready to be evoked. You see it in young children, especially in the ease with which they acquire the art of rhythmic dancing to complicated patterns—an art which Plato thought was the right beginning for the education of the citizen.

A remarkable testimony to the same effect can be found in one of the last writings that came from the pen of Thomas Carlyle—a writer from whom one would hardly expect it. The passage is well worth quoting. It contains a hint of great practical value to all educators.

"It is strange to me," he says, "that in all education of mankind the value of *combined rhythmic action* has been overlooked by pedagogues and professors. I believe the vulgarest Cockney crowd flung out millionfold on Whit Monday with nothing but beer and dull folly to depend on for amusement, would at once kindle into something human if you set them to do almost any regulated act in common. They would dismiss their beer and dull folly, in the silent charm of rhythmic human companionship, in the practical feeling that all of us are made on one pattern and are brothers one to another" ("Shooting Niagara," 1867).

"Rhythmic human companionship"—I ask you to make a note of that phrase and carry it with you in your efforts to promote the community spirit. The other day I had the opportunity of witnessing an exhibition of what is known as "Dalcroze eurythmics"—one of the many efforts now being made by far-seeing educators to develop this wonderful gift for rhythmic human companionship which all young people possess, but are apt to lose when the shades of the prison house begin to close round them. I was profoundly impressed. I felt, as I had never felt before, that the human body is a creative instrument, endowed with marvellous powers for "rhythmic human companionship."

I WOULD develop the body as the creative instrument nature intended it to be, on the lines of "rhythmic human companionship," and I would make that education accessible to every member of the community. That, I would say, is the sort of education that is needed if the world is to be made safe for democracy, which is the political form of rhythmic human companionship. I would get at the mind less through the spoken word that enters by the ears and more by the skill that comes out of the five fingers; and not only from the five fingers, but from the body as a whole. I would train the body as a skilful community instrument both in work and in play—and more perhaps in play than in work—for the playtime of the people is the great field where the new education must look for its conquests.

For my own part I am looking forward to the day when the whole movement for adult education will take that direction, and I rejoice to see it is already beginning to do so. It has been held too long in academic fetters. It must shake them off, and instead of feebly following in the footsteps of schools and colleges, must seek rather to set an example for them to follow. The education of the whole man, as an inseparable unity of mind and body, created for "rhythmic human companionship," and finding his highest joys in the beautiful art of coöperation—I give you that as a summary formula for adult education.

ITS practical application has already been worked out by an Institute for Adult Education in a great American city. They found that the young men and women who came to the Institute, mostly workers in shops and factories, were too tired, too listless, to take any interest in the cultural opportunities that were offered to them. All they wanted was some form of external excitement, some form of ready-made pleasure.

The management then decided to attack this problem of devitalization. All the classes and lectures were scrapped and a new start was made with community dancing under the direction of a gifted instructor who was aware of the fact, which the Greeks knew long ago, that the human body is a natural musical instrument, and who was prepared to treat dancing as a fine art, somewhat on the principles of Dalcroze.

The results were astonishing. Through the awakening of this unsuspected power the young people began to discover themselves. Rhythmical human companionship began. The instinct for skill was roused into action, and with that the devitalization began to disappear. And as it disappeared there arose among these shopgirls and factory workers a spontaneous demand for skill in many directions, mostly in the direction of the arts.

Such an institution, if started anywhere, would soon be besieged by the classes for whom it was intended. It would rapidly develop from its first beginnings. Skilful occupations of all kinds would be demanded—arts, crafts, and interesting hobbies. It would gradually work its way to the finer arts. Unsuspected gifts for music, for singing, for painting and sculpture, would disclose themselves. And all this would take place in a social atmosphere where fellowships would form themselves spontaneously.

I know of few better ways of promoting the community spirit; of few more likely to prove attractive and fruitful. Don't begin, I would say, by *talking* to young people about the community spirit, by giving them lectures on it. Keep all that for a later stage. Begin by getting them busy *together* on something that is worth while, and if possible beautiful. So long as you get their instinct for coöperation awakened, it matters little in how humble a form you begin. Once awakened, it will grow of itself into higher forms. And, of course, the younger you catch them, the better your chance of success.

The best opportunity that now exists for developing the community spirit lies in the field of recreation, the leisure end of life, the playtime of the people, both children and adults. Get it started there and it will soon react on the work-field and become a vital element in the building up of good citizenship.

To Make Better Citizens

WE have been told so often that education is the remedy for the evils of democracy, that many of us take it as an axiomatic truth. And so perhaps it is. As a general statement it seems to me indisputably true that education is the safeguard to which democracy must look. At the same time I take leave to doubt whether education, as now carried on in schools and colleges, state supported or not, is at all likely to achieve the end in view—that of raising the political capacity of the masses to the level which democracy requires. The situation seems to be this: we have got democracy; we have got agreement that democracy must be educated; we have got universal education; but the kind of education we have got, though not without its merits, *is not the kind of education democracy requires.*

Political capacity is a very high form of human endowment. It involves a breadth of vision, a long foresight, a degree of detachment from our own interests, a sense of responsibility, a steadfastness of purpose, a sweep of imagination and a power of dealing with technical problems that are not easily acquired by those who lack them to begin with. Are those qualities being produced, are they even being led up to, by the type of education now being given to the rising generation? I believe they are not.

And there is another point rarely mentioned by those who believe that education is the remedy. Education is a slow process. It takes time. Suppose, then, that it were possible to set on foot tomorrow a perfect system for training the young citizen, how long would it be before the effects of that training became visible in the life of democracy? How long would it be before the new system began to tell? A long time, certainly. Well, I may be mistaken, but if so I am mistaken along with some very high authorities, when I say that the fate of democracy is not going to wait a long time to get itself decided. It will be decided not by those who are going to have to vote fifty years hence, but by those who have the vote now.

IN the next place I would call your attention to the difficulty, the extreme delicacy and highly technical nature, of many of the public questions with which the fortunes of the community are now involved. There is a growing complexity about these matters which puts them beyond the range of the average voter and can only be dealt with by the highest degree of expert knowledge and skill.

I would no more trust my own judgment in deciding some of them than I would trust myself to regulate the treatment of disease in a large hospital.

The question I would ask then is this: Can we hope, by our existing system of training, to raise the voting power of our enormous electorate to the point of competent judgment on these complicated questions? Can that lowest level of political capacity which does not even know what an election is "all about," which may even have been deliberately misinformed, be educated into intelligent dealing with the gold standard or the balancing of a modern budget? Can the intermediate levels, represented, let us say, by voters like myself, be turned by education into equality with the experts who have devoted their lives to these matters?

Frankly, I think it impossible. The course of education is not moving in that direction, nor towards that goal. I doubt if we are appreciably nearer to it than we were when compulsory education was established. And there is this difference between then and now—the voting masses have become vastly greater and the problems to be handled vastly more difficult.

Creating the All-Round Man

IF that hope must be abandoned, does it follow that the training of the citizen must be abandoned altogether? I should despair if I thought so. Only those will think so who make the mistake I spoke of at the beginning—that of treating the citizen as though he were a voter and nothing more, and voting the only thing he needs training for.

Fortunately, the citizen has other fields of activity open to him in which he can render service of the utmost value to his fellow citizens and enrich the value of his own life at the same time. It is for these I would chiefly train him. It is for these I would be trained myself.

I would try, if I had the opportunity, to make an all-round complete man of him—intellectually and morally. I would rethink and revise the whole system of national education with the conception of the *whole man* constantly in mind. My training of him or his training of me—put it which way you will—should be *human* throughout and not merely political, not merely scientific, nor *merely* anything else. And I would do all that—or have all that done to me—not because I regard voting as unimportant, but because I believe that your complete citizen, your all-round man, is the man least likely to make a mess of his voting, least likely to follow the instincts of the herd, least likely to be cajoled, flattered, or bribed by people who are out to capture his vote.

The school I would send him to—or go to myself—should be called the School of Excellence; I would place him there almost from the time he could stand on his feet, and I would find some means of keeping him there till the time when his work and play were done.

And what would I teach him, or be taught myself? I would teach him in the first place the excellent management of his own body, a very beautiful art, of which the average pedagogue knows nothing, and the athletic trainer hardly more, but which every human being is capable of learning and ought to learn as the foundation or growing point of all the qualities that make a good citizen.

Along with the mental training of the three R's, which saves him from illiteracy, I would give him the physical training which saves him from becoming a neurasthenic, a degenerate, or a hospital patient; and I would make that beautiful art accessible to all classes of the community in exactly the same way as the art of reading books and newspapers is made accessible now.

And then, having taught my young citizen the excellent management of his body, I should be in a position to proceed, stage by stage, to the excellent management of his life as a whole—the life of a self-controlling, self-respecting individual, a life of ordered coöperation and voluntary discipline, the creator of his own pleasures, instead of a purchaser of pleasure ready made, a life of skilful activity, enjoyable in itself and socially valuable to the world at large. The beginning of all that lies in the *body*.

If such a method were applied to the training of our citizens, I feel confident that the voting part of the citizen's business would soon get itself better done. How can we expect the citizen to vote wisely while the rest of his life is all in a muddle—his body distracted, unmanaged, and tending to the "C3" condition; dependent for its pleasures on the external excitements of the cinema, the racecourse, the night clubs, and the sex novel; his mind equally dependent on the ready-made opinion of the newspaper or the street corner or the first canvasser who happens to get him by the buttonhole—a poor judge of values and a creator of nothing.

AND not only would the voting be better done, but the things we vote about would be more worth while. Most of the things we are voting about now—our social problems, as we call them—are the direct outcome of the muddled lives that most of us live in the intervals between the elections. They are the products of personal confusion, of the want of self-control on the part of these very people—the majority of us—who are called upon at election time to set

it all right by voting for remedial legislation. It is a vicious circle—as though a man were trying to fill a tank with water while all the time the spigot is wide open at the other end.

One word in conclusion. Let nobody think that I expect the millennium to follow from anything I have suggested. I gave up belief in the millennium long ago. I have long reconciled myself to the belief that whoever created man, whether nature or God, intended him for hard fighting all along the line of his advance, and equipped him with powers and faculties to play the part of a brave pioneer. The pursuit of excellence, for which man was created, is a very difficult affair. I not only accept that, but welcome it and rejoice in it.

Real Health

WE NEED a much deeper conception of bodily health than that which underlies our current quotation of a sound mind in a sound body.

The health of a human being, though having something in common with the health of an ox, is nevertheless on a different level and is altogether misconceived when we think of it in terms appropriate only to the ox. A human being has other functions to perform than that of wholesomely digesting fodder and converting it into succulent beef, and would be incompetent to perform them if endowed only with the ox's health. The only healthy mind that could exist in such a body would be the mind of an ox; to the healthy mind of a human being it would be an utterly inadequate instrument, even though it stood upright on two feet and wore the human shape.

I would even go the length of saying that a healthy human mind might be more at home with a body crippled by disease and destined to a premature death (like Keats, for example) than with a body whose health consisted only in qualities appropriate to the health of an ox.

Following upon that comes a sugges-

tion, which I now make, that the perfect health of the body demands, when all its other demands have been satisfied, that opportunity shall be found and training given for the exercise of creative activity. Short of this, the perfect health of the body is not attainable. The "exercise" it demands is essentially *skilful* exercise and not mere *exertion.* An unskilled body is a thwarted body—thwarted, not in some minor detail, but in the very core and essence of its nature. And because thwarted, unhealthy.

Even those elements of health which it shares with the body of an ox will suffer through the essential thwarting of its *human* nature—unless, indeed, the owner of it manages (as some do) to accommodate that nature to an oxlike level. These thwarted human bodies exist in millions among the massed population of our great cities, and every one of them represents a thwarted *mind, a* thwarted human being.

VOICES have recently been heard among us—my own has been one of them—earnestly pleading for reformed methods of education in which the acquisition of skill, and not the acquisition of knowledge alone, should be the object aimed at from the earliest stage and steadily pursued to the last. The plea has naturally aroused a good deal of criticism, especially among professional educators, which has sometimes gone the length of accusing us of contempt for "knowledge."

This, of course, is absurd. Skill is nothing else than knowledge in action, or, better, wisdom completing itself by wisely doing what is accurately known. My conviction is that until knowledge is thus transformed into skill it has no vital connexion with the personality of the knower; it is superficial, precarious, unfixed, unassimilated, so that most of it is destined to be lost sight of, neglected, misapplied, forgotten, or even despised in the stages of life which follow the stage known as education.

As friends and lovers of knowledge we are pleading for a type of education which shall incorporate knowledge into the personality of the knower and for the conversion of it, thereby, into creative activity. This conversion of knowledge into creative activity, through incorporation with the "whole man" of the knower, is precisely what we mean by skill. A little knowledge thus converted seems to us of higher value than much knowledge in the unfixed and half-formed condition represented by certificates, credits, matriculation tests, and university degrees.

Dull and drab at the best is the life of the man or woman incapable of creative activity; dull and drab, and often vicious in the vain effort to escape the dullness and the drabness—the origin of most of the vices that disfigure and poison our civilization. That man desires happiness and can never be diverted from the pursuit of it is true; but the happiness he desires is not of the kind that "ready-made pleasures" can supply or money purchase, no matter how abundant and varied. It is the joy of *work*—which at its highest level is indistinguishable from play, as the highest levels of play are indistinguishable from it—the joy of creative activity, which the whole structure of his mind and body, evolved through long ages of struggle with nature, designs him to exercise.

Illusions About Leisure

Leisure is a difficult subject to discuss, owing to the crop of mistaken ideas which have grown up around it and obscure its significance. I will begin by cutting a path through this jungle.

The commonest error is the idea of leisure as always pleasant. This, of course, is not so. Whether leisure is pleasant or not depends on circumstances, and still more on the kind of man who has it. There is all the difference in the world between the leisure of wise men and the leisure of fools. Leisure is not pleasant—at least as a rule—when it has to be spent in gaol or on a sick-bed or in listening to the conversation of a bore. Which leads, by the way, to an important rule about the use of leisure, one of the very few that can be laid down, "Don't spend your leisure in ways that spoil the leisure of your friends." Some of my own best friends seem to be ignorant of this rule and I am not sure that I always observe it myself!

Even playing games is not always a pleasant occupation for leisure, especially if one plays them badly. Pleasure resorts where this kind of recreation is catered for often turn out very disappointing. At Monte Carlo, for example, there are many unhappy faces and suicides are not uncommon.

Another common mistake is to draw a sharp line between labor and leisure, putting labor occupations into the left-hand column and leisure occupations into the right; or treating leisure as though it began where labor left off. This clearly will not do, because the labor occupation of one man is often the leisure occupation of another. A country walk is a leisure occupation for many of us, but not for a country postman who walks fifteen miles every day in delivering his letters. But on the highest levels of life the distinction between labor and leisure or between work and play fades out. A great artist finds his play in his work. Play becomes art when raised to its highest excellence, its highest beauty, and its highest power. Anything that one does, from cooking a dinner to governing a state, becomes a work of art if motivated by the passion for excellence and done as well as it can be. A man who does his job in that spirit will be the one who gets the most satisfaction out of life.

A MISTAKE of another kind is often made by people who talk about "education for leisure," as so many of us are now doing. Education for leisure

is greatly needed, and I am inclined to think the fate of civilization depends on our getting it. But we can easily go about it in the wrong way. We go about it in the wrong way when we give it in the form of detailed instruction as to how leisure should be spent, so much time for this, so much for that. Leisure is precisely one of those things which cannot be dealt with in that way.

The essence and the charm of a leisure occupation arise from the fact that we have freely chosen it, that it represents our self-expression and is not a thing which some expert in leisure has told us we ought to do. If we ruled our leisure in that way we should soon be in the condition of the lady who spent so much time in playing bridge that she had no leisure at all.

Awakening the Creative Faculties

EDUCATION for leisure is imperatively needed, but it must take a different line. What we can do and ought to do is to train young people, beginning in earliest childhood, up to the point where they will be able to make a good choice of their leisure occupations for themselves. We do that *by awakening the creative side of them,* by giving them opportunities for using those creative faculties which all human beings possess to some degree, but which are often killed out by the education young people are getting now, to their great detriment in after life, in regard to both happiness and character.

The reason so many people are at a loss what to do with themselves in their leisure time, and make a stupid use of it in consequence, is that their creative faculties were never awakened when they were young. A person whose creative faculties have been awakened will seldom be at a loss for an enjoyable and worthwhile leisure occupation.

It is a fatal mistake to suppose that creative activity has its place in leisure occupations only. The need for it is equally great in the occupations of labor, in the work of every day, in the work

of the head as well as the work of the hand, and perhaps in the work of the head most of all. What kind of creativeness is more precious than *creative thinking*—in business, in economics, in politics, in international affairs, in religion? When was creative thinking so urgently needed as it is today? Are not our present troubles largely due to the fact that creative thinkers are so rare? The chief fault of our present methods of education is that they produce so many people who can't *think for themselves.*

There is this hopeful thing about creativeness—if you get the creative spirit into the activities of a human being at any point it will soon spread to other points. Teach a child to play creatively in his games and he will soon begin to think creatively in his lessons. Get it into leisure and it will soon spread into labor. Get it into the fingers and it will soon find its way to the brain. Provided always that you catch the pupil young enough. If you wait till he is middle aged and his habits have formed themselves, the creative spirit will be difficult to start, and when started at one point will be much slower in finding its way to the others.

Higher Recreation

There is yet another common mistake that I must refer to. It is the notion that recreation consists only in the playing of games—golf, bridge, tennis, baseball, and all the others that are played by children and adults.

Of course, recreation does include all that, but, much as I value games, I should not have undertaken my present mission if recreation consisted in them alone.

There is something more. Recreation includes all the beautiful skills, crafts, and hobbies that human beings can practise, on and up to the finest of the fine arts. I call this the Higher Recreation. You may think of music as a typical form of it, though, of course, there are a hundred others. We need playgrounds for the body, but we need also playgrounds for the soul, and it is in them, I think, that the most enjoyable recreation, the most delightful and lasting of leisure occupations, are to be found.

The wonderful art of the ancient Greeks was largely due to their fine physical culture, which they coördinated with the culture of the mind, and expressed in beautiful games. Their games were the growing point of their arts. Through their physical culture and through the games they grafted on to it, in which rhythmical dancing played an important part, they learnt how to bring their bodies under the control of their intelligence, and having established skill in that fundamental form they went on from it, step by step, to the higher recreation in art and thought, not only producing works of visible beauty which are joys for ever, but creative thinkers whose wisdom is still one of our greatest treasures.

There is no reason why we should not do likewise. But we shall never do it so long as we think of recreation as a mere affair of playing games. We must include the higher recreation and provide for the lower recreation trained leaders who understand, as the Greeks understood, how to make the lower into the growing point of the higher.

Let me tell you a story to illustrate what I have been saying.

Some months ago when I was in New York I was standing one day on Fifth Avenue in company with a friend. We were looking at the Empire State Building. I told my friend what I thought of it; I said that it appealed to me as a great work of art, a wonderful combination of mechanical science and creative imagination. My friend assented. I then asked him, "When was that building begun?" And he gave me an answer which bewildered me at first, but which, when I came to think it over, struck me as profoundly significant. "That building," he said, "was begun *long ages ago*. It was begun when the first boy made the first mud pie and it was finished when that boy, now grown into a twentieth-century man, had been taught by mechanical science how to raise the walls of his mud pie into a thing of beauty with its head among the clouds."

The studious class are their own victims; they are thin and pale, their feet are cold, their heads are hot, the night is without sleep, the day a fear of interruption,—pallor, squalor, hunger, and egotism. If you come near them and see what conceits they entertain—they are abstractionists, and spend their days and nights in dreaming some dream; in expecting the homage of society to some precious scheme built in a truth, but destitute of proportion in its presentment, of justness in its application, and of all energy of will in the schemer to embody and vitalize it.

—*Emerson*

T. S. STRIBLING

THE STORE

THIS is a story of the South in the 1880's, of a South that has been ravaged by war and carpet-baggers, of blacks who are only nominally free, of whites who are slaves to their lust for power. "The Store" won the Pulitzer Prize in 1932 for its author, T. S. Stribling (1881-   ), and has been widely hailed as the most dramatic novel of the "reconstructed" South and its effort to recreate the graciousness of its pre-war civilization. Lawrence Stallings says: "It has gusto. . . . By comparison with Stribling, most American novelists seem to be suffering from pernicious anaemia."

IN RESPONSE to his wife's uncertain inquiry about the political speaking, Colonel Miltiades Vaiden called back from his gate that he did not think there would be any ladies at the courthouse that evening.

The heavy wife in the doorway hesitated. She had wanted to go. She felt the gregarious impulse of fleshy persons to foregather with crowds, to laugh and fraternize with the audience, to propel her large body among her lighter fellows with the voluptuous and genial ruthlessness of a fat person. However, on the other hand, her feminine fear of being the only woman in the audience stood in her path.

But behind these two antagonistic impulses lay another cause of depression which the ponderous wife knew too well but which she never frankly had admitted even to herself. This was that her husband did not want her to go with him to this or to any other public gathering; it was . . . that he was ashamed of her.

This fact wavered in the woman's mind until she expelled it by calling out:

"Oh, Mr. Milt, there'll be a lot of leading men down there, I expect. Maybe some of 'em will offer you a—a better position. . . ."

At this mention of position a disagreeable tickle went through the husband's chest, but he answered in an impassive, corrective tone:

"Not likely such a topic will come up at a political meeting, Ponny."

"Well . . . if it does . . . you . . you mustn't repulse 'em, Mr. Milt."

"No, I won't, Ponny."

He let himself into the street and closed the gate after him. As he did thi the looseness of the hinges, the broke palings, the gaunt outline of his rente house here on this back street in Flo ence, all combined to give him a twi of repulsion when connected with th thought of a "position."

Because, as a matter of fact, the Co onel had no position. Ever since the Civ War had lost him his place as an ove seer on a cotton plantation, he had d sired the post and circumstance of country gentleman. Only nowadays the were no country gentlemen. Nowada one reached gentility by other method but Colonel Vaiden, somehow, had n succeeded in fitting himself into tho other methods.

For a long stretch the Colonel's failu had been a kind of standing riddle persons who had known of his disti guished services during the war and l leadership of the Klan during the R construction. But this riddle gradual lost point with time. So now, as the C onel glanced back in the twilight a saw in the doorway the bulky outline his wife, he knew that, besides himse she was the only human being on ea who believed that upon him, eventual would fall some great, noble, a extraordinary estate. She was constan expecting it out of a persistent faith a admiration for her husband's ability.

As the Colonel stepped across a gully
the neglected street he rewarded her
yalty by thinking in a kind of annoyed
shion:

"I should have asked her to go with
e . . . damn it . . . Ponny's a good
irl. . . ."

Cherry Street, along which Colonel
aiden moved, was bordered by bare
eed-grown lots and an occasional stark
ame house with a chicken coop and a
rivy in the rear. Two or three squares
urther on the pedestrian turned west-
ard toward Market Street. Here the
eighborhood began to improve: dark
asses of magnolias and live oaks
reened the houses. Opening on the
sidewalks were double gates to admit a
horse and carriage, or perhaps a milk
cow of mornings and evenings.

These were still ordinary middle-class
homes, but this evening they stiffened a
determination in Miltiades to reach this
stage of luxury. Yes, and, by gravy, he
would do even better than that! These
frame houses with magnolias and live
oaks, he would have something better
than that . . . he did not know just
what that better ménage would be, but a
quiver of impatience went through him
to be at it. Whatever he did he must do
quickly; whatever he gained he must
gain with speed; . . . he was forty-eight
years old.

Out of the Past

HALF an hour later, as Colonel Vaiden
approached Courthouse Square, a
istant burst of cheering told him that the
peaking already had begun. As he drew
earer the lilt of the voice of an orator
me to his ears.

As Miltiades passed a small single
uggy with a pretty bay mare between
s shafts, he heard a lover's tiff going
n in undertones. A girl's voice was say-
g tautly:

"Lucius, I—I'll get out!"

A youth's voice replied hastily:

"No, don't get out, Miss Sydna. . . ."

"Then sit on your side and listen to
e Governor," advised the girl in an-
yance.

"I was listening to him, too," teased
er companion.

Colonel Vaiden caught a glimpse of
e girl's face, a graceful face filled with
e embarrassment of a young girl who
ad not yet learned to deal with the
mall improprieties of the admirers
hom she attracted. He recognized her
Sydna Crowninshield, the daughter of
s old sweetheart Drusilla Lacefield.
Drusilla. . . . Drusilla had been en-
aged to be married to him, and she had
oped with another man, Emory Crown-
shield, on the night before their wed-
ing. . . . Again he recalled very dis-
nctly his return home after the war,
how he had engaged himself to Drusilla
once more and had seduced and jilted
her. That was a long time ago, yet
Drusilla's gift of herself to him still stood
like a far-away light amid the foggy
commonplaces of his succeeding love
life.

However, it seemed to Miltiades that
after all it was a good thing that he
had not married Drusilla. He had not
made a success, and their contemplated
marriage always tacitly had been
founded on his becoming wealthy and
successful. He still believed he was going to be successful, but he would not
have liked to share with Drusilla this
long flat stretch of poverty. For Ponny—
for his fat wife Ponny—it was all right,
but for Drusilla it would have been
impossible.

The expression of Miss Sydna aroused
in him a sharp disapproval of the youth
in the buggy. Without glancing around
he said in a curt undertone:

"Young man, in a lady's presence you
should imitate a gentleman, at least temporarily." And with that he walked on.

Miltiades thought of the honor in
which Southern men held their women.
Take, for example, his own action in
rebuking the youth in the little hug-me-
tight buggy. A Northern man would
perhaps have laughed, or have listened

and said nothing, but he, a Southern man, had reproved the misdemeanant with a phrase. . . . He continued slowly and aimlessly across the Square.

A VOICE behind him calling out, "Mr. Bivins! Oh, Mr. Bivins, just a moment!" caused the Colonel to look around.

A middle-aged man came hurrying up.

"Mr. Bivins, add three rolls of plow lines and a dozen mule collars to my order. . . ."

When the man came closer, Colonel Vaiden saw who it was and felt a sharp impulse to turn and walk on without a word. His dignity, however, forbade that, so he said briefly:

"I am afraid you have made a mistake, Mr. Handback."

Then the merchant discovered his own error and began begging Miltiades' pardon. He explained, with considerable confusion, that in the dark he had mistaken Miltiades for a hardware drummer who was staying at the hotel.

"That's all right, Mr. Handback," interrupted the Colonel with an ancient resentment flatting his tones.

The Colonel recalled clearly the offense which now reduced the merchant to such an embarrassed favor currier. Handback had accepted twenty-five hundred dollars' worth of the Vaiden cotton in his store on the very day he made an assignment in bankruptcy. It was all the cotton which Miltiades and Augustus and Cassandra and Marcia Vaiden had raised in a season; their whole year's work gone without a penny. That had been twenty years ago.

Now, with this ancient transaction in their thoughts, the two men would probably have walked to the hotel in silence, had not another group of men entering the Square created a diversion.

J. Handback pointed across the dimly lighted plaza.

"Look yonder, won't you? That damned Landers and his nigger meeting just now breaking up!"

Miltiades looked without enthusiasm and said nothing.

J. Handback began again, exaggerating his contempt to cover his own silently arraigned case.

"I swear I wouldn't affiliate with them black monkeys, not to be postmaster all the rest of my life. I wouldn't do it!"

"A man'll do most anything for money," observed Miltiades drily.

"Uh . . . m-m . . . yes, but I wouldn't do that," stammered the merchant. "It cuts a man off from the society of decent men and women. It's social suicide even to vote the Republican ticket here in Florence, much less bob-bashiely with niggers!"

"I never heard anybody accuse Landers of stealing anything."

"No, but I say a man who'll do what Landers does will steal!"

"M-m . . . yes . . . he might. . . ."

"Well, I for one can't stand to rub shoulders with a coon. In my store I keep 'em on the other side of the counter; in my fields I keep 'em at the business end of a plow."

"That's right." Miltiades admitted this reluctantly, because it condoned in a subtle way the merchant's theft of the cotton from his family.

The merchant stood looking down on Lump when a burst of laughter from the hotel lobby seemed to turn his thoughts from the negro. He looked at Miltiades and asked tentatively:

"Colonel Vaiden . . . might I ask you to do me a favor?"

"What is it?" inquired the Colonel dubiously.

"Would you mind stepping in the lobby and telling Slim Bivins to add three rolls of plow lines and a dozen assorted mule collars to my order?"

"No-o. . . . I don't mind. . . ."

"Thank you very much, Colonel—very much," said the merchant gratefully. "Good-night."

"Thank you very much, Colonel—very much," said the merchant gratefully. "Good-night."

"Good-night," returned Miltiades

wondering a little to hear himself saying good-night to J. Handback. Then he gave an inaudible sniff of laughter.

J. Handback moved off toward Market Street, apparently going to his home in the northern end of town. At last, when he became a dim blur against the walls of the opposite stores, Miltiades saw him change his course in the general direction of East Florence.

A vague speculation floated through the Colonel's mind as to why J. Handback should have turned toward East Florence, but he neither pressed the point, nor did he care. Any unconventionality which the merchant probably had in mind was no more in the Colonel's estimation than where some dog buried a bone. The fellow was a thief. . . .

One Way to a Store

INSIDE the lobby of the Florence Hotel Colonel Vaiden found a group of five commercial travelers with cigars cocked at optimistic angles as they retold bawdy-house yarns and spat at dirty brass cuspidors.

The Colonel explained the extra items which J. Handback wanted to add to his order. Mr. Bivins became business-like at once. He went to a desk in the lobby, drew out his order book, and poised his pencil.

As he did so a faint tentative design began to grow in Miltiades' thoughts. He began mentally taking stock of every available resource which he possibly might scrape together. He was considering borrowing some money. The sum he had in mind was five hundred dollars. He wondered if he could start a little business on a capital of five hundred dollars, but then he knew he would never be able to raise that amount among his brothers and sisters, and the notion faded from his thoughts.

A sudden impulse made him draw Mr. Bivins aside and question him about the price of stocking a store. The sales-man, immediately interested, rapidly began reeling off necessary items and when Miltiades made no move to stop him, jotted them down in his order book. After several hours of such figuring, Bivins presented him with a bill for 916.

Miltiades, profoundly embarrassed, said that he could only pay in small in-stallments. Bivins immediately checked his credit with bystanders and found that it was nil. This infuriated the Colonel who stormed out of the hotel saying that the salesman would be sorry some day.

Miltiades was not, as he fatuously had forecast, as well off now as he had been before he was refused credit. He had felt all the time that he would be re-fused, but now that it had come to pass, he was morally wounded and deeply incensed.

But presently this drifted from his mind and left him thinking of the com-missary he had run before the war on the old Lacefield plantation down in the Reserve. He had controlled two hundred negroes, fifteen hundred acres of cotton, and the commissary. The commissary itself had been a mere detail in those days, but what he had learned about it would become important when he finally obtained a store of his own.

THE sound of footsteps filled the last of the night with a far-reaching, uneven clacking. The Colonel stood looking down the milky blur of Market Street with a faint curiosity as to who could be walking away from town at such an hour. Presently the figure of J. Handback defined itself against the gray pall of the morning, weaving a little from side to side.

The identity of the befuddled man caused Miltiades not so much surprise as a sort of contemptuous recognition of something he should have guessed. He turned to walk away when the figure came on again as if touched off by a button.

"Why, it's my frien' Colonel Vaiden,"

it babbled. "Thought for a moment . . . might be somebody . . . wouldn't want to see me out . . . you know . . . late like this . . . but . . . but see I'm in han's of a frien' . . . eh, Colonel? . . . we're frien's, ain't we, Colonel?"

Miltiades stood with military erectness looking at the fellow.

"Well, yes," he agreed drily, "you might say we're friends, barring the fact that you stole twenty-five hundred dollars from me twenty years ago."

J. Handback came to a pause.

"Still think o' that?"

"Now and then."

"No . . . no . . . won't go into that. . . ." Handback stood for a moment or two, ill at ease; then, by way of changing the topic, "Didn't see nothin' more of that damn nigger-lovin' Landers, I s'pose?"

"No, and I hope I won't."

"Amen to that, Colonel. . . . Disgrace . . . 'filiatin' with a lot o' damn dirty niggers . . . ort to be drummed out o' town. . . ." Here he came to another conversational dead end and stood looking around in the graying morning. "Well . . . better be movin' 'long."

Miltiades stood considering what was best to do. He disliked the man, but Handback had a very good reputation. He was a deacon in the Methodist church, and the Colonel did not have the petty spite to allow the fellow to waste his good name by wandering around on the streets drunk. So now he took his arm and started thoughtfully back down Market Street toward town.

Handback offered no objection, but began explaining himself more fully.

"Jess been to see a frien' o' mine, Colonel . . . lady 'frien' . . . sh-she's damn near a lady . . . damn near white, too, even if I do say it."

"M-m," said the Colonel, with the disapproval of one man for another man's unconventionalities.

"Now . . . now . . . man needs a li'l' relaxation," defended the merchant, "relieves business strain. . . . Whicherway we goin'?"

"To the hotel."

"By George . . . good idyah . . forgot we had a hotel." The merchant steps depended more and more on th Colonel. "But I should uh stayed out th night at Gracie's . . . ver' nice woma Colonel . . . kep' her for years . . Clean . . . discreet, an' . . . an' o ligin'. . . ."

They were approaching Courthous Square again. Some of the lamps, whic were gauged to extinguish themselves the morning, were out. Miltiades quickl made his way across the square with h burden.

The single night light burning in th lobby had faded to a small pale tongu of flame in the gray morning. The nigl clerk dozed with his head on the regi ter. Miltiades did not waken the ma but maneuvered his charge up the fligl of stairs into the first empty bedroom h found. He stood for a moment breathin deeply from his exertion, then tiptoe down again.

Jo HANDBACK arose painfully from hi bed the next morning, swearing t himself that he would never again visi the establishment which he kept in Eas Florence. The whole encounter wit Miltiades came to him, nebulously, bu with complete certainty. He even remem bered what he had said to the Colone his arguments for going to his quadroo mistress . . . of all men in Florence t pick out Miltiades Vaiden for such confession! The most unforgiving enem he had in the world!

After considerable thought J. Hand back drew out a memorandum book an scribbled a note to Colonel Vaiden ask ing him to meet him after church.

Miltiades had also given considerabl thought to the events of the previou evening. Finally he determined to us what he knew about J. Handback as means of getting himself a position i his store.

Mr. Handback could not refuse thi suggestion so the Colonel became a cler in the Handback store at $7.50 a week

A Pound of Bacon

THE report that Colonel Miltiades Vaiden was a clerk in J. Handback's store affected a number of persons, each in a different manner.

To Mrs. Drusilla Crowninshield it brought an empty conclusion to a sort of half sad triumph that her old lover's marriage with Ponny BeShears for her money had gained him, in the end, nothing at all.

The daughter Sydna fell into a vague wonderment if, by any possibility, Colonel Vaiden were entering the Handback store to scrutinize more carefully the character of Lucius Handback. Such extreme knight errantry Sydna felt possible in Miltiades. The girl had never spoken a word to the Colonel that she remembered. Her mother's attitude toward Colonel Vaiden had impressed a reticence upon the daughter. At times Sydna thought of what she would say if she should speak to him; she would try to thank him for his care over her, for being a kind of invisible guardian over her . . . here her thoughts lost the form of words and became a feeling of sweetness and gratitude.

To Gracie, the quadroon seamstress of East Florence, the news had disturbing overtones.

She had dispatched Toussaint several days before to go to town and get a pound of bacon. When she gave him this commission her almost white son had asked in an intent, even voice:

"Am I going to stand up for a whole pound, Mammy?"

Gracie became at once uneasy about her restive, unadjustable son.

"No," she cried sharply, then tempered her voice to a persuasive tone: "No, Toussaint, don't say anything about the pound. . . . If it looks too little, you might say, 'I wanted a pound . . .' no, I wouldn't say anything at all about it."

Her whole body felt jumpy lest her son should speak his bitter thoughts before white folk. She would get him

North as soon as possible. A romantic notion of installing herself in some Northern city as a Mexican woman continually dwelt in Gracie's mind. Toussaint would go through college; he would become a professional man, and he would marry . . . the rest Gracie never really put into words, but she always saw her white son married to a white woman and the long stain of negrohood in her line brought to an end.

Toussaint set off toward Old Florence on the mission, hazardous for precisely him, of buying a pound of bacon. Toward the rear of the store a number of negroes were waiting for somebody in their midst. Toussaint went closer and saw a middle-aged man writing on the back of a negro's due bill.

As Toussaint recognized this clerk a queer sensation went over him. It was Colonel Miltiades Vaiden. He stared, hardly crediting the enormity. Moreover, it had a very personal bearing on himself. He knew that Colonel Vaiden's family once had owned his mother and his grandmother, Hannah, before her. From these Vaidens, he had derived, through his mother, whatever education he possessed. Now to see the former owner of his family weighing goods out to a bunch of cotton-field negroes, it pinched something in Toussaint's chest.

When Toussaint's turn came, the Colonel carefully weighed out a full pound of bacon for him. For he did not stand with J. Handback's policy of cheating the negroes.

Toussaint asked to see the scales in order to see if it really was a pound.

"Why, you damned gingerbread nigger! Insinuating I'd short-weight . . ."

The next thing Toussaint knew a terrific force whirled him around. The store spun about him. The next instant terrific shocks went through his spine as the Colonel kicked him toward the door. The door itself made a flying leap at him. He flung out his arms and crashed down on his hands and knees. Before he could scramble up another kick mashed his face down in the tobacco spittle on the floor.

Some of the negroes around the door began laughing with the loud clacking of field hands. Presently a middle-aged black man came out of the store bringing Toussaint's hat and his pound of bacon. He gave Toussaint this advice: "Lissen to me, yellow boy, it is much mo' dangerous to accuse a white man of shawt-weightin' you when he ain't 'an when he is."

Handback wondered uneasily what Gracie would think about the Colonel having kicked Toussaint. She might very well be angry and difficult to propitiate. She might say, "You let one of your clerks kick Toussaint." That one specific thing would lie between them,

and it might cost him five, ten, or eve. twenty dollars.

He decided that he would not go t Gracie's that Saturday night. He did nc care much about it anyway. He wa tired. They had had a rushing trade. I would do him good to go home an sleep. Then he wondered what Graci would say to a shoe store. He wanted t talk about it to some disinterested per son. Not that he expected any directin wisdom in the quadroon's replies, but i clarified his own ideas to talk them ove

The merchant was conscious of thi liberating effect the colored woman ha upon his ponderings, and he reflecte that, since he had paid for her service anyway, it was nothing but good busi ness for him to go down and collect.

So he turned his steps toward Eas Florence.

The Colonel Is Promoted

HIS very first evening at work showed the Colonel the huge volume of his employer's business. Grist mills, saw mills, cotton gins, lumber yards, cross-tie yards, and of course cotton plantations, marched through page after page.

At first Miltiades was simply astonished, but now, as he walked home, he began to think that the money of the Vaidens was part of the original capital of the store. The nest egg he should have had lay embedded in the base of this vast complex of enterprises. And now here he was, a clerk, in the system of properties which he had helped to fund, drawing from it, by dint of endless labor, seven dollars and a half a week! This was the cause of his ironic amusement and indignation.

Soon after this Miltiades was promoted to the job of overseer of Handback's properties and his salary raised to $10 a week. Handback knew that he lost money by the Colonel's honest dealings with the blacks and felt that it was better to have him out of the store most of the time.

The thing that gyved the Colonel was the use to which all the cotton yield

would be put. J. Handback would take it all, use a negligible fraction on hi family and quadroon mistress, and with the rest he would buy more gins, more plantations, increase the stock in hi store, and none of it would ever come to anything more than that. The ironic part of it was that he, Miltiades Vaiden, was one of the units in Handback's pointless accumulation.

At a turn of the road he saw the gin with rapid puffs of steam rising above its roof. Lines of wagons stood in the gin yard awaiting their turn at unloading. From a platform at the height of the second floor, negroes slewed the bales onto an inclined plane, and rolled them down into the gin yard below. A little distance out in the yard, other negroes with a tripod and scales weighed the bales and daubed their weights on their ends with black paint. The seed of the cotton was carted out of the gin yard and left to decay in a great pile.

As the Colonel got out of the wagon and went about the building he had an odd feeling that the bales which rolled down in the yard were the self-same cotton which he and his sister Cassandra had picked and delivered to the Hand-back store twenty years before.

He and his family had grown five bales of cotton . . . the Colonel continued thinking about it. At that time cotton was worth a dollar a pound. Every bale he had lost to Handback was worth five of these modern bales. It was as if he had delivered to the merchant twenty-five present-day bales.

From the gin loft Miltiades looked down in the yard and began counting twenty-five bales. They made a big pile of cotton. On the end of each bale were its weight and the initials, "J. H."

The Colonel discovered a plan of action precipitating itself in his head. He gave the teamsters their orders.

"I want you boys to haul some of this cotton to the railroad yard in Florence, and I want some of it laid down at Connors' Landing. I'm going to ship it by boat," he directed. Then he added, "River rates are cheaper than railroad rates."

"Yes, suh," agreed a negro, "I bet it 'ud take a fo'chune to move dat cotton eidah by train aw boat."

One of the men asked in a matter-of-fact way how many bales went to Florence and how many to Connors' Landing.

The Colonel hesitated.

"Lemme see, I believe I'll have . . . twenty-five bales hauled to Connors'," he directed.

Bales of Cotton

As MILTIADES drove home that evening he went over in his mind all sorts of explanations to an imaginary J. Handback why he had dispatched twenty-five bales of cotton to Connors' Landing.

He tried out in his soliloquy a casual reference:

"I had twenty-five bales hauled to Connors' Landing today. . . ."

After a space he tested a fuller explanation:

"I sent twenty-five bales to Connors' Landing today; freight rates are so much cheaper by boat than by train."

As Miltiades thought these words, the merchant's answer sounded from nowhere in his ears:

"How came you to take it on yourself to say how my cotton should be shipped?"

The actual breaking of the news to J. Handback that his cotton had been hauled to Connors' Landing fell out quite otherwise than Miltiades had anticipated.

"How many bales did you say you sent down?" Handback demanded.

"Twenty-five."

"How come you to start with just twenty-five?"

"Well . . . I had to start with some number."

"I mean, whyn't you send more?"

"I thought maybe you needed some quick cotton on the market. I didn't know how your finances were."

"M—m, I do need some quick cotton, and my finances are dern low," admitted the merchant, frowning; "that's one of the things that always stopped me—that and the freight agent." He picked up a pencil and began figuring on the back of an old envelope. "Put five hundred more bales down there," he directed finally.

This sudden determination of the merchant to bank five hundred bales of cotton at Connors' Landing had a queerly depressing effect upon Miltiades. He set out for his round of the plantations with a feeling that some ill thing had befallen him. Exactly why, he could not say. Still, somewhere in the Colonel's heart he had had a feeling that the twenty-five bales at Connors' Landing in some vague way belonged to him, and that the new cotton which presently would be hauled and cover up the twenty-five bales would lose him some sort of intangible property rights in them. It was, of course, a purely nonsensical fancy, but still, it was enough to depress the Colonel for several days after that.

THOSE original twenty-five bales of cotton, after they had become lost among the five hundred J. Handback had piled down at Connors' Landing, became a kind of obsession with Colonel Vaiden. With no intention of doing so, he was continually thinking of ways to repossess this cotton, although, as a matter of fact, he never had possessed it.

With a wagon and team he might haul the twenty-five bales to the old Vaiden place and store them in the shed of the forge which his father had built long before the war.

Then he began thinking over the negroes he might possibly get to haul the cotton for him. A notion popped into the Colonel's head to use Gracie's boy. The Colonel held a sort of authority over Gracie and her son—an authority undefined on the one hand and unacknowledged on the other: it was a vague relation that persisted between ex-master and ex-slave. There was something between them. They were not just a white man and two negroes.

One afternoon, in the shortening autumn day, Mr. Klem called out in neighborly fashion as Miltiades passed the Klem home:

"Hope it doesn't raise the river. I waded Mr. Boggus' cattle over to the island to graze yestiddy. I added two yearlings of my own for luck."

"Is it as low as that?"

"Why, there hasn't been a steamboat up for weeks. . . . Er—I understand there's going to be something doing up your way, soon, Colonel."

This observation startled Miltiades. He thought for an instant Klem meant something about cotton.

"What sort of doings, Mr. Klem?" he asked soberly.

"My wife says your troubles are going to be little ones purty soon." He gave a respectful laugh.

"Oh . . . well, I don't know," said the Colonel, not much relishing the subject with Klem.

Miltiades walked on to his own home with his thoughts divided by the prospects of autumnal rains and the possibility that Ponny was pregnant. Both these topics bore somewhat on the matter of cotton. When the river rose Handback would ship his cotton on the first steamboat that came up over the shoals. If his wife should have a child it would make the repossession of his cotton all the more imperative.

However, Miltiades did not really believe in his wife's pregnancy. He had been married to her for twenty years, and if she ever intended to have a child . . . His thoughts moved on in vague negation.

On this point, however, Ponny herself was in quite a different mind. When Miltiades reached home she told him she had rested very well that day. The Colonel said he was glad to hear it and began thinking again of the cotton.

A few days later the Colonel heard of the arrival of the steamboat, *Zebulon D,* captained by a person who was known to wink at the law for a price.

After locating him the Colonel explained that he wanted to ship five hundred bales of cotton to New Orleans. The Captain agreed to do it for $3000. This included shipping all of the negroes who loaded the cotton so that they wouldn't spread the story.

Aftermath

IN THE rainy morning the *Zebulon D.* steamed away from Connors' Landing. From where he stood on the bank, Miltiades Vaiden watched the whitened water flung up by her stern wheel and the black rolls of smoke from her chimneys beaten down to the surface of the river by the rain. Ahead of the boat he had just a glimpse of the barge piled high with cotton bales.

On the bank Colonel Vaiden stood speculating on how long before the roustabouts would get back to Florence from New Orleans. He would have just that length of time to receive and dispose of the returns for the cotton he was shipping. Even with the boat and barge still in sight, he felt pressed for time. The cotton would be missed, he believed, within twenty-four hours. The bank of the river was trampled into a loblolly by the night-long labor of the roustabouts. . . . The Colonel glanced about him in the gray descending curtain. No one, he supposed, would be abroad on such a morning. Then he planned, if he were seen, if the loss of the cotton should be attributed to him, to claim that he was attempting to collect an old debt. In reality he stood within his rights. When it came right down to the justice of it, no grand jury would say he had committed a theft.

He and his brothers and sisters had been cheated out of their cotton crop by Handback. He, Miltiades Vaiden, had collected five hundred bales of cotton for an original five. But cotton just after the war was worth a dollar a pound, while now it was worth only twenty cents a pound. Handback had had the money for twenty years. At ten per cent that would double twice . . . twenty-five bales would be, fifty . . . a hundred bales. But he had collected five hundred bales. That would be fifty per cent, doubled twice.

These figures moved through Miltiades' head with the repetition of things heard in a fever. He walked on through the woods thinking five . . . five hundred . . . fifty per cent, when a cry startled him out of this mental repetend.

"Milt Vaiden! Miltiades Vaiden! Hold on a minute! Wait!"

A shock of resistance and antagonism went through the Colonel. It aroused him completely and suddenly put the whole street right.

"What do you want, Handback?" he asked, and awaited his approach.

"My God, man!" gasped the merchant. "You've ruined me! You've broken me up!"

Miltiades stared at the fellow's clay-colored face. His heart began beating in his heavy chest. He wondered swiftly if there were a possibility of instituting a lawsuit to hold the cotton he had seized upon.

"What you talking about?" The Colonel wetted his lips.

"You've cost me ever' damned bale of cotton I've got!"

Miltiades wondered how Handback came to know so quickly. He drew in his breath to say, "And you cost me every bale I had once." He was interrupted by the merchant rushing on in the wildest manner:

"It's all gone. . . . Ever' bale we had down there's washed away. . . . It's scattered down the river from here to Padooky!"

The merchant was staring at his clerk in the utmost anguish of soul. A sharp, almost painful twist went through Miltiades as he reoriented his thoughts to Handback's point of view.

"They're washed away!" he echoed in amazement.

"Ever' damn bale! Telephone! Telegraph! Set guards out below and save what we can! God damn it! Hell fire! That was what the freight agent said would happen. He warned me. A man's a damn fool not to listen to somebody with sense!"

"Mr. Handback," cried the Colonel in spontaneous sympathy, "I'm awfully sorry I got you to put your cotton——"

"Oh, hell . . . my cotton . . . I had it done . . . it was my fault!"

Miltiades went to a desk and scribbled a message to the ferryman at Savannah saying five hundred bales of Handback cotton washed away . . . hold . . . reward. J. Handback & Son, Florence, Ala.

He handed it to the merchant. Handback read it.

"Put down ten dollars' reward for each bale," he dictated.

Miltiades added the figures. The merchant looked at it again and passed it on to the operator.

"Let's go," he said.

Miltiades was overcome by the sinking realization that he was no longer collecting a just debt—he was making a grab.

The Other Side of the Grave

Early Sunday morning two weeks later, Miltiades was awakened out of his sleep by either a dream or an impression that his draft had come. He sat up in bed and blinked his eyes. His heart beat. A kind of agonized near possession of the draft tingled through him.

He had an impulse to get up immediately and hurry down to the post office and look in his box. But it was Sunday, and there would be nobody in the office to hand out his mail. He decided to drop down there anyway.

As he drew near the musty building his heart began beating. He entered the door and tried to look across the lobby at once into his box. The lobby itself was empty. He walked across to his call box with his eyes fixed on his number. The narrow tallish box was empty.

A negro's voice behind him said:

"Is you lookin' fuh a postmaster, Col'l Milt?"

"Yes, I'm looking for Landers. Where do you s'pose I'd find him?"

"Well, Ah do' know zackly, Col'l Milt. Mist' Landahs, he walk out on de creek nea'ly evah Sunday mawn'n'."

"Well, I know damn well he won't be there," growled the Colonel, "and if he is there he won't come to the office and see if I've got any mail . . . such a damn set of unaccommodating Republican post-office employees. . . ."

The Colonel strode out of the office already in a dudgeon at Landers for being about to refuse to come and look for his mail.

The Colonel's way lay along Pine Street, which was continued out of town as Waterloo Road. At the end of the street it turned left down a wooded hillside, then led through a scattering of negro cabins and so to the creek.

A thin man of medium height, wearing the baggy clothes of a post-office employee, appeared walking along the opposite side of the creek.

Miltiades moved toward the edge of the creek, waving a hand with an irra-tional feeling that the man might vanish as unexpectedly as he had appeared.

"Mr. Landers! Oh, Mr. Landers!" he called above the watery baritone of the stream.

The postmaster walked with head down and hands behind him.

Now he looked up and around.

"Yes," he said, "what is it?"

"Will you let me in the post office?"

Landers collected himself.

"Do you want in right now?"

"Well . . . before long."

"I'm going to walk down the creek way," said Landers; "I'll be there in about half an hour."

"Well . . . all right," called back Miltiades.

But when Landers resumed his musing posture and started forward once more, the habitual loneliness of the man impressed the Colonel.

What Landers had said about meeting him at the post office in half an hour was a lonely phrase. It implied that of course the Colonel would not want to walk back to town in Landers' company. Yet the fellow was granting him a favor. Suddenly it seemed boorish to accept it in such a fashion. The Colonel quickened his gait, paralleling the postmaster.

"Mr. Landers," he called, "you are going to the post office and so am I . . . Wait there a minute. . . ."

The thin man stopped walking and sat down on a stone. The Colonel turned back to the bridge at a quick pace. As he went he reflected that never in his life had he seen a white man walk the streets with Landers. He half regretted his rashness. He would think up some good reason for separating from Landers when they reached the edge of town.

He joined the postmaster, commenting on the beauty of the day.

"They told me at the office you walked out here," explained the Colonel. "Do you always walk by yourself?"

"I don't know."

The Colonel looked at him, rather surprised.

"You don't know whether you walk by yourself or not?"

Landers glanced at his companion and then said in a hesitant manner:

"Not with anybody on this side of the grave, of course. I'm glad you came along. I've often wanted to talk about it with somebody."

The Colonel walked for several moments in silence at being shifted so abruptly to this unusual mental plane. He felt the utter loneliness of this man who moved about imagining such extraordinary communications with never a person to mention them to.

"Don't you ever talk about it to . . ." the Colonel almost said "niggers" but changed it to "your friends?"

"No, they would just get nervous about it."

"Yes, I fancy they would," agreed Miltiades.

"Do you think—er—some particular person is with you?"

"My sister," nodded Landers. "She has been dead a year."

"How did you know it was your sister?"

"I didn't. One day an old gentleman came to me in the post office and asked for his mail. I looked, and he didn't have any. Then he said, 'A woman wants to speak to you.' I said, 'Where is she?' He said, 'In the back part of your post office, where we can be by ourselves for a few minutes.' I looked around and didn't see anybody and asked what woman it was. The old man said her name used to be Ora Landers. Well, I looked at him for about a minute; then I said, 'Ora Landers was my sister. She is dead'; and the old man said, 'I know it.'

"I had the queerest feelings, of course. I said to him, 'I think you must be a humbug . . . or crazy'; but I opened the door and let him in."

"And what did he do?" asked Miltiades.

"Why, he said my sister wanted to tell me I was not by myself all the time like I thought I was, that she was with me whenever she could be, and I wouldn't be lonesome long."

Miltiades pondered this. Then he said: "What made you think it was really your sister, anyway? . . . Did you take the whole thing on the old man's say-so?"

"Why . . . not exactly. . . ." The postmaster seemed a little uncertain and ill at ease. "I—I believe I'll tell you just what did happen. . . . I'd like to have your opinion on it.

"Well, I said, 'How do I know you are Ora?'

"And she sort of laughed and said, 'Do you remember old Marth Killicut.'

"Did she laugh and say this or did the old man do it?" probed the Colonel.

"Why, really, the old man, but I was considering him as Ora."

"I see. . . . Go ahead."

"I said, 'Yes, I remember Marth Killicut.

"And she said, 'Yes, and you ought to be ashamed, Manuel, you gave her a little son.'

"What do you make out of that?"

Miltiades shook his head blankly.

"Nothing at all. . . . Who was Marth Killicut?"

"A street walker I knew a long time ago. I had forgot all about her until the old man said I had given her a son.

"How would she have known whose son it was? Why would she have picked out me?"

The Colonel stood faintly shaking his head.

"And he didn't ask you for any money?"

"No, when we got through, he walked out, just like I told you, and I've never seen him again."

The Colonel stood nodding faintly and looking at the postmaster.

"If he'd only tried to hold you up for some money . . . but he didn't do that. . . ."

$48,751.37

FINALLY they returned to the post office and Landers handed him his letter. The Colonel put the letter in his pocket and kept his hand over the pocket. He walked across the street, past the Florence Hotel, and stopped under one of the twisted, misshapen mulberry trees in front of Intelligence Row. Then he opened the envelope with fingers that trembled lest they tear the enclosure.

Inside was a bill of sale and a draft for forty-eight thousand, seven hundred and fifty-one dollars and thirty-seven cents.

The draft was light blue. The figures and letters were a deeper blue and written in a clerkly hand. The Colonel stood looking and looking at it, breathing rapidly through his open mouth. Forty-eight thousand. . . .

The blood beat in his temples and throat.

The draft could not be cashed on Sunday. How much time Miltiades would have to cash it, he did not know. If Handback got a hint of it he might have the payment stopped in New Orleans. He, Miltiades, could not hope to draw such a sum from one of the Florence banks without investigation.

He decided to take the train to Tuscumbia the next day and cash the check there.

The Colonel's reflections were disturbed by some negroes loitering up Intelligence Row, talking, guffawing, and slapping each other on the back.

When the black men saw Miltiades under the mulberry, they abruptly dropped their horseplay and moved past him in decorum.

The manner of the negroes caught the attention of the ex-overseer. He wondered why their sudden change. Was it something about him, or did they think that he knew something about them? Some knowledge somewhere had caused the black men to quiet down like that. Normally they would have exaggerated their horseplay in an effort to amuse a white onlooker. A suspicion went through the Colonel.

"Look here, did any of you niggers ship on a towboat a week or so ago?"

"Yes, suh, we all of us ship on de *Zeb'lon D.,*" stated a brown man with a faint touch of antagonism in his voice.

An odd feeling as if Intelligence Row were sinking beneath him caught the Colonel.

"But, Col'l Milt, even if we is back we still 'membahs what white man weighed us out a whole poun' of sugah an' coffee fuh ouah money an' wha did'n'."

And with this vague encouragement the group shuffled on toward the hotel corner.

The discovery that every negro in town knew the facts about the Handback cotton dismayed the Colonel. And now, suddenly, he realized that in their eyes he was an arch thief. The way they quieted before him and gave him side glances showed that. All the negroes knew it, and hanging immediately over his head, like a knife just ready to drop was the time when every soul in Florence, white and black, would know it and then what was he to do?

The Colonel put his envelope into an inner pocket and straightened his shoulders.

"Well," he thought with a tang of defiance, "I have collected an old debt, and the niggers can look wall-eyed about it if they want to, and if anybody else wants to follow their—er—example, they can . . . start."

The next day he was able to cash the check after the Tuscumbia bank had wired to the New Orleans bank on which it was drawn. Miltiades returned home with a heavy valise filled with bills.

As Miltiades walked along the road with his valise he saw free negroes, as useless as free horses, walking to and fro, and him with forty-eight thousand dollars to safeguard somehow. The irony of the situation bit at the Colonel's nerves.

The road from the depot led at first eastward to the Florence-Sheffield road, then northward into Market Street. Mil-tiades walked to the main thoroughfare, but instead of turning north he continued straight along a secondary road that led to East Florence and the home of his ex-slave.

Master and Slave

WHEN Colonel Vaiden reached Gracie's cottage its whiteness and neatness touched the visitor with the ironic fact that his family's former slave lived in a better house than his own.

An inner door opened, and Gracie came out. Her eyes were full of one kind of questioning which changed to another kind when she saw who it was.

"Why, Colonel Milt!" she gasped. "What's happened?"

She saw the new leather case and knew this had something to do with her. A fear went through her mind that it contained pistols and ammunition; that the Colonel was fleeing from officers and had come for her to hide him.

"Gracie, I've got this thing." He swung the valise a bit. "I want you to take care of it for me." His tone took instant and unquestioning possession of her. "Can you put it up in the loft? . . It's heavy."

"I don't know. . . ."

Gracie came forward to take the bag, but she was so shaken she could hardly lift it. She knew perfectly well that the money belonged to Handback, that Miltiades had stolen it.

"Oh, my Jesus," thought the quadroon, "here he comes again, knocking me out of my place." As she took the bag and carried it into the kitchen she thought, "This'll get me into terrible trouble! I know it'll do it! In the kitchen I'll tell him I can't do it!"

She walked into the kitchen, trying to hold the bag away from her as if it were venomous. Every moment she planned to turn around and tell him she couldn't hide his bag.

The Colonel's rush pushed them both hurriedly into the kitchen.

There was a little square manhole through the ceiling, above the stove. Gracie seized her broom and began knocking it open with the handle. The Colonel watched her.

"I don't believe anybody will think to look up there," he said, staring at the manhole.

"I reckon not," said Gracie, in despair at what she was doing.

"If anybody asks you, tell 'em you don't know anything about it."

"Mr. Milt!" cried Gracie, "what do you want with so much for, anyway?"

"There, it's giving," said the Colonel.

Miltiades helped push up the bag with the straw end of the broom, while Gracie strained to lift it in the manhole.

"Col'l Milt," she said, looking terrified at the ceiling, "won't that get you into lots of trouble?"

"I don't know," said Miltiades. "I suppose I'll find out."

"Col'l Milt, whatever made you do it to begin with?" she asked, overwhelmed by the magnitude of her former master's swindle.

"Do what?" asked Miltiades, with a faint, sardonic sense of humor.

Gracie could insinuate what she knew, but she could not speak of it openly.

"Well . . . you having so much money," replied the quadroon vaguely. She thought a moment and then asked, "What will I say you come here for, Col'l Milt?"

"If anybody saw me, they can guess what they want to.

"Now, Gracie," he directed, "I am depending upon you to keep absolutely quiet about this."

"You know I'm not going to say anything," said Gracie gloomily.

"I mean inadvertently—by accident," impressed Miltiades.

He walked slowly to the kitchen door, opened it, and let himself out.

Gracie watched him go with her heart beating heavily in her chest. She felt sick. The body of her thought forecast unhappily what the future would bring and what had happened to her in the past through Miltiades.

It was Miltiades, long ago, who had forced her child upon her and this child finally had broken off her concubinage with General Beekman. She had persisted in keeping Toussaint, so Beekman had sent her away from Montgomery back to Florence. Now she had found

an even, unemotional haven in this cottage which Handback had given her and Miltiades had caught her up again and was using her under compulsion.

She had tried not to let him use her long ago, in the stable loft, but she had been his slave. Today, in her cottage she had become his servant again. She could not prevent him. His entrance and exit had been as brusque and matter of course as ever they had been on the old Vaiden place, when she was a slave girl in her white father's family.

Two Under Arrest

WITH Miltiades the thought of Gracie lingered a bare moment after he stepped out of her door. She lived in a better house than he did: that was ludicrous. The heart of his thought was his money. Was it safe? Suppose some unforeseen thing happened to him; suppose he did not get back for his money for a term of years, how safe was Gracie's stewardship?

The phrase, "a term of years," banished the quadroon woman completely from the Colonel's mind. The Colonel admitted the possibility of being sent to the coal mines. He began dividing forty-eight thousand dollars by three, four, five, six. If they sentenced him for five years, he would be drawing nine thousand dollars a year during his imprisonment. He had never earned that much in his life.

But this wage depended upon Gracie.

As Miltiades turned off toward Cherry Street, a very extraordinary idea struck him: to go to Handback and have it out with him. Settle it one way or the other. The plan was as imprudent as a jump in the dark, but the simple belligerence of the idea appealed to the Colonel.

Handback had changed in the weeks since Miltiades had left him. His face was whiter, his eyes were not so full, his features were drawn, and he seemed grayer about the temples.

When the two were safely behind the rail, the merchant looked at his former clerk intently.

"I went out among the niggers and begun inquiring about my cotton," he said. "Nobody knew anything about it till I struck Fo' Spot. He said maybe it was washed away and maybe a towboat took it. I said, 'What makes you think a towboat took it?' He said, 'Well, one thing, I he'p load it on the Zeb'lon D.'"

The merchant began a sort of laugh.

A quiver of the pleasure and the power of anger swept through the Colonel.

"That's exactly what I came here to tell you," he nodded crisply. "I'm damned glad Fo' Spot saved me the trouble."

"To tell me!"

"Hell, yes, what else would I want to see you for?"

There was a silence. Handback began trembling.

"Where is the money, Milt?"

The Colonel leaned across and tapped the smaller man on the chest.

"It's . . . paying . . . for . . . the cotton . . . you . . . stole . . . from . . . me . . . right . . . after . . . the . . . war."

THE shorter man swore an oath and jerked open a drawer in his desk. Miltiades jammed an arm into the open drawer and felt a pistol. At that moment the drawer rammed shut on his hand and Handback struck him, full swing on the head.

A gong-like ring and flames of fire

filled the Colonel's ears and eyes. With his free hand he caught the smaller man's throat.

An odd fight ensued: Handback pounding at Miltiades' face and jamming the drawer shut on his hand; Miltiades jerking at the pistol in the drawer and sinking his fingers into the merchant's throat.

At the fight under the bright illumination the whole store fell into an uproar. Negroes yelled. A voice shouted:

"Colonel's got a gun!"

And black men scrambled and fought to get to the door.

A man with a policeman's star forced his way through the pandemonium. He made toward Miltiades and Handback.

"Here, you're under arrest," he shouted. "Stop that! What in the hell are you two old men fighting about?"

"He's a thief!" yelled Handback. "That cotton that washed away! He stole ever' bale of it!"

"Stole it!" cried the officer, coming up and stopping the men.

"Shipped it out on a towboat!"

"The Colonel did! Why, Mr. Handback, you're bound to be wrong!"

"I collected a debt he's been owing me ever since he bankrupted twenty years ago!" quivered Miltiades.

"Well, well, gentlemen!" cried the officer, amazed. "I'll have to arrest you both."

Both men were fined $5 and costs for disorderly conduct. Handback was told that he could not get a remedy for the theft of his $48,000 in a police court. Then both men were released.

As Miltiades made his way home, shunned by all, he was accosted by Jaky Sandusky, a local law student who offered to be his lawyer. The Colonel refused him, rather hotly.

Before he had gone much farther the sheriff stopped him and politely suggested that he was wanted in jail. Miltiades did not protest.

Just then a gang of little boys broke into a shrill chanting:

"There goes Colonel Towboat Cotton and the sher'f! There goes Colonel Towboat Cotton and the sher'f!"

They shrieked with laughter.

Miltiades clenched his fingers with desire to choke their scrawny throats. Suddenly he observed that he was in front of the Crowninshield home.

"Come on," he said to the sheriff with a dry mouth, "let's move on!"

The sheriff was as furious as his prisoner. "I'll pick the little rascals up. . . ."

At that moment a slender girl came running out of the Crowninshield gate. She dashed across the road into the gang.

"You bad little boys!" she cried. "You are mean! You are outrageous! I'll tell your mothers on you! I'll tell your mothers on every single one of you!"

She was crying. She spread her arms and bore down on them as if she would physically stop their advance.

The gang fell back shouting: "Oh, we ain't skeered of you! You can't do nothing to us!" They went trooping back up the street hooting this new jest.

The two men looked after the vanishing children still vibrating with detestation.

"Wasn't that Miss Sydna Crowninshield?" asked the sheriff.

"Yes," said the Colonel.

"I didn't know she was a particular friend of yours."

"Neither did I," said the Colonel, in the tone of a man who could not understand the incident himself.

Always a Vaiden

IN JAIL the Colonel was again approached by Jaky Sandusky, the young lawyer. He advised Miltiades to sit tight in jail because Handback had nothing but a civil suit against him and

the Colonel could take action against him for false arrest and damages to character and reputation.

The Colonel grudgingly decided to take the suggestion.

The next day Sandusky came back with the news that he had seen Handback who had sworn to send Colonel Vaiden to the coal mines. Sandusky had told Handback that he couldn't do it because he had appointed the Colonel as his agent to handle the cotton and he had simply taken advantage of his position to collect an old debt. Therefore no criminal action could be taken.

Sandusky warned the Colonel, however, that neither of the two litigants had a clear case against the other and said that the best way out was to make a financial settlement, both men making a compromise.

Colonel Vaiden agreed to see Handback but when he came to the jail, both men were so unreasonable that a deadlock was reached.

The Colonel was sitting alone, several hours later when Sandusky came rushing back to say that Handback would settle for $10,000. Miltiades was astonished and thought that there was some trick to it but Sandusky had the agreement there in black and white.

As Miltiades walked out on the street with his shoulders back the sheriff said: "I declare, no matter what kind of scrape one of them Vaiden boys gets into, he acts just like a Vaiden!"

Nothing could divert Colonel Vaiden's mind from the astounding turn of fortune in the Handback matter. He glanced backwards now and then to see if he were being followed. Then he pursued his way along the deserted road to Gracie's cottage in East Florence.

As he walked he wondered if he would possibly have any trouble getting the money back from Gracie. The mere thought of a Vaiden negro failing to safeguard his spoil, or failing to return it when he was ready for it, filled the Colonel with a kind of anticipatory grimness.

His very freedom from criminal prosecution depended upon Gracie's faithfulness. He wondered what he would do to a Vaiden nigger woman if she should spoil the sudden and miraculous fortune which had befallen him?

Gracie's cottage was deserted. The white man knocked at the door, then entered, going directly to the kitchen, where the valise was concealed.

When he entered the kitchen he saw some boards laid on the top of the kitchen stove, and the cover of the manhole in the ceiling was gone, leaving a square black aperture.

As the Colonel stared at the hole in the ceiling a homicidal wrath rose up against the colored woman. He tingled to do some terrible violence to her. For a Vaiden nigger . . . one his own family had raised . . .

He studied the aperture, then suddenly climbed up on the stove and felt into the dark loft. His hand touched the valise. He gripped the leather corner and almost fell off the stove. He pulled the case to the edge of the manhole. He was trembling so violently that it almost fell out of his hands. He caught it against his chest, with the boards on the stove teetering under his feet. Then he saw that the valise had been opened and one of the packages broken into.

When the Colonel saw this a queer change came into the quality of his wrath. The broken package was Gracie's own theft. It was a nigger's trick to take a little out of much, to pilfer a dollar or two, to commit beggarly thefts. The Colonel got off the stove, put the valise on the table and began examining the torn package. It had a bill or two left in it. There had been five hundred-dollar packages and thousand-dollar packages in the container. At the very least Gracie had taken something near five hundred dollars.

This increase in the quadroon's theft worked another turn in Miltiades' complicated fury.

"God damn such a wench!" he shivered, "running off with hundreds of dollars. . . ."

The noise of the opening of the front door went through his nerves like the plucking of violin strings. He ought to beat her with a stick of her own stove wood. He took a step backward so he could look through the kitchen door into the hall.

Gracie was just entering her room when she saw Miltiades in the kitchen. She gave a little cry and stood looking at him.

The man moistened his lips.

"You have taken some of my money," he said in a monotone.

The quadroon nodded with a strange heartbroken expression in her face.

"Y-yes, sir . . . th-three hundred dollars," she said unsteadily.

"What did you take it for?" trembled the Colonel.

"For—for Miss Ponny, Colonel Milt."

"Ponny! Ponny! What did Ponny want with three . . ."

"Oh, Mas' Milt!" gasped Gracie, "to buy a coffin . . . to buy a coffin for her and her little baby. . . ."

And the quadroon began weeping, with a faint gasping sound, battling against her emotions like a white woman.

Death Insures Fortune

IN THE shabbily built boom house on Cherry Street the two front windows were alight. This double lighting silently reaffirmed to Miltiades the tragedy of which Gracie, the quadroon, already had informed him.

The house where Ponny and her baby were laid out for burial was, paradoxically, more astir with life than Miltiades had ever known it. The living room on the right-hand side seemed to be full of people. The company room on the left was lighted but appeared unoccupied. But as Miltiades moved up the dark walk to his door he saw through the window, lying on the bed of the company room, a great bulk covered with a sheet.

The ladies were talking excitedly, telling what had happened.

"I jest felt something was wrong," said Mrs. Klem, "when I saw the sheriff and Mr. Handback coming away from Miss Ponny's. . . ."

"Yes, yes, naturally," agreed Mrs. Ashton, frowning slightly at Mrs. Klem and trying to get her to hush now that Miltiades had entered the house.

"So, thinks I," proceeded Mrs. Klem, "I'll jest step over and see what's happened to Miss Ponny, and over I goes. And there she was. . . . Law, Miss Ashton, you'll never know how she looked, there on the floor, caught in . . ." Mrs. Klem paused significantly, shaking her head. After a moment she added, "And it was all brought on by that stinking sheriff and that hawg of a Handback tumbling ever'thing in her house upside down and digging in her yard looking for the money."

They had convicted Miltiades of wife murder. If Miltiades had not stolen the cotton the sheriff would never have frightened poor Ponny into a miscarriage with his search warrants.

Then, as he sat there, a queer thought came to Miltiades. It was Ponny, whom years ago he had married for her money, who at last, with her life, had countersigned his title to the fortune he now possessed. This bizarre fact, once it had come upon him, held his mind with a sort of fascination. Ponny's death really had rescued him from jail, delivered him from a criminal prosecution, and handed him a fortune. Because what chance would Handback have in any suit after he had done Ponny to death in his misuse of the sheriff and the search warrant?

At this turn of his thoughts Miltiades' wrath began to rise against the merchant. He wished he had been at home when the sheriff and Handback were frightening his sick and pregnant wife! It was an outrage us misuse of official power! A prospecti e mother: to come turning her house upside down, no doubt demanding to know where the money was and abusing her for not being able to tell! The full cruelties enacted against Ponny grew upon the Colonel. No wonder they kept him locked up in jail without bond or bondsmen! No wonder when Ponny was dying they had come flying back to the jail and had compromised on ten thousand dollars and no criminal actions on either side!

The Colonel had known of Ponny's death when he returned with the money. He had cursed the Handbacks for damned unscrupulous murders, and he had said to the jailer that, as far as his liberty was concerned, he need not pay a cent. But he had paid over the money because he had said he would, because the word of a Vaiden was as good as another man's bond!

Then he had sent a negro to ask a bank to take the remainder of the money in their back door. Later he had walked openly up Market Street with the return of his old debt and had deposited it.

But the money, the compromise money which he had left with the jailer to be paid to the Handbacks, he felt had been tricked from him. It was their damned slippery double dealing again!

Sandusky presented the Colonel with a bill for $500 to cover his legal services. The Colonel was incensed that he should ask for so much for one day's work. Sandusky replied that lawyer's fees were determined by the amount of money involved. The Colonel finally decided to give the young man $2.50 for getting him out of his difficulty with Handback, thereby stimulating an enormous grudge against him.

Catastrophic Memories

IN the meantime the Colonel was rapidly investing his money. He bought the old Lacefield plantation and put Gracie and Toussaint on it. Gracie was conscience-stricken over having hidden Handback's money and refused to be kept by him any longer. Thus the quadroon gave up all idea of taking Toussaint North and making a white man of him.

Now her surroundings filled Gracie with the most painful memories. Down this rutted Reserve road, her little Missy, the gray-eyed Marcia, had ridden to be imprisoned in the Yankee camp. At the Crossroads store, old man Be-Shears had sold Solomon, her first husband, to a negro dealer.

The last time Gracie had seen the Lacefield plantation its meadows were full of Yankee tents. In one of these tents she had sojourned as the mistress of a Federal officer named Beekman. Her father, old man Jimmie, had tried to reclaim her as his property from Beekman, but the Yankee soldiers had laughed at him; and she saw her father, who was also her owner, ride away cursing her and on the verge of apoplexy.

But above all the scene around her reminded Gracie of Beekman. She and Beekman had walked along these lanes. An old sedge field which she was passing had been a meadow then, and here was pitched the tent of her uncandled honeymoon. The impression of the Yankee officer became so strong that she almost expected to see him at some turn of the road. The cream-colored girl had loved Beekman.

The old Lacefield manor itself was deplorable. The silver poplar grove that had stood on its lawn had long since been used for firewood. All that was left of a flower pit that had lain back of the mansion was a depression three or four feet deep and choked with weeds. The great gate was gone, and Miltiades could have driven his buggy anywhere across the scattered stones of the wall. He drew up in front of the chipped columns of the portico.

"Gracie," said the Colonel, "you can stay here, or I'll put you in one of the cabins on the place. You have your choice."

"This is a strange thing that I am going to live in the Lacefield manor," said Gracie.

And for a moment she and the Colonel stood as man and woman who felt each other's involved and tragic rôle in a catastrophe which was so great that it stretched beyond both their comprehensions.

The Colonel gave more instructions to Toussaint about the rehabilitation of the place, and then started to his buggy to drive away. Gracie told Toussaint to hurry and unhitch the Colonel's buggy for him.

The son moved deliberately. He undid the bridle from the ancient hitching post, hooked it over the catch at the top of the collar, and stood holding the bits, looking at the white man with appraising gray eyes. There was a quality in him which Miltiades could not quite fathom. The Colonel referred this to the man who he thought was the boy's father. "If he takes after Beekman," thought the owner of the plantation, "he will at least be energetic." And a droll notion struck him that the solitary benefit of the Yankee invasion during the war was that it had improved the energy of some of the negroes in the second generation in the South.

Unfulfilled Ambitions

THE Colonel also bought a store which was as dingy as Handback's. It was stocked with supplies for negroes who were kept in bondage to the land by the due bills which they owed the store. With his store, Miltiades also made good his prophecy to the salesman who had insulted him by refusing him credit.

But any satisfaction he might have gotten from this was offset by the fact that he was shunned by everybody in town as a thief.

One day he met the Methodist minister who approached him on the subject of giving some money to the new church. To the minister's amazement Miltiades pulled out $50 from his roll and gave it to him.

When the report of his donation got abroad at the next meeting of the Methodist deacons, gossip was rampant. The malevolent said it was conscience money. The ambitious said Colonel Vaiden was trying to buy his way into respectable society again.

The point that really stuck in Miltiades' mind after his contribution was the manor which he had always wanted to have and which the bare foundations of the church had suggested.

So now, today, as he walked up Pine Street, he was thinking that for all the edification he was getting out of his money he might as well be J. Handback and have done with it.

He had no manor; he had no liberal and cultivating amusements, nor was he a patron of the arts. He pursued none of the *post bellum* graces of life, and for all he was getting out of his money, he might just as well be Handback, or any other of the ten thousand money grubbers in the South. He was disturbed and disappointed in himself. After he had transferred the ownership of the cotton from Handback to himself it was a sort of moral duty for him to use it at least with more enlightenment than Handback had been doing.

AT this psychological moment he met Bradley, the local real estate man. The question of a manor house came up and Bradley suggested that he might buy Drusilla Crowninshield's house which was then heavily mortgaged. The Colonel had some misgivings about buying the house over his old sweetheart's head —but allowed himself to be taken to look the old showplace over.

At this moment the door of the manor opened and a girl appeared against the light in the hallway. She probably saw the coal of Bradley's cigar, for she said in a startled voice: "Who's there?"

"It's just us, Miss Sydna," interposed Bradley in the casual tone of a neighbor. "I was just showing a prospect your house to see if it was anything like what he wanted."

"Mr. Bradley, you're not going to sell him our place!" called Sydna in apprehension.

Bradley broke into a laugh.

"How could I sell your mammy's own property if she didn't want me to?"

The girl on the porch hesitated.

"Who is your prospect?" asked Sydna.

"Colonel Milt Vaiden."

Sydna gave a little gasp. She felt as if a violin string had been twanged in her chest.

"Won't you come in, Colonel Vaiden?" she invited, in some excitement.

Miltiades was disconcerted that Bradley had got him into such a situation. He thought sharply to himself, if he ever did buy anything at all, it wouldn't be from Bradley.

"I wish I could, Miss Sydna, but I haven't time. I was not making a call."

"You and Mother are such old friends, it looks as if . . ."

"Well, yes . . . I suppose I ought . Drusilla and I——" He broke off, oppressed by the enigmatic complication of their two lives, their changing relations to each other, until now he stood on her lawn in the darkness, with a real-estate dealer, planning to foreclose the mortgage against her home. . . .

At that moment an interior door opened, and a voice called:

"Sydna darling, it's getting late. Who are you talking to, honey?"

"I'm talking to Colonel Vaiden, Mother," called back Sydna triumphantly and expectantly.

Came a pause; then Drusilla's voice said:

"Oh!"

And the interior door was shut.

A Christmas Call

For several days, on the strength of Sydna's cordiality, Colonel Miltiades Vaiden pondered writing a note, asking permission to call at the Crowninshield home. But the impulse somehow held within itself a queer unrealizable feeling, and so it was delayed and delayed.

But on Christmas Day he put on his best clothes and called at the Crowninshields'. Drusilla remained with him a short time but finally excused herself and left him with her daughter, Sydna.

The girl was really chagrined to see her mother go to the kitchen. She went to her mother's chair and sank into it. She kept glancing at the Colonel across the hearth, sometimes with direct scrutiny, sometimes out of the corners of her eyes. . . . He was a powerfully built man, with his shoulders heavier than his girth, even in the middle of middle age. Sydna thought he looked like a general. It was comfortable to sit in the room with Colonel Vaiden after listening to the moonstruck vagaries of the town youths.

"Do you remember sitting on my knee once, up in your mother's room?"

"Was that you?" asked Sydna, looking curiously at him. "I feel like we've been friends, Colonel Milt . . . always.

I really do remember seeing you on the plantation. You and Mother were sitting on a settee. Mother called me to you. You took me up on your knee and kissed me."

The Colonel sat for several moments in silence. Preceding that scene with the child he recalled Drusilla's sudden and amazing bestowal of herself upon him, and after their gust, little Sydna had come in, and he kissed her.

And now here sat he and Sydna before this Christmas fire. His gustiness for Drusilla was quite gone. Indeed, his gustiness for all women had changed into a kind of poetry. They could be exquisitely sweet and comforting to him across the expanse of a whole hearth, as was Sydna.

The Colonel's thoughts wandered on and on and presently came out an odd door.

"I imagine," he said, "the first man who ever built a church completely bewildered all the women of his tribe."

"Why so?" inquired the girl curiously.

"Because it was the first house ever built not to be used as a home. The women must have been astonished."

The girl studied the Colonel intently for several moments.

"How came you to say that?"

The Colonel tried to think his thoughts backwards but could not.

"I haven't the slightest idea."

"I believe you were thinking about that house you want to build. You don't want it to be just a home—you want it to be something more than that."

"Well, that's true, but I couldn't have been thinking about that just then."

"That's all right. . . . Tell me, why do you want more than a home?"

The Colonel sat some moments looking into the coals.

"I want a justification."

"A what?"

"If I have money I think I ought to do some beautiful thing with it. It's a kind of obligation to live a fine life, Sydna. The old South before the war realized this. They tried to create around them a magnificence that had nothing to do with making more money. That's why Handback always gave me a sort of repulsion. Besides starting out with my money, he did nothing beyond make more money. He was like an unfriendly boy in a ball game who grabs the ball and then refuses to play but just sits and holds it. . . ."

In the midst of this illustration came the sharp clacking of a woman's heels on the piazza. The hall door was flung open. The steps hurried to the sitting room.

"Sydna, where's your mother?" called a woman's voice.

"In the kitchen. . . . Why . . . what's happened?"

"Mr. Handback's killed himself! He went down to your mother's old home place and blew his head off with a shotgun. I hope Miltiades Vaiden is satisfied now!"

And she clicked hurriedly down the hall toward the kitchen.

Some Other Country

GRACIE was the last person to see Handback alive. He had come to her saying that he was ruined but could salvage enough money to take her and Toussaint to New Orleans where they could all live as white people.

Gracie caught her breath with a great dawning happiness. The whole of her uttermost dreams abruptly had come into sight. The woman stood in the old dining room thinking for several moments.

"Mr. Handback," she said, turning to him slowly, "you don't know why I left your house in Florence, do you?"

"Well," he said, after a moment, "it doesn't make any difference why you left me, Gracie."

"Oh, yes, it does," persisted the cream-colored woman quickly. "I couldn't possibly go to New Orleans with you . . ."

"Then what?" asked the merchant reluctantly.

"Because . . . Colonel Miltiades Vaiden . . . is my half brother."

The man looked at her curiously.

"You were taking up the family quarrel?"

"Oh, no. . . . When—when you were hunting everywhere for your—your money, Mr. Handback, I—" her voice sank to a bare whisper—"I had it. . . ."

"You . . . had it?"

"I was keeping it for him."

The merchant stared at her, at first, almost with simple astonishment, then his comprehension went dropping down through the gulfs of his business cataclysm, his agony and despair and final ruin. For Gracie to have helped her white half brother steal him out!

The woman groped behind her for a chair and sat down, for the first time in the white man's presence.

Handback said:

"I——"

He stopped and started again with a dry mouth:

"Didn't I always——"

Gracie understood everything that he could not say. She nodded faintly and whispered from chalky lips:

"Yes . . . you always did. . . ."

Handback saw the carving knife on the table. Then he thought of his shotgun. He started into the kitchen to go out the back door. He turned once to ask a question. He could not frame it because he could imagine no answer at all. Why she should have betrayed him, why turn all he had over to her white half brother, who, he knew, had never been anything to her. Of the lingering dominance between ex-master and ex-slave he understood nothing . . . nor did Gracie. It was all as insane as the cursings of the mad.

T̲HE merchant walked through the kitchen into the back yard. His shotgun leaned against the woodpile. He knew if he went back and killed her nothing would be done to him. His trial would be postponed court after court and finally dropped. He picked up his gun with a shaking hand to go back and kill her. His very unsteadiness halted him for a moment. Suppose he shook so that he crippled her and would have to stand firing shot after shot into her breast. He could not mutilate the creamy, graceful thief.

He loosed his mare's rein and then held to the saddle as if he were about to fall. He led the animal to the doorstep and got shakily on her back. He drew up his gun, turned the mare through the weed-grown lawn, and went out into the public road again.

He rode at a walk for nearly a quarter of a mile. Then he got down and hitched his mare to the fence and cocked his gun. He looked about, then walked up the fence row for twenty or thirty yards. He laid the stock of the gun across the top rail with the muzzle toward him. He thought of some money which he had put in his cash drawer and which would have been enough to take him and Gracie to some other country . . . a little money which she had not got.

Around him stretched the plantations which once were his. He had done no wrong thing. He had given no cause of offense to any man. The work of his life had been taken away from him by a woman he had kept . . . more gently than his wife . . . for years.

Not once did it pass through Handback's mind that he loved Gracie Vaiden; not once, even up to the moment of his death, did he realize that he was doing this thing not for the loss of his wealth, but for the final loss of his love.

The negro boy on the mule trotted merrily on to the manor. He was the bearer of happy news. When he came in sight of the white-faced woman in the door he yodeled gleefully across the unkempt lawn:

"Toussaint sho' wucked a Chrismus' trick on evahbody today, Miss Gricie. Him an' that black Lucy Lacefiel' got married at Mount Olive chu'ch in Eas' Flaunts 'bout two houahs ago."

Repercussions

A̲LTHOUGH all Florence believed that J. Handback had committed suicide on account of business reverses, the *Florence Index* took a more charitable view of his death. The paper attributed it to the fact that he carried a new style hammerless shotgun which would fire prematurely upon a mere jar, and the merchant had jarred his gun as he climbed the fence into the field.

The article went on to relate how Handback's last act had been to arrange some deeds relating to the old Lacefield place ready for delivery to its present owner, Colonel Miltiades Vaiden, but since his death, the son of the deceased, Mr. Lucius Handback, had been unable to locate the papers.

The article concluded with praise of the dead man as a tender father, a kind and loving husband, and a consistent member of the First Methodist Church in Florence for a period of more than twenty years.

This article gave Jaky Sandusky an idea. He went to Lucius Handback, son of the deceased, and told him that if the deeds for the Lacefield plantation were lost, Colonel Vaiden's ownership of the property was null and void, even though he had paid for it. Lucius Handback was far from a friend of Miltiades, himself, and urged Sandusky to see what he could do about getting the property away from him.

J. Handback's suicide caused Miltiades' life in Florence to become a little more isolated than it had been formerly. In the irrational way such things work, public opinion had balanced the merchant's suicide against Ponny's death, and this left Miltiades with the theft of the Handback cotton unatoned for. It would be held against him with renewed bitterness until Handback's tragedy also drifted out of the common mind.

But although the suicide worked against the Colonel socially, it looked as if it might aid him financially. All the Handback plantations were put up for sale, and Miltiades had bargained for three more with long extensions of credit. It was the Colonel's idea to buy. He wanted to buy to the limit of his cash and credit during the present depression and enjoy the benefits of recovering prices within the next few years. While he executed this financial maneuver he damned Wall Street and the Yankee nation for their plot in creating a panic just to discredit the Democratic Administration.

As the Colonel moved along, other questions began to disturb him. He wondered if it would be a proper act for him to visit the Crowninshield home under the renewed opprobrium of J. Handback's death. He would not want to bring Sydna's and Drusilla's name under the shadow of that tragedy. But he did want to show Drusilla the plans of his new house anyway.

The Manor

SYDNA was in the living room, reading. Drusilla was in the kitchen, going into the higher mysteries of cornbread.

Sydna arose quickly and gave both her hands to the caller.

"You've been away a long time, Colonel Milt," she said reproachfully.

The Colonel immediately became concerned.

"Well . . . considering everything, Sydna, I thought that was the best thing to do. I have brought something for you to see."

Sydna withdrew her own hands with a touch of color in her face.

"Now, what is it?"

"It's the plans and prices of that house we've all been talking about."

"Oh, you want to show them to Mother!" exclaimed the girl.

"Well, I thought I would, if she had time."

"She'll take time. I'll do whatever she's doing in the kitchen and send her in."

"If you will, Sydna," agreed the Colonel, watching her.

"And—and, Colonel—I do hope she . . likes everything."

The Colonel looked at the daughter.

"I hardly know what I'll do, Sydna, if she doesn't."

The daughter was moved. She came forward and squeezed the Colonel's hands.

"And listen . . . please . . . may I come back afterwards . . . and see if she did?"

"Yes, Sydna, I wish you would."

The girl, still pressing his fingers, leaned forward and kissed him.

"That's for luck," she said.

As she disappeared through the doorway Miltiades had a queer impression that the Drusilla whom he had known on the plantation in the Reserve was tripping away from him once more.

Sydna really was not at all like Drusilla. She was taller, slenderer, with blonde hair and more melting brown eyes. In temperament she was quite different from her mother, yet to Miltiades, some transportation of personality seemed to have taken place, and in Sydna, during little glimpses like these, the real Drusilla laughed and moved and breathed again.

This odd impression, which lingered for perhaps half a minute after Sydna had gone, was presently dissipated by Drusilla entering the door.

THE Colonel's enthusiasm for his manor mounted again as he took his hostess's fingers.

"I've just got the figures on that house, Drusilla." He opened his linen envelope again. "I can get it built on payments of three thousand a year. It's on account of bad times. The contractor says I'll never get such an offer again."

He spread his blueprints and estimates out on a table, and the two looked at them together.

"The real house," suggested Drusilla, "when it's up, and a lawn and trees around it, will look much softer and more livable than this."

"Yes, of course, an architect's drawing always looks hard." He paused a moment, and then saw an opening toward his original point: "What a home finally looks like will depend a good deal on who lives in it, Drusilla."

"Yes, of course, that's true."

"If it's a manor at all, it will have to have a woman in it."

Drusilla looked at him thoughtfully.

"And you are going to ask me to be the woman?" she suggested slowly.

The Colonel was not expecting such a remark, but he said simply:

"I have wanted you for a long, long time, Drusilla. When I ask you to be the mistress of my home I must tell you I have done many things I could wish I had never done. If you are willing to take the sort of man I am, Drusilla, it would be far beyond my deserts if you would marry me."

"What do you want with a woman of my age in a house of fourteen rooms, Miltiades?" she asked with a faint propitiatory smile.

"Why, Drusilla, because I love you," exclaimed the Colonel, quite taken aback; "because I have loved you ever since—ever since your father gave me my first job as a man. Now, look here,"

he pleaded in a lighter tone, "you might as well marry me. You said yourself we Vaidens kept after what we wanted till we got it."

"Well, you are going to get it, Milt," ejaculated Drusilla.

"Do you mean you are going to marry me?"

"No."

"Then I'm getting what?"

"Why, the manor. You're going to build a finer one than Father ever possessed."

"But I want you!" cried the Colonel. "I've thought of you every day through all these years. I have walked past your home here at night, and stopped and thought of you being just across here behind these brick walls, until I was ashamed of myself for thinking such thoughts when I was married to Ponny."

"I know all that, Milt," said the woman softly; "in fact, I've seen you once or twice. I have always been a kind of symbol to you of the manor and the station you wanted. Once you thought you saw a way to get it through Ponny. Your marriage to Ponny taught me a great deal, Milt. Up to that time I thought you wanted me because I was I. . . . People said you married Ponny because I had jilted you. But I knew better. I saw that you never had wanted me, you had always wanted the manor."

She sat looking at him without reproach or resentment, simply telling at last what the years had taught her.

Miltiades had never dreamed of such a view of himself and his life. He knew he had married Ponny for the money her father was reputed to possess. But always he had supposed his passion for Drusilla sprang out of the charms of the woman herself.

"Why do I want you now?" he asked at last. "I can get the manor without you."

"Why, you think probably that I am part of the interior decoration of a manor. . . . You've seen me in one."

"But, listen, Drusilla," begged Miltiades, getting up and going toward her: "Be the interior decoration of one!"

"No."

He stopped, looking at her intently.

"It really isn't . . . Handback, is it?"

"Miltiades!" She arose with a little stamp of her foot. "Of course it isn't Handback! Didn't my father build that first manor . . . out of slaves?"

"THEN what is your real reason?" "You went off and left me without telling me why, when it concerned me vitally."

"Why, Drusilla," said the Colonel in a shocked voice, "I didn't dream . . . you remember you . . . you went away once with Colonel Crowninshield. . . ."

"I was a romantic girl then, Miltiades, but you deserted a woman who loved you."

Colonel Vaiden stood looking at her with nothing at all to say.

"After you married Ponny you became a sort of ghost to me," went on Drusilla. "I would see you passing along the street, the ghost of somebody I had loved."

Miltiades listened, moistening his lips with his tongue.

"Sydna watched you too," continued the woman. "When she was a little thing she would call to me 'Mamma, there goes Colonel Milt.'"

"Yes?" said the man in a low tone.

"She has looked for you and talked about you all her life. Here, of late, since this trouble came up, she cannot bear to hear anyone speak ill of you . . . no matter what happened."

Miltiades nodded. He could well believe that.

"That morning when she ran out in the street and chased away those boys, she went back to her room and cried all the rest of the day."

"I declare," breathed the Colonel with a fixed frown, "I didn't know . . . I didn't dream . . . that's pitiful. . . ."

"Here, lately, she can't endure any of her usual callers. Young Jerry, Lucius Handback, Alfred Thorndyke . . . she says they are so silly and kiddish. She won't have them around."

"Yes?" nodded the Colonel, looking intently at her.

"And these last few days, when you have persistently stayed away from us, she has been sick. . . . You see . . . Sydna has loved you a long time, Miltiades."

"Me! Me!" whispered the Colonel. "Sydna love me! . . . How is that possible? . . ."

The mother made a helpless gesture falling back in her chair.

"I have wondered a thousand times, Miltiades. . . . God knows why."

Dreams Come True

DRUSILLA thought it best to make the wedding a very quiet affair: just the two immediate families, a few intimate friends, with the Reverend Mathers, the Episcopal minister, officiating.

Sydna told her mother that she was willing to stand on the highest mountain before all the world and marry Miltiades. She said she only wished her own character measured up to his.

Drusilla reminded her daughter that it was not what people were, but what other people thought they were, that counted, and that she still considered it best to make it a very quiet affair.

As to the actual quietness of the affair,

only the form of the announcement was subdued. The news traveled over the town instantly by back-yard telegraph.

Within six hours it was known from old Florence to East Florence that Sydna Crowninshield was going to marry her mother's old beau for his money.

A great many experienced persons applauded Miltiades' wisdom in picking a young nurse for his old age.

Old Mrs. Waner on Tombigbee Street prophesied spitefully,

"This 'un'll run off the night before the weddin' jest like her mammy did before her."

Old Mrs. Waner disliked the whole

kit and bi'ler of the Vaidens with an old woman's thoroughgoing detestation, because her brother, old Parson Bennie Mulry, a Methodist circuit rider, now dead, had praised the Vaidens too enthusiastically when he was at home.

Nobody in Florence could understand how Sydna could take a man old enough to be her father, and who came within an ell of being it, too.

These old women gossips quite forgot how charming certain middle-aged men had appeared when they were girls; those recollections having been effaced by more recent memories of how middle-aged men had appeared when they themselves were middle-aged.

During these days his approaching wedding held the Colonel in a state of dreamlike cheerfulness. Sydna was perfect. Sydna was all the things that Ponny had never been. And he was getting his manor at last.

Miltiades' passion to build finally had settled on the remodeling of the Crowninshield home. A contractor already had torn away the old piazza and was now replacing it with a tiled floor above which presently would arise six great granite columns.

The family had planned for the wedding to take place when the piazza and the observatory were finished. Then the old place would be a worthy foil, thought the Colonel, for the flower-like charm of Sydna.

Miltiades did not entirely understand his prospective mother-in-law. She seemed pleased with her daughter's approaching nuptials and used toward Miltiades a humorous and slightly ironic wisdom. The Colonel fell in the way of asking her advice about all sorts of things.

"Look here, Drusilla," said Miltiades uncertainly, "do you approve of me or not?"

"Of course I do, Miltiades. I was the first one to accept you. Then came the ministers of the various churches, then the poorer members of your own family. In the not distant future everybody in Florence with any claim to station and respectability will accept you warmly and sincerely, but I was first, Miltiades, because you loved me once."

LATE that night the last of the revelers in the manor had gone away. Drusilla had wished her new son-in-law and his bride a long and happy life. She had wished it tenderly and had gone her way to her own solitary apartment on the first floor.

Miltiades and Sydna went up the stairs together. Each was exquisitely conscious and shy of the other. To Miltiades the girl he was escorting lived in some pure remote zone of a child's dream. The gentle blossoming of her bosom and the curve of her waist were to the Colonel the unfolding buds of spring, and not the fruit of summer. He went with her into her boudoir, where the neighbor girls had laid out a lace gown on the foot of the bed. The Colonel observed the gown; he complimented Sydna upon being a princess in her wedding dress and presently asked if she would excuse him and let him smoke a cigar on the little balcony in the front piazza.

The girl flushed slightly and said he might. The Colonel went through the upper hall and stepped out on the little inset balcony. He was up within ten or twelve feet of the ceiling of the piazza. Three of the granite columns were not yet finished and stood dressed in dark scaffolding.

The Colonel smoked his cigar in slow, meditative puffs. Sydna, disrobing in their boudoir, was quite near and intimate to him at one moment, and then seemed to recede at a great distance the next. It seemed quite unbelievable. His long-gone courtship and relations with Drusilla were a hundred times more credible than this. That had been a flesh-and-blood affair. This was a dream, a sacrament, a kneeling before an altar.

The Colonel smoked slowly with long intervals between his puffs. The moonlight shifted imperceptibly on the new columns.

Nemesis

An interruption of Colonel Vaiden's idyllic mood was created by the service upon him of Lucius Handback's bill of complaint in chancery.

It was a long document, and it stated in one unending sentence that Lucius Handback had come into possession of the title of one Erasmus Ham and Polly Ham, his wife, which title was of record in Volume 86 Page 714 of the Deed Book in the Lauderdal County Courthouse of the State of Alabama.

Although Miltiades had had many warnings that such a bill would be filed against him, he was both surprised and incensed at its actual service.

The bill, however, had to be answered, even if it was nefarious. So in the course of a day or two the Colonel went down to Intelligence Row to the office of Governor Terry O'Shawn.

"Look here, Governor, what worries me, I've got all my money tied up in farms. If I should lose the Lacefield place it will upset my plans a great deal."

"Well, now, about your place," said the Governor coming down to business at last, "you got your deed from old man Handback?"

"That's right, one that his heirs and assigns guarantee forever. Now, I say, if his heir should take my place back I would recover it because the heir himself guarantees my title. "

"According to that," smiled the Governor, "the title would travel round and round between you and Lucius Handback, and perpetual motion would be discovered at last."

The two men laughed at this.

"Now listen," concluded the Governor. "Usually I can't accept suits, you know that, but chancery is a very convenient court to defend in. We can easily put it off until my term of office has expired, and even then our suit in chancery will be young."

Both men laughed again. There was something comforting about the Governor.

"And even if we never get the title cleared up, at least you will have the plantation you paid for. And in the meantime, in order to meet necessary legal expenses, file answers, and so forth and so on, probably it would be a good idea for you to deposit a small retainer."

"About how much?" asked Miltiades.

"Oh, about five hundred dollars," said the Governor, who had given Mr. Sandusky some advice during the Colonel's previous difficulty.

Nemesis had overtaken Colonel Miltiades Vaiden, and Florence was variously glad.

There were multiplied reasons for their pleasure. Not only was Miltiades a dour, thievish man, but Lucius Handback was a tippler, a gamester, a pursuer of women, and of such frailties are often compounded very lovable and popular men. Moreover, Miltiades had used his wealth to build a beautiful home, and nobody enjoyed seeing Cherry Street riff-raff bloom out in a mansion on Pine. Behind all this lay the basic distaste of any self-respecting, order-loving, God-fearing community to see a poor man suddenly turned prosperous . . . it always seems such a waste of money.

Even the preachers whom the Colonel had subsidized felt a quiet satisfaction in the thought that, no matter how far the ministerial judgment might be betrayed by wolves in sheep's clothing, God was not mocked.

Colonel Vaiden himself did not inquire into the heavenly machinery that had led to his downfall. He asked Governor O'Shawn to make the best terms he could with Lucius Handback.

Sandusky, Lucius' lawyer, would agree to no terms at all except delivery of the plantation. Sandusky said he was sure Miltiades was headed for bankruptcy, and he did not want the Lacefield estate mixed up with the common funds of a bankrupt.

The handsome fence and the stately manor behind the parked trees set up a kind of helpless ache in Miltiades. Just to have achieved such a home and such a wife, just to have touched for a moment the goal of his life, and then suddenly to lose it. He thought again, with a self-contemptuous thankfulness, that the home belonged to Drusilla Crowninshield and could not be sold for his debts. But he doubted if he would live more comfortably as a hanger-on in Drusilla's home than he had done in his own mean tenement.

An Astral Wag

He glanced back down the street and saw the lanky form of Landers following him.

The Colonel was forced to wait for him.

"What do you want?" he asked, with his repulsion in his voice.

"I have a message for you," said the postmaster.

"What is it?"

"It's from a man, a young man, not quite as tall as I am but much heavier set . . . a very jolly young man."

"You don't know him?"

"No, he just asked me to take this message to you, and I said I would."

The Colonel looked at the postmaster a little curiously. He was exactly the sort of man to accept a commission and never ask for whom he was doing it. There were some good points about Landers if he wasn't such a damned niggerlover.

"Well . . . what was the message?" asked the Colonel at last. "Was it about some bill?"

"I don't think so," said Landers, a little puzzled in his turn.

"Well, what did he say?"

"He said you would find what you needed in the cash drawer."

The Colonel frowned in surprise.

"What I *needed* . . . in the *cash drawer?*"

"That's what he said," nodded Landers.

Miltiades laughed the brief laugh of amazement.

"What I need usually stays in cash drawers, but I be damned if it's in mine."

Landers appeared a little taken aback.

"Well . . . that's all I know," said the postmaster uneasily. "I didn't ask him anything else. I thought you would know what he meant."

"You didn't think to ask the man's name so I could get in touch with him again?" asked the Colonel, with a hint of reproach.

"No, I didn't," said Landers regretfully. "I was sure you'd recognize him . . . a youngish man with a wide forehead . . . gray eyes and very level eyebrows, like your own. And somehow, when he appeared before me, I got the impression that he had come to his death by violence . . . probably shot and killed."

The postmaster's explanation left Colonel Vaiden in a state of shocked incredulity. The Colonel, of course, went and looked in his cash drawer. He found four dollars and eighty cents, the amount which Love had sold since the drummer had ascertained the color of his money. The cash drawer did hold what Miltiades needed, but not in sufficient quantity. The thought came to Miltiades' mind that possibly an astral wag had visited the postmaster; some ghost with an annoying sense of humor.

The Only Way Out

The merchant had gone to his store very early next morning because he meant to ride out to the country and stay all day, in order, mainly, to avoid being dunned.

Colonel Vaiden rode out to his plantation concerned mostly about his debts, but thinking now and then of Landers. The postmaster's message had been proved empty, but what puzzled Miliades was how Landers knew that he was on the edge of ruin? But, of course, so many duns and everything coming through the post office. . . . The Colonel dropped the subject.

Miltiades now began thinking how he could get some concealable money out of his holdings before he was forced into bankruptcy.

He decided that the only thing to do was to sell the equipment he had bought for the Lacefield plantation. Toussaint had raised a fine crop of cotton which he could never pick and market without the equipment. The Colonel's desperate step would mean ruin for Gracie and her family.

"Toussaint . . . you . . . you'll have to give them up," said Gracie shakenly after he had broken the news to them.

"Now, dat's right, you lissen to huh," nodded Lump, pointing at Gracie.

"But, Mother Vaiden," protested her daughter-in-law Lucy, trying to keep respectful to her mother-in-law, "don't you see all our work here will be thrown away? We won't have anything at all to show for what we've done!"

Gracie looked at her daughter-in-law.

"What colored person ever has anything to show for what he's done?" she asked bitterly. "I've always wanted to go away from here! But you would stay . . . and keep Toussaint!"

Gracie was only a little removed from weeping. Her own shock and loss in the death of Handback had been overwhelming, but for Toussaint, her son, to lose his whole year's work, broke Gracie's heart. He had worked so hard . . . like a white man. Now to have all his tools taken from him on the verge of a heavy crop. . . .

"But I tell you, Mother Vaiden," repeated Lucy in controlled desperation, "Toussaint doesn't have to take his tools back. Colonel Vaiden is under a contract."

"Contract!" repeated Gracie hopelessly.

"At least he might have spirit enough to ask a lawyer about it before he turns everything over to him," cried Lucy.

"Oh, Lawd, a lawyah!" gasped Lump. "Whut chanst has a niggah got in co't again Col'l Milt Vaiden?"

"Toussaint," asked Lucy, shifting back to her major premise, "aren't you going to stand up for yourself in this matter? I—I admired you, Toussaint, in the beginning, because you stood up for yourself."

"What do you think I ought to do, Lucy?"

"Why, tomorrow, when you go to town, see a lawyer. Even the white people can't say there's any harm in asking the advice of a lawyer. Surely we've got a right to do that."

Vaiden vs. Vaiden

So Toussaint went to Sandusky and the case came up in court a few days later. For a Vaiden to submit to being sued by a negro was unbelievable and feeling ran high.

For several minutes there were the usual preliminaries of clerk and judge and lawyers, through which the audience waited patiently.

Then Sandusky arose and stated the position of his client, that Miltiades was under a contract to furnish him mules and implements until his crop was gathered, and he prayed the court to restrain the landlord from selling the said mules and implements.

There was some hissing when Sandusky sat down. The Judge quelled this, and Governor O'Shawn arose.

"Your honor," he began, looking first at Judge Abernethy and then at his audience, "I will plunge straight at the heart of this action. Your petitioner, Toussaint Vaiden, colored, asks an injunction on the strength of a contract.

"Your honor, your respondent to this action comes forward and denies that there is or ever has been a contract to furnish the petitioner stock and implements for any specified time. It is a contract, sir, terminable at the will of the respondent. Why do I say that?

"Your honor, it is a well known fact in Alabama that no negro tenant obtains any further returns from the crop he raises than his board and keep.

"At the end of any agricultural year, your honor, the negro share cropper comes out exactly even. His account at the store balances with his share of the crop. No one owes him anything.

"Therefore a negro tenant's connection with a plantation may be severed by the landlord at any stage of the planting because the negro has had his board and keep up to that point, and that is as much as he will ever get, no matter how long he toils.

"In brief, your honor, the negro share cropper in Alabama has no share in the crop he cultivates. And any contract which contemplates the negro as having a share in such a crop cannot be made the foundation of a suit in equity."

Handclapping and applause interrupted the orator. Judge Abernethy rapped for order, and O'Shawn concluded his oration:

"The above is the *de facto* estate of the negro in Alabama, your honor; it now lies to your hand to make it the *de jure* estate.

"Let your honor in this decision be the first great jurist to reconcile Alabama's laws and her practice. Let her be the spokesman to the nation for the South that, politically, religiously, socially, and agriculturally, the South is and of a right must be now and forever a white man's country! I thank you."

The small chancery court broke into a tumult of approval of the orator's sentiments. Judge Abernethy did not attempt to suppress the applause. When it quieted he picked up his papers and announced the court would take a recess until four o'clock.

Sandusky, who had been twisting in his seat under the Governor's speech, took his hat from the desk and was about to leave the courtroom.

Governor O'Shawn addressed the court again.

"May I suggest, your honor, that you appoint the constable to keep the petitioner in safe keeping until he returns here at four o'clock for your honor's decision?

"The petitioner in this cause is probably an innocent negro egged on to this foolish action by unscrupulous advice. His cause is most unpopular. He has been threatened with a whipping. Your respondent has no desire for such an outcome. That is why I suggest that your honor offer the petitioner the asylum of the county jail for his own safety and protection."

Judge Abernethy took off his glasses and polished them.

"If the petitioner desires such sanctuary the court is disposed to grant it."

No Money for Justice

MEN from all over the house were pushing their way to O'Shawn to congratulate him on his defense when a larger commotion grew up in the Square outside. Miltiades was afraid that something was happening to Toussaint. He pushed his way to the window and saw a great swarm of men collected around two horsemen and a horse and buggy in the middle of the Square.

In the buggy sat two neatly dressed white men whom the Colonel had never seen before. His own curiosity arose.

"What's the hullabaloo about?" he inquired of the man next to him.

At first nobody knew, but at last Miltiades understood a man shouting from below.

"It's the robbers!" cried the fellow. "Sheriff Mayhew's got the robbers!"

Miltiades stood for a moment staring in amazement into the plaza. The horsemen with rifles and the horse and buggy began moving again, this time toward the county jail, following in the wake of Toussaint and the constable.

Since the prisoners were taken away, the interest of the crowd centered on the horse and buggy. The onlookers began asking questions: how did the sheriff know where the robbers were, and how was he sure that these were the thieves? They looked like very well to do men.

For answer Mayhew got into the captured buggy, reached up into the top, and unbuttoned a false lining. He opened it and discovered a glittering loot, watches, rings, bracelets, pistols, small clocks; all hung on rings in the buggy top. It looked like a jeweler's display. He lifted the cushion of the front seat and exposed rings of keys, a jimmy, a steel saw, a slender bag of brown leather stuffed with sand.

"Anybody ought to be shot," said a voice, "that would slip into another man's house at night with one o' them damn things. . . ."

"What the hell do you want to have a trial of them damn cutthroats for? They're guilty. What you want to spend the county's money on 'em for?"

Half a dozen voices in the crowd took it up. "They ain't no use spendin' money on them damn sandbaggers."

Now and then a stone banged against the jail-house door. A louder noise arose farther down the street and Sheriff Mayhew saw a knot of men dragging something through the crowd, and divined it was a log to batter the door.

The sheriff shoved and strong-armed his way toward the jail, shouting against the uproar:

"Hey, men! Be quiet! Stop!" He jerked a boy around and kicked him. "Lay down that rock!" He began struggling toward the steps, hauling men out of his path by their collars. "Get out of here! Clear out, or I'll land *you* in jail."

Voices yelled:

"Open the door, Mayhew! Go in there and bring out them damned thieves, Mayhew!"

As the knowledge widened in the crowd that the sheriff was among them, a medley of shouts boiled up:

"Bring 'em out!" "Open the door!" "Let Mayhew to the door, he's go'n' to open it!" "Let the sheriff to the door!"

The crowd suddenly began pushing

him. Mayhew stumbled up the treads and stood above the mob.

"Men! Gentlemen!" he shouted, waving his arms. "What the hell do you mean? What do you want?"

"Them sandbaggers! Them dirty, thievish devils!"

"They'll be tried and sentenced! Let the courts do it! We've got enough evidence against them to send a dozen men to the coal mines!"

The crowd took on a semblance of more orderly determination. The red-faced man called from the foot of the steps:

"Hell fire, we don't want no trial! Bring 'em out, Mayhew, or we'll bust in the door!"

The officer looked over the brilliant packed street for a glimpse of O'Shawn.

"Fellows," he temporized, "you know I haven't got any right to hand the prisoners over to you! The law makes me responsible for 'em! It's my duty. . . ."

Shouts interrupted:

"Hell fire, we know that! Git out o' the way! Bring that lawg on, fellers!"

Postmaster Landers went out into the shimmering street. In his thoughts it was not the death of the two men in jail that sent his thin legs hurrying through the heat: it was the sharp and ruinous dislocation of their lives. For the lives of the thieves to be snapped off in tension and agony and terror and to be begun anew with these horrors trailing after them sickened the mystic. Who would disrupt the unending and mysterious processes of the soul for a handful of watches and rings?

The postmaster stopped at Simpson's drug store, and only old man Simpson was in the place. The old druggist stood in his doorway staring toward Courthouse Square.

"When are they going to hang 'em?" he asked excitedly as Landers came up. "I might as well lock the store."

He looked at his watch and began closing the door.

At the corner of Tombigbee and

Market the postmaster almost ran into the Reverend B. Alvin Puckett. The minister ejaculated:

"What time have you got? Isn't this a terrible thing! They say the Governor got them to put it off till four. Such terrible things happen! I feel I ought to get within sight of it. A minister ought to see the sins and cruelties of life in order to strike home at the devil from his pulpit!"

In his heart the Reverend Puckett was glad he had met no person more important than Landers, the Republican postmaster. He walked on toward town through the burning sunshine.

The Lynching

A WAGON, oddly loaded, came rattling and jouncing up Market Street. Over its sides thrust hoes, the handles of plows, rakes, what-not. On the seat in front of the hotch-potch sat two women. One, who might have been a white woman, was driving, urging her blown and lathered mules with a whip. By her side jounced an ashen-hued girl, heavy with child, clutching the seat, on the brink of child-bearing.

The frightened driver turned the wagon across to Pine Street. She laid the whip on the spent mules. The team lurched along far in arrears of her haste. She turned into Pine under the dust-filmed trees.

She drew up her team at the Crowninshield residence and almost fell, scrambling, down over the front wheel.

The quadroon rushed out her words at Miltiades.

"Oh, Col'l Milt, get Toussaint out! They're going to kill him just for a lawsuit! Col'l Milt, please . . . please . . ."

She knelt before him, catching his hand and weeping.

"There a—a thousand white men around the jail-house with guns . . . waiting for him to come out!"

Miltiades was disgusted.

Gracie became inexpressibly agitated.

"Why, Col'l Milt, don't you know they'll do something to Toussaint? Don't you know? . . . Col'l Milt, go down and get him out! Please! Please do . . . before four o'clock. . . . What time is it now?"

The Colonel drew out his watch deliberately as he answered her.

"I don't know that I have any call to get Toussaint out of his trouble. I didn't get him into it. I told him to bring me those mules. And did he do it? No. Damn his yellow skin. He come up here and started a lawsuit against me!"

"I told him not to! I begged, I prayed for him not to."

"Then what in the hell did he do it for?" cried Miltiades, growing angry again.

"Oh, Col'l! Col'l! Get him . . . get Toussaint out! He can't help being bull headed and starting lawsuits!"

"Why can't he?" cried the white man

Gracie glanced at the empty door She took a step closer.

"Because he's your boy . . . he's you own boy! He's a Vaiden! Whoever hear tell of a Vaiden . . . giving in?"

She fell to weeping silently, like white woman, her face distorted an tears running from her eyes.

The white man stood incredulous.

"Why, he—he's Beekman's boy!"

Gracie shook her head.

"N-no . . . don't you remember . . the time you took me . . . in the loft?

The Colonel gazed at the woman moment longer. Suspicion of deceit flic ered through his head but was instant gone. Gracie did not lie. He snappe out his watch again.

"Hell, I haven't got time to hitch the carriage . . . we can't walk to tov in twelve minutes!"

"I brought the wagon," hurried t woman, beginning to run back down t driveway.

A NOISE began to grow down the stre It was the myriad noise of a gr crowd. It was purfled by shouts, outcri Its ground tone was a persistent ro

At a certain point came an outburst of yelling, then an abrupt and shocking silence.

The Colonel headed the stumbling mules into the Square. The crowd swarmed around the gnarled and twisted mulberries along Intelligence Row.

On three of these trees, in the center of the mob, swung three figures. Miltiades jerked his reins and stopped.

Lucy sat staring and motionless in the seat beside the Colonel. Gracie stepped over the front wheel and leaped to the ground. She fell heavily, but instantly was up, running toward the trees. A big man hung from one tree, a little man from another. Toussaint was in the middle.

From the moment she reached the outskirts of the silent crowd she screamed, "Let me by! Let me by!"

The middle tree was low. The white negro's feet were just off the pavement.

The mob became aware of the woman. They took their eyes off their handiwork to look at her as she pushed her way in. They made way for her.

She reached the body and began clawing at the knot. Her fingers could do nothing. She reached frantically toward the faces around her.

"Gimme a knife! Gimme a knife! Oh, Lordy! Lordy! Gimme a knife!"

Two open knives clattered on the brick pavement in the little open ring around the trees.

Gracie caught up one and began slashing the rope. It was tough. She haggled and haggled with the dull knife. At last a strand held it. Another stroke cut it apart. Toussaint collapsed. His mother, trying to held him up, fell with him.

A dozen drunken voices in the mob broke into laughter at the downfall of the negro mother and her dead son.

Revelations

THREE or four men bore the body of Toussaint to the wagon and laid it on the hotch-potch in the wagon bed.

Miltiades said to the bearers:

"What did you hang the nigger for?"

And one of the men answered with the detachment of an onlooker:

"Why, I think they done it jest to make a clean sweep of the jail. He was here in a cage, so they took him along with the others."

"Did he . . . fight?" asked Miltiades, with a queer twinge.

"No, he didn't fight or beg or anything; when Alex Cady tied the rope around his neck, the nigger spit."

The Colonel gave over the wagon and mules to the two colored women. They drove away and left him in the hot Square under the westering sun.

The show was over. The mob had become a crowd again, and some of them were going home. A sprinkling of men flowed away in all directions. Miltiades had no heart to return to the Crowninshield manor. He did not want to see Drusilla or Sydna now. A thought came to him that the negro woman, Gracie, had come closer to some inner reality of his life than any other human being would ever come again . . . his boy . . . their boy . . . had looked at Alex Cady when the hillman put the rope around his neck . . . and had spat. The Colonel bit his lip to imprison within himself a throb of strange and tragic triumph, and his grief which all but overwhelmed him.

Out of necessity to go somewhere, Miltiades walked across the Square to his store. The merchant took out his key and let himself into the hot dark interior. It smelled of bacon and calico and coal oil. There were some bolts of cloth on one end of the drygoods counter. The Colonel lay down on the counter and put his head on the bolts. After a moment he sat up, thinking if his boy had not started an injunction against him . . . if Bradley had not lost the deeds . . . if Sandusky had not been admitted to the bar . . . a long string of "ifs" upon which every life hangs suspended.

THE rattling of a wagon outside his store drew the Colonel out of his thoughts and off of his counter. A figure paused in front and called in a hillman's voice:

"Hello! Hello!"

"Why, hello, Stebbins," said Miltiades recognizing Handback's clerk. "Did you want to see me? . . . Come in."

"Yes, I did, Colonel. I've got something here I believe is yours," he said.

"What is it?"

"Why, I'm still rooming at the Handback store to keep up the insurance. This afternoon I got to rummaging around looking for a pistol to take to the lynching bee, and I found them old deeds of yores stuck away in the old cash drawer."

A sort of weak sensation went over the Colonel.

"Deeds to my place . . . the old Lacefield place?"

"Why, ye'es," drawled Stebbins. "I figgered Mr. Han'back must 'a' put 'em in there before he started out huntin' last Chris'mus Day. He yelled an' tole Lucius he put 'em in the safe. But instid of that he put five thousan' dollars in the safe, an' he put the deeds in the cash drawer. I've been thinkin' and wonderin' about it. I imagine he got 'em mixed up, somehow. He meant to put the deeds in the safe and the money in the cash drawer. But if he done that he meant to come back. And if he meant to come back, then he didn't kill hisse'f like ever'body thinks; the gun must of gone off by accident, after all. . . ."

The Colonel was paying no attention to the quandary into which J. Handback's former clerk had fallen.

The information which had been given him to find the deeds had been true . . . Landers' message that what he needed was in the cash drawer. Its truthfulness now came to him with a terrible mockery. If only he had known which cash drawer . . . Sandusky's suit would never have overthrown him . . . Toussaint would never have been. . . . The closeness to avoiding all that had happened tortured the Colonel.

He pushed aside the strange affliction of a white man who has hanged his negro son. He said aloud in an ordinary voice:

"I must tell Landers about the papers. He came to me one day and said . . ."

"Why, Colonel," ejaculated Stebbins "hadn't you heard?"

"Heard what?"

"Why, Landers got bad hurt. He was trying to get the men to turn the white nigger a-loose when somebody knocked him in the head with a rock. . . . I—r'ally guess he's dead now. I heard the niggers mournin' in his house as I come by."

How Beautiful Is Night

How beautiful is night!
A dewy freshness fills the silent air;
No mist obscures, nor cloud, nor speck, nor stain,
    Breaks the serene of heaven;
In full-orbed glory yonder moon divine
Rolls through the dark blue depths.
    Beneath her steady ray
    The desert-circle spreads,
Like the round ocean, girdled with the sky.
How beautiful is night!

—*Robert Southey*

Romain Rolland

JEAN-CHRISTOPHE

BEFORE the first of the ten volumes of "Jean-Christophe" was published in 1905, Romain Rolland was known as an able professor of music with liberal ideas at the Sorbonne in Paris. By the time the last volume was published in 1912, Rolland was hailed as one of the greatest writers of modern times. "Jean-Christophe" is not so much a novel as a rambling romance of a German musician and his contacts with the problems of the time which the author interprets with a universal significance. While the style is sometimes uneven there is brutal strength and poetry in its passages and characters which remind one of the art of Michelangelo and the music of Beethoven.

Dawn

JEAN-CHRISTOPHE was the eldest son of Melchior-Krafft and grandson of Jean Michel Krafft, musicians both, and well known and esteemed in their own little Rhineland town, as indeed they were throughout the whole district between Cologne and Mannheim. Melchior was first violin at the Hof-Theater, while the grandfather had once been conductor of the Grand Duke's concerts. Not wholly German—there was Belgian blood somewhere—the Kraffts had a touch of that superiority often found in men of mixed race; and though of peasant origin their art had done much to tone down, if not quite to obliterate, the native roughness. Physically big, strong and healthy, they had transmitted their rude health and muscularity to the boy—which was just as well, since he needed all his inherited roughness before many years had passed. Jean-Christophe's mother—good, kind, patient Louisa—frankly peasant throughout and all-German—was rather despised by her husband Melchior, who was always tormented by the thought that, with his gifts and presence, he ought to have married higher, perhaps "married money." Vain and self-indulgent, he turned into an incurable tippler, and in his bad moments was certainly a most undesirable husband and parent.

When little Jean-Christophe, at the age of six or seven, showed clearly that he had inherited the family talent for music, the father took him in hand—often too literally—and tried his hardest to make him a child-prodigy, a second Mozart. The boy loved music, while detesting Melchior's method of teaching, which was all drudgery, and for some time his life was almost a martyrdom. Luckily, the grandfather had more intelligence and sympathy and, thanks to him, Jean-Christophe made rapid progress. At last he actually achieved a little composition of his own which, "by permission," was dedicated to the august ruler and performed in his presence before the whole Court. The infant composer, ridiculously dressed up in conventional evening clothes, like a miniature man, had to climb on to the music stool, while everyone laughed at his appearance; but the performance was a huge success, and when, after the concert, he was presented to the Grand Duke, his master and patron, and petted by one of the little princesses, the pride of Melchior and his father knew no bounds. It was characteristic of the boy, and of the man he was to become, that he should have confided to the princess that the work performed was not entirely his own—that grandfather had written the trio in the minuet.

ABOUT this time Gottfried, Louisa's brother, one of the author's best-drawn and most sympathetic figures, enters the story. Gottfried was a humble little peddler, bald and bent, prematurely old, but infinitely patient and philosophical; also, he had an intuitive sense of what music should be. The rough, hasty brother-in-law and his father made a butt of the decent, self-effacing little man, to whom Jean-Christophe—at first inclined to ridicule, like his elders—soon became deeply attached. The boy hears his uncle singing softly to himself one evening by the riverside, and realizes that what he hears is *music*. Another sunset hour found the pair together again, but indoors. Gottfried will not sing; he cannot, unless he feels in the mood. So Christopher—let us call him so, for convenience sake—ventures to play one of his own compositions, a song. Gottfried is not impressed; frankly, he thinks it very ugly. Perhaps there are others better? So the boy plays and sings all the airs he has composed. But the critic shakes his head.

"They're uglier still."

Christopher hardly kept back his tears.

"But why do you say they're ugly?"

Gottfried looked at him with his frank eyes

"Why? . . . I don't know. . . . Stay . . your music is ugly—in the first place—because it is silly. Yes, that's it. . . . It is silly because it means nothing. When you wrote that you had nothing to say. Why did you write it?"

"I don't know," said Christopher sadly. "I wanted to write something pretty."

"So! You wrote just for the sake of writing You wrote to be admired. You were proud, you were false, and you have been punished. You see, you are always punished for being vain and untrue in music. Music must be humble and sincere—otherwise, what is it? Something impious, something blasphemous against the Lord, who has given us lovely song that we may utter that which is true and honest."

Christopher had had his first real music lesson, and it was to sink deeper

Morning

THINGS went badly with the Kraffts. Melchior's drinking bouts grew more and more frequent, his private lessons fewer. Louisa was so hard pressed for money that she had to find work as a daily cook in the Grand Ducal kitchen; Christopher, now ten, brought a little grist to the mill by playing the violin in the Court orchestra. His delight and consolation were the evening walks and talks with wise, honest Gottfried. Then Jean-Michel, the kindly old grandfather, had a stroke and died.

With the mainstay of the family gone, Melchior grew daily more reckless, drinking heavily and neglecting his work in the orchestra. The piano had to be sold, and the salary he received from the Grand Duke was transferred for safety's sake to Christopher, who finds himself head of the house at fourteen! One night Louisa's husband did not return. This causes little surprise, for he has no regular hours; but presently there was a confusion of hushed voices; Melchior's dripping body was brought home; he had fallen in the mill-stream and been drowned.

There were two younger brothers—both commonplace, and one rather vicious. They left home, and Christopher, whose industry and whose devotion to his poor, struggling mother were beyond praise, found for Louisa and himself another and a smaller home It was a lodging house, occupied by several sets of tenants, among them a young widow of not more than twenty, with a little daughter. Christopher, now seventeen or so, was gradually attracted by Madame Sabine Froehlich, an inscrutable creature with a certain fascinating, cat-like indolence about her. She grew fond of the big, awkward, gifted boy; encouraged him till he declares his love, then went away for a little holiday, and died of pneumonia.

A LITTLE later Christopher came across a shop girl, whose rather vulgar charms he could not resist, and for a time Ada monopolised all his leisure, by no means platonically. Meanwhile, his scallywag brother Ernst turned up in rags, and billeted himself on his mother. When Christopher discovered that Ada had no objection to flirting with this young man he very wisely cast her off. But the goody-goody family in whose house the Kraffts are lodging were, or professed to be, so shocked at the young musician's conduct, and made things so unpleasant for him and for Louisa, that they were compelled to find other quarters. The quarrel with flighty Ada, added to all the other troubles, made Christopher reckless. To the grief of the long-suffering Louisa, he began to drink more than is good for him, until one day he met Gottfried, who pretended to mistake him for his dead father, and addressed him as 'Melchior.' The lesson is not wasted; so again the despised peddler was of service to the lad he loves and understands, as no one else does.

Adolescence

BEFORE they parted company Christopher recovered his balance and his self-respect. Clear-eyed and calm, now that he was free from the degrading companionship of the shop girl and her set, he devoted himself entirely to his work, determined to win through sooner or later. Strong within him was the resolve to create something of real worth. "To create is to kill death!" he exclaims, in his new-born enthusiasm. Henceforth he did not write a single note unless he felt inspired to write it. Having thus begun to criticise himself, it was but natural that he should criticise others, and soon he was finding fault with even his best-loved composers. As for the music he heard in his home town, he despised it utterly, making not the slightest effort to conceal his opinions. It can easily be understood that this contemptuous attitude soon made him unpopular with his neighbours, who at last came to the conclusion that the boy is "quite cracked."

He gave a concert; but the enemies he made conspire to spoil it. The Grand Duke was absent; the singer—a local favourite—flatly refused to interpret her part as Christopher intended; the instrumentalists played abominably, and the conductor was completely apathetic. Result—hideous failure, and impotent fury on the part of the baffled composer.

Christopher found sympathisers in a group of young *dilettanti* who started a high-brow magazine called *Dionysos.* With one or two exceptions, they were sons of Jewish millionaires, and they wrote just for the fun of the thing. They offered the post of music critic to Christopher, who jumped at the chance of being able to reply to the attacks made on him in the Rhineland newspapers.

HOWEVER, the *Dionysos* people soon tired of their too earnest critic; and after a time they went so far as to tone down his contributions—which he never troubled to read in print—and even to reverse their sense completely. When Christopher accidentally discovered the tricks played on him he threw up the job in furious indignation and, without thinking of the consequences, undertook the musical criticism of a Socialist sheet notorious for its attacks on the Grand Duke and his entourage. Christopher's patron was, of course, informed of what had happened. He sent for his *Hof Musicus,* to know what it all meant. The august personage was very angry, but not more angry than honest, blundering Christopher, who, at the end of a stormy scene, was practically kicked out of the place, and actually kicked out of his miserably-paid official position. Nothing dismayed, he gave another concert, at which his latest composition, a symphonic poem, was produced for the first time. The performance was simply a burlesque of his intentions, and the newspapers tore the work and its unfortunate author to pieces.

He set to work again; wrote some *Lieder,* and had them published. But "stiff in opinions, always in the wrong," he would not have them advertised, loathing even the suspicion of *réclame.* Naturally, the venture was still-born; scarce one copy of the songs was sold.

Revolt

Someone gave Christopher a box at the theatre, where a French company was playing Hamlet. In the foyer he noticed a young girl who was going away disappointed, all the seats being booked. Timidly he asked her if she would join him, as he was alone. As timidly, after a good deal of hesitation, she accepted and, being French, got real enjoyment from hearing her own tongue spoken. She and Christopher said very little to each other; he did not ask her name, nor she his; and when he left her in the box, before the play was finished, all he could recall of her is her shy but trustful glance; he would never forget her beautiful eyes.

A day or two later he went to Frankfort. On his return, during a halt at a station, he noticed a girl seated in a carriage going in the opposite direction. It was she who had been with him in the box at the theatre, and he wondered where she could be going. Home again, and chaffed by one of his friends on his "French conquest," Christopher discovered that the unknown possessor of the haunting eyes was, or rather had been, a governess employed in the town; that her presence with him in the box had been considered scandalous by her employers, who promptly dismissed her; and that she was on her way back to Paris when he saw her in the train.

Her name was Antoinette Jeannin, a brave, devoted creature. Antoinette's brother Olivier later became Christopher's bosom friend in Paris.

Christopher, looking about for friends —Gottfried, to his deep sorrow, is dead—suddenly remembered having been presented, while still quite a tiny boy, to Hassler, the famous composer, then conducting in Berlin. The great man had embraced him, and told him to come and see him when he was grown up. So Christopher took his latest MSS in his pocket, went off and found Hassler, who, of course, had forgotten all about him, and showed not the least interest in his career. True, Hassler repented of his callous behaviour soon after, sent a letter to Christopher's hotel to ask him to call again; but already the indignant, disillusioned lad was on his way home, and the letter never reached him.

On his way back, Christopher bethought him of an old gentleman named Schulz, who had once written to him in enthusiastic appreciation of some of his compositions. Accordingly, he broke his journey and called on his admirer. This excellent old fellow, with a couple of musical cronies, made a tremendous fuss over the youngster. Having made the acquaintance of a fascinating actress who played Ophelia in Hamlet, Christopher resolved to go to Paris, if only his mother would consent. As it turned out, he went sooner than he expected. In fact, he had to clear out of Germany, after a row in a country inn, where he got into a fight with a band of drunken soldiers and left the sergeant senseless on the floor. A warrant was soon issued for his arrest, but he got quickly away to the Belgian frontier, and there took train to Paris.

Exile in Paris

In Paris Christopher was at first utterly desolate and miserable, among a strange people whose language he spoke very imperfectly. He hunted up a couple of German friends, who introduced him here and there, and by degrees he got lessons enough to save him from starvation. One of the music publishers to whom he showed his works wanted the young composer to "simplify" Schumann's "Carnival" and other classics for the benefit of the ignorant; but, sick and hungry though he is, Christopher instantly quarrels with him and stalks out of his shop. The old pride never deserts him; in fact, his absolute honesty and disregard of consequences cause him before long to make almost as many enemies in Paris as he had left in his Rhineland home.

When things were at their most desperate, Christopher made the acquaintance of a Socialist deputy and his wife, M. and Madame Roussin, who, unlike some others, are not shocked by his bluntness and his rather coarse, provincial manners and appearance. There were pupils to be had in their circle, and one who came to him is Grazia, an Italian child of fourteen. Although adoring her stern teacher, especially when she hears him reviled and ridiculed, she showed so little promise that very soon Christopher refused to continue the lessons, and the girl was broken-hearted.

Christopher had been in Paris a year or two when at an evening reception at the Roussins he noticed a timid, delicate, rather distinguished-looking young man whose eyes, which seemed familiar, again and again sought and then avoided his own. They became acquainted, and though his expression never failed to recall something familiar to Christopher it was not until long after that he discovered Olivier Jeannin was the brother of the young governess, Antoinette. From acquaintances they became fast friends; inseparable when they decided to live together. David and Jonathan were not more devoted than this strong, self-willed, obstinate musician and this fragile, cultured, affectionate poet—so typically French.

The Friends

THE pair were really happy together in their modest rooms in the Montparnasse quarter, and each of them worked hard and well. Olivier soon published a book of verse, the failure of which—because it is not "pushed"— exasperated his friend. In his usual clumsy way, Christopher tried to influence the newspapers in its favour, but with no success. Then he gave a concert —to empty benches. But though very hard up, the pair were strong and brave, and Christopher as aggressive as ever. In turn he fought a bloodless duel with a tiresome French literary dandy; had his symphonic work, "David," published and performed with éclat; received letters from publishers, "asking for more"; in fact, he had "arrived"—or nearly so.

All this time—for Christopher was away some years, and was no longer a boy—his patient old mother had not set eyes on him, though they corresponded regularly. One day he received a letter from her; she was not very well, and longed to see him again. By scraping together all the little money they possess, and pawning a few things, the two friends managed to find enough to pay their fares to Germany, and they went off without a moment's delay. Chris-

topher, of course, risked arrest for the old offence; but that didn't trouble him. Louisa died in her son's arms soon after his arrival. Friends warned him that he has been recognized, and should hurry away. With difficulty he was persuaded to go, Olivier staying behind for the funeral.

Back in Paris, Christopher was invaded by newspaper interviewers. The *Grand Journal* published his portrait, with a fulsome article proclaiming him a genius; the bumptious, all-powerful editor had to have the new celebrity— *his* "discovery"—lunch with him; more interviews and articles followed, and for a fortnight the composer was in the limelight. He hated it, and could not understand why suddenly everybody seemed so fond of him. Nor could he understand why, a little later, this same newspaper should turn and rend him in a series of bitterly hostile articles. Christopher did not yet realize what the Press is!

THE long and happy association of Christopher and Olivier came to an end when the poet married a rich girl, Jacqueline Longeais, who carried him off on a long honeymoon, leaving the

German half of the partnership desolate and feeling like a widower. Christopher knew that Olivier would always be his dearest friend; but it could never be the same again, for "a married man is only half a man." Olivier and his bride were madly, selfishly in love at first. Now that they were rich there was no need for Olivier to work, and gradually he lost tone. Jacqueline had a son; but soon she grew restless, having exhausted her passion; and in a year or two she ran away with an elderly man of the world who soon tired of his easy conquest, and disappeared. Before this she had even tried to beguile Christopher himself.

Olivier came back to Paris, crushed and despairing since Jacqueline's flight. Even Christopher, with all his true, understanding affection, could not console his friend; yet the renewal of their comradeship was a source of satisfaction to both. For some time past the attacks on Christopher in the *Grand Journal* and other papers, already mentioned, had

been regular and bitter. Suddenly they ceased, and in their place came praise unlimited. About the same time a Leipzig firm offered him good terms for the publication of his works. What was the cause of this change in his fortunes? And when he let it be known that he had an urgent desire to revisit the old home on the Rhine, he was astonished to receive an intimation from the German Embassy that he has permission to stay forty-eight hours in the Fatherland.

On his return he was told by one of his hostesses that Comte and Comtesse Berény were anxious to make his acquaintance. They had for years taken a keen interest in his career, he learned, and the husband, holding a high diplomatic position, was emphatically a man to know. When Comtesse Berény comes forward, smiling and holding out her hand, Christopher recognized the little Grazia of old. So the secret was out; *she* had been his guardian angel all the time.

The Burning Bush

ALTHOUGH they no longer lived together, Christopher and Olivier saw one another daily. Somehow the composer, who was always by instinct in sympathy with the under dog, got in touch with the workers of the district, and he took Olivier to their meeting places. The Frenchman, with his aristocratic prejudice, found it hard, even for his friend's sake, to take much interest in these Socialists and Syndicalists, with whom the peasant-born German was on such familiar terms. Christopher talked to them quite frankly. It had not taken him long to discover that the last thing these "brothers" wanted was honest work. And when they taunted him with being a lazy "artist," an idler, he retorts that he had to struggle hard for a living from the time he was a little boy. Yet, for all his contempt of these so-called "workers," Christopher was sufficiently sympathetic to write them a Revolutionary song. He laughed when warned that the police were watching him.

The First of May arrived, with a general strike threatened, by way of celebration. Christopher took Olivier—rather against his will, for he was weak and listless after influenza—into the streets, and they immediately were in a dense crowd. *Cuirassiers* trotted up, to disperse the mob, and then the *ágents* came on the scene. In the rush, Olivier was separated from his friend and knocked down; while Christopher, resenting interference, found himself at grips with two policemen. One of them drew his sabre, and it would have gone hard with the German but for his sinewy hand. Seizing his opponent's wrist, he turned the weapon from his own breast to that of the *ágent* and, in the fury of the moment, slew him.

BY THIS time the Red Flag was flying; revolvers and knives were out; fighting was going on all over the place. An omnibus, thrown over on its side by a score of grimy hands, served as a barricade. Mad with excitement, Christopher found himself the leader of a cause he despised. He would inevitably have been shot or arrested had not a calmer friend dragged him away and put him in a motor car, which immediately drove off at full speed.

Arriving at Laroche, Christopher and the other man took the train for Switzerland. Constantly inquiring for Olivier, Christopher was told he is hurt, but will rejoin them over the border on the morrow; the truth being that the fragile little poet had been trampled to death under "the wild mob's million feet."

When a letter arrived the next day, telling him Olivier was dead, Christopher was frantic with grief. He tried to get back to Paris, but after several days and nights of wandering, returned to Switzerland to find shelter with an old German friend, Dr. Erich Braun, and his strange, silent wife. It was weeks before Christopher could pull himself together sufficiently to get a few music lessons; he had no money, and could not billet himself indefinitely on the kind-hearted friend without making some payment for his board. Anna, the doctor's wife, was an unforgettable woman, full of fire, hiding her passion, until at last it burst into flame suddenly and terrifically. Christopher was well-nigh consumed in the outbreak. Flight alone preserved him. He passed, not wholly unscathed, through "the burning bush."

Journey's End

YEARS pass. Jean-Christophe made his name; he conquered. And though his hair whitened, he was still young at heart, still full of force, and more than ever full of the simple faith he had so long renounced. Germany was free to him now, he can go where he will, and his pleasure was to roam from place to place, resting nowhere long.

In Switzerland he met Grazia again. Widowed, and with two children. Full of joy at recovering a real friend, and longing for affection—since no one has taken Olivier's place in his heart—Christopher, revived by the warmth of her gracious presence, would have had her marry him. But she, though she had loved him always, felt she must refuse, lest marriage spoil that more perfect thing which is friendship. So, Grazia urging him, he went on to Paris to conduct a series of concerts, while she stayed in Switzerland with her boy and girl. There was still some of the old Adam left in him. He quarreled, quite unnecessarily, with the management on some quixotic point concerning a new opera of his; and, when he was attacked in the Press, young Georges Jeannin, son of Olivier and Jacqueline, annoyed him deeply by fighting a duel in his behalf. But he was very fond of Georges, and soon forgave him.

A little later Christopher received Fate's rudest blow. Grazia fell ill, and died almost suddenly. He took his punishment with wonderful calm. A large, benignant philosophy assuages his sorrow; and to console himself for the loss of the two people he has loved best in the world—Olivier and Grazia—he set about uniting their children, Georges and Aurora.

Gradually Christopher's health gave way, and he felt he must see his native place once more. But everything was changed in the old home; a street was named after him, and he heard, almost without recognizing, a work of his own performed in a gigantic new concert hall. So he returned to Paris and hid his illness until the young people are married. Then he broke down, and took to his bed as a dying lion to his lair. Obstinate to the last, he would not have a nurse. He murmured to himself, *Ich hab' genug* —"I can stand no more." One night in his delirium he conducted an orchestra, playing his own music, and died content, with its strains still in his ears.

Sigmund Freud

PSYCHO=ANALYSIS

Although it was as long ago as 1899 that Freud published "Traumdeutung," it was not until 1913 that an English translation appeared under the title "Interpretation of Dreams." Of the numerous books which he has published in the intervening years translations have appeared of many, including "Three Contributions to the Theory of Sex"; "The Psycho-pathology of Everyday Life"; and "Group Psychology and the Analysts of the Ego." In 1922 he published his "Introductory Lectures on Psycho-analysis," and it is this book which Dr. Stanford Read outlines in the following pages. Freud went to London as a refugé from Austria and died there on September 23, 1939.

I—The Psychology of Errors

This distinguished Viennese physician, whose genius has so greatly revolutionised the science of psychology, has been the author of many works which have been translated into English. His greatest and most important contribution was "The Interpretation of Dreams," written in 1899. Since then his publications have taken an ever widening sphere in the realms of the mind in both its normal and morbid aspects. Though known popularly as the originator of the body of doctrine and form of treatment known as "psycho-analysis," his theories have a far wider application, and challenge the very foundations of the hitherto current ideas concerning psychic life. In 1922 there appeared his "Introductory Lectures on Psycho-analysis," which contains in simpler form an exposition of his views and may be profitably studied by laymen interested in a subject whose increasing importance is undeniable.

It is pointed out how our accustomed mode of thought must inevitably lead to hostility to psycho-analysis, because it is a displeasing proposition that mental processes are essentially unconscious, and also that impulses which can only be described as sexual, in both the narrower and the wider sense, play a peculiarly large part in the causation of nervous and mental disorders: nay, more, that these sexual impulses have contributed invaluably to the highest cultural, artistic and social achievements of the mind.

In order to lead his readers up logically to his belief in motivation through the influence of an unconscious mind, Freud devotes three chapters to an investigation of "the psychology of errors." He refers to those familiar and common phenomena which may be observed in every healthy person, such as slips of the tongue or pen, mis-reading or mis-hearing, temporarily forgetting names or appointments, mislaying things. Though usually considered trivialities and accidental, the thesis is that these have a meaning, and cannot be explained by fatigue, excitement, or lack of attention.

In the illustrations given of misprints we can easily read the hidden motivation. A social-democratic paper, giving an account of a festivity, printed the words "Amongst those present was His Highness, the Clown Prince." In a war-correspondent's account of meeting a famous general whose infirmities were pretty well known, a reference to the general was printed as "this battle-scared veteran," and later corrected to "this bottle-scarred veteran." A slip of the tongue may be perseveration but it often makes sense and shows a suppressed motive. That is, the result may have a right to be regarded in itself as a valid mental process following out its own purpose, and as an expression having content and meaning. A lady appearing to compliment another, says: "I am sure you must have *thrown* this delightful hat together" instead of "sewn it together." Nothing can prevent us from seeing in the slip the thought that the hat is an amateur production. In other cases, the slip adds a second meaning to the one intended, as in the case of the young man who offered to "insort" an unknown lady (condensation of escort and insult).

From these examples we can see that the explanation lies in the concurrence or interference of two different intentions of speech with one another. That is, these slips are not accidents; they are serious mental acts; they have their meaning. Though the victim of the tongue slip may repudiate the meaning read into his act, an analysis of his mind will confirm the hidden intention.

In other fields of error, if anyone forgets an otherwise familiar proper name and has difficulty in retaining it in his memory, it is not hard to guess that he has something against the owner of the name. The forgetting of resolutions can in general be referred to an opposed current of feeling which is against carrying out the intention. It may seem incredible that a person could have any purpose in losing things, which is often such a painful accident, and yet there are innumerable instances of this kind. A young man lost a pencil which he valued greatly. A few days before he

had received a letter from his brother-in-law which concluded with the words: "I have neither time nor inclination at present to encourage you in your frivolity and idleness." Now the pencil was a present from this brother-in-law. Similar cases are very numerous. One loses objects when one has quarrelled with the giver and no longer wants to be reminded of him. Dropping, breaking, and destroying things serve a similar purpose. The essential element in the error is not its form but the *tendency* which makes use of it and can achieve its end in the most various ways. It is told of a famous German chemist that his marriage never took place because he forgot the hour of the ceremony and went to the laboratory instead.

Hitherto psychology has known nothing of such interferences or of the possibility that they could occasion manifestations of this kind. In slips of the tongue the interfering tendency is forced back. The speaker had determined not to convert the idea into speech and the tendency which is debarred from expression asserts itself against his will and gains utterance, either by altering the expression of the intention permitted by him, or by mingling with it, or actually by setting itself in place of it. This, then, is the mechanism of the slip of the tongue. Thus psychology brings home to us the great prevalence of mental conflict in our purposive life, and the great tendency to ward off from memory that which is unpleasant.

II—A Theory of Dreams

In part II Freud passes on to his theory of dreams. In his investigation of nervous patients he found that in speaking of their symptoms, which were discovered to have a meaning, they also mentioned their dreams. The suspicion thereupon arose that dreams too had a meaning. The aim is now to demonstrate the meaning of dreams in preparation for the study of the neuroses; for a dream itself is a neurotic symptom and occurs in all healthy people. Thus

psycho-analysis takes up research into what has been regarded as ordinary and of no practical value, like "errors." We know from our own experience that the mood in which we awake from a dream may last throughout the day; cases have been observed in which mental disorder began with a dream, the delusion which had its source in this dream persisting.

What exactly is a dream? It seems to be an intermediate condition between sleeping and waking. What then is

SIGMUND FREUD

sleep? It is a condition in which I refuse to have anything to do with the outer world and have withdrawn my interest from it. Our relationship with the world seems to be excusable only with intermission. Why does not mental life go off to sleep? Probably because there is something that will not leave the mind in peace; stimuli are acting upon it and to these it is bound to react. We note, too, that the character of mental processes during sleep is different from that of waking ones. Dreams not only consist of mental images, but differ in so many ways. There is proof that internal and external stimuli brought to bear during sleep make their appearance in dreams, but they are interpreted and elaborated differently in each instance. Some dreams are meaningless and confused, but some are sensible. Often in the latter there occur recollections of daily life, or matters connected with it, but in most dreams there is no seeming connexion with the day before, and no light is thrown upon the absurd dreams. Daydreams, which are phantasies, and are the product of thinking, not seeing, we shall find later have much in common with night-dreams. The content of them is dictated by a very transparent motivation. They are scenes and events which gratify either the egoistic cravings of ambition or thirst for power, or the erotic desires of the subject.

Let us start with the hypothesis that dreams are not a bodily but a mental phenomenon. Why not *ask the dreamer the meaning of the dream?* It is highly probable that the dreamer really does know the meaning of his dream: *only he does not know that he knows, and therefore thinks that he does not.* Such an assumption is confirmed by the study of dreams suggested during hypnotic or artificial sleep. We do not expect the dreamer at once to tell us what his dream means, but we do think he will be able to discover its source, from what circle of thoughts and interests it is derived.

This ensues from the use of what Freud terms "free association" which follows when the subject keeps in mind the original dream ideas one by one, and allows any associated ones to come without conscious direction or criticism. It is not altogether fantastic to suppose that these associations connected with the elements of the dream are determined by no other complex (group of emotionally toned and repressed ideas) than that which has produced the particular element itself, and that they will lead to the discovery of that complex. The dream element is not a thought proper but a substitute for something the knowledge of which is indeed possessed by the dreamer but is inaccessible to him. For reasons which will be noted later there will be found an unconscious resistance on the part of the dreamer to link the associations with the dream elements. The dream as related Freud terms the "manifest dream content," and the hidden meaning come to by following out the associations, the "latent dream thoughts." The two are intimately related in various ways.

Much light is thrown on interpretation by examining children's dreams, which are commonly easy to understand and reveal themselves as direct and undisguised fulfilment of wishes, like day-dreams. *Distortion is not therefore essential to the dream.* In adults we see the same type as reactions to internal bodily stimuli occasioned by thirst, hunger or sexual desire. The dream thus acts the purpose of protecting sleep from the stimulus, impelling us to wake up, and acts by calling up hallucinatory satisfaction. It is the guardian of sleep. Because, however, our wishes are often contrary to our personality, the dream becomes distorted and disguised so that the desires are hidden. This is called "the dream-work" which is carried out by a hypothetical dream censor. The dreamer's own self appears in every dream and plays the principal part, even if it knows how to disguise itself completely as far as the manifest content is concerned. Much that appears in a dream, too, cannot be interpreted solely through free association because some elements are symbolic, and by a knowledge of the meaning of these symbols it is often possible to interpret a dream without questioning the dreamer. The number of things which are represented symbolically in dreams is not great: the human body as a whole, parents, children, brothers and sisters, birth, death, nakedness and sex.

The dream-work causing the main distortion Freud divides into four processes: (1) Condensation—by means of which many latent elements are blended. (2) Displacement—where the accent is transferred from an important element to another which is unimportant or where the latent element is replaced by something more remote. (3) The transformation of thoughts into visual images. These features may be termed archaic in that they involve primitive modes of expression of language. (4) Secondary elaboration, which combines the immediate results of the other mechanisms into a single and coherent whole.

Freud concludes, then, that wish-fulfilment is, too, the essence of the distorted dream, but that the wish has been out of tune with the personality, has been repressed, and can therefore only appear in its disguised form. The infantile dream is an open wish-fulfilment admitted by the dreamer; the ordinary distorted dream is the disguised fulfilment of a repressed wish; while the anxiety dream (nightmare) is the open fulfilment of a repressed wish. In the last named the fear experienced arises from the dreamer nearly becoming aware of the desire he has repressed and is anxious not to recognize as part of himself. In dreams it is the unconscious wish which supplies the necessary fund of mental energy, and some residue thought from the previous day is usually the stimulus.

III—The Psycho-Analytic Theory of Neuroses

IN CHAPTER III Freud passes to his psycho-analytic theory of the neuroses. Here he endeavours to show that the comprehension of neurotic phenomena has much in common with what he has discussed in his previous chapters, and points out that his theory is the result of experience and founded on direct observation or on conclusions drawn from observation.

He starts by discussing symptomatic acts and delusions, and shows that they are not accidents but have their motive, meaning and intention; that they belong to a mental context which can be specified, and that they provide a small indication of a more important mental process not known to the individual himself. So neurotic symptoms have meaning like errors and like dreams, and are closely connected with the events of the patient's life. This is illustrated by brief reference to the symptoms of cases in which the impression is gained that the patients are "fixed" to a particular point in their past, and are thus alienated from both present and future. This is specially noted in the so-called "traumatic neuroses" (*i.e.* those developing after some accident or some terrifying experience) where the experience fixated is regularly reproduced in dreams. Always the meaning of the symptoms is unknown to the sufferer, but analysis invariably shows that they are derived from unconscious processes which can under favourable conditions become conscious. Memory gaps, or amnesias, are commonly found on analysis, which point to the fact that certain experiences have been relegated to an unconscious part of the mind. In many subtle ways the patient will manifest resistance against cure, as not only does he wish to remain ignorant of his unconscious but, in a distorted way, some gratification is gained through the symptom. The powerful forces here at work must be the same forces that originally induced the condition.

The unconscious system of the mind is compared to a large ante-room in which the various mental excitations are crowding upon one another like individual beings. Adjoining this is a second, smaller compartment in which consciousness resides. On the threshold between the two stands a sort of door-keeper who examines the various mental excitations, censors them and denies them admittance when he disapproves of them. The excitations in the unconscious, in the antechamber, are not visible to consciousness, which is in the other room, so to begin with they remain unconscious. When they have pressed forward to the threshold and been turned back by the door-keeper, they are incapable of becoming conscious; we call them repressed. The second chamber is called "the preconscious system." Thus the neurosis is brought about through the repression of wishes which the censor will not admit to conscious awareness, and the symptoms are the disguised morbid gratification of them. The purpose of the symptom is either a sexual gratification or a defence against it; in hysteria the positive character predominates, and in the obsessional type the negative ascetic character. The symptoms are the effects of compromise between the two opposed tendencies.

IV—The Sexual Instinct in Human Life

This leads Freud on to that realm of his theory which has brought about such intense opposition to psycho-analysis, viz. the sexual instinct, its place in human life and its relation to the neuroses. He uses the term "sexual" in a very broad sense. In perverts the sexual aim or the sexual object may be altered, and he endeavours to show that perverted sexuality is nothing else but infantile sexuality. The term *libido* is used to indicate sexual desires and longings in all their aspects as we should speak of "hunger" in relation to the instinct of nutrition.

In the first three or four years of life libidinous gratification is centred in sensations derived from stimulation of what are known as erogenous zones represented by the mouth, anal orifice and genitalia. The child is auto-erotic in that it seeks and finds its objects in its own person. Certain partial impulses appear early—sadism and masochism, the impulse to show and to look, to touch and be touched, and a curiosity impulse. These are readily identified as forerunners of tendencies apparent in the sex life of the normal adult. Perversions in after life represent the great exaggeration or over-development of one or other of these early tendencies present in every child. A sense of guilt through the influence of these impulses, and enhanced perhaps by possible threats, will arise in the child, and this will play a large part in the formation of character if he remains healthy, and of his neurosis if he falls ill. This is but another aspect of the idea that our earliest experiences are impressed on our unconscious.

Even in this *pregenital stage* one will see the beginning of object-love and the *libido* soon shows a preference for the opposite sex. This gives rise to the "Oedipus Complex" which is of such ast importance in the psycho-analytic xplanation of the neuroses, the boy and he mother, the girl and the father, being the emotional links. In neurotics his bond has not been relinquished in ater life as it should. Freud has no loubt but that one of the most important sources of the sense of guilt which o often torments neurotic people is to e found in the Oedipus Complex. He uspects, too, that perhaps the sense of uilt of mankind as a whole, which is he ultimate source of religion and moality, was acquired in the beginnings f history through this same complex. There thus grows up a conscious love or the parents with a repressed (and herefore unconscious) hate and perhaps leath wish against the parent of the ame sex from the spirit of rivalry.

From about the sixth or eighth year onwards a standstill or retrogression s observed in the sexual development, alled the "latency period." It may be bsent and if present it does not necesarily entail an interruption of sexual activities and interest over the whole ield. Most of the mental experiences and excitations occurring previously become repressed and forgotten, which veils our earliest childhood from us. It is he task of every psycho-analysis to oring this forgotten period of life back o recollection.

From the time of puberty onwards the human individual must devote himself to the great task of freeing himself from his parents; and only after the detachment is accomplished can he cease to be a child, and so become a member of the social community. For a son the task consists in releasing his desires from his mother in order to employ them in the quest of an external love-object in reality; and in reconciling himself with his father if he has remained antagonistic

to him, or in freeing himself from his domination if, in the reaction to the infantile revolt, he has lapsed into subservience to him. These tasks are seldom carried through ideally. In neurotics this detachment from the parents is not accomplished at all; the son remains all his life in subjection to his father and is incapable of transferring his *libido* to a new love-object. In the reversed relationship, the daughter's fate may be the same. In this sense the Oedipus Complex is the kernel of the neuroses.

Freud then goes on to discuss how these early factors produce neurotic disorders in later life. First there will arise a faulty development in the sexual instinct so that one or more of its early component impulses may be arrested and fixated, although other portions of it may have reached their final goal. When in adult life powerful external obstacles prevent adequate gratification of the *libido,* there will always be the tendency to regress to those fixated impulses which formerly afforded an outlet. Neurotics fall ill in consequence of a "privation" and their symptoms are actually substitutes for the missing satisfaction. In these people signs of mental conflict are found. One side of the personality stands for certain wishes, while another part struggles against them. This conflict is between the Ego instincts and the sexual instincts. The Ego has formed ideals which are found to be incompatible with the early form of desires. In its infancy the Ego only followed the pleasure principle, but has later become trained to be "reasonable," to face reality and thus repudiate what once gave it pleasure. If the regression does not call forth a prohibition on the part of the Ego, there is no conflict and no neurosis results, but real satisfaction is found in the form of some perversion.

V—Formation and Aim of Neurotic Symptoms

WE CANNOT here follow Freud in detail as he discusses the formation of neurotic symptoms, but in short we may state it as follows: Through

some situation which denies satisfaction to the *libido,* this latter is withdrawn from reality and turns back into the self (introversion), when in its dammed up state it partially overcomes what had been repressed in childhood and re-arouses unconscious phantastic wishes which correspond to an early developmental phase. An introverted person is unstable and not yet neurotic, but he will become so unless some other outlet for his pent-up *libido* is found. The symptoms arise as the result of a conflict between an unconscious wish which is striving to realize itself consciously and the repressing wish of the Ego to prevent such awareness. The symptom is a compromise between the two forces and can only appear in distorted form so that it is not recognised for what it really is. Thus, we note that dreams and neurotic symptoms have both a like formation and both can be viewed as the disguised manifestation of a repressed wish fulfilment. Freud points out that in Art there is a path for phantasy back to reality. The artist is introverted and has not far to go to become neurotic. He has great instinctive needs and with unsatisfied longing turns away from reality and transfers all his *libido* on to the creation of his wishes in the life of phantasy.

In neurotic symptoms there is also a secondary aim. The illness is used as a means to various ends and the neurotic takes advantage of it to gain attention, sympathy and love, to avoid disagreeable things, to revenge himself on others, or to punish himself and do penance for what he conceives to be his sins.

The neuroses are divided into the actual neuroses—neurasthenia, anxiety-neurosis and hypochondria, and the psycho-neuroses—hysteria and the obsessional neurosis. In the former the symptoms are more bodily in origin, while in the latter the symptoms can be shown to be the last links in a long chain of mental processes. Very commonly the two are combined.

Morbid anxiety and phobias are then discussed, these being very frequent phenomena in these conditions. It is suggested that the first anxiety state arose from the process of birth. Normal anxiety is the reaction of the Ego to danger and the signal preparatory to flight. In neurotic anxiety the Ego is attempting a flight from the unconscious demands of the *libido* and is treating the internal danger as though it were an external one. We thus tend to be afraid of our repressed desires. The damming up of the *libido* causing morbid fear may result mainly from physical factors in the sexual sphere where there is unsatisfactory or inadequate outlet, or arise as the result of psychic factors, such as repressions, resistances and conflicts.

FREUD then develops a later and more intricate theory with regard to the relation of *libido* to the Ego or self. He comes to the conclusion that the *libido* (sexual hunger) may be attached to the Ego either partially or wholly. In the latter case he terms the condition as one of Narcissism (after the fable of Narcissus who fell in love with his own reflection in the water). When one speaks of egoism one is thinking only of the *interests* of the persons concerned; Narcissism relates also to the satisfaction of his libidinal needs. There is in childhood such a phase of development interposed between the auto-erotic stage of infancy and the later stage of object-love. It is distinguished by the fact that for the time being the individual's sexual impulses and interests are directed towards himself in much the same manner as in the adult they are normally directed towards another person. He is in love with himself. There may, therefore, be fixation at this point of sexual development predisposing to morbid conditions in later life. Such ideas are believed to throw much light on such conditions as homosexuality, and the mental diseases of dementia praecox, paranoia and melancholia.

The final chapters are devoted to a discussion of psycho-analytic treatment and how through this the steps of the development of the nervous disorder are retraced through bringing the unconscious mental factors into awareness.

VI—Fundamental Principles of Freud's Theories

Though this is an epitome of Freud's great work on psycho-analysis in which his main ideas are expounded, it must be realized that one can give no adequate indication of the stupendous research this psychological genius has undertaken or the fruit that it has borne. Psycho-analysis in the hands of Freud and his disciples has taken on an ever widening sphere and has endeavoured to throw light on far reaching problems in the realms of religion, history, folk-lore, artistic and literary creation, characterology, and the study of superstition.

Though one can understand how his revolutionary theories have been heralded with intense opposition, yet his basic ideas are more and more being absorbed into current psychological thought. His fundamental principles consist in a rigid determinism as regards psychical events; in a dynamic nature of mental processes; in the importance of the mental processes in infantile life; in his theory of sexual development; in his views on mental energy, the unconscious, repression and mental conflict. Through his work for the first time a meaning has been given to mental symptoms which hitherto had been shrouded in obscurity. The real value of any pioneer work can only be appraised by posterity.

AS YE CAME FROM THE HOLY LAND

As ye came from the holy land
    Of Walsinghame,
Met you not with my true love
    By the way as you came?

How should I know your true love,
    That have met many a one
As I came from the holy land,
    That have come, that have gone?

She is neither white nor brown,
    But as the heavens fair;
There is none hath her form divine
    In the earth or the air.

Such a one did I meet, good sir,
    Such an angelic face,
Who like a nymph, like a queen, did appear
    In her gait, in her grace.

She hath left me here alone
    All alone, as unknown,
Who sometime did me lead with herself,
    And me loved as her own.

What's the cause that she leaves you alone
    And a new way doth take,
That sometime did love you as her own,
    And her joy did you make?

I have loved her all my youth,
    But now am old, as you see:
Love likes not the falling fruit,
    Nor the withered tree.

Know that Love is a careless child,
    And forgets promise past:
He is blind, he is deaf when he list,
    And in faith never fast.

Of womenkind such indeed is the love,
    Or the word love abusèd,
Under which many childish desires
    And conceits are excusèd.

But true love is a durable fire,
    In the mind ever burning,
Never sick, never dead, never cold,
    From itself never turning.
        —Anonymous (16th Cent.).

Hilaire Belloc

THE PATH TO ROME

Fɪʀsᴛ published in 1902, "The Path to Rome" deservedly remains its author's most popular achievement. Comparable with Stevenson's "Travels with a Donkey," it captivates all readers by its engaging style of narrative and its gay philosophy of life. Mr. Belloc was born in France in 1870.

1—I Set Out Upon My Journey

Iᴛ ᴡᴀs the very beginning of June, at evening, but not yet sunset, that I set out from Toul by the Nancy gate; but instead of going straight on past the parade-ground, I turned to the right immediately along the ditch and rampart, and did not leave the fortifications till I came to the road that goes up alongside the Moselle. For it was by the valley of this river that I was to begin my pilgrimage, since, by a happy accident, the valley of the Upper Moselle runs straight towards Rome, though it takes you but a short part of the way.

I walked along the valley of the Moselle, and as I walked, the long evening of summer began to fall. The sky was empty, and its deeps infinite; the clearness of the air set me dreaming. I passed the turn where we used to halt when we were learning how to ride in front of the guns. Everything about me conduced to reminiscence and to ease. A flock of sheep passed me with their shepherd, who gave me a good-night. I found myself entering that pleasant mood in which all books are conceived (but none written). I wasted in the contemplation of that silent hollow many miles of marching.

As I left the last house of the village I was not secure from loneliness, and when the road began to climb up the hill into the wild, I was wondering how the night would pass.

With every step upward a greater mystery surrounded me. A few stars were out, and the brown night mist was creeping along the water below; but there was still light enough to see the road, and even to distinguish the bracken in the deserted hollows. The highway became little better than a lane; at the top of the hill it plunged under tall pines, and was vaulted over with darkness. The kingdoms that have no walls, and are built up of shadows, began to oppress me as the night hardened. Had I had companions, still we would only have spoken in a whisper, and in that dungeon of trees even my own self would not raise its voice within me.

The air was full of midsummer, and its mixture of exaltation and fear cut me off from ordinary living. I now understood why our religion has made sacred this season of the year; why we have, a little later, the night of St. John, the fires in the villages, and the old perception of fairies dancing in the rings of the summer grass. A general communion of all things conspires at this crisis of summer against us reasoning men that should live in the daylight, and something fantastic possesses those who are foolish enough to watch upon such nights.

Wʜᴇɴ I awoke it was full eight o' clock, and the sun had gained great power. I saw him shining at me through the branches of my trees like a patient enemy outside a city that one watches through the loopholes of a tower, and I began to be afraid of taking he road. I looked below me down the teep bank between the trunks and saw he canal looking like black marble; ind I heard the buzzing of the flies ibove it, and I noted that all the mist iad gone. A very long way off, the noise of its ripples coming clearly along the floor of the water, was a lazy barge and a horse drawing it. From time to time the tow-rope slackened into the still surface, and I heard it dripping as it rose. The rest of the valley was silent except for that under-humming of the insects which marks the strength of the sun.

II—Landscapes from the Heights

THE delightful thing in Charmes is its name. Of this name I had indeed been thinking as I went along the last miles of that dusty and deplorable road—that a town should be called "Charmes." Not but that towns, if they are left to themselves and not hurried, have a way of settling into right names suited to the hills about them and recalling their own fields.

I climbed, then, over slippery pine needles and under the charged air of those trees, which was full of dim, slanting light from the afternoon sun, till, nearly at the summit, I came upon a clearing which I at once recognized as a military road, leading into what we used to call a "false battery," that is, a dug-out with embrasures into which guns could be placed but in which no guns were. For ever since the French managed to produce a really mobile heavy gun they have constructed any amount of such auxiliary works between the permanent forts.

This false battery was on the brow of the hill, and when I reached it I looked down the slope, over the brushwood that hid the wire entanglements, and there was the whole valley of the Moselle at my feet.

As this was the first really great height, so this was the first really great view that I met with on my pilgrimage. I drew it carefully, piece by piece, sitting there in the declining sun and noting all I saw.

THIS is the peculiar virtue or walking to a far place, and especially of walking there in a straight line, that one gets these visions of the world from hilltops.

When I call up for myself this great march, I see it all mapped out in landscapes, each of which I caught from some mountain, and each of which joins on to that before and to that after it, till I can piece together the whole road. The view here from the Hill of Archettes, the view from the Ballon d'Alsace, from Glovelier Hill, from the Weissenstein, from the Brienzer Grat, from the Grimsel, from above Bellinzona, from the Principessa, from Tizzano, from the ridge of the Apennines, from the Wall of Siena, from San Quirico, from Radicofani, from San Lorenzo, from Ronciglione, and at last from that lift in the Via Cassia, whence one suddenly perceives the city.

These vistas unroll themselves all in their order till I can see Europe, and Rome shining at the end. Then I went up to that valley of the Moselle over which I was gazing, until I came to the sources of the river deep in the fold of the great hills.

IT WAS my delight to lie upon a bank of the road and to draw what I saw before me, which was the tender stream of the Moselle slipping through fields quite flat and even and undivided by fences. Its banks had here a strange effect of Nature copying man's art; they seemed a park, and the river wound through it full of the positive innocence that attaches to virgins; it nourished and was guarded by trees.

There was about that scene something of creation and of a beginning, and as I drew it, it gave me, like a gift, the freshness of the first experiences of living, and filled me with remembered springs. I mused upon the birth of rivers, and how

they were persons and had a name—
were kings, and grew strong and ruled
great countries, and how at last they
reached the sea.

The afternoon and the evening followed as I put one mile after another
behind me. The frontier seemed so close

that I would not rest. I was in a grand
wonderment for Switzerland, and
wished by an immediate effort to conquer the last miles before night. Also,
will confess to a silly pride in distances
and a desire to be out of France on my
fourth day.

HILAIRE BELLOC born July 27, 1870, is one of the most accomplished and versatile of English
men of letters. An essayist of lightest touch, deft artist in descriptive narrative, an engaging novelist,
brilliant biographer, a writer of verse, learned exponent of French history, authoritative critic of
military affairs, a student of politics—he is of the few who, in an age of narrow specialization,
have maintained the larger tradition of the finest periods of literature by displaying a wide range
of interest and confident power in many branches of the art. Perhaps his most notable gift is a
humor that is at once urbane and hearty. It lights up all his works, and none more happily than
"The Path to Rome," which appeared in 1902. Although he has written more than two score books
since then, it remains one of his most individual works and we are fortunate in being able to include
a little version of it made by Mr. Belloc himself.

The light still fell, and my resolution stood, though my exhaustion undermined it. The line of the mountains rose higher against the sky, and there entered into my pilgrimage for the first time the loneliness and the mystery of meres. Something of what a man feels in East England belonged to this last of the plain under the guardian hills. Everywhere I passed ponds and reeds, and saw the level streak of sunset reflected in stagnant waters.

The marshy valley kept its character when I had left the lane and regained the high road. Its isolation dominated the last effort with which I made for the line of the Jura in that summer twilight, and, as I blundered on, my whole spirit was caught or lifted in the influence of the waste waters and of the birds of evening.

At last I came within one mile of the Swiss frontier. When I guessed that I had covered this mile, I saw a light in the windows on my left, a trellis and the marble tables of a café. I put my head in at the door.

"Am I in Switzerland?" said I.

A German-looking girl, a large heavy man, a Bavarian commercial traveller, and a colleague of his from Marseilles, all said together, in varying accents. "Yes!"

"Then," I said, "I will come in and drink."

III—The Vision of the Alps

THIS book would never end if I were to attempt to write down so much as the names of a quarter of the extraordinary things that I saw and heard on my enchanted pilgrimage, but let me at least mention the commercial traveller from Marseilles.

He talked with extreme rapidity for two hours. He had seen all the cities in the world, and he remembered their minutest details. He was extremely accurate, his taste was abominable, his patriotism large, his vitality marvellous, his wit crude but continual, and to his German friend, to the host of the inn, and to the blonde serving-girl, he was a familiar god. He came, it seems, once a year, and for a day would pour out the torrent of his travels like a waterfall of guide-books—for he gloried in dates, dimensions and the points of the compass in his descriptions; then he disappeared for another year, and left them to feast on the memory of such a revelation.

For my part I sat silent, crippled with fatigue, trying to forget my wounded feet, drinking stoup after stoup of beer and watching the Phocean. He was of the old race you see on vases in red and black—slight, very wiry, with a sharp, eager, but well-set face, a small, black, pointed beard, brilliant eyes like those of lizards, rapid gestures, and a vivacity that played all over his features as sheet lightning does over the flow of midnight in June.

I watched the Phocean. I thought of a man of his ancestry three thousand years ago sitting here at the gates of these mountains talking of his travels to dull, patient, and admiring northerners, and travelling for gain up into the Germanies, and I felt the changeless form of Europe under me like a huge, solid rock.

Having passed the valley of the River Doubs and getting over into the heart of Switzerland, I got to the top of the ridge. A young man was chopping wood outside a house, and I asked him in French how far it was to Moutier. He answered in German, and I startled him by a loud cry, such as sailors give when they see land, for at last I had struck the boundary of languages, and was with pure foreigners for the first time in my life. I also asked him for coffee, and, as he refused it, I took him to be a heretic, and went down the road making up verses against all such, and singing them loudly through the forest that now arched over me and grew deeper as I descended.

A LITTLE after this I saw between the branches of the trees in front of me a sight in the sky that made me stop breathing, just as great danger at sea, or great surprises in love, or a great deliverance will make a man stop breathing. In between the branches of the trees was a great promise of unexpected lights beyond.

I pushed left and right along the edge of the forest and along the fence that bound it, until I found a place where the pine-trees stopped, leaving a gap, and where on the right, beyond the gap, was a tree whose leaves had failed.

There the ground broke away steeply before me, and the beeches fell, one below the other, like a vast cascade, towards the limestone cliffs that dipped down still further. I looked through this framing hollow and praised God. For there, thousands of feet below me, was what seemed an illimitable plain; at the end of that world was an horizon, and the dim bluish sky that overhangs an horizon.

There was brume [mist] in it and thickness. One saw the sky beyond the edge of the world getting purer as the vault rose. But right up—a belt in that empyrean—ran peak and field and needle of intense ice, remote, remote from the world. Sky beneath them an[d] sky above them, a steadfast legion, the[y] glittered as though with the armor o[f] the immovable armies of Heaven. Tw[o] days' march, three days' march away they stood up like the walls of Eden.

So little are we, we men; so much ar[e] we immersed in our muddy and imme[diate] diate interests that we think, by num[bers] bers and recitals, to comprehend di[s]tance or time, or any of our limitin[g] infinites. Here were these magnifice[nt] creatures of God—I mean the Alps— which now for the first time I saw fro[m] the height of the Jura; and because the[y] were fifty or sixty miles away, and be cause they were a mile or two high, the[y] were become somewhat different fro[m] us others, and could strike one motio[n]less with the awe of supernatural things Up there in the sky, to which only clouds belong and birds and the last trem[b]ling colours of pure light, they stoo[d] fast and hard; not moving as do th[e] things of the sky. They were as distan[t] as the little upper clouds of summer, a[s] fine and tenuous; but in their reflectio[n] and in their quality, as it were, of weap ons—like spears and shields of an un known array—they occupied the sk[y] with a sublime invasion; and the thing[s] proper to the sky were forgotten by m[e] in the presence as I gazed.

IV—I Am Conquered by the Alps

NEXT let me describe how I attempted to cross the last Alpine snows from the northern to the southern side.

At three o'clock the guide knocked at my door, and I rose and came out to him. We drank coffee and ate bread. We put into our sacks ham and bread, and he white wine and I brandy. Then we set out. The rain had dropped to a drizzle, and there was no wind. The sky was obscured for the most part, but here and there was a star. The hills hung awfully above us in the night as we crossed the spongy valley. A little wooden bridge took us over the young Rhône, here only a stream, and we followed a path up into the tributary ravine which leads to the Nufenen and the Gries passes. In a mile or two it was a little lighter, and this was as well, for some weeks before a great avalanche had fallen.

Beneath the wide cap of frozen snow ran a torrent roaring. I remembered Colorado, and how I had crossed the Arkansas on such a bridge as a boy. We went on in the uneasy dawn. The woods began to show, and there was a cross where a man had slipped from above that very April and been killed. Then, most ominous and disturbing, the drizzle changed to a rain, and the guide shook his head and said it would be snowing higher up. We went on, and it grew lighter. Before it was really day (or else the weather confused and darkened the sky), we crossed a good bridge, built long ago, and we halted at a shed where the cattle lie in the late summer when the snow is melted.

The guide said it could not be done, but I said we must attempt it. I was eager, and had not yet felt the awful grip of the cold. We left the Nufenen on our left, a hopeless steep of new snow buried in fog, and we attacked the Gries. For half an hour we plunged on through snow above our knees. So far the guide knew we were more or less on the path, and he went on and I panted after him. Neither of us spoke, but occasionally he looked back to make sure I had not dropped out.

The snow began to fall more thickly, and the wind had risen somewhat. I was afraid of another protest from the guide, but he stuck to it well, and I after him, continually plunging through soft snow and making yard after yard upwards. The snow fell more thickly, and the wind still rose.

We came to a place which is, in the warm season, an alp; that is, a slope of grass, very steep but not terrifying; having here and there sharp little precipices of rock breaking it into steps, but by no means (in summer) a matter to make one draw back. Now, however, when everything was still Arctic, it was a very different matter. A sheer steep of snow whose downward plunge ran into the driving storm and was lost, whose head was lost in the same mass of thick cloud above, a slope somewhat hollowed and bent inwards, had to be crossed if we were to go any farther.

The guide said there was little danger, only if one slipped one might slide down to safety, or one might (much less probably) get over rocks and be killed. I was chattering a little with cold; but as he did not propose a return, I followed him. The surface was alternately slabs of frozen snow and patches of soft new snow. In the first he cut steps, in the second we plunged, and once I went

right in and a mass of snow broke off beneath me and went careening down the slope. He showed me how to hold my staff backwards, and to use it as a kind of brake in case I slipped.

WE HAD been about twenty minutes crawling over that wall of snow and ice; and it was more and more apparent that we were in for danger. Before we had reached the far side, the wind was blowing a very full gale, and roared past our ears. The surface snow was whirring like dust before it; past our faces and against them drove the snow-flakes, cutting the air; not falling, but making straight darts and streaks. They seemed like the form of the whistling wind; they blinded us.

The rocks on the far side of the slope, rocks which had been our goal when we set out to cross it, had long ago disappeared in the increasing rush of the blizzard. Suddenly, as we were still painfully moving on, these rocks loomed up over as large as houses, and we saw them through the swarming snow-flakes as great hulls are seen through a fog at sea. The guide crouched under the lee of the nearest; I came up close to him and he put his hands to my ear, and shouted to me that nothing further could be done—he had so to shout because in among the rocks the hurricane made a roaring sound, swamping the voice.

I asked how far we were from the summit. He said he did not know where we were exactly, but that we could not be more than 800 feet from it. I was but that from Italy, and I would not admit defeat. I offered him all I had in money to go on, but it was folly in me, because if I had had enough to tempt him, and if he had yielded we should both have died. Luckily it was but a little sum. He shook his head. He would not go on, he broke out, for all the money there was in the world. He shouted me to eat and drink, and so we both did.

We returned and were ultimately safe, but it is a dreadful thing to give up one's sword. The Alps had conquered me. I went round over the Furka and then over the St. Gothard until, as I descended the southern slope of that pass, a hint or memory of gracious things ran in the slight breeze, the wreath of fogs would lift a little for a few yards, and in their clearings I thought to approach a softer and more desirable world. I was soothed as though with caresses, and when I began to see somewhat farther, and felt a vigour and fullness in the outline of the trees, I said to myself:

"I know what it is! It is the South and a great part of my blood. They may call it Switzerland still, but I know now that I am in Italy, and this is the gate of Italy lying in groves."

Then and on till evening I reconciled myself with misfortune, and when I heard again at Airolo the speech of civilized men, and saw the strong Latin eyes and straight forms of the race after all those days of fog and frost and German speech and the north, my eyes filled with tears, and I was as glad as a man come home again.

V—Wayside Adventures and Reflections

THE wine of Airolo and its songs, how greatly they refreshed me! To see men with answering eyes and to find a salute returned; the noise of careless mouths talking all together; the group of cards, and the laughter that is proper to mankind; the straight carriage of the women, and in all the people something erect and noble as though indeed they possessed the earth. I made a meal here, talking to all my companions left and right in a new speech of my own, which was made up, as it were, of the essence of all the Latin tongues.

The Italian lakes have that in them and their air which removes them from common living. Their beauty is not the beauty which each of us sees for himself in the world; it is rather the beauty of a special creation; the expression of some mind.

To eyes innocent, and first freshly noting our great temporal inheritance—I mean to the eyes of a boy and girl just entered upon the estate of this glorious earth, and thinking themselves immortal—this shrine of Europe might remain for ever in the memory; an enchanted experience, in which the single sense of sight had almost touched the boundary of music. They would remember these lakes as the central emotions of their youth. To mean men also, who, in spite of years and of a full foreknowledge of death, yet attempt nothing but the satisfaction of sense, and pride themselves upon the taste and fineness with which they achieve this satisfaction, the Italian lakes would seem a place for habitation, and there such a man might build his house contentedly. But to ordinary Christians I am sure there is something unnatural in this beauty of theirs, and they find in it either a paradise only to be won by a much longer road or a bait and veil of sorcery, behind which lies great peril.

Now, for all we know, beauty beyond the world may not really bear this double aspect, but to us on earth—if we are ordinary men—beauty of this kind has something evil. Have you not read in books how men when they see even divine visions are terrified? So, as I looked at Lake Major in its halo, I also was afraid, and I was glad to cross the ridge and crest of the hill and to shut out that picture framed all round with glory.

I went across the Lombard Plain in cold weather, and wet; I struck the Apennines, and forded their rivers. I was imprisoned and let loose again, and I made for a pass in the Apennines which was on the right road to Rome. But the night before I came to it the country was so deserted that I had to sleep out, and I was without food for nearly a day.

I have waited for the dawn a hundred times, attended by that mournful, colourless spirit which haunts the last hours of darkness, and influenced especially by the great timeless apathy that hangs round the first uncertain promise of increasing light. For there is an hour before daylight when men die, and when there is nothing above the soul or around it, when even the stars fail. And this long and dreadful expectation I had thought to be worst when one was alone at sea in a small boat without wind, drifting beyond one's harbour in the ebb of the outer channel tide, and sogging back at the first flow on the broad, confused movement of a sea without any waves. In such lonely mornings I have watched the Owers light turning, and I have counted up my gulf of time, and wondered that moments could be so stretched out in the clueless mind. I have prayed for the morning or for a little draught of wind, and this I have thought, I say, the extreme of absorption into emptiness and longing.

I HEARD no sound of animals or birds. I passed several fields, deserted in the half-darkness, and in some I felt the hay, but always found it wringing wet with dew; nor could I discover a good shelter from the wind that blew off the upper snow of the summits. For a little space of time there fell upon me that shadow of sleep which numbs the mind, but it could not compel me to lie down, and I accepted it only as a partial and beneficent oblivion which covered my desolation and suffering as a thin, transparent cloud may cover an evil moon.

Then, suddenly, the sky grew lighter upon every side. That cheating gloom—which I think the clouds in purgatory must reflect—lifted from the valley as though to a slow order given by some calm and good influence that was marshalling in the day. Their colors came back to things; the trees recovered their shape, life and trembling; here and there, on the face of the mountain opposite, the mists by their movement took part in the new life, and I thought I heard for the first time the tumbling water far below me in the ravine.

That subtle barrier was drawn which marks to-day from yesterday; all the night and its despondency became the past and entered memory. The road before me, the pass on my left (my last ridge, and the entry into Tuscany), the mass of the great hills, had become mixed into the increasing light, that is, into the familiar and invigorating present which I have always found capable of opening the doors of the future with a gesture of victory.

NEXT, I went down the Garfagnana to Lucca, and then on to Siena, until at last, when I was within a three days' march of Rome, I happened to come, in a very uninhabited plain, upon a farm. I saw lights shining in the large farmhouse, and I went in.

There, in a very large room, floored with brick and lit by one candle, were two fine old peasants, with faces like apostles, playing a game of cards. There also was a woman playing with a strong boy child, that could not yet talk; and the child ran up to me. Nothing could persuade the master of the house but that I was a very poor man who needed sleep, and so good and generous was this old man that my protests seemed to him nothing but the excuses and shame of poverty.

He asked me where I was going. I said: "To Rome." He came out with a lantern to the stable, and showed me there a manger full of hay, indicating that I might sleep in it. His candle flashed upon the great silent oxen standing in rows; their enormous horns, three times the length of what we know in England, filled me with wonder.

Rather than seem to offend him, I lay down in that manger, though I had no more desire to sleep than has the flittermouse in our Sussex gloamings; also I was careful to offer no money, for that is brutality.

When he left me, I took the opportunity for a little rest, and lay on my back in the hay, wide awake and staring at darkness.

VI—At the Journey's End

THE rest is easily told. I went through Viterbo and Ronciglione—passing on my way a dark and lonely lake called the Pond of Venus—until I came to a little inn where again they let me sleep upon some hay.

But as I slept, Rome, Rome still beckoned me, and I woke in a struggling light as though at a voice calling, and slipping out, I could not but go on to the end.

The small, square paving of the Via Cassia, all even like a palace floor, rang under my steps. The parched banks and strips of dry fields showed through the fog—for its dampness did not cure the arid soil of the Campagna. The sun rose and the vapor lifted. Then, indeed, I peered through the thick air; but still I could see nothing of my goal, only confused folds of brown earth and burnt-up grasses, and farther off rare and un-northern trees.

I passed an old tower of the Middle Ages that was eaten away at its base by time or the quarrying of men; I passed a divergent way on the right where a wooden sign said, "The Triumphal Way," and I wondered whether it could be the road where ritual had once ordained that triumphs should go.

The road fell into a hollow where soldiers were maneuvring. Even these could not arrest an attention that was fixed upon the approaching revelation. The road climbed a little slope where a branch went off to the left, and where there was a house with a plate to Pio Nono's visit, and an arbor under vines, It was now warm day; trees of great height stood shading the sun; the place had taken on an appearance of wealth and care. The mist had gone before I reached the summit of the rise.

There, from the summit, between the high villa walls on either side—at my very feet I saw the city.

AT THE foot of the hill I prepared to enter the city, and I lifted up my heart. There was an open space; a tramway; a tram upon it about to be drawn by two lean and tired horses whom in the heat many flies disturbed. There was dust on everything around. A bridge was immediately in front. It was adorned with statues in soft stone, half-eaten away, but still gesticulating in corruption, after the manner of the seventeenth century.

And beneath the bridge there tumbled and swelled a great confusion of yellow water—it was the Tiber. Far on the right were white barracks of hideous appearance; over these the Dome of St. Peter's rose and looked like something newly built. It was of a delicate blue, but made a metallic contrast against the sky.

Then, along a road perfectly straight and bounded by factories, mean houses and distempered walls—a road littered with many scraps of paper, bones and dirt—I went on for several hundred yards, having the old wall of Rome before me all the time, till I came right under it at last; and with the hesitation that befits all great actions I entered, putting the right foot first lest I should bring further misfortune upon that capital of all our fortunes.

And so the journey ended.

IF IT is the love of that which your work represents—if, being a landscape painter, it is love of hills and trees that moves you—if, being a figure painter, it is love of human beauty, and human soul that moves you—if, being a flower or animal painter, it is love, and wonder, and delight in petal and in limb that move you, then the Spirit is upon you, and the earth is yours, and the fullness thereof. —Ruskin.

SIR GILBERT PARKER

THE RIGHT OF WAY

ALTHOUGH Sir Gilbert Parker's literary reputation rests mainly on his work as a novelist, it was as a playwright that he first came before the public, his maiden venture being a version of Goethe's "Faust," which was successfully produced in 1888 at Sydney where he was temporarily associate editor of the Sydney *Morning Herald*. In 1892 he published his first volume of fiction, a number of short stories under the general title of "Pierre and His People." From that time a brilliant succession of novels has appeared from his pen, each notable for its high literary quality. "The Right of Way," published in 1901, exhibits its author in his most characteristic mood. Like nearly all his stories, it is a tale of the North, told with humor and pathos, and with a rare gift for depicting human emotions and scenery. Sir Gilbert Parker himself prepared this epitome before his death.

I—A Soul of Ashes

To Charles Steele, lawyer, of Montreal, at his birth nature had been kind. She had given him a remarkable intellect, a dazzling brilliancy and personal comeliness of an almost exaggerated kind. One thing she had denied him, however—the imagination of the spirit. He was born incredulous, he grew to be an incarnate question, his soul was stunted. Men called him Charley, but he was no man's intimate or friend. They named him "Beauty Steele," but while men and women admired, they found in him nothing to love. Cold, cynical, his very courtesy an impertinence, his eyeglass a weapon of offence, his foppishness aggression, he walked apart—*non-intime,* with a deadly intelligence and a soul of ashes. But sometimes the soul flickered into life—under the influence of drink. And then, intoxicated, his great powers reached their zenith, the cold intellect grew warm; for the moment the man came into touch with fellow men.

So it was when Beauty Steele was defending Joseph Nadeau on a charge of murder. Hour by hour the Crown piled up damning evidence, but Charley, the defending lawyer, sat unmoved, careless, while the prisoner gave no answer, no explanation, and the onlookers became anxious—not lest a man should be sentenced to death, but lest Beauty Steele should cynically throw away his unbroken record of success.

Then, on the third day, he spoke, infecting the jury with his own scepticism as to the prisoner's guilt, until they could not believe even the obvious facts, swaying their judgment, moulding them as wax to his will, and securing the acquittal of the man to whom he said contemptuously when the trial was ended: "Get out of my sight. You're as guilty as hell!"

ON that day Fate laid its hand upon Charley Steele. In the audience which hung on his words was a girl, beautiful as he was handsome, and, like him, passionless and formal. With her heart, such as it was, drawing her towards Fairing, the honest English soldier, her intellect surrendered to the dominating intellect of the orator, to the fascination of his personality. As he spoke their eyes met, and the bargain was sealed which ended in a union, cerebral, intellectual, temperamental, aesthetic, unwarmed by any spark of passion; a union which gave the girl—Kathleen—the right of way, and barred the path to happiness against the man for ever, and the happiness of another also.

Five years pass, and then the punishments which the cold, agnostic intellect has made for itself begin to find the man. John Brown, the shallow, theatrical, eloquent parson, whom Charley Steele had corrupted with his eternal question, "Who knows?" comes back to Montreal, which he has scandalised, a broken speculator. Billy Wantage, Kathleen's brother, has forged Steele's name, and drawn out twenty-five thousand dollars belonging to a charity for which the lawyer was trustee. Drink, once the servant which Charley brought to the service of his mind, has become his master. And Kathleen, the wife, at last arraigns him.

"Look at what you've made of Billy," she cries. "You ruined John Brown with your dissipations and your sneers at religion, and your 'I wonder nows.' Of what use have you been, Charley? Oh, you fop, you fool; you have ruined my brother, you have ruined my life, and I hate and despise you for a cold-blooded, selfish coward."

It is an unjust accusation. It misconceives the man. For Beauty Steele is not all bad. He gives his wife the title-deeds of his fine mansion, in place of a smaller settlement he had made on his marriage, covers up Billy's crime and bears the financial loss himself. He has in him the germs of a great nobility, the seeds of a high nature; but they are merely germs, checked in growth, because he was born with some fertilising element absent from his being, and a soul which is only stimulated into flickering life by alcohol, which lifts him into an atmosphere of warmer, almost understanding life. So by the people his wife is pitied, and men speak of him disparagingly as "poor Charley Steele" as they see him frequenting the bars, and hear of his constant visits to a low public-house, the Côte Dorion, by the riverside.

To the Côte Dorion he turns when his wife and he part after their great quarrel—to the inn where he can drink and think; where he can speak with Suzon, the ill-educated barmaid, with the touch of native genius, of divination, of elemental humanity, who alone has the gift of answering his questions, pouring doubt upon his doubt. He realizes the danger of such visits, for the rough river-men, mistaking his relations, or would-be relations, with Suzon, have sworn vengeance on him. But he is reckless, defiant, indifferent, and he will go to the Côte Dorion once again.

T HE river folk are rough, suspicious; Charley is intoxicated, reckless, jealous, daring to insanity. He drives the crowd in the bar-room mad by gazing at them through his eyeglass, with studied insolence and murmured mockery.

Then he is challenged to give them a sermon, and he responds with a biting, searching commentary on religion, life and all its strivings. His hearers grow ominously sullen. He is reputed to be an infidel, and they are good Catholics. They find an insulting challenge in his ribald treatment of sacred things. But, as he speaks, inspired by drink, his eloquence conquers prejudice for a moment. He tells them how they get tired with work, with play; that it is not always summer, that nothing blooms all the year round, that rest is sweet, and that all men long sooner or later for the sweet fields of Eden. What are they like, those fields? No one knows. The One Man who knew never told. Why not? The cynicism of his undeveloped soul peers out almost viciously, with destructive questioning. Who knows? What's the good of asking? It's better to go it blind.

The hearts of the river-men harden against him once more; they become angered as he winds up with a Protestant hymn, grow hot as he turns insolently from them to Suzon. They jostle him; he replies with flippant impertinence. A tumbler is thrown, a lamp is broken. The only Englishman there offers to stand by Charley, only to be repelled by a cold stare through the eyeglass, and the words, "I beg your pardon, but have I ever been introduced to you?"

Left to his fate, Beauty Steele fights hard—in vain. He is struck down, flung senseless into the river, and the dark waters close over his old life.

II—Ghosts of the Past

H E opens his eyes on a new life in a woodman's cottage in the Vadrôme Hills, over Chaudière, a hundred miles down the river—a backwater of the world. The hut belongs to one Jo Portugais, whom, as Joseph Nadeau, Charley Steele had saved from the gallows five years before. Drifting on his log raft past the Côte Dorion, Jo had heard the fight, had drawn from the water the man who had saved him, had nursed him back to life. But not to reason. Memory was gone; the capacity to think was numbed; the cynical philosopher, the brilliant lawyer, wakes—a child. And so he remains through seven months, living the simple life of a child, helping Portugais in his work of carpentering, quenching his thirst with pure water, purging himself of the past, of which he remembers nothing, until there comes M. Loisel, a great surgeon of Paris, to visit his brother, the curé of Chaudière. The curé tells him of the stranger in Jo Portugais' hut; his professional interest is aroused; he visits Charley and proposes an operation.

But yet he hesitates, man of the world as he is. Suppose that with memory restored should come again shame, or sin, or crime, would the patient thank him? Now, the man is living without stain. But what has he been; what, if intellect be restored, may he be? The curé, however, overcomes his brother's scruples. The man must face his life, taking its responsibility in his hands, trusting to God. The operation is performed, and Beauty Steele awakes to consciousness of his old life, with mind and memory undimmed.

It is to Charley as though he had slept

but for a few hours. He only wonders that his head is so clear after last night's debauch at the Côte Dorion. And then full knowledge comes to him from a fragment of newspaper which has been used as a tablecloth. In it he sees the announcement of the marriage of his wife Kathleen to Captain Fairing, her old admirer. He reads the newspaper comment on his wife's previous unhappy marriage, of which he was, in public estimation, the cause; he reads of his obscure end, of the discovery that he had embezzled twenty-five thousand dollars—"the final seal of shame upon a mis-spent life, destined for brilliant and powerful uses."

His brain burns as he scans the dreadful epitaph upon Beauty Steele. What an *impasse* is before him! He can only return to his life and his career by shaming his wife, the woman he has injured, for whom he is sorry; he can only clear his own name by branding her brother as a felon. He will not go back. Since people think him dead, then dead he will be to the world. Charley Steele shall die—but Charles Mallard shall live.

But the old Charley does not die suddenly, nor without a struggle. The old cynicism springs up betimes, to be repressed because the people about him are so simple, have been so good to him. The old thirst comes on him, memories of the sweet smell of the cool beer in the saloon yonder; but he quenches it with cold water—fights it down. The French surgeon, who knows his weakness, writes to him, sending drugs which will help him in the struggle. He disdains to use them, however; he will rely on his own will.

The seven months' purgation in Jo Portugais' hut helps him, though he suffers terribly, to overcome the temptation. But the seven months have done more: they have given his conscience a chance

to grow. He looks back on the old life with stirrings of remorse; he sets himself to find a new life. Down in Chaudière village old Louis Trudel, the tailor is known to have but a short while to live; Charles Mallard enters his shop and instals himself, uninvited, as apprentice.

So the brilliant lawyer becomes a tailor, learning his trade with rare facility, an object of curiosity to the villagers. They dub him "M'sieu," seeing something under his rough garb of *habitant* different from themselves. He is an object of admiration, since he speaks as well as the curé or the seigneur; above all, an object of interest to the girl who stands on the threshold of his life, her hand upon the door.

Rosalie Evanturel, the postmaster's daughter, of gentle though reduced family, educated as befitted her birth rather than her position, high-souled, made for love and to love, of virginal purity—such a woman as Beauty Steele had never known, or could never have understood, she comes slowly into the life of Charles Mallard.

Louis Trudel was a fanatic in religion. Finding a scrap of paper on which his assistant had written some pungent sentences, he is convinced that the writer is an infidel. The words are part of an outpouring of doubt: "This tailor here. . . . This stingy, hard, unhappy tailor. . . . If there is a God . . . Therefore, wherefore, tailor-man? Therefore, wherefore, God? . . . Show me a sign from Heaven, tailor-man!"

The tailor will give the sign. From the church door he steals a small iron cross, a precious relic, heats it red-hot and brands the breast of his assistant while he sleeps.

Rosalie, who has suspected something evil—she knows not what—steals from the post-office across the road, and with Trudel's old servant, Margot, comes on him in the act. Old Trudel falls in a fit, Margot dies soon after, and love springs from the shared secret of the branded cross.

Wɪᴛʜ love, the heart and soul of the man open for the first time. Now he does good, not ill, to those around him; his eyeglass is no longer a weapon of offence; cold cynicism dwindles, the old doubts, indeed, obtrude themselves, but the eternal question takes a new form.

What is the token—
Bruised and broken,
Bend I my life to a blossoming rod?
Shall, then, the worst things
Come to the first things,
Finding the best of all, last of all, God?

The ghosts of the past are not wholly laid; one comes—John Brown, the derelict parson, now quack doctor, vending his nostrums at the village fair, beguiling his audience with snatches of bawdy song.

The village tailor has saved the quack from a fatal accident as he came; but he does not know that the tailor is Charley Steele—the man who, in the shadow of the trees, sees the ruin he has made, hears the renegade priest, now sunk so low, singing a drinking-song he himself had often sung in old times. Hearing it again, Charley, in a passion of remorse and weakness, flies to drink once more, and almost kills himself with the debauch.

III—A Dead Soul Awakened

Hᴇ comes back from his illness to find the old life at his door. In Jo Portugais he recognizes the murderer he had defended; from him he hears of Kathleen, his wife, of her child—not his. Suddenly he is threatened with arrest for a crime of which he knows nothing, from which he can only clear himself by revealing his identity. From such an *impasse* death is the only escape, and he is ready to drink the laudanum which will end all, but Rosalie intervenes. She threatens to die with him. And Portugais, to save him, confesses his crime, and tells who Charles Mallard is to the abbé who has accused him.

His dormant soul has at last found its inspiration. It blooms forth in his overwhelming love for Rosalie, transfiguring him. Charity and humanity take the place of ambition, he sees life now at last through the lens of personal duty.

But the penalty of his past finds him. Kathleen has the right of way; he cannot give Rosalie the name of wife without crime and wrong to her—yet, nevertheless, she is wronged as it is. Whilst Kathleen lives, he must make Rosalie unhappy.

Once the way out offered itself to him. Rosalie has taken her father to the hospital to Montreal—to die, and Charley, following, creeps back to the town disguised as a *habitant*. At dead of night he enters his old house to possess himself of some jewels he had left in a secret place, and as he is leaving, Kathleen, his wife, comes after him, walking in her sleep. Unconscious, she crosses the garden towards a gate that opens on the edge of the cliff where the river runs fifty feet below. Temptation comes to him, as he watches. Shall he let her go to her death and so free himself for ever? He is dead to Kathleen—shall his ghost save her? But a voice speaks to him, the voice of a man with a conscience—"Save her!" He rushes past her noiselessly and closes the gate.

The end is very near for Charley Steele—the tremendous nemesis, born of the ill-doing of the past, working out its end in the well-doing of the present. Chaudière is to have a Passion Play. In the intention of the curé, it is to be for purely local instruction, to purify his flock, perhaps to help him in his great desire, his pure ambition—to bring

Charley, whom he loves, into the bosom of the Church. He has pressed Charley into the service, made him helper.

THAT night the parish church of Chaudière bursts into flames. One of the ghosts of Charley's past, John Brown, crawls into the building to sleep, and, by accident, sets it alight. It is left for Charley and Jo Portugais, the agnostic and the murderer, to rush into the flames and save the few treasures of the church; for Rosalie, to try to bear away the iron cross which has given and yet cost her so much. Rosalie is cut off in the flames, but Charley, at the risk of life, rescues her. As he lies unconscious, his shirt torn open, the brand of the cross on his breast meets the awe-stricken eyes of the watchers.

But the church is gone. There are no means to build another, no way—until the infidel shows them one! He talks to the crowd, with all the old power, the old convincing eloquence, of the church sacred by the burial of their beloved, by the christening of their children, the marriages which have given them happy homes, the sacraments which are to them the laws of their lives. Never have they heard any man speak as he speaks. At his bidding they open their little hoards; they give notes of hand which their seigneur discounts; every man gives to the building fund one-fortieth of his possessions. Day by day the offerings come in. The money is placed in the safe in the tailor's shop, and Charley and Jo Portugais keep guard over the treasure.

But the story of the fund has been noised abroad; criminals from Quebec follow on the track headed by Billy Wantage, another ghost from the past, and guided by John Brown. The gang attacks the tailor's shop, and its defenders save their sacred charge by giving up their lives. It is the hand of Billy Wantage that slays Beauty Steele.

So the infidel dies for the church; and the people whom he loves, and whom he has won from distrust to confidence, wait and pray outside the house, while their curé within strives, ere it be too late, to bring his field to harvest.

"Will you not come to the bosom of the Church for which you have given all?" he says, and Charley whispers, "Tell them so."

From the window the curé tells the glad news to the crowd below. "Oh, my dear people," he says, "God has given him to us at last." The end comes with Rosalie beside him. At the last, in delirium, he sees a tall, white form. "Who is it?" he asks.

"It is Death, my son," was the priest's low reply.

And then, for a moment, he becomes Charley Steele. He gropes for the eyeglass, and speaks to the imaginary figures, as he spoke at Côte Dorion two years ago.

"I beg your pardon. Have I—ever—been—introduced—to you?" he murmurs.

"At the hour of your birth, my son," is the curé's reply: and it is all done for ever.

Years later, the woman he had loved, who, faithful to his memory, had given her life to good works, could speak of him with the priest who also had loved him, and say of him with pride, "He was a great man."

Great, because she had made him so, because she, her love, had awakened the dead soul, had given him belief. Seeking inspiration in liquor, he could reach great heights, pinnacles of intellect, where humanity could find no place, where he was alone in a cold solitude, where evil was his good. Inspired by love, mind finding warmth in the kindled soul, he had at last sought his work among men, being a man, and found his reward where he had found his inspiration.

RALPH CONNOR

THE SKY PILOT

THIS is a very human story of west-central Canada,—the Province of Alberta, which from Montana on its southern border extends north about 750 miles and averages about 300 miles across from east to west. It lies in the great American wheat belt. Its two leading cities today are Edmonton and Calgary, the population of each of which is now approaching 100,000 while that of the Province is roughly 800,000. Its farmers include not a few Americans who sold their farms in the States at good prices and emigrated to newer fields. This story, however, goes back to the latter years of the last century, when cattle-raising, lumbering, and mining held sway. Its author, who wrote under the pen name of Ralph Connor, was a Presbyterian minister, Charles William Gordon, born in Glengarry, Ontario, in 1860. He was graduated from Toronto University, and then studied theology in Canada and took a post-graduate course at New College in Edinburgh, Scotland, the land of his ancestors. Before becoming pastor of St. Stephen's Church in Winnipeg in 1894, he served four years as a missionary at Banff, in the Canadian Rockies. Much of the present story is no doubt autobiographical, and otherwise based on his own experience and observations. All his books are marked by vivid description and delineation of character. Besides "The Sky Pilot" they include "Black Rock," "Beyond the Marshes," "Gwen's Canyon," "Ould Michael," "The Man from Glengarry," "Glengarry School Days," and "The Prospector." Mr. Connor died during 1937.

BECAUSE, first, I was a failure as a college student, and, second, because I had a cousin in the wilds of Alberta, I was permitted to try what good I could do for myself, and possibly for others, in that country; and so, having passed somewhat beyond the tenderfoot stage, I became the school-teacher at Swan Creek. At the time of my arrival, and for some time thereafter, the dominating social force of that neighborhood was the Noble Seven. Whatever this was originally, it had long outgrown its numerical limitation, and its present purpose was to give periodical opportunity for whisky-drinking and poker-playing. Liquor-selling is prohibited by law in Alberta, but one may make medicinal use of whisky in case of illness; and when the Noble Seven were about to meet, one or more, usually more, of its members fell conveniently ill, and enough whisky was brought in to cure all the disorders of the entire community.

As the meetings were usually held on the first day of the week, the occasion came to be known as Permit Sunday.

The most conspicuous member of the Noble Seven was "the Duke." We never learned his name. It was known, doubtless, to the Hon. Fred Ashley, of Ashley Ranch, for there the Duke was a frequent and familiar visitor; but neither the Hon. Fred nor his wife, Lady Charlotte, ever mentioned it. The Duke was the coolest gambler and the most reckless drinker and rider of them all. Next to him came a cross-grained Scotchman named Bruce. I put him next, not because he so much excelled the others in such matters as pertain to ranch life, as because he was so devoted to the Duke as to seem in some sort a part of him. Bruce submitted to no control save that of the Duke, and endured from him what others of us probably would have resented. He was a University of Edinburgh man, while Hi Kendal and Bronco Bill, the Hon. Fred's two cowboys, were as ignorant as they were untamed.

The rest of the company consisted of just such brave-hearted men, recognizing none but their own laws, as are to be found wherever cattle-raising is carried on in an unfenced country. It was to this country and this sort of men that Arthur Wellington Moore came. I was the first to know of his coming, because he announced his intentions with regard to Swan Creek in a letter addressed to the schoolmaster. It informed me that he purposed to do missionary work there, and a notice of the first meeting was enclosed, which he asked me to post in some conspicuous place. Moreover, he left it to me to find the place for holding the meeting, and I selected the parlor of the Stopping-Place, which in another community might have been called a hotel, the parlor likewise being the barroom of the establishment.

THE time appointed for the meeting fell on a Permit Sunday, so there was sure to be plenty of persons for the making of an audience; but a baseball game was scheduled for that day, and I appointed the time for religious services immediately after the game. The cowboys were disgusted when they read the announcement. They foresaw that their Sunday diversions would come in for criticism. Who invented the title I do not know, but before Moore arrived his real name was forgotten and he was known only as the "Sky Pilot." This was soon abbreviated to Pilot, and he was seldom addressed or alluded to by any other term. His appearance was as much against him as his vocation; for he was slight of figure, young to boyishness, and easily embarrassed.

The first service was enough to dampen the ardor of an older, more experienced missionary. Perhaps it was his very youth and innocence that made him persevere. The men were inclined to interrupt his remarks, and would have behaved much worse than they did if the Duke had not restrained them; but at the end of the sermon they took to arguing with the boy on the subject of his discourse, and Bruce, with his university training and his Scottish pugnacity, had the little Pilot sadly flustered. When the dreadful ordeal was over, he told me sadly that he could not understand it. Then his eyes flashed, and he declared that he knew he was right; men could not be men without Him, and he would not give up the attempt.

It seemed a hopeless, pitiable enthusiasm. The Noble Seven laughed at, ignored, or despised the Pilot, according to each man's temperament. One day a ball game was on, and Bronco Bill, the pitcher for one side, failed to appear. Hi, the catcher, was in despair when somebody ironically suggested putting the Pilot into the box. The Pilot was looking on, his face expressive of puzzlement, pain, and some sort of longing. Hi contemptuously asked him whether he could pitch, and when the Pilot admitted that he could, "a little," he was allowed to try. The result was a revelation to Swan Creek. Such pitching never had been dreamed of, much less seen, in that country. Nobody could hit the little man's curves effectively. He couldn't do very well at the bat himself, but, having got to first base on a short hit, he usually made home by clever running that completely outwitted the field side. Hi's nine won the game by thirty-seven to nine, or some such overwhelming score, and the Pilot scored relatively for his own standing.

But that, of course, did not make the men his religious followers; it simply established him higher in their respect for him as a man. They had already begun to like his enthusiastic way of telling a story, and he had made more than one heart ache by unexpectedly reviving past memories in singing a song; but it was not till Bruce's misadventure that he really won them.

BRUCE had been drinking more and more heavily. The Pilot, who blinked at nothing and feared nobody, had taken the Duke to task for not exercising his evident influence over the Scotchman to make him more temperate in his habits, and had been coldly rebuffed for his pains. The climax came at a meeting of the Seven, when Bruce, very drunk, began to shoot the lights out. The others hurried to places of safety, but the Duke tried to get Bruce's revolver away from him. In the scuffle the weapon went off, and an ugly hole was torn in the fleshy part of Bruce's arm. The wound alone was not dangerous, but Bruce's general condition made his case hopeless. He went into a delirium, and the Duke rode over to my shack to get me to take my bromides to the sufferer. I returned with him, and the Pilot accompanied us uninvited. When we arrived at Bruce's cabin, he was lying on his bed, singing a hymn, and punctuating the stanzas by shooting at snakes and demons. Neither the Duke nor I cared to enter while that fusillade was in progress, but the Pilot, in spite of our appeals, went to the door, waited until a shot had been fired, stepped in, and asked interestedly, "Did you get him?"

"No," said Bruce, "he dodged like the devil."

"Then we'll smoke him out," said the Pilot, and began to put wood in the stove. He talked cheerfully while he worked, assuring poor Bruce that wood smoke was the one thing demons feared, and in short order he had water boiling and tea made. It was an exhibition of courage and tact that completely won the Duke.

"There'll be no more Permit Sundays," he whispered, and he kept his word, with the exception that on the Permit Sundays that followed the Pilot occupied the chair.

All night long the Pilot stayed at Bruce's bed, singing to him, telling him stories of the old country, soothing his fears. The Duke galloped away for a doctor, who came and did all that a doctor could do. It was no more than to prolong the man's life a bit and make the end a little easier, perhaps, though to us who watched it was patent enough that Bruce's pathetic lucidity at the last was due more to the Pilot than to medicines.

The Duke stretched his hand across the dead man's bed and asked the Pilot to pardon him for his former rudeness. "Don't," was the Pilot's reply, almost sobbing, "I can't stand it."

ANOTHER conquest awaited the Pilot— the conquest of Gwen, much more difficult than that of Bruce and the Duke. Gwen was the only child of the first settler thereabout. Her mother had died when she was little more than a baby, and she had grown up unlettered and unrestrained, a daredevil on horseback, a tyrant in her home. Her father, Meredith, had no influence over her, though she loved him deeply, and, as in Bruce's case, the one human being she bowed to was the Duke. It was only the Duke's influence that induced her to submit to my instruction in the rudiments of learning, and even he could not prevail on her to see the Pilot. Old Meredith had well-nigh moved out of the country because of the Pilot's coming, and Gwen shared his prejudice.

But one day the Pilot tried to ford the Swan not far from the old settler's ranch. His horse was unequal to the task, and the Pilot would have drowned if Gwen had not used her lariat cleverly and brought him to shore. The plain, human man that he was, and that it took most of us so long to discover, was magnificently displayed in his behavior on that occasion. He was nettled, humiliated to be saved by a girl! She gleefully compelled him to admit that she had saved him, and he professed gratitude enough, but, with as much stubborn spirit as she herself had, he declared that he could make the ford, and what was more, he would; and what was more still, he tried to, in spite of Gwen's frightened warnings. His horse came ashore again after a furious struggle, and the Pilot was "all in," but Gwen brought him to and insisted that he come to the house for dry clothes, and to wait till the weather was more favorable.

The Pilot went with visible unwillingness. His purely human side, which, when you knew it, was as big as all outdoors, was crushed, but the spiritual side came to the rescue when once he was in the house and had dry clothes on. There was an old parlor organ there, unused since the death of Gwen's mother. The moment the Pilot saw it, he ran to it uninvited, sat down and went to singing songs to his own accompaniment. This was entertaining enough, but presently we were amazed to see the old settler crying. Gwen was indignant, but "Oft in the Stilly Night," as Meredith chokingly explained, was her mother's song. That opened the way to the bringing forth of her mother's Bible, and a long evening of reading followed, broken by Gwen's amazed questions and the Pilot's elucidations in quaint, easily comprehended language.

The Pilot thereafter was more welcome in the old settler's house than was the schoolmaster; but Gwen was as wilful and perverse with him as she had been with me, or with anybody. He tried to teach her of God's omnipotence, and she wouldn't have it. "I've always had my way, and I always will," she cried. He gravely assured her that the time would come when she could not do as she wished, and she flouted him. Her attitude was nothing short of a challenge to the Almighty.

Within a week the test came. She was saving the life of an Indian boy, riding with him before a stampede of cattle. Her horse, forced to the edge of the canyon, refused to obey the bridle and pounded on a bit of turf where the bank bit in. The turf collapsed. Gwen could not jump for safety because she clung to the Indian, and they all went down, thirty feet, in a heap. The Indian was the only one unhurt. Gwen received such injuries that, although she had the best of surgical attention, she never could walk or ride again.

We kept this sad certainty from her as long as we could, else she would have died; but she had to know some time, and when the truth was told her rebellion was at once pathetic and terrible. Not to ride again! Why, it was her life! She *would* ride! Nothing should prevent her from getting well. Helpless on her cot, suffering frightful physical agony, she defied God.

THE Pilot dreaded to go to her. We told him he was the one person who could help her, and he turned on us fiercely. We were all to blame. The fault was all ours. What! because of her physical wreck? No! No! Because her spirit was so proud and ungovernable. Had we not, everyone, from her father down, always yielded to her, always declared that her childish tyrannies were pretty? Had we not done every mortal thing fool men could do to make her proud and perverse?

In this frame of mind he set out, with apparent reluctance, to visit the sufferer. Our way lay through the canyon, Gwen's favorite spot in all the world she knew. She never could ride there again, and the Pilot groaned at thought of it. "What can I say to her?" he cried despairingly. What did he say? Why, the moment he was in her room he burst into an enthusiastic description of the canyon, just as he had then seen it. With his vivid word-painting he made her see it, till her eyes brightened and she forgot her pain. Day after day he called, and always his talk was of the beauties of the things she could not again see with her own eyes.

Naturally enough the time came when there was a reaction in Gwen's spirit. The old imperiousness broke forth, and she complained of God that He had afflicted her. She asked such questions about God's goodness as children will, such as most of us find unanswerable; but Gwen had more than a child's comprehension, and the Pilot more than most men's share of prophetic vision. He had brought her that day a handful of flowers plucked in her canyon. After the conventional answers to her questions had failed to satisfy her, he told of the time when there were no canyons, only broad prairies. The Master wished to see flowers growing there, and the prairies told him the winds carried away the seeds the birds dropped, so that none would grow. Then the Master smote the prairie and made a terrible gash in it, so that for long the earth groaned with pain; but the Swan poured its waters along the wound, and in time, when the birds dropped the flower-seeds, they fell where the winds could not reach them. They fell, too, on well-watered soil, and so grew and flourished in all their beauty. He likened the canyon flowers to gentleness, meekness, and self-control, and Gwen understood him.

"But there are only ragged rocks in my canyon," she said sadly.

"They will bloom some day," he assured her. "God will find them and we shall see them."

And we did, for Gwen gradually grew to be a marvel of patience—not one of your doleful, resigned-because-she-had-to-be kind, but a cheerful sufferer whom it delighted you to visit, for you saw how much pleasure your visit gave to the poor thing, and you derived as much if not more good from it yourself.

THE Pilot's hold was now more complete on the cowboys than on the professing church people of the country. They would do anything for him, as witness their endeavors to realize for him the Pilot's chief ambition. He wanted a church building, but the amount of money needed, about seven hundred dollars in addition to labor, seemed to be out of proportion to the resources of the district. The church people were backward, more than hesitant, and the Pilot was in despair. It was then that Bronco Bill took hold.

Bill's attitude toward Christianity may be inferred from his treatment of an agnostic who had strayed into one of the Pilot's meetings. He was a young chap, barely out of his tenderfoot days, and he ventured to argue with the Pilot as Bill and his friends had argued at the first meeting. Several times Bill called him to order, trying to make him see that he had struck a false note, and that doubters of the Pilot's doctrines should have the good taste to be silent. The young chap wouldn't take the hint, and Bill, exasperated beyond endurance, yanked him out of doors, where he proceeded to make him "walk turkey," up and down, back and forth, in the snow, until Mr. Agnostic, utterly exhausted, was ready to cry "Credo" to Calvinism, Presbyterianism, Methodism, or any other "ism" it might please Bill to nominate.

Bill took hold of the church building. He told the regular church people that if they would put up two hundred dollars he would see that the cowboys supplied the other five hundred dollars. This was regarded, even by his friends, as a bluff, and the church people paid no attention to it. But Bill meant business and knew what he was about. He got at the cowboys of the region just after they had been paid off, and in his uncouth but effective way started a subscription. This soon amounted to a good fraction of the total.

Then he had recourse to Gwen's assistance. She it was who had secretly inspired him to make the "bluff," and she was eager to contribute her share. As she never could ride again, she asked Bill to sell her pinto pony. He said he would try, and by a horse-trading trick he hocus-pocused the Hon. Fred Ashley into paying one hundred dollars for a forty-dollar animal. To this purchase-price he secretly added fifty dollars, so that Gwen's contribution was one hundred and fifty dollars. In such ways he raised the five hundred dollars, and the regular church people, out of pure shame, had to put up the rest.

After that Bill took financial charge of the work of construction, beating down the lumber-dealers, and contriving by all means, no matter how they smacked of sharp practice, to get the building up without wasting a dollar in profit to anybody. It was the Pilot's hope that the structure could be completed in time to open it for services on Christmas, and this was accomplished; but, most unhappily, the dear Pilot himself could not conduct the first service, or any other, in it.

W E HAD not noticed it until near the end, but as we looked back we could see that the Pilot had been failing for a long time. The rigorous life of the foothills had not hardened him. Some of us thrive on it; others are so constituted that it kills them. The Pilot sent word on Christmas morning, from Meredith's ranch, where he had been ill for many days, that he could not come to service, and that Bill must open the church for him. It was a task that, in the circumstances, might have abashed even a clergyman; Bill would have run from much less if it had not been the Pilot's bidding. There had to be a psalm and a prayer. We managed the psalm somehow, but the prayer! Bill asked

for volunteers, and nobody offering, he was compelled to attempt it himself.

It was not good English; it had not even Bill's ordinary fluency of utterance; in his very opening he told the Almighty that it was doubtless "persoomin' to try this sort o' business"; but it was comprehensible to us as a passionate appeal that the Pilot might be spared because we needed him; and if we understood it there can be no doubt that God felt the full force of it. At the end, Lady Charlotte timidly began the Lord's Prayer, and those who could do so joined in it. Then, after an awkward pause, Bill said abruptly, "This here church is open. Excuse me!" and rushed to his horse, that he might go to the bedside of the dying Pilot.

It was not in the Divine plan that the Pilot should preach in the church that had been built in the main by those whom he had conquered, but if ever a man preached unceasingly by his influence, Moore did, for I have seen evidence of it whenever I have met the men who were my companions during those two years in the foothills.

High Wisdom

REMEMBER first of all, virtuous reader, that it is high wisdom and great perfection thyself to know and then thyself to despise. Thou must know that thou hast nothing that good is of thyself, but of God. For the gifts of nature and all other temporal gifts of this world, which be lawfully and truly obtained, well considered, be come to thee by the infinite goodness and grace of God, and not of thyself. But in especial it is necessary for thee to know that God of his great grace hath made thee his image, having regard to thy memory, understanding, and free will, and that God is thy Maker and thou his wretched creature; and that thou art redeemed of God by the passion of Christ Jesus, and that God is thy helper, thy refuge, and thy deliverer from all evil, and to consider and know the goodly order which God of his infinite wisdom hath ordained thee to be ordered by. As to have these temporal goods for the necessity of thy body: the body and sensual appetites to be ordered by thy soul, thy soul to be ordered by reason and grace: by reason and grace to know thy duty to God and to thy neighbour, and by all common reason if thou keep this convenient order to God and his creatures, they shall keep their order to thee. But if thou break thine order to them, of likelihood they shall break their order to thee.

John Colet—"The Order of a Good Christian Man's Life"

Vicente Blasco Ibañez

THE FOUR HORSEMEN OF THE APOCALYPSE

Ever since they were first described in the Revelation of St. John the Divine, "The Four Horsemen of the Apocalypse"—Conquest, War, Famine and Death—have inspired painters and writers to create masterpieces. In 1918 the revolutionary Spanish author, Vicente Blasco Ibañez (1867-1928), took them for the title of his extraordinarily forceful novel about war in general and the first World War in particular, which has been translated into many languages and had an enormous sale. A famous movie was made from it in 1921, starring Rudolph Valentino.

The dark outline of the *Arc de Triomphe* stood forth clearly in the starry expanse. The avenues extended in all directions, a double file of lights. Those around the monument illuminated its gigantic bases and the feet of the sculptured groups. Further up, the vaulted spaces were so locked in shadow that they had the black density of ebony.

Upon passing under the Arch, which greatly intensified the echo of their footsteps, three men came to a standstill.

"How beautiful it is!" exclaimed Tchernoff who was seeing something beyond the shadows. "An entire civilization, loving peace and pleasure, has passed through here."

"This Arch," the Russian continued speaking to Desnoyers and Argensola, "is French within, with its names of battles and generals open to criticism. On the outside, it is the monument of the people who carried through the greatest revolution for liberty ever known. Here there is more than the glory and egoism of a great nation. All Europe is awake to new life, thanks to these Crusaders of Liberty. . . . Here in the *Arc de Triomphe* is the symbol of revolutionary France."

The Arch was even more, according to the Russian. It represented a great historical retaliation; the nations of the South, called the Latin races, replying, after many centuries, to the invasion of the northern tribes which had destroyed the Roman jurisdiction—the Mediterranean peoples spreading themselves as conquerors through the lands of the Teutonic barbarians. Retreating immediately, they had swept away the past like a tidal wave—the great surf depositing all that it contained.

"If *they* should return!" added Tchernoff with a look of uneasiness. "If they again should tread these stones! they will not be the soldiers only who march against Paris. At the tail of the armies come the maddened canteen-keepers, the Herr *Professors,* carrying at the side the little keg of wine with the powder which crazes the barbarian, the wine of *Kultur.* And in the vans come also an enormous load of scientific savagery, a new philosophy which glorifies Force as a principle and sanctifier of everything, denies liberty, suppresses the weak and places the entire world under the charge of a minority chosen by God, just because it possesses the surest and most rapid methods of slaughter. Humanity may well tremble for the future if again resounds under this archway the tramp of boots following a march of Wagner.

They left the Arch, following the *avenue Victor Hugo.* Tchernoff walking along in dogged silence as though the vision of this imaginary procession had overwhelmed him. Suddenly he continued aloud the course of his reflections.

"And if they should enter, what does it matter? . . . On that account, the course of Right will not die. It suffers eclipses, but is born again; it may be ignored and trampled under foot, but it does not, therefore, cease to exist, and all good souls recognize it as the only rule of life. A nation of madmen wishes to place Might upon the pedestal that others have raised to Right. Useless endeavor! The eternal hope of mankind will ever be the increasing power of more liberty, more brotherliness, more justice."

THE Russian appeared to calm himself with this statement. He and his friends spoke of the spectacle which Paris was presenting in its preparation for war. Tchernoff bemoaned the great suffering produced by the catastrophe, the thousands and thousands of domestic tragedies that were unrolling at that moment.

The houses appeared wrapped in slumber, but behind the closed windows might be surmised the insomnia of the reddened eyes, the sighs from hearts anguished by the threatened danger, the tremulous agility of the hands preparing the war outfit, perhaps the last loving greetings exchanged without pleasure, with kisses ending in sobs.

Tchernoff thought of his neighbors, the husband and wife who occupied the other interior apartment behind the studio. There had begun to develop on the other side of the wall a regulation drama—a repetition of hundreds of others, all taking place at the same time.

"She is German and he is French. Now he has gone to join his regiment. Last night I could hardly sleep. I heard the lamentations through the thin wall partition, the steady, desperate weeping of an abandoned child, and the voice of a man who was vainly trying to quiet her! For the unhappy creature is going to be a mother," he said sadly.

"Now she is thinking all the time of her nationality which is separating her from her husband; she is thinking of the concentration camp to which they will take her with her compatriots. She is fearful of being abandoned in the enemy's country obliged to defend itself against the attack of her own country. . . . And all this when she is about to become a mother. What miseries!"

The three reached the *rue de la Pompe* and on entering the house, Tchernoff began to take leave of his companions; but Desnoyers wished to prolong the conversation. The conversation with the Russian interested him, so they all went up in the elevator together. Argensola suggested that this would be a good opportunity to uncork one of the many bottles which he was keeping in the kitchen.

Tchernoff drank two glasses, testifying to the excellence of the liquid by smacking his lips. The three were silent with the wondering and thoughtful silence which the grandeur of the night imposes.

"I wonder if any star knows that Bismarck ever existed!" Tchernoff muttered. "I wonder if the planets are aware of the divine mission of the German nation!"

The Four Horsemen

TCHERNOFF continued drinking, but with a distracted air, his eyes fixed on the red cloud that floated over the roofs. Suddenly he leaped from thought to word without any forewarning, continuing aloud the course of his reasoning.

. . . "And when the sun arises in a few hours, the world will see coursing through its fields the four horsemen, enemies of mankind. . . . Already their wild steeds are pawing the ground with impatience; already the ill-omened riders have come together and are exchanging the last words before leaping into the saddle."

"What horseman are these?" asked Argensola.

"Those which go before the Beast."

The two friends thought this reply as unintelligible as the preceding words. Desnoyers again said mentally, "He is drunk," but his curiosity forced him to ask, "What beast is that?"

"That of the Apocalypse."

Tchernoff described the Apocalyptic beast rising from the depths of the sea. He was like a leopard, his feet like those of a bear, his mouth like the snout of a lion. He had seven heads and ten horns. And upon the horns were ten crowns, and upon each of his heads the name of a blasphemy. Blasphemies against humanity, against justice, against all that makes life sweet and bearable. "Might is superior to Right!" . . . "The weak should not exist." . . . "Be harsh in order to be great." . . . And the Beast in all its hideousness was attempting to govern the world and make mankind render him homage!

"But the four horsemen?" persisted Desnoyers.

Tchernoff began to describe the four scourges of the earth exactly as though he were seeing them:

"The first horseman appears on a white horse. In his hand he carries a bow, and a crown is given unto him. He is Conquest, according to some, the Plague according to others. The second rider dashes out brandishing over his head an enormous sword. He is War. Peace flees from the world before his furious gallop; humanity is going to be exterminated. A black horse appears. He who mounts it holds in his hand a scale in order to weigh the maintenance of mankind. He is Famine. And there appears a pale-colored horse. His rider is

"Suddenly something happened which startled the three men from their contemplative admiration—a dreadful sound."

From the movie starring Rudolph Valentino.
Courtesy of the Museum of Modern Art.

called Death, and power is given him to destroy with the sword and with hunger and with death, and with the beasts of the earth.

"The four horsemen are beginning their mad, desolating course over the heads of terrified humanity.

"Poor Humanity, crazed with fear, is fleeing in all directions on hearing the thundering pace of the Plague, War, Hunger and Death. Men and women, young and old, are knocking each other down and falling to the ground overwhelmed by terror, astonishment and desperation. And the white horse, the red, the black and the pale, are crushing all with their relentless, iron tread—the athletic man is hearing the crashing of his broken ribs, the nursing babe is writhing at its mother's breast, and the aged and feeble are closing their eyes forever with a childlike sob.

"God is asleep, forgetting the world," continued the Russian. "It will be a long time before he awakes, and while he sleeps the four feudal horsemen of the Beast will course through the land as its only lords."

TCHERNOFF was overpowered by the intensity of his dramatic vision. Springing from his seat, he paced up and down with great strides; but his picture of the fourfold catastrophe revealed by the gloomy poet's trance seemed to him very weak indeed. A great painter had given corporeal form to these terrible dreams.

"I have a book," he murmured, "a rare book." . . .

Tchernoff placed his precious book under the light. It was a volume printed in 1511, with Latin text and engravings.

Desnoyers read the title, "The Apocalypse Illustrated." The engravings were by Albert Dürer, a youthful effort, when the master was only twenty-seven years old. The three were fascinated by the picture portraying the wild career of the Apocalyptic horsemen. The quadruple scourge, on fantastic mounts, seemed to be precipitating itself with a realistic sweep, crushing panic-stricken humanity.

Suddenly something happened which startled the three men from their contemplative admiration—something unusual, indefinable, a dreadful sound which seemed to enter directly into their brains without passing through their ears—a clutch at the heart.

Through the open door, a cry of alarm came up from the patio. With a common impulse, the three ran to the interior window. Looking down, they could see lights below, people moving around a form stretched out on the tiled floor.

"She has killed herself," said a voice which seemed to come up from a well. "The German woman has committed suicide."

The Russian was shaking his head with a fatalistic expression. The unhappy woman had not taken the death-leap of her own accord. Someone had intensified her desperation, someone had pushed her. . . . The horsemen! The four horsemen of the Apocalypse! . . . Already they were in the saddle! Already they were beginning their merciless gallop of destruction!

The blind forces of evil were about to be let loose throughout the world.

The agony of humanity, under the brutal sweep of the four horsemen, was already begun!

New Life

JULIO DESNOYERS was hoping to continue his life as though nothing had happened. It was enough for him that Marguerite should continue faithful to their past. Together they would see events slipping by them with the cruel luxuriousness of those who, from an inaccessible height, contemplate a flood without the slightest risk to themselves.

This selfish attitude had also become habitual to Argensola.

"Let us be neutral," the Bohemian would say. "Neutrality does not necessarily mean indifference. Let us enjoy the great spectacle, since nothing like it will ever happen again in our lifetime."

Meanwhile Julio was continuing the course of his own reflections. Marguerite! . . . She had come back at last.

Her first care was to explain to Julio the conservatism of her tailored suit, the absence of jewels in the adornment of her person. "The war, my dear! Now it is the *chic* thing to adapt oneself to the depressing conditions, to be frugal and inconspicuous like soldiers."

Julio noticed a persistent absent-mindedness about her. It seemed as though her spirit, abandoning her body, was wandering to far-away places. Her eyes were looking at him, but she seldom saw him. She would speak very slowly, as though wishing to weigh every word, fearful of betraying some secret. This spiritual alienation did not, however, prevent her slipping bodily along the smooth path of custom, although afterwards she would seem to feel a vague remorse. "I wonder if it is right to do this! . . . Is it not wrong to live like this when so many sorrows are falling on the world?" Julio hushed her scruples with:

"But if we are going to marry as soon as possible! . . . If we are already the same as husband and wife!"

She replied with a gesture of strangeness and dismay. To marry! . . . Ten days ago she had had no other wish. Now the possibility of marriage was recurring less and less in her thoughts. Why think about such remote and uncertain events? More immediate things were occupying her mind.

At the station entrance, while she was kissing her brother for the last time, she had an encounter, a great surprise. "He" had approached, also clad as an artillery officer.

Julio shot her a questioning look. Who was "he"? He suspected, but feigned ignorance, as though fearing to learn the truth.

"Laurier," she replied laconically, "my former husband."

The lover displayed a cruel irony. It was a cowardly thing to ridicule this man who had responded to the call of duty. He recognized his vileness, but a malign and irresistible instinct made him keep on with his sneers in order to discredit the man before Marguerite. Laurier a soldier!—He must cut a pretty figure dressed in uniform!

"No . . . no, he didn't look so bad. Quite the contrary. Perhaps it was the uniform, perhaps it was his sadness at going away alone, completely alone, without a single hand to clasp his. I didn't recognize him at first. Seeing my brother, he started toward us; but then when he saw me, he went his own way. . . . Poor man! I feel sorry for him!"

Her feminine instinct must have told her that she was talking too much, and she cut her chatter suddenly short. The same instinct warned her that Julio's countenance was growing more and more saturnine, and his mouth taking a very bitter curve. She wanted to console him and added:

"What luck that you are a foreigner and will not have to go to the war! How horrible it would be for me to lose you!" . . .

This did not please his amorous egoism—to be placed apart from the rest as a delicate and fragile being only fit for feminine adoration. He preferred to inspire the envy that she had felt on beholding her brother decked out in his warlike accoutrement. It seemed to him that something was coming between him and Marguerite that would never disappear, that would go on expanding, repelling them in contrary directions. . . .

War was obliterating all her winning vanities. She was no longer fluttering about in bird-like fashion. Her feet were treading the earth with resolute firmness, calm and secure in the new strength which was developing within. When one of his caresses would remind her that she was a woman, she would always say the same thing,

"What luck that you are a foreigner! . . . What happiness to know that you do not have to go to war!"

"Your reign is over," laughed Argensola. "The fact that you are a handsome fellow doesn't help you one bit nowadays. In a uniform and with a cross on my breast, I could soon get the best of you in a rival love affair. Before a uniform, they feel the humble and servile enthusiasm of the female of the lower animals before the crests, foretops and gay plumes of the fighting males.

Look out, master! . . . We shall have to follow the new course of events or resign ourselves to everlasting obscurity."

And Desnoyers agreed that truly they were two beings on the other side of the river of life which at one bound had changed its course. There was no longer any place in the new existence for Argensola, that poor painter of souls, nor for him, the hero of a frivolous life.

Unfulfilled Obligations

UPON being convinced that war really was inevitable, Julio's father was filled with amazement. Humanity had gone crazy. Capital was master of the world, and war was going to wipe it out. In its turn, war would be wiped out in a few months' time through lack of funds to sustain it. His soul of a business man revolted before the hundreds of thousands of millions that this foolhardy event was going to convert into smoke and slaughter.

For him war meant disaster writ large. He had no faith in his country. France's day had passed. Now the victors were of the Northern peoples, and especially that Germany which he had seen so close, admiring with a certain terror its discipline and its rigorous organization.

The former working-man felt the conservative and selfish instinct of all those who have amassed millions. He scorned political ideals, but through class interest he had of late years accepted the declarations against the scandals of the government. What could a corrupt and disorganized Republic do against the solidest and strongest empire in the world? . . .

"We are going to our deaths," he said to himself. "Worse than '70! . . . We are going to see horrible things!"

The good order and enthusiasm with which the French responded to their country's call and transformed themselves into soldiers were most astonishing to him. This moral shock made his national faith begin to revive.

Finally, against his will, Desnoyers was drawn into the whirlpool of enthusiasm and emotion. Like everyone around him, he lived minutes that were hours, and hours that were years. Events kept on overlapping each other; within a week the world seemed to have made up for its long period of peace.

The old man fairly lived in the street, attracted by the spectacle of the multitude of civilians saluting the multitude of uniformed men departing for the seat of war.

All his past was looming up before his eyes with such extraordinary clearness that it seemed as though until then his mind must have been in hopeless confusion.

The threatened land of France was his native country. Many generations of Desnoyers had prepared for his advent into life by struggling with the land and defending it that he might be born into a free family and fireside. . . . And when his turn had come for continuing this effort, when his time had arrived in the rosary of generations—he had fled like a debtor evading payment! . . . Ah, miserable coward! The material success of his life, the riches acquired in the Argentine, were comparatively of no importance. There are failures that millions cannot blot out. The uneasiness of his conscience was proving it now. Proof, too, was in the envy and respect inspired by the poor men marching to meet death with others equally humble.

IN HIS dreams, he was constantly feeling the anguish of an upright and desperate man who wishes to meet his obligations.

Pay! . . . and how? It was now very late. For a moment the heroic resolution came into his head of offering himself as a volunteer. But he was over seventy, and only the young make good soldiers. No; it was too late. He could not even leave an illustrious name that might serve as an example.

Instinctively he glanced behind. He was not alone in the world; he had a son who could assume his father's debt . . . but that hope only lasted a minute. Julio was not French; he belonged to another people; half of his blood was from the Argentine. Besides, how could the boy be expected to feel as he did? Would he even understand if his father should explain it to him? . . . It was useless to expect anything from this lady-killing, dancing clown. What was his son doing? . . . Undoubtedly continuing his gay and useless life. Such men only existed for their own selfish folly.

A sub-lieutenant of the Reserves, with his bag on his shoulder, was accompanied by his father toward the file of policemen keeping the crowds back. Desnoyers saw in the young officer a certain resemblance to his son. The father was wearing in his lapel the black and green ribbon of 1870—a decoration which always filled Desnoyers with remorse. He was tall and gaunt, but was still trying to hold himself erect, with a heavy frown. He wanted to show himself fierce, inhuman, in order to hide his emotion.

"Good-bye, my boy! Do your best."

"Good-bye, father."

They did not clasp hands, and each was avoiding looking at the other. The official was smiling like an automaton. The father turned his back brusquely, and threading his way through the throng, entered a café, where for some time he needed the most retired seat in the darkest corner to hide his emotion.

And Don Marcelo envied his grief.

The Slacker

ONE morning Julio received a note from Marguerite—only two lines scrawled in great haste. She was leaving, starting immediately, accompanied by her mother. Adieu! . . . and nothing more. The panic had caused many love-affairs to be forgotten, had broken off long intimacies, but Marguerite's temperament was above such incoherencies from mere flight. Julio felt that her terseness was very ominous. Why not mention the place to which she was going? . . .

Why remain longer in Paris? His family was away. Now Marguerite's mysterious flight was leaving him entirely alone, in a solitude that was filling him with remorse.

That afternoon, when strolling through the boulevards, he had stumbled across an acquaintance in the fencing club which he used to frequent. This was the first time they had met since the beginning of the war, and they ran over the list of their companions in the army.

Desnoyers' inquiries were answered by the older man. So-and-so? . . . He had been wounded in Lorraine and was now in a hospital in the South. Another friend? . . . Dead in the Vosges. Another? . . . Disappeared at Charleroi. And thus had continued the heroic and mournful roll-call. The others were still living, doing brave things.

The members of foreign birth, young Poles, English residents in Paris and South Americans, had finally enlisted as volunteers. The club might well be proud of its young men who had practised arms in times of peace, for now they were all jeopardizing their existence at the front. Desnoyers turned his face away as though he feared to meet in the eyes of his friend, an ironical and questioning expression. Why had he not gone with the others to defend the land in which he was living? . . .

"To-morrow I will go," repeated Julio, depressed by this recollection.

But he went toward the South like all those who were fleeing from the war.

For four days the distracted lover lived in Bordeaux, stunned and bewildered by the agitation of a provincial city suddenly converted into a capital. The hotels were overcrowded, many notables contenting themselves with servants' quarters. There was not a vacant seat in the cafés; the sidewalks could not accommodate the extraordinary assemblage.

All his investigations proved fruitless. The friends whom he encountered in the fugitive crowd were thinking only of their öwn affairs. Finally, a friend of his days of glory, whose former elegance was now attired in the uniform of a nurse, gave him some vague information. "The little *Madame* Laurier? . . . I remember hearing that she was living at Lourdes." . . . Julio needed no more than this to continue his journey. To Lourdes!

Lourdes, formerly visited by the hopeful, Catholic sick, was now invaded by a crowd no less dolorous but clad in carnival colors. The first encounters in Belgium and in the East, a mere half-dozen battles, had been enough to produce physical wrecks still showing a manly nobility in spite of the most horrible outrages. Their organisms, struggling so tenaciously to regain their hold on life, bringing their reviving energies out into the sunlight, represented but the most minute part of the number mowed down by the scythe of Death.

Back of them were thousands and thousands of comrades groaning on hospital beds from which they would probably never rise. Thousands and thousands were hidden forever in the bosom of the Earth moistened by their death agony—fatal land which, upon receiving a hail of projectiles, brought forth a harvest of bristling crosses!

War now showed itself to Desnoyers with all its cruel hideousness. He had been accustomed to speak of it heretofore as those in robust health speak of death, knowing that it exists and is horrible, but seeing it afar off . . . so far off that it arouses no real emotion.

The explosions of the shells were accompanying their destructive brutality with a ferocious mockery, grotesquely disfiguring the human body. He saw wounded objects just beginning to recover their vital force who were but rough skeletons of men, frightful caricatures, human rags, saved from the tomb by the audacities of science—trunks with heads which were dragged along on wheeled platforms; fragments of skulls whose brains were throbbing under an artificial cap; beings without arms and without legs, resting in the bottom of little wagons, like bits of plaster models or scraps from the dissecting room; faces without noses that looked like skulls with great, black nasal openings.

And these half-men were talking, smoking, laughing, satisfied to see the sky, to feel the caress of the sun, to have come back to life, dominated by that sovereign desire to live which trustingly forgets present misery in the confident hope of something better.

So strongly was Julio impressed that for a little while he forgot the purpose which had brought him thither. . . . If those who provoke war from diplomatic chambers or from the tables of the Military Staff could but see it—not in the field of battle fired with the enthusiasm which prejudices judgments—but in cold blood, as it is seen in the hospitals and cemeteries, in the wrecks left in its trail! . . .

Desnoyers wandered a long time around the basilica where, in the shadow of the trees, were long rows of wheeled chairs occupied by the wounded. Officers and soldiers rested many hours in the blue shade, watching their comrades who were able to use their legs. The sacred grotto was resplendent with the lights from hundreds of candles. Devout crowds were kneeling in the open air, fixing their eyes in supplication on the sacred stones whilst their thoughts were flying far away to the fields of battle, making their petiions with that confidence in divinity which accompanies every distress.

Near him, in the diaphanous white of a guardian angel, was a nurse. Poor blind man! . . . Desnoyers was passing on when a quick movement on the part of the white-clad woman, an evident desire to escape notice, to hide her face by looking at the plants, attracted his attention. He was slow in recognizing her. Her face was pale and sad. There wasn't a trace left in it of the old vanities that used to give it its childish, doll-like beauty. In the depths of those great, dark-circled eyes life seemed to be reflected in new forms. . . . Marguerite!

They stared at one another for a long while, as though hypnotized with surprise. She looked alarmed when Desnoyers advanced a step toward her. Fear that he might come near her, made her go toward him.

She led the way to a side path from which she could see the blind man confided to her care. They stood motionless, face to face. Desnoyers wished to say many things; many . . . but he hesitated, not knowing how to frame his complaints, his pleadings, his endearments. Far above all these thoughts towered one, fatal, dominant and wrathful.

"Who is that man?"

"It is Laurier. . . . It is my husband."

Laurier! . . . Julio looked doubtfully and for a long time at the soldier before he could be convinced. That blind officer motionless on the bench, that figure of heroic grief, was Laurier! . . .

He spoke with the fury of a lover who discovers an infidelity. "And for this thing you have run away without warning, without a word! . . . You have abandoned me in order to go in search of him. . . . Tell me, why did you come? . . . Why did you come?" . . .

"I came because it was my duty."

Then she spoke like a mother who takes advantage of a parenthesis of surprise in an irascible child's temper, in order to counsel self-control, and explained how it had all happened. She had received the news of Laurier's wounding just as she and her mother were preparing to leave Paris. She had not hesitated an instant; her duty was to hasten to the aid of this man. She had been doing a great deal of thinking in the last few weeks; the war had made her ponder much on the values in life. Her eyes had been getting glimpses of new horizons; our destiny is not mere pleasure and selfish satisfaction; we ought to take our part in pain and sacrifice.

She had wanted to work for her country, to share the general stress, to serve as other women did; and since she was disposed to devote herself to strangers, was it not natural that she should prefer to help this man whom she had so greatly wronged? . . .

"How you love him!" exclaimed Julio.

Fearing that they might be overheard and in order to keep him at a distance, she had been speaking as though to a friend. But her lover's sadness broke down her reserve.

"No, I love you. . . . I shall always love you. But I love him, too."

She said it with a look that seemed to implore pardon, with the sad sincerity of one who has given up lying and weeps in foreseeing the injury that the truth must inflict.

"I am here where I ought to be. I need his forgiveness, but if he does not pardon me, I shall stay with him just the same. . . . There are moments when I wish that he may never recover his sight, so that he may always need me, so that I may pass my life at his side, sacrificing everything for him."

"And I?" said Desnoyers.

Marguerite looked at him with clouded eyes as though she were just wakening. "It is better for us to part. Go your way, alone and untrammelled. Leave me; you will meet other women who will make you more happy than I. Yours is the temperament that finds new pleasures at every step."

SHE stood firmly to her decision. Her voice was calm, but back of it trembled the emotion of a last farewell to a joy which was going from her forever. The man would be loved by others . . . and she was giving him up! . . . But the noble sadness of the sacrifice restored her courage. Only by this renunciation could she expiate her sins.

Julio dropped his eyes, vanquished and perplexed. As though he had suddenly found a solution which was reviving his courage, Desnoyers said:

"Listen, Marguerite; I can read your soul. You love this man, and you do well. He is superior to me, and women are always attracted by superiority. . . . I am a coward. Yes, do not protest, I am a coward with all my youth, with all my strength. Why should you not have been impressed by the conduct of this man! . . . But I will atone for past wrongs. This country is yours, Marguerite; I will fight for it. Do not say no. . . ."

"No, no!" interrupted Marguerite in an anguished tone. "You, no! One is enough. . . . How horrible! You, too, wounded, mutilated forever, perhaps dead! . . . No, you must live."

Then in a last desperate attempt at explanation she again repeated what she had said at the beginning of their interview. She loved Julio . . . and she loved her husband. They were different kinds of love. She could not say which was the stronger, but misfortune was forcing her to choose between the two, and she was accepting the most difficult, the one demanding the greatest sacrifices. Hopeless words came between the two like an obstacle momentarily increasing in size, impelling them in opposite directions. Why prolong the painful interview? . . . Marguerite showed the ready and energetic decision of a woman who wishes to bring a scene to a close. "Good-bye!" She must go to her patient.

She went away without looking at him, and Desnoyers instinctively went in the opposite direction. As he became more self-controlled and turned to look at her again, he saw her moving on and giving her arm to the blind man, without once turning her head.

Desnoyers

TWO mornings later, the Desnoyers' door bell rang. A visitor!

There came toward the old man a soldier—a little soldier of the infantry, timid, with his kepis in his hand, stuttering excuses in Spanish:—

"I knew that you were here . . . I come to . . ."

That voice? . . . Dragging him from the dark hallway, Don Marcelo conducted him to the balcony. . . . How handsome he looked! . . . The kepis was red, but darkened with wear; the cloak, too large, was torn and darned; the great shoes had a strong smell of leather. Yet never had his son appeared to him so elegant, so distinguished-looking as now, fitted out in these rough ready-made clothes.

"You! . . . You! . . ."

The father embraced him convulsively, crying like a child.

He had always hoped that they would finally understand each other. His blood was coursing through the boy's veins; he was good, with no other defect than a certain obstinacy. He was excusing him now for all the past, blaming himself for a great part of it. He had been too hard.

When the delighted father was finally able to control his emotion, his eyes, still filled with tears, glowed with a malignant light. A spasm of hatred furrowed his face.

"Go," he said simply. "You do not know what war is; I have just come from it; I have seen it close by. This is not a war like other wars, with rational enemies; it is a hunt of wild beasts. . . . Shoot without a scruple against them all. . . . Every one that you overcome rids humanity of a dangerous menace."

He hesitated a few seconds, and then added with tragic calm:

"Perhaps you may encounter familiar faces. Family ties are not always formed to our tastes. Men of your blood are on the other side. If you see any one of them . . . do not hesitate. Shoot! He is your enemy. Kill him! . . . Kill him!"

In the Studio

JULIO was a sergeant after having been only two months in the campaign. The captain of his company and the other officials of the regiment belonged to the fencing club in which he had had so many triumphs.

"What a career!" Argensola enthused. "He is one of those who in youth reach the highest ranks, like the Generals of the Revolution. . . . And what wonders he has accomplished!"

Julio had been the first to attack many trenches and had saved many of his comrades by means of the blows from his bayonet and hand to hand encounters. Whenever his superior officers needed a reliable man, they invariably said, "Let Sergeant Desnoyers be called!"

Argensola rattled off all this as though he had witnessed it, as if he had just come from the seat of war, making Don Marcelo tremble and pour forth tears of joy mingled with fear over the glories and dangers of his son. That Argensola certainly possessed the gift of affecting his hearers by the realism with which he told his stories! His friend's father had aged greatly since the beginning of the war. Argensola, who had always dodged him in the street and had thrilled with fear when sneaking up the stairway in the avenue home, now felt a sudden confidence. The transformed old man was beaming on him like a comrade, and making excuses to justify his visit.

He had wished to see his son's home. The letters from Julio were not enough; he needed to see his old abode, to be on familiar terms with the objects which had surrounded him, to breathe the same air, to chat with the young man who was his boon companion.

His fatherly glance now included Argensola. . . . "A very interesting fellow, that Argensola!" And as he thought this, he forgot completely that, without knowing him, he had been accustomed to refer to him as "shameless," just because he was sharing his son's prodigal life.

And he actually had to make an effort to recall the dignity of his years, in order not to ask Argensola to present him to the fair fugitives whose presence he suspected in the interior rooms. Perhaps they had been his boy's friends, too. They represented a part of his past, anyway, and that was enough to make him presume that they had great charms which made them interesting.

He was beginning to hate the ostentatious splendors of his home on the *avenue Victor Hugo*. He now recalled without a regretful pang, the destruction of the castle. No, he was far better off there . . . and "there" was always the studio of Julio. The painter described Julio's life before the war as an existence dedicated completely to art. The father ignored the inexactitude of such words, and gratefully accepted the lie as a proof of friendship. Argensola was such a clever comrade, never, in his loftiest verbal flights, making the slightest reference to Madame Laurier.

A NEW talker took part in these conversations. Desnoyers had become acquainted with the Russian neighbor of whom Argensola had so frequently spoken. Since this odd personage had also known his son, that was enough to make Tchernoff arouse his interest.

In normal times, he would have kept him at a distance. The millionaire was a great believer in law and order. He abominated revolutionists, with the instinctive fear of all the rich who have built up a fortune and remember their humble beginnings. Tchernoff's socialism and nationality brought vividly to his mind a series of feverish images—bombs, daggers, stabbings, deserved expiations on the gallows, and exile to Siberia. No, he was not desirable as a friend. . . .

But the gentleness of Tchernoff, his original ideas, his incoherencies of thought, bounding from reflection to word without any preparation, finally won Don Marcelo so completely over that he formed the habit of consulting him about all his doubts.

What was most irritating Tchernoff was the moral lesson born of this situation which had ended by overwhelming the world—the glorification of power, the sanctification of success, the triumph of materialism, the respect for the accomplished fact, the mockery of the noblest sentiments as though they were merely sonorous and absurd phrases, the reversal of moral values . . . a philosophy of bandits which pretended to be the last word of progress, and was no more than a return to despotism, violence, and the barbarity of the most primitive epochs of history.

Desnoyers once recalled the four horsemen, and all that Argensola had told him before presenting him to the Russian.

"Blood!" he shouted jubilantly. "All the sky seems to be blood-red. . . . It is the apocalyptic beast who has received his death-wound. Soon we shall see him die."

Tchernoff smiled, a melancholy smile.

"No; the beast does not die. It is the eternal companion of man. It hides, spouting blood, forty . . . sixty . . . a hundred years, but eventually it reappears. All that we can hope is that its wound may be long and deep, that it may remain hidden so long that the generation that now remembers it may never see it again."

15 Days Leave

JULIO was wounded. But at the same time that this news came, lamentably delayed, he found that Julio's wound was almost healed and, thanks to the wire-pulling of the senator, he was coming to pass a fortnight with his family while convalescing.

Don Marcelo gloated over the fifteen days of satisfaction ahead of him. Sub-Lieutenant Desnoyers found it impossible to go out alone. Scarcely had Julio put it on his head before his sire appeared, also with hat and cane, ready to sally forth.

"Will you permit me to accompany you? . . . I will not bother you."

This would be said so humbly, with such an evident desire to have his request granted, that his son had not the heart to refuse him. In order to take a walk with Argensola, he had to scurry down the back stairs, or resort to other schoolboy tricks.

Never had the elder Desnoyers promenaded the streets of Paris with such solid satisfaction as by the side of this muscular youth in his gloriously worn cloak, on whose breast were glistening his two decorations—the cross of war and the military medal. He was a hero, and this hero was his son.

All the other military men that they met, no matter how many bands and crosses they displayed, appeared to the doting father mere embusqués, unworthy of comparison with his Julio. . . . The wounded men who got out of the coaches by the aid of staffs and crutches inspired him with the greatest pity. Poor fellows! . . . They did bear the charmed life of his son. No one would kill him!"

Julio was content. For the first time in his life he was tasting the delights of knowing that he was a useful being, that he was good for something, that his passing through the world would not be fruitless. He recalled with pity that Desnoyers who had not known how to occupy his empty life, and had filled it with every kind of frivolity. Now he had obligations that were taxing all his powers; he was collaborating in the formation of a future.

"I am content," he repeated with conviction.

His father believed him, yet he fancied that, in a corner of that frank glance, he detected something sorrowful, a memory of a past which perhaps often forced its way among his present emotions. There flitted through his mind the lovely figure of Madame Laurier. Her charm was, doubtless, still haunting his son.

ONE evening as Don Marcelo was accompanying his son down the *Champs Elysées,* he started at recognizing a lady approaching from the opposite direction. It was Madame Laurier. . . . Would she recognize Julio? He noted that the youth turned pale and began looking at the other people with feigned interest. She continued straight ahead, erect, unseeing. He turned his head involuntarily to look after her, but had to avert his inquisitive glance immediately. He had surprised Marguerite motionless behind them, pallid with surprise, and fixing her gaze earnestly on the soldier who was separating himself from her. Don Marcelo read in here eyes admiration, love, all of the past that was suddenly surging up in her memory.

Poor woman! . . . He felt for her a paternal affection as though she were the wife of Julio. He knew that Marguerite was going to become a mother, and the old man, without taking into account the reconciliation nor the passage of time, felt as much moved at the thought of this approaching maternity as though the child were going to be Julio's.

Meanwhile Julio was marching right on, without turning his head, without being conscious of the burning gaze fixed upon him, colorless, but humming a tune to hide his emotion. He always believed that Marguerite had passed near him without recognizing him, since his father did not betray her.

"No One Will Kill Him"

WHEN he least expected it, Don Marcelo found himself at the end of that delightful and proud existence which his son's presence had brought him. The fortnight had flown by so swiftly! The sub-lieutenant had returned to his post, and all the family, after this period of reality, had had to fall back on the fond illusions of hope, watching again for the arrival of his letters, making conjectures about the silence of the absent one, sending him packet after packet of everything that the market was offering for the soldiery —for the most part, useless and absurd things.

The mother became very despondent. Julio's visit home but made her feel his absence with greater intensity. Seeing him, hearing those tales of death that her husband was so fond of repeating, made her realize all the more clearly the dangers constantly surrounding her son. Fatality appeared to be warning her with funereal presentiments.

"They are going to kill him," she kept saying to Desnoyers. "That wound was a forewarning from heaven."

Desnoyers waxed very indignant over his wife's low spirits, retorting:

"But I tell you that Nobody will kill Julio! . . . He is my son. In my youth I, too, passed through great dangers. They wounded me, too, in the wars in the other world, and nevertheless, here I am at a ripe old age."

Events seemed to reinforce his blind faith. Calamities were raining around the family and saddening his relatives, yet not one grazed the intrepid sub-lieutenant who was persisting in his daring deeds with the heroic nerve of a musketeer.

On entering his house, he was met in the hall by his wife, who told him that a senator was waiting for him.

"Very good!" he responded gaily.

His good wife was uneasy. She had felt alarmed without knowing exactly why at the senator's solemn appearance;

with that feminine instinct which perforates all masculine precautions, she surmised some hidden mission.

Moved by an irresistible impulse, she hovered near the closed door, hoping to hear something definite. Her wait was not long.

Suddenly a cry . . . a groan . . . the groan that can come only from a body from which all vitality is escaping.

From the luxurious rooms came forth the world-old cry, always the same from the humblest home to the highest and loneliest:—

"Oh, Julio! . . . Oh, my son, my son!" . . .

The Burial Fields

THE automobile was going slowly forward under the colorless sky of a winter morning.

"How many are dead!" sighed Don Marcelo's voice from the automobile.

Tombs . . . tombs on all sides! The white locusts of death were swarming over the entire countryside. The soil seemed to be clamoring, and its words were the vibrations of the restless little flags. And the thousands of cries, endlessly repeated across the days and nights, were intoning in rhythmic chant the terrible onslaught which this earth had witnessed and from which it still felt tragic shudderings.

The automobile came to a standstill. The guide was running about among the crosses, stooping over in order to examine their weather-stained inscriptions.

"Here we are!"

All the family were soon grouped around a heap of earth in the vague outline of a bier, and beginning to be covered with herbage. At the head was a cross with letters cut in deep with the point of a knife, the kind deed of some of his comrades-at-arms—"DESNOYERS." . . . Then in military abbreviations, the rank, regiment and company.

The father was staring at the rustic grave in dumb amazement. His son was there, there forever! . . . and he would never see him again! He imagined him sleeping unshrouded below, in direct contact with the earth, just as Death had surprised him in his miserable and heroic old uniform. He recalled the exquisite care which the lad had always given his body—the long bath, the massage, the invigorating exercise of boxing and fencing, the cold shower, the elegant and subtle perfume . . . all that he might come to this! . . . that he might be interred just where he had fallen in his tracks, like a wornout beast of burden!

Before the uselessness of his bitter plaints, Don Marcelo's former dominant character had come to life, raging against destiny.

He looked at the horizon where so often he had imagined the adversary to be, and clenched his fists in a paroxysm of fury. His disordered mind believed that it saw the Beast, the Nemesis of humanity.

It appeared to him that from afar was echoing the gallop of the four Apocalyptic horsemen, riding rough-shod over all his fellow-creatures. He saw the strong and brutal giant with the sword of War, the archer with his repulsive smile, shooting his pestilential arrows, the baldheaded miser with the scales of Famine, the hard-riding spectre with the scythe of Death. He recognized them as only divinities, familiar and terrible—which had made their presence felt by mankind. All the rest was a dream. The four horsemen were the reality . . . nothing mattered.

Whatever the end might be, it would be sure to turn out badly. Although the Beast might be mutilated, it would again come forth years afterward, as the eternal curse of mankind. . . .

For him the only important thing now was that the war had robbed him of his son. All was gloomy, all was black. The world was going to its ruin. . . . He was going to rest.

Katherine Mayo

MOTHER INDIA

Few books have ever created such a sensation as Katherine Mayo's "Mother India," published in 1927. The people of India themselves considered it such as unfair representation of their country that one of their number hastened to write "Uncle Sham," which discloses some of the most unpleasant features of conditions in the United States. In this condensation we have tried not to give undue prominence to the inherently repulsive passages, and to present India as an admittedly backward country but one which, under the guidance of occidentals and enlightened natives, is making notable progress.

Our Near Neighbor

The area we know as India is nearly half as large as the United States. Its population is three times greater than ours.

Under present conditions of human activity, whereby the roads that join us to every part of the world continually shorten and multiply, it would appear that some knowledge of the main facts concerning so big, and today so near, a neighbor should be a part of our intelligence and our self-protection.

But what does the average American actually know about India? That Mr. Gandhi lives there; also tigers. His further ideas, if such he has, resolve themselves into more or less hazy notions more or less unconsciously absorbed from professional propagandists out of one camp or another; from religious or mystical sources; or from tales and travel books, novels and verses, having India as their scene.

It was dissatisfaction with this status that sent me to India, to see what a volunteer unsubsidized, uncommitted, and unattached person could observe of common things in daily human life.

Leaving untouched the realms of religion, of politics, and of the arts, I would confine my inquiry to such workaday ground as public health and its contributing factors. None of these points could well be wrapped in "Eastern mystery" and all concern the whole family of nations in the same way that the sanitary practices of John Smith of 23 Main Street concern Peter Jones at the other end of the block.

For if Peter cultivates habits of living and ways of thinking that make him a physical menace not only to himself and his family, but to all the rest of the block, then practical John will want details.

"Why," ask modern Indian thinkers, "why, after all the long years of British rule, are we still marked among the peoples of the world for our ignorance, our poverty, and our monstrous death rate? By what right are light and bread and life denied? Our very souls are poisoned by the shadow of the arrogant stranger, blotting out our sun. Nothing can be done—nothing, anywhere, but to mount the political platform and faithfully denounce our tyrant until he takes his flight. When Britain has abdicated and gone, then, and not till then, free men breathing free air, may we turn our minds to the lesser needs of our dear Mother India."

Now it is precisely at this point, and in the spirit of hearty sympathy with the suffering peoples, that I venture my main generality. It is this:

The British administration of India, be it good, bad, or indifferent, has nothing whatever to do with the conditions above indicated. Inertia, helplessness, lack of initiative and originality, lack of staying power and of sustained loyalties, sterility of enthusiasm, weakness of life-vigor itself—all are traits that truly characterize the Indian not only of today, but of long past history. All furthermore, will continue to characterize him, in an increasing degree, until he admits their causes and uproots them.

Economic "Drains"

THE welfare of any people, we are wont to agree, must finally rest upon economic foundations.

Of cotton, the Indian's persistent statement is that the country's raw crop, selfishly cornered, is sent to England to give employment to Lancashire spinners, and then, brought back as cloth, is forced upon Indian purchasers.

The facts are: (a) The English market stands sixth on the list of purchasers of Indian cotton. (b) Indian cotton, being of poor quality, does not meet the requirements of English cotton cloth manufacturers. (c) The cotton for the looms of Lancashire is supplied from America and the Sudan. (d) The little Indian cotton used in the United Kingdom goes chiefly to making lamp-wicks, cleaning cloths and other low-grade fabrics.

The Government, meantime, has been sparing no pains to improve the quality of the cotton crop. In the endeavor to induce the growers to put more intelligence into the work, experimental farms and model stations have been established in the cotton areas, inspectional teaching has been set up, and improved implements and good seed provided, with an active propaganda as to the feasibility of higher prices.

"India is actually a better cotton country than is the United States," an American authority has said, "but the people will not put their backs into the work, and the Home Rule politician does what he can to discourage improved production, on the ground that 'India must not help England by growing cotton that Lancashire will use.'"

"But consider the question of tea," replied the Indian economist quickly. "We raise great crops of tea, and almost the whole is swept out of India—another exhausting drain upon the country."

"Do you sell your tea, or give it away?"

"Ah, yes—but the *tea*, you perceive, is *gone*."

The third "drain" upon the country as named above, is the interest upon Government's Public Utility bonds, paid to London.

But the net profits of the Government of India brought in by the railways after payment of interest, sinking funds, annuity charges, etc., were, in 1924-25, $58,736,000.

MR. GANDHI's views on railways, being a conspicuous feature of his anti-British propaganda, may be noted here:

"Good travels at a snail's pace—it can therefore, have little to do with the railways. Those who want to do good . . are not in a hurry. . . . But evil has wings. . . . So the railways can become a distributing agency for the evil one only."

Yet Mr. Gandhi himself sets the example of braving that danger, in his many political tours about the country. And, despite his doubts on the point, one effect of the existence of the railroads has certainly been to wipe out the mortal terror of famine in India. Whereas in the old days that threat hung always over the land, waiting only the failure of a monsoon to reap its human harvest, deaths from this cause are now almost unknown.

Beyond the railheads run the British built network of good highroads, speeding motor traffic where bullock cart alone used to creep and wallow.

"And every time I think of famine and the desperate work and the wholesale death it used to mean," said one old Deputy District Commissioner, "I say 'God bless Henry Ford!'"

The Idle "Wealth of the Indies"

Now, leaving matters of argument, let us face about and look at indisputable wastages of India's vital resources. The major channels have been shown in earlier pages, but these leave untouched a list of points only second in importance, such as caste marriage costs, the usurer, the hoarding of treasure, and mendicancy.

Marriage expenses and funeral expenses, love of litigation, thriftlessness and crop failures are among the chief loads that lead the Indian into debt. The Indian money-lender, or *bania,* is the man who, foreseeing a short crop, corners all the grain in his region, and at sowing time sells seed grain to his neighbors at 200 per cent profit, taking the coming crop as security.

Once in debt to a *bania,* few escape. Clothing, oxen, and all purchased necessities are bought of the same wise old spider. Compound interest rolls up in the good old way as the years pass, and posterity limps under the load into the third and fourth generation.

Everywhere, whether openly or covertly, the usurer opposed the education of the people, because a man who can read will not sign the sort of paper by which the *bania* holds his slave, and a man who can figure will know when his debt is cleared. As two Indian members of the profession warmly told me, the *bania* hates "this meddlesome and unsympathetic foreign government that has introduced a system of cooperative credit, which, wherever a Briton directs it, is ruining our good old indigenous banking business. Moreover, not content even with that mischief, it is pushing night school and adult-education schemes to upset the people's mind."

A THIRD actual drain upon prosperity, seldom advertised, yet affecting not only India but the rest of the world, is India's disposition of bullion. Since the early days of the Roman Empire, western economists have been troubled over India's intake of precious metals, rather than of foreign goods, in payment for her produce. These metals she has always swallowed up.

In 1889 it was estimated that India held imprisoned "a stock of gold bullion wholly useless for commercial purposes and increasing at the rate of nearly $14,000,000 annually, of the value of not less than $1,312,000,000." This ever-accumulating treasure lies in the hands of all conditions and orders of men, from the poorest laborer to the most eminent prince. In 1927, Mr. D. C. Bliss, American Trade Commissioner in Bombay, wrote of treasure in India:

"Vast reserves have been accumulated, . . . estimated as amounting to more than five billion dollars—but they have been jealously hoarded in the form of unproductive precious metals. Put to productive uses, or loaned out in the world's money-markets, they would suffice to make India one of the powerful nations of the world. The traditional 'wealth of the Indies' is there, but in such a form that it yields nothing to its possessors."

Turning now to the drain incurred through robbing the soil: India, as we know, is pre-eminently an agricultural country. But she has never fertilized her soil. Continually taking from it, she puts nothing back—and yet laments the thinness of her crops. Having but little firewood, she burns her cow-dung for fuel. And, being under religious taboo against the handling of dead animal substance, the Hindu majority will not use for bone manure the cattle bones of which they have such store, but, instead, sell them to be exported to foreign parts. And they cultivate with a little wooden plow that barely scratches the surface of the ground.

Suppose that, still respecting the taboo, they used some of their idle buried cash, or the interest it would bring, put to work, to buy fertilizer and machinery, what far-reaching profit might not that one step effect, did but their general way of life permit enduring prosperity!

And here, too, must be mentioned the enormous dead loss incurred by the country through the maintenance of its seventy-odd millions of unprofitable cattle which, because of religious inhibitions, may but rarely contribute even hides and bones to the country's profit.

LAST on our list of draughts upon the wealth of India, we find the item of mendicancy.

The Brahmanic code commends renunciation of active life and the taking up of a life of contemplation and beggary as the proper terminal half of man's earthly career. At the same time it teaches that he who gives to the beggar is in reality a debtor to that beggar, in that he who receives affords the giver a priceless opportunity to establish credit in the life to come.

In the Indian Legislative Assembly, on February 2, 1926, Sir Hari Singh Gour said that there were 5,800,000 beggars, vagrants, witches and wizards recorded and an additional 1,452,174 of saints and fakirs who lived by beggary.

AND now we come to a more obscure question, that of the present economic status of the peoples in comparison with their condition in past eras. Mr. Gandhi and his school affirm that the peoples of India have been growing steadily poorer and more miserable, as a result of British rule. To form a close surmise of the facts is difficult indeed.

The masses have, as a whole, little ambition to raise or to change actual living conditions. Their minds as a rule do no turn to the accumulation of things.

But their margin of safety is indubitably greater, their power of resistance to calamity increased, and, allegations to the contrary notwithstanding, means of enlarging their income lie at all times now, within their hands. In just such measure as the desire for material advance awakens, one sees this demonstrated in individual lives. The question whether or not such desire is good underlies one of the prime differences between eastern and western thought and practice.

Now in assigning value to these factors, one must remember that the soil of India is today supporting the pressure of over 54,000,000 more human beings than it sustained fifty years ago, plus an increase of 20 per cent.

This, again, is a result of freedom from wars and disorders and from killing famines; of the checking of epidemics; and of the multiplied production of food—all elements bound to produce ever greater effect as essential features of an established government. And the prospects it unfolds, of sheer volume of humanity piling up as the decades pass, is staggering. For, deprived of infanticide and of her other escape-valves, yet still clinging to early marriage and unlimited propagation, India stands today at that point of social development where population is controlled by disease, and disease only.

The World Menace

NOBODY knows the exact incidence of malaria in India, for village vital statistics are, perforce, kept by primitive village watchmen who put down to "fever" all deaths not due to snake-bite, cholera, plague, a broken head or the few other things they recognize. But a million deaths a year from malaria may be regarded as a conservative estimate of India's loss by that malady.

Under present conditions of Indianized control, governmental anti-malarial work, like all other preventive sanitation, is badly crippled. Yet it generally contrives to hold its own, though denied the sinews of progress.

And one recognizes with satisfaction, here and there, a few small volunteer seedlings springing up, strangers and aliens to the soil. Preeminent among these is the Anti-Malaria Co-operative Society of Bengal, an Indian organizaion now trying to bring control of malaria into the lives of the people, through educating the villagers in means of protecting their own health. They are also raising funds to make available to the Bengali villagers the services of Indian doctors properly trained in western medicine.

One of the great objectives of the British Sanitary Administration is to put good wells into the villages and to educate the people in their proper use. Now, this matter of Indian wells is of more than Indian importance. For cholera is mainly a water-borne disease, and "statistics show that certain provinces in British India are by far the largest and most persistent centers of cholera infection in the world."

The malady is contracted by drinking water infected with the faeces of cholera patients or cholera carriers, or from eating uncooked or insufficiently cooked infected food. It finds its best incubating grounds in a population of low vitality and generally weak and unresisting condition. There is a vaccine for preventive inoculation but, the disease once developed, no cure is known. Outbreaks bring a mortality of from 15 to 90 per cent., usually of about 40 per cent. The area of Lower Bengal and the valley of the Ganges is, in India, the chief cholera center, but "the disease is very generally endemic in some degree throughout the greater part of the whole Indian peninsula."

Since the year 1816, ten pandemics of cholera have occurred. In 1893 the United States was attacked, and in this explosion the speed of travel from East to West was more rapid than ever before.

Without fear of the charge of alarmism, international Public Health officers today question whether they can be sure that local controls will always withstand unheralded attacks in force. With that question in mind, they regard India's cholera as a national problem of intense international import.

In the normal course of events, how-ever, the main danger source for widespread cholera epidemics is the periodic concentration of great masses of people in fairs and festivals and in pilgrimages to holy cities. During the past twelve years or more, the British sanitary control of the crowds, in transit and also in concentration, where temporary latrines are built, pipe-lines for water laid, wells chlorinated and doctors and guards stationed, has been so efficient as greatly to lessen the risks.

Bubonic plague was first introduced into India in 1896, coming from China. Today India is the world's chief reservoir of infection, and has lost, since 1896, some 11,000,000 lives by that cause alone: The case mortality is about 70 per cent. Of pneumonic plague, which sometimes develops in conjunction with the other form, only an occasional case survives.

Plague uncontrolled at its source may at any time become an international scourge, a danger to which international health officers are the more alive since latter-day observations continue to show the disease breaking out in regions where its occurrence has been unknown before.

Plague, unlike cholera, is not communicated by man to man, but to man by fleas from the bodies of sick rats. When plague breaks out in a village, the effective procedure is to evacuate the village at once and to inoculate the villagers with plague vaccine. In most countries you simultaneously proceed to real control by killing the rats. But this, in a Hindu land, you cannot effectively do, because of the religion which prohibits the killing of animals.

With repeated examples, however, of the results of following Government's behests, a degree of improvement has taken place. In some places where plague has struck often, the people have begun to evacuate of themselves, when rats begin to die, and to flock into the nearest dispensary begging for inoculation. But the darkness of their minds is still deep.

Child Marriage

A STUDY of the attitude of the Government of India as to the subject of child-marriage shows that, while steadily exercising persuasive pressure toward progress and change, it has been dominated, always, by two general principles —the first, to avoid as far as possible interference in matters concerning the religion of the governed; the second, never to sanction a law that cannot be enforced.

To run counter to the Indian's tenets as to religious duties, religious prohibitions, and god-given rights has ever meant the eclipse of Indian reason in madness, riot and blood. And to enforce a law whose keeping or breaking must be a matter of domestic secrecy is, in such a country as India at least, impossible.

Indian and English authorities unite in the conviction that no law raising th marriage age of girls would be today e fectively accepted by the Hindu people The utmost to be hoped, in the presen state of public mentality, is, so these ex perienced men hold, a raising of th age of consent within the marriag bonds. A step in this direction was ac complished in 1891, when Government backed by certain members of the ad vanced section of the Indians, after a ho battle in which it was fiercely accuse by eminent orthodox Hindus of assailing the most sacred foundations of th Hindu world, succeeded in raising tha age from ten years to twelve. In latte day Legislative Assemblies the struggl has been renewed, non-official India Assemblymen bringing forward bill aiming at further advance only to se them defeated by the strong orthodo majority.

HUSBAND AND WIFE

SUCCESSIVE debates expose the fact that few or none of the Indian par liamentarians dispute the theoretical wis dom of postponing motherhood until th maturity of the mother; but all agre that it is impossible to effect such a resul without prohibiting the marriage of girl of immature age. Yet this they say, wit one accord, cannot be done—and fo three reasons:

First, because immutable custom for bids, premarital pubescence being gen erally considered, among Hindus, a so cial if not a religious sin.

Second, because the father dares no keep his daughter at home lest she b damaged before she is off his hands And this especially in joint family house holds, where several men and boys— brothers, cousins, uncles—live under th same roof.

Third, because the parents dare no expose the girl, after her dawning pu berty, to the pressure of her own desir unsatisfied.

Some speakers point to the gradua growth of public opinion as expressed i

aste, party and association councils as
he best hope of the future. These de-
recated legislation as both irritating
nd useless, calling attention to the fact
hat the orthodox community, compris-
ng as it does the great majority of
Hindus all over India, would regard
egal abolition of child-marriage as, liter-
lly, a summons to holy war.

Similarly, any active attempt to protect
he child wife during her infancy would,
was shown, be held as an attack upon
ne sacred marital relation, impossible
) make effective and sure to let loose
bloodshed and chaos."

Throughout the Hindu argument,
owever, the general conviction appears
that law-making for social advance,
while entirely hopeless of enforcement,
exerts an educational influence upon the
community and is therefore to be regarded with satisfaction as a completed
piece of work.

And the significance of this legislation
is further driven home by the estimate
that in India each generation sees the
death of 3,200,000 mothers in the agonies
of childbirth—a figure greater than that
of the united death roll of the British
Empire, including India, France, Belgium, Italy and the United States, in the
World War; and that the average physical rating of the population is at the
bottom of the international list.

Girl Liabilities

A GIRL child, in the Hindu scheme, is
usually a heavy and unwelcome
ash liability. Her birth elicits the formal
ondolences of family friends.
"The parents look after the son, and
od looks after the daughters." The re-
alt is that the female death-rate be-
ween one and five is almost invariably
omewhat higher than the male death-
ate.

Rich or poor, high caste or low caste,
ne mother of a son will idolize the
aild. She has little knowledge to give
m save knowledge of strange taboos
ad fears and charms and ceremonies to
ropitiate a universe of powers unseen.
ne would never discipline him, even
ough she knew the meaning of the
ord. She would never teach him to re-
rain passion or impulse of appetite.
ae has not the vaguest conception of
ow to feed him or develop him. Her
ea of a sufficient meal is to tie a string
ound his little brown body and stuff
m till the string bursts. And so
rough all his childhood he grows as
ew his father before him, back into
e mists of time.

Yet when the boy himself assumes
arried life, he will honor his mother
ove his wife, and show her often a real
fection and deference. Then it is that
e woman comes into her own, ruling
indoors with an iron hand, stoutly maintaining the ancient tradition, and, forgetful of her former misery, visiting
upon the slender shoulders of her little
daughters-in-law all the burdens and the
wrath that fell upon her own young
back. But one higher step is perhaps reserved for her. With each grandson laid
in her arms she is again exalted. The
family line is secure. Her husband's soul
is protected. Proud is she among women.
Blessed be the gods.

THE reverse of the picture shows the
Hindu widow—the accursed. That
so hideous a fate as widowhood should
befall a woman can be but for one cause
—the enormity of her sins in a former
incarnation. From the moment of her
husband's decease till the last hour of
her own life, she must expiate those sins
in shame and suffering and self-immo-
lation, chained in every thought to the
service of his soul. Be she a child of
three, who knows nothing of the marriage that bound her, or be she a wife
in fact, having lived with her husband,
her case is the same. The widow becomes the menial of every other person
in the house of her late husband or she
may be turned adrift. Then she must
live by charity—or by prostitution, into
which she not seldom falls. And her

dingy, ragged figure, her bristly shaven head, even though its stubble be white over the haggard face of unhappy age, is often to be seen in the temple crowds or in the streets of pilgrimage cities, where sometimes niggard piety doles her a handful of rice.

As to remarriage, that, in orthodox Hinduism, is impossible. Marriage is not a personal affair, but an eternal sacrament. Of recent years, however, the gradual if unrecognized influence of western teaching has aroused a certain response. In different sections of India, several associations have sprung up, having the remarriage of virgin widows as one of their chief purported objects. The movement, however, is almost wholly restricted to the most advanced element of Hindu society, and its influence is, as yet, too fractional appreciably to affect statistics.

For the number of widows in India is according to the latest published official computation, 26,834,838.

"You cannot hustle the East." But the underground workings of western standards and western contacts, and the steady, quiet teachings of the British official through the years have done more, perhaps, towards ultimate change than any coercion could have effected.

The Untouchables

"WHY, after so many years of British rule, do we remain 92 per cent illiterate?" reiterates the Hindu politician, implying that the blame must be laid at the ruler's door.

But in naming his figure, he does not call to your attention a fact which, left to yourself, you would be slow to guess: he does not tell you that of the 247,000,-000 inhabitants of British India, about 25 per cent—60,000,000—have from time immemorial been specially condemned to illiteracy, even to sub-humanity, by their brother Indians.

The old lawmakers in devising the caste system, placed themselves at the head thereof, under the title of "earthly gods"—Brahmans. Next beneath them they put the Kshattryas, or fighting men; after the fighters, the Vaisyas, or cultivators, upon whom the two above look down, and finally, the fourth division, or Sudra caste, born solely to be servants to the other three. Of these four divisions, themselves today much subdivided, was built the frame of Hindu society. Outside and below all caste, in a limbo of scorn earned by their sins of former existences, must forever grovel the Untouchables.

Regarded as if sub-human, the tasks held basest are reserved for them; dishonor is associated with their name; and to all of them the privilege of any sort of teaching is sternly denied. They may not enter a court of justice; they may not enter a dispensary to get help for their sick; they may stop at no inn. Some, in the abyss of their degradation, are permitted no work at all. These may sell nothing, not even their own labor. They may only beg. If alms be given they must be tossed on the ground, well away from the road, and when the giver is out of sight and the roads empty then and not until then, the watcher may creep up, snatch, and run.

Under such conditions of preordained misery, certain communities among the Untouchables have developed a business in the practice of crime. These communities specialize, one in pocket-picking, another in burglary, yet others in foraging in highway robbery, in murder, etc., often combining their special trade with prostitution as a second industry. Scattered all over India and known as the Criminal Tribes, they number today about four and a half million persons.

Now it must not be forgotten that the matter of Untouchability, like almost all other Hindu concerns, is woven, warp and woof, into the Hindu religion; and that the Hindus are a tremendously religious people. Nevertheless the immediate impulse of the Briton in India was to espouse the cause

f the social victim. The Directors of the
East Indian Company, as early as 1854,
recommended "that no boy be refused
admission to a Government school or
college on ground of caste," and stuck
o the principle until their authority was
sunk in that of the Crown.

Thenceforward it was continually reaffirmed, yet pushed with a caution that
might seem faint-hearted to one unfamiliar with the extreme delicacy of the
ground. Little or nothing was to be
gained in any attempt to impose a foreign idea, by force, on unready and non-
understanding millions.

Today almost all that can be accomplished by civil law for the untouchable
has been secured. Government has
freely opened their way, as far as Government can determine, to every educational advantage and to high offices.
And Government's various land development and cooperative schemes, steadily
increasing, have provided tremendous
redeeming agencies and avenues of
escape.

But for Provincial Governments to
pass legislation asserting the rights of
every citizen to enjoy public facilities,
such as public schools, is one thing; to
enforce that legislation over enormous
countrysides and through multitudinous
small villages without the cooperation
and against the will, of the people, is
another.

The economic situation of the Untouchables under Government's steady
effort, is, in some communities, looking
up. With it their sense of manhood is
developing in the shape of resentment
f the degradation to which until now
hey have bowed. Among them a few
men of power and parts are beginning
o stand out.

Finally, their women, as Christian

THE UNTOUCHABLE

converts, furnish the main body of Indian teachers for the girls of India of all
castes, and of trained nurses for the
hospitals; both callings despised and rejected by the superior castes, both neces-
sitating education, and both carrying the
possibility of increasing influence.

As to the rating of the Untouchables
converted to Christianity—there are now
about five million of them—opinions
differ; but in any case the fact stands
that these converts are set free, as far
as they can grasp freedom, from caste
bonds. The faces of the Hindus are fixed
against them, to be sure. But of the converts of the third generation many experienced persons are found to say that
they are the hope of India.

Could They Rule Themselves?

Self-government is not a thing that
can be 'given' to any people. . . .
To people can be 'given' the self control
f maturity." President Wilson once
aid.

The British are trying to draw the Indians into responsible participation in
Government. India's outburst of loyalty
in the World War, her whole-hearted
contribution of men and means from

every province and state save Bengal, prompted a responsive flood of feeling in Britain and a desire to requite one demonstration of confidence and sympathy with another in kind.

The scheme in its shape of today has not the stability of the slow-growing oak, root for branch, balanced and anchored. Rather, it is a hothouse exotic, weedy, a stranger in its soil, forced forward beyond its inherent strength by the heat of a generous and hasty emotion.

An outsider sitting today through sessions of the Indian legislature, Central or Provincial, somehow comes to feel like one observing a roomful of small and rather mischievous children who by accident have got hold of a magnificent watch. They fight and scramble to thrust their fingers into it, to pull off a wheel or two, to play with the mainspring; to pick out the jewels. They have no apparent understanding of the worth of the mechanism, still less of the value of time. And when the teacher tries to explain to them how to wind their toy up, they shriek and grimace in fretful impatience and stuff their butterscotch into the works.

As to the relation of these people to their supposed job, its most conspicuous quality, today, is its artificiality. Adepts in the phraseology of democratic representation, they are, in fact, profoundly innocent of the thought behind the phrase. Despotisms induce no growth of civic spirit, and the peoples of India, up to the coming of Britain, had known no rule but that of despots. Britain, by her educational effort, has gradually raised up an element before unknown in India —a middle class. But this middle class— these lawyers and professional men—are in the main as much dominated today as were their ancestors five hundred years ago by the law of caste and of transmigration—completest denial of democracy. They talk of "the people" simply because the word bulks large in the vocabulary of that western-born representative government which they now essay.

One of the chief reasons for the non existence of an electorate is that whil less than 8 per cent of the people ca read at all, that literate fraction is co centrated almost entirely in the larg towns and cities, leaving the great mass spread over the great spaces of the lan unreached and unreachable by th printed word.

This illiterate peasantry, these illitera landholders, have no access to and no i terest in the political game, nor in an horizon beyond that which daily mee their physical eyes. The town politicia the legislator actual or aspirant, rarel comes near them unless it be at electio or as in the period of the "non-violenc agitations, to stir them with some repo of evil to rise in blind revolt.

But we should be fairer to the India as well as wiser ourselves if w looked in his mind, rather than in our for light on causes. Then we should s that no white man in office ever labo under such a handicap as does the ave age Indian official, or ever is so large foredoomed to defeat, in effort towar disinterested public service.

With the Hindu comes, first, the a cient religious law of the family cla because of this system the public offic holder who fails to feather the nest of h kin will be branded by all his world n only a fool but a renegade, and will fir neither peace at home nor honor abroa No public opinion sustains him.

Second, beyond the family line com the circle of caste. The Hindu-offic holder who should forget his caste's i terests for interests lying outside that c cle would bring down upon his he the opprobrium, perhaps the disciplir of his orthodox fellow caste men. A this, be it remembered, means not on temporal discomfort, but also dire pe alties inflicted upon his soul, determi ing the miseries of future incarnations.

Third, the political struggle betwe people of the Hindu faith, which co prise three-quarters of the populatio and those of the Muslim, which r resents one-quarter, brings tremendous pressure to bear upon the official from either camp, practically compelling him to dispense such patronage as he enjoys among his co-religionists only.

With these points in mind, one views with more charity and understanding the breakdown of allegiance to western ideals that generally occurs in even the staunchest of Indian public officials when the British superior officer who has backed him through thick and thin in free work for general good, is replaced by an Indian, himself subject to the ancient code.

It is stiff work to maintain, alone and accursed, an alien standard among one's own people.

The Alternatives

THUS far we have been dealing mainly with British India, as distinct from the Indian Empire composed of British India and the Indian States. The Indian States hold 39 per cent of the area of the whole Empire and about 3 per cent of the population. Individually, the states vary in size from properties of twenty square miles or less to a domain as large as Italy, and each is governed by its own prince.

The princes know well that if Britain were to withdraw from India, they themselves, each for himself, would at once begin annexing territory; that all would be obliged to live under arms, each defending his own borders; and that the present day politician would in the first onset finally disappear like a whiff of chaff before flame.

The princes, however, want no such issue. They frankly say that they enjoy the *pax Britannica,* which not only relieves them from the necessity of sustaining larger military establishments, but which gives them the enjoyment of public utilities, as railroads, good highways, ports, markets, mail, and wires, while permitting them to develop their properties in peace. Their attitude during the War was wholly loyal, and they contributed munificently of money, men and goods to the Empire's cause.

In a word, they are a company of high-spirited, militant aristocrats strongly interested that the British Crown shall remain suzerain in India, but absolutely refusing to carry their complaisance so far as to admit the Indian politician of the Reforms Government as an agent to their courts.

"We shall never deal with this new lot of Jacks-in-office," they say. "While Britain stays, Britain will send us English gentlemen to speak for the King-Emperor, and all will be as it should be between friends. If Britain leaves, we, the princes, will know how to straighten out India, even as Princes should."

Then I recall a little party given in Delhi by an Indian friend in order that I might privately hear the opinions of certain Home Rule politicians. Most of the guests were, like my host, Bengali Hindus belonging to the western-educated professional class. They had spoken at length on the coming expulsion of Britain from India and on the future in which they themselves would rule the land.

"And what," I asked, "is your plan for the princes?"

"We shall wipe them out!" exclaimed one with conviction. And all the rest nodded assent.

WHETHER British or Russians or Japanese sit in the seat of the highest; whether the native princes divide the land, reviving old days of princely dominance; or whether some autonomy more complete than that now existing be set up, the only power that can hasten the pace of Indian development toward freedom, beyond the pace it is traveling today, is the power of the men of India, wasting no more time in talk, recriminations, and shiftings of blame, but facing and attacking, with the best resolution they can muster, the task that awaits them in their own bodies and souls.

RUDYARD KIPLING'S
"KIM OF THE RISHTI"

A Study by E. B. Osborn

"THIS picture of India (published in 1901) is one of the most elaborate ever executed by a western writer between the covers of an imaginative book," said Mark and Carl Van Doren. "Not only for that reason but because it expresses most sides of Kipling's nature, 'Kim' may outlive many of his lighter works; it may come in time to represent the best of him that is worth preserving." Kipling was born in Bombay, India, in 1865; he died in London, England, in 1936, and was buried in Westminster Abbey.

THERE IS no more wonderful tale of adventure in the language than Kim, which represents the genius of Rudyard Kipling at its culmination. It is not only the story of a boy with a quite unique gift for the subtle intelligence work—espionage would be a gross and unjust name for it—which anticipates and arrests the intrigues that might break the peace of India, but also a romance of spirituality, of mankind's unending quest for the divinely ordained road, the strait pathway, leading out of the vast and bewildering illusion of mortal life.

Kim and the old Lama from Tibet, who becomes his travelling companion, are the heroes of the twofold drama of action and the soul's high enterprise. But India, like Egdon Heath in "Hardy's Return of the Native," is really the chief character, making or unmaking men and dominating either side of the story.

There is, depicted before us with all the author's skill, the visible India with its wondrous variety of scenery and of human types busy with worldly affairs. But there is also the invisible India, the most ancient of man's spiritual homes, with its old religions and cosmogonies, towering heavenward like the Himalayas and white with the snows of eternal thought. The dust and turmoil of the populous and picturesque scene move the reader—but he is more profoundly stirred by entering into the secret Orient where a man of affairs may give up all worldly honour and glory to meditate and make his soul,

To learn and discern of his brother the clod,
His brother the brute, and his brother the god

and so round off his life into a perfect whole.

KIM'S FATHER was a colour-sergeant of the Mavericks, an Irish regiment, and his mother had been a nurse-maid in a colonel's family. Kimball O'Hara had in the end "gone native altogether," as the saying is, had learn to love opium, and had died as poor whites die in India. His whole estate at death consisted of three papers: one he called his *ne varietur,* because those words were written under his signature thereon; his "clearance-certificate"; and Kim's birth-certificate. In his glorious opium hours he warned Kim not to part with them on any account, for they would some day make a man of him. The half-caste woman with whom he lived sewed these papers after his death into a leather amulet-case, which she strung round Kim's neck. "And some day," she told the little boy, confusedly remembering O'Hara's prophecies, "there will come for you a great Red Bull on a green field, and the Colonel riding on his tall horse, and"—dropping into English—"nine hundred devils."

If, indeed, any authoritative person had seen those papers, Kim would have been aught and brought up normally, perhaps at the Masonic Orphanage in the Hills. But he escaped and lived in Lahore like a native child, and what he did not know about the customs, stories and proverbs of his associates was really not worth knowing.

All castes and conditions were familiar to him, but he was puzzled at his first sight of the Lama.

He was nearly six feet high, dressed in fold upon fold of dingy stuff like horse-blanketing. At his belt hung a long open-work iron pen-ase and a wooden rosary such as holy men wear. On his head was a gigantic sort of tam-o'-shanter. His face was yellow and wrinkled, like that of Fook Sing, the Chinese bootmaker in the bazaar. His eyes turned up at the corners and looked like little slits of onyx.

A scholar of parts, once a ruler in his Tibetan lamassery, he had come down into Hind to visit the Holy Places of Buddhism and to find the "River of the Arrow"—the mystic stream which gushed forth where fell the shaft shot by the young Buddha from a bow none could bend, and which washes away all taint and speckle of sin.

Kim, who is known as the "Little Friend of all the World," being kind and tolerant to all people and a born lover of human nature, sees that the good old pilgrim is helpless in a strange environment, four months' journey from his lamassery, and appoints himself as his guide and disciple. It is surprising how he wheedles good living for him out of the people they meet.

Mahbub Ali, an Afghan horse-dealer who dyes his beard scarlet to hide the signs of coming age, is one of the intimate friends Kim falls in with on the way. Kim does not know that he is a sort of super-spy, who gives the Government from time to time invaluable information concerning out-of-the-way mountain principalities, which his caravans visit, explorers of nationalities other than English, and the progress of the gun trade. Just then five confederated kings, who had no right to confederate, were meditating trouble, serious trouble. Mahbub Ali had hurried south, avoiding a halt at the insalubrious city of Peshawur, in order to deliver the report of R.17, another wary watcher, on the peril that threatened. Dynamite was milky and innocuous in comparison with this report which most scandalously betrayed the five kings, a sympathetic Northern Power, a Hindu banker in Peshawur, and a semi-independent Mahomedan ruler in the south.

It falls to Kim's lot to deliver this report into the hands of the Head of the Secret Service, and he assists unseen, out of childish curiosity, at the immediate interview between the latter and the Commander-in-Chief. It is there and then arranged that a punitive expedition of eight thousand men, with the guns required, shall at once be mobilised to deal with the crisis. Not knowing—then —what he had been doing, Kim's act had set in motion a great military demonstration. But he talks about it and prophesies war to those he meets, including an old Ressaldar who had been faithful to his salt and fought in the Mutiny; a fine old veteran with three sons who were Ressaldar-majors in their regiments, and he had come out to show the pilgrims a short lane leading into the chief thoroughfare in Hindustan.

The Great Road

AND so the feet of the Lama and his chela (disciple and servitor) are set upon the Grand Trunk Road, which runs straight, bearing without crowding the traffic of Hindustan, for fifteen hundred miles—a river of life that has not its like for colour and picturesque variety and ceaseless flowing anywhere else in the whole wide world. "For the most part it is shaded, as here," says the old retired Ressaldar, "with four lines of trees; the middle road—all hard—takes the quick traffic. In the days before rail-carriages the Sahibs travelled up and down here in hundreds. Now there are only country carts and such like. Left and right is the rougher road for the heavy carts—grain and cotton and timber, bhoosa, lime and hides. A man goes in safety here—for at every few *kos* is a police-station." When "Kim" was written, the motor-car had not yet arrived to bring the Sahibs (who are still in a hurry!) back again to the famous thoroughfare.

It was a moving museum of races and castes, trades and professions. The Lama, his soul busied elsewhere, kept his eyes fixed steadily on the ground, but Kim watched the passing pageant with huge delight.

Here and there they met or were overtaken by the gaily dressed crowds of whole villages turning out to some local fair; the women, with their babes on their hips, walking behind the men, the older boys prancing on sticks of sugar-cane, dragging rude brass models of locomotives such as they sell for a halfpenny, or flashing the sun into the eyes of their betters from cheap toy mirrors. . . .

A solid line of blue, rising and falling lik the back of a caterpillar in haste, would swin up through the quivering dust and trot pas to a chorus of quick cackling. That was a gan of *changars*—the women who have taken a the embankments of all the Northern railwa under their charge—a flat-footed, big-bosome strong-limbed, blue-petticoated clan of earth carriers, hurrying north on news of a job. . . They belong to the caste whose men do no count.

A little later a marriage procession woul strike into the Grand Trunk with music an shoutings, and a smell of marigold and jasmin stronger even than the reek of the dust.

One could see the bride's litter, a blur of re and tinsel, staggering through the haze, whi the bridegroom's bewreathed pony turned asid to snatch a mouthful from a passing fodde cart. . . .

Still more interesting and more to shouted over it was when a strolling juggle with some half-trained monkeys, or a pantin feeble bear, or a woman who tied goat's horn to her feet and with these danced on a slack rope, set the horses to shying and the wome to shrill, long-drawn quavers of amazement.

Friends and Adventures

KIM makes friends for himself and the innocent old Lama in this happy Asiatic confusion in which, if only you have a little patience, all that a simple man needs is forthcoming. One very good friend he finds is an old lady of substance going on a visit to a son-in-law in a gaily ornamented family bullock-cart with a retinue that includes hillmen from the North. Kim's skill in abusive chaff and treasure of stories and songs picked up in Lahore city amuse the old dame; moreover, being from the Hills herself, she reveres the Lama whose blessing, she hopes, will bring her many grandsons. So they all travel together comfortably, master and disciple subsisting on the pious old hill-woman's bounty. And then—he is found by his father's regiment, and the sign of the Red Bull on a green field, which is the crest of the Mavericks, is seen by him on a camp marking-flag! The column crawls in sight, the band plays it to camp, for the men are route-marching with all their baggage, and with wondrous speed a white city of tents, all twinkling with fires, come silently int being. Never before had Kim watche the routine miracle of a seasoned reg ment pitching camp in thirty minute He crawls to the mess-tent door, and se the red-gold bull, fashioned from ol time loot from the Summer Palace Pekin, which is the sole ornament of th officers' table on the line of marc ramping on a field of Irish green. An he is caught by the Church of Englan chaplain, who finds the amulet-case co taining the documents that identify th boy. So Kim enters into his racial he itage and his feeling about it is that the Prodigal Son, as set forth in the lin invented for a chapter heading:

> The fatted calf is dressed for me,
> But the husks have greater zest for me,
> I think my pigs will be best for me,
>   So I'm off to the styes afresh.

And the reader, too, resents the fa that the story, like Kim of the Rish (Ey-Rishti = Irish) now become youn Kimball O'Hara, must leave the Roa for a while. The sorrow of the old Lam at the loss of his *chela* is contagious,

Kim at School

THE Church of England padre, a stupid man with very little Hindustani and still less knowledge of the innumerable types of native character, has the sense to ask the Roman Catholic chaplain's advice about his captive. Father Victor is learned in human nature, and he feels, if he cannot understand, the beauty of holiness that shines about the Lama and the pain in every sentence of his lamentation over the loss of the child disciple, of whom he says: "My heart went out to thee for thy charity and thy courtesy and the wisdom of thy little years." He bears it patiently, however, thinking he has sinned in allowing himself to be beguiled by yet another phase of the great illusion. But he thinks it right that Kim should learn to be a sahib, and decides to give three hundred rupees a year that the boy may get the best schooling to be had in India.

Meanwhile, before he goes to St. Xavier's in Partibus, the school recommended by Father Victor, Kim becomes an object of wonderment to the regiment. He tells them all that they will not go to Sanawar, but to "thee war" (talking in "the tinny, saw-cut English of the native-bred"). As he sits silent as a trapped wild thing, newly washed all over and dressed in a horrible stuff suit which rasps his limbs, the official opinion of him is declared. "A most amazin' young bird," says the sergeant. "He turns up in charge of a yellow-headed buck-Brahman priest, with his father's lodge-certificates round his neck, talkin' God knows what all of a red bull. The buck-Brahman evaporates without explanations, and the bhoy sets cross-legged on the chaplain's bed prophesyin' bloody war to the men at large."

Next morning, as the Mavericks take a side road to Umballa, the order to go to the front comes along, and a hoarse and joyful clamour rolls down on him through the thick dust, and someone smites Kim on the back, crying: "Tell how ye knew, ye little limb of Satan.

He is in the custody of a fat, freckled drummer boy, however, and loathes his new life. So he gets a native letter-writer to write him a letter to Mahbub Ali, asking for help or money, and the scarlet-bearded Afghan horse-dealer carries him off to Umballa race-course, after laying into the detested drummer-boy with a peculiarly adhesive quirt. But he gives the "Little Friend of all the World" clearly to understand that he cannot honourably connive at his escape—"Once a sahib, always a sahib," sagely observes Mahbub Ali. But they meet Creighton (of the Ethnological Survey) at the psychological moment, and it is decided not to waste the boy's peculiar gifts. Kim thinks his friend has played him false and says bitterly, quoting a proverb: "Trust a Brahman before a snake, and a snake before a harlot, and a harlot before an Afghan, Mahbub Ali."

But it is all settled for the best. The Lama has sent the first three hundred rupees (in one of Gobind Sahai's notes of hand which are "good from here to China," says Colonel Creighton to Father Victor), and due attention has been paid to the scarlet-bearded Afghan's metaphorical advice: "As regards that young horse I say that when a horse is born to be a polo-pony, closely following the ball without teaching—when such a colt knows the game by divination—then I say it is a great wrong to break that colt to a heavy cart, sahib."

ON THE way to St. Xavier's at Lucknow, whither he travels by train in a second-class compartment next to the colonel's first, his future is unfolded to him. He is to enter the Survey as a chain-man, provided he is diligent at school, and it is explained to him what that will mean. "Thou art a sahib and the son of a sahib," the colonel warns him, "therefore do not at any time be led to contemn the black men. I have known boys newly entered into the service of the Government who feigned not to understand the talk or the customs of black men. Their pay was cut for ignorance. There is no sin so great as ignorance. Remember this." He has a farewell meeting with the old Lama who is living in the Temple of th Tirthankers at Benares—and the gate close on him with a clang.

The First Holiday

KIM was diligent at St. Xavier's, and he passed an examination in elementary surveying "with great credit," his age being fifteen years and eight months. His name does not appear in the year's batch of those who entered for the subordinate Survey of India, but against it stand the words "removed on appointment." During those three years the old Lama made many journeys, following the traces of the Blessed Feet through all India, but always casting up at the Temple of the Tirthankers and then visiting Lucknow, to see his beloved *chela*. It became Kim's sanctioned custom to work faithfully during term-time at St. Xavier's, but to spend his holidays among his own people, so that the other side of his special intelligence might be developed. As his feeling is expressed in one of the two stanzas used as a chapter heading:

> I would go without shirts or shoes,
> Friends, tobacco or bread,
> Sooner than for an instant lose
> Either side of my head.

When his first August to October holidays began, it was arranged that he should be kept out of mischief at a barrack school in the hills behind Umballa. But he had himself stained and disguised in a house of light women, and joyously vanished in the guise of a low-caste Hindu boy, sending a letter of explanation to Mahbub Ali, hoping that "the Hand of Friendship would turn aside the Whip of Calamity." Mahbub convinced the colonel that such conduct was as inevitable as that of a horse which needs salt, and if it is not in the mangers, must lick it up from the earth.

After some glorious adventures on his own (with a capital of two rupees and three annas, for the disguising cost him four annas) he falls in with Mahbub, whose life he has the good luck to save.

Camping with the horse-dealer's re tainers beside the railway, he overhear two would-be assassins whispering be hind his horse-truck, and is able to war him in safety, though the night is ful of eyes. They go up from Umballa t Simla together, and Kim finds th journey all pure delight, as the roa climbs deviously and the vista of th Plains rolls out far below. He then re ceives orders from the colonel to lodg in Lurgan Sahib's house until it is tim to go back to school.

Lurgan, who keeps a shop full of th most amazing curios, is also a membe of the secret service, and he tests Kim' capacity in various unlikely ways. A gramophone, which abuses him at night does not frighten the stout-hearted boy and he breaks it by stuffing his coat int the trumpet-like mouth. Other and mor perilous magic is tried on him. A wate jar is smashed and its contents spilt, and Lurgan tries to hypnotise him into seeing it magically mended and restored to its original shape—it is the same method whereby the great hallucination of the Indian Rope Trick may have been accomplished. The boy sees the shadowy shape of the pot growing like a flower from the ground, but his mind and will are too strong to be convinced by suggestion that the phantasm is real. Afterwards he and the passionate, jealous child who guards Lurgan's jewels, play at the game, excellent for training eye and memory to work together, of looking at a number of unfamiliar objects for a minute, and then making an accurate catalogue of them.

KIM is deeply interested in Lurgan's many and very curious visitors, of whom an obese, fat-legged Babu, Hurree Chunder Mookerjee (R. 17 in the "Great Game") helps on his special education by showing him how to record distances measured in his own foot-paces by means of a rosary and by presenting him with a brass betel-box filled with little bottles of tabloids, quinine and other "good departmental drugs." Later holidays are used, under Mahbub's supervision, to put a fine finish on his special gifts; for example, he makes a secret survey and description of the mysterious capital of an independent native state, which would be useful to the Jung-i-Lat Sahib (Commander-in-Chief) if he went there with an army.

The Finished Expert

At sixteen Mahbub and Lurgan assured the colonel that Kim was ready for work and ought to be released from school. He is put on the pay-list, has his colour changed, and is protected against devils by the witch-like Huneefa (here we get a glimpse into the India of other-worldly spirits and dark magic, the oldest India of all) and left to follow the Lama for six months with the yellow complexion of a Tibetan *chela* and the other paraphernalia, such as the sand-coloured robe, begging-gourd, rosary and ghost-dagger.

He goes to the Temple at Benares to meet his Master. On the way he falls in with a Jat, bearing his poor little sick son in his arms, who complains that all the priests are most holy and—most greedy. "I have walked the pillars and trodden the temples till my feet are flayed, and the child is no whit better." Quinine and dark brown meat-lozenges out of Kim's quaint medicine-chest cure the child, and the pilgrims have not only acquired merit, but also made a new good friend.

It was as well they did, else Kim could never have saved the life of E.23, who has been bringing a most important letter from the "King's country" in the South and tumbles into the Delhi train, wounded and half-starving and well aware that he will be arrested at Delhi on a charge of murder, for which both the corpse and the witnesses had been provided in a southern city. When arrested he would be sent back to an independent state where he would be made to die slowly, as a warning to other spies. With the oddments in the Jat's bundle Kim changes the despairing fugitive from a Mahratta trader into an all-but naked ash-smeared, ochre-barred, dusty-haired Saddhu, his legs crossed under him, Kim's brown rosary about his neck, and a scant yard of worn flowered chintz on his shoulders. So E.23 escapes the net and is able to tell one of his chiefs where the letter has been hidden.

No wonder that this feat is described as "an extraordinary efficient performance" by the ubiquitous Mookerjee, who turns up at the house in Sharunpore of the son-in-law of the garrulous, lively, pious, good-hearted old dame met on the road during Kim's first journey. He is disguised as a *hakim,* and so cleverly that Kim does not at first recognize him.

In the High Hills

The Babu has orders to investigate the doings of two Russian envoys in the Far North, who are posing as sportsmen in quest of wild goats, but are actually engaged in making a military survey of the territory of two of the five confederated kings already mentioned. He asks Kim to help him, being an "awfully fearful" man ("God made the Hare and the Bengali," comments Kim, quoting the proverb), and so all three journey toward the Himalayas.

"Who goes to the Hills goes to his mother," runs the proverb, and the strength of the old Lama mightily increases as he strides up and on towards the snow-peaks afar. He is a power, moreover, in his own steep countryside. "The Plains had treated him as a holy man among holy men. But the Hills worshipped him as one in the confidence of all the devils."

This part of the story is full of wonderful pictures of the mountain vastnesses and fastnesses, which are among the finest of Kipling's masterpieces of description. Reading them, we are as dizzy and daunted as any plainsman suddenly thrown among snowy steeps and dark abysms—our wonder at the great artist's power becomes a kind of vertigo. Presently the travellers fall in with the Russian envoys, to whom Mookerjee has attached himself as guide and counsellor. They do not know how to treat the natives, and when one of them strikes the old man full on the face, the horror of the observers is beyond all bounds. "He struck the Holy One—we saw it!" cries a hillsman. "Our cattle will be barren—our wives will cease to bear! The snows will slide on us as we go home." Only because the Lama forbids any killing are their lives spared. But their papers are taken away by Mookerjee, their other belongings being cast down thousands of feet deep into "Shamlegh midden." So the object of the secret service is achieved.

But the spirit of the Lama is sad and broken within him, because he has been betrayed into anger—so that he put his hand upon his iron pen-case, the weapon of Tibetan monks quarrelling among one another. The traces of human feelings left in the saintly old man may please the Western reader. We are no more shocked at his momentary wrath with Ignorance and Lust than we were when, in an early chapter, he trailed his rosary on the grass to please a baby and sang a little song to it:

> This is a handful of cardamoms,
>   This is a lump of *ghi:*
> This is millet and chillies and rice,
>   A supper for thee and me.

Such trifling weaknesses, though for the faithful Buddhist they hinder the way to the peace that passes mortal understanding, endear him to us as they endeared him to Kim, his loving disciple and servitor. His quest is accomplished, for his spirit is miraculously disembodied for a time—they think him dead—and plunged into the cleansing flood of his life-long vision, but it returns to the body in order that he may promise the certainty of salvation to his beloved Kim. "Son of my soul," he says at the long last, "I have wrenched my soul back from the Threshold of Freedom to free thee from all sin—as I am free and sinless. Just is the wheel! Certain is our deliverance. Come!"

So ends this twofold romance of mortal journeyings and of the Mystic Way.

A Poet's Prayer

Almighty Father! let thy lowly child,
Strong in his love of truth, be wisely bold—
A patriot bard by sycophants reviled,
Let him live usefully, and not die old!
Let poor men's children, pleased to read his lays,
Love, for his sake, the scenes where he hath been;
And, when he ends his pilgrimage of days,
Let him be buried where the grass is green;
Where daisies, blooming earliest, linger late
To hear the bee his busy note prolong,—
There let him slumber, and in peace await
The dawning morn, far from the sensual throng,
Who scorn the wind-flower's blush, the redbreast's lonely song.
                                        —*E. Elliott*

GEORGE BERNARD SHAW

BACK TO METHUSELAH

A Study by Edgar Preston

SAUL among the Prophets! — Shaw among the hagiographers! which is the more surprising? Flippant, irreverent "G.B.S.," who frankly confesses to cutting cerebral capers and letting off "aphoristic fireworks," comes solemnly forth with 'Back to Methuselah': a Metabiological Pentateuch.

At the outset the unsophisticated reader scarce knows whether his attitude should be grave or gay. Soon, of course, he will discover, as he might have guessed, that it is all a prodigiously witty fantasy, serving as vehicle for the satire of the alertest, most whimsical mind at work to-day. He will find it all brain and no heart: which must be very much what Mr. G. K. Chesterton meant when he described George Bernard Shaw as "Light without heat."

Having left the Preface (of nearly ninety pages!) till the end—a course I would recommend—I half expected to find in the opening Part, "In the Beginning," things reminding me a little of "La Bible Folichonne"; but I was wrong. To be sure, subjects commonly regarded as sacred are handled very frankly and unceremoniously, as is the fashion of the "Intellectuals" of to-day; but I found nothing that should really shock the sensibilities of even the most old-fashioned. Yet every page contained matter apt to make one think—and sometimes "furiously."

How is the "average, sensual man" to approach a work so subtle, so variegated as this? and how do anything like justice to the arguments, the reasonings, the deductions—religious, scientific, political, social, artistic and what not—of a writer so various as Mr. Shaw (b. 1856), whose bewildering habit it is to start hare after hare—and leave his readers to chase 'em! A perfect description of his methods is supplied in his own words, applied to Comedy, which is: "destructive, derisory, critical, negative." So, realizing this, let us watch the gifted author as he "takes the Garden of Eden and weeds it properly."

In the Beginning

THE date of "In the Beginning" is 4004 B.C.; and the scene, of course, is the Garden. The characters are Adam and Eve—and the Serpent.

EVE: But who taught you to speak?

THE SERPENT: You and Adam. I have crept through the grass, and hidden, and listened to you. I am the most subtle of all the creatures of the field. I can talk of many things. I am very wise. It was I who whispered the word to you that you did not know—Dead—Death—Die.

[EVE had just been shocked at the sight of a fawn that had fallen from a height and broken its neck. ADAM has taken the body away to bury it.]

EVE (*shuddering*): Why do you remind me of it? I forgot it when I saw your beautiful hood. You must not remind me of unhappy things.

SERPENT: Death is not an unhappy thing when you have learnt how to conquer it.

EVE: How can I conquer it?

SERPENT: By another thing, called Birth.

EVE: What is birth?

SERPENT: The serpent never dies. Some day you shall see me come out of this beautiful skin, a new snake with a new and lovelier skin. That is birth.

EVE: I have seen that. It is wonderful. But

the rest of us will die sooner or later, like the fawn.

SERPENT: That must not be—I worship you, Eve—I must have something to worship. There must be something greater than the snake.

With Adam still away, the Serpent continues Eve's education, explaining to her that although she and Adam—who had thought themselves immortal—must die some day, they may be succeeded by new Adams and new Eves. When Adam returns Eve tells him the great news.

EVE: I will make other Adams, other Eves.
ADAM: I tell you you must not make up stories about this. It cannot happen.
SERPENT: I can remember when you were yourself a thing that could not happen, yet you are.
ADAM (struck): That must be true.
SERPENT: I will tell Eve the secret; and she will tell it to you.
ADAM: The secret! (He turns quickly towards the serpent, and in doing so puts his foot on something sharp.) Oh!
EVE: What is it?
ADAM (rubbing his foot): A thistle—and there, next to it, a briar—and nettles, too! I am tired of pulling these things up to keep the garden pleasant for us for ever.
SERPENT: Why should you trouble yourself? Let the new Adams clear a place for themselves.
EVE (to Adam): You must clear away some of those horrid things, or we shall be scratched and stung.
ADAM: Oh yes, some of them, of course. I will clear them away to-morrow. (The SERPENT laughs.) What a funny noise to make—I like it.
EVE: I do not. Why do you make it again?
SERPENT: Adam has invented something new—he has invented to-morrow. You will invent things every day now that the burden of immortality is lifted from you.
EVE: Immortality? What is that?
SERPENT: My new word for having to live for ever.
EVE: The serpent has made a beautiful word for being. Living.
ADAM: Make me a beautiful word for doing things to-morrow.

SERPENT: Procrastination.
EVE: That is a sweet word. I wish I had a serpent's tongue.
SERPENT: That may come too. Everything is possible.

ACT II is "a few centuries later," with the scene laid in an oasis in Mesopotamia. Adam delves in his garden, "looking worried, like a farmer," and Eve sits spinning flax in the shadow of a tree. Enter Cain, a warlike figure, with spear and shield. His reception by his parents is far from cordial; the prejudice caused by that little affair with Abel seems to linger. Cain is rather proud of his exploit. He despises his old father for a mere plodder; while he, Cain, is an adventurer, a man of spirit. A general wrangle ensues, with a lot of plain speaking all round. In fact, it might be a Saturday night family squabble in a Camden Town kitchen with Adam a "labourer," Eve a "charlady," and Cain —from the way he "chucks his weight about"—a rough sort of Tommy but lately demobbed. Altogether an unedifying scene, especially when Cain and his father nearly come to blows, after Eve has said many nasty things—as mothers-in-law have continued to do, so they say—about her son's wife. However, when .Cain has left them, Adam and Eve resume their monotonous tasks.

EVE (slowly taking up her distaff): If you were not a fool you would find something better for both of us to live by than this spinning and digging.
ADAM: Go on with your work, I tell you or you shall go without bread.
EVE: Man need not always live by bread alone. There is something else. We do not yet know what it is; but some day we shall find out; and then we shall live on that alone; and there shall be no more digging, no spinning, nor fighting, nor killing.
(She spins resignedly! he digs impatiently.)

The Gospel of the Brothers Barnabas

FROM first to last "The Gospel of the Brothers Barnabas," which constitutes Part II, is a truly brilliant piece of comedy. It is of the present day, and to a large extent political, two of the more important characters, Joyce Burge and Henry Hopkins Lubin, being easily recognizable caricatures of famous Liberal leaders. Their manners, opinions points of view and modes of speech are

arodied with delightful felicity, while
he mutual leg-pulling of the pair is ex-
ilarating in the extreme. The brothers
Barnabas may be taken to represent the
ducated, enlightened, thinking public,
Conrad being professor of biology at
arrowfields University, and Franklyn a
man of means and leisure, at one time
n the Church, "instead of which" he
ow lectures.

The scene is laid in the study of
Franklyn Barnabas's house, overlooking
Hampstead Heath. Both have come to
he same conclusion, namely, that life is
oo short for men to take it seriously,
nd they are agreed that its term should
e extended to at least three centuries.
That is their Gospel. The new rector,
Mr. Haslam, is introduced. He is a
oung, jolly, honest parson of the mod-
rn type, who "doesn't think he could
tick the Church" all his life, and to
whom the possibility of hundreds of
ears of it is by no means alluring. A
right little niece, Cynthia—"usually
alled Savvy, short for Savage," Dr.
Conrad explains—then comes in. A
"simple-lifer," frank, slangy and
obbed, she hits it off at once with the
padre who, unlike the uncles, has no
sort of objection to her manners. Then
here is a parlour-maid, who has "given
notice" because she feels that, since she
has only one life, it behooves her to
marry a village woodman with poetic
eyes and a moustache. She turns up in a
surprising way later, and is altogether
an engaging creature.

Joyce Burge, the eminent politician,
is announced. The brothers hastily
decide to try their new Gospel on him,
but without much hope of success.
"Why," declares Conrad, "Joyce Burge
has talked so much in the House of
Commons and out of it that he has lost
the power of listening." In reality Burge
wants Franklyn Barnabas, whose reputation and real character give him
weight, to stand for a Liberal seat. Soon
they are in the thick of an argument
which waxes hotter and hotter.

BURGE (*testily*): I wish you would come to
your point. Half the time you are saying that
you must have principles; and when I offer
you principles you say they won't work.

FRANKLYN: You have not offered me any
principles—your party shibboleths are not principles. If you get into power again you will
find yourself at the head of a rabble of Socialists and anti-Socialists, of Jingo Imperialists
and Little Englanders, of cast-iron Materialists
and ecstatic Quakers, of Christian Scientists and
Compulsory Inoculationists, of Syndicalists and
Bureaucrats: in short, of men differing fiercely
and irreconcilably on every principle that goes
to the root of human society and destiny: and
the impossibility of keeping such a team together will force you to sell the pass again
to the solid Conservative Opposition.

BURGE (*rising in wrath*): Sell the pass again!
You accuse me of having sold the pass! I solemnly declare that this is a false and monstrous
accusation.

FRANKLYN: Do you deny that the thing occurred? Were the uncontradicted reports false?
Were the published letters forgeries?

BURGE: Certainy not. But *I* did not do it. I
was not Prime Minister then. It was that old
dotard, that played-out old humbug Lubin.
He was Prime Minister then, not I.

FRANKLYN: Do you mean to say you did
not know?

BURGE (*sitting down again with a shrug*):
Oh, I had to be told. But what could I do?
If we had refused we might have had to go
out of office.

FRANKLYN: Precisely.

BURGE: Well, could we desert the country,
in such a crisis? The Hun was at the gate.
Everyone has to make sacrifices for the sake of
the country at such moments. We had to rise
above party; and I am proud to say we never
gave party a second thought. We stuck to—

CONRAD: Office?

BURGE (*turning on him*): Yes, sir, to office:
that is, to responsibility, to danger, to heart-
sickening toil, to abuse and misunderstanding,
to a martyrdom that made us envy the very
soldiers in the trenches. If you had had to live
for months on aspirin and bromide of potassium to get a wink of sleep, you wouldn't talk
about office as if it were a catch.

FRANKLYN: Still, you admit that under our
parliamentary system Lubin could not have
helped himself?

BURGE: On that subject my lips are closed.
Nothing will induce me to say one word against
the old man.

Mr. BURGE is proceeding to say every
sort of disparaging thing about
"the old man" when the parlour-maid
announces Mr. Lubin. Affable, kindly,
self-possessed, easily dignified, he is at

home at once. Very soon he is seated beside Savvy and patting her hand in a nice, paternal way; she interests him far more than do any of the others. It is not long before the rival leaders are saying very plain, straight things to one another. They. differ profoundly on every subject, but, of course, are debarred from quarrelling openly in their friends' study.

I could quote further from this—to my mind, the best—part of the work; but I want to get on to the "Gospel," which would have had no sort of chance amidst the politicians' chatter had not bright little Savvy insisted on making her uncles expound it. When Burge and Lubin hear the brothers' "Back to Methuselah" programme they are mildly interested, and not disinclined to agree that, after all, seventy years or so *is* a somewhat brief term in which to bring to perfection the great schemes they have at the back of their minds. At the same time they are both politely sceptical as to its possibility; and Lubin sarcastically enquires whether the elixir is lemons, or sour milk, or of what it consists?

Burge, on the other hand, thinks he sees political capital to be made out of it. "Back to the Bible!" that's the cry for the next election. Think of the effect on the Nonconformist vote! "You have put the Liberal Party into power for the next thirty years, Doctor; that's what you've done." Then Lubin cuts in once more. "Are the citizens to live three hundred years, as well as the statesmen?" "Of course," replies Conrad. Whereupon Lubin, remarking "that had not occurred to me," sits down abruptly, evidently very unfavourably affected by this new light.

Before the talk comes to an end the brothers have explained that they don't know when "the thing's going to happen." They can't make it happen; they can put it into men's heads that there is nothing to prevent its happening but their own wish to die before their work is done, and their own ignorance of the

splendid work there is for them to d In a word, it's all a matter of Will.

LUBIN: Why do you fix three hundred yea as the exact figure?
FRANKLYN: Because we must fix some figu Less would not be enough; and more wou be more than we dare as yet face.
LUBIN: Pooh! I am quite prepared to fa three thousand, not to say three million.
CONRAD: Yes, because you don't believe y will be called on to make good your word.
FRANKLYN (*gently*): Also, perhaps, becau you have never been troubled much by visio of the future.
BURGE (*with emphasis*): The future does n exist for Henry Hopkins Lubin.
LUBIN: If by the future you mean the m lennial delusions which you use as a bunch carrots to lure the uneducated British donk to the polling booth to vote for you, it ce tainly does not.

As they go out Lubin remarks Burge: "You don't suppose, do you, th our friends here are in earnest? The have just been pulling our legs ve wittily."

IN THE summer of the year A.D. 21 "the thing" has happened. We fin ourselves in the official parlour of th President of the British Islands. The have, indeed, been many changes in th two hundred and fifty years that hav elapsed since the scene in the Hampstea study, but Conrad Barnabas—or som one very like him—survives, and pre ently he is in conversation with th President, Burge-Lubin, "a stoutish middle-aged man, good-looking an breezily genial, dressed in a silk smoc stockings, handsomely ornamented sa dals, and a gold fillet round his brows. He is like Joyce Burge, yet also lik Lubin, as if nature had made a com posite photograph of the two me Burge-Lubin sits down in the pres dential chair. After putting a peg i his switchboard, he turns the pointer o the dial, puts another peg in and presse a button. At once a silvery screen hidin the end wall vanishes, and in its plac appears another office, wherein is di covered a man who looks like Conra He is the Accountant-General. At th resident's request, he goes off to inrview an American who claims to have vented a method of breathing under ater. It is suggested that Barnabas, as ie greatest living authority on the duraon of human life, should enquire into , as the invention may upset his estiate of that duration. When he has one, Confucius, the Chief-Secretary, omes in. Burge-Lubin wishes the peole would take a serious interest in olitics.

CONFUCIUS: I do not agree. The Englishman s not fitted by nature to understand politics. ver since the public services have been manned y Chinese, the country has been well and honstly governed. What more is needed?

BURGE-LUBIN: What I can't make out is that China is one of the worst governed countries n earth.

CONFUCIUS: No. It was badly governed twenty ears ago; but since we forbade any Chinaman o take part in our public services, and imported atives of Scotland for that purpose, we have lone well.

BURGE-LUBIN: People don't seem to be able to govern themselves. I can't understand it. Why should it be so?

CONFUCIUS: Justice is impartiality. Only strangers are impartial.

Other characters introduced in this topsy-turvy scene are the Minister of Health (a handsome negress), and Archbishop Haslam (our old friend the rector), who does not look a day over sixty, but is actually two hundred and eighty-three. He estimates that he has four million relatives. Then the Domestic Minister, Mrs. Lutestring, calls. She is a fine, young-looking woman, and the Archbishop is struck by her appearance. They begin to talk about ages, and the lady feels sure she has met him before; in fact, has opened the door for him many a time. She is, or was, the parlour-maid, now aged two hundred and seventy-five. There is general jealousy of the young-old pair, especially when they go off together.

The Tragedy of an Elderly Gentleman

WE COME next to the "Tragedy of an Elderly Gentleman," the date of which is A.D. 3000, and the scene Burrin pier, on the south shore of Galway Bay, Ireland. The Elderly Gentleman is discovered seated on an ancient stone stump. He has come from Bagdad, the capital of the British Commonwealth, on a pious pilgrimage "to one of the numerous lands of his fathers." The lady with whom he converses—one of the guardians of the district—can hardly understand his speech. She smiles gravely at his appearance, observing that it must be at least a hundred and fifty years since she last laughed. He is too old for such frivolity. A male inhabitant is called upon to try what he can make of the stranger; but he has no more luck than the lady; and at length the Elderly Gentleman, who, it appears, is a Vice-President the Travellers' Club, and no end of a swell, is turned over to a young woman who looks no older than Savvy Barnabas, whom she resembles somewhat, looked

a thousand odd years before. Her name is Zoo. They get on fairly well.

THE ELDERLY GENTLEMAN: Pray, is there no one in these islands who understands plain English?

ZOO: Well, nobody except the oracles. They have to make a special historical study of what we call the dead thought.

ELDERLY GENTLEMAN: Dead thought! I have heard of the dead languages, but never of the dead thought.

ZOO: Well, thoughts die sooner than languages. I understand your language, but we do not always understand your thought. The oracles will understand you perfectly. Have you had your consultation yet?

ELDERLY GENTLEMAN: I did not come to consult the oracle, madam. I am here simply as a gentleman travelling for pleasure in the company of my daughter, who is the wife of the British Prime Minister, and of General Aufsteig, who I may tell you in confidence is really the Emperor of Turania. The greatest military genius of the age.

ZOO: Why should you travel for pleasure? Can you not enjoy yourself at home?

ELDERLY GENTLEMAN: I wish to see the world.

ZOO: It is too big. You can see a bit of it anywhere.

ELDERLY GENTLEMAN (*out of patience*): Damn it, madam, you don't want to spend your life looking at the same bit of it! (*Checking himself.*) I beg your pardon for swearing in your presence.

Zoo: Oh! That is swearing, is it? I have read about that. It sounds quite pretty. Dammit-madam, dammitmadam. Say it as often as you please. I like it.

ELDERLY GENTLEMAN (*expanding with immense relief*): Bless you for those profane but familiar words! Thank you, thank you. I begin to feel at home.

QUITE the brightest thing in this section of the book is, I think, the Elderly Gentleman's outburst on the subject of Ireland—much too long to quote, unfortunately—which is a sheer masterpiece of *malice,* with a lot of truth mingled with its laughter. None but an Irishman could so perfectly have hit off his native land.

The rest of the party from Bagdad now arrive. Among them is "a man of compact figure, clean-shaven, saturnine, and self-centred, very like Napoleon I." They all proceed to a courtyard before a temple, where presently the Oracle is to be consulted by the Envoys. Napoleon—otherwise Emperor of Turania—encounters a Veiled Woman who, when she has dressed for the part, becomes the Oracle, and there is a very amusing trial of will power between them, the Man of Destiny coming off second best, needless to say. All this scene is first-rate burlesque. The visitors remark a statue, and enquire whose it is. Zoo volunteers to tell them the story of the statue:

A thousand years ago, when the whole world was given over to short-lived people, there was a war called the War to End War. In the war that followed it about ten years later, none of the soldiers were killed; but seven of the capital cities of Europe were wiped out of existence. It seems to have been a great joke; for the statesmen, who thought they had sent ten million common men to their deaths, were themselves blown into fragments, with their houses and families, while the ten million men lay snugly in the caves they had dug for themselves. Later on even the houses escaped, but their inhabitants were poisoned by gas that spared no living soul.

Of course, the soldiers starved and ran wild;

and that was the end of pseudo-Christian civilization. The last civilized thing that happened was that the statesmen discovered that cowardice was a great patriotic virtue; and a public monument was erected to its first preacher, an ancient and very fat sage called Sir John Falstaff. Well (*pointing*), that's Falstaff.

The rest of the Act, like that which follows, is frank farce. A lot of elaborate tomfoolery, more effective acted than read, with plenty of creepy "effects," scenic and otherwise, finds its culmination in the Oracle's blunt reply to the fussy Envoy: "Go home, poor fool." This, Zoo informs the party, is "the same reply, word for word, that your illustrious predecessor got fifteen years ago. You asked for it, and you got it."

But the Envoy's grand-daughter is not satisfied. That was not the answer given before. She can remember it, having learnt it at school. And she quotes: "When Britain was cradled in the west, the east wind hardened her and made her great. Whilst the east wind prevails Britain shall prosper. The east wind shall wither Britain's enemies in the day of contest."

They come to the conclusion that the former Envoy, on hearing the Oracle's reply, faked up an answer fit for publication—and won an election with it. "He was capable of anything," adds the present Envoy bitterly; "I knew his private secretary.

IN Part V we find ourselves "As Far as Thought can Reach." It is some distance, certainly, the date being A.D. 31,920! In my innocence I had supposed all along that the solution of all this joyous nonsense, masquerading so gravely in the garb of wisdom, might be found herein; but I was mistaken. If solution there be, each of us must discover it for himself, or "give it up," as I confess myself compelled to do.

Among the characters is Pygmalion, a sculptor, who, with the aid of a noted biologist, has constructed a synthetic man. Alas! he turned out a most dangerous beast, and had to be destroyed.

Next a synthetic couple are introduced; they, too, are all right up to a certain point, but the woman bites her creator, Pygmalion, and he falls dead. It was necessary to kill the couple also. So all the laboratory work was wasted.

Last of all come Ghosts—Adam's, Eve's, Cain's, the Serpent's, Lilith's. All but the last-named say a few words in justification of the part each played "in the Beginning." Eve concludes with: "My clever ones have inherited the earth. All's well." The Serpent declared himself content, since "there is now no evil, and wisdom and good are one." Cain says: "None can deny that mine was a splendid game while it lasted." Adam says—and it may well be the father of mankind speaks for the vast majority—"I can make nothing of it, neither head nor tail. What is it all for? Why? Whither? Whence? . . . Foolishness, I call it."

To Lilith is left the final word: "Of Life only is there no end . . . It is enough that there is a Beyond."

So THIS is Mr. Shaw's "beginning for a Bible of Creative Evolution"; these are the books forming his "Metabiological Pentateuch"; and, having read them with great care—often puzzled, at times rather bored (for these notes were nothing unless perfectly frank), frequently filled with admiration and astonishment and amusement—having duly done my utmost to meet my author half-way, I come to the conclusion that this is a brilliant achievement, especially for one who would have us believe "his sands are running out"! Garrulity, to which he rather unnecessarily pleads guilty, there is, of course, but this is not the garrulity of age—which is intolerable.

No; let Mr. Shaw say what he will, the author of this extraordinarily suggestive, provocative work is just as "unbearably brilliant"—to use his own perfect piece of self-criticism—to-day, as he was in what he likes to regard as his prime, a quarter of a century, or more, ago. Time has left G.B.S. untouched. And really, when you come to think of it, there would seem to be no reason why, as a disciple of his delightful Brothers Barnabas, Mr. Shaw should not be found, some time about the year 2170, correcting the final proof sheets of the concluding portion of the "Bible" he has now so engagingly commenced. His "Revelation" would be worth reading!

LOVE, DRINK, AND DEBT

I HAVE been in love, and in debt, and in drink,
    This many and many a year,
And those are three plagues enough, any should think,
    For one poor mortal to bear.
'Twas love made me fall into drink,
    And drink made me run into debt,
And though I have struggled, and struggled, and strove,
    I cannot get out of them yet.

There's nothing but money can cure me,
    And rid me of all my pain!
    'Twill pay all my debts,
    And remove all my lets,
And my mistress, that cannot endure me,
    Will love me, and love me again:
Then I'll fall to my loving and drinking amain!

                    —A. Brome

GABRIELE D'ANNUNZIO
1864–1938

THE GIOCONDA

With a Biographical and Critical Study by Robert Musgrove Scott

GABRIELE D'ANNUNZIO —the name evokes such a tumult of recollections that it seems to designate not one man, but many. Seldom has a man of letters played such varied parts so seriously and conspicuously as this dramatist, poet, novelist, soldier, ruler, and apostle of Italian patriotism. He has had adventures so romantic that the history of them seems almost too improbable to be taken seriously.

Throughout the whole of his career, however, and in all his rôles, d'Annunzio has had one very prominent characteristic—a tremendous vitality that reminds us of the artists of the Renaissance. He considered that the most precious quality of the beautiful Duchess of Scerni, a figure in his novel, "The Child of Pleasure," was the splendour of her unaffectedly youthful spirit. The same judgement might be passed on himself; for in his life and writing alike we find a young impetuousness, daring and appetite for beauty. This is natural in the case of his literary work, for the best was done in the nineteenth century; but considering his political career, it seems incredible that he should have been born in 1864.

Until 1915, d'Annunzio attracted the attention of the world only as a great writer. His life was eccentric, of course, but eccentricity is expected of a distinguished artist. His work was fervently acclaimed in his own country and admired throughout the rest of Europe. He seemed destined to the materially comfortable but uneventful life of a genius whose pre-eminence receives

pecuniary recognition. The Great War came, and Italy at first took no part in it, so that it did not seem to concern in the least her greatest author. In May 1915, however, d'Annunzio returned to Italy from France, blazing with generous anger because of the German atrocities. It was evidence of his youthful spirit, this spectacular indignation, as was also the energy with which he set about finding a practical outlet for his feeling. Writing, speaking in public, demonstrating, he began to influence the rather uncertain temper of the Italian public. His great literary reputation, his intoxicating articles and furious declamations completely appealed to the imagination of his countrymen. Italy entered the war with enthusiasm—a step for which d'Annunzio's propaganda had largely prepared it.

DURING the war he served as an airman, and was distinguished for his bravery and skill. Then came the holiday adventure of Fiume—an incident that reads like extravagant comic opera, but which had a great effect on the minds of Italians. Italy had hoped to receive the great Hungarian port of Fiume after the war; but it was decided at the peace negotiations that this was impracticable, principally owing to the attitude of Yugoslavia.

Italian opinion bitterly resented the decision; the citizens of Fiume were no less angry. Italy was too much weakened by internal dissension to take any kind of action. Class and industrial disputes tore the nation, and the patriotism that had been very real during the war had become a catchword. D'Annunzio, however, with a distinctly self-conscious air of heroism, snapped his fingers in the face of Europe. In September 1919 he occupied Fiume with an army of ill-clad and ill-armed volunteers, and encouraged the people with placards and banners to shout: "Italy or Death!"

He reigned in Fiume until January 1921, although the treaty of Rapallo had made the city an independent state in the previous November. His administration was not remarkably efficient, but neither was it discreditable; and when he returned to his own land his departure was deeply regretted by his late subjects. It might be thought that the whole adventure was a foolish melodrama—a schoolboy game played on a large scale. So far as Italy was concerned, however, the impression that it made was far different. D'Annunzio had once more captured the imagination of Italians; had fired them with renewed patriotism, and given them a greater national self-respect. As a reward he was created Prince of Montenevoso. He retired from public affairs to develop his theories of life, and to patrol (quite unnecessarily) the Lake Garda in an armed motor-boat.

I T MAY seem that so many biographical details are out of place in a study of d'Annunzio's art. Apart from the fact, however, that he has lived in a manner at least reminiscent of one of those heroes for whom he has so often expressed his reverence, there is a close connection between his literary and his political work. Both are fruits of the same inspiration—a love of Italy, young and old: a love of the modern nation that has amounted almost to folly; a love of the immortal guardian of an ancient culture that has amounted to worship. His war-time and post-war adventures are part of his poetry—a stirring and formless epic; his poetry contains the spiritual essence of his patriotism.

That part of d'Annunzio's life which we have considered in detail might lead us to expect that his works would be filled with the spirit of romance. It is true that his earlier poetry is in the grand, rhetorical style of the much recited verse of his compatriot, Carducci—a style which suggests that the poet has had a dictionary of classical and historical allusions constantly before him.

As a whole, however, although they show many varied influences, d'Annunzio's writings have few romantic tendencies. The most remarkable quality, indeed, that they have in common, next to their vigour, is the fidelity with which they accord to classical traditions. His poems echo the lyric cadences of the Golden and Silver ages of Roman literature; his novels have the Latin virtues of crystal clarity and epigrammatic description; and his successful tragedies have the restraint and sense of form of the tragedies of ancient Greece.

In his "New Song," published in 1882, d'Annunzio prays:

To me now the serene rhythm of Albius Tibullus, where laughs the vast peace of the country in flower.
Where laugh the azures of the Latin sky, and the pale suns and the clouds—as in a clear brook.

So, in his verse, it is not only the rhythm, the music, that remind us of the poets of ancient Rome. D'Annunzio's sensuousness, his delight in colour, in "the azures of the Latin sky and the pale suns," in physical beauty of every kind, in love, in poetry, clearly show what tradition he follows. But his pagan love for nature (in its widest sense) is no mere literary admiration as was Swinburne's. It is his deepest and most genuine sentiment. His ardour and passionate sincerity, whether he be writing of love and death in "The Chimera," or of Rome in "Roman Elegies," show him to be a true countryman of Horace and Catullus, having similar tastes and a similar philosophy.

Sing of the huge joy of living, of being strong, of being young; of biting earthly fruits with strong, white, greedy teeth.

And of hearing all music, and of looking
with eyes of flame on the divine face of the
world, as a lover looks on his beloved.

He is a miserable slave, he who makes sorrow his garment.

To live intensely is to develop one's
personality to the full; to look on the
world and find it good; these are
d'Annunzio's favourite themes, and all
his poetry resounds with his praise of
earth. His creed is no blind atheism; it
is a vital pantheism. His is the oldest
kind of song; yet it is perpetually young.

IN CONSIDERING d'Annunzio's novels,
we are immediately struck by their
confusing variety of styles. Even though
he has divided the more important novels
into three cycles, the Romances of the
Rose, of the Lily, and of the Pomegranate, each consisting of three works,
this does not altogether mean that each
group represents a stage in his artistic or
intellectual development. Within a single
cycle his outlook and method of treating
his subjects change. To illustrate this,
we might instance two of the Romances
of the Rose. "The Child of Pleasure"
(1888) is written under the influence of
de Maupassant's works; in "The Intruder" (by which title "L'Innocente"
has been translated into English)
although the creative hand is the hand
of d'Annunzio the voice is the voice of
Dostoievsky. Both these tales and "The
Triumph of Death" (1894), the third
of this cycle, are remarkable for their
realism. The Romances of the Lily show
d'Annunzio still wandering inconse-
quently about the fields of literature. He
toys—always in his vivid style—with
vague philosophies: in "The Virgins of
the Rocks" (1896), for example, he
thinks that he has found his ideal hero
in the Teutonic Superman.

In the Romances of the Pomegranate
—"The Flame," "The Victory of Man,"
and "The Triumph of Life"—we find
that d'Annunzio has arrived at something definite. He begins at last to give
expression to his own ideas—those ideas
that are the inspiration of his poetry.

He writes in frank and passionate praise
of pagan loveliness and earthly joys.
Throughout he asserts the glory of
material existence. He is no longer at
all derivative; his prose is richer and
more poetic than in his other words.
These three, however, show the weakness of all his novels. His arguments
are always partisan, although expressed
with a clarity and force that are almost
startling, so that the reader may with
equal justification accept or reject them.
Therefore, even if nobody can deny the
technical excellence of his novels, any
estimation of their value as serious contributions to literature must depend on
individual taste.

IT IS in his tragedies that d'Annunzio
shows his genius most clearly. With
the exception of the more ambitious (and
far less able) poetical dramas such as
"Phedra," they are all concerned with
extremely fascinating problems of common interest, and have this mark of
great literature: that, however original,
however unfamiliar to us their characters may be, the plots woven about them
are of universal application. In them
d'Annunzio develops his themes honestly—his plays are almost entirely free
from the special pleading that mars his
novels. In them, too, his insight into
psychology is shown to be very great—
as when he presents the tragedy of
blindness in "The Dead City." An idea
of his powers as a dramatist might best
be given, however, by outlining his
tragedy, "The Gioconda."

"THE GIOCONDA" is the story of the
unhappy married life of a sculptor,
Lucio Settala, and his wife, Silvia.
Broadly speaking, the question that
d'Annunzio asks and answers in the play
is this: "Have two persons, one of an
artistic temperament, fine but unstable,
and the other of a domestic temperament, placid and tender, enough in common to enable them to live happily
together?" D'Annunzio decides that they
have not. The beauty, the strength and

the weakness of both of the principal characters are drawn with unerring skill. We see that Silvia's love for Lucio is as much the cause of the final tragedy as the fact that he is tired of her, and that this love is really a desire for possession that makes Silvia use any weapons—even bluster and conscious lies—in her fight to retain her husband's affections. At the same time, we are made to feel Lucio's unconscious hypocrisy in persuading himself that it is his art that separates him from Silvia, when it is actually his love for another woman. We cannot be sure whether we most admire the author's wonderful dissection of character or the sense of proportion that is maintained throughout the play.

Many critics have raised the objection that there is too little action in d'Annunzio's dramas. To hold this opinion is, however, to miss their essential quality. They are modelled on classical tragedy, so that much action would be out of place. D'Annunzio's stage-craft, moreover, makes action unnecessary as a means of holding the attention of the audience. He creates his situations almost entirely by words.

For example, the first scene of Act I of "The Gioconda" consists of a conversation between Silvia and a family friend, Lorenzo Gaddi, who taught Lucio the rudiments of the sculptor's art. Almost immediately after the rise of the curtain Gaddi says:

"The storm is passed, and here is Lucio coming back to you, full of thankfulness and tenderness, after so much wrong." We know immediately that something has happened—something that is going to be of consequence to the development of the play. And we are all agog to know what the mysterious wrong has been when Silvia speaks:

"Sometimes all that has been, all the evil, all the sorrow and even the blood and the scar, all disappear, vanish; everything is forgotten; everything ceases to have been. Sometimes all that has passed, all the horrible burden of memory, so tightly packed, so overloaded, becomes solid and real and hard, like a wall; like a rock barrier that I must never cross."

We are told that the event that caused all her trouble has been connected with Lucio, and that the blood was shed at his studio. Later in the scene we discover that Lucio tried to commit suicide, being the most complete victim of a woman, who is not named. It has been a great tragedy, and Silvia is apprehensive as to its effect on her husband. Will he really love her again; will he return to his work? Lorenzo Gaddi assures her that all will be well, but he does not speak with great conviction. Despite her rather forced cheerfulness, there is obvious apprehension in Silvia's manner.

IN THE next scene we learn a little more of what has happened from Francesca Doni, Silvia's sister, when she talks with Cosimo Dalbo, a friend of Lucio's, who has been absent on a visit to Egypt. The doctors despaired of saving Lucio's life, and it was only Silvia's selfless devotion that brought the artist back to health. The designing woman, Gioconda Dianti, has not given up hope of winning Lucio—like Silvia, Francesca will not impute unfaithfulness to the man. Then Lucio appears. He has not seen Cosimo since the latter's return from his holiday, and each has much to say to the other.

We hear that Lucio has attempted suicide after completing a marvellous statue, which no longer interests him he maintains, although we see clearly that his attitude is a pose. Cosimo, however, says that something will have been saved from the wreck of the tragedy—the statue; and that "so much suffering will not have been in vain, and so much misfortune will not have been entirely useless if a beautiful thing is added to the decoration of life." Lucio agrees, and thus shows how different are his ideas from those of his wife, who will be content to account as naught the suffering and wrong if her husband loves her again.

Silvia comes to her husband, and

Cosimo leaves. The interview between husband and wife is sketched with great delicacy and a wonderful depth of feeling. So constrained are they at the beginning of their talk, and so hysterical is their reconciliation that it does not seem probable that it will endure long. But the first act ends in an atmosphere of tranquil beauty—of calm so perfect that we suspect that it is the traditional herald of a storm.

WE ARE not kept long in suspense, for in the first scene of Act II d'Annunzio analyzes the mind of Lucio Settala, showing that his love for Gioconda Dianti is still a consuming passion. Cosimo and Lucio are sitting together, and the latter mentions that he has had a love letter from Gioconda that "burnt his fingers."

"You still love her?" Cosimo asks.

Lucio denies it, but on being pressed he admits that he is worried by the knowledge that the girl waits for him every day at the foot of his statue—his masterpiece. His nervous condition is so obvious that Cosimo proposes that he should go away for a long holiday, and so come to forget the temptress. Lucio refuses.

"She will have imparted more subtly her spirit to that house which I love because of the work that it represents to me," he says. "I shall see her from these distant places as the guardian of a statue over which I spent the most vivid moments of my life. No, I do not love her. But she will me; she will always be the stronger; she knows that she can conquer me and bind me; she is armed with a fascination before which I cannot maintain my own will without tearing my heart to shreds . . . and she waits confidently."

Cosimo shows the most downright common sense, suggesting that Lucio must either deprive Gioconda of the key of the studio, or sell the studio itself. Lucio argues hotly against following either of these courses; but it is plain that he is hiding his real reason for wishing to retain the studio, and to allow Gioconda to keep her key to it. At last Cosimo cries:

"I thought, at the beginning, that all that was necessary was that you should be freed from an importunate woman. I recognize now that what I have advised was childish."

Lucio's reserve breaks down, and he mutters:

"I should have been left to die."

It was only because he was possessed of the artist's impatience of facts—because he found the life that convention expected of him unsupportable—that he had tried to kill himself.

Cosimo sets about appealing to Lucio's emotions—to his love for Silvia as the mother of their one child, Beata. He goes too far, however; he becomes very sentimental. Lucio answers his reasoning bitterly. Cosimo is very patient, and still urges him to go away with Silvia for a holiday, maintaining that he "will again find the goodness which will be an inspiration" to him.

"The goodness! The goodness!" Lucio exclaims, "Do you think that inspiration comes from goodness, and not from some deep instinct within me! I am within my own law, so that I am also within the law of Good."—One of the most forcible expositions in literature of the divine selfishness of art.

He then proceeds to give reasons for his love for Gioconda—declaring throughout that she is part of his art. Here d'Annunzio's prose is seen at its best, crisp, marvellously vivid and fluent. She is a thousand statues, Lucio cries, and the ancients were blinded by the glory of statues. Her beauty lives in all marble. When he went with her to the quarries at Carrara, a "confused aspiration" seemed to leap to her from the motionless white of the marble. "The wind, the sun, the vastness of the mountains, the long lines of yoked oxen, and the antique curves of the yokes, and the grinding of the loads, and the cloud that was trickling from the Tirreno, and the incredibly high flight of an eagle—all these filled me with an exaltation that was like infinite poetry."

As if to justify his conduct further in his friend's eyes (and incidently in ours), Lucio describes how, just before he tried to kill himself, he had begun to model another statue in plaster. It would have crumbled to dust had not Gioconda, during his illness, kept damp the cloths that covered it. She was the preserver of his art.

"While the other (Silvia) was preserving your life?" Cosimo interrupts reproachfully.

"Which of the two things is the more valuable?" Lucio demands. "Life would be intolerable to me if it were to mean the agonising surrender of one of my conceptions . . . But I have told you already, I ought to have been allowed to die . . . Now that I have recovered, you find in me the same man, and the same influences. What would you advise? Shall I follow my destiny?"

Before Cosimo can answer the cruel question, however, the two are interrupted by Silvia and Francesca Doni. Cosimo leaves, and Lucio goes with him. But we see that his pretense of irresolution is at an end; he knows that he will "follow his destiny." D'Annunzio has almost finished with him; he has shown the beauty and the hypocrisy of the artistic mind.

Francesca tells her sister that old Lorenzo Gaddi has seen Gioconda, and that the girl has refused to have any dealings with anybody not sent by Lucio himself. Silvia, burning with anger, says that she will go and see Gioconda, will confront her and will find some means of driving her out. Silvia is the personification of outraged conventional propriety. She knows that Lucio has been receiving letters from Gioconda; and where and when the girl waits for her husband. She will keep the appointment for him. Francesca is timid, but practical; Silvia, however, is too excited to listen to her mild counsels. She announces her intention of going immediately to meet Gioconda; and Francesca decides to accompany her. So the second act ends, with tragedy impending.

We watch the next act in horrified anticipation. The scorn, the virtuous indignation of the wife which is opposed to the sentimentally poetic and altogether impertinent attitude of the model make a quarrel inevitable. We can imagine the terror of Francesca, who is hiding in a room off the studio. Events march swiftly. Silvia persuades Gioconda that Lucio no longer cares for her in any way, and the girl rushes behind a curtain to smash Lucio's statue—his masterpiece. Silvia follows her, and there is a scuffle, in the course of which the statue is overthrown and broken to fragments. In attempting to prevent this disaster, however, Silvia has her hands terribly cut. Lucio appears, and Silvia realizes that he has come to see Gioconda. Her mental and physical agony are too great for her endurance, and she faints, knowing that she has finally lost Lucio's love.

The play does not end here, although it has given an answer to the problem with which it deals. According to classical tradition, the audience could not be dismissed so soon after the emotional crisis of a play. D'Annunzio, accordingly, gives us a picture of Silvia, deserted by her husband and with her two hands amputated at the wrists, living a secluded life by the sea. The act is filled with great poetry, but is intensely sad because of the fruitless efforts that Silvia makes to keep all knowledge of her tragedy, including her own maimed condition, from her child.

So the play ends—pathetically rather than tragically. It is typical of d'Annunzio's art that it should be like this. He has always striven after realism, and the after-effects of tragedy are much more often pathetic than tragic; that is to say, they are invested with a sadness that appeals to the emotions raher than with a horror that appeals to the intellect.

H. M. Tomlinson

THE SEA AND THE JUNGLE

Outlined by the Author

IMMEDIATELY upon the publication of this book in 1912 discerning critics declared that a new author had "arrived" to claim a secure place in the front rank of literary artists. Its full title was "The Sea and the Jungle, Being the Narrative of the Voyage of the Tramp Steamer *Capella* from Swansea to Pará in the Brazils and thence 2,000 Miles along the Forests of the Amazon and Madeira Rivers to the San Antonio Falls, Afterwards Returning to Barbadoes for Orders and Going by way of Jamaica to Tampa in Florida where She Loaded for Home. Done in the years 1909 and 1910." This title is virtually a synopsis of the book, and how enchanting that book is may be gauged from the following outline. Bibliophiles treasure the first edition. Mr. Tomlinson's later books include "Old Junk," "London River," "Waiting for Daylight," "Tidemarks," "Under the Red Ensign" and "Gifts of Fortune."

Outward Bound from Swansea to Brazil

"I'VE NEVER seen her as dirty as this," grumbled the chief engineer apologetically, peeping from his cabin at green water lopping casually over the after-deck. "It's that patent fuel —it's stowed wrong. Now she'll roll— you can feel it—the cat she is, she's never going to stop. It's that patent fuel and her new load line."

Certainly she sat close to the sea. I had never before seen so much lively water so close. She wallowed, she plunged, she rolled, she sank heavily to its level. I looked out from the window of the Chief's cabin, and those green mounds of the swell swinging under us and away were superior, in apparition, to my outlook.

We rolled. I grasped the rail of the weather-cloth, in the drive of wind and spume, and rode our charger like a valiant man; like a valiant man who is uncertain of his seat. Something like a valiant man. We advanced to the attack, masts and funnel describing great arcs, and steadily our bows shouldered away the foe. I think sailors deserve large monies. Being the less valiant—for the longer I watched, the more grew I wet and cold—it came to my mind that

where we were, but a few weeks before, another large freighter had her hatches opened by the seas, and presently was but a trace of oil and cinders on the waters. You will remember I am on my first long voyage.

We rounded Hartland. It was growing dark, the weather was now directly upon our starboard beam, and the waves were coming solidly inboard. The main deck was white with plunging water. We rolled still more.

"I can't make out why you left London when you didn't have to," said the grinning sailor. "I'd like to be on the Stratford tram, going down to Forest Gate."

This was nearly as bad as the Chief's flute. I held up two fingers over those hatches of ours, called silently on blessed Saint Anthony, who loves sailors, and went down the ladder; for night had come, and the prospect from the *Capella* was not the less apprehensive to the mind of a landsman because the enemy could not be seen, except as flying ghosts. The noises could be heard all right.

I SHUT my heavy teak door amidships, shut out the daunting uproar of floods and the sensation that the night was collapsing round our heaving ship.

There was a home light far away, on some unseen Cornish headland, rising and falling like a soaring but tethered star. Nor did I want the lights of home.

I turned up the dull and stinking oil lamp, and tried to read; but that fuliginous glim haunted the pages. That black-edged light too much resembled my own thoughts made manifest. There were some bunches of my cabin mate's clothes hanging from hooks, and I watched their erratic behaviour instead. The water in the carafe was also interesting, because quite mad, standing diagonally in the bottle, and then reversing. A lump of soap made a flying leap from the washstand, and then slithered about the floor like something hunted and panic-stricken. I listened to numerous little voices. There was no telling their origins. There was a chorus in the cabin, whispers, plaints, creaks, wails and grunts; but they were foundered in the din when the spittoon, which was an empty meat tin, got its lashings loose, and began a rioting fandango on the concrete. Over the clothes chest, which was also our table, and a cabin fixture, was a portrait of the mate's sweetheart, and on its frame was one of my busy little friends the cockroaches; for the mate and I do not sleep alone in this cabin, not by hundreds. The cockroach stood in thought, waving his hands interrogatively, as one who talks to himself nervously. The ship at that moment received a seventh wave, lurched and trembled. The cockroach fell. I rose, listening. I felt sure a new clamour would begin at once, showing we had reached another and critical stage of the fight. But no; the brave heart of her was beating as before. I could feel its steady pulse throbbing in our table. We were alive and strong, though laboring direfully.

It was when I was thinking whether bed would be, as I have so often found it, the best answer to doubt, that I heard a boatswain's pipe.

I fought one side of the door, and the wind fought the other. My hurry to open the door was great, but the obstinate wind held it firmly. Without warning the wind released its hold, the ship fell over to windward, the door flew open, and forth I went, clutching at the driving dark. Then up sailed my side of the ship, and the door shut with the sound of gunfire. I had never before experienced such insensate violence. These were the unlawful noises and movements of chaos. Hanging to a rail, I was puzzling out which was the head and which the stern of the ship, when a flying lump of salt water struck me in the face just as a figure (I thought it was the chief officer) hurried past me, bawling "All hands."

The figure came back. "That you, purser? Number three hatch has gone," it said, and disappeared instantly.

So then this very thing had come to me, and at night. Our hatches were adrift. It was impossible. Why, we had only just left Swansea. It could not be true; it was absurdly unfair. This was my first long voyage, and it had only just begun. I stood like the cricketer who is out for a duck.

If I could tell you how I felt, I would. Somebody was shouting somewhere, but his words were cut off at once by the wind and blown away. I felt my way along a wet and dark alleyway which was giddily unstable, for sometimes it pressed hard against my feet, and then it would fall from under me. I got round by the engine-room entrance. Small gleams, shavings of light, were escaping from seams in the unseen structure, but they illuminated nothing, except a length of wet rail or a scrap of wet deck. The ship itself was a shade, manned by voices.

I could not see that anything was being done. Were they allowing her to fill up like an open barge? I became aware my surcharged feelings were escaping by my knees, which kept knocking in their tremors against a lower rail. I tried to stop this trembling by hardening my muscles, but my fearful legs had their own way. Yet it is plain there was nothing to fear. I told my legs so. Had we not but that day left Swansea? Besides, I had already commenced a letter which was to be posted at Pará. The letter would have to be posted. They were waiting for it at home. Somewhere below me a heavy mass of water plunged monstrously, and became a faintly luminous cloud over all the main deck aft, actually framing the rectangular form of the deck in the night. This was unreasonable. I was not really one of the crew either, though on the articles. I was there by chance. No advantage should be taken of that. A torrent poured down the athwartships alleyway, and nearly swept me from my feet.

One could not watch what was happening. That was another cruel injustice. The wind and sea could be heard, and the ship could be felt. But how could I be expected to know what to do in the dark in such circumstances? There ought to be a light. This should have happened in the daytime. My garrulous knees struck the lower rail violently in their excitement. I leant over the rail, shading my eyes. I grew savagely indignant with something having no name and no shape. I cannot even now give a name to the thing that angered me, but can just discern, in the twilight which shrouds the undiscovered, a vast calm face the rock of which no human emotion can move, with eyes that stare but see nothing, and a mouth that never speaks, and ears from which assailing cries and questions fell as mournful echoes, ironic repetitions. This flung stone falls from it, as unavailing as your prayers; but we shall never cease to pray and fling stones, alternately, up there into the twilight.

Nevertheless, when the Chief, with his hurricane lamp, found me he says I was smiling. The youth who was our second mate ran up and stood by us, the better to shout to the deck below. He shouted, bending over the rail, till he was screaming through hoarseness. He turned to us abruptly. "They don't understand a word

I say," he cried in despair. "There isn't a sailor or an Englishman in the crowd the—German farmers." This, I found afterwards, was nearly true. These men had been signed on at a continental port. It was really our Dutch cook who saved us that night. It was the cook who first saw the hatch covers going.

THE SHIP's head had been put to the seas to keep the decks as clear as possible, and as I was now more accustomed to the gloom I could make out the men below busy at the hatch. Most conspicuous among them was the cook, who had taken charge there, and he, with three languages, bludgeoned into surprising activity the inexperienced youngsters who were learning for the first time what happens to a ship when the carpenter's chief job on leaving port has its defects discovered by exceptional weather. They were wading through swirling waters as they worked, and once a greater wave sprang bodily over them, and when the hatch showed through the foam again some of the men had gone, as though dissolved. But it was found they had kept the right side of the bulwarks, and the elderly carpenter, whose leg had got wedged in a winch, was the only one damaged.

If you ask me when I shall be pleased to allow the necessary sun to rise upon this narrative to give it a little warmth, then I must tell you it cannot be done till we have fastened down the *Capella's* number two hatch, at least. That hatch has gone now, and if hatches one and four give way while number two is getting attention from the weary, soaked and frozen crowd which has just had an hour's desperate work at number three, then I fear the sun will never rise on this narrative. (How Bates got over to his wonderful blue butterflies in those Amazonian forest paths under a tropical sun in thirty-eight words I do not know. He must have been thinking of nothing but his butterflies. I cannot do it, with the seas and the ship keeping my mind so busy.)

Luckily, the other hatches kept staunch. We were watertight again. When the Old Man, the Chief, the Doctor and the Purser gathered late that night in the Chief's cabin to see what it was he had secreted in his cupboard, we sat where we could, and I never knew tobacco could taste like that. I felt as if never before had I found such large leisure for extracting its full flavour. From a sudden limitation within a space which gave me a brief outlook of a few hours, I was presently released into the open again and of what might remain to me of the usual gift of ample years. I had all that time to smoke in. Never did a pipe taste so sweet. It is idle for good and serious souls to think me graceless here with this talk of tobacco immediately after such a release. Let me tell them my sacrificial smoke rose up straight and accepted. Looking through the smoke, I saw clearly how worthy, kind and lovable were the faces of my comrades. I warmed to this voyage for the first time, as though, after a test, I had been initiated. This was the place for me, with men like these about me, and such great affairs to be met. I revelled in the thought of our valorous bluff, insignificant as we were in that malign desolation, sundered from our kind.

"Chief," said the Old Man, "it was my department that time. None of your old engines did it."

"You've got a good cook," said the Chief. "I saw that."

Then the Chief, remembering something, turned in his seat to the picture hanging above his desk of a smiling and handsome matron. "Here's luck, old girl," he said, holding up his glass, "you can still send me some letters."

Up the Para River

"LAND Ho!" That was the Skipper's own perfunctory cry. He had saved his pound of tobacco.

It was two in the afternoon. There was America. I rediscovered it with some difficulty. All I could see was a mere local thickening of the horizon, as though the pen which drew the faint line dividing the world ahead into an upper and a nether opalescence had run a little freely at one point. That thickening of the horizon was the island of Monjui. Soon, though, there was a palpable something athwart our course. The skyline heightened into a blush barrier, which, as we approached it, broke into sections. The chart told us that a series of low, wooded islands skirts the mainland. Yet it was hard to believe we were approaching land again. What showed as land was of too unsubstantial a quality, too thin and broken a rind on that vast area of water to be of any use as a foothold. Where luminous sky was behind an island groups of diminutive palms were seen, as tiny and distinct as the forms of mildew under a magnifying glass, delicate black pencillings along the foot of the sky-wall. Often that hairlike tracery seemed to rest upon the sea. The *Capella* continued to stand in, till Brazil was more than a frail and tinted illusion which sometimes faded the more the eye sought it. Presently it cast reflections. The islands grew into cobalt layers, with vistas of silver water between them; they acquired body. The course was changed to west, and we cruised along for Atalaia Point, towards the pilot station. Over the thin and futile rind of land which topped the sea —it was thin enough to undulate on the low swell—ponderous thunder clouds towered, continents of night in the sky, with translucent areas dividing them which were brightly illuminated from the hither side. Curtains as black as bitumen draped to the waters from great heights. Two of these appalling curtains, trailing over America, were drawn a little apart. We could see beyond them to a diminishing array of glowing cloud summits; far through those parted black curtains of storm we saw an accidental revelation of a secret and wonderful region with a sun of its own. And all, gigantic clouds, the sea, the far and frail coast, were serene and still. The air had ceased to breathe. I thought this new lucent world we had found might prove but a lucky dream after all, to be seen but not to be entered, and that some noise would presently shatter it and wake me. But we came alongside the white pilot schooner, and the pilot put off in a boat manned by such a crowd of grinning, ragged and cinnamon-skinned pirates as would have broken the fragile wonder of any spell. Ours, though, did not break, and I was able to believe we had arrived. At sunset the great clouds were full of explosions of electric fire, and there were momentary revelations above us of huge impending shapes. We went slowly over a lower world obscurely lighted by phosphorescent waves.

Jan. 9. The *Capella* left Pará at three o'clock this morning, and continued up the Pará River. Daylight found us in a wide, brownish stream, with the shores low and indistinguishable on either beam. When the sun grew hot, the jungle came close in; it was often so close that we could see the nests of wasps on the trees, like grey shields hanging there. Between the Pará River and the Amazon the waters dissipate into a maze of serpentine ditches. In width these channels usually are no more than canals, but they were deep enough to float our big tramp steamer. They thread a multitude of islands, islands overloaded with a massed growth which topped our mast heads. Our steamer was enclosed within echoing chasms; the noise and incongruity of our progress awoke deep protests there.

The dilated loom of the rains, the cloud shapes so continual that they occupy, where they hang not so far away, all the space between the earth and sky, bulge over the forest at the end of every vista. The heat is luscious; but, then, I have nothing to do but to look on from a hammock under the awning. The foliage which is pressed out over the water, not many yards from the hurrying *Capella*, has a closeness of texture astonishing, and even awful, to one who knows only the thin woods of the north. It ascends directly from the water's edge, sometimes out of the water, and we do not often see its foundation. There are no shady aisles and glades. The sight is stopped on a front of polished emerald, a congestion of stiff leaves. The air is still. Individual sprays and fronds project from the mass in parabolas with flamboyant abandon and poise; they are as rigid as metallic and enamelled shapes. The diversity of forms, and especially the number and variety of the palms, so overload an unseen foundation that the parapets of the woods occasionally lean outwards to form an arcade above our masts. One should not call this the jungle; it is even a soft and benignant Eden. This is the forest I had really wished to find. Often the heavy parapets of the woods are upheld on long colonnades of grey palm boles; or the whole upper structure appears to be based on green arches, the pennant fronds of smaller palms flung direct from the earth.

There is not a sound but the noise of our intruding steamer. Occasionally we brush a projecting spray, or a vine pendant from a cornice. We prove the forest then. In some shallow places are regiments of aquatic grasses bearing long plumes. There are trees which stand in the water on a tangle of straight pallid roots, as though on stilts. This up-burst of intense life so seldom shows the land to which it is fast, and the side rivers and paranas are so many, that I could believe the forest afloat, an archipelago of opaque green vapours. Our heavy wash sways and undulates the aquatic plants and grasses, as though disturbing the fringe of those green clouds which cling to the water because of their weight in a still air.

There is seldom a sign of life but the infrequent snowy herons, and those curious brown fowl, the ciganas. The sun flames on the majestic assembly of the storm. The warm air, broken by our steamer, coils over us in a lazy flux. We all hung over the *Capella's* side, gaping.

Sometimes we pass single habitations on the water side. Ephemeral huts of palm-leaves are forced down by the forest, which overhangs them, to wade on frail stilts. A canoe is tied to a toy jetty, and on the jetty a sad woman and several naked children stand, with no show of emotion, to watch us go by. Behind them is the impenetrable foliage.

Nightfall, and there is a doubt as to whether our pilots should anchor or not. They decide to go on. We do not go the route of Bates, via Breves, but take the Paraná de Buyassa on our way to the Amazon. It was dark when we got to the Paraná, and but for the trailing lights, the fairy mooring lines of habitations in the woods, and what the silent explosions of lightning revealed of great heads of trees, startlingly close and monstrous, as though watching us in silent and intent regard, we saw nothing of it.

In the Heart of the Virgin Forest

THE equatorial forest is popularly pictured as a place of bright and varied colours, with extravagant flowers, an abundance of fruits and huge trees hung with creepers where lurk many venomous but beautiful snakes with gem-like eyes, and a multitude of birds as bright as the flowers; paradise indeed, though haunted by a peril. Those details are right, but the picture is wrong. It is true that some of the birds are decorated in a way which makes the most beautiful of our temperate birds seem dull; but the toucans and macaws of the Madeira forest, though common, are not often seen, and when they are seen they are likely to be but obscure atoms drifting high in a white light. About the villages and in the clearings there are usually many superb butterflies and moths, and a varied wealth of vegetation not to be matched outside the tropics, and there will be the fireflies and odours in evening pathways.

But the virgin forest itself soon becomes but a green monotony which, through extent and mystery, dominates and compels to awe and some dread. You will see it daily, but will not often approach it. It has no splendid blossoms; none, that is, which you will see, except by chance, as by luck one day I saw from the steamer's bridge some trees in blossom, domes of lilac surmounting the forest levels. Trees are always in blossom there, for it is a land of continuous high summer and there are orchids always in flower, and palms and vines that fill acres of forest with fragrance, palms and other trees which give wine and delicious fruits, and somewhere hidden there are the birds of the tropical picture, and dappled jaguars perfect in colouring and form, and brown men and women who have strange gods. But they are lost in the ocean of leaves as are the pearls and wonders in the deep. You will remember the equatorial forest but as a gloom of foliage in which all else that showed was rare and momentary, was foundered and lost to sight instantly, as an unusual ray of coloured light in one mid-ocean wave gleams, and at once goes, and your surprise at its apparition fades too, and again there is but the empty desolation which is for ever but vastness sombrely bright.

ONE morning, wondering greatly what we should see in the place where we should be the first men to go, Hill and I left Camp 22 and returned a little along the track. It was a hot, still morning. A vanilla vine was in fragrant flower somewhere, unseen, but omnipresent. My little unknown friend in the woods, who calls me at odd times—but I think chiefly when I am near a stream —by whistling thrice, let me know he was about. Hill said he thinks he has seen him, and that my little friend looks like a blackbird. On the track in many places were objects which appeared to be long cups inverted, of unglazed ware. Picking up one I found it was the cap to a mine of ants. The inside of the clay cup was hollowed in a perfect circle, and remarkably smooth. A paca dived into the scrub near us. It was early morning, scented with vanilla, and the intricacy of leaves was radiant.

Nowhere in the screen could I see a place through which it was possible to crawl to whatever was behind it. The front of leaves was unbroken. Hill presently bent double and disappeared, and I followed in the break he made. So we went for about ten minutes, my leader cutting obstructions with his machete, and usually we had to go almost on hands and knees. The undergrowth was green, but in the etiolated way of plants which have little light, though that may have been my fancy. One plant was very common, making light-green feathery barriers. I think it was a climbing bamboo. Its stem was vapid and of no diameter, and its grass-like leaves grew in whorls at the joints. It extended to incredible distances.

We got out of that margin of undergrowth, which springs up quickly when light is let into the woods, as it was there through the cutting of the track, and found ourselves on a bare floor where the trunks of arborescent laurels grew so thickly together that our view ahead was restricted to a few yards. We were in the forest. There was a pale tinge of day, but its origin was uncertain, for overhead no foliage could be seen, but only deep shadows from which long ropes were hanging without life. In that obscurity were points of light, as if a high roof had lost some tiles.

Hill set a course almost due south, and we went on, presently descending to a deep clear stream over which a tree had fallen. A beam of daylight came down to us there. It made the sandy bottom of the stream luminous, as by a lantern, and betrayed crowds of small fishes. As we climbed the tree, to cross upon it, we disturbed several morphos. We had difficulties beyond in a hollow, where the bottom of the forest was lumbered with fallen trees, dry rubbish and thorns, and once, stepping on what looked timber

solid enough, its treacherous shell collapsed, and I went down into a cloud of dust and ants.

In clearing this wreckage—which was usually as high as our faces, and was doubly confused by the darkness, the involutions of dead thorny creepers, and clouds of dried foliage—Hill got at fault with our direction, yet reassured himself, though I don't know how; but I think with the certain knowledge that if we went south long enough we should strike the Madeira somewhere, and on we went. For hours we continued among the trees, seldom knowing what was ahead of us for any distance; we were surviving points of noise intruding again after long in the dusk of limbo. So still and nocturnal was the forest that it was real only when its forms were close. All else was phantom and of the shades. There was not a green sign of life, and not a sound. Resting once under a tree I began to think there was a conspiracy implied in that murk and awful stillness, and that we should never come out again into the day and see a living earth. Hill sat looking out, and said, as if in answer to an unspoken thought of mine which had been heard because there was less than no sound there, that men who were lost in those woods soon went mad.

THEN he led on again. This forest was nothing like the paradise a tropical wild is supposed to be. It was as uniformly dingy as the old stones of a London street on a November evening. We did not see a movement, except when the morpho butterflies started from the uprooted tree. Once I heard the whistler call us from the depths of the forest, urgent and startling; and now, when in a London by-way I hear a boy call his mate in a shrill whistle, it puts about me again the spectral aisles, and that unexpected quiet of the sepulchre which is more than mere absence of sound, for the dead should have no voice.

This central forest was really the vault of the long-forgotten, dank, mouldering dark, abandoned to the accumulations of eld and decay. The tall pillars rose, upholding night, and they might have been bastions of weathered limestone and basalt, for they were as grim as ancient and ruinous masonry. There was no undergrowth. The ground was hidden in a ruin of perished stuff, uprooted trees, parchments of leaves, broken boughs and mummied husks, the iron globes of nuts, and pods. There was no day, but some breaks in the roof were points of remote starlight. The crowded columns mounted straight and far, almost branchless, fading into indistinction. Out of that overhead obscurity hung a wreckage of distorted cables, binding the trees, and often reaching the ground.

The trees were seldom of great girth, though occasionally there was a dominant basaltic pillar, its roots meandering over the floor like streams of old lava. The smooth ridges of such a fantastic complexity of roots were sometimes breast high. The walls ran up the trunk, projecting from it as flat buttresses, for great heights. We would crawl round such an occupying structure, diminished groundlings, as one would move about the base of a foreboding, plutonic building whose limits and meaning were ominous but baffling. There were other great trees with compound boles, built literally of bundles of round stems, intricate gothic pillars. Every tree was the support of a parasitic community, lianas swathing it and binding it. One vine moulded itself to its host, a flat and strangling compress, as though it were plastic. We might have been witnessing what had been a riot of manifold life. It had been turned to stone when in the extreme pose of striving violence. It was all dead now.

But what if these combatants had only paused as we appeared? It was a thought which came to me. The pause might be but an appearance for our deception. Indeed, they were all fighting as we passed through, those still and fantastic shapes, a war ruthless but slow, in which the battle-day was ages long. They seemed but still. We were deceived. If time had been accelerated, if the movements in that war of phantoms had been speeded, we should have seen what really was there, the greater trees running upwards to starve the weak of light and food, and heard the continuous collapse of the failures, and have seen the lianas writhing and constricting, manifestly like serpents, throttling and killing their hosts. We did see the dead everywhere, shells with the worms at them. Yet it was not easy to be sure that we saw anything at all, for these were not trees, but shapes in a region below the day, a world sunk abysmally from the land of living things, to which light but thinly percolated down to two travellers moving over its floor trying to get out to their own place.

THE WALTZ

BEHOLD with downcast eyes and modest glance,
In measured step, a well-dressed pair advance,
One hand on hers, the other on her hip,
For thus the law's ordained by Baron Trip.
'Twas in such posture our first parents moved,
When hand in hand through Eden's bowers they roved,
Ere yet the devil with practice foul and false
Turned their poor heads and taught them how to waltz.

—*R. B. Sheridan*

JOHN GALSWORTHY'S "FORSYTE SAGA"

A Study by Edgar Preston

Before attempting the study of a work of such magnitude as "The Forsyte Saga" of Mr. John Galsworthy (1867-1933) I think it safer to let the author himself, by way of prelude, tell us in his own words what his book is designed to be.

"This long tale," he says, "is no scientific study of a period; it is rather an intimate incarnation of the disturbance that Beauty effects in the lives of men. The figure of Irene, never present except through the sense of other characters, is a concretion of disturbing Beauty impinging on a possessive world."

"But," adds Mr. Galsworthy, "though the impingement of Beauty and the claims of Freedom in a possessive world are the main prepossessions of the Forsyte Saga, it cannot be absolved from the charge of embalming the upper middle-class. As the old Egyptians placed around their mummies the accessories of a future existence, so I have endeavoured to lay beside the figures of Aunts Ann and Juley and Hester, of Timothy and Swithin, of old Jolyon and James, and of their sons that which shall guarantee them a little life hereafter, a little balm in the hurried Gilead of a dissolving 'Progress.' "

Well, the author of the Saga—a term used, as he points out, "with a suitable irony," seeing that the pages contain so little that is heroic or poetical—has elected to work on an unpromising, because a prosaic, material, and for that reason alone, if there were no other, his triumph is all the more notable. One thinks of Théophile Gautier's familiar:

Oui, l'oeuvre sort plus belle
D'une forme au travail Rebelle,
Vers, marbre, onyx, émail.

But there is this difference: the Carrara, the Paros which Gautier had in mind is far from being the medium in which John Galsworthy has worked here. Instead of hard marble he has put his deft hands to the common clay, and has fashioned it into a form at once precise yet grand, clear-cut yet massive. Or, to vary the metaphor, he has brought the art of the miniaturist to bear on a canvas of huge dimensions without becoming petty or finicky.

In other words, the characters in the three books comprising the Saga are very ordinary people—with one or two exceptions, perhaps—viewed and portrayed minutely, intimately, and at the same time with a big, ironic *bonhomie* that takes away all sense of littleness. There is much of Thackeray in this treatment: that is one's first, even one's last, impression; yet the outlook, the point of view, is ever individual, ever Galsworthy, pure and undiluted.

It was objected by some critics of Flaubert, one remembers, that his theme in "Madame Bovary" was "common," even repulsive; that his characters were the same—just plain, unremarkable, provincial folk, scarce worthy of notice. Yet all are agreed the work is a master-work; and such, surely, must be the verdict on Mr. Galsworthy's elaborate, remarkable story.

Originally, as the preface tells us, "The Forsyte Saga" was the title destined for that part of it called "The Man of Property," published in 1906. But when that opening volume was completed, it became evident to all that the story could not be ended there, with so much left to tell. So a second part, "In Chancery," followed, but not until fourteen years had elapsed. Nor was the interest in the Forsytes gone or even abated in 1920; when that book came to its conclusion another volume was inevitable. This appeared in the following year under the significant title of "To Let," and everyone, I suppose, was more or less agreed that, with the marriage of Soames's daughter Fleur to honest Michael Mont the time had come to close the long narrative. All the older generation were gone, and most of the younger. Of these latter only Soames and his two wives—Annette the present, Irene the past—survived, apart from one or two having no very prominent part in the history.

So, obviously, this was the appropriate moment to write "finis," and when the three volumes bound in one were published in 1922 the big tome was recognized as the complete Saga, which it is. But Mr. Galsworthy's interest in his subject was evidently not exhausted. For lo! within two years appears "The White Monkey," a sequel in which Soames and Fleur and young Mont and others with whom we are familiar take the stage once more. This however, is no part of the Saga proper, which suffices of itself; so I do not propose in these pages to touch the sequel, although the temptation to do so is not easily resisted!

First of all, who *are* these Forsytes? Once, when the family had definitely settled down as genuine "upper middle-class," all six sons of the founder of their fortunes—Jolyon, the builder, known as "Superior Dosset," it occurred to some one of them to make inquiry in Devonshire, whence came the first Jolyon of all, a farmer. The result was not particularly gratifying to those of the family who had hoped to discover that perchance they were "somebody." For the investigator's frank report was to the effect that the Forsytes appeared to have been nothing more than farmers from

time immemorial. One or two of them might perhaps have been styled "yeomen"—there being a grain of comfort in this—but generally, it would seem, they must have been "very small beer." The subject was not pursued further—indeed only the indiscreet like dear old Aunt Juley, "who could always be relied on to say the wrong thing"—ever thought of alluding to it again.

"Superior Dosset" Forsyte, busy any time between 1800 and 1850—London's very worst architectural period, perhaps —building ugly houses, reached the age of fourscore years and left behind him a nice little fortune of £30,000 or so. Also he left ten children, not one of whom failed to "make old bones." At one period of the story it was calculated that the average age of this second generation of Forsytes was eighty-seven, and that the six sons were worth a good deal over a million between them. A tough, tenacious lot!

They had all done so well for themselves, these Forsytes, that (in 1886, when the tale opens) they were all what is called "of a certain position." They had shares in all sorts of things, not as yet—with the exception of Timothy—in consols, for they had no dread in life like that of 3 per cent, for their money. They collected pictures, too, and were supporters of such charitable institutions as might be beneficial to their sick domestics. From their father, the builder, they inherited a talent for bricks and mortar. Originally, perhaps, members of some primitive sect, they were now in the natural course of things members of the Church of England, and caused their wives and children to attend with some regularity the more fashionable churches of the Metropolis. . . .

Their residences, placed at stated intervals round the park, watched like sentinels, lest the fair heart of this London, where their desires were fixed, should slip from their clutches and leave them lower in their estimations.

There was old Jolyon in Stanhope Place; the Jameses in Park Lane; Swithin in the lonely glory of orange and blue chambers in Hyde Park Mansions—he had never married, not he! —the Soameses in their nest off Knightsbridge; the Rogers in Prince's Gardens; the Haymans— Mrs. Hayman was the one married Forsyte sister—in a house high up on Campden Hill, shaped like a giraffe, and so tall that it gave the observer a crick in the neck; the Nicholases in Ladbroke Grove, a spacious abode and a great bargain; and last, but not least, Timothy's on the Bayswater Road, where Ann and Juley and Hester lived under his protection.

Old Jolyon, it should be stated, was in the tea trade, and chairman of sundry companies; James, a solicitor, founder of the firm of Forsyte, Bustard and Forsyte —the last-named being his only son Soames, who combined the business of collecting pictures with that of the law; Swithin, an estate and land agent; Roger, who speculated in house property; Nicholas, ditto, with mines and railways thrown in; and Timothy, a publisher, "in consols."

We meet all these good people, and many others, for the first time at the At Home given by old Jolyon—long since a widower—at Stanhope Gate. The family is assembled on a June afternoon in 1886 to meet Philip Bosinney, who has just become engaged to June Forsyte, the host's grand-daughter. And let me confess that by the time Mr. Galsworthy had presented the entire company I felt dazed and bewildered, and perhaps slightly irritated that they should be so many. I feared I should be bored; but I was wrong, for the Forsytes proved, on better acquaintance, to be full of interest, quaint or otherwise.

PHILIP BOSINNEY is somewhat distrusted. In the first place, he has no money—a very bad sign; then, he is something of an artist, and a Forsyte, though respecting successful art, is instinctively suspicious of those who make it—"flighty, unsubstantial fellows, you never can depend on 'em!" And, to crown it all, the news leaks out that June's intended has come "in a soft, grey hat, not even a new one—a dusty, shapeless thing!" Big, bulky George (Roger's son), the accredited wit of the family, at once christened Bosinney "the dashing buccaneer," and the word "buccaneer" stuck.

Never had there been so full an assembly, for, mysteriously united in spite of all their differences, they had taken arms against a common peril. Like cattle when a dog comes into the field, they stood head to head and shoulder to shoulder, prepared to run upon and trample the intruder to death. They had come, too, no doubt, to get some notion of what sort of presents they would ultimately be expected to give; for though the question of wedding gifts was usually graduated in this way: "What are *you* givin'? Nicholas is givin' spoons!" so very much depended on the bridegroom. If he were sleek, well-brushed, prosperous-looking, it was more necessary to give him nice things; he would expect them.

In Bosinney's case, as it turned out, no presents at all were required—but that is to anticipate.

Like "Vanity Fair," this is a novel without a hero—or a heroine. The figures that loom largest in the picture are Soames and his wife Irene, and they are rather tragic figures. "The Man of Property" is the title, half chaffing, half malicious, by which James's son and partner is known in the family; for, although only thirty-five, he bids fair to pay more in death duties than any of the others, having something like a genius for business and a real *flair* for that which is destined to "boom" in art.

Already Soames has many possessions, chiefest among them being his beautiful wife. She did not want to marry him, but, after a considerable period of waiting, he got her in the end, just as, by patient diplomacy, he had got many of his most treasured canvasses. Irene had no money, but her loveliness atoned for that defect. She did not love him. That was a pity, for in his crude, proprietorial way, Soames was very fond of her and, as he often said, gave her everything she asked for. Right to the end of the chapter he could never understand why he was disliked—by her, and by others as well. In discussing the ill-matched pair I have found that women generally have more tolerance for Soames than for Irene; while most men disclose a marked partiality for that silent, elusive woman.

IRENE, with her lovely "figure"— strange word, in these days when women have no "figures"!—her caressing, brown eyes, her pale, straight feaures and her mass of burnt-umber hair, exercised, indeed, a curious fascination over men of all types and all ages. "What is she like?" asked someone who had not seen her. "She's like Venus in beautiful clothes," was the answer. One thinks Helen of Troy, whose face wrought such wonders, might have been an apter comparison! The influence Soames's wife had over Philip Bosinney is not easy to define. That she inspired passion in him, and returned it, is certain. In the circumstances we must, I suppose, regard this influence as bad; yet she had the power to bring out the best rather than the worst in men, as witness the two Jolyons and her own son Jon.

Nothing in the book is quite so charming, to my mind, as the episode with old Jolyon Forsyte, told in the Interlude which follows "The Man of Property" and precedes "In Chancery." The rupture with Soames is some years old. Since Bosinney's tragic death and her flight from home Irene has been living in Chelsea very quietly, alone—"Yes, alone," as she replies to a rather pointed inquiry—earning a bare livelihood by giving music lessons. One day she takes it into her head to pay a visit to Robin Hill, the beautiful house near town that had really been designed for herself but had been sold in disgust by Soames to his cousin Jolyon. There she renews acquaintance with the elder Jolyon, who finds her strolling in the grounds and makes her stay to dinner.

Before long Irene—who, of course, by all the rules of respectability, should be an outcast, seeing that she has deserted her husband—is a frequent visitor at Robin Hill, and once a week or so old Jolyon goes up to town and takes her out to dinner, with the Opera or a theatre to follow. Warmed by her gracious presence, the game old octogenarian enjoys a sort of Indian summer, all forgetful of the pain in his side, the scantness of breath, the occasional fainting fits. None would recognize in this kind, thoughtful, courtier-like host the stern, unbending, arbitrary Chairman of Companies, whose determination to have his own way has been proverbial in the City for nearly half-a-century.

Unwittingly, the woman he had once described as "dangerous" has restored for him the joy of life and made him loth to leave it.

But at length, hearing that June is returning to her grandfather—June, whom she robbed of her lover years before—Irene thinks it best to bring her visits to an end, and writes to old Jolyon, telling him so very gently. His reply is so pathetic that she sends him a wire to say she is coming, after all. Her message gives him the greatest delight, and he goes into the grounds to watch for her coming.

Coming down! After all! Then she did exist—and he was not deserted. A glow ran through his limbs; his cheeks and forehead felt hot . . . . He meant to go down and meet her in the coppice, but felt at once he could not manage that in this heat. He sat down instead under the oak tree by the swing, and the dog Balthasar, who also felt the heat, lay down beside him. . . .

The stable clock struck four; in half an hour she would be here. He would have just one tiny nap, because he had had so little sleep of late; and then he would be fresh for her, fresh for youth and beauty, coming toward him across the sunlit lawn—lady in grey! And settling back in his chair he closed his eyes. Some thistledown came on what little air there was, and pitched on his moustache, more white than itself. He did not know; but his breathing stirred it, caught there. A ray of sunlight struck through and lodged on his boot. A humble-bee alighted and strolled on the crown of his Panama hat. And the delicious surge of slumber reached the brain beneath that hat, and the head swayed forward and rested on his breast. Summer—summer! So went the hum.

The stable clock struck the quarter past. The dog Balthasar stretched and looked up at his master. The thistledown no longer moved. The dog placed his chin over the sunlit foot. It did not stir. The dog withdrew his chin quickly, rose, and leaped on old Jolyon's lap, looked in his face, whined; then, leaping down, sat on his haunches, gazing up. And suddenly he uttered a long, long howl.

But the thistledown was still as death, and the face of his old master.

Summer—summer—summer! The soundless footsteps on the grass!

THE ARRIVAL of Philip Bosinney in the Forsyte circle had the disturbing effect that the artistic temperament so often produces when it happens to clash —as here—with plain, prosperous Philistinism. June should no more have become engaged to this impecunious "buccaneer" than Irene should have allowed herself to be persuaded to marry Soames. When the architect and the beauty meet they recognize one another as kindred souls, instinctive enemies of the moneyed mediocrities around them, and alliance between the pair is almost inevitable.

I find Bosinney the least satisfactory character in the triology. Certain traits but half revealed make one inclined to like him; and I, for one, feel a certain disappointment at not being allowed to know him better, for he was an artist, and an "original." His mysterious death in the fog seems appropriate to one so nebulous himself; but I wish he could have been spared a little longer.

A character of extraordinary consistency and sustained interest is that of Soames, who never disappoints one, even for a moment. He is indeed superbly drawn. While the others die off one by one—even old Timothy, who "reaches three figures," as the cricket reporters say, cannot last for ever—"The Man of Property" survives all his disappointments and troubles and seems almost as strong as ever at the end. One is really glad to find him staying the course, after a second unsatisfactory marriage experience. Having at length, after twelve years, got free by divorcing Irene—not on poor Bosinney's account, but with his cousin, young Jolyon, of all people, as co-respondent—Soames takes to wife Annette, daughter of Madame Lamotte, whose acquaintance he had made at their restaurant in Soho—the region which, as he remarks, "always gave him a feeling of property improperly owned."

HE HAD a good deal of trouble in finding evidence sufficient to get him his divorce, and some of his efforts to procure it provide perhaps the finest of the numberless fine touches of comedy in which the book abounds. His experiences with the detective agency, for example. Seven months, at fifteen pounds a week! It's an expensive business, he finds, especially when the young woman who is "shadowing" Irene in Paris can find nothing worth reporting in that time. So Soames goes across himself, not so much to get evidence as to make a last effort to induce his wife—for such she still is—to return to him, "and no questions asked." She refuses absolutely to have anything to do with him; so he writes her a letter the same day and, to save time, takes it to her hotel himself and leaves it in her room. When he comes down he is told that Irene has just left.

So he returns to London, utterly disgusted, but now fully resolves to marry Annette at the earliest possible moment. He is hardly back before Mr. Polteel, the detective agency man arrives, full of importance. At last he has got what they want, and he proceeds to read the latest information received from the "shadow" in Paris. She has seen another "party" with Irene—young Jolyon, her trustee under his father's will, was the first—and can swear to having seen him coming out of her bedroom at ten o'clock at night.

"Who is this new person?" asked Soames abruptly.

"That we don't know. She'll swear to the fact, and she's got his appearance pat."

Mr. Polteel took out a letter, and began reading:

" 'Middle-aged, medium height, blue dittoes in afternoon, evening dress at night, pale, dark hair, small dark moustasche, flat cheeks, good chin, grey eyes, small feet, guilty look——' "

Soames rose and went to the window. He stood there in sardonic fury. Congenital idiot—spidery, congenital idiot! Seven months at fifteen pounds a week—to be tracked down as his own wife's lover! "Guilty look!" He threw the window open.

"It's hot," he said, and came back to his seat. Crossing his knees, he bent a supercilious glance on Mr. Polteel.

"I doubt if that's quite good enough," he said, drawling the words, "with no name or address. I think you may let that lady have a rest, and take it up at this end." Whether

Polteel had spotted him, he could not tell, but he had a vision of him in the midst of his cronies dissolved in inextinguishable laughter. "Guilty look!" Damnation!

Here's the true playwright touch. What a "curtain"!

By now we have journeyed far into "In Chancery," before the end of which Soames has got his decree and has married the placid, business-like, very French young woman, Annette. He had already bought the Soho restaurant, and put in a manager. Of course it was impossible for his wife's mother to live "over the business," in the changed conditions.

Young Jolyon and Irene also are wedded, and, both having had their fill of excitement—this is Jolyon's third experience of marriage, are perfectly happy. Soon they have a son—Jolyon, which quickly becomes Jon. A few months later Annette presents Soames with a child—the first and last. Of course, it is a girl, because Soames would have given half he possessed for a son! Irene has borne the male child to his rival—"that fellow Jolyon." But there is some consolation for Soames. It's only a daughter—but at any rate, she is *his*. They call the dark-eyed, sweet thing Fleur.

This vital sense of possession is seen as triumphant in Soames.

IN LESS THAN twenty years the Fates have willed that Jon and Fleur shall meet, and love. They are, of course, "a pair of star-crossed lovers," and I think someone should have made it his or her business to tell them sooner what Jon's father tells them later—the whole story of Irene's divorce, etc., of which the young people had been kept in ignorance. Fleur, it will be remarked, is much less impressed by the old scandal than is Jon; but the boy so loves the girl that he would probably have married her, *coûte que coûte,* were it not for Irene, his mother. His devotion to her just turns the scale against Fleur, who has to console herself with Michael Mont, a future baronet, and altogether a shrewd, alert, decent fellow—a typical modern product.

SOAMES parts with his one child very reluctantly. Annette has not turned out to be an ideal wife by any means; but since she has served her purpose in giving him Fleur, the "Man of Property" cares mighty little how his rather sulky, indifferent spouse flirts and gads about with the wealthy Belgian loafer, Prosper Profond. Fleur, who knows her mother, has no real home life; better, Soames regretfully concludes, that she should settle down in a place of her own.

So Fleur and Mont became man and wife, with the ceremony at St. George's, Hanover Square. At the ensuing reception nearly all the surviving members of the Forsyte family, with Michael Mont's parents and sundry friends and relatives, are gathered together, and soon "the room was full of the bubble and squeak of conversation." To the surprise of many, June appeared, weirdly dressed in a djibbah, an oldish woman now, with streaks of white in the red hair.

When "going-away" time drew near, Fleur asked June to go upstairs with her while she changed her dress.

June sat down on the bed, thin and upright, like a little spirit in the sere and yellow. Fleur locked the door.

"I suppose you think me a fool," she said, with quivering lips, "when it was to have been Jon? But what does it matter? Michael wants me, and I don't care. It'll get me away from home." Diving her hand into the frills on her breast, she brought out a letter. "Jon wrote me this."

June read: "Lake Okanagen, British Columbia.—I'm not coming back to England. Bless you always.—Jon."

"She's made safe, you see," said Fleur.

June handed back the letter.

"That's not fair to Irene," she said; "she always told Jon he could do as he wishes."

Fleur smiled bitterly.

"Tell me, didn't she spoil your life, too?"

June looked up.

"Nobody can spoil a life, my dear. That's nonsense. Things happen, but we bob up."

With a sort of terror she saw the girl sink on her knees and bury her face in the djibbah. A strangled sob mounted to June's ears.

"It's all right—all right," she murmured. "Don't! There, there!"

But the point of the girl's chin was pressed

even closer into her thigh, and the sound of her sobbing was dreadful.

"Don't sit down under it, my dear," said June at last. "We can't control life, but we can fight it. Make the best of things; I've had to. I held on, like you; and I cried, as you're crying now. And look at me!"

Fleur raised her head; a sob merged suddenly into a little choked laugh.

"All right!" she said. "I'm sorry. I shall forget him, I suppose, if I fly fast and far enough." And, scrambling to her feet, she went over to the wash-stand.

"Give me a kiss," said June, when Fleur was ready, and dug her chin into the girl's warm cheek.

"I want a whiff," said Fleur; "don't wait."

In the hall Fleur turned her lips up to her father, and pressed them in the middle of his cheek.

"Daddy," she said, and was past and gone. Daddy! She hadn't called him that for years! Soames stood on the bottom step but three, whence he could see above the heads—the silly hats and heads. They were in the car now; and there was that stuff showering, and there went the shoe. A flood of something welled up in Soames, and—he didn't know—he couldn't see!

I CONFESS to a feeling akin to sadness at reaching the end of this long story.

In this brief study of what I have not the slightest doubt is a great and an enduring work of art it has been impossible to convey more than a suggestion of its rich and abundant qualities. Here, one feels, is something really, essentially English—something those of us who have lived as long as Mr. Galsworthy, or perhaps a little longer, know to be true. Here, in these pages, is crystallised a phase of London life that deserved preservation. It needed a master hand to shape this matter, *au travail rebelle,* into the shapely, meaning thing which is this Forsyte Saga.

---◆---

DAFFODILS

I WANDER'D lonely as a cloud
   That floats on high o'er vales and hills,
When all at once I saw a crowd,
   A host, of golden daffodils;
Beside the lake, beneath the trees,
Fluttering and dancing in the breeze.

Continuous as the stars that shine
   And twinkle on the Milky Way,
They stretch'd in never-ending line
   Along the margin of a bay:
Ten thousand saw I at a glance,
Tossing their heads in sprightly dance.

The waves beside them danced, but they
   Out-did the sparkling waves in glee:
A poet could not but be gay,
   In such a jocund company:
I gazed—and gazed—but little thought
What wealth the show to me had brought:

For oft, when on my couch I lie
   In vacant or in pensive mood,
They flash upon that inward eye
   Which is the bliss of solitude;
And then my heart with pleasure fills,
And dances with the daffodils.

          —William Wordsworth

Morley Roberts

RACHEL MARR

Morley Roberts (1857-) has some sixty odd books to his credit, of which his Cornish romance, "Rachel Marr," is a representative work. When British Imperialism was at its zenith in the eighteen-nineties, Roberts kept the British public supplied with tales of the seven seas, serious and humorous, and stories of primitive life in the outposts of the Empire. Roberts' writings are the usufruct of broad experiences in many parts of the world; in Australia, South Africa, New South Wales, the United States, Canada and South and Central America. He also sailed before the mast.

How Rachel, Naiad and Dryad Succoured Mary

"Rachel Marr" appeared in 1903 and met with a rather uncertain reception. Time's revenges came however in 1925, when the novel was re-published for the benefit of a later generation. It was again submitted to critical opinion, which on this occasion was prompt to recognize that it was confronted by a master-study of elemental passions. Even that small and perhaps too fastidious minority, which found the accent of the hero's more emotional monologues occasionally unauthentic, which quarreled with the pattern of the prose harmonies as now and then too mannered and too elaborate, and which complained that the atmosphere of Pantheism with which the book is permeated is too industriously introduced, was the first to recognize that the analysis of character and mood, the descriptions of woodland, sky and sea, the ruminations on seasons human and terrestrial, and the comments of the chorus (*or rather raisonneur*)—the drunken ex-preacher Steve Penrose—on men and women's aspirations, futilities and self torturings, were elements of a work nobly planned and nobly executed and constituted separable but organic parts of

A hymn divine of high and passionate love
To its own music chanted.

Morley Roberts's *magnum opus,* a tale of life in a Cornish fishing village, is the story of the reactions of Rachel Marr, last of a line of small landowners, to the personalities of two brothers whose family have been farmers on her estate, Anthony Perran, who still holds land from her, and John Perran, who has returned to Cornwall with a fortune made in America. Rachel, nominally a Roman Catholic, is pagan and passion-swayed like her mother, but virginal. Anthony, Methodist and ascetic, believes in crucifying the flesh. John, joyous, laughter-loving and loose-living, takes days and women as he finds them. Both men however are shaken wholly out of themselves by a passion for Rachel, a passion which, as the narrative shows, neither is able to gratify or to subdue.

The opening scene takes place on a summer midnight when Anthony, riding home accompanied by Sigurd, his great Dane, comes upon Rachel swimming in the sea. "Would you do anything for me if I asked you?" she questions. "Aye, anything that was right," he answers. "If I liked you," she replied, "and I don't to-night, I'd do anything that you wanted, and I wouldn't crawl about trying to find out whether it was right or not. I'd do it and confess afterwards—if I had to!"

That Rachel was guided by no conventional patterns of propriety she showed the following day when, reclining on the pine needles in her favourite wood, she heard a woman sobbing, who turned out to be her old playfellow

Mary, the daughter of William Jose, the village blacksmith. The girl had returned home from Plymouth unmarried, but a mother; and she was weeping because she feared that she and her baby boy would get but a hostile reception from her stern old father. Rachel, who loved all children, comforted her and dandled her baby; and in return learnt things which gave her a knowledge of her own strong instincts. But when she had conducted Mary and her baby to the blacksmith's shop and had taken part in a violent scene in which old Jose had taken his daughter by the throat to choke out of her the name of her lover, she decided to give Mary shelter in her own home at Morna House.

Anthony again asked the inexperienced seventeen-year-old girl "if it was right." But Martha, Rachel's old nurse, gave her grumbling assent to the proposal; while Rachel's mother, who scarcely ever left her bedroom, gave her indifferent consent, merely muttering "Poor fool!" Martha, however, soon saw that complications would arise out of the business; for she recognized in the eyes of Mary's baby the unmistakable blue eyes of John Perran. She told Rachel therefore that John was the father of the child and she warned Anthony that she

had long had a mind to set Rachel against the Perrans.

When Anthony asked "Why, woman, why?" she told him that he was stubborn in his faith and "would never marry a Papist" and that "if Miss Rachel ever loved anyone, 'twould be terrible hard upon her, for her soul would be in it." To this solicitation Anthony made no reply. Despite his remembrance of the glowing vision she made swimming in the sea Rachel appeared to him a mere girl, a child. She surrendered her soul to a priest, and if they married there would be disputes about the religion of the children. Moreover he had pledged his word to Winnie, his cousin. Riding home he met Rachel's confessor, Father Brant, and Steve Penrose, the relapsed preacher. To the latter, "obviously advanced in liquor and most remarkably cheerful," he remarked "If I had my way I'd have you flogged."

"Bless your soul, sir," said Steve, "I've stopped whipping myself. But the whip's for you, sir; 'tis you uses it on yourself. And a lot you gain. There's more of the sad priest in you than in his reverence here."

Meantime Rachel, in a mood of curiosity, sought out again the spiteful, lecherous, "whey-faced" Winnie who, speaking of Anthony, declared "I believe you are in love with yourself."

How Rachel Came into Her Inheritance

"WHAT's Miss Rachel's mother but a walking ghost callin' on ghosts?" Martha had exclaimed to Anthony Perran when, as Rachel's real mother, she had besought him to let the girl alone. The old servant was right; and her mistress, who had kept and paced her room so many years, talking to herself, calling out to her Antonio, refusing to see either priest or doctor, and addressing scarce a word to the daughter she could not love, was now approaching the kingdom of the shades.

Mary Tregilgas had married Richard Marr, a Londoner, a painter of the sea, and an alien from religion like her father. But her daughter Rachel was the child, as Father Brant knew, not of

Richard Marr, but of a Roman Catholic priest called Antonio who had met and loved Mary at Naples and who, having eventually repented of his sin, had been sent by his superiors to labor in South America, whence he had sent her as his sole message an old ivory crucifix sheathing a dagger inscribed with the legend *Non venio pacem mittere sed gladium.* Rachel could remember the time at Naples—when her mother clad herself in scarlet and gold. But now for years she had worn nothing but black and kept the crucifix always hidden in her bosom, repenting of her sin but unrepentant, and content, like Bardolph, to be with the man she loved "either in Heaven or in Hell." Of late her pacing of her room had grown more incessant and had been prolonged into the night; while her outcries had become more vehement and more continuous.

She gave up the ghost, as was but fitting, on a night when a storm of thunder, lightning and rain burst upon the land. As a sign that she cast out God she threw the crucifix into the garden. But Rachel recovered it and Martha persuaded her to take it back. She then locked herself into her bedroom, arrayed herself once more in scarlet, lighted candles at the head and foot of the bed, and took her life by opening the veins of her arm with the dagger in the crucifix.

In this grisly and terrible scene, a scene enacted behind closed doors which its fascinated and horrified spectators are powerless to break open, Morley Roberts sounds a note of stark intensity.

Why Anthony, Loving Rachel, Married Winnie

IT was not until fourteen months after Mrs. Marr's death that William Jose learnt—by mere accident—that John Perran was the father of his daughter's child. And about the same time Anthony Perran, beginning to desire Rachel and thinking all desires and affections equally evil, deliberately and formally engaged himself to Winnie and bestowed his dog Sigurd upon Rachel. And one night, as Rachel lay sleeping in the pine wood and dreaming that children were born to her of whom Anthony was the father, Sigurd who months before had found her swimming in the sea again directed Anthony to her. But though he recognized her mood he would not yield to it. Two months later indeed he took Winnie for his wife, who on her wedding-eve was told by her befuddled father, John Perran's sometime boon companion, that she was marrying within the table of prohibited degrees. Something to the same effect was whispered to the bride as she was returning from the marriage ceremony by old Steve Penrose; but though his boldness cost him a bleeding mouth he seemed to think it worth while.

Bitter of mood Rachel attended by Sigurd ventured out into the storm that raged on the wedding-eve and sheltering herself and her dog in a hollow cave near Pentowan House, where Anthony lived, stopped there till long past midnight. On the wedding-day, after seeing the wedded pair, she unlocked her grandfather's dusty library and spent several hours there, strangely ignorant as she was of books. In the evening she returned there and despite Martha's entreaties read till dawn; about which time Anthony Perran rose gladly from his bridal couch and went among his cattle. Several months later, when it was said that Winnie was to become a mother, Martha intercepted Anthony, who confessed to her that he had loved Rachel and to himself that he still loved her.

Martha laughed even as the tears ran down her face. "And this (she said) is a man, oh, and a fine man; and he lets the thoughts of a girl on things the world is in division about keep him from his love. . . . Take this thought home and live with it, that her heart's a woman's, and that her religion was no more to her than it is to most of us women, something to hold till the man comes, as a child plays with dolls till nature gives her a babe to suckle."

ABOUT the same time Rachel, who had a kindly feeling for Steve Penrose, learnt from him that John Perran was returning to Morna. She accordingly sought out the blacksmith, who still completely ignored his daughter, and tried to obtain from him a promise that he would take no vengeance on her betrayer. But, since all that the old man would promise was that he would not seek out John and since she herself knew that John would make no smallest effort to avoid Jose, she told Anthony plainly how matters stood. Moreover in a final effort to avert catastrophe, when she heard that John had actually arrived in the village and was stopping with George Perran, his uncle, she sent Steve Penrose to warn him of his danger. But John took the matter quite calmly, invited Steve to drink with him, and cheerfully announced his intention to see Jose, Mary, and if possible Rachel Marr.

And Rachel made these efforts on behalf of others, though her own soul was in deep water. She had now finally refused to confess to or to pray with

Father Brant. Moreover, she had had another bitter interview with Winnie who, having boasted that she and Anthony laughed in bed at her of nights for her love-sickness and that she was about to bear a child to Anthony, heard the sentence, "It may never be born."

How Anthony and John Quarrelled Over Rachel

JOHN PERRAN soon saw Mary, who called him "Sir," having never called him "Jack," and brought down her baby for him to see. But, though he undertook to look after the boy, he never promised to marry the mother; and Mary recognized that he loved her no more. John, in fact, had previously seen Rachel, and her beauty had set him aflame. In two or three broken sentences he contrived to tell her what he thought of Winnie, what he thought of himself, and what he thought of her.

For a time Rachel was a little troubled by his words; for John was as sunshine to Anthony's shadow. Besides she could not help thinking that "her strength could raise John to her own level far easier than she could draw back Anthony to the dear and usual earth." Soon, however, she was more troubled by the man's actions; for John bearded Jose at his forge, who threatened to kill him if he went near Mary again, and was only kept back from making an immediate assault upon him by Rachel's entreaty. At his dire peril John remained in Morna, remained because he wanted to be near Rachel, to gain her respect and to win her smile. And in a foolish impulse Steve Penrose encouraged him, admitting that Rachel loved Anthony, but yet, advising John "to make up" to her:

"She loved him, and it's folly; and he's married to one we know of, and that finishes him. But you, sir, are free, and are like him as two peas, save that you are more the kind that women love, being blithe and bright."

The result was that John came lurking around Morna House of nights, hoping to get a glimpse of Rachel, and that old Jose, thinking he sought to keep a midnight assignation with Mary, kept watch, too, and finding him there one

evening felled him to the ground with his hammer, fracturing the base of his skull.

In this eerie night-piece, which shows three women, Martha, Mary and Rachel, listening intently inside the house to mysterious movements in the darkness of the garden, while the rain pours down and Sigur rattles his chain and barks, the author plays on the nerves of apprehension and fear with quite a Maeterlinckean art. Thereby, too, he conducts his story appreciably nearer to its dénouement; for he is now enabled to lodge the wounded John in Rachel's house and so to afford Anthony easy access to her.

OF SUCH access Anthony took advantage to make open love to Rachel, who, in the heartbreaking scene that followed, "offered him more than words." And she, gazing down one day on John as he lay in bed "the exact and awful image of his dearer brother, "bent and kissed him on the brow, not unseen of Mary, who straightway hated her bitterly. John, too, was no longer himself, but ached for Rachel. So before he was quite out of danger he fled from Morna House, fearing lest he might commit some mad folly, and went to live with George Perran again. And soon afterwards the two brothers met and John confessed his own love for Rachel and his knowledge of Anthony's love for her. "But, if she's yours," he cried, "or if she will be, I'll go." But the voice of Anthony was terrible and he laughed as he declared:

"Her heart's mine, you fool. Take her if you can. She'll be sorry for you; but not I. Get out of my sight, or I shall forget you are maimed and a madman and my brother."

Winnie's Plot and How it was Foiled

AND now Winnie, who had hitherto been passive, began to take an active part in what had now developed into a quadrilateral entanglement, aided unwittingly by John Perran. He, who bore no malice and would give no evidence against old Jose, thereby securing his speedy release from imprisonment, went to see her in Anthony's absence, thinking to sift her. But she sifted him, who was no longer his own man for good and evil, and told him that Rachel had been fond of him when a young girl and had kissed him as he lay a sick man at her house. So John declared his love to Rachel, asserted that he knew she loved him, and was dismissed by her in indignation which turned all too soon to pity. She was restless now; but she had one moment of happiness when, with Anthony for company, she went across the bay to the river in Sam Burt's boat and narrowly escaped drowning.

Winnie meantime was contriving a great plot against her. Playing on Mary's jealousy and on John's infatuation—for she had half convinced him that she wished for his happiness—she persuaded the woman to hand over Sigurd to her custody and to carve John's name on the pine tree beneath which Rachel was wont to recline, and she plied the man with neat brandy and undiluted lies till he was ready to believe that Rachel had acted like love-sick Orlando, and would be only too glad to keep a midnight tryst with him in the wood. The hideous plot might have succeeded had not Winnie, resenting the growls of the chained-up dog, lashed him so unmercifully that he broke loose, threw her violently to the ground, and nearly got Anthony by the throat. Bleeding as he was from the lashes of the whip and from the prongs of the hayfork with which one of the farm servants had attacked him, Sigurd raced off home, arriving at the wood just in the nick of time to hurl John Perran to the ground and to save Rachel from dishonour.

It is a thrilling scene; though it must be confessed that Winnie's wickedness smacks too much of the villainy of the Webster and Tourneur school of dramatists to be quite credible. Sigurd's appearance too as *deus ex machina* is undeniably a device borrowed from melodrama. It must be remembered however that the frustrated attack is a difficult business for the novelist to tackle. Here Morley Roberts deals with the situation with at least dignity and a fine reticence; while he metes out poetic justice to Winnie by condemning her to give birth to a still-born child.

Henceforward the story moves rapidly to its conclusion. To free Anthony, John made love to Winnie and asked her to elope with him; but finding she detected his loathing of her he denounced her as "liar" and "harlot" and left her. In revenge Winnie told her husband that John and Rachel had had a meeting in the pine wood, and that John had just bade her tell him that he was welcome now to someone, if he'd take her. Quite beside himself, Anthony rushed off to Morna House, where he and Rachel put together some of the elements of Winnie's plot, those that were missing being extracted by Rachel from Mary after Anthony had left the house, vowing to slay his brother. To avert such fratricide, Rachel sent Mary to George Perran's house to warn John of his danger; but John returned to Morna House resolved to meet his brother, and only with great difficulty did Rachel persuade him to leave.

WHILE Anthony, armed with his gun, was riding through the wood in search of him, the two distraught women, Rachel and Martha, unburdened their hearts to one another, the younger telling the whole story of her love for Anthony, the elder confessing that she had had a lover who perished at sea, leaving her a baby who had died when only three months old.

A little later the rattle of wheels was heard outside the house and John's voice roaring out a song. In he came, the merry wooer, and before Rachel and Martha were able fully to comprehend things, he had got Mary out of bed and dressed, had forced her on her knees to beg for forgiveness of Rachel, and had carried her and her baby off in his horse and trap. And no sooner had the sound of the wheels died away than Anthony came back quite cured of his madness.

Rachel then told him the whole story of the plot, and besought him in the most moving fashion to leave his wife and to go off with her. But he would not; wherefore Rachel polished the blade of the crucifix until it was exceedingly bright. Some weeks later in the summer old Steve mustered up courage to make the same appeal which she had made and was refused by Anthony, who went a little later to Morna House at night and begged Rachel to wait until the summer was ended. And when that season came they met one evening and talked and kept watch until the dawn. And this is how they found surcease of their agony.

"I'm happy, Anthony."

"Is that the dawn?"

"It comes, dear, but not yet. Are you happy, my beloved?"

"If I could die so."

She bent over and kissed him tenderly; and in the faint light of the growing dawn, which put the great stars out one by one, her face was sweet and wonderful and as strong as death.

She reached out her hand and took the crucifix.

But, though her story ends in frustration and defeat, Rachel Marr herself is surely destined to immortality. Already she seems to have joined that great-hearted and high-souled company in which are numbered heroines so noble as Richardson's Clarissa, George Eliot's Romola, Meredith's Emilia and Hardy's Tess.

◆

HUMAN DISCONTENT

WHENCE is it, sir, that none contented lives
With the fair lot which prudent reason gives,
Or chance presents, yet all with envy view
The schemes that others variously pursue?
Broken with toils, with ponderous arms oppressed,
The soldier thinks the merchant solely blest.
In opposite extreme, when tempests rise,
"War is a better choice," the merchant cries.
When early clients thunder at his gate,
The barrister applauds the rustic's fate;
While, by *sub-poenas* dragged from home, the clown
Thinks the supremely happy dwell in town!
Not to be tedious, mark the moral aim
Of these examples. Should some god proclaim,
"Your prayers are heard: you, soldier, to your seas;
You, lawyer, take that envied rustic's ease,—
Each to his several part—What! Ha! not move
Even to the bliss you wished!" And shall not Jove,
With cheeks inflamed and angry brow, forswear
A week indulgence to their future prayer?

—Horace

Maurice Barrès

UPROOTED

Maurice Barrès, born in Lorraine in 1862, was like most Lorrainers an extreme Nationalist. His writings, which were largely fictional, exercised a powerful influence over his generation of Frenchmen and contributed to the inveterate antagonism of the French to Prussianized Germany that resulted in the World War. During the conflict he supported the French cause with daily articles in *Echo de Paris*. What is noteworthy concerning this Lorrainer is that his earlier writings were expositions of a philosophy of egotism, which is significantly expressed in the general title of his three volumes called "Le Culte de Moi." In 1897, "Les Déracinés" (Uprooted) professed his conversion to gallicism about which he wrote with an almost mystical fervor. This book was the first of a trilogy including "L'Appel au Soldat" and "Leurs Figures." At his death in 1923, he was compared with Anatole France as one of the representative figures of the literature of 19th and early 20th century France.

Modern Adventurers

At two o'clock on May 5, 1884, seven lads held a meeting before the tomb of Napoleon, under the solemn dome of the Hôtel des Invalides. None of them had been long in Paris. They spoke with a Lorraine accent, and their heavy winter clothes were worn threadbare. But shabby though they were to look at, there was a resolute strength in their fresh faces which distinguished them from the metropolitan crowd. Seven young students from Nancy, they had suddenly been uprooted from the rich soil of Lorraine and thrown on the bare, dusty asphalt of Paris.

Among them were at least five of the best minds of the younger generation of their province. Maurice Roemerspacher, for instance, the broad-shouldered, robust, red-haired youth, who stood gazing at the sarcophagus of the great emperor, had already written an article which had been praised by the master spirit of the age, Taine. Next to him, leaning a hand on his shoulder, was a pale, excitable lad, who was speaking with great passion and gesticulating violently. This was François Sturel, who was making a name as a wild, but very original poet. Then there were Renaudin, a rising

journalist, Suret-Lefort, a rising barrister, and the philosophic Saint-Phlin. Even Racadot, a wealthy farmer's son, with a low brow and heavy features, and Mouchefrin, his penniless boon companion, were not negligible forces; one had at least tenacity of character, the other cleverness and ambition.

"Napoleon was but a poor, friendless young man," Sturel was saying, "but he was true to himself—to himself alone—and he made his mark. Well, we have finished our studies; what are we going to do with ourselves? Shall we be lost in the crowd, and let others win dominion? Look at it—the vast, dim mass of men of our own generation. It contains somewhere the coming leaders, the captains of the new age. Let us be the leaders! Let us be the captains! Swear it on the tomb of Napoleon—of Napoleon the preacher of the gospel of energy! We will be great men!"

It was vainglorious, it was violent, it was extravagant; but it was effective. Sturel was a poet, and he gave expression to the master passion of his contemporaries. It was young France speaking. Napoleon to them was neither a lover and servant of France, nor a liberator of humanity, but a hard, fierce, splendid free-lance, fighting only for his own hand. As such, they admired him. Taine had destroyed their faith in humanitarianism; Renan had destroyed their faith in revealed religion; Darwin had opened their eyes to the struggle for life. Well, what was there to live for? The struggle itself, and the fierce joy of it! So they admired Napoleon as a sublime example of the energy which gives a man victory in this pitiless struggle.

"Napoleon" said Mouchefrin, "was fitted to preside over the reorganization of a new France because he was a foreigner. None of our institutions had any power over his alien imagination. What do we feel for our republican form of government? Contempt and hatred! It is utterly corrupt, utterly feeble, utterly ineffectual. It lies with us to destroy it."

"But how?" said Renaudin.

NOBODY answered. Young France was not prepared with any plan of campaign. It was merely an aimless, disorganized, discontented multitude. Gambetta, the founder of the Third Republic, had tried to stamp out all monarchial and imperial sentiment in France by educating the younger generation to disregard the prejudices and feelings of their parents, and to examine everything from the point of view of French revolutionary thought.

The seven students from Nancy were the products of this destructive system. They had been instructed by one of the most brilliant teachers of the day, Paul Bouteiller, a friend and follower of Gambetta. He had taught them to criticise the traditions and ways of life of Lorraine, in the light of the abstract ideas of liberty, equality and fraternity. They had done so. Then, however, instead of accepting the theories of the French Revolution, as Gambetta and his followers intended them to do, they had gone on to criticise and explode these theories in the light of Darwinism and other modern branches of science. They were no longer Republicans, but Anarchists; and they hated the republican government with the blind, savage idealism of youthful rebels.

"But how are we to make your attack?" Renaudin had asked.

"All this talk about Napoleon," said Racadot, with a glance at Sturel, who had called the meeting and done nearly all the speaking, "is beside the point. None of us is the leader of a victorious army. We can't climb to power that way. We must adopt the modern method, the Press. Let us found a paper. I can get the funds."

The fact was Racadot had just received a legacy of $8,000, and he saw a way of increasing his fortune. It may seem a wild folly to try to start a newspaper on this small sum. Nowadays one wants about a quarter of a million. But in Paris in the early 'eighties a skilful intriguer, with a capable staff, did not require much capital. Though the circulation of his paper was poor and the advertisement revenue scanty, a little daring soon made up for that.

A crowd of company promoters and ambitious politicians required a means of influencing public opinion, and they generally subsidised any clever journal that was waiting to be bought up. That was how *The True Republic* was founded.

Young Sturel was made editor; Roemerspacher, Saint-Phlin and Suret-Lefort, chief contributors. They all agreed to give their services until the paper became a paying concern; but they did not know anything about the subsidies. They would have withdrawn had they done so, for they still retained certain unreasonable traditions regarding personal honour.

This part of the business, however, was secretly managed by Renaudin, Racadot and Mouchefrin. They began boldly, as soon as the first number was issued.

"Will you make an enemy for the sake of five hundred dollars?" said Renaudin to the agent of the Panama Canal Company.

The money was paid. The company was about to float a large issue of new shares.

Castles in the Air

WHILE the blackmailing was going on, Sturel, Saint-Phlin, Roemerspacher and Suret-Lefort were engaged in building castles in the air. In one column of the newspaper, Sturel was continually proclaiming that France needed a strong man of the Napoleonic type. In another, Roemerspacher tried to found a new system of morality on the basis of modern science. Saint-Phlin was busy constructing a scheme of religious philosophy; while Suret-Lefort, the most practical member of the group, wrote on modern politics. The articles were well done, but they were not journalism. The result was that *The True Republic* never had a circulation of more than 4,500 copies.

Even the virtue of the austere Saint-Phlin and of the studious Roemerspacher gave way to the common temptation of bohemianism. Strangely enough, Sturel, who had the wildest imagination of them all, was the only one who thought of marriage. The allowance which he received from his parents enabled him to live in a good boarding-house in the Rue Sainte-Beuve. Here he had met a charming girl of seventeen years of age, Thérèse Alison, who was staying with her mother in Paris for the season.

Thérèse also came from Lorraine, and was another example of an uprooted and endangering mind. All the year round she wandered with her mother about Europe, lost in that idle, aimless multitude of pleasure-seekers which floats continually between the German spas, Paris and the cities of the Riviera. A quarrel between her parents had deprived her of the sweet and strengthening influences of home life, just at the age in which her character was being formed. A variety of chance acquaintanceships had already given her a self-assurance and a certain facility and forwardness of manner which would have brought her under suspicion in old-fashioned circles.

But the fact was that if she had remained shy and maidenly, she would never have had any social intercourse. As it was, until she met François Sturel, she never knew the intimate joys of human companionship. Under the eyes of Mme. Alison the young pair flirted and quarrelled, and made excursions together into the country. In another month, it seemed, they would be betrothed. On both sides the match was a desirable one in all respects.

But even the best of Parisian boarding-houses is not as safe a place for a young poet as a quiet home in Lorraine. One evening Sturel found a strange and marvellous creature sitting opposite to him at table. Astiné Aravian, a Turkish lady of high rank and remarkable beauty, had lived, up to the age of thirty, at Constantinople, in the harem of one of the chief officials of the Ottoman Empire. Her husband had just died, leaving her possessed of great wealth.

During her married life she had amused herself by reading French novels of the worst type, and now that she was free, she had journeyed to Paris to try and live the life of wild pleasure which she had admired in her favourite books. She came straight from the railway station to the boarding-house, still dressed in her native costume, and wearing long strings of splendid turquoises. All the romance of the Orient hung about her. Her fine oval face, her black hair, long black eyelashes and sombre blue eyes fascinated Sturel.

And, unfortunately, she in turn was attracted by François Sturel. That pale, good-looking young man a French poet? How interesting! Perhaps if Thérèse had not remained in her room all that day —she had had a tiff with her sweetheart—the result might have been different. But who knows? The Oriental woman was extraordinary quick and direct when once her desire and curiosity were excited.

"Won't you come and read some of your poems to me in my room?" she said.

HE ENTERED the room, and did not leave until the morning. It was not until she quitted the boarding-house, as suddenly as she entered it—after a stay of three weeks—that Sturel recovered from the fever of the senses and the disorder of the imagination which she had provoked in him. He then returned to Thérèse; but he had lost his purity and freshness of feeling, and she was vexed with him, and showed it by exaggerating the rather loud manners which she had learnt at fashionable watering-places. Both of them concealed the true and touching simplicity of their youthful souls. They were secretly discomfited by the brilliant, worldly tone in which they now conversed. They thwarted the happy chance which had brought them together; and, just for the vanity of astonishing each other, they spoilt the hours of joy and youth and ardour which would have led them hand in hand down the road to marriage.

The New Morality

RACADOT succeeded in getting *The True Republic* a bad name, without converting it into a profitable concern; and by the end of September his legacy was almost expended. He resolved to call in an expert.

"My dear editor," he said to Sturel, "the paper is admirably done, but it doesn't bring in money. The fact is we don't know the ropes. I have got a new contributor, and I should like you to come and dine with him this evening at the Champs Elysées."

Later Sturel was introduced to the expert.

"A scandalous case," said the new contributor, "has just been tried in private at the law-courts. A barrister and a merchant are badly mixed up in it. I will write you a note giving the name of the barrister—he hasn't a penny, so we can't bleed him. Then we will announce an inquiry to discover the name of the merchant. I know him also, and I will call on him, under the pretext of an interview, and I'm sure he'll stump up a round sum to keep us quiet."

"That's enough," said Sturel.

He took his hat, stick and gloves, paid his bill, and went off. Racadot followed him, explaining the difference between making a bargain to keep silent, "which really isn't dangerous," and forcing payment by defamatory attack, "which, of course, one must beware of doing."

Sturel hurried out of earshot. He wanted to get somewhere on to firm ground. He felt beneath his feet the quaking surface of the vast bog into which journalism has been transformed by the system of blackmail that constitutes parliamentary government in France.

He gave up editing *The True Republic*, and the expert was taken on the staff. But still things did not go well with the newspaper. Racadot's legacy was exhausted, and he wanted ready money to keep the newspaper running. Hearing that his old teacher, Paul Bouteiller, had gone into politics, and was standing as deputy for Nancy, he offered to put *The True Republic* at his service for the election.

In return, Bouteiller arranged to get the newspaper subsidised both by the Ministry for Home Affairs and by the Ministry for Foreign Affairs.

Where could Racadot get the money to bring out the paper in the meantime? He announced a lecture by himself on "The New Morality," and got off about forty tickets on his friends and acquaintances. He cut down expenses to the last penny, and lived himself on short rations. But bills poured in that he had to meet; and on May 21, 1885, the printer of the newspaper refused to prepare the issue for the following day unless his account was paid. He gave Racadot two hours to find the money.

THE only rich person Racadot knew who was likely to befriend him was Astiné Aravian, the strange Turkish woman. She had returned to Paris, and taken a suite of rooms in the Rue de Balzac, and she often came to the office of *The True Republic,* in the hope of meeting Sturel again. But instead of helping her to find him, Racadot tried to win her favour.

In the low-browed, heavy-featured peasant there was nothing to tempt the splendid Oriental adventuress. She amused herself, sometimes, by going out at night with him and Mouchefrin, and exploring the scenes of Paris night life in their company; but that was all.

She was now going to spend an evening with them, wandering among the taverns on the hills above the Seine, and Racadot was resolved to get some money out of her one way or another.

About ten o'clock that night, Sturel and the Alisons were returning in a landau from an excursion to the Bois de Boulogne.

"Oh, the poor lady!" said Mme. Alison, as they passed by Billancourt. "She'll never get a carriage, here, this time of night!"

On the edge of the road a lady was wildly waving to the driver of the landau. Two men stood behind her, but they did not call or make any sign. Seeing that the carriage did not stop, the lady hastened towards Billancourt, and the men followed her.

"They're going the wrong way to get to town," said Thérèse to François. "Jump out and tell them."

Sturel never moved. The light from the carriage lamps had fallen on the face of the lady—she was Astiné Aravian. And the two men in the shadow were Racadot and Mouchefrin. Why, then, did Astiné have so strange a look of anguish? Still, as she had left him for two men of that sort, he had no call now to interfere.

The next day, all the press was full of the news of the illness of Victor Hugo. On his way to lecture on The New Morality, Sturel bought a newspaper, and read: "Victor Hugo died this afternoon at twenty minutes past one."

And underneath, in small type: "The body of a young woman of marvellous beauty was found this morning at Billancourt. Her head was smashed in and her clothes removed. She has been identified as Madame Aravian, a close relation of the Turkish Ambassador at St. Petersburg. No arrest has yet been made."

Sturel found about forty persons assembled in the lecture-hall. Roemerspacher came and sat beside him, and was surprised at his strange, distracted air. Sturel waited in a sort of cold, shuddering impatience. Racadot came on the platform. He had shaved his beard off. His face was thinner than it used to be; his eyes had more flame and more intelligence. He seemed to have been refined by illness. There was less of the peasant about him, and more of the thinker.

He began by boldly attacking the great man whom everybody was praising:

"Victor Hugo is a perfect example of the modern hypocrite. Sceptical in regard to the dogmas of ancient religion, he is credulous to the point of superstition in regard to the myths of modern politics. He pretends to be a modern thinker, but all he does is to play with words that are now empty of meaning. I mean words like duty, liberty, fraternity. He talks about going back to nature, but he never goes. What is the 'duty' that nature teaches us? The duty of self-preservation. There is for each of us an absolute necessity to persist in living. To live at the expense of others, and by all possible means; such is the beautiful lesson of nature. That is her idea of 'fraternity.' "

"There is certainly some truth in what he says," said Roemerspacher to Sturel. "It is necessary to find a new basis for morality. But what a vile point of view he takes of a delicate problem!"

Sturel did not respond. He was staring at Racadot, but not listening clearly to what he said. "Did he kill her? Did he kill her?" he kept asking himself.

The lecturer concluded by affirming that nature insisted that we should put aside our false and ineffectual moral sentiments, and boldly engage in the struggle for life.

"Science teaches us that every living being must strike to dominate and crush its neighbours. So does history. Who are the men who really fascinate the imagination? The Killers! The Conquerors! The Caesars! The Bonapartes!"

"Here," said Roemerspacher to Sturel, "Racadot is echoing you. Do you remember your speech at the tomb of Napoleon?"

There was no applause at the conclusion of this strange lecture, and Roemerspacher, who was annoyed at having been referred to, caught up Racadot.

"My dear friend," he said, "your laws of nature that invite us to crush our neighbours, and so on, may be true, in theory, for an imaginary monster living all alone on some unknown island. But man is really a social being, a political animal. For his own protection he must respect the laws of society. Besides, if he doesn't, society will soon protect itself. You haven't thought of the guillotine!"

Strangely pale, Racadot hurried off.

The End of the Compact

ALONE with Roemerspacher, Sturel told him everything; the scene at Billancourt between Astiné Aravian and Racadot and Mouchefrin: the news of the murder.

"You and I are partly responsible," said Roemerspacher, after a long pause. "I taught Racadot to talk about the struggle for life, and the new morality. You taught him to talk about fighting against the world for his own hand, as your hero, Napoleon, did."

"And who taught us?" said Sturel. "We only handed on to Racadot and Mouchefrin the results of the education that Paul Bouteiller gave us. Yes; Racadot was right in what he said about Victor Hugo and all the ranters of the modern liberal, democratic sort. They take away from us the faith and traditions of our fathers, but what do they put in their place? A vague, sentimental humanitarianism that will not stand examination!"

"But I still think," said Roemerspacher, "that we could found a new morality of a really solid kind on science."

"A morality that would help a poor, hungry, hard-pressed, miserable creature in the hour of temptation?" exclaimed Sturel. "No. I've done with it all. I do not wish to be a citizen of the universe, living according to the rule of universal reason, as Paul Bouteiller used to say.

What is Bouteiller now doing himself? Truckling to the Republican ministers in order to get a chance of entering parliament and sharing in the spoils! No. Let me be a humble, faithful son of Lorraine, holding to the honest traditions of the people from whom I spring."

The next day, that brilliant but rather obscure paper, *The True Republic,* was not published. Its staff was dispersed, and its proprietor imprisoned, and Paul Bouteiller had to find another organ of public opinion to assist him in winning his election at Nancy. Racadot had been arrested on the charge of murdering Astiné Aravian. As the police had traced the jewels which he had taken from his victim, he confessed that he had committed the crime. He was guillotined, and Mouchefrin acquitted.

THE trial excited an extraordinary amount of interest, and nearly lost Bouteiller his seat. There happened at the time to be a fierce dispute between the clerical and the anti-clerical Press. The clerical Press seized upon the fact that Racadot was a pupil of Bouteiller, and instanced the "crime of Billancourt" as an effect of the system of education established by the Third Republic. Racadot's lecture was printed by a Catholic journal, and the bishop of Nancy took it as the text for a manifesto against the official philosophy of the Republic.

Bouteiller defended himself in an interview, in the course of which he said:

"The miserable creature, Racadot, was a lad with a practical mind, and nothing of a theoriser. He committed a murder to try to keep his paper, *The True Republic,* alive. The idea of founding the rag he got from the actual editor, François Sturel, a brilliant boy, but wild and undisciplined. As for the divagations about 'a new morality,' by means of which the criminal tried to excuse his infamy, no doubt young Roemerspacher was responsible for these—a very distinguished lad, by the way, who has attracted the notice of Taine. The amusing thing in the dreadful tragedy is that these young men, whom the clerical Press now make such a row over, were anti-Republicans. So you see I had no influence whatever over their minds."

His statement, which did not grow less malevolent as it passed from mouth to mouth, had the effect of incriminating Sturel and Roemerspacher.

"I was always suspicious of M. Sturel. I knew that he kept bad company," said Mme. Alison afterwards to her friends.

Thérèse and François had not been formally betrothed, and the match was now abandoned. Sturel returned to his home in Lorraine, and there he heard that Thérèse had become engaged to a certain Baron de Nelles, and that Bouteiller had been returned to parliament as the deputy for Nancy. "To Bouteiller, from grateful Lorraine," that was the toast given at a banquet in commemoration of the Republican victory at the polls.

"To Bouteiller, from grateful Lorraine!"

MAY

MAY! queen of blossoms,
    And fulfilling flowers,
With what pretty music
    Shall we charm the hours?
Wilt thou have pipe and reed,
Blown in the open mead?
Or to the lute give heed
    In the green bowers?

Thou hast no need of us,
    Or pipe or wire;
Thou hast the golden bee
    Ripen'd with fire;
And many thousand more
Songsters, that thee adore,
Filling earth's grassy floor
    With new desire.

Thou hast thy mighty herds,
    Tame and free-livers;
Doubt not, thy music too
    In the deep rivers;
And the whole plumy flight
Warbling the day and night—
Up at the gates of light,
    See, the lark quivers!
        —*Edward Thurlow, Lord Thurlow*

EDEN PHILLPOTTS

THE MOTHER

IN 1890 Eden Phillpotts (1862–) quit the insurance business to become an actor. He drifted from the stage to journalism, and in 1890 assumed authorship with the publication of his first novel of Dartmoor, "Sons of the Morning." "The Mother" which appeared in 1908, has been selected as representative of his work. Mother-love is his theme, and his outlook optimistic.

THE scene is laid throughout in Merivale, a moorland hamlet under the shadow of Vixen Tor, and the story opens on an afternoon in late October on the fringe of Devon's central waste beneath the woods. Here Avisa Pomeroy, the placid, wise and gentle mother of headstrong Ives Pomeroy, falls in with Rachel Bolt, the aged and doting mother of an only child Samuel. Their talk is of a great matter; nothing less than the news that Jill Wickett has accepted Samuel Bolt in preference to the younger, passionate Ives Pomeroy who also has long been set upon her. Avisa feels no regret at the news; only surprise at any girl choosing the simple, uninteresting Samuel when she might have had such a wonder of young manhood as Ives; but other thoughts about him stir uneasiness in her heart and it is with a grave face that she goes home to meet her boy.

She finds him in the kitchen of Vixen Tor farmhouse, his face dark and malignant with passion. Fiercely he accuses her of having helped Bolt to win the girl from him, and scornfully refuses to acknowledge that his own hectoring behaviour has been responsible for her choice. Finally he blazes out:

"Curse the lot of you—narrow, hard-hearted, frozen up creatures that you be! You talk so wise, and me robbed of the only thing in the world I cared about. Precious comfort—the likes of you—to a miserable man. But I'll go my own way—to hell if I choose. And 'twill be your fault—yours, mother, as much as any— for you never liked her and never helped me

to win her. And now—be damned to everybody! I don't care what becomes of any living soul on God's earth no more. And I'll be free, mark me, from this day—free to do what I please and think what I please. So now you know, mother!"

He took his cap, rose and went out of the house; while Mrs. Pomeroy bent and brushed up the dirt that his boots had left by the hearth.

"He'll be the death of us yet," said Lizzie mournfully; but her mother shook her head and smiled. She was looking after Ives.

"Don't think it," she answered. " 'Tis the other way; we'll be the life of him."

In almost every small village the public-house serves as the gossip exchange, and The Jolly Huntsmen at Merivale was no exception to the rule. It was kept by two brothers, Peter and Joel Toop. Into their lives had come lately an object of immense significance in the person of an orphaned young kinswoman, Ruth Rendle, to whom, having recently lost their barmaid, they had offered a home in exchange for service. A slim, dark-faced girl of twenty-one, with black hair and rather heavy brows, silent and sensible, she awoke in the breasts of both brothers something more than a flicker of passion and put thoughts of matrimony into their heads which they ought to have entertained thirty years before if at all. Much of the comedy of the book is provided by the development of the tender passion in the hearts of these elderly men and by their separate proposals of marriage to Ruth.

But Ruth plays a much more important part in this peasant drama than by thus opening a subsidiary plot in which Eden Phillpotts can exercise his rich and racy humour. For she awakens passion in the heart also of Matthew Northmore, the master of Stone Park, a shy and sensitive man of thirty-eight, in whose life women had figured little, and love not at all. A man of immense vigour, with a temper, naturally morose, made gloomier by a lonely life on his moorland farm, Northmore becomes a dangerous enemy to Ives Pomeroy when, proposing in his turn to Ruth, he discovers that the girl's affections secretly are set upon that passionate, unmoral, reckless and, as yet, unbroken-in youth, who not only does not love her but is of the type not destined to make any woman happy.

In the meantime, however, Ives can think of nothing but the shameful way in which he has been jilted by Jill Wickett, and wearies every ear with the recital of his wrongs. Even to Ruth Rendle he tells the story, entering the bar with his now most sympathising crony, Mr. William Cawker, the irrepressibly humorous, graceless, rascally poacher invariably known as Moleskin, who is one of Eden Phillpotts's most delightful creations.

Moleskin knows human nature as well as he knows the nature of fur and fin and feather, and he purposely catches Ives Pomeroy on the rebound from Jill Wickett, who in due course became the wife of Samuel Bolt.

Moleskin has heard that Squire Serpell at Oaktown aims at having the biggest head of game this fall that ever has been known; "hundreds and hundreds of eggs is bought," and Moleskin, "a free trader to the backbone and all for liberty in these matters," has his own plans for the disposal of some of the resulting pheasants. But an accomplice is desirable, even necessary if Moleskin is to elude interfering keepers successfully, and in Ives, in his present mood, he knows he has found the right man.

"Ban't my way to count my chickens afore they are hatched, let alone another person's; but a very grand lot of birds there ought to be; and since you'm the only chap in these parts

with a head on his shoulders and right principles——"

"You can trust me all right, Moleskin."

"I know it. Wish there was more like you."

And poor deluded Ives is committed to participating in a raid upon the Oaktown coverts, he to act as the decoy, while Moleskin as the more experienced hand is to do the shooting with an air gun in another preserve. One attempt to save Ives from his folly and danger is made by Moleskin's wife and daughter. But it is worse than vain. For they ask Emmanuel Codd, head man at Vixen Tor Farm, to warn Ives to keep away from Moleskin, not knowing that there is bad blood between Codd and his young master. And Codd wishing to do an ill turn to Ives passes the news on to Matthew Northmore, who finds himself perplexed; knowledge of what is impending puts a weapon in his hand, which he yet hesitates to use; finally, he decides to try to help the younger man by asking the inspector of police to give him a word of warning. And thereby he is Pomeroy's undoing.

For the raid takes place; Ives with a fowling-piece sets dogs and keepers running after him, while Moleskin noiselessly kills twenty pheasants. Both get away, but Ives has been seen in the moonlight running across a drive; the gamekeeper cannot positively identify him; but Northmore's well-meant request to the inspector to warn Pomeroy furnishes virtual confirmation, and three days later the hand of the law falls upon him.

At the moment Ives was in the very act of confessing to his mother what he had done, and he was disconcerted at finding that for once her unfailing patience before his escapades appeared to desert him. A passionate scene is interrupted by Lizzie Pomeroy's excited announcement that three policemen are coming through the meadow.

Avisa looked at her son and world of sudden grief appeared upon her face.

"Ives! Ives!" she said.

"I know! It's all right; they've smelt a rat! You can guess where I shall be. Let me have some food when the coast's clear, and then I'll be away till the storm's blown over. Find out if Moleskin's took and let me know up on the Vixen after dark."

And he fled through a back entrance to a little niche among the rocks on the summit of Vixen Tor which had been his secret lair since early boyhood, where, undisturbed, he could dream his day-dreams or cool his heart and brain when fevers of passions consumed him.

Left alone with her daughter, Avisa told her what Ives was wanted for.

Her mind worked swiftly and her lips moved. "Lord have mercy on my son! Lord have mercy on my son!" she whispered to herself again and again. Then she felt her daughter's hand and heard Lizzie cry "Save him, mother, save him!"

It seemed now that Avisa came to herself. "Bear yourself braver, Lizzie. Yes—yes; I'll save him, please God." She turned to the men. "Good morning, Mr. Bachelor."

"Good morning, ma'am. I'm sorry for our errand and I hope with all my heart that your son will be able to clear himself; but 'tis rather bad against him. Anyway, he must come with us, please. 'Tis feared that he had a hand in that business to Oaktown."

"Yes, he had," she answered quietly. "You will find him hidden up in the rocks there. I'll show you where he is."

The policeman stared.

"'Tis a terrible thing for you—a terrible thing. I wish to God, ma'am, you'd not been called to do this," he said earnestly.

Her sad eyes met his.

"So do I," she answered. "Love's a hard task-master sometimes."

AND then Avisa leads the constables to the foot of Vixen Tor, watched with incredulous astonishment by Ives aloft among the rocks, who boils with passion against his mother for betraying him and shouts curses after her retreating figure before surrendering himself.

Reaching home, Avisa is greeted by her daughter:

"Ives will never darken our doors again," sobbed Lizzie.

Then Avisa spoke. She took out her handkerchief and wiped Lizzie's eyes with it. Her own were dry.

"Darken our doors he can't, my pretty. Better than sunshine always. I doubt you'm wrong. My son will come home to me a wiser man—some day—yes, he'll come home, if I know him true."

Upon such a matter Avisa's instinct could not err, and a few days after his release from prison Ives came home, his love for his mother undiminished by her surrender of him to justice, the motivation of which he may perhaps have come to understand in the interval, though he never spoke of it. But even in her recovered happiness Avisa knew that Ives had not yet found himself, and time mattered, for she knew also that she was in the grip of malignant disease and would not be spared very long to exercise influence over him from this side of the grave. And in the meantime there was Jill Bolt, unsuitably mated to a fatuous man wholly unable to satisfy her needs and in dangerous proximity to her former lover, upon whose passionate nature her super-abundant physical womanhood still had inflammatory effect. They met soon and often, and it was not long before pity and desire wrought upon him so far that he resolved to carry her off, as usual disregarding everything except fulfilment of his own will and purpose.

BUT, also as usual, Ives could not refrain from taking his mother into his confidence. A conflict of wills ensued of terrible intensity to his mother. Only twenty-four hours lay between him and ruin, for Ives had arranged to meet Jill at three o'clock the following morning at the ancient granite Windystone up on the moor. Avisa knew that this was the supreme battle of her life for her son, and she did not spare herself. Hour after hour she poured out words and only desisted when, threatened by physical collapse, she extracted a promise from him upon his honour that he would do nothing until he had spoken with her on the morrow.

Not until the following evening did she learn that the victory was hers. No urge of conscience impelling him to do what was right had made Ives change his mind. Knowledge of facts of which Jill had kept him in ignorance had enabled Avisa to convince him against his will that sordid material considerations had decided Jill to throw in her lot with him, not love for himself alone, and all the romance was eliminated from the adventure and his pride was wounded to the quick.

He told his mother that evening, and with native wisdom she forbore from comment. On her advice he wrote a note to Jill, announcing his intention not to meet her as arranged or proceed with the elopement, and scrawling the one word "Jill" upon the envelope, went up to her cottage and slipped the letter under the front door.

But Jill had gone to bed early, to get a few hours' sleep before her exodus, and it was the husband, not the wife, who found the letter when he came in about ten o'clock. Always a feeble creature, Samuel Bolt was completely at a loss to know what to do in such a tremendous crisis. For two hours he sleepily pondered the matter and then, slowly coming to his senses, had a great idea. He would do nothing at all! Unheroic as the plan was, it yet would have considerable consequences, for his silence would mean that Jill would endure the trouble and mortification of a fruitless journey to the Windystone, and meantime he could go to bed and find in sleep restoration of energy to cope with the problem in some more effective way.

Presently Jill woke up, and stealthily moving, dressed in the dark and fared forth under the stars to the Windystone. A church clock struck three, and she strained her ears for the step of Ives.

Light began to be felt rather than seen and the eastern hills were defining themselves; but the world still slept; the stars still shone overhead, and the water at her feet still reflected their light. The morning wind awoke, sighed out of his deep, hungry heart, and roamed restless until dawn should come and throw her rosy loveliness into his bosom. Waking creatures shambled past Jill. Mares and little foals went by; cattle stirred and blew sleep from their nostrils and rose out of their beds in the fern. Pure silver light stole over the sky and drowned the stars, but the earth was still very dark. Birds called; the world revolved to the sun and soon a rusty red lattice and tangle of dim fire fretted the east. Every stone and bush shone clear against the increasing glory of the day; but no sign of Ives appeared upon the path that he should have trodden an hour ago.

Furious at her lover's defection, still more furious at his failure to prevent her from keeping a tryst which he either would not or could not keep himself, Jill Bolt made her way back to her husband's house, changed her gown, hid her soaking boots and stockings for the present, then lighted the fire and prepared breakfast. Anxious to postpone discussion of the letter yet a little longer, Samuel announced his intention of not going to work that day, and offered to take his wife to Tavistock cattle market and revel. The holiday passed prosperously and it was not until, supper finished, they were on the point of going to bed, that Samuel gave her Pomeroy's letter to read. His pusillanimity astonished Jill.

"Why for didn't you wake me last night and have this out then?"

"Because—for several reasons. One was I hadn't the heart. You must remember this comed as a terrible shock to me; it made my flesh water and my bones jelly—"

"Why didn't you come upstairs and pull me out of bed by the hair and cut my throat?"

" 'Twould only have been one more nastiness in the newspapers. I hope to God whatever happens I shall never get in print; besides, I'm not that sort. But I said to myself, sternlike, that you'd got to suffer, Jill. So what did I do but just harden my heart against you, and go to bed. and let you march off to cool your heels and wait for the rascal. And I thought the cross of Christ up along in the shape of the Windystone night very likely do the rest; and I'm sure I hope it have."

Even with regard to the attitude it behooved him as a man to adopt towards Ives Pomeroy, Samuel could say no more than "I ought to go to the length of being vexed with the man in public, ought really to pull his nose before people." To bleating like this Jill was incapable of reply, but she knew she was well out of an awkward predicament; she could make shift to put up with this pusillanimous husband. And the lover? "Leave him to me," she said. "My quarrel's quite as big as yours—maybe bigger"—words ominous of trouble to Ives.

At this point in his career his mother died. For some little time before, Ruth Rendle had been staying with Avisa Pomeroy at Vixen Tor Farm, being glad to escape from The Jolly Huntsmen where vexation constantly beset her since her refusal of the Toop brothers and of Matthew Northmore. Thwarted love indeed had so embittered the last that he had become a morose, hard-drinking man, dangerous when angered, and always gloomy. Under Avisa Pomeroy's roof the girl found a home and Avisa rejoiced when she became aware of Ruth's secret love for Ives. Here, the mother knew, was the sure promise of ultimate happiness for her son. But others were aware of it too; Matthew Northmore long since; and quite recently Jill Bolt, widowed now by an accident that had befallen Samuel; and jealousy, added to her bitterness, inspired her to fiendish action.

Mutual dislike had developed into active hatred between Northmore and Pomeroy, leading actually to blows, and it was in one of these quarrels that Northmore's hasty words gave Pomeroy knowledge of Ruth's feeling for himself. The seed thus sown grew rapidly and, all his lower passion for Jill Bolt extinguished, Ives knew he loved and was loved by Ruth. Their engagement was virtually in being, and then Jill struck. As her tool she used Emmanuel Codd, the discontented former headman at Vixen Tor Farm who, dismissed by Ives after his mother's death, had found employment with Matthew Northmore. The master of Stone Park was away and Ives, passing the place, caught sight of Codd and went into the rickyard to talk to him. Inadvertently he dropped a matchbox given him by Ruth and a let-ter, and went on his way unknowing. Half an hour later Jill Bolt sat with Codd in the same place, and with devilish cunning told Codd what to do. That night Northmore's stacks were fired, three pedigree heifers were roasted in a shippon, and next morning Northmore found under the edge of a haystack to the rear of those consumed by fire Ruth's letter to Ives, half-burnt, and the matchbox.

Northmore spent a night of torment debating the matter with himself, and next day rode to Tavistock where Ruth was employed in a shop. Briefly he recited the facts, put the evidence into her hand and then told her to choose.

"You must marry me, Ruth. This leaves you no loophole. I'll say nothing more but that I know in a very little time you'll bless the change that has made you do it. I see the future crystal clear. Speak then. If Pomeroy's to go to prison, say so. If he's to be free, say so. . . . I know 'twill be your love for him will make you take me. But I'll suffer even that torture; because I'll look forward. You'll change when you get to find the kind of husband I am, I'm sure of that."

"You've planned this, Matthew?"

"Fate planned it. God Almighty planned it. Don't decide afore the full meaning and force of the thing is made clear to your mind. I've waited long enough; I can wait a bit more yet."

Northmore waited in silence while the girl concentrated her thoughts upon all that had happened between these two men, and what she knew of the character of both of them. It took her long to decide, but the proofs that lay under her hands seemed quite conclusive, and at last her mind was made up. She took the match-box and the damning papers and threw them in the fire.

"You understand what that means, Ruth?"

"Yes," she answered, "I understand. It means that I'll marry you, Matthew, and make you the best wife I can—"

Frenzied denunciations of her and of all other women pour from the lips of Ives Pomeroy when shortly afterwards, asking Ruth to marry him, he learns from herself that she has accepted Northmore, and two days later he confronts his rival and insists upon getting to the bottom of the matter. So violent is the scene that Northmore realizes things cannot be left as they are, and the men arrange to meet on the next day but one at the Lone Stones up on the moor, where they will be undisturbed, Northmore's intention being to tell Pomeroy that his crime of arson is known; Pomeroy's purpose being nothing less than death for himself or murder.

But in the short interval of time the purpose of both men is changed. To Northmore comes Jill Bolt who having, not a little to her own surprise, been sought successfully in marriage by Peter Toop, has forgiven Ives Pomeroy and wishes to clear him of the suspicion of arson. Calmly she tells him the whole story, makes clear to him what his marriage to Ruth Rendle will mean both in his own eyes and his wife's—if Ruth becomes his wife—and leaves him to contemplate a future without Ruth, which he knows will be unendurable. Only one way of escape from an intolerable situation seems open to the unhappy man, and forgetting all about his appointment there with Ives, he determines to go next day to the Lone Stones and there take his own life since it was there he had first asked Ruth to marry him and had been refused.

Upon Pomeroy falls his mother's influence. Almost exhausted by one of his characteristic outbursts of passion he picked up Avisa's Bible and found in it a slip of paper on which a list of references to many texts was written. Idly he turned to the first: *And teach us what we shall do unto the child that shall be born.* He sought the second: *God hath judged me and hath also heard my voice, and hath given me a son.* The third: *God be gracious unto thee my son.* The fourth: *His mother made him a little coat.* Seldom if ever has so pathetic a token of his mother's love fallen into the hands of a son; for here was a chronicle of Ives Pomeroy's headstrong, troubled career from infancy to man-

hood, clearly to be read through the words in the Bible in which his mother had found comfort or hope when heart-stricken or crushed by grief or agony he had caused her. Two hours and more did the man spend, reading and musing on these texts for the tale of his life. And then:

From this great survey he came back to the present; but he did not come back alone. His mother's heart was beating in his; her spirit belonged to him as the intrinsic controller of his own. Again he turned to the Bible for a text that he remembered dimly. He knew the source of it and came upon it anon. *Thy mother is like a vine in thy blood.*

What fruit should the scion of this stock ripen in the world's garden? Can we gather a thorn from a grape?

"That woman's son have got no choice," he said to himself, and in ignorance uttered truth.

Thus it was brought to pass that when Ives Pomeroy came to the spot appointed for the meeting he came with empty hands, resolved to do no hurt to Northmore. But a wave of hatred swept over him when the other man appeared, for Northmore staggered as if he were drunk and his eyes blazed with misery. Any meeting with him was foolish under these conditions and Ives crouched out of sight the better to judge of the other's state. Northmore was not drunk, but his excitement was terrible; he flung himself down on the reeking earth and then suddenly tore open his coat and shirt, drew a revolver from his pocket and cocked it and held it to his side; then he changed his mind and lifted it to his head. That movement saved his life. Ives sprang forward with a shout and Northmore turned and started as he pulled the trigger, with the result that the bullet missed his temple. He had no chance to fire again, for Ives tore the weapon away.

Dazed, obscured, inconsequent, Northmore was long in returning to a state of mind sufficiently normal for him to explain the facts, but he told his story by degrees. One salient fact emerged. Ruth was free.

Dixon Wecter
THE SAGA OF AMERICAN SOCIETY

*"The Colonel's Lady and Sally O'Grady
are sisters under the skin."*

Y**ou** will find when you read "The Saga of American Society" that these lines from Kipling contain more truth than poetry. For this book shows that our *Mayflower* descendants and "first families" had very humble beginnings. If you ever thought that the flamboyant people in the society columns were the real American aristocrats, you will discover here how wrong you were. But down below the surface of this lively account, you will find in broad outline much of the cultural, economic and political history of our country. Dixon Wecter, whose family settled in the South before the Revolution, and who was born in Houston, Texas, in 1906, has the scholarly background, sense of humor and modern viewpoint necessary to make his story of the ups and downs of American high life authentic and amusing. He has received degrees from Baylor University, Yale and Oxford, and is now a professor in the Southern Branch of the University of California, at Los Angeles, and a Research Fellow of the Huntington Library in nearby San Marino. He is also the author of "Edmund Burke and His Kinsmen," and has contributed to the *Atlantic Monthly* and other periodicals.

T**he** late Major Henry Lee Higginson in giving to Harvard College the grounds now known as Soldiers Field, conceded that democracy and socialism having got fast hold of the world would dominate the future, and therefore called upon those with social background, knowledge, and cultivation faithfully to help the new masters of the world rule "more wisely and more humanely than the kings and nobles have done. Our chance is *now*—before the country is full and the struggle for bread becomes intense. I would have the gentlemen of this country lead the new men, who are trying to become gentlemen, in their gifts and in their efforts to promote education."

These are wise and generous though belated words which make a victory of defeat, and suggest perhaps a way in which Jerusalem may yet be builded here amid these dark Satanic mills.

The late years of economic tension have demonstrated to everybody certain painful weaknesses in the fabric of American life. We have attempted too much to wealth and bluff indiscriminate philanthropy, and too little to the quieter obligations of an aristocracy. Today the cry for social justice is articulate.

But the classic plutocrat today is no more than a bogey in the Marxist nursery. In fact he has been so harassed by levies, laws, codes, public criticisms, and gruelling committees of investigation that a lover of paradox might forecast the day when a hard-bitten plutocracy, driven to its burrows, would revolt and assert the claims of human brotherhood against a pampered, effete proletariat.

The distaste of the American rich for politics has finally drawn a heavy penalty by leaving them at the mercy of a democratic electorate. This plight of the millionaire from a purely economic viewpoint is not likely to draw many tears from the impartial, who cannot regard the discharge of a second gardener or the reduction of sixteen cylinders to twelve as an essentially tragic privation. Last year at the Newport Flower Show America's last great hostess—who, like the readers of the tabloids, still believes in Society—remarked to friends with a certain ethereal complacency, "Isn't it terrible?—And you know, *our* heads will be the first to fall!"

But much more serious losses would now follow the complete cancellation of that margin of sumptuary grace and leisure which America has managed to attain. Its aristocracy is on the whole not a very well seasoned one; the behavior of the rich and conspicuous in so-called Society has often been cheap, snobbish, and absurd, as the following chapters from its history may indicate. Yet its destruction, root and branch, would do little good and much irreparable harm. The distribution of a few dollars per capita and the conversion of a fleet of steam yachts into proletarian picnic-boats would hardly compensate for the annihilation, among some members of that aristocracy, of gentle manners, beautiful speech, and the connoisseurship of gracious living. Mr. Edward F. Hutton, with the arrogance of the newly rich, and Mr. Michael Gold, with the desperation of the eternally poor, are both equally blind to the ancient Hellenic wisdom of Santayana's words: "You individually can't raise the lowest level of human life, but you may raise the highest level."

Plutocracy, Aristocracy and Society

At the outset one might notice the difference between Plutocracy, Society, and Aristocracy in America. It is easy to see the difference in texture between the stout garment of aristocracy and that fringe of its gold braid called Society. Society is the overt manifestation of caste. It is active, conspicuous, articulate, specialized. Many people of birth and breeding as well as fortune prefer to live quietly, not a little bored with the social game of ceaseless entertaining, sponsorship, and snubbing—which they are glad enough to leave to their more restless cousins, to lavish spenders, and to flashy newcomers who have done so much to bring the word Society into disrepute. To the old aristocrat notoriety is a type of social nudism, and a number of ultra-conservative families today from New York to San Francisco pay a mild sort of blackmail to keep their names out of the press, travel under assumed names, and with mortal fear and hatred flee the photographers, reporters, and kidnappers whom they lump together.

Society however generally delights in publicity and novelty, though in recent years it has learned in self-defense to affect some protective coloration along with the old guard. Another earmark of Society is the extreme seriousness with which it takes itself. The seasoned aristocrat accepts social life as a passing amusement, a decorative puppet-show, an escape from work or boredom; the *nouveau* regards it as an end to itself. He never bivouacs upon the level earth, content to eat and drink and watch the stars come out, but thinks of human existence as an inclined plane upon which going upward is the only alternative to slipping back.

The absence of an hereditary governing class has had the effect of removing all bounds from social ambition. If every boy can be President, then surely every girl can sit in Marble House at Newport. In this sense Society is more characteristic of America at large than is aristocracy; it is the symbol of a chiefly feminine achievement as impressive in its way as the Brooklyn Bridge and the transcontinental railway. But the traditional aristocrat is born not made, as Doctor Holmes knew when he answered an anxious mother's inquiries by predicating that "a child's education should begin at least one hundred years before he was born." That at any rate is beyond purchase or enterprise.

What then is the relation between wealth and aristocracy? If any one still believes they are synonymous let him go to Charleston, South Carolina, the home of the stranded gentry, and then travel on to Palm Beach where every prospect pleases. Yet social distinctions sooner or later disappear when they have lost all economic bulwarks. Privacy, leisure, cultivation, and beauty—things vital as bread and meat to the aristicratic life—are increasingly expensive in this modern world. The center of gravity must therefore always remain among the well-to-do, though possessing this equilibrium the true aristocracy will readily extend its privileges to those whose charm, gentleness, consideration for others, and good manners have persisted in the face of poverty. They bear the symbols of its freemasonry, and are admitted without having to show their bank-books at the door.

The self-assured aristocrat—who can most readily be distinguished from the arrivist by the nonchalance with which he invites the world in general to go to hell—has passed beyond the servility of regarding wealth as the measure of success. Rich enough to take it for granted, or else poor enough to ignore it, he under no circumstances crooks the knee.

Some years ago a great lady of Charleston was being regaled by her grandchildren concerning the sights they had seen in Paris. They dwelt in particular upon their visit to the Louvre, and the knots of people who were always found in rapt contemplation before Whistler's *Mother*. The old lady listened attentively, and when they paused for breath she inquired with all imaginable sweetness, "But why? After all, she was only a MacNeill of North Carolina."

Social Cake without Icing

No one is more incurably romantic than a democrat, and we in America have fostered the legendary glamor of a Virginia peopled exclusively by Cavaliers fleeing the axe of Cromwell's headsman with their pockets stuffed with crested silver and a family portrait or two under their arm, a New York colonized by lordly patroons stepping off *The Little Sea-Mew* straight from Amsterdam with Indians genuflecting on the shore, and a Plymouth Rock on which was kindled the blaze of religious liberty to illuminate the world.

Idealists have often forgotten the fact that trade and the hope of better fortune were the mainsprings of immigration to America during the seventeenth and eighteenth centuries, when first the Puritan shopkeeper, and later the Whig merchant, were in flower in England. Their social ambitions as well as their commercial enterprise were infused into the New World. Almost without exception the permanent settlers in America—F. F. V.s, *Mayflower* passengers, Knickerbockers, and Quakers—were drawn from the middle and lower classes, from the aggressive, the dissenter, the ne'er-do-well, the underprivileged, and the maladjusted. The aristocrat whose birth and heritage gave him a stake in the old order had no reason for uprooting himself; if indeed he visited these coasts. He came for riches, adventure, or a term of exile as colonial governor. As has often been said, "Dukes don't emigrate." A true picture of the origins of Colonial Society must begin, then, by expunging the pious frauds of romance and amateur genealogy.

The Colonies are fairly described by James Truslow Adams as the social cake with the icing left off. Instead of the multiple layers of British society from plowman to prince, there were only two classes in America: indentured servants or slaves, and freemen. Among the freemen certain distinctions were felt by those of English origin—in regard to breeding, learning, seniority of residence, political influence, and public service—but they were ill-defined, vague, and constantly in need of revision. In general, however, what has been called the "vacuum in the accustomed social structure" was quickly filled by the ambitious, assertive, and able. Since the Norman Conquest the climber had never had so magnificent an opportunity.

In the beginning, land was the criterion of power and social position. The necessary simplicity of life and the less potent power of gold in the midst of a wilderness hampered any other display of pomp and circumstance than that marked by the surveyor's chain. Great landowners were the familiars and favorites of royal governors, who not only helped to enlarge their holdings, and flattered their social vanity, but also recommended to the King their appointment as members of the Council in each colony.

Gradually in the course of the eighteenth century, after most of the desirable land had been claimed and cities firmly planted, the mercantile class began its irresistible rise to dominance. The Amorys, Faneuils, Hancocks, and Boylstons of Boston; the Wartons of Newport and the Browns of Providence; the Crugers, Waltons, and Lows of New York; the Willings, Morrises, Pembertons, and Whartons of Philadelphia—

these merchants, traders, and shippers were the second growth of plutocracy in America, the heralds of that New World equivalent for the ancient aristocrat, the successful business man.

It was a type one stage further removed from the English country gentry, a departing path which later followed the track of steamship owners, railroad magnates, steel and iron manufacturers, down to our most recent fortunes in oil, automobiles, chain-stores, and patent medicines. Yet the absence of a recognized social order or an hereditary peerage with its theory that "by their roots ye shall know them," has caused such distinctions as do exist, or are imagined, to be taken seriously and self-consciously. This fact is borne out in the history of all the Colonies.

First Families of Virginia

FIRST in point of time was the settlement of Virginia.

Of the 295 men who founded Jamestown, 92 were classified on contemporary records as "gentlemen." Yet these gallants met not only cruel disappointment but frequently death itself from disease, famine, and redskins; aside from the descendants of John Rolfe, a man of petty rank, there is not a single American family today which stems from the first settlers of Jamestown.

Soon the Virginia Company discovered that the colonists who throve most contentedly as tobacco planters were those recruited from the middle class, with some mixture from below. As Sir William Berkeley, crustiest of Tories, was to remark in 1651, hundreds of examples showed that no man in Virginia, however lowly his origin, was denied the opportunity to rise in the social and economic scale. Of the forty-four burgesses in the Assembly of 1629—the only elective body in the Colony—seven had been listed as servants in the muster-roll of only five years before; in the Assembly of 1632 there were at least six former indentured servants, while thirty years later we find that 43 per cent of the

House of Burgesses had had their way paid to Virginia as bondsmen. In fact, many snobs in England were coming by hearsay to regard Virginia as an aristocracy of ex-footmen and of jail-birds with new plumage. It was a notion as absurd as the cisatlantic theory that all First Families sprang from belted earls.

Till well after 1700 it may safely be said that there was not a gentleman of leisure in Virginia or in fact the whole of North America, unless, as Mr. Adams observes, "he were a jailbird or a redskin." But in the course of the next quarter century several important events took place which gave the planter of Virginia, Maryland, and the Carolinas that relief from toil, or the personal supervision of it, which meant cultivation of the arts of living and social intercourse, as well as an increasing snobbishness of class.

First was the introduction of slavery by "the Saints of New England," as the second Colonel Byrd ironically called them in 1736, who "import so many Negroes hither that I feal the Colony will some time or other be Confirmed by the name of New Guinea." Slavery placed a stigma hitherto unknown upon working with the hands, and also drove a sharp cleavage between even the modest owner of one or two slaves, and the farmer or mechanic who did everything.

The poor white, that plague of the Southern aristocracy, was thus created; if a commoner had spirit he usually packed his tools and moved beyond the mountains toward the frontier—which, steadily advancing westward, for more than a century took up the slack of an underprivileged and disgruntled demos.

THE quarter-century from 1740 to 1765 saw the greatest fluorescence of luxury which this land had ever known—silks, jewels, gold and silver plate, French and Spanish wines, portrait-painting, carriages from London, horse-racing for high stakes, fox-hunts, concerts, balls and plays in the theatres at Williamsburg and Charleston—a social manifestation so widespread and competitive that it can be compared only to the Gilded Age three decades before the Great War. People of means felt no need to affect that later republican simplicity which became fashionable and perhaps expedient, after revolutions in America and France. The deluge had not yet come.

The mould of fashion was indisputably the Virginian or the Carolinian, celebrated not only for elegance in dress, speech, dining, and sport, but also for that graceful lotus-eating in a land where the abundance of nature had made hard work seem almost an act of ingratitude. Félix de Beaujour in the course of his travels later observed: "A Bostonian would seek his fortune in the bottom of hell, but a Virginian would not go four steps for it." Furthermore, sectional snobbery was already in the air: Virginians begin to bring home tidings that the ladies of Philadelphia are "homely, hard favored, and sour," and another citizen of the Old Dominion calls the Scotch-Irish "a spurious race of mortals," while farther south dwellers in Charleston were already coming to despise the tar-heels of their sister-colony.

The late President Alderman of the University of Virginia voiced an immemorial attitude when he pleasantly observed, "I come from North Carolina, that lowly valley between twin-peaks of conceit." Long before the initials F. F. V. were popularized early in the nineteenth century, the family pride for which they stood was proverbial. The type seems to have changed little up to the Civil War; and in 1853 in a book by Joseph G. Baldwin we find this timeless sketch:

> How far back he traced his lineage I do not remember, but he had the best blood of both worlds in his veins; sired high up on the paternal side by some Prince or Duke, and dammed on his mother's side by one or two Pocahontases. . . . The Virginian is a magnanimous man. He never throws up to a Yankee the fact of his birthplace. He feels on the subject as a man of delicacy feels in alluding to a female indiscretion, where there has been some scandal concerning the family. So far do they carry this refinement, that I have known one of my countrymen, on occasion of a Bostonian owning where he was born, generously protest that he had never heard of it.

But he adds that the Virginian excels in all the social arts—in getting up a good dinner, a picnic, or a fish fry, in promoting horse-races and fox-hunts, in mixing juleps or an apple toddy with nutmeg on top, and also in the strategy of "filling up of the chinks of conversation with small fugitive observations, the supplying the hooks and eyes that keep the discourse together." Unlike most of his compatriots, who knew nothing but trade and commerce, the Virginian had a fund of social small-talk.

Class Distinction in New England

THE THEORY that upper-class Southerners were scions of Old World aristocracy went hand in hand with the prejudice that Yankees of wealth and power were the grandsons of blue-nosed tailors, runaway 'prentices, and the off-scourings of ship-yards. John Fiske was probably the first historian of national standing to point out the truth, which now seems self-evident, that the leading families of New England—Saltonstall, Lowell, Cabot, Dudley, Winthrop, Peabody, and the rest—were recruited from the same essentially middle-class stratum which had produced Randolph, Cary, Cabell, and Lee

Whatever differences there were between the social structure of Virginia and Massachusetts sprang not from any essential difference in original rank, but from environment—plantation versus township, slavery as opposed to free labor, rich soil and mild weather against the rock-bound coast and winter storm, sympathy or hostility toward kingship in England, and the choice between sporting parson and Calvinist divine.

Well-descended Bostonians today deprecate the dourness, grimness, and bigotry of their forefathers—but they are intensely proud of them. With the card-playing, horse-racing, fox-hunting round of the planter it had no traffic—and in spite of its recent apologists often looked upon social gaiety in a peculiarly theological light. There are distinctly morbid implications in a social scheme which led one of the leaders of public life in seventeenth century Massachusetts to amuse himself by rearranging the coffins in the family vault and speak of the chore as "an awful yet pleasing Treat."

As in the case of the permanent settlers of Virginia, the first immigrants to arrive in New England—the *Mayflower* group, from which descended Brewsters, Bradfords, Allertons, Standishes, and Winslows—were people of extremely humble origin in comparison with the later arrivals. Of the forty-one men who signed the Covenant of the *Mayflower,* eleven bore the title of "Mr." but none that of "Gent." A group of English emigrants more socially insignificant could hardly be imagined; time and sentiment alone have given them the luster they possess.

The upper middle class did not begin to arrive till after the chartering of the Massachusetts Bay Company in 1629, which began as a trading enterprise but soon undertook to furnish an asylum to the English Puritan gentry as well. With approval of the Earl of Warwick, leadership was assumed by the country squire, John Winthrop, with his wealth, his Cambridge education, his stiff-necked piety, and his equally inflexible will.

GOVERNOR WINTHROP and his powerful henchman, the Reverend John Cotton, believed firmly in an aristocracy of Zion in which the clergy—most of them men of humble birth—should be the ranking class. Winthrop said, regarding democracy, that "among nations it has always been accounted the meanest and worst of all forms of government," and of society in general that "the best part is always the least, and of that part the wiser part is always the lesser."

The Rev. Mr. Cotton agreed fully: "Democracy I do not conceive that God did ever ordain as a fit government for either church or commonwealth. If the people be governors, who shall be governed? As for monarchy and aristocracy, they are both clearly approved and directed in the Scriptures. . . . He setteth up theocracy . . . as the best form of government in the commonwealth as in the church."

Under this system it was natural that election by God should be the basis of rank and that the names inscribed in the Lamb's Book of Life should be also first in the social register. Accorded the place of honor on all occasions official and social, the clergy ruled with absolute power until 1691 when Massachusetts received a new royal charter, much like that of Virginia, which set up a representative assembly and a franchise based no longer upon church membership but on property.

Four social classes are pretty clearly defined in early New England. The first was made up of the ministers, as indicated, plus a sprinkling of gentlemen—Saltonstalls, Dudleys, Bradstreets, Pynchons—who brought with them from England a middling social rank which in Massachusetts Bay became the top. In time these folk admitted to their company the successful merchant, whose fortune in merchandise, timber, ships, fishing, spermaceti, and speculation in land and townships, made him vital to the economic life of New England and, by inevitable logic, soon acceptable socially as well. Rising from obscurity of birth to a place of eminence made possible by brains, thrift, and industry was approved as part of the Divine economy of the universe, a kind of social predestination which it would be impious to challenge.

Below them were artisans and freeholders, who did most of the skilled work—cobbling, weaving, tinkering, farming, fishing. They called each other "Goodman" and "Goodwife," being very particular about the social earmarks which set them apart from the third class of unskilled laborers, wage-earners and journeymen, addressed by their Christian name alone. The fourth class was composed of indentured servants, who seem often to have been very unsatisfactory to their betters: John Winthrop justified his wife for beating their "lubberly" serving-maid, and Cotton Mather made it "an Article of special Supplication before the Lord, that He would send a good Servant into" his household.

In the course of time a very small fifth class, of Indian and Negro slaves, was added, but in general New England industry was grounded not upon servant or slave labor but upon the small farmer, skilled craftsman, fisherman, and sailor. Unlike the Spaniard who chose exploitation rather than extermination of the red man, and unlike the Southerner who presently came to see the advantages of slave labor, the Yankee attempted to do everything for himself, and as a result never attained that spacious margin of leisure in which Society of the Old World pattern flourished.

SOCIAL life in early Massachusetts was simple: a mid-week lecture in church was considered the convivial flood-mark, and among minor indulgences was

counted a stroll on Boston Common "where the Gallants a little before sunset walk with their Marmalet Madams . . . till the Nine-a-clock Bell rings them home."

But class distinctions were solemnly respected. As in Virginia, gentlemen were exempt from corporal punishment. In 1651 the Massachusetts General Court expressed its "utter detestation that men and women of meane condition, education, and calling, should take vppon them the garb of gentlemen by wearinge of gold or silver lace, or buttons or poynts at their knees, or walke in great boots, or women of the same ranke to weare silke or tiffany hoods or scarfs." It was decreed that ladies and gentlemen might wear lace, silver and gold thread, slashed sleeves, hat-bands, and elaborate girdles, belts and ruffs—but that goodman and goodwife could not do so. In 1653 two women were arrested at Newbury for wearing silk hoods and scarves, but were released upon proving that their husbands were worth £200 apiece.

But no kind of social gradation was more jealously guarded than seating in church, according to "dignity, age and estate." There were laborious rules of precedence, such as that "the fore seat in the front gallery shall be equall in dignity with the second seat in the body"; at Saco the people were separated into seven classes and seated correspondingly by a vote of the town. People often crowded into pews above their station, were ejected, and sometimes heavily fined. In old Newbury social climbers were fined up to £27 for persistently attempting to sit in the wrong pew.

Quite naturally the same attitude was carried over into other spheres. In the college founded in 1636 and named in honor of the Reverend John Harvard, the son of a butcher, students were listed in the catalogue according to their social rank up to 1773.

Society in Colonial Boston never wholly lost the artlessness of its earliest phase. The fashionable dinner hour was three o'clock; supper parties came in the early evening, followed by cards. Etiquette demanded that a bride receive her friends daily for four successive weeks after the wedding. Among the most popular social occasions were funerals, to which private invitations as well as public announcements were issued. As a modern critic of Boston, Charles Macomb Flandrau from Minnesota, has observed, funerals are "the only form of social gathering at which absolutely no one, under any circumstances, is ever expected to be either amusing or amused."

Yet in the last half of the Eighteenth Century Boston began to assume a rich magnificence—solid as a silver tankard by Paul Revere—thanks to its godly prosperity. French nobles in the Revolutionary War were vastly pleased with Boston—like the Comte de Ségur, who found that "democracy has not banished luxury," the Marquis de Chastellux who attended the Tuesday Evening Club and was charmed with a certain "*ton* of ease and freedom," and the Prince de Broglie who was enchanted by the good dinners, elegant napery, and plates changed whenever you wished.

Founders of the Empire State

THE earliest white settlers of Manhattan—some thirty families of sturdy Walloons, chiefly artisans, who came over in 1623 in the *Nieu Nederlandt* under the governorship of Cornelis Jacobsen May—were in general vigorous pioneer stock.

They are well described by Augustus Van Buren, who writes in the *Proceedings of the New York Historical Society,* vol. xi, p. 133: "Most of them could neither read nor write. They were a wild, uncouth, rough, and most of the time a drunken crowd. They lived in small log huts, thatched with straw. They wore rough clothes, and in the winter were dressed in skins. They subsisted on a little corn, game, and fish. They were afraid of neither man, God, nor the devil. They were laying deep the foundation of the Empire State."

Holland was just then in her renascence of commerce, learning, and political independence after the long tyranny of Spain, and there was little reason for anybody save those at the bottom of the ladder to leave. Hence the early Dutch settlers were of lowest social rank, unlike the middle and occasionally upper class colonists of Virginia, New England, New France, and New Spain. Illiterate, quarrelsome, fond of cheating the Indians and each other, they were nevertheless tough and plucky, like most men with their backs to the wall. Their

descendants are with us today. Walter P. Chrysler, automobile manufacturer, states in *Who's Who in America* that he is descended from the first male child born in New Amsterdam, Tuenis Van Dolsen.

Financial power in the planting of this colony came from the Dutch West India Company, composed of self-made Amsterdam merchants who—despised by the old aristocracy—longed to become founders of great estates and feudal barons, even by proxy in lands beyond the seas. One of them was Kiliaen Van Rensselaer, who had made a fortune trading in pearls and precious stones. In 1629 he and others persuaded the States General of Holland to encourage settlement by making any man "a patroon with all the rights of lordship" who within a space of six years should found a colony of fifty adults. The next year Van Rensselaer's agents bought from the Indians in exchange for "certain quantities of duffels, axes, knives, and wampum," a tract of some 700,000 acres along the west bank of the Hudson. The title of Rensselaerwyck was vested in him and his heirs for ever, and he was entitled to an oath of fealty from tenants.

THE Dutch system was more autocratic in political than in social ways, largely because the colony was directed by bourgeois enterprise and because one's status as a "great" or a "small" burgher was quite frankly bought in cash. Most high-handed of the governors was Peter Stuyvesant, whose blood still flows in the veins of New York lawyers, congressmen, and bankers. Suffering a sea-change from his mediocre status in Amsterdam, he arrived in New Netherland with a bearing described as that "of a peacock," kept the good burghers standing with uncovered head for more than an hour in his presence, and a little later dispersed a popular delegation which had come to offer suggestions about the defences of the colony with the words "We derive our authority from God and the Company, not from a few ignorant subjects, and we alone can call the inhabitants together."

With the final overturn of Dutch power and the Treaty of Westminster in 1674 which gave the colony into English hands, the lineage of royal governors began. Sometimes they were cultivated and just like William Burnet, but often venal like the notorious Fletcher, or bankrupt rakes trying to recoup their fortune like Lord Cornbury. Though some of the Dutch families refused sullenly to admit it at first, the "governor's set" with its tone set from London society, assumed the social hierarchy and in time assimilated to itself the more prosperous and eligible Knickerbocker families—Beekmans, Schuylers, Cuylers, Van Renssalaers, Van Cortlandts, and a few others.

Although the attempt to create an aristocracy of patroons had failed—for indeed Rensselaerwyck was unique in its success—the impulse toward a landed gentry was still strong. And so, corresponding to the Spanish encomiendas, the French seigniories, and the Virginia plantations, arose the English manors of the Hudson Valley. Among the new creations was Livingston Manor, which went to Robert Livingston in 1686, Pelham Manor to Thomas Pell a year later, Philipsborough to Frederick Philipse in 1693, Morrisania to Lewis Morris and

the Manor of Cortlandt to Stephen Van Cortlandt in 1697, and Scarsdale to Caleb Heathcote in 1701. Together with Rensselaerwyck, and early grants to John Archer and Thomas Chambers, this completes the tally of the nine actual manors—though for more than a century later heads of families up the river who owned large tracts, like the Schuylers around Albany, were popularly styled "patroons."

So late as 1838 James Silk Buckingham, visiting Stephen Van Rensselaer, "last of the Patroons," with an income "said to be a million dollars yearly," wrote of these old upstate families unchanged by the metropolitan ways of Manhattan:

These, in their number and ramifications, give a great gravity and decorum to the general tone of society here. There is less of show in houses, carriages, and horses; less of ceremony and etiquette in visiting; very early hours for meals: seven for breakfast, two for dinner, and six for tea; plainer and more simple fare at each than in the larger towns . . . every family here lives much within its income, and lays by accumulated means for the succeeding generation.

In fact the simplicity of life in colonial New York made ostentation almost impossible, though keeping one's own carriage was the notable badge of social plutocracy. Maria De Peyster Spratt, whose husband was president of the Council, seems to have been the first woman to own her own coach and four; the Van Rensselaer patroons imported Dutch coaches in which they rumbled down to New York for the winter season.

But New York lost its social simplicity during the later eighteenth century with perhaps more celerity than Boston. Its brief regime as the national capital, and its enduring status as the national metropolis, attracted rich and sophisticated visitors from the South, England, and the Continent. Like all great commercial ports it was washed by the tides of world culture, and lacking the Puritan reënforcement soon succumbed to the Parisian elegance and frivolity brought home by Mrs. John Jay and her circle. In its brief heyday in 1789 as the capital city, the Boston *Gazette* rejoiced that "our beloved President stands unmoved in the vortex of folly and dissipation which New York presents."

Among other worldly influences should not be forgotten the presence of Brillat-Savarin, who spent the years 1793-96 in New York as an emigré from the horrors of Girondist cookery. He gave French lessons, played in theatre orchestras, and taught Julien in Boston to cook eggs with cheese.

Other exiles of more conventional rank added to the gaiety of Manhattan, and impoverished as they were, received eager welcome from Hamiltons, Morrises, Wolcotts and Livingstons—Louis Philippe and his two brothers, the Duc de Montpensier and the Comte de Beaujolais, who spent the winter of 1798-99 in New York in lodgings over a bakery, where the painter Copley attended a distinguished dinner given by Louis Philippe at which one half of the guests sat upon the side of the bed because there were no more chairs.

Colonial Philadelphia

LOUIS PHILIPPE while in Philadelphia—where he wore his rue with a difference, and lived over a barbershop—once proposed to a daughter of Senator William Bingham, but was refused by her father the financier patrician, who told the Duke: "Should you ever be restored to your hereditary position, you will be too great a match for her; if not, she is too great a match for you." That reply is redolent of the solid assurance which has always characterized Philadelphia Society.

The founder of Pennsylvania, William Penn, was the son of a British admiral; while receiving an aristocratic education at Christ Church, Oxford, he began to attend Quaker meetings, renounced the scarlet coat for gray, and in 1681 received a charter to found a colony of Friends. The Quaker movement was itself essentially democratic—the use of "thee" and "thou," for example, and the occasional startling habit of riding naked through the streets "shouting for King Jesus" being symbols of the attempt to strip away the trappings of rank. The colonists whom Penn brought over were, at their best, of the thrifty, prosperous middle class. These were the Logans, the Shippens, the Pembertons, the Norrises, the Lloyds, the Wynnes, and the Peningtons.

Up to the Revolution they were the leaders in finance, trade, and law-making in the Commonwealth, though in numbers they had soon been swamped by Germans and Scotch Irish. Often they built massive houses, comfortable but not showy—like Edward Shippen's on South Second Street, with its gardens, summer-house, and deer-park, or country places like Cliveden, Stenton, Belmont, and Landsdowne, seat of the Penns. Here they entertained simply but substantially, with dinner at the traditional hour of four which was maintained down to the Civil War.

These Quakers, as a group, had little knowledge of or interest in Society, and in the course of the eighteenth century a strong social leadership was assumed by families of later settlers—merchants, lawyers, government officials—who were chiefly Church of England folk. We hear disparagements about Philadelphia ladies of quality from the Prince de Broglie who wrote: "The ladies of Philadelphia, although magnificent enough in their costumes, generally do not wear them with much taste. . . . While they have good figures, they lack grace and make their curtsies badly." La Rochefoucauld assures us in 1797 that Society is indiscriminately mad after European visitors—philosophers, preachers, literary men, princes, dentists, wits, and idiots—but we cannot accept such crabbing too seriously.

According to general opinion, Philadelphia at the close of the Revolution shared with Charleston the social palm among American cities—thanks in large measure to the effective leadership of Mrs. Bingham. Among the most celebrated parties of the century were the fête called the Meschianza, held during the War, and a little later the grand ball given by M. Luzerne, the French Minister, to celebrate the birth of the Dauphin. He erected a building just for the occasion, in the midst of a garden "with groves and fountains, spacious walks and numerous seats. . . . For ten days before the event nothing else was talked of in the city. The shops were filled with customers; hair-dressers were retained . . . and so great was the demand on their attention, that many ladies were obliged to have their heads dressed between four and six o'clock in the morning." There were cotillions, fireworks at nine, supper at twelve prepared by thirty cooks borrowed from the French army, and a merry good-night at three.

Society in the Revolution

BEFORE closing the account of eighteenth century aristocracy one cannot well overlook the part it played in the Revolution. The mainspring of rebellion came from the encroachment of a stupid Parliament upon the rights of trade. Organized by the prosperous merchant class with the help of lawyers—who were just gaining for their profession a certain amount of social recognition—the impulse to revolt spread among backwoodsmen, "buckskins," and farmers, who when victory was once gained suffered repudiation from the councils of the nation.

The avalanche of Revolution had been started in Virginia, for example, by such patricians in the House of Burgesses as Peyton Randolph, Richard Bland, Robert Carter Nicholas, John Robinson, and George Wythe. They drew into the campaign a young back-country lawyer, Patrick Henry, who stirred the simple folk and sounded the alarm more clearly than they—aware of their aristocratic bonds with Britain—had ever dared to do. The same collaboration between two classes, the humbler discovering that it was just as good as the British excisemen sent to tax it, and the prouder knowing its superiority, may be seen among the Signers of the Declaration and the Framers of the Constitution.

In all civil wars people of fortune and heredity rank are apt to cling to the old order, and although the circumstances of the American Revolution created a multitude of exceptions, yet the Loyalist cause attracted many of the proud and rich—Fairfaxes, Galloways, Penns, Dulaneys.

Perhaps a little exaggerated is the pessimism of Mr. Porter Sargent, native Bostonian, in the preface to his annual *Private Schools: 1936:* "The aristocrats of Boston all left with Lord Howe. The old Boston families of today are for the most part derived from the rabble of smugglers and privateers-men who poured in as the Tories left with the British fleet."

Some of the French allies, coming over to fight a war for oppressed classes, expected to find complete absence of social distinction. They were mistaken. In Philadelphia Lambert Cadwalader had organized and outfitted a band of young blue-bloods to give their all for the self-evident truth that men are created free and equal, called the Silk Stocking Company. George Washington—who in 1777 had reminded Congress that it would be necessary to receive the Marquis de Lafayette well because of his high social standing—wrote to a friend about the choice of officers: "Take none but gentlemen."

A London newspaper during the War generously said of George Washington "There is not a king in Europe but who would look like a *valet de chambre* by his side." He never forgot his Virginia pride. His very leadership of the cause was in fact a tribute to the aristocratic British tradition of public service to which he was faithful in his fashion.

The Polka Fashions, Godey's "Lady's Book," November, 1845

Although he did not warm to the proposal of Colonel Lewis Nicola that he should become King George I of America, probably looked with disapproval upon Gouverneur Morris's suggestion that members of the United States Senate be chosen for life, and despite inner sympathy passed over Hamilton's frank plea that "the rich and well-born" be given "a distinct, permanent share in the government," Washington was no democrat by heredity or taste.

The Revolution had an immense effect upon American Society. On the one hand the presence of French allies, officered by the cream of Gallic nobility, speeded the urge toward new worldliness and luxury—even though some French visitors professed themselves scandalized by the extravagance of American ladies of fashion. So widespread was the blossoming of French taste and the corresponding *savoir faire* it implied, that—so Chateaubriand tells us at any rate—even the Iroquois tribe had their French dancing-master, M. Violet.

In the second place the Revolution, like all wars, pullulated with profiteers.

In the year peace was declared James Bowdoin wrote from Boston to ex-Governor Pownall: "When you come you will see scarcely other than new faces. The change which in that respect has happened within the few years since the revolution is as remarkable as the revolution itself." It was a story to be repeated in 1865 and 1918. Upon riches there was a sharply growing emphasis, which happens in every epoch of shattering and remoulding. Chastellux describes an assembly in Philadelphia at which, "on passing into the dining room, the Chevalier de Luzerne presented his hand to Mrs. [Robert] Morris, and gave her the precedence, an honor pretty generally bestowed on her, as she is the richest woman, and all ranks here being equal, men follow their natural bent, by giving preference to riches."

Talleyrand once was talking to a man in Maine who had never visited Philadelphia, the capital. "When you go there you will be glad to see General Washington." "Yes," the man answered, and with his eyes sparkling added, "and I also want to see Bingham who they say is so rich!"

Grand Manner on the Wane

AMERICA during the early nineteenth century witnessed the liquidation of one type of plutocrat and—while the plaudits of democracy rang loud for three decades—the upsurge of another. To Thomas Jefferson the dangerous aristocrat was the great landowner, devouring small farm after farm, and passing on this vast feudality to his eldest son and so on to the end of time, preventing "that equal distribution of property which was the legitimate reward of industry"—and therefore to tear out "every fibre of ancient or future aristocracy," as Jefferson wrote in his Autobiography, he took aim squarely against primogeniture and entail, against Carrolls, Livingstons, Schuylers, and Van Rensselaers, and made it quite certain that these at any rate would never be the great American fortunes. Then he rested from his labors.

And behold, on a new horizon another plutocrat arose, the Federal banker —Nicholas Biddle in Philadelphia, Robert Lenox in New York, Colonel Thomas H. Perkins in Boston—and against this "hydra" of "moneyed capitalists" Andrew Jackson charged as savagely as he had assailed the British at New Orleans, and with temporary success. But from the hydra other heads were to spring—the international banker, the great real estate speculator, the Civil War profiteer, the railroad magnate and Wall Street operator, the manipulator of trusts in oil and steel—which became objects of passing democratic indignation, were attacked, and often died in the hope of a glorious resurrection.

These vicissitudes belong not only to the history of American economics but to Society as well—a connection which has existed to some extent everywhere, but which in the United States is peculiarly compelling because of that development in the national state of mind traced in the previous chapter. Yet the years from the death of planter and patroon to the final solidification of the city industrialist are years of rampant theoretical democracy, of renewed earnestness in attempting to achieve the ideal of the Declaration of Independence.

As a result, social records during the first forty years of the nineteenth century are more barren and inglorious than in any other span of our national life. It was not by any means a period of proletarian rule in the Marxist sense, but one dominated by a rising bourgeoisie. Significantly Fredrika Bremer wrote in 1849 that "here, where almost every person works for his living, one cannot properly speak of a working class, but quite correctly of people of small means and somewhat limited environment and circumstances—*a class which has not yet worked itself up.*"

Every ambitious shopkeeper in shirtsleeves regarded himself as a potential John Jacob Astor or Stephen Girard. In his Sunday clothes he even tried to look as though he had already arrived, thanks to the short-cut of a detachable collar or shirt with a "dickey," while his wife hung her gingham apron behind the pantry-door and appeared by his side in a dress copied by a third-rate mantua-maker from the *Petit Courier des Dames de Paris*. Even in the last years of the eighteenth century La Rochefoucauld found that workingmen and their families ordered sedan-chairs on holidays and were conveyed to public-houses in the neighborhood, to take their gin-sling or threepennyworth of stout.

Lavish expenditure seems to have received popular approval save when it came from those who could really afford it. Sir Charles Lyell tells of an Alabama girl, daughter of a prosperous candidate for the legislature, who after visiting Mobile returned home with a dress made with Parisian flounces à la mode—wherefore her father lost the election. A wiser candidate for office in the same state, well able to afford a carriage, chose instead to stump the rural districts on foot.

In this era arose the American paradox of the gentleman of classical education feigning illiteracy to get votes—like the Jim Fergusons and Alfalfa Bill Murrays of a later day—and for the first time in our history the comedy of slang, cracker-box philosophy, and smokehouse humor came to seem irresistibly delightful, heralding the cult of Arkansas, Bill Nye, Hosea Bigelow, and Mark Twain. It was the discovery of a great common denominator, a backhand blow at the precise and supercilious East. The grand manner was on the wane everywhere, except perhaps in a few drawing-rooms in Beacon Street or Washington Square and a score of stately houses in Charleston and New Orleans.

The stronghold of political and social democracy was the frontier, where, as it used to be said, "the rifle and the axe made all men equally tall"—the original democratic thesis in America. Bacon's Rebellion, Shays's Rebellion, the Whiskey Insurrection, and other protests against the rich and powerful seemed to brew there, as storms in a cyclone belt, and move eastward. What had been true of an earlier time grew even more valid in the nineteenth century as the frontier grew longer and the seaboard more entrenched in tradition. A gentleman of the British Court, Charles Augustus Murray, in his book of travels published in 1839, noted that while distinctions of fortune and family were sharply felt in conservative circles of the East, in the West he saw the clerk of a steamboat and a grocer in a small Missouri River town sit down to grog and a game of cards with a Congressman and an army officer—all chatting, swearing, laughing, and calling each other by their first names.

The manner in which the spirit of frontier democracy asserted itself in national affairs, and to some extent deflected the course of American Society, might be sketched. First of all, the Revolution itself not only helped to set up new plutocrats, as has been noted, but also broke down much of the reverence that hedged the old.

Early in the Revolution, on July 13, 1776, the radical *Pennsylvania Evening Post* called upon Americans to abandon all titles of Excellency and Honorable, and a little later *The Boston Daily Advertiser* declared "Americans should have but one denomination—the People." The Constitution was careful to provide that the United States should grant no titles of nobility, and that no office-holder should without the consent of Congress accept any title, office, or present from a king or foreign power. Jefferson insisted, in the teeth of Federalist opposition, that no titled foreigner could be admitted to U. S. citizenship until he had renounced his title.

Jeffersonian Democracy

JEFFERSON was the first who dared challenge the old hereditary principles of Europe. Primogeniture, long entrenched in English common law, was of very slow growth in America during the seventeenth century, partly because land was cheap and abundant, partly because there were so few means of livelihood, other than farming, for younger sons. But in the eighteenth century its practice was on the increase, especially among families of great pride, like the Byrds, Carrolls, Calverts, Livingstons, and Van Rensselaers, who wished to keep up their name in suitable style. In Virginia, the stronghold of both, Jefferson mobilized his energy and rhetoric for the attack, and in 1776 by a small majority the Legislature prohibited entail. Exultingly Jefferson said:

To annul this privilege, and instead of an aristocracy of wealth, of more harm and danger than benefit to society, to make an opening for the aristocracy of virtue and talent, which nature has wisely provided for the direction of the interests of society, and scattered with an equal hand throughout all its conditions, was deemed essential to a well-ordered republic.

As early as 1839 Francis J. Grund, an inquiring young German who made a special study of aristocracy in America, predicted that no sort of permanent caste would ever be possible because "scarcely one fourth" of the then rich men had inherited their wealth and the traditions of wealth, while their heirs scattered it as quickly as it had been gathered. Unlike the *ancien régime* in Europe, the American plutocracy was not self-perpetuating.

The present drift toward the confiscation of large fortunes through inheritance-taxes is but another and finally decisive step in the same direction. At first bound by a few strands of Lilliputian cord of which he was scarcely aware, the titan of wealth now finds himself so beset with legal hindrances against accumulations that he can no longer make the gesture of handing intact a princely fortune to his heirs.

Though Jefferson dealt the old aristocracy its deepest wound by his overthrow of hereditary principles, he commenced in later life to flaunt gayer social heresies. Before he succeeded Adams as

President in 1801, and for some weeks after inauguration until the White House was finished, Jefferson lived at Conrad's boarding-house on Capitol Hill, and there as his friend Margaret Bayard Smith recalled, he "occupied during the whole winter the lowest and coldest seat at a long table at which a company of more than thirty sat down." In vain the proprietress of the boarding-house attempted to coax him to a higher seat at least among the Congressmen, but with his usual exquisite courtesy the President of the United States declined, and continued at the foot.

When the White House at last was opened, and he began giving dinner parties himself, he always seated his guests at a circular table—on the principle of *inter pares* which seems to have been invented by King Arthur. Straightway he abolished the weekly levees in which Washingtons and Adamses had rejoiced, and when a group of indignant ladies appeared in their best party-dresses at the customary hour of the levee they found Jefferson out riding. They grimly resolved to wait, and have a Presidential

Lady Washington's Reception at the White House
After a painting by Daniel Huntington

levee willy-nilly. Soon the President appeared in boots and dusty clothes, gracious and suave as only a Randolph of Virginia who had lived long at the Court of Louis XVI knew how to be, and treated the call as a delightful surprise, with such adroitness that the ladies left charmed, bewildered, and routed.

Unlike Washington he assumed no trappings of royal dignity, but even when receiving foreign ministers remained dressed in "a blue coat, a thick gray-colored hairy waistcoat, with a red underwaist lapped over it, green velveteen breeches with pearl buttons, yarn stockings, and slippers down at the heels," as Senator Maclay describes him, generally sitting "in a lounging manner, on one hip commonly." One foreign ambassador, going in the morning to pay him a visit of ceremony, was deeply shocked to find him blacking his own shoes; Jefferson explained that he hated to cause his servants needless trouble.

There is no gainsaying the fact that Jefferson, more than any other man in American history, curbed at the crucial time the power and glory to which the Society of a new republic aspired. He belongs in fact at the well-spring of a tradition which so far has received little notice from our social historians—that of the radical aristocrat in America, the man or woman whose blue blood or wealth, or both, have lent a keener appreciation of social justice, together with the resources for doing something about it.

In the great shadow of Jefferson the sapling of democracy grew, protected from the withering scorn of Federalism —which, like the sun at noonday in Washington's and Hamilton's time, sank rapidly after their death until it set about 1815. Jefferson passed on his protectorship to Madison (1809-1817) and to Monroe (1817-1825), who although at heart less zealous democrats, could not but regard the trust as binding.

Low-Water Mark of American Society

AFTER an interlude of four years under cold, well-meaning, but unpopular John Quincy Adams, the democrats returned to power with the first plebeian President of the United States, Andrew Jackson. Here at last were the theories of Jefferson in a tenement of common clay. Of poor Scotch-Irish squatter stock, Old Hickory never learned to speak or write correctly, chewed tobacco incessantly, and shifted from riding-boots to stocking feet. With his stout, florid wife, "Aunt Rachel"—who was given lessons in table-manners by Mrs. Edward Livingston, after the Battle of New Orleans —Jackson responded to applause at the grand ball given him by the flower of Creole aristocracy, by showing the city folks what real dancing was, to the tune of *Possum up de Gum Tree*. Following Jackson's election to the Presidency in 1828, the death in Tennessee that winter of Aunt Rachel was learned by Washington society circles, as a contemporary tells us, with "a sense of relief."

The Inauguration of Jackson on March 4, 1829 marks, beyond much doubt, the low water-mark of official Society in America. It was the People's saturnalia. After the Oath had been taken, thousands of people—buckskins, poor whites, cross-roads politicians, mulattoes and blacks, who had come to Washington to see the investiture of their idol—made a wild dash for the White House. When the doors were jammed the assault was carried to the windows. Waiters bearing trays of orange punch, saw the glasses snatched away before they were well into the room. Many were borne to the floor to scramble helplessly among rivulets of punch and shards of broken glass and china.

Twenty thousand people, it was said, had broken "cut glass and china to the amount of several thousand dollars . . . in the struggle to get the refreshments." "What a pity—what a pity!" wrote Margaret Bayard Smith to Mrs. Kirkpatrick.

"Ladies fainted, men were seen with bloody noses and such a scene of confusion took place as is impossible to describe—those who got in could not get out by the door again, but had to scramble out of windows."

Good form was now in eclipse. Every guest at a White House dinner was provided with two forks, steel and silver, to take his choice; Jackson preferred steel. Friends dropped in before breakfast, or in the evening, as inclination prompted. At the later hour they were sure to find him in the White House living-room, smoking a reed pipe with a red clay bowl, with his niece Mrs. Donelson sewing, and half a dozen children playing on the floor. His critics, especially the feminine precursors of the later "cave-dwellers" of Washington, were uncommonly severe. When he gave large parties they complained of the presence of "Irish laborers . . . in their shirt sleeves," and when parties were small they sneered at "a little set of exclusives . . . under the immediate patronage of the President."

In Washington, meanwhile, socially minded optimists predicted with every change in the White House that at last the golden age had come. We find a prophecy about aged General Harrison in 1840: "He will make these gorgeous halls reverberate with merry peals of laughter, refined repartee, excruciating anecdotes and sparkling bonmots"—but, without much chance to show of what social mettle he was made, old Tippecanoe died just one months after his inauguration. Tyler, who succeeded him, turned out to be so excessively democratic that several ladies of *ton* in Washington boasted they had not set foot in the White House since General Harrison's death.

In general it may be said that, despite tight little coteries in New York, Philadelphia, Boston, and Charleston, the keynote of social intercourse in *ante bellum* America—particularly as set by the nation's capital—was one of breezy camaraderie, founded at its best upon the theory that everybody could be a gentleman or a lady. At its worst it was characterized by Thoreau, the hermit of Walden Pond: "What men call social virtues, good fellowship, is commonly but the virtue of pigs in a litter, which lie close together to keep each other warm."

Those who had tried to climb and received a kick in the face swelled the ranks of the disgruntled, defeated, and savagely impatient who made this an era unparalleled in American history for riots, street-fights, and incendiarism. Those who met better luck and mounted steadily upward had only one gauge of measuring distance—the whispered commentary which Fredrika Bremer heard as she walked the streets of Boston in 1850: "He is worth so many dollars. . . ." Though she did hear of a small remote band, almost as mythical as the Lost Tribes, who were "above fashion"— probably because their money was made so long ago that the public had lost track of its exact amount.

The Bitch-Goddess Success

AT LARGE however that cult was evolving—less known to a frugal Colonial New England or a gay, spendthrift Virginia—which William James toward the end of its cycle called "the moral flabbiness born of the exclusive worship of the bitch-goddess SUCCESS."

It was inevitable that in a democracy which plumed itself on equal opportunities for all, the hero should be the man who had made the most of his golden chances. Moreover, already in the making was that peculiarly American psychology—symbolized in the great caravans moving westward—of keeping up with one's neighbors, of regarding solitude and independence as a little eccentric, if not dangerous. In business and mechanics the most daring of innovators, the American was already developing that social and personal timidity, that love of conformity, which is the hallmark of the parvenu. Only the born aristocrat takes for his motto that saying with which the grandest of Boston *grandes dames* used to explain herself, "C'est mon plaisir." Only the most honest plebeian makes the reply Abraham Lincoln did when a waiter at his first state-dinner inquired whether he would take white wine or red. "I don't know," said Lincoln simply. "Which would you?"

On the eve of the Civil War two kinds of aristocracy were struggling for mastery in America. In the North it was a plutocracy of bankers, mill owners, shipping magnates, and most notable of all, speculators in city real estate. The Astors, Goelets, Schermerhorns, and Rhinelanders in New York had had the good fortune in the early nineteenth century to hitch their family carriages to the rising star of Manhattan real estate. The South had come with increasing boldness to repudiate Jefferson. Setting out to justify slavery it ended by vindicating social gradations everywhere. Chancellor Harper of the Supreme Court of South Carolina declared that "through the evolution of men in society . . . each man or class of men comes to find the proper place and level, and society then crystallizes and legalizes the resulting differences."

At the top were the plantation aristocrats, comprising the approximately one thousand families who in 1850 received over $50,000,000 a year, while the remaining 666,000 families all together had an income of only $60,000,000. In the ranking class belonged some of the old eighteenth-century grandees—Lees, Bollings, Carters, Randolphs, and others— who had salvaged enough despite laws against entail to keep the family name in style, and with them newer and even richer slave-owners and planters like the Hairstons with 1700 slaves and vast plantations in three states.

Below them was the numerous middle class: small slave-holding farmers, professional men, and prosperous tradesmen, and like the corresponding group in the North they looked emulously toward their betters. Descending the ladder one came upon the petty farmer who did all his own work and lived on "hog and hominy," the "poor white," and finally the Negro, free or slave. Social lines in the South were everywhere sharply marked, because of a slavery which made the rich much prouder and the poor more scorned.

At first the Civil War, like other great conflicts, caused an acceleration of pulse, a gaiety, a hectic flush of prosperity even in the doomed South. Even during the black winter of 1864-65 when the real aristocrats were giving "starvation parties" — cheerful foregatherings without food or drink—Mrs. Jefferson Davis startled Virginia with her midnight suppers and inexhaustible cellars of champagne. Seldom has display been more unfortunately timed.

At that, Mrs. Davis was not so abysmally impossible as her rival in the White House, stout, ill-dressed Mary Todd Lincoln, who appeared at her first levee in pink silk décolletage with a floral headdress "which ran down to her waist," and at a reception given to her husband in New York appeared carrying "a small ivory fan with which she occasionally fanned some of the gentlemen who paid their respects to her, playfully telling them 'not to get too warm in the cause.'" The later career of Mrs. Lincoln grew darker even to insanity. She was in some ways the heaviest cross borne by her patient and great-souled husband.

Throughout the North, the Civil War ushered in an epoch of lavish moneymaking and spending, which, unlike the tarantella of Mrs. Davis, was more prolonged and secure. Wives of war profiteers, called by Knickerbocker aristocrats "the Sybarites of 'shoddy,'" began to appear at Pike's Opera House and at Wallack's with more diamond stomachers and tiaras of emeralds than had ever been seen in public before. To show the wealth of their husbands, ladies took up the fashion of powdering their hair with gold and silver dust.

Men, heralding the tastes of Jim Brady and H. A. W. Tabor, sported waistcoat buttons made from diamonds of the first water. In smart turn-outs they drove to Jerome Park and the races at a scintillating clip. New opera houses, theatres, luxury hotels, and a fresh crop of brownstone mansions along Fifth Avenue arose—for, as we are told by a sober historian, a hundred thousand New Yorkers were now making some pretense to "fashion."

We read that during the season of 1865-66 six hundred balls, "more or less public," were given in New York City, with the cost to ball-goers estimated at seven million dollars, "the average cost of a suitable dress being a thousand dollars, without jewelry." Relieved from the scourge of bread-winning and penny-pinching, life came perhaps unduly to revolve about the luxuries—sport and social concourse and the exploration of the senses.

It was the threshold of what Mark Twain christened "The Gilded Age."

Plutocracy to Aristocracy

THE assimilation of plutocracy to aristocracy has been the vital problem of Society in America since its beginnings, but particularly since the rise of great industrial fortunes. It has been imperative somehow to translate *richesse permet* into *noblesse oblige*. Behind endless manuals of etiquette and blue books of behavior, scrapbooks of culture and outlines of knowledge, and all the nostalgia for European titles as well as Old Masters, lies the aspiration of a rising middle class attempting to seize, even by casual symbols, upon some guiding wisdom, upon the art of being rich gracefully, which Americans are accused of lacking. "Who knows how to be rich in America?" demanded Godkin in *The Nation* in 1866. "Plenty of people know how to get money; but not very many know what best to do with it. To be rich properly is indeed a fine art. It requires culture, imagination, and character." And Henry Adams a little later spoke for the older aristocracy of cultivation when he observed that the lives of the very rich were "no more worth living than those of their cooks."

Of course to the mass of people, in the time of Jackson as well as in the time of McKinley, the individual of dazzling wealth was the happiest, most glamorous, and most enviable of men—just as he is today to the avid reader of Society Notes in the tabloid newspapers, going home on the six o'clock subway to his walk-up flat or hall bedroom. Admiration of the millionaire, which survives a thousand disillusionments and a dozen depressions with their cries against "hydras of corruption" and clamors to "soak the rich," always stirs a democracy where gold is the visible ensign of power. The hereditary aristocrat, to whom Marco Millions is an old story, is perhaps the only sort who comes close to freeing himself from this servility to mere wealth—even more than the professed Communist of water front and ghetto who has made a gospel of defeat.

Theodore Roosevelt once wrote: "I am simply unable to make myself take the attitude of respect toward the very wealthy men which such an enormous multitude of people evidently really feel. I am delighted to show any courtesy to Pierpont Morgan or Andrew Carnegie or James J. Hill, but as for regarding any one of them as, for instance, I regard Professor Bury, or Peary, the Arctic explorer, or Rhodes, the historian—why, I could not force myself to do it even if I wanted to, which I don't." Yet it is probable that Theodore Roosevelt's ancestors, when they were founding their fortunes in sugar, trade, and real estate, looked with vast respect and emulation toward Kiliaen Van Rensselaer or Robert Livingston.

A review of the older commercial families may well begin with the Roosevelts, who trace their descent from one

Klaes Martensen van Rosenvelt, who came to New Amsterdam about 1649 as a "settler," which as his descendant the twenty-sixth President of the United States remarked, was "the euphemistic name for an immigrant who came over in the steerage of a sailing ship of the seventeenth century." The progress of the Roosevelts from steerage to peerage was at first a slow and laborious climb. The immediate descendants of Klaes added to the family tree by marriage with the stock of a Puritan wheelwright and several strains of Scotch-Irish and Quaker origin. Not until the times of Johannes Roosevelt, forbear of Theodore, and his nephew Isaac, ancestor of Franklin Delano, in the eighteenth century did the family begin to acquire wealth and power.

Isaac's son James, born in 1828, father of the present President of the United States, increased his accumulation by a venture into railroads and settled at Hyde Park. He married first Rebecca Howland, and had a son James who married Helen Astor, aunt of Vincent Astor; the father married secondly Sara Delano, who still survives. Other Roosevelts, sprung from Johannes, showed a preference for Southern wives, usually of aristocratic blood and wealth, and entertained New York Society with conservative dignity in brownstone houses filled with black hair-cloth furniture, mahogany sideboards, and ornate gas chandeliers—belonging distinctly to the "nobs" rather than the "swells."

After the Roosevelts come the great fortunes in real estate which were amassed between the Revolutionary War and the heyday of the railroads. Up to about 1825 it was doubtful whether New York, Philadelphia, Boston, or Baltimore would yield the richest harvest to landlords, but the opening of the Erie Canal determined the future of New York. The Schermerhorns, represented by Peter the ship-chandler who after the Revolution began buying Manhattan real estate with every penny he could scrape, and his shrewd son Peter "the Younger" who

was a director of the Bank of New York from 1814 to his death in 1852, rose rapidly in importance, and through marriage to Hones, one-time auctioneers, and to Astors, carried even newer families along in their triumphant march.

THE most fabulous accumulation of the early nineteenth century was that of John Jacob Astor. The father of the first American Astor was Jacob Ashdor of Waldorf, Germany, whom Parton, earliest of reliable biographers, describes as "a jovial, good-for-nothing butcher . . . much more at home in the beerhouse than at his own fireside." His son came by steerage to America, landing in New York, where another brother Henry was a prosperous butcher. There the boy peddled cakes for a baker until he found employment in Robert Browne's fur store, beating furs to keep out moths.

Having resolved from the start "to be honest, to be industrious, and not to gamble," he soon saved enough to begin to buy furs himself, and presently set up his own business. The expansion of Astor's business, slow at first and then increasing prodigiously, is a legend as fabulous as the rise of London's Dick Whittington. Astor sent ships to Europe and to China, exchanging furs for musical instruments, silk, tea, and other commodities; soon he had set up the village of Astoria on the Columbia River as the trading-post of his American Fur Company.

He bought New York real estate and heavily mortgaged farms in the environs. As he fondly remembered in old age, "the first hundred thousand were the hardest" and nobody suspected him of being so rich when he quietly reached his first million. The Panic of 1837 and the steep climb of land values in Manhattan increased that fortune many-fold, but he still remained the lower-class German immigrant, barely able to read and write enough for business purposes; Albert Gallatin, former Secretary of the Treasury, declined to manage his estates because "he dined here and ate his ice cream and peas with a knife."

The Astor fortune grew from twenty to fifty million under the care of his son William Backhouse Astor, whose elder brother John Jacob lived, a hopeless imbecile, for seventy-six years. William, born in 1792, had attended public schools till the age of sixteen, helping his father at the store after school hours; then he was sent to Germany for a university education. His marriage in 1818 to Margaret, daughter of General John Armstrong of Rhinebeck, New York, gave him a footing in Society.

He left one-third of his fortune to his younger son William, husband of Caroline Schermerhorn, "the Mrs. Astor" of the Four Hundred, and two-thirds to his elder son John Jacob. The latter's marriage in 1846 to the daughter of Thomas L. Gibbes of the South Carolina gentry occasioned a grand reception—"the spacious mansion in Lafayette Place," wrote Philip Hone, "was open from cellar to garret, blazing with a thousand lights." The Astors were becoming magnificent.

The Astor family is now represented in America in the male line solely by stock descended from William and Caroline Astor. Their son the fourth John Jacob, born in 1864, married Ava Willing of Philadelphia, built the Astoria section of the Waldorf Hotel in 1897, had a yacht the *Nourmahal* whose name has become an Astor tradition.

Vincent Astor, present head of the family and childless, was a phlegmatic youth at St. George's School and Harvard, but has developed by slow and steady degrees, plus hard work and serious-mindedness, until he has become the most progressive of all the Astors—founding model farms and building model tenements for the poor, as well as running de luxe apartments and the St. Regis for the rich. His wife, Helen Dinsmore Huntington of a Hudson Valley family, has loyally shared these interests. With such hobbies as oceanography, practical science, and liberal

journalism, and his preference for men of affairs over sacrosanct Society, has gone Mr. Astor's passionate Americanism in speech, clothes, and habits.

THE richest of social families in the United States are the Vanderbilts. Cornelius Vanderbilt was born in 1794 on Staten Island, the fourth of nine children of a Dutch farmer and ferryman, who spelled his name Van Der Bilt, and his wife Phebe Hand, a New Jersey farmer's daughter. The Van Der Bilts were miserably poor squatters who had come over in the seventeenth century, to wrest a living through four generations from a stony and sandy soil. The mother, Phebe, was superior in brains and industry to her husband.

Hard-working and ambitious, Cornelius at the age of sixteen had his own boat, a periagua, for ferrying passengers and freight, and was soon saving a thousand dollars a year. During the War of 1812 he was given a small Army contract. In 1818, owner of several sailing boats, he sold them all and staked his future upon steam navigation; soon he was running a line of ships on the Hudson, in those early days of steam.

From Hudson River shipping he soon expanded into the North Atlantic and presently the Pacific, and made his first ten million.

After the close of the Civil War he astonishingly increased his wealth from ten to one hundred million dollars within twelve years, through dazzling speculations in railroads. The New York Central became, and still remains, the backbone of the Vanderbilt fortune. Though the Commodore's tight-fisted control was broken after another generation, and the accumulation dissipated by extravagance and titled marriages, between 200,000 and 300,000 shares of stock still remain in the family.

The son increased the fortune to two hundred million, but split it equally between his two sons Cornelius, who married Alice Gwynne of Cincinnati, and William Kissam, married first to

Alva Smith of Mobile, later Mrs. O. H. P. Belmont, and later to Anne Harriman Sands Rutherfurd. Each successive generation marked a gain in social grace and the uncommercial interests. William Henry, who according to his early biographer Croffut, "liked pictures which told a story, with either strong or cheerful subjects," bought Meissoniers, Millets, and Rosa Bonheurs at the rate of some $1,500,000; he loved horses and owned the famous trotter "Maude S."; he moved Cleopatra's Needle from Egypt to Central Park at the cost of $100,000; and he built the great twin mansions on Fifth Avenue between 51st and 52nd Streets for himself and his daughters, employing 600 artisans for a year and a half. Of him Gladstone is said to have remarked to the Vanderbilt lawyer, Chauncey Depew: "The Government ought to seize his property and take it away from him, as it is too dangerous a power for any one man to have."

The family passed through a phase of running after European titles and recognition which gave them a temporary though unfortunate notoriety; the youngest generation seems however to have grown blasé to such pomps and vanities. Its only liability is found in the person of Cornelius Vanderbilt, Jr., with his cheerfully irresponsible career of rash books and marriages; he nevertheless offered an *amende honorable* for a harsh saying attributed to his great-grandfather (the public be damned) by starting a tabloid newspaper in Los Angeles in 1923 with the slogan "The Public Be Pleased." That revision is perhaps significant of the growing humility among American plutocrats, as well as of the fact that sixty years after the great Commodore the Vanderbilt family has rapidly completed the typical cycle into the sere and yellow leaf of wealth, vigor, and enterprise.

THE Rockefellers, unlike Vanderbilts and Astors have had little to do with foreign titles, Newport, and lavish pageantry, but have stuck loyally by their business origins and made a career of hard work, simple living, and planned philanthropy. According to a family anecdote, the young sons of John D. Rockefeller, Jr., Winthrop and David, were ragged by a playmate for tinkering with a dilapidated rowboat, for, he suggested, they might at least ask their father for an outboard motor; they are said to have replied indignantly, "Who do you think we are, Vanderbilts?"

The tally-ho of Mr. F. Ambrose Clarke arriving at the estate of Mr. Hugh A. Murray, Roslyn, L. I., with a group of friends for the United Hunts Meet, May 20, 1933.

Certain American fortunes are linked with social names, while others are not —a difference doubtless explained by the time and circumstances of foundation, the personality and ambition of the founders. Thus the great wealth amassed in iron and steel by Andrew Carnegie, grandson of a Scotch shoemaker, has had very little impact upon American Society.

For three generations the Morgans have been entitled, by reason of their great wealth and almost overpowering respectability, to as much social position in New York as they cared to claim. But neither Juliet Pierpont Morgan nor Francis Louise Tracy Morgan chose to assume the social leadership whose weight would have been to them—with their quiet, simple, reticent lives—more of a cross than a crown.

Conservative American Society has other criteria besides sheer wealth, and to neglect this fact would be a grave injustice. Among the new families who have obtained a measure of social notice, one can trace year by year an upward or downward curve, usually conditional upon the behavior of their members. It is perhaps discouraging to add that, aside from judicious entertaining of the right people, the art of quietude is the recipe for success. An aspirant makes the lower rungs of the social ladder by getting his name in the newspapers, but achieves the higher levels by keeping it out of them. The Woolworth heirs, for example, have suffered during the past three years by the floodlights focused upon Countess Barbara von Haugwitz-Reventlow, though after her less flashy second marriage and increasing domesticity, her standing is now convalescent; the rather obvious social ambitions of her rowdy kin the Donahues have been even more maladroit, while their relatives the McCanns have been in *The Social Register* since 1928.

How to Play the Social Game

WHAT does it mean to play the social game? Briefly, to entertain frequently and well the other best people who can return the favor; and to be seen on every fashionable occasion. To dress in smart clothes, a little ahead of the popular style, and to be gay and amusing are very important. A young Chicago couple who devote themselves systematically to its pursuit are typical. Born of good families and educated at fashionable schools, they are not too rich and therefore have to plan their disbursements with care. They live in a suite in the city's most eligible hotel, and entertain at carefully thought-out intervals and in novel ways. Their lists of guests are painstakingly made, involving no social risks, but mixing just the right celebrity of literature, art, or drama, with the fashionable set. The wife specializes in services to friends, from helping select the latest ball gown to arranging flowers at a funeral; in social life she plays her charming and highly keyed part as skilfully as a comedienne, and after a dinner or dance at which she has been the life of the party is as drained and dispirited as though she had borne the ordeal by footlights.

The husband, who, unlike many American men, keenly relishes society, is tall, handsome, graceful, and an excellent dancer and bridge player. "I always drink one good glass of champagne before this sort of thing, and stay in bed the next day," he says, admitting that late hours and nervous effort "take it out of me," and adding that if his business life were less flexible he would find the training for society almost an impossibility.

It is a game which implies also the art of social climbing. Rare indeed is the type of hostess who once remarked to the author: "If I ever do any social climbing I shall have to start by climbing down." If one belongs merely to the industrial rich, whose social consciousness is just being stirred out of the lethargic commerce of chain stores and soothing-syrup, one begins to aspire toward that group which has been called "exclusive bar society"—the unattached socially who eddy about El Morocco and Bradley's Casino. Next one may pass to the Palm Beach and racing set, with a dash of smart Bohemia and the reward of a nod from Beatrice Lillie. If one gambles sportingly, dances well, and uses horses up the hill of social difficulty, he may graduate into the international set. By this time he will bestow a patronizing smile as he passes the locked portal of the old guard, for ahead of him stretches presentation at Court and hobnobbing with Mountbattens or Athlones. The royal family of Great Britain is the *ne plus ultra* of American Society—for after that, one has only death to apprehend, and the ultimate presentation.

The grossest technique in social climbing is known as gate crashing. Apparently it was sponsored first by Socrates, who persuaded Aristodemus to assist at Agathon's party by suggesting that "to the feasts of the good, the good unbidden go." Its great modern vogue seems however to date from the Great War and the attendant social disintegration. When society was a small, compact group of those who knew each other well and entertained sedately, gate crashing was seldom inspired by either opportunity or desire. An unknown man or woman in the ballroom of Mrs. Astor would have been as uneasy as a sinner upon the griddle of hell.

But the War brought in large parties of casual, even indiscriminate guests, and the private dances of the 1920's for a thousand or more people—approximating the numbers hitherto known only at subscription fêtes—relieved the interloper, who had come to see the sights, hear the music, and drink the champagne, of any discomfiture. Sometimes a hostess had only the vaguest ideas about the people to whom she sent hundreds of her invitations. The story is told of a Harvard undergraduate who replied in writing to a hostess of whom he had never heard, "I should be pleased to accept your invitation, but I think I ought to tell you that I am a Negro."

The patronage of charity, church settlement work (Episcopalian), the financial support of hospitals, clinics, and opera are probably the safest route which the newcomer can travel. After she has given her cheque for a substantial sum and shown her eagerness to work for the cause, she will be asked to become a sustaining member and sit on the board with women she has wanted to know. Probably they will begin to ask her to tea, then to large parties and luncheons, and finally to dinner. If fortune has blessed her with a small daughter, let her be sent to a fashionable day school, where she will have classmates to be invited to a birthday party, and given expensive souvenirs; in this way a little child may lead them.

The Childish Life

WITHOUT some mention of the dictatorship of the young, any chapter on American manners would be incomplete. No other country in the world has made so much of its children, or given them so free a hand in shaping its customs and lending their exuberant naïveté to its social scene.

The surprise of visitors from abroad over the autocracy of our youth has never ceased. At the turn of the century Doctor James F. Muirhead, compiler of the American Baedeker, noted particularly the tyranny of the American débu-

tante, who coolly assumed the center of every stage, accepted homage as her undoubted right, allowed her young admirers to spend far too much upon her, and moved a little too insolently against a background of orchids and American Beauty roses. Henry James, revisiting these shores in 1906 after many years of absence, saw American Society as "a great circle of brilliant and dowered débutantes and impatient youths, expert in the cotillion, waiting together for the first bars of some wonderful imminent dance music."

The eagerness yet unsureness, the lack of discipline and restraint, the wandering attention and quick boredom, the susceptibility to suggestion and whim—all these things impressed him as characteristic of Society in the United States, with "the sawdust of its ripped-up dolls" still in its hair. "The immensity of the native accommodation, socially speaking, for the childish life, is not that exactly the key to much of the spectacle?"

Few things are so revealing of this state of mind as the popularity of the word "sophistication." As a term of praise it is unknown in other languages and even in England, except in certain circles which have consciously borrowed from us. The great Oxford Dictionary defines it in no sense but a vicious one, meaning adulteration, impurity, specious value, or an affectation of wisdom. Yet in America—where sophistication may mean anything from painted toe-nails to intellectual urbanity—it was for some years the rallying-cry of tailors and dressmakers, the appeal of advertising in those magazines which address the gentry of sport and fashion, and the envy of college sophomores and parvenus from the middle class.

Just after the War the bright young people of America, in their myopic search for wisdom, seized upon sophistication instead. It flourished naturally in little coteries of its own, because nobody can be sophisticated all by himself, for example, a man climbing into an unshared bed—after, of course, his valet has left him. This generation blissfully believed that it had invented sophistication, without realizing that the most blasé societies of history—the Age of Pericles, the times of Confucius, and the reign of the Roi Soleil—had not talked about it because they took it completely for granted. The fledgling preens its feathers most frequently.

Chief among social traits was its cynicism about morals. The tastes of "advanced" Society in the post-War years, as reflected in the drama, the novel, and the quality magazine, ran to sexual comedy—the peccadilloes of husbands and wives, the finesse of seduction, the humors of divorce, the innuendoes of perversion. Situations which once would have called for the problem play or reform novel became fit topics for jest in the dialogue of Noel Coward and Philip Barry, or the caricatures of Peter Arno. The disillusionment of returned editors of *The Stars and Stripes* and the keen satire of young Jews founded *The New Yorker;* its wit—best described as the uprush of the under-dog—has given nervous enjoyment to the upper classes.

The advent of the talkies in the closing years of this decade introduced the great inland public to a dash of the irony, the *double entendre,* and gay flippancy of the Broadway theatre. For the first time, perhaps, the citizen of Middletown or the sophomore of Siwash College could observe through the none too accurate lens of Hollywood how the smart set talks and behaves. The effect upon the population at large was not so great as one might have supposed, partly because the double meanings went unperceived by the majority, including the censors; partly because the plain man continued to find more thrills in the ocular simplicities of musical comedy; and finally because the onset of the lean years had a far more powerful effect in bringing to a close the excesses of that era.

Now, with the waning of great fortunes and the vast uncertainty of our economic and social future, "sophistication," with its thin veneer of Byronism, has already passed its peak. In fact, the paradox is dawning upon a rather serious younger generation that sophistication may also be enlisted upon the side of virtue, as it appears in that wittily urbane letter which Madame de Sévigné wrote to her cousin Bussy, when he urged that she revenge herself upon an unfaithful husband by embarking upon an affair with him.

At any rate, despite its early kinship with pose and cheap cynicism, the word has fought hard for an honorable place —evidently because a need is felt in America to express some undefined aspect of the art of living. Mere etiquette is not enough; there must be charm, suavity, and distinction besides. In this sense sophistication is one of those additional bulwarks which minorities continue jealously to build in the midst of a democracy.

Is Society Justified?

In Washington in February, 1936, Mr. J. P. Morgan, relaxing from the ordeal of another investigation, told reporters: "If you destroy the leisure class, you destroy civilization. . . . By the leisure class I mean the families who employ one servant, 25,000,000 or 30,-000,000 families." The president of the Housewives League of America and a dozen editors immediately seized upon the blurred and magnified image which Mr. Morgan had of American domesticity—pointing out that according to the 1930 census there were less than 30,000,000 families in the whole United States, and fewer than 2,000,000 cooks and other servants to attend them all.

But Mr. Morgan's cardinal belief was much more important than his statistics. The relation between leisure and civilization has fascinated a great many thinkers from Plato to Thorstein Veblen. In America it was argued with greatest heat just before the Civil War, when all the rationale of slavery seemed to hinge upon the answer; today it is inseparable from the claims of Marxism. If the mazes of that argument are too long here to trace, one can at least point out certain bonds which unite the social plutocracy to art, music, letters, learning, philanthropy, public service, and religion in America.

But the self-justifications of society in America are none too impressive. It has bought Old Masters, but fed few living artists. Its tastes in music and opera have been both timid and grandiose, and its patronage of literature has been negligible. Unhappily it forsook politics more than a century ago, though for reasons not wholly unselfish it longs just now to return. With generosity it has sometimes given to charity and education, though it has wasted other great sums in foolish ways. To the wisdom, goodness, and piety of mankind it has afforded at best an erratic and whimsical support. In all these ways American society has shown characteristic short-sightedness.

A favored minority which nourishes well the arts and good works gives hostages for its own safety; one which slights them for selfish ends—"conspicuous waste," lavish living and dining, amusement and sport—loses its compass of idealism and invites disaster. This fact has been dimly recognized at all times, though it is a far cry from the Cæsars lulling the mob with bread and circuses to the American banker winning his way from odium to fame with schools and clinics. Lacking the English tradition of public service, or the feudal bond between lord and liege, plutocracy in America has seldom sat at ease on its pyramid of privilege. Every depression will bring more cries of "soak the rich," fresh criticism from intellectuals, and new defection of rebels from plunder on the left, in the Jeffersonian tradition. Only the rash will dare forecast the future.

It is a little hard triumphantly to vindicate society in the economy of human life. Without some tincture of snobbery, society is never found; and snobbery is more amusing than admirable. Originally "snob" meant a cobbler's helper, a person of low birth and breeding, and then came to signify a person ashamed of his low birth and breeding. That snobbery and eminent rank have become linked, at least in the popular mind, is an irony due largely to the mediation of society.

The acute social awareness which

society has come to typify is chiefly the result of this modern world—with its industrialism, competition, insecurity, and whirligig of quick riches today and poverty tomorrow. In this hasty exchange of identifications society is the chevron worn on the sleeve rather than the inner grace. Or, to change the metaphor, society is the flower which blooms in economic springtime upon the stout boughs of an aristocracy. It is ornamental and transitory, as well as attractive to the bees of cross-fertilization, but sustenance must be drawn through the tap-root. Many an aristocracy fallen upon wintry days has lost its social blossoms, and withdrawn quietly into that deeper life which may truly find some sort of justification.

All human experience, as the biographer of Doctor Samuel Johnson long ago remarked, cries out irresistibly, "a gentleman is always a gentleman." Lacking the simplicity, courage, generosity, and honor of this ideal the life of mankind would indeed be poorer.

———◆———

The Land Which No One Knows

Dark, deep, and cold the current flows
Unto the sea where no wind blows,
Seeking the land which no one knows.

O'er its sad gloom still comes and goes
The mingled wail of friends and foes,
Borne to the land which no one knows.

Why shrieks for help you wretch, who goes
With millions, from a world of woes,
Unto the land which no one knows?

Though myriads go with him who goes,
Alone he goes where no wind blows,
Unto the land which no one knows.

For all must go where no wind blows,
And none can go for him who goes;
None, none return whence no one knows.

Yet why should he who shrieking goes
With millions, from a world of woes,
Reunion seek with it or those?

Alone with God, where no wind blows,
And Death, his shadow—doomed, he goes:
That God is there the shadow shows.

O shoreless Deep, where no wind blows!
And thou, O Land which no one knows!
That God is all, His shadow shows.

—E. Elliott

Sir John Arthur Thomson

THE OUTLINE OF SCIENCE

U NTIL recently books about science have been too complicated for the man in the street to read with enjoyment. "The Outline of Science" is one of the best of the recent books which open to everyone, in accurate and fascinating form, the marvels of the heavens and the earth. Its distinguished author, Sir John Arthur Thomson (1861-1933) was for many years Regius Professor of Natural History in the University of Aberdeen in Scotland.

In the Heavens

T HE story of the triumphs of modern science naturally opens with Astronomy. The picture of the Universe which the astronomer offers to us is imperfect; for while there are many problems which have been solved, there are just as many about which there is doubt.

The heavenly bodies fall into two very distinct classes so far as their relation to our Earth is concerned; the one class, a very small one, comprises a sort of colony of which the Earth is a member. These bodies are called *planets,* or wanderers. There are eight of them, including the Earth, and they all circle round the sun. Their names, in the order of their distance from the sun, are Mercury, Venus, Earth, Mars, Jupiter, Saturn, Uranus, Neptune, and of these Mercury, the nearest to the sun, is rarely seen by the naked eye. Uranus is practically invisible, and Neptune quite so. These eight planets, together with the sun, constitute, as we have said, a sort of little colony; this colony is called the Solar System.

The second class of heavenly bodies are those which lie *outside* the solar system. Every one of those glittering points we see on a starlit night is at an immensely greater distance from us than is any member of the Solar System. Yet the members of this little colony of ours, judged by terrestrial standards, are at enormous distances from one another. If a shell were shot in a straight line from one side of Neptune's orbit to the other it would take five hundred years to complete its journey. Yet this distance, the greatest in the Solar System as now known (excepting the far swing of some of the comets), is insignificant compared to the distances of the stars. One of the nearest stars to the earth that we know of is Alpha Centauri, estimated to be some twenty-five million millions of miles away. Sirius, the brightest star in the firmament, is double this distance from the earth.

We must imagine the colony of planets to which we belong as a compact little family swimming in an immense void.

The Earth, the planet on which we live, is a mighty globe bounded by a crust of rock many miles in thickness; the great volumes of water which we call our oceans lie in the deeper hollows of the crust. Above the surface an ocean of invisible gas, the atmosphere, rises to a height of about three hundred miles, getting thinner and thinner as it ascends.

Except when the winds rise to a high speed, we seem to live in a very tranquil world. At night, when the glare of the sun passes out of our atmosphere, the stars and planets seem to move across the heavens with a stately and solemn slowness. It was one of the first discoveries of modern astronomy that this movement is only apparent. The apparent creeping of the stars across the heavens at night is accounted for by the fact that the earth turns upon its axis once in every twenty-four hours. When we remember the size of the earth we see that this implies a prodigious speed.

In addition to this the earth revolves round the sun at a speed of more than a thousand miles a minute. Its path round the sun, year in year out, measures about 580,000,000 miles. The earth is held closely to this path by the gravitational pull of the sun, which has a mass 333,432 times that of the earth. If at any moment the sun ceased to exert this pull the earth would instantly fly off into space straight in the direction in which it was moving at the time, that is to say, at a tangent. This tendency to fly off at a tangent is continuous. It is the balance between it and the sun's pull which keeps the earth to her almost circular orbit. In the same way the seven other planets are held to their orbits.

Circling round the earth, in the same way as the earth circles round the sun, is our moon. Sometimes the moon passes directly between us and the sun, and cuts off the light from us. We then have a total or partial eclipse of the sun. At other times the earth passes directly between the sun and the moon, and causes an eclipse of the moon. The great ball of the earth naturally trails a mighty shadow across space, and the moon is "eclipsed" when it passes into this.

The other seven planets, five of which have moons of their own, circle round the sun as the earth does. The sun's mass is immensely larger than that of all the planets put together, and all of them would be drawn into it and perish if they did not travel rapidly round it in gigantic orbits.

So the eight planets, spinning round on their axes, follow their fixed paths round the sun.

IF WE could be transported in some magical way to an immense distance in space above the sun and could see our Solar System, say trillions of miles away, the planets would fade entirely out of view, and the sun would shrink into a point of fire, a star. And here you begin to realize the nature of the universe. *The sun is a star. The stars are suns.* Our sun looks big simply because of its comparative nearness to us. The universe is a stupendous collection of millions of stars or suns, many of which may have planetary families like ours.

How many stars are there? Astronomers have counted the stars in typical ditricts here and there, and from these partial counts we get some idea of the total number of stars. There are estimated to be between two and three thousand million stars.

Yet these stars are separated by inconceivable distances from each other, and it is one of the greatest triumphs of modern astronomy to have mastered, so far, the scale of the universe. For several centuries astronomers have known the relative distances from each other of the sun and the planets. If they could discover the actual distance of any one planet from any other, they could at once tell all the distances within the Solar System.

The sun is, on the latest measurements, at an average distance of 92,-830,000 miles from the earth, for as the orbit of the earth is not a true circle, this distance varies. This means that in six months from now the earth will be right at the opposite side of its path round the sun, or 185,000,000 miles away from where it is now. Viewed or photographed from two positions so wide apart, the nearest stars show a tiny "shift" against the background of the most distant stars, and that is enough for the mathematician. He can calculate the distance of any star near enough to show this "shift." We have found that the nearest star to the earth, a recently discovered star, is twenty-five trillion miles away. Only thirty stars are known to be within a hundred trillion miles of us.

This way of measuring does not, however, take us very far away in the heavens. There are only a few hundred stars within five hundred trillion miles of the earth, and at that distance the "shift" of a star against the background (parallax, the astronomer calls it) is so minute that figures are very uncertain. At this point the astronomer takes up a new method. He learns the different types of stars, and then he is able to deduce more or less accurately the distance of a star of a known type from its faintness. He, of course, has instruments for gauging their light. As a result of twenty years work in this field, it is now known that the more distant stars of the Milky Way are at least a hundred thousand trillion (100,000,000,000,000,000) miles away from the sun.

Our sun is in a more or less central region of the universe, or a few hundred trillion miles from the actual centre. The remainder of the stars, which are all outside our Solar System, are spread out, apparently, in an enormous disc-like collection, so vast that even a ray of light, which travels at the rate of 186,000 miles a second, would take 50,000 years to travel from one end of it to the other. This, then is what we call our universe.

Why do we say "our universe?" Why not *the* universe? It is now believed by many of our most distinguished astronomers that our colossal family of stars is only one of many universes. By a universe an astronomer means any collection of stars which are close enough to control each other's movements by gravitation; and it is clear that there might be many universes, in this sense, separated from each other by profound abysses of space. Probably there are.

Vast as is the Solar System, then, it is excessively minute in comparison with the Stellar System, the universe of the Stars, which is on a scale far transcending anything the human mind can apprehend.

The Sun

BUT now let us turn to the Solar System, and consider the members of our own little colony.

In the Solar System we include all those bodies dependent on the sun which circulate round it at various distances, deriving their light and heat from the sun—the planets and their moons, certain comets and a multitude of meteors: in other words, all bodies whose movements in space are determined by the gravitational pull of the sun.

Thanks to our wonderful modern instruments and the ingenious methods used by astronomers, we have to-day a remarkable knowledge of the sun.

The actual temperature at the sun's surface, or what appears to us to be the surface—the photosphere—is, of course, unknown, but careful calculation suggests that it is from 5,000° C. to 7,000° C. The interior is vastly hotter. We can form no conception of such temperatures as must exist there. Not even the most obdurate solid could resist such temperatures, but would be converted almost instantaneously into gas. But it would not be gas as we know gases on the earth. The enormous pressures that exist on the sun must convert even gases into thick treacly fluids. We can only infer this state of matter.

It is in the brilliant photosphere that the dark areas known as sun-spots appear. Some of these dark spots—they are dark only by contrast with the photosphere surrounding them—are of enormous size, covering many thousands of square miles of surface. What they are we cannot positively say. They look like great cavities in the sun's surface. Some think they are giant whirlpools. Certainly they seem to be great whirling streams of glowing gases with vapors above them and immense upward and downward currents within them. Round the edges of the sun-spots rise great tongues of flame.

Perhaps the most popularly known fact about sun-spots is that they are somehow connected with what we call magnetic storms on earth. These magnetic storms manifest themselves in interruptions of our telegraphic and telephonic communications, in violent disturbances of the mariner's compass, and in exceptional auroral displays. The connection between the two sets of phenomena cannot be doubted, even although at times there may be a great spot on the sun without any corresponding "magnetic storm" effects on the earth.

A surprising fact about sun-spots is that they show definite periodic variations in number. The best-defined period is one of about eleven years. During this period the spots increase to a maximum in number and then diminish to a minimum, the variation being more or less regular. Now this can only mean one thing. To be periodic the spots must have some deep-seated connection with the fundamental facts of the sun's structure and activities. Looked at from this point of view their importance becomes great.

It is from the study of sun-spots that we have learned that the sun's surface does not appear to rotate all at the same speed. The "equatorial" regions are rotating quicker than regions farther north or south. A point forty-five degrees from the equator seems to take about two and a half days longer to complete one rotation than a point on the equator. This, of course, confirms our belief that the sun connot be a solid body.

WHAT is its composition? We know that there are present, in a gaseous state, such well-known elements as sodium, iron, copper, zinc, and magnesium; indeed, we know that there is practically every element in the sun that we know to be in the earth.

In 1868 Sir Norman Lockyer detected a light coming from the prominences of the sun which was not given by any substance known on earth, and attributed this to an unknown gas which he called helium, from the Greek *helios,* the sun. *In 1895 Sir William Ramsay discovered in certain minerals the same gas identified by the spectroscope.*

We can say, therefore, that this gas was discovered in the sun nearly thirty years before it was found on earth; this discovery of the long-lost heir is as thrilling a chapter in the detective story of science as any in the sensational stories of the day, and makes us feel quite certain that our methods really tell us of what elements sun and stars are built up. The light from the corona of the sun, as we have mentioned indicates a gas still unknown on earth, which has been christened Coronium.

To us on the earth the most patent and most astonishing fact about the sun is its tremendous energy. Heat and light in amazing quantities pour from it without ceasing.

Where does this energy come from? Enormous jets of red glowing gases can be seen shooting outwards from the sun, like flames from a fire, for thousands of miles. Does this argue fire, as we know fire on the earth? On this point the scientist is sure. The sun is not burning, and combustion is not the source of its heat. If the sun were composed of combustible material throughout and the conditions of combustion as we understand them were always present, the sun would burn itself out in some thousands of years, with marked changes in its heat and light production as the process advanced. There is no evidence of such changes. There is, instead, strong evidence that the sun has been emitting light and heat in prodigious quantities, not for thousands, but for millions of years. Every addition to our knowledge that throws light on the sun's age seems to make for increase rather than decrease of its years. This makes the wonder of its energy greater.

The best explanation that we have to-day of this continuous accretion of energy is that it is due to shrinkage of the sun's bulk under the force of gravity.

Gravity is one of the most mysterious forces of nature, but it is an obvious fact that bodies behave as if they attracted one another, and Newton worked out the law of this attraction. We may say, without trying to go too deeply into things, that every particle of matter attracts every other throughout the universe. If the diameter of the sun were to shrink by one mile all round, this would mean that all the millions of tons in the outer one-mile thickness would have a straight drop of one mile towards the centre. And that is not all, because obviously the layers below

this outer mile would also drop inwards, each to a less degree than the one above it. What a tremendous movement of matter, however slowly it might take place! And what a tremendous energy would be involved! Astronomers calculate that the above shrinkage of one mile all round would require fifty years for its completion, assuming, reasonably, that there is close and continuous relationship between loss of heat by radiation and shrinkage. But we need not feel over-anxious, before the sun becomes too cold to support life many millions of years would be required.

Does Life Exist on Stars?

IT is quite clear that there cannot be life on the stars. Nothing solid or even liquid can exist in such furnaces as they are. Life exists only on planets, and even on these its possibilities are limited.

In considering the possibility of life as we know it we may at once rule out the most distant planets from the sun, Uranus and Neptune. They are probably intrinsically too hot. We may also pass over the nearest planet to the sun, Mercury. We have reason to believe that it turns on its axis in the same period as it revolves round the sun, and it must therefore always present the same side to the sun. This means that the heat on the sunlit side of Mercury is above boiling-point, while the cold on the other side must be between two and three hundred degrees below freezing-point.

The planet Venus, the bright globe which is known to all as the morning and evening "star," seems at first sight more promising as regards the possibility of life. It is of nearly the same size as the earth, and it has a good atmosphere, but there are many astronomers who believe that, like Mercury, it always presents the same face to the sun, and it would therefore have the same disadvantage—a broiling heat on the sunny side and the cold of space on the opposite side. We are not sure.

We turn to Mars; and we must first make it clear why there is so much spec-

ulation about life on Mars, and why it is supposed that, if there is life on Mars, it must be more advanced than life on the earth.

The basis of this belief is that if, as we saw, all the globes in our solar system are masses of metal that are cooling down, the smaller will have cooled down before the larger, and will be further ahead in their development. Now Mars is very much smaller than the earth, and must have cooled at its surface millions of years before the earth did. Hence, if a story of life began on Mars at all, it began long before the story of life on the earth. We cannot guess what sort of life-forms would be evolved in a different world, but we can confidently say that they would tend toward increasing intelligence; and thus we are disposed to look for highly intelligent beings on Mars.

But this argument supposes that the conditions of life, namely air and water, are found on Mars, and it is disputed whether they are found there in sufficient quantity. The late Professor Percival Lowell, who made a lifelong study of Mars, maintained that there are hundreds of straight lines drawn across the surface of the planet, and he claimed that they are beds of vegetation marking the sites of great channels or pipes by means of which the "Martians" draw water from their polar ocean. Professor

W. H. Pickering, another high authority, thinks that the lines are long, narrow marshes fed by moist winds from the poles. There are certainly white polar caps on Mars. They seem to melt in the spring, and the dark fringe round them grows broader.

Other astronomers, however, say that they find no trace of water-vapor in the atmosphere of Mars, and they think that the polar caps may be simply thin sheets of hoar-frost or frozen gas. They point out that, as the atmosphere of Mars is certainly scanty, and the distance from the sun is so great, it may be too cold for the fluid water to exist on the planet.

Astronomers who are sceptical about life on Mars are often not fully aware of the extraordinary adaptability of life. There was a time when the climate of the whole earth, from pole to pole, was semi-tropical for millions of years. No animal could then endure the least cold, yet now we have plenty of Arctic plants and animals. If the cold came slowly on Mars, as we have reason to suppose, the population could be gradually adapted to it. On the whole, it is possible that there is advanced life on Mars, and it is not impossible, in spite of the very great difficulties of a code of communication, that our "elder brothers" may yet flash across space the solution of many of our problems.

NEXT to Mars, going outward from the sun, is Jupiter. The surface which we see in photographs is a mass of cloud or steam which always envelops the body of the planet. It is apparently red-hot. A red tinge is seen sometimes at the edges of its cloud-belts, and a large red region (the "red spot"), 23,000 miles in length, has been visible on it for half a century. There may be a liquid or solid core to the planet, but as a whole it is a mass of seething vapors whirling round on its axis once in every ten hours. As in the case of the sun, however, different latitudes appear to rotate at different rates. The interior of Jupiter is very hot, but the planet is not self-luminous. The planets Venus and Jupiter shine very brightly, but they have no light of their own; they reflect the sunlight.

Saturn is in the same interesting condition. Saturn is so far away from the sun that the vaporization of its oceans must necessarily be due to its own internal heat. It is too hot for water to settle on its surface. Like Jupiter, the great globe turns on its axis once in ten hours—a prodigious speed—and must be a swirling, seething mass of metallic vapors and gases. It is instructive to compare Jupiter and Saturn in this respect with the sun. They are smaller globes and have cooled down more than the central fire. There is no evidence of life on Saturn.

Mars and Venus are therefore the only planets, besides the earth, on which we may look for life; and in the case of Venus, the possibility is very faint. But what about the moons which attend the planets? They range in size from the little ten-miles-wide moons of Mars, to Titan, a moon of Saturn, and Ganymede, a satellite of Jupiter, which are about 3,000 miles in diameter. May there not be life on some of the larger of these moons? We will take our own moon as a type of the class.

The Moon

THE moon is so very much nearer to us than any other heavenly body that we have a remarkable knowledge of it. Our large telescopes bring the moon to within about fifty miles of us. We could see a city like London as a dark, sprawling blotch on the globe. We could just detect a Zeppelin or a Diplodocus as a moving speck against the surface. But we find none of these things. It is true that a few astronomers believe that they see signs of some sort of feeble life or movement on the moon. Professor Pickering thinks that he can trace some volcanic activity. He believes that there are areas of vegetation, probably of a low order, and that the soil of the moon may retain a certain amount of water in it. He speaks of a very thin atmosphere, and of occasional light falls of snow.

But there are many things that point to absence of air on the moon. Even the photographs we reproduce tell the same story. The edges of the shadows are all hard and black. If there had been an appreciable atmosphere it would have scattered the sun's light on to the edges and produced a gradual shading off such as we see on the earth. This relative absence of air must give rise to some surprising effects. There will be no sounds on the moon, because sounds are merely air waves. Even a meteor shattering itself to a violent end against the surface of the moon would make no noise. Nor would it herald its coming by glowing into a "shooting star," as it would on entering the earth's atmosphere. There will be no floating dust, no scent, no twilight, no blue sky, no twinkling of the stars. The sky will be always black and the stars will be clearly visible by day as by night. The sun's wonderful corona, which no man on earth, even by seizing every opportunity during eclipses, can hope to see for more than two hours in all in a long lifetime, will be visible all day. So will the great red flames of the sun. Of course, there will be no life, and no landscape effects and scenery effects due to vegetation.

For fourteen days there is continuous night, when the temperature must sink away down towards the absolute cold of space. This will be followed without an instant of twilight by full daylight. For another fourteen days the sun's rays will bear straight down, with no diffusion or absorption of their heat, or light, on the way. It does not follow, however, that the temperature of the moon's surface must rise enormously. It may not even rise to the temperature of melting ice. Seeing there is no air there can be no check on radiation. The heat that the moon gets will radiate away immediately.

The actual temperature of the moon's surface by day is a moot point. It may be below the freezing-point or above the boiling-point of water.

The moon is interesting to us precisely because it is a dead world. It seems to show how the earth, or any cooling metal globe, will evolve in the remote future. We do not know if there was ever life on the moon, but in any case it cannot have proceeded far in development. At the most we can imagine some strange lowly forms of vegetation lingering here and there in pools of heavy gas, expanding during the blaze of the sun's long day, and frozen rigid during the long night.

In this simple outline we have not touched on some of the more debatable questions that engage the attention of modern astronomers. Many of these questions have not yet passed the controversial stage; out of these will emerge the astronomy of the future. But we have seen enough to convince us that, whatever advances the future holds in store, the science of the heavens constitutes one of the most important stones in the wonderful fabric of human knowledge.

The Origin of the Earth

Several theories have been propounded to account for the origin of the earth, but the one that has found most favor in the eyes of authorities is that of Chamberlin and Moulton. According to this theory a great nebular mass condensed to form the sun, from which under the attraction of passing stars planet after planet, the earth included, was heaved off in the form of knotted spiral nebulae, like many of those now observed in the heavens.

Of great importance were the "knots," for they served as collecting centres drawing flying matter into their clutches. Whatever part of the primitive bolt escaped and scattered was drawn out into independent orbits round the sun, forming the "planetesimals" which behave like minute planets. These planetesimals formed the food on which the knots subsequently fed.

The material of the earth is similar to that of many of the other members of the Solar System, though of course the materials may not exist in the same proportion. In its primitive stage, the earth in its outer parts was liquid or gaseous; it was from its outer part that the moon was detached and became a separate body. The friction of the tides has carried the moon farther and farther away from the earth. The primitive earth, it is estimated, had a diameter of about 5,500 miles; it grew larger by drawing into itself more nebulous materials or meteorites until it had a diameter of 8,100 miles at the end of its growing period.

After *the growing period* was over, the earth began to lose volume. To-day it has a diameter of 7,900 miles. It was cooling, and that usually means becoming smaller. It was also consolidating internally. On the surface the earth was probably like a mass of lava, alternately passing from crust-making to boiling over. The boiling process must have brought about a sorting of materials, the lighter materials coming to the top and the heavier sinking to lower levels. The more acid, granitic materials would rise; basaltic materials would sink. Thus, roughly speaking, arose the rigid, rocky, relatively cool shell of the earth, perhaps fifty miles thick, shutting in the internal heat. The continents are, on the whole, built of the lighter materials, *e.g.*, granites, while the depressions that form the floor of the oceans have more of the heavier basaltic rocks beneath them. In any case a rocky shell or litho-

sphere was formed, and the romance of the rocks is concerned with the permutations and combinations of the materials of the earth's crust.

IN ALL probability, the earth contains a metal core embedded in a mantle of rocks some 50 miles thick. The centre of the earth is about 4,000 miles beneath us; the deepest shaft ever bored reached a depth of only some 6,500 feet, or less than one and a half miles. For a knowledge of the conditions existing in the interior of the earth, therefore, we must depend on the resources of scientific investigation. It is probable that the rocky crust of the earth changes in its nature at a uniform rate, as the temperature rises, down to a certain depth, and beneath that there is a sudden change in the conditions; we reach the beginning of the metal core which is enveloped by the earth's mantle of rocks. We owe a great deal of our knowledge of the interior of the earth to earthquake waves and to volcanic eruptions. There are many seismologic stations at different places with instruments so fine, and so carefully watched, that the earthquake phenomena can be studied with utmost precision. By studying the manner of the propagation of earthquake waves it is possible, with the aid of mathematical reasoning, to calculate their paths in the interior of the earth, and the velocity of their propagation. By such means the composition of the earth's interior is ascertained.

That the temperature of the interior of the earth is very high, is shown by the existence of hot springs and volcanoes, and by the rapid rise in temperature observed in mining operations, tunnelling and drilling.

Land and Water

THE question of the *plan of the earth,* and the distribution of land and water over its surface, is a very fascinating one. When we consider that animals and plants of the same families and even of the same species are found in

equal abundance in widely separated regions, and that this is true of all geological ages, we are forced to conclude that continents now separated by oceans must once have been connected by bridges of land. Oftener than once, dry land has disappeared below the surface of ocean water; the bed of oceans has been raised above the surface and become dry land; but some areas have continued as land throughout nearly the whole of geological time. The fabled continent of Atlantis was supposed to have existed in the North Atlantic Ocean. Whether Plato's description of prehistoric Atlantis—and the high state of the civilization of its inhabitants—is credible or not, there is little doubt that in very remote times there was a large land mass between the Eastern and Western Continents.

There was a time in the earth's history when there was no sea. The surface of the young earth was too hot to allow the accumulation of water in basins. More than that, *there were no basins,* for the surface of the young earth must have been at any one place as flat as a pancake. If the young earth was uniformly spherical (apparently flat at any point) there could be no separate *seas.* If the young earth had on its surface a high temperature, there could be no *sea:* the water would evaporate. But there is another factor: that the growing earth was originally too *small* to hold even a gaseous envelope (the atmosphere), still less an aqueous envelope (the hydrosphere).

As the earth gradually grew in diameter it acquired an atmosphere—differing from that of to-day in having but little oxygen. For the oxygen of our air is mostly due to the activity of green plants. As the earth reached its limit of growth and began to cool and shrink, a rocky shell (or lithosphere) was formed, seething and swaying at first, but gradually gaining stability. The probability is that as the result of surface boilings lighter materials rose higher to form CONTINENTS, while heavier materials sunk lower to form OCEAN BEDS. It is probable that over-weighting of vast areas resulted in the formation of ocean basins, which have become steadily larger as the quantity of water on the earth has increased. Over limited areas

the floor of the sea has sometimes been raised into dry land, and a large part of a continent has sometimes sunk down and formed the floor of a sea, but the trend of opinion among geologists seems to be in favor of the view that the present positions of the great masses of land and water have remained on the whole the same since continents and ocean basins were first established.

To the natural question, Where did all the water come from? geology answers, "From the earth itself." When we visit hot springs or watch the clouds of steam rising from volcanoes, we probably get more than a hint of how the water of the sea began. It is supposed that from a quarter to a half of the present-day volume of the seas was in existence before the Cambrian period. The rest has been added since—expressed from the earth itself. There is, of course, an endless circulation of water, on which the economy of Nature largely depends. The mist rises from the sea and clouds are formed which condense into rain or snow on the cold mountains or in cool strata in the air. The rain falls, the springs are fed, the streamlets become rivers, and these return to the parent sea. And it is the sun that keeps this water going round; for without the sun we could not have either rain or rivers.

On an average there are 3½ pounds of salty material to every 100 pounds of sea-water; and the great bulk of this has been dissolved out by the rain from the rocks of the dry land. In a very real sense the continents are always flowing into the sea.

There are dissolved salts and other solids in the water of rivers and lakes just as there are in the sea, but those in the latter are nearly 200 times as abundant as those in the former, so we speak of *fresh* water and *salt* water.

A very interesting fact in, regard to the salts of the sea is their correspondence with the salts in the blood of land animals! If the percentages of sodium, magnesium, calcium, potassium, and chlorine in sea-water be compared with the percentages in blood serum, the figures are respectively 30.5 and 39; 3.79 and 0.4; 1.2 and 1.0; 1.11 and 2.7; 55.27 and 45.0. There are striking resemblances especially in the proportion of potassium and calcium to sodium. So it has been suggested by Macallum and Quinton that in Cambrian times an equilibrium was established between the living matter of marine animals and the composition of the surrounding water.

And as to the differences which the percentages we have quoted also reveal, these may be interpreted in terms of the changes in the composition of the sea since the close of the Cambrian period. The composition of our blood is a telltale relic.

What Is the Universe Made Of?

OUR mind craves for some explanation of the matter out of which the universe is made. For this explanation we turn to modern Physics and Chemistry. Both these sciences study, under different aspects, matter and energy; and between them they have put together a conception of the fundamental nature of things.

More than two thousand years ago the first men of science, the Greeks of the cities of Asia Minor, speculated on the nature of matter. You can grind a piece of stone into dust. You can divide a spoonful of water into as many drops as you like. Apparently you can go on dividing as long as you have got apparatus fine enough for the work. But there must be a limit, these Greeks said, and so they supposed that all matter was ultimately composed of minute particles which were indivisible. That is the meaning of the Greek word "atom."

The whole physical and chemical science of that century is now based upon the atom. An atom is the smallest particle of a chemical element. No one has ever seen an atom. Even the wonderful new microscope which has just been invented cannot possibly show us particles of matter which are a million times smaller than the breadth of a hair; for that is the size of atoms. We can weigh them and measure them, though they are invisible, and we know that all matter is composed of them. It is a new discovery that atoms are not indivisible. They consist themselves of still smaller particles, as we shall see. But the atoms exist all the same, and we may still say that they are the bricks of which the material universe in its entirety is built.

But if we had some magical glass by means of which we could see into the structure of material things, we should not see the atoms put evenly together as bricks are in a wall. As a rule, two or more atoms first come together to form a large particle, which we call a "molecule." Single atoms do not, as a rule, exist apart from other atoms; if a molecule is broken up, the individual atoms seek to unite with other atoms of another kind or amongst themselves. For example, three atoms of oxygen form what we call ozone; two atoms of hydrogen uniting with one atom of oxygen form water. It is molecules that form the mass of matter; a molecule, as it has been expressed, is a little building of which atoms are the bricks.

In this way we get a useful first view of the material things we handle. In a liquid the molecules of the liquid cling together loosely. They remain together as a body, but they roll over and away from each other. There is "cohesion" between them, but it is less powerful than in a solid. Put some water in a kettle over the lighted gas, and presently the tiny molecules of water will rush through the spout in a cloud of steam and scatter over the kitchen. The heat has broken their bond of association and turned the water into something like a gas; though we know that the particles will come together again, as they cool, and form once more drops of water.

In a gas the molecules have full individual liberty. They are in a state of violent movement, and they form no

Molecules are, of course, invisible. Two or more atoms form a molecule which is the basis of all matter. A molecule of water is made up of two atoms of hydrogen and one atom of oxygen. Molecules of different substances, therefore, are of different sizes according to the number and kind of particular atoms of which they are composed. A starch molecule contains no less than 25,000 atoms.

union with each other. If we want to force them to enter into the loose sort of association which molecules have in a liquid, we have to slow down their individual movements by applying severe cold. That is how a modern man of science liquefies gases. No power that we have will liquefy air at its ordinary temperature. In *very* severe cold, on the other hand, the air will spontaneously become liquid. Some day, when the fires of the sun have sunk very low, the temperature of the earth will be less than —200° C.: that is to say, more than two hundred degrees Centigrade below freezing-point. It will sink to the temperature of the moon. Our atmosphere will then be an ocean of liquid air, 35 feet deep, lying upon the solidly frozen masses of our water-oceans.

In a solid the molecules cling firmly to each other. We need a force equal to twenty-five tons to tear asunder the molecules in a bar of iron an inch thick. Yet the structure is not "solid" in the popular sense of the word. If you put a piece of solid gold in a little pool of mercury, the gold will take in the mercury *between* its molecules, as if it were porous like a sponge. The hardest solid is more like a lattice-work than what we usually mean by "solid"; though the molecules are not fixed, like the bars of a lattice-work, but are in violent motion; they vibrate about equilibrium positions. If we could see right into the heart of a bit of the hardest steel, we should see billions of separate molecules, at some distance from each other, all moving rapidly to and fro.

Most people have heard of "atomic energy," and the extraordinary things that might be accomplished if we could harness this energy and turn it to human use. A deeper and more wonderful source of this energy has been discovered in the last twenty years, but it is well to realize that the atoms themselves have stupendous energy. The atoms of matter are vibrating or gyrating with extraordinary vigor. The piece of cold iron you hold in your hand, the bit of brick you pick up, or the penny you take from your pocket is a colossal reservoir of energy, since it consists of trillions of moving atoms. To realize the total energy, of course, we should have to witness a transformation such as we do in atoms of radio-active elements, about which we shall have something to say presently.

If we put a grain of indigo in a glass of water, or a grain of musk in a perfectly still room, we soon realize that molecules travel. Similarly, the fact that gases spread until they fill every "empty" available space shows definitely that they consist of small particles travelling at great speed. The physicist brings his refined methods to bear on these things, and he measures the energy and velocity of these infinitely minute molecules. He tells us that molecules of oxygen, at the temperature of melting ice, travel at the rate of more than a quarter of a mile a second.

Molecules of hydrogen travel at four times that speed, or three times the speed with which a bullet leaves a rifle. Each molecule of the air, which seems so still in the house on a summer's day, is really travelling faster than a rifle bullet does at the beginning of its journey. It collides with another molecule every twenty-thousandth of an inch of its journey. It is turned from its course 5,000,-000,000 times in every second by collisions. If we could stop the molecules of hydrogen gas, and utilize their energy, as we utilize the energy of steam or the energy of the water at Niagara, we should find enough in every gramme of gas (about two-thousandths of a pound) to raise a third of a ton to a height of forty inches.

The Smallest Units of Matter

BUT these wonders of the atom are only a prelude to the more romantic and far-reaching discoveries of the new physics—the wonders of the electron.

The discovery that the atom was composed of smaller particles was the welcome realization of a dream that had haunted the imagination of the nineteenth century. Chemists said that there were about eighty different kinds of atoms—different kinds of matter—but no one was satisfied with the multiplicity. Science is always aiming at simplicity and unity. It may be that science has now taken a long step in the direction of explaining the fundamental unity of all the matter. The chemist was unable to break up these "elements" into something simpler, so he called their atoms "indivisible" in that sense.

But one man of science after another expressed the hope that we would yet discover some fundamental matter of which the various atoms were composed —one primordial substance from which all the varying forms of matter have been evolved or built up.

With the discovery of radium it was learned that nearly every form of matter can be stimulated to radio-activity; which, as we shall see, means that *its atoms break up into smaller and wonderfully energetic particles which we call "electrons."* This discovery of electrons has brought about a complete change in our ideas in many directions.

"What a wonder, then, have we here!" says Professor R. K. Duncan. "An innocent-looking little pinch of salt and yet possessed of special properties utterly beyond even the fanciful imaginings of men of past time; for nowhere do we find in the records of thought even the hint of the possibility of things which we now regard as established fact. This pinch of salt projects from its surface bodies [*i.e.* electrons] possessing the inconceivable velocity of over 100,-000 miles a second, a velocity sufficient to carry them, if unimpeded, five times around the earth in a second, and possessing with this velocity, masses a thousand times smaller than the smallest atom known to science. Furthermore, they are charged with negative electricity; they pass straight through bodies considered opaque with a sublime indifference to the properties of the body, with the exception of its mere density; they cause bodies which they strike to shine out in the dark; they affect a photographic plate; they render the air a conductor of electricity; they cause clouds in moist air; they cause chemical action and have a peculiar physiological action. Who, to-day, shall predict the ultimate service to humanity of the electron from radium!"

ALTHOUGH we have discovered a great deal about the electron and the constitution of matter, and while the physicists of our own day seem to see a possibility of explaining positive and negative electricity, the nature of them both is unknown. There exists the theory that the particles of positive and negative electricity, which make up the atoms of matter, are points or centres of disturbances of some kind in a universal ether, and that all the various forms of energy are, in some fundamental way, aspects of the same primary entity which constitutes matter itself.

But the discovery of the property of radio-activity has raised many other interesting questions, besides that which we have just dealt with. In radio-active elements, such as uranium for example, the element is breaking down; in what we call radio-activity we have a manifestation of the spontaneous change of elements. What is really taking place is a transmutation of one element into another, from a heavier to a lighter. The element uranium spontaneously becomes radium, and radium passes through a number of other stages until it, in turn, becomes lead. Each descending element is of lighter atomic weight than its predecessor. The changing process, of course, is a very slow one. It may be that all matter is radio-active, or can be made so. This raises the question whether all the matter in the universe may not undergo disintegration.

There is, however, another side of the question, which the discovery of radio-activity has brought to light, and which has effected a revolution in our views. We have seen that in radio-active substances the elements are breaking down. Is there a process of building up at work? If the more complicated atoms are breaking down into simpler forms, may there not be a converse process— a building up from simpler elements to more complicated elements? It is probably the case that both processes are at work.

There are some eighty-odd chemical elements on the earth to-day: are they all the outcome of an inorganic evolution, element giving rise to element, going back and back to some primeval stuff from which they were all originally derived infinitely long ago?

Is there an evolution in the inorganic world which may be going on, parallel to that of the evolution of living things; or is organic evolution a continuation of inorganic evolution? We have seen what evidence there is of this inorganic evolution in the case of the stars. We cannot go deeply into the matter here, nor has the time come for any direct statement that can be based on the findings of modern investigation. Taking it altogether the evidence is steadily accumulating, and there are authorities who maintain that already the evidence of inorganic evolution is convincing enough. The heavier atoms would appear to behave as though they were evolved from the lighter. The more complex forms, it is supposed, have *evolved* from the simpler forms.

Discoveries have been made which point to the conclusion that the elements are built up one from another.

We may here refer to another new conception to which the discovery of radio-activity has given rise. Lord Kelvin, who estimated the age of the earth at twenty million years, reached this estimate by considering the earth as a body which is gradually cooling down, "losing its primitive heat, like a loaf taken from the oven, at a rate which could be calculated, and that the heat radiated by the sun was due to contraction." Uranium and radio-activity were not known to Kelvin, and their discovery has upset both his arguments.

Radio-active substances, which are perpetually giving out heat, introduce an entirely new factor. We cannot now assume that the earth is necessarily cooling down; it may even, for all we know, be getting hotter. At the 1921 meeting of the British Association, Professor Rayleigh stated that further knowledge had extended the probable period during which there had been life on this globe to about one thousand million years, and the total age of the earth to some small multiple of that. The earth, he considers, is not cooling, but "contains an internal source of heat from the disintegration of uranium in the outer crust." On the whole the estimate obtained would seem to be in agreement with the geological estimates. The question cannot be completely settled within fixed limits that meet with general agreement.

Ether and Energy

THERE are other fundamental existences which give rise to more complex problems. The three great fundamental entities in the physical universe are matter, ether, and energy; so far as we know, outside these there is nothing. We have dealt with matter, there remain ether and energy. We shall see that just as no particle of matter, however small, may be created or destroyed, and just as there is no such thing as empty space—ether pervades everything —so there is no such thing as *rest*. Every particle that goes to make up our solid earth is in a state of perpetual unremitting vibration; energy "is the universal commodity on which all life depends." Separate and distinct as these three fundamental entities—matter, ether, and energy—may appear, it may be that, after all, they are only different and mysterious phases of an essential "oneness" of the universe.

The whole material universe is supposed to be embedded in a vast medium called the ether. It is true that the notion of the ether has been abandoned by some modern physicists, but, whether or not it is ultimately dispensed with, the conception of the ether has entered so deeply into the scientific mind that the science of physics cannot be understood unless we know something about the properties attributed to the ether.

The ether was invented to explain the phenomena of light, and to account for the flow of energy across empty space.

Light takes time to travel. We see the sun at any moment by the light that left it 8 minutes before. It has taken that 8 minutes for the light from the sun to travel that 93,000,000 miles odd which separates it from our earth. Besides the fact that light takes time to travel, it can be shown that light travels in the form of waves. We know that sound travels in waves; sound consists of waves in the air, or water or wood or whatever medium we hear it through. If an electric bell be put in a glass jar and the air be pumped out of the jar, the sound of the bell becomes feebler and feebler until, when enough air has been taken out, we do not hear the bell at all. Sound cannot travel in a vacuum. We continue to *see* the bell, however, so that evidently light can travel in a vacuum. The invisible medium through which the waves of light travel is the ether, and this ether permeates all space *and all matter*.

Between us and the stars stretch vast regions empty of all matter. But we see the stars; their light reaches us, even though it may take centuries to do so. We conceive, then, that it is the universal ether which conveys that light. All the energy which has reached the earth from the sun and which, stored for ages in our coalfields, is now used to propel our trains and steamships, to heat and light our cities, to perform all the multifarious tasks of modern life, was conveyed by the ether. Without that universal carrier of energy we should have nothing but a stagnant, lifeless world.

Energy is indispensable if the world is to continue to exist, since all phenomena, including life, depend on it. Just as it is humanly impossible to create or to destroy a particle of matter, so is it impossible to create or to destroy energy. This statement will be more readily understood when we have considered what energy is.

Energy, like matter, is indestructible, and just as matter exists in various forms so does energy. And we may add, just as we are ignorant of what the negative and positive particles of electricity which constitute matter really are, so we are ignorant of the true nature of energy. At the same time, energy is not so completely mysterious as it once was.

The existence of various forms of energy had been known, of course, for ages; there was the energy of a falling stone, the energy produced by burning wood or coal or any other substance, but the essential *identity* of all these forms of energy had not been suspected. The conception of energy as something which, like matter, was constant in amount, which could not be created nor destroyed, was one of the great scientific acquisitions of the past century.

It is not possible to enter deeply into this subject here. It is sufficient if we briefly outline its salient aspects. Energy is recognized in two forms, kinetic and potential. The form of energy which is most apparent to us is the *energy of motion;* for example, a rolling stone, running water, a falling body, and so on. We call the energy of motion *kinetic energy.* Potential energy is the energy a body has in virtue of its position—it is its capacity, in other words, to acquire kinetic energy, as in the case of a stone resting on the edge of a cliff.

Energy may assume different forms; one kind of energy may be converted directly or indirectly into some other form. The energy of burning coal, for example, is converted into heat, and from heat energy we have mechanical energy, such as that manifested by the steam-engine. In this way we can transfer energy from one body to another. There is the energy of the great waterfalls of Niagara, for instance, which are used to supply the energy of huge electric power stations.

What Is Heat?

An important fact about energy is, that all energy *tends to take the form of heat energy.* The impact of a falling stone generates heat; a waterfall is hotter at the bottom than at the top—the falling particles of water, on striking the ground, generate heat; and most chemical changes are attended by heat changes. Energy may remain latent indefinitely in a lump of wood, but in combustion it is liberated, and we have heat as a result. The atom of radium or of any other radio-active substance, as it disintegrates, generates heat. "Every hour radium generates sufficient heat to raise the temperature of its own weight of water, from the freezing point to the boiling point."

And what is heat? *Heat is molecular motion.* The molecules of every substance, as we have seen on a previous page, are in a state of continual motion, and the more vigorous the motion the hotter the body. As wood or coal burns, the invisible molecules of these substances are violently agitated, and give rise to ether waves which our senses interpret as light and heat. In this constant movement of the molecules, then, we have a manifestation of the energy of motion and of heat.

That energy which disappears in one form reappears in another has been found to be universally true. It was Joule who, by churning water, first showed that a measurable quantity of mechanical energy could be transformed into a measurable quantity of heat energy. By causing an apparatus to stir water vigorously, that apparatus being driven by falling weights or a rotating flywheel or by any other mechanical means, the water became heated. A certain amount of mechanical energy had been used up and a certain amount of heat had appeared. The relation between these two things was found to be invariable. Every physical change in nature involves a transformation of energy, but the total quantity of energy in the universe remains unaltered. This is the great doctrine of the Conservation of Energy.

Energy may become dissipated. Where does it go? since if it is indestructible it must still exist. It is easier to ask the question than to give a final answer, and it is not possible in this OUTLINE, where an advanced knowledge of physics is not assumed on the part of the reader, to go fully into the some-what difficult theories put forward by physicists and chemists. We may raise the temperature, say, of iron, until it is white-hot. If we stop the process the temperature of the iron will gradually settle down to the temperature of surrounding bodies. As it does so, where does its previous energy go? In some measure it may pass to other bodies in contact with the piece of iron, but ultimately the heat becomes radiated away in space where we cannot follow it. It has been added to the vast reservoir of *unavailable* heat energy of uniform temperature. It is sufficient here to say that if all bodies had a uniform temperature we should experience no such thing as heat, because heat only travels from one body to another, having the effect of cooling the one and warming the other. In time the two bodies acquire the same temperature.

Before heat energy can be utilized we must have bodies with different temperature. If the whole universe were at some

NATURE'S TRANSFORMATIONS OF WATER. The water-vapour of the air falls as frozen snow, then thaws into running water, and again freezes into icicles.

uniform temperature, then, although it might possess an enormous amount of heat energy, this energy would be unavailable.

And what does this imply? It implies a great deal: for if all the energy in the world became unavailable, the universe, as it now is, would cease to be. It is possible that, by the constant interchange of heat radiations, the whole universe is tending to some uniform temperature, in which case, although all molecular motion would not have ceased, it would have become unavailable. In this sense it may be said that the universe is running down.

The primary reservoir of energy is the atom; it is the energy of the atom, the atom of elements in the sun, the stars, the earth, from which nature draws for all her supply of energy. Shall we ever discover how we can replenish the dwindling resources of energy, or find out how we can call into being the at present unavailable energy which is stored up in uniform temperature?

It looks as if our successors would witness an interesting race, between the progress of science on the one hand and the depletion of natural resources upon the other. The natural rate of flow of energy from its primary atomic reservoirs to the sea of waste heat energy of uniform temperature, allows life to proceed at a complete pace sternly regulated by the inexorable laws of supply and demand, which the biologists have recognized in their field as the struggle for existence.

It is certain that energy is an actual entity just as much as matter, and that it cannot be created or destroyed. Matter and ether are receptacles or vehicles of energy. As we have said, what these entities really are in themselves we do not know. It may be that all forms of energy are in some fundamental way aspects of the same primary entity which constitutes matter.

The Number of Things in the World

Perhaps the biggest revelation of chemistry for ordinary people is that, in spite of the immense variety of things in the world, there are only a relatively small number of things that are really different, namely, *the eighty or so chemical elements*. We do not know how many words there are in the English language, but there are only about twenty-six generally recognized letters. It is the same in chemistry. [According to the physical tables of the Smithsonian Institute, as cited in the World Almanac for 1940, there are ninety-two chemical elements. A number of new elements have been discovered since "The Outline of Science" was written. *Ed.*]

We have seen that all the observed phenomena of Chemistry and Physics are regarded as indications of the fundamental unity of matter. All matter, in short, is supposed to be, in its final analysis, essentially the same in constitution. The atoms of all matter consist of particles of positive and negative electricity; the simplest atom, that of hydrogen, is a unit of negative electricity, called an electron, revolving round a nucleus of positive electricity, called a proton.

Electrons obtained from different atoms are found to be the same; in an atom of hydrogen there is one electron, in an atom of helium two, in an atom of lithium three. The addition of further electrons to the system gives rise to the atoms of all other elements. All matter is thus supposed to be electrical in its nature. The atom, since its disintegration is seen to take place, is no longer the atom indivisible or incapable of being broken up into something simpler.

It is not now believed that each of the eighty or so elements known to us has its own kind of atom, each stamped with its own properties. The properties and qualities of the different elements, it is believed, depend on the number and arrangement of the particles of negative electricity (electrons) and of positive particles (protons) contained in the atoms of the various elements. The view is that all the elements, though they have different chemical qualities, are built up out of the same material; thus our ideas regarding the constitution of matter and the framework of the Universe have been completely changed. "The superlatively grand question" is, what is the inner mechanism of the atom?

IT is the business of the Chemist to attempt to fathom the mysteries of the properties of the various chemical elements, to evolve order and system out of them. It is to the Chemist that we owe our knowledge that the atoms of different substances can be arranged in a definite order, and also that they show an increasing complexity of structure. Heavier atoms appear to behave as though they were evolved from the lighter.

It is well known to everybody that the atom of one chemical element may combine with one or more atoms of another element. When the chemist speaks of the *valency* of an element, he means the number of other atoms, with which

one atom of this element can directly combine. For example, one atom of hydrogen combines with one atom of chlorine, and the result is hydrochloric acid; or one atom of oxygen will combine with two atoms of hydrogen and the result is water; one atom of nitrogen and three of hydrogen make ammonia.

Each of these combinations represents a *chemical* process, that is to say, a chemical change which produces a substance which is totally distinct, not a substance which merely partakes of the characters of the two component elements.

Thus are the various substances built up; the elements are mostly found in mutual combinations, and the combinations are sometimes of course, very complex. While a particle, or molecule, of water consists of two atoms of hydrogen and one of oxygen, the molecule of the proteid called "albumen" is built up by 72 atoms of carbon, 112 atoms of hydrogen, 18 atoms of nitrogen, all brought into association with one atom of sulphur. In all protoplasm of living matter there is a mixture of proteins, carbohydrates, and fats, with intricate chemical and physical inter-relations.

The Riddle of Life

IT is highly improbable that there is any one substance which deserves to be called *the* living matter or protoplasm. What we actually know is a complex and heterogeneous system in which various chemical reactions take place simultaneously. There is always involved, as life goes on, a breaking down and a building up of proteins. But the riddle is still unread.   •

Of the fourscore and more elements, no fewer than twenty-nine are known to occur in living creatures; but twelve of these are rare. Those that are always present are hydrogen, carbon, oxygen, nitrogen, phosphorus, sulphur, potassium, magnesium, calcium, and iron, and to these there should probably be added sodium, chlorine, and silicon. Not uncommon are iodine (*e.g.,* in brown seaweeds and the thyroid gland), manga-

nese (a trace in most animals and in some plants), bromine (in brown seaweeds, a trace in some animals), and fluorine (in bones and a few plants).

The first big fact is that the elements invariably present in organisms are common in the inorganic world. The second big fact is that the essential and most important elements in living creatures are hydrogen, carbon, oxygen, and nitrogen. In most animal and plant proteins sulphur is also present in addition to the Big Four. In nucleo-proteins, like the chromatin of the nuclei of all cells, there is likewise phosphorus.

Thus as far as the constituent *elements* go, there is nothing peculiar in living matter.

Various concrete suggestions have been made in regard to the possible origin of living matter, which will be dealt with in a later section. So far as we know of what goes on to-day, there is no evidence of spontaneous generation; organisms seem always to arise from pre-existing organisms of the same kind; where any suggestion of the contrary has been fancied, there have been flaws in the experimenting.

If the synthetic chemists should go on surpassing themselves, if substances like white of egg should be made artificially, and if we should get more light on possible steps by which simple living creatures may have arisen from not-living materials, this would not greatly affect our general outlook on life, though it would increase our appreciation of what is often libelled as "inert" matter. If the dust of the earth did naturally give rise very long ago to living creatures, if they are in a real sense born of her and of the sunshine, then the whole world becomes more continuous and more vital, and all the inorganic groaning and travailing becomes more intelligible.

From "A Song of The Rolling Earth"

A song of the rolling earth, and of words according——

. . . .

Amelioration is one of the earth's words,
The earth neither lags nor hastens,
It has all attributes, growths, effects, latent in itself from the jump,
It is not half beautiful only, defects and excrescences show just as much as per-
    fections show.

The earth does not withhold, it is generous enough,
The truths of the earth continually wait, they are not so conceal'd either,

. . . .

The earth does not argue,
Is not pathetic, has no arrangements,
Does not scream, haste, persuade, threaten, promise,
Makes no discriminations, has no conceivable failures,
Closes nothing, refuses nothing, shuts none out,
Of all the powers, objects, states, it notifies, shuts none out.

The earth does not exhibit itself nor refuse to exhibit itself, possesses still under-
    neath,
Underneath the ostensible sounds, the august chorus of heroes, the wail of slaves,
Persuasions of lovers, curses, gasps of the dying, laughter of young people, accents
    of bargainers,
Underneath these possessing words that never fail.

To her children the words of the eloquent dumb great mother never fail,
The true words do not fail, for motion does not fail and reflection does not fail,
Also the day and night do not fail, and the voyage we pursue does not fail.

Of the interminable sisters,
Of the ceaseless cotillons of sisters,
Of the centripetal and centrifugal sisters, the elder and younger sisters,
The beautiful sister we know dances on with the rest.

                                        —*Walt Whitman*

JAMES OLIVER CURWOOD

THE RIVER'S END

Yᴏᴜ don't have to be ashamed of a taste for "Westerns" when you are reading something by James Oliver Curwood (1878-1927). For his books have all the blood and thunderish excitement of the typical variety plus a certain amount of literary quality and authenticity. In fact, he became such an authority on Northwest Canada that the Dominion Government employed him as an explorer. He is famous for his books about the Royal Mounted Police of which "The River's End" is one of the best examples.

Bᴇᴛᴡᴇᴇɴ Conniston, of His Majesty's Royal N o r t h w e s t Mounted Police, and Keith, the outlaw, there was a striking physical and facial resemblance. Both had observed it, of course. It gave them a sort of confidence in each other. Between them it hovered in a subtle and unanalyzed presence that was constantly suggesting to Conniston a line of action that would have made him a traitor to his oath of duty.

For nearly a month he had crushed down the whispered temptings of this thing between them.

He represented the law. He was the law. For twenty-seven months he had followed Keith, and always there had been in his mind that parting injunction of the splendid service of which he was a part—"Don't come back until you get your man, dead or alive." Otherwise——

A racking cough split in upon his thoughts. He sat up on the edge of his cot, and at the gasping cry of pain that came with the red stain of blood on his lips Keith went to him and with a strong arm supported his shoulders. He said nothing, and after a moment Conniston wiped the stain away and laughed softly, even before the shadow of pain had faded from his eyes. One of his hands rested on a wrist that still bore the ring-mark of a handcuff. The sight of it brought him back to grim reality.

After all, fate was playing whimsically as well as tragically with their destinies.

"Thanks, old top," he said. "Thanks." His fingers closed over the manacle-marked wrist.

Over their heads the arctic storm was crashing in a mighty fury, as if striving to beat down the little cabin that had dared to rear itself in the dun-gray emptiness at the top of the world, eight hundred miles from civilization.

Queer and Funny

"Iᴛ's queer, devilish queer," Conniston said finally. "Don't you think so, Keith?" He was an Englishman, and his blue eyes shone with a grim, cold humor. "And funny," he added.

"Queer, but not funny," partly agreed Keith.

"Yes, it is funny," maintained Conniston. "Just twenty-seven months ago, lacking three days, I was sent out to get you, Keith. I was told to bring you in dead or alive—and at the end of the twenty-sixth month I got you, alive. And as a sporting proposition you deserve a hundred years of life instead of the noose, Keith, for you led me a chase that took me through seven different kinds of hell before I landed you. I froze, and I starved, and I drowned. I haven't seen a white woman's face in eighteen months. It was terrible. But I beat you at last. That's the jolly good part of it, Keith— I beat you and *got* you, and there's the proof of it on your wrists this minute. I won. Do you concede that? You must be fair, old top, because this is the last big game I'll ever play."

Keith nodded. "You won," he said. "You won so square that when the frost got your lung——"

"You didn't take advantage of me," interrupted Conniston. "That's the funny part of it, Keith. That's where the humor comes in. I had you all tied up and scheduled for the hangman when —bing!—along comes a cold snap that bites a corner of my lung, and the tables are turned. And instead of doing to me as I was going to do to you, instead of killing me or making your getaway while I was helpless—Keith—old pal— *you've tried to nurse me back to life!* Isn't that funny? Could anything be funnier?"

He reached a hand across the table and gripped Keith's. And then, for a few moments, he bowed his head while his body was convulsed by another racking cough. When Conniston raised his face, the red stain was on his lips again.

"I've got two sure days ahead of me, possibly a third," Conniston went on. "Then you'll have to dig a hole and bury me. After that you will no longer be held by the word of honor you gave me when I slipped off your manacles. And I'm asking you—*what are you going to do?*"

Keith's face aged even as the dying Englishman stared at him. "I suppose— I'll go back," he said heavily.

"You mean to Coronation Gulf? You'll return to that stinking mess of Eskimo igloos? If you do, you'll go mad!"

"I'm sorry," he said again. "I—like you. Do you know, Keith, I wish we'd been born brothers and you hadn't killed a man. That night I slipped the ring-dogs on you I felt almost like a devil. I wouldn't say it if it wasn't for this bally lung. But what's the use of keeping it back now? It doesn't seem fair to keep a man up in that place for three years, running from hole to hole like a rat, and then take him down for a hanging. I know it isn't fair in your case. I feel it. I don't mean to be inquisitive, old chap, but I'm not believing Departmental 'facts' any more. I'd make a topping good wager you're not the sort they make you out. And so I'd like to know— just why—you killed Judge Kirkstone?"

Keith's two fists knotted in the center of the table. Conniston saw his blue eyes darken for an instant with a savage fire. In that moment there came a strange silence over the cabin, and in that silence the incessant and maddening yapping of the little white foxes rose shrilly over the distant booming and rumbling of the ice.

Behind Departmental Facts

"WHY did I kill Judge Kirkstone?" Keith repeated the words slowly. His clenched hands relaxed, but his eyes held the steady glow of fire. "What do the Departmental 'facts' tell you, Conniston?"

"That you murdered him in cold blood, and that the honor of the Service is at stake until you are hung."

"There's a lot in the view-point, isn't there? What if I said I didn't kill Judge Kirkstone?"

"I'm after facts, and you can't lie to a dying man. Did you kill Judge Kirkstone?" Conniston demanded.

"I — don't — know," replied Keith slowly, looking steadily into the other's eyes. "I think so, and yet I am not positive. I went to his home that night with the determination to wring justice from him or kill him. I wish you could look at it all with my eyes, Conniston. You could if you had known my father. You see, my mother died when I was a little chap, and my father and I grew up together, chums. I don't believe I ever thought of him as just simply a father. Fathers are common. He was more than that. From the time I was ten years old we were inseparable. I guess I was twenty before he told me of the deadly feud that existed between him and

Kirkstone, and it never troubled me much—because I didn't think anything would ever come of it—until Kirkstone got him. Then I realized that all through the years the old rattlesnake had been watching for his chance. It was a frame-up from beginning to end, and my father stepped into the trap. Even then he thought that his political enemies, and not Kirkstone, were at the bottom of it. We soon discovered the truth. My father got ten years. He was innocent. And the only man on earth who could prove his innocence was Kirkstone, the man who was gloating like a Shylock over his pound of flesh. Conniston, if you had known these things and had been in my shoes, what would you have done?"

Conniston, lighting another taper over the oil flame, hesitated and answered: "I don't know yet, old chap. What did you do?"

"I fairly got down on my knees to the scoundrel," resumed Keith. "If ever a man begged for another man's life, I begged for my father's—for the few words from Kirkstone that would set him free. I offered everything I had in the world, even my body and soul. God, I'll never forget that night! He sat there, fat and oily, two big rings on his stubby fingers—a monstrous toad in human form—and he chuckled and laughed at me in his joy, as though I were a mountebank playing amusing tricks for him—and there my soul was bleeding itself out before his eyes! And his son came in, fat and oily and accursed like his father, and *he* laughed at me. I didn't know that such hatred could exist in the world, or that vengeance could bring such hellish joy. I could still hear their gloating laughter when I stumbled out into the night. It haunted me. I heard it in the trees. It came in the wind. My

brain was filled with it—and suddenly I turned back, and I went into that house again without knocking, and I faced the two of them alone once more in that room. And this time, Conniston, I went back to get justice—or to kill. Thus far it was premeditated, but I went with my naked hands. There was a key in the door, and I locked it. Then I made my demand."

Keith rose from the table and began to pace back and forth.

"The son began it," said Keith. "He sprang at me. I struck him. We grappled, and then the beast himself leaped at me with some sort of weapon in his hand. I couldn't see what it was, but it was heavy. The first blow almost broke my shoulder. In the scuffle I wrenched it from his hand, and then I found it was a long, rectangular bar of copper made for a paper-weight. In that same instant I saw the son snatch up a similar object from the table, and in the act he smashed the table light. In darkness we fought. I did not feel that I was fighting men. They were monsters and gave me the horrible sensation of being in darkness with crawling serpents. Yes, I struck hard. And the son was striking, and neither of us could see. I felt my weapon hit, and it was then that Kirkstone crumpled down with a blubbery wheeze. You know what happened after that. The next morning only one copper weight was found in that room. The son had done away with the other. And the one that was left was covered with Kirkstone's blood and hair. There was no chance for me. So I got away. Six months later my father died in prison, and for three years I've been hunted as a fox is hunted by the hounds. That's all, Conniston. Did I kill Judge Kirkstone? And, if I killed him, do you think I'm sorry for it?"

Trading Identities

"SIT down!"

The Englishman's voice was commanding. Keith dropped back to his seat, breathing hard. He saw a strange

light in the steely blue eyes of Conniston.

"Keith, when a man knows he's going to live, he is blind to a lot of things.

But when he knows he's going to die, it's different. If you had told me that story a month ago. I'd have taken you down to the hangman just the same. It would have been my duty, you know, and I might have argued you were lying. But you can't lie to me—now. Kirkstone deserved to die. And so I've made up my mind what you're going to do. You're not going back to Coronation Gulf. You're going south. You're going back into God's country again. And you're not going as John Keith, the murderer, but as Derwent Conniston of His Majesty's Royal Northwest Mounted Police! Do you get me, Keith? Do you understand?"

Keith simply stared. The Englishman scratched his cheek, a half-humorous gleam in his eyes. He had been thinking of this plan of his for some time, and he had foreseen just how it would take Keith off his feet.

"Quite a scheme, don't you think, old chap? I like you. I don't mind saying I think a lot of you, and there isn't any reason on earth why you shouldn't go on living in my shoes. There's no moral objection. No one will miss me. I was the black sheep back in England— younger brother and all that—and when I had to choose between Africa and Canada, I chose Canada. An Englishman's pride is the biggest fool thing on earth, Keith, and I suppose all of them over there think I'm dead. They haven't heard from me in six or seven years. I'm forgotten. And the beautiful thing about this scheme is that we look so deucedly alike, you know. Cut off that mustache and beard of yours, add a bit of a scar over your right eye, and you can walk in on old McDowell himself, and I'll wager he'll jump up and say, 'Bless my heart, if it isn't Conniston!' That's all I've got to leave you,

Keith, a dead man's clothes and name. But you're welcome. They'll be of no more use to me after tomorrow."

"Impossible!" gasped Keith. "Conniston, do you know what you are saying?"

"Positively, old chap. I count every word, because it hurts when I talk. So you won't argue with me, please. It's the biggest sporting thing that's ever come my way. In the next twenty-four hours you've got to learn by heart the history of Derwent Conniston from the day he joined the Royal Mounted. We won't go back further than that, for it wouldn't interest you, and ancient history won't turn up to trouble you. Your biggest danger will be with McDowell, commanding F Division at Prince Albert. He's a human fox of the old military school, swaggers and all, and he can see through boiler-plate. But he's got a big heart. He has been a good friend of mine, so along with Derwent Conniston's story you've got to load up with a lot about McDowell, too. There are many things—*oh, God*——"

He flung a hand to his chest. Grim horror settled in the little cabin as the cough convulsed him.

That night, in the yellow sputter of the seal-oil lamp, the fight began. Grim-faced—one realizing the nearness of death and struggling to hold it back, the other praying for time—two men went through the amazing process of trading their identities.

Through the terrible hours that followed Keith felt the strength and courage of the dying man becoming slowly a part of himself. The thing was epic. Conniston, throttling his own agony, was magnificent. And Keith felt his warped and despairing soul swelling with a new life and a new hope, and he was thrilled by the thought of what he must do to live up to the mark of the Englishman.

Back to Civilization

DAWN—the dusk of another night—and Keith raised his haggard face from Conniston's bedside with a woman's sob on his lips. The Englishman had

died as he knew that he would die, game to the last threadbare breath that came out of his body. For with this last breath he whispered the words which he had repeated a dozen times before, "Remember, old chap, you win or lose the moment McDowell first sets his eyes on you!" And then, with a strange kind of sob in his chest, he was gone, and Keith's eyes were blinded by the miracle of a hot flood of tears, and there rose in him a mighty pride in the name of Derwent Conniston.

It was his name now. John Keith was dead. It was Derwent Conniston who was living. And as he looked down into the cold, still face of the heroic Englishman, the thing did not seem so strange to him after all. It would not be difficult to bear Conniston's name; the difficulty would be in living up to the Conniston code.

"I am Derwent Conniston," he kept telling himself. "John Keith is dead—dead. My name is Conniston—"

In his years of aloneness he had grown into the habit of talking to himself—or with himself—to keep up his courage and sanity. "Keith, old boy, we've got to fight it out," he would say. Now it was, "Conniston, old chap, we'll win or die." After that he never spoke of John Keith except as a man who was dead. And over the dead John Keith he spread Conniston's mantle. "John Keith died game, sir," he said to McDowell, who was a tree. "He was the finest chap I ever knew."

Days grew into weeks, and under Keith's feet the wet, sweet-smelling earth rose up through the last of the slush snow. Three hundred miles below the Barrens, he was in the Reindeer Lake country early in May. For a week he rested at a trapper's cabin on the Burntwood, and after that set out for Cumberland House. Ten days later he arrived at the post, and in the sunlit glow of the second evening afterward he built his camp-fire on the shore of the yellow Saskatchewan.

For a week John Keith followed up the shores of the Saskatchewan. The seventh day a new sound came to his ears at dawn. It was the whistle of a train at Prince Albert.

There was no change in that whistle, and every nerve-string in his body responded to it with crying thrill. It was the first voice to greet his home-coming, and the sound of it rolled the yesterdays back upon him in a deluge. He knew where he was now; he recalled exactly what he would find at the next turn in the river.

A few minutes later he heard the wheezy chug, chug, chug of the old gold dredge at McCoffin's Bend. It would be the Betty M., of course, with old Andy Duggan at the windlass, his black pipe in mouth, still scooping up the shifting sands as he had scooped them up for more than twenty years. He could see Andy sitting at his post, clouded in a halo of tobacco smoke, a red-bearded, shaggy-headed giant of a man whom the town affectionately called the River Pirate. And then, coming suddenly to the edge of the clearing at McCoffin's Bend, he saw the dredge close inshore, and striding up from the beach Andy Duggan himself! In another moment Keith had stepped forth and was holding up a hand in greeting.

As Duggan advanced, he was moved by a tremendous desire to stretch out his hand and say: "I'm John Keith. Don't you know me, Duggan?" Instead, he choked back his desire and said, "Fine morning!"

Duggan nodded uncertainly. He was evidently puzzled at not being able to place his man. "It's always fine on the river, rain'r shine. Anybody who says it ain't is a God A'mighty liar!"

He was still the old Duggan, ready to fight for his river at the drop of a hat! Keith wanted to hug him. He shifted his pack and said:

"I've slept with it for a week—just to have it for company—on the way down from Cumberland House. Seems good to get back!" He took off his hat and met the riverman's eyes squarely. "Do you happen to know if McDowell is at barracks?" he asked.

"He is," said Duggan.

That was all. He was looking at Keith

with a curious directness. Keith held his breath. He would have given a good deal to have seen behind Duggan's beard. There was a hard note in the riverman's voice, too. It puzzled him. And there was a flash of sullen fire in his eyes at the mention of McDowell's name.

"The Inspector's there—sittin' tight," he added, and to Keith's amazement brushed past him without another word.

To Keith this first experiment in the matter of testing an identity was a disappointment. It was not only disappointing but filled him with apprehension. It was true that Duggan had not recognized him as John Keith, *but neither had he recognized him as Derwent Conniston!* And Duggan was not a man to forget in three or four years—or half a lifetime, for that matter. He saw himself facing a new and unexpected situation. What if McDowell, like Duggan, saw in him nothing more than a stranger? The Englishman's last words pounded in his head again like little fists beating home a truth, "You win or lose the moment McDowell first sets his eyes on you." They pressed upon him now with a deadly significance.

Win or Lose?

H IS head was in a whirl when he came to barracks. Life was good, after all. It was worth fighting for, and he was bound to fight. He went straight to McDowell's office. A moment after his knock on the door the Inspector's secretary appeared.

"The Inspector is busy, sir," he said in response to Keith's inquiry. "I'll tell him——"

"That I am here on a very important matter," advised Keith. "He will admit me when you tell him that I bring information regarding a certain John Keith."

The secretary disappeared through an inner door. It seemed not more than ten seconds before he was back. "The Inspector will see you, sir."

Squaring his shoulders Keith entered to face McDowell, the cleverest man-hunter in the Northwest.

K EITH's first vision, as he entered the office of the Inspector of Police, was not of McDowell, but of a girl. She sat directly facing him as he advanced through the door, the light from a window throwing into strong relief her face and hair. The effect was unusual. She was strikingly handsome. The sun, giving to the room a soft radiance, lit up her hair with shimmering gold; her eyes, Keith saw, were a clear and wonderful gray—and they stared at him as he en-tered, while the poise of her body and the tenseness of her face gave evidence of sudden and unusual emotion. These things Keith observed in a flash; then he turned toward McDowell.

The Inspector sat behind a table covered with maps and papers, and instantly Keith was conscious of the penetrating inquisition of his gaze. He felt, for an instant, the disquieting tremor of the criminal. Then he met McDowell's eyes squarely. They were, as Conniston had warned him, eyes that could see through boiler-plate.

He felt creeping over him a slow chill. There was no greeting in that iron-like countenance, for full a quarter-minute no sign of recognition. And then, as the sun had played in the girl's hair, a new emotion passed over McDowell's face, and Keith saw for the first time the man whom Derwent Conniston had known as a friend as well as a superior. He rose from his chair, and leaning over the table said in a voice in which were mingled both amazement and pleasure:

"We were just talking about the devil —and here you are, sir! Conniston, how are you?"

For a few moments Keith did not see. *He had won!* The blood pounded through his heart so violently that it confused his vision and his senses. He felt the grip of McDowell's hand; he heard his voice; a vision swam before his eyes—and it was the vision of Derwent Conniston's triumphant face.

McDowell's military voice was snapping vibrantly, "Conniston, meet Miss Miriam Kirkstone, daughter of Judge Kirkstone!"

He bowed and held for a moment in his own the hand of the girl whose father he had killed. It was lifeless and cold. Her lips moved, merely speaking his name. His own were mute. McDowell was saying something about the glory of the service and the sovereignty of the law. And then, breaking in like the beat of a drum on the introduction, his voice demanded,

"Conniston—*did you get your man?*"

The question brought Keith to his senses. He inclined his head slightly and said, "I beg to report that John Keith is dead, sir."

He saw Miriam Kirkstone give a visible start, as if his words had carried a stab. She was apparently making a strong effort to hide her agitation as she turned swiftly away from him, speaking to McDowell.

"You have been very kind, Inspector McDowell. I hope very soon to have the pleasure of talking with Mr. Conniston—about—John Keith."

She left them, nodding slightly to Keith.

Post Mortems

WHEN she was gone, a puzzled look filled the Inspector's eyes. "She has been like that for the last six months," he explained. "Tremendously interested in this man Keith and his fate. I don't believe that I have watched for your return more anxiously than she has, Conniston. And the curious part of it is she seemed to have no interest in the matter at all until six months ago. Sometimes I am afraid that brooding over her father's death has unsettled her a little. A mighty pretty girl, Conniston. A mighty pretty girl, indeed! And her brother is a skunk. Pst! You haven't forgotten him?"

He drew a chair up close to his own and motioned Keith to be seated. "You're changed, Conniston!"

The words came out of him like a shot. So unexpected were they that Keith felt the effect of them in every nerve of his body. He sensed instantly what McDowell meant. He was *not* like the Englishman; he lacked his mannerisms, his cool and superior suavity, the inimitable quality of his nerve and sportsmanship. How the Englishman's ghost must be raging if it was in the room at the present moment! Keith grinned and shrugged his shoulders.

"Were you ever up there—through the Long Night—alone?" he asked. "Ever

been through six months of living torture with the stars leering at you and the foxes barking at you all the time, fighting to keep yourself from going mad? I went through that twice to get John Keith, and I guess you're right. I'm changed. I don't think I'll ever be the same again. Something—has gone. I can't tell what it is, but I feel it. I guess only half of me pulled through. It killed John Keith. Rotten, isn't it?"

He felt that he had made a lucky stroke. McDowell pulled out a drawer from under the table and thrust a box of fat cigars under his nose.

"Light up, Derry—light up and tell us what happened. Bless my soul, you're not half dead! A week in the old town will straighten you out."

He struck a match and held it to the tip of Keith's cigar.

For an hour thereafter Keith told the story of the man-hunt. It was Conniston who spoke from within him. It was the Englishman who told how terribly John Keith had been punished, and when he came to the final days in the lonely little cabin in the edge of the Barrens, Keith finished with a choking in his throat, and the words,

"And that was how John Keith died— a gentleman and a *man!*"

"After two and a half years of *that*

even a murderer must have seemed like a saint to you, Conniston," McDowell said. "You have done your work splendidly. The whole story shall go to the Department, and if it doesn't bring you a commission, I'll resign. But we must continue to regret that John Keith did not live to be hanged."

"He has paid the price," said Keith dully.

"No, he has not paid the price, not in full. He merely died. It could have been paid only at the end of a rope. His crime was atrociously brutal, the culmination of a fiend's desire for revenge. We will wipe off his name. But I can not wipe away the regret. I would sacrifice a year of my life if he were in this room with you now. It would be worth it. God, what a thing for the Service—to have brought John Keith back to justice after four years!"

He was rubbing his hands and smiling at Keith even as he spoke. His eyes had taken on a filmy glitter. The law! It stood there, without heart or soul, coveting the life that had escaped it. A feeling of revulsion swept over Keith.

A knock came at the door.

McDowell's voice gave permission, and the door slowly opened.

"Shan Tung is waiting, sir," he said.

An invisible hand reached up suddenly and gripped at Keith's throat. He turned aside to conceal what his face might have betrayed. Shan Tung!

The Unholy Power

IN the hall beyond the secretary's room Shan Tung waited. As McDowell was the iron and steel embodiment of the law, so Shan Tung was the flesh and blood spirit of the mysticism and immutability of the Chinese race. His face was the face of an image made of an unemotional living tissue in place of wood or stone, dispassionate, tolerant, patient. What passed in the brain behind his yellow-tinged eyes only Shan Tung knew. It was his secret. And McDowell had ceased to analyze or attempt to understand him. The law, baffled in its curiosity, had come to accept him as a weird and wonderful mechanism—a thing more than a man—possessed of an unholy power. This power was the oriental's marvelous ability to remember faces. Once Shan Tung looked at a face, it was photographed in his memory for years. Time and change could not make him forget—and the law made use of him.

This was the man whom Keith now dreaded to meet. Only the slight sound made by the opening and closing of a door gave evidence of his entrance into the Inspector's room. Shan Tung and no other could open and close a door like that.

Keith, facing the window, was wait-ing. The moment the door was opened, he felt Shan Tung's presence. Every nerve in his body was keyed to an uncomfortable tension. The thought that his grip on himself was weakening, and because of a Chinaman, maddened him. And he must turn. Not to face Shan Tung now would be but a postponement of the ordeal and a confession of cowardice.

Forcing his hand into Conniston's little trick of scratching his cheek, he turned slowly, leveling his eyes squarely to meet Shan Tung's.

To his surprise Shan Tung seemed utterly oblivious of his presence. He had not, apparently, taken more than a casual glance in his direction. In a voice which one beyond the door might have mistaken for a woman's, he was saying to McDowell:

"I have seen the man you sent me to see, Mr. McDowell. It is Larsen. He has changed much in eight years. He has grown a beard. He has lost an eye. His hair has whitened. But it is Larsen."

The faultlessness of his speech and the unemotional but perfect inflection of his words made Keith shiver where he stood.

"He had no suspicion of you, Shan Tung?" McDowell asked.

"He did not see me to suspect. He will be there—when——" Slowly he faced Keith. "—When Mr. Conniston goes to arrest him," he finished.

He inclined his head as he backed noiselessly toward the door. His yellow eyes did not leave Keith's face. In them Keith fancied that he caught a sinister gleam. There was the faintest inflection of a new note in his voice, and his fingers were playing again, but not as when he had looked out through the window at Miriam Kirkstone. And then —in a flash, it seemed to Keith—the Chinaman's eyes closed to narrow slits, and the pupils became points of flame no larger than the sharpened ends of a pair of pencils. The last that Keith was conscious of seeing of Shan Tung was the oriental's eyes. They had seemed to drag his soul half out of his body.

"A queer devil," said McDowell. "After he is gone, I always feel as if a snake had been in the room. He still hates you, Conniston. Three years have made no difference. He hates you like poison. I believe he would kill you, if he had a chance to do it and get away with the business. And you—you blooming idiot—simply scratch your cheek and laugh at him! I'd feel differently if I were in your boots."

Inwardly Keith was asking himself why it was that Shan Tung had hated Conniston.

McDowell added nothing to enlighten him.

"You're going to reënlist, aren't you, Conniston?" the Inspector asked.

"I still owe the Service a month or so before my term expires, don't I? After that—yes—I believe I shall reënlist."

"Good!" approved the Inspector. "I'll have you a sergeancy within a month. Meanwhile you're off duty and may do anything you please. You know Brady, the Company agent? He's up the Mackenzie on a trip, and here's the key to his shack. I know you'll appreciate getting under a real roof again, and Brady won't object as long as I collect his thirty dollars a month rent. Of course Barracks is open to you, but it just occurred to me you might prefer this place while on furlough. Everything is there from a bathtub to nut-crackers, and I know a little Jap in town who is hunting a job as a cook. What do you say?"

"Splendid!" cried Keith. "I'll go up at once, and if you'll hustle the Jap along, I'll appreciate it. You might tell him to bring up stuff for dinner," he added.

McDowell gave him a key. Ten minutes later he was out of sight of barracks and climbing a green slope that led to Brady's bungalow.

As he entered the bungalow he was startled by the ringing of the telephone. After four years the sound was one that roused with an uncomfortable jump every nerve in his body. Probably it was McDowell calling up about the Jap or to ask how he liked the place. With a jerk he unhooked the receiver.

It was not McDowell who answered him. To his amazement, coming to him through the tumult of the storm, he recognized the voice of Miriam Kirkstone!

East Meets West

Miss Kirkstone was telling him that she had telephoned McDowell but had been too late to catch him before he left for Brady's bungalow; she was asking him to pardon her for intruding upon his time so soon after his return, but she was sure that he would understand her. She wanted him to come up to see her that evening at eight o'clock.

Before Keith had taken a moment to consult with himself he had replied that he would. He heard her "thank you," her "good-by," and hung up the receiver, stunned. So far as he could remember, he had spoken no more than seven words.

When Wally, the Jap, came it gave him an excuse to call up McDowell. He confessed to a disquieting desire to hear the inspector's voice again. In the back of his head was the fear of Shan Tung, and the hope that McDowell might throw some light on Miriam Kirkstone's unusual request to see her that night.

To Keith's surprise it was McDowell who spoke first of Miss Kirkstone.

"She seemed unusually anxious to get in touch with you," he said. "I am frankly disturbed over a certain matter, Conniston, and I should like to talk with you before you go up tonight."

Keith sniffed the air. "Wallie is going to ring the dinner bell within half an hour. Why not join me up here? I think it's going to be pretty good."

"I'll come," said McDowell. "Expect me any moment."

Fifteen minutes later Keith was helping him off with his coat

McDowell was silent for a space, looking steadily at Keith, as if measuring him up to something.

"I don't mind telling you that I am very deeply interested in Miss Kirkstone," he said. "You didn't see her when the Judge was killed. She was away at school, and you were on John Keith's trail when she returned. I have never been much of a woman's man, Conniston, but I tell you frankly that up until six or eight months ago Miriam was one of the most beautiful girls I have even seen. I would give a good deal to know the exact hour and date when the change in her began. I might be able to trace some event to that date. It was six months ago that she began to take an interest in the fate of John Keith. Since then the change in her has alarmed me, Conniston. I don't understand. Will you help me to discover her secret?"

He leaned toward Keith. He was no longer the man of iron. There was something intensely human in his face.

"There is no other man on earth I would confide this matter to," he went on slowly. "It will take—a gentleman— to handle it, someone who is big enough to forget if my suspicion is untrue, and who will understand fully what sacrilege

means should it prove true. It is extremely delicate. I hesitate. And yet—I am waiting, Conniston. Is it necessary to ask you to pledge secrecy in the matter?"

Keith held out a hand. McDowell gripped it tight.

"It is—Shan Tung," he said, a peculiar hiss in his voice. "Shan Tung—and Miriam Kirkstone! Do you understand, Conniston? Does the horror of it get hold of you? Can you make yourself believe that it is possible? Am I mad to allow such a suspicion to creep into my brain? Shan Tung—Miriam Kirkstone! And she sees herself standing now at the very edge of the pit of hell, and it is killing her."

Keith felt his blood running cold as he saw in the inspector's face the thing which he did not put more plainly in word. He was shocked. He drew his hand from McDowell's grip.

"Impossible!" he cried. "Yes, you are mad. Such a thing would be inconceivable!"

"No. The suspicion came less than a month ago. No one that I know has ever had the opportunity of looking into Shan Tung's private life. The quarters behind his café are a mystery. I suppose they can be entered from the café and also from a little stairway at the rear. One night—very late—I saw Miriam Kirkstone come down that stairway. Twice in the last month she has visited Shan Tung at a late hour. Twice that I know of, you understand. And that is not all—quite."

Keith saw the distended veins in McDowell's clenched hands, and he knew that he was speaking under a tremendous strain.

"I watched the Kirkstone home—personally. Three times in that same month Shan Tung visited her there. The third time I entered boldly with a fraud message for the girl. I remained with her for an hour. In that time I saw nothing and heard nothing of Shan Tung. He was hiding—or got out as I came in."

"Why don't you demand an explanation of Miss Kirkstone?" Keith asked.

"I have, and she denies it all absolutely, except that Shan Tung came to her house once to see her brother. She says that she was never on the little stairway back of Shan Tung's place."

"And you do not believe her?"

"Assuredly not. I saw her. To speak the cold truth, Conniston, she is lying magnificently to cover up something which she does not want any other person on earth to know."

Keith leaned forward suddenly. "And why is it that John Keith, dead and buried, should have anything to do with this?" he demanded. "Why did this 'intense interest' you speak of in John Keith begin at about the same time your suspicions began to include Shan Tung?"

McDowell shook his head. "It may be that her interest was not so much in John Keith as in you, Conniston. That is for you to discover—tonight. It is an interesting situation. It has tragic possibilities. The instant you substantiate my suspicions we'll deal directly with Shan Tung. Just now—there's Wallie behind you. His dinner must be a success."

The Fatal Room

"OF COURSE you remember this room?" said Miriam Kirkstone as she led Keith into the living room where he had killed her father.

He nodded. "Yes. It was night when I came, like this. The next day I went after John Keith."

She leaned toward him, her hands clasped in front of her on the table. "You will tell me the truth about John Keith?" she asked in a low, tense voice. "You swear that it will be the truth?"

"I will keep nothing back from you that I have told Inspector McDowell," he answered, fighting to meet her eyes steadily. "I almost believe I may tell you more."

"Then—did you speak the truth when you reported to Inspector McDowell? *Is John Keith dead?*"

Clearly he was facing suspicion. She could not have driven the shaft intuitively. The unexpectedness of the thing astonished him and then thrilled him, and in the thrill of it he found himself more than ever master of himself.

"Would you like to hear how utterly John Keith is dead and how he died?" he asked.

"Yes. That is what I must know."

He noticed that her hands had closed. Her slender fingers were clenched tight.

He did not repeat the story exactly as he had told it to McDowell. The facts were the same, but the living fire of his own sympathy and his own conviction were in them now. He told it purely from Keith's point of view, and Miriam Kirkstone's face grew whiter, and her hands grew tense again, as she listened for the first time to Keith's own version of the tragedy of the room in which they were sitting. And then she followed Keith up into that land of ice and snow and gibbering Eskimos, and from that moment he was no longer Keith but spoke with the lips of Conniston. He described the sunless weeks and months of madness until the girl's eyes seemed to catch fire, and when at last he came to the little cabin in which Conniston had died, he was again John Keith. He could not have talked about himself as he did about the Englishman. And when he came to the point where he buried Conniston under the floor, a dry, broken sob broke in upon him from across the table. But there were no tears in the girl's eyes. Tears, perhaps, would have hidden from him the desolation he saw there. But he did not give in. Her white throat twitched. Then she said:

"And that—was John Keith!"

He bowed his head in confirmation of the lie, and, thinking of Conniston, he said: "He was the finest gentleman I ever knew. And I'm sorry he is dead."

"And I, too, am sorry."

She was reaching a hand across the table to him, slowly, hesitatingly. He stared at her.

"You mean that?"

"Yes, I am sorry."

He took her hand. For a moment her fingers tightened about his own. Then they relaxed and drew gently away from him. In that moment he saw a sudden change come into her face. She was looking beyond him, over his right shoulder. Her eyes widened, her pupils dilated under his gaze, and she held her breath.

He knew that she had seen something, something that had startled her for a moment, but he did not question her. Instead, as if he had noticed nothing, he asked if he might light a cigar.

"I see someone smokes," he excused himself, nodding at the cigarette butts.

He was watching her closely and would have recalled the words in the next breath. He had caught her. Her brother was out of town. And there was a distinctly un-American perfume in the smoke that someone had left in the room. He saw the bit of red creeping up her throat into her cheeks, and his conscience shamed him. It was difficult for him not to believe McDowell now. Shan Tung had been there. Probably it was Shan Tung whose face she had seen.

She looked pathetically helpless, and he thought that someone ought to be there with the right to take her in his arms and comfort her.

"You will come again?" she whispered.

"Yes, I am coming again," he said. "Good-night."

He passed out into the drizzle. The door closed behind him, but not before there came to him once more that choking sob from the throat of Miriam Kirkstone.

The Surprise of a Lifetime

HE dropped into a dimly lighted shop to purchase a box of cigars. It was deserted except for the proprietor. His elbow bumped into a telephone. He would call up Wallie and tell him to have a good fire waiting for him, and in the company of that fire he would do a lot of thinking before getting into communication with McDowell.

It was not Wallie who answered him, and he was about to apologize for getting the wrong number when the voice at the other end asked,

"Is that you, Conniston?"

It was McDowell. The discovery gave him a distinct shock.

"Don't ask questions but hustle up here," McDowell fired back. "I've got the surprise of your life waiting for you!"

Keith heard the receiver at the other end go up with a bang. Something had happened at the Shack, and McDowell was excited. He went out puzzled. For some reason he was in no great hurry to reach the top of the hill. Finally he opened the door of his bungalow and entered, taking swiftly the two or three steps that carried him across the tiny vestibule to the big room. His entrance was so sudden that the tableau in front of him was unbroken for a moment. Birch logs were blazing in the fireplace. In the big chair sat McDowell, partly turned, a smoking cigar poised in his fingers, staring at him. Seated on a footstool, with her chin in the cup of her hands, was a girl.

Slowly the girl rose to her feet. Perhaps she was eighteen, a slim, tired-looking, little thing, wonderfully pretty, and either on the verge of laughing or crying. Perhaps it was halfway between. To his growing discomfiture she came slowly toward him with a strange and wonderful look in her face. And McDowell still sat there staring.

"Derry, don't you know me? *Don't you know me?*"

It was a sob, a cry. McDowell had risen. Overwhelmingly there swept upon Keith an impulse that rocked him to the depth of his soul. He opened his arms, and in an instant the girl was in them. Quivering, and sobbing, and laughing she was on his breast. He felt the crush of her soft hair against his face, her arms were about his neck, and she was pulling his head down and kissing him —not once or twice, but again and again, passionately and without shame. His own arms tightened. He heard Mc-Dowell's voice—a distant and non-essential voice it seemed to him now—saying that he would leave them alone and that he would see them again tomorrow. He heard the door open and close. McDowell was gone. And the soft little arms were still tight about his neck.

"You—you don't seem very glad to see me, Derry."

"I—I'm just stunned," he managed to say. "You see——"

"It *is* a shocking surprise, Derry. I meant it to be. I've been planning it for years and years and *years!* And I'm never going back again—to *them*," he heard her say, something suddenly low and fierce in her voice. *"Never!* I'm going to stay with you always, Derry!"

She put her lips close to his ear and whispered: "I knew I'd find you somewhere—sometime. I haven't slept two winks since leaving Montreal! And I guess I really frightened that big man with the terrible mustaches, for when I rushed in on him tonight, dripping wet, and said, 'I'm Miss Mary Josephine Conniston, and I want my brother,' his eyes grew bigger and bigger until I thought they were surely going to pop out at me. And then he swore. He said, 'My Gawd, I didn't know he had a sister!' "

Keith's heart was choking him. So this wonderful little creature was Derwent Conniston's sister! And she was claiming *him*. She thought he was her brother!

The Splendid Lie

HER VOICE was small and troubled, yet the pain was slowly fading out of her eyes as she felt the passionate embrace of his fingers in her hair. "You are changed."

"Yes, I am changed. A part of Derwent Conniston died seven years ago. That part of him was dead until he came through that door tonight and saw you. And then it flickered back into life. It is returning slowly, slowly. That which was dead is beginning to rouse itself, beginning to remember. See, little Mary Josephine. It was this!"

He drew a hand to his forehead and placed a finger on a scar. "I got that seven years ago. It killed a half of Derwent Conniston, the part that should have lived. Do you understand? Until tonight——"

Her eyes startled him, they were growing so big and dark and staring, living fires of understanding and horror. It was hard for him to go on with the lie. "For many weeks I was dead," he struggled on. "And when I came to life physically, I had forgotten a great deal. I had my name, my identity, but only ghastly dreams and visions of what had gone before. I remembered you, but it was in a dream, a strange and haunting dream that was with me always. It seems to me that for an age I have been seeking for a face, a voice, something I loved above all else on earth, something which was always near and yet was never found. It was you, Mary Josephine, you!"

Was it the real Derwent Conniston speaking now? He felt again that overwhelming force from within which was not his own. The thing that had begun as a lie struck him now as a thing that was truth. It was he, John Keith, who had been questing and yearning and hoping. It was John Keith, and not Conniston, who had returned into a world filled with a desolation of loneliness, and it was to John Keith that a beneficent God had sent this wonderful creature in an hour that was blackest in its despair.

He was not lying now. He was fighting. He was fighting to keep for himself the one atom of humanity that meant more to him than all the rest of the human race, fighting to keep a great love that had come to him out of a world in which he no longer had a friend or a home, and to that fight his soul went out as a drowning man grips at a spar on a sea.

As the girl's hands came to his face and he heard the yearning, grief-filled cry of his name on her lips, he no longer sensed the things he was saying, but held her close in his arms, kissing her mouth, and her eyes, and her hair, and repeating over and over again that now he had found her he would never give her up. Her arms clung to him. They were like two children brought together after a long separation, and Keith knew that Conniston's love for this girl who was his sister must have been a splendid thing. And his lie had saved Conniston as well as himself.

There had been no time to question the reason for the Englishman's neglect —for his apparent desertion of the girl who had come across the sea to find him. Tonight it was sufficient that *he* was Conniston, and that to him the girl had fallen as a precious heritage.

He stood up with her at last, holding her away from him a little so that he could look into her face wet with tears and shining with happiness. She reached up a hand to his face, so that it touched the scar, and in her eyes he saw an infinite pity, a luminously tender glow of love and sympathy and under-standing that no measurements could compass. Gently her hand stroked his scarred forehead. He felt his old world slipping away from under his feet, and with his triumph there surged over him a thankfulness for that indefinable something that had come to him in time to give him the strength and the courage to lie. For she believed him, utterly and without the shadow of a suspicion.

"Tomorrow you will help me to remember a great many things," he said. "And now will you let me send you to bed, Mary Josephine?"

She was looking at the scar. "And all those years I didn't know," she whispered. "I didn't know. They told me you were dead, but I knew it was a lie. It was Colonel Reppington——" She saw something in his face that stopped her. "Derry, *don't you remember?*"

"I shall—tomorrow. But tonight I can see nothing and think of nothing but you. Tomorrow——"

She drew his head down swiftly and kissed the brand made by the heated barrel of the Englishman's pistol. "Yes, yes, we must go to bed now, Derry," she cried quickly. "You must not think too much. Tonight it must just be of me. Tomorrow everything will come out right, everything. And now you may send me to bed."

Message in the Night

It was midnight when he rose from the big chair and went to his room. The door was closed. He opened it and entered. Even as his hand groped for the switch on the wall, his nostrils caught the scent of something which was familiar and yet which should not have been there. It filled the room, just as it had filled the big hall at the Kirkstone house, the almost sickening fragrance of agallochum burned in a cigarette. It hung like a heavy incense.

Keith's eyes glared as he scanned the room under the lights, half expecting to see Shan Tung sitting there waiting for him. It was empty. His eyes leaped to the two windows. The shade was drawn at one, the other was up, and the window itself was open an inch or two above the sill. Keith's hand gripped his pistol as he went to it and drew the curtain. Then he turned to the table on which were the reading lamp and Brady's pipes and tobacco and magazines. On an ashtray lay the stub of a freshly burned cigarette. Shan Tung had come secretly, but he had made no effort to cover his presence.

It was then that Keith saw something on the table which had not been there before. It was a small, rectangular, teakwood box no larger than a half of the palm of his hand. He had noticed Miriam Kirkstone's nervous fingers toying with just such a box earlier in the evening. They were identical in appearance. Both were covered with an exquisite fabric of oriental carving, and the wood was stained and polished until it shone with the dark luster of ebony. Instantly it flashed upon him that this was the same box he had seen at Miriam's. She had sent it to him, and Shan Tung had been her messenger. The absurd thought was in his head as he took up a small white square of card that lay on top of the box. The upper side of this card was blank; on the other side, in a script as

exquisite in its delicacy as the carving itself, were the words:

"With the compliments of Shan Tung."

In another moment Keith had opened the box. Inside was a carefully folded slip of paper, and on this paper was written a single line. Keith's heart stopped beating, and his blood ran cold as he read what it held, a message of doom from Shan Tung in nine words:

"What happened to Derwent Conniston? Did you kill him?"

Near-Explosion

CRUZE, McDowell's young secretary, was pacing slowly up and down the hall when Keith entered the building in which the Inspector had his offices the next morning. His face bore a perplexed and rather anxious expression. At Keith's appearance he brightened up a bit.

"Don't know what to make of the governor this morning, by Jove I don't!" he explained, nodding toward the closed doors. "I've got instructions to let no one near him except you. You may go in."

"What seems to be the matter?" Keith felt out cautiously.

The Secretary shrugged his thin shoulders, flipped the ash from his cigarette, and with a grimace said, "Shan Tung."

Keith wanted to call him back, to leap upon him, if necessary, and drag him away from that deadly door. But he neither moved nor spoke until it was too late. The door opened, he heard Cruze announce his presence, and it seemed to him the words were scarcely out of the secretary's mouth when McDowell himself stood in the door.

"Come in, Conniston," he said quietly. "Come in."

It was not McDowell's voice. It was restrained, terrible. It was the voice of a man speaking softly to cover a terrific fire raging within. Keith felt himself doomed. Therefore his amazement was unbounded when McDowell, closing the door, seized his hand in a grip that made him wince.

"I'm not condemning you, of course," he said. "It was rather beastly of me to annoy your sister before you were up this morning. She flatly refused to rouse you, and by George, the way she said it made me turn the business of getting into touch with you over to Cruze. Sit down, Conniston. I'm going to explode a mine under you."

Keith saw the other was like an animal ready to spring and anxious to spring, the one evident stricture on his desire being that there was nothing to spring at unless it was himself.

"What happened last night?" McDowell asked.

KEITH's mind was already working swiftly. McDowell's question gave him the opportunity of making the first play against Shan Tung.

"Enough to convince me that I am going to see Shan Tung today," he said.

He noticed the slow clenching and unclenching of McDowell's fingers about the arms of his chair.

"Then—I was right?"

"I have every reason to believe you were—up to a certain point. I shall know positively when I have talked with Shan Tung."

He smiled grimly. McDowell's eyes were no harder than his own. The iron man drew a deep breath and relaxed a bit in his chair.

"If anything should happen," he said,

looking away from Keith, as though the speech were merely casual, "if he attacks you——"

"It might be necessary to kill him in self-defense," finished Keith.

McDowell made no sign to show that he had heard, yet Keith thrilled with the conviction that he had struck home. He went on telling briefly what had happened at Miriam Kirkstone's house the preceding night. McDowell's face was purple when he described the evidences of Shan Tung's presence at the house on the hill, but with a mighty effort he restrained his passion.

"That's it, that's it," he exclaimed, choking back his wrath. "I knew he was there! And this morning both of them lie about it—both of them, do you understand! And on top of that he told me something that I *won't* believe!"

He jumped to his feet and began pacing back and forth, his hands clenched behind him. Suddenly he whirled on Keith.

"Why in heaven's name didn't you bring Keith back with you, or, if not Keith, at least a written confession, signed by him?" he demanded.

This was a blow from behind for Keith. "What—what has Keith got to do with this?" he stumbled.

"More than I dare tell you, Conniston. But *why* didn't you bring back a signed confession from him? A dying man is usually willing to make that."

"If he is guilty, yes," agreed Keith. "But this man was a different sort. If he killed Judge Kirkstone, he had no regret. He did not consider himself a criminal. He felt that he had dealt out justice in his own way, and therefore, even when he was dying, he would not sign anything or state anything definitely."

McDowell subsided into his chair. "And the curse of it is I haven't a thing on Shan Tung," he gritted. "Not a thing. Miriam Kirkstone is her own mistress, and in the eyes of the law he is as innocent of crime as I am. If she is voluntarily giving herself as a victim to this devil, it is her own business—legally, you understand. Morally——"

He stopped, his savagely gleaming eyes boring Keith to the marrow.

"I think, old chap, I'd better be going. I'm rather anxious to see Shan Tung before dinner," Keith said.

McDowell followed him to the door. His face had undergone a change. There was a tense expectancy, almost an eagerness there. Again he gripped Keith's hand, and before the door opened he said,

"If trouble comes between you let it be in the open, Conniston—in the open and not on Shan Tung's premises."

Keith went out, his pulse quickening to the significance of the iron man's words, and wondering what the "mine" was that McDowell had promised to explode, but which he had not.

The Missing Brother

HE went directly to Shan Tung's café and sauntered in. He gave a waiter one of Conniston's cards and said,

"Take this to Shan Tung. He is expecting me."

"Shan Tung no home. Gone away," the Chinaman said, stupidly.

That was all. Where he had gone or when he would return Keith could not discover.

Ten minutes later he determined on a bold stroke. There was no time for indecision or compromise. He must find Shan Tung and find him quickly. And he believed that Miriam Kirkstone could give him a pretty good tip as to his whereabouts. But Miss Kirkstone was not at home. If she was, she did not answer to his knocking and bell ringing.

His imagination pictured Shan Tung at that moment with Miriam Kirkstone, and at the thought his disgust went out against them both. In this humor he returned to McDowell's office. He stood before his chief, leaning toward him over the desk table. This time he was the inquisitor.

"Plainly speaking, this liaison is their

business," he declared. "Because he is yellow and she is white doesn't make it ours. I've just had a hunch. Where is that big fat brother of hers?"

McDowell hesitated. "It isn't a liaison," he temporized. "It's one-sided—a crime against——"

"*Where is that big fat brother?*" With each word Keith emphasized his demand with a thud of his fist on the table. "*Where is he?*"

McDowell was deeply perturbed. Keith could see it and waited.

"I don't know," the Inspector said. "He disappeared from town a month ago. Miriam says he is somewhere in British Columbia looking over some old mining properties. She doesn't know just where."

"And you believe her?"

The eyes of the two men met. There was no longer excuse for equivocation. Both understood.

McDowell smiled in recognition of the face. "No. I think, Conniston, that she is the most wonderful little liar that lives. And the beautiful part of it is, she is lying for a purpose. Imagine Peter Kirkstone, who isn't worth the powder to blow him to Hades, interested in old mines or anything else that promises industry or production! And the most inconceivable thing about the whole mess is that Miriam worships that fat and worthless pig of a brother. I've tried to find him in British Columbia. Failed, of course. Another proof that this affair between Miriam and Shan Tung isn't a voluntary liaison on her part. She's lying."

"There are some truths which one cannot tell about oneself," interrupted Keith. "They must be discovered or buried. And I'm going deeper into this prospecting and undertaking business this afternoon. I've got another hunch. I think I'll have something interesting to report before night."

The Means to an End

TEN minutes later, on his way to the Shack, he was discussing with himself the *modus operandi* of that "hunch." It had come to him in an instant, a flash of inspiration. That afternoon he would see Miriam Kirkstone and question her about Peter. Then he would return to McDowell, lay stress on the importance of the brother, tell him that he had a clew which he wanted to follow, and suggest finally a swift trip to British Columbia. He would take Mary Josephine, lie low until his term of service expired, and then report by letter to McDowell that he had failed and that he had made up his mind not to reënlist but to try his fortunes with Mary Josephine in Australia. Before McDowell received that letter, they could be on their way into the mountains. The "hunch" offered an opportunity for a clean getaway, and in his jubilation Miriam Kirkstone and her affairs were important only as a means to an end. He was John Keith now, fighting for John Keith's life—and Derwent Conniston's sister.

Mary Josephine herself put the first shot into the fabric of his plans. She must have been watching for him, for when halfway up the slope he saw her coming to meet him. She scolded him for being away from her, as he had expected her to do. Then she pulled his arm about her slim little waist and held the hand thus engaged in both her own as they walked up the winding path. He noticed the little wrinkles in her adorable forehead.

"Derry, is it the right thing for young ladies to call on their gentlemen friends over here?" she asked suddenly.

"I suppose you mean Miss Kirkstone?"

"Yes. She was frightfully anxious to see you, Derry."

"And what did you think of her, dear?"

She cast a swift look up into his face. "Why, I like her. She's sweet and pretty, and I fell in love with her hair. But something was troubling her this morning. I'm quite sure of it."

He nodded. He saw his horizon aglow with the smile of fortune. Everything was coming propitiously for him, even this unexpected visit of Miriam Kirkstone. He did not trouble himself to speculate as to the object of her visit, for he was grappling now with his own opportunity, his chance to get away, to win out for himself in one last masterstroke, and his mind was concentrated in that direction. The time was ripe to tell these things to Mary Josephine. She must be prepared.

THEREAFTER for many minutes he spoke his plans. Mary Josephine's cheeks grew flushed. Her eyes shone with excitement and eagerness. She thrilled to the story he told her of what they would do in those wonderful mountains of gold and mystery, just they two alone. He made her understand even more definitely that his safety and their mutual happiness depended upon the secrecy of their final project, that in a way they were conspirators and must act as such. They might start for the west tonight or tomorrow, and she must get ready.

There he should have stopped. But with Mary Josephine's warm little hand clinging to his and her beautiful eyes shining at him like liquid stars, he felt within him an overwhelming faith and desire, and he went on, making a clean breast of the situation that was giving them the opportunity to get away. He felt no prick of conscience at the thought of Miriam Kirkstone's affairs. Her destiny must be, as he had told McDowell, largely a matter of her own choosing. Besides, she had McDowell to fight for

her. And the big fat brother, too. So without fear of its effect he told Mary Josephine of the mysterious liaison between Miriam Kirkstone and Shan Tung, of McDowell's suspicions, of his own beliefs.

Not until then did he begin to see the changing lights in her eyes. Not until he had finished did he notice that most of that vivid flush of joy had gone from her face and that she was looking at him in a strained, tense way. He felt then the reaction. She was not looking at the thing as he was looking at it. He had offered to her another woman's tragedy as *their* opportunity, and her own woman's heart had responded in the way that has been woman's since the dawn of life.

She snatched her hand from his with a suddenness that startled him. Her eyes, so beautiful and soft a few minutes before, scintillated fire. "Derry, if you don't fix this heathen devil—*I will!*"

Even as he saw his plans falling about him, he opened his arms and held them out to her, and with the swiftness of love she ran into them, putting her hands to his face while he held her close and kissed her lips.

"You bet we'll fix that heathen devil before we go," he said. "You bet we will—*sweetheart!*"

His next move was to go straight to the Kirkstone house on the hill. There he got Miriam to admit that she hated Shan Tung and would like to see him dead. But she would not tell him why. After insistent questioning she admitted that Shan Tung would be out of town for ten days and agreed to let Keith know when he returned.

A Year in a Week

THE next ten days contained both joy and pain for Keith. For even in the fullest hours of his happiness there was a thing eating at his heart, a thing that was eating deeper and deeper until at times it was like a destroying flame within him. One night he dreamed; he dreamed that Conniston came to his

bedside and wakened him, and that after wakening him he taunted him in ghoulish glee and told him that in bequeathing him a sister he had given unto him forever and forever the curse of the daughters of Achelous. And Keith, waking in the dark hour of night, knew in his despair that it was so. For all time, even though he won this fight he was fighting, Mary Josephine would be the unattainable. A sister—and he loved her with the love of a man!

In a week they lived what might have been encompassed in a year. So it seemed to Keith, who had known her only so long. With Mary Josephine the viewpoint was different. There had been a long separation, a separation filled with a heartbreak which she would never forget, but it had not served to weaken the bonds between her and this loved one, who, she thought, had always been her own. To her their comradeship was more complete now than it ever had been, even back in the old days, for they were alone in a land that was strange to her, and one was all that the world held for the other. So her possessorship of Keith was a thing which—again in the dark and brooding hours of night—sometimes made him writhe in an agony of shame. Hers was a shameless love, a love which had not even the lover's reason for embarrassment, a love unreserved and open as the day.

Each morning she greeted him with a kiss, and each night she came to him to be kissed, and when it was her pleasure she kissed him—or made him kiss her—when they were on their long walks. It was bitter-sweet to Keith, and more frequently came the hours of crushing desolation for him, those hours in the still, dark night when his hypocrisy and his crime stood out stark and hideous in his troubled brain.

ON the ninth day he had finished supper with Mary Josephine when the telephone rang. He rose to answer it. It was Miriam Kirkstone.

"He has returned," she said.

That was all. The words were in a choking voice. He answered and hung up the receiver. He knew a change had come into his face when he turned to Mary Josephine. He steeled himself to a composure that drew a questioning tenseness into her face. Gently he stroked her soft hair, explaining that Shan Tung had returned and that he was going to see him. In his bedroom he strapped his Service automatic under his coat.

At the door, ready to go, he paused. Mary Josephine came to him. Something whispered to him that it was the last time. Whatever happened now, tonight must leave him clean. His arms went around her, he drew her close against his breast, and for a space he held her there, looking into her eyes.

"You love me?" he asked softly.

"More than anything else in the world," she whispered.

"Kiss me, Mary Josephine."

Her lips pressed to his.

He released her from his arms, slowly, lingeringly.

After that she stood in the lighted doorway, watching him, until he disappeared in the gloom of the slope. She called good-by, and he answered her. The door closed. And he went down into the valley, a hand of foreboding gripping at his heart.

Behind the Secret Door

HE CAME to Shan Tung's. Beyond the softly curtained windows it was a yellow glare of light. He entered and met the flow of life, the murmur of voices and laughter, the tinkle of glasses, the scent of cigarette smoke, and the fainter perfume of incense.

"I have come to see Shan Tung," said Keith to a waiter.

He had half expected to be refused, in which event he was prepared to use his prerogative as an officer of the law

to gain his point. But the waiter did not hesitate. He was almost eager. And Keith knew that Shan Tung was expecting him.

They passed behind one of the screens and then behind another, until it seemed to Keith their way was a sinuous twisting among screens. They paused before a panel in the wall, and the waiter pressed the black throat of a long-legged, swan-necked bird with huge wings and the panel opened and swung toward them. It was dark inside, but the waiter turned on a light. Through a narrow hallway ten feet in length he led the way, unlocked a second door, and held it open, smiling at Keith.

"Up there," he said.

"Good evening, John Keith!" It was Shan Tung. An oriental gown fell about him, draping him like a woman. It was a crimson gown, grotesquely ornamented with embroidered peacocks, and it flowed and swept about him in graceful undulations as he advanced, his footfalls making not the sound of a mouse on the velvet floors.

Keith did not take the hand. He made as if he did not see it. He was looking into those glowing, confident eyes of the Chinaman. A Chinaman! Was it possible? Could a Chinaman possess that voice, whose very perfection shamed him?

Shan Tung seemed to read his thoughts. And what he found amused him, and he bowed again, still smiling. "I am Shan Tung," he said with the slightest inflection of irony. "Here—in my home—I am different. Do you not recognize me?"

He waved gracefully a hand toward a table on either side of which was a chair. He seated himself, not waiting for Keith. Keith sat down opposite him. Again he must have read what was in Keith's heart, the desire and the intent to kill, for suddenly he clapped his hands, not loudly, once—twice——

"You will join me in tea?" he asked.

Scarcely had he spoken when about them, on all sides of them it seemed to Keith, there was a rustle of life. He saw tapestries move. Before his eyes a panel became a door. There was a clicking, a stir as of gowns, soft footsteps, a movement in the air. Out of the panel doorway came a Chinaman with a cloth, napkins, and chinaware.

"Quick service," Keith acknowledged. "*Very* quick service. Shan Tung! But I have my hand on something that is quicker!"

Suddenly Shan Tung leaned over the table. "John Keith, you are a fool if you came here with murder in your heart," he said. "Let us be friends. It is best. Let us be friends."

He met Keith's eyes squarely and in silence for a moment. "We are both *men,* John Keith." His voice was soft and calm. His tapering fingers with their carefully manicured nails fondled a roll of parchment, and then unrolled it, and held it so the other could read.

It was a university diploma. Keith stared. A strange name was scrolled upon it, Kao Lung, Prince of Shantung. His mind leaped to the truth. He looked at the other.

The man he had known as Shan Tung met his eyes with a quiet, strange smile, a smile in which there was pride, a flash of sovereignty, of a thing greater than skins that were white. "I am Prince Kao," he said. "That is my diploma. I am a graduate of Yale."

KEITH's effort to speak was merely a grunt. He could find no words. And Kao, rolling up the parchment and forgetting the urn of tea that was growing cold, leaned a little over the table again. And then it was, deep in his narrowed, smoldering eyes, that Keith saw a devil, a living, burning thing of passion, Kao's soul itself. And Kao's voice was quiet, deadly.

"I recognized you in McDowell's office," he said. "I saw, first, that you were not Derwent Conniston. And then it was easy, so easy. Perhaps you killed Conniston. I am not asking, for I hated Conniston. Some day I should have killed him, if he had come back. John Keith, from that first time we met, you were a dead man. Your life is mine. I can save it. I can destroy it. And you, in turn, can be of service to me. You help me, and I save you. It is a profitable arrangement. And we both are happy, for you keep Derwent Conniston's sister—and I—I get my golden-headed goddess, Miriam Kirkstone!"

"That much I have guessed," said Keith. "Go on!" For a moment Kao seemed to hesitate, to study the cold, gray passiveness of the other's face. "You love Derwent Conniston's sister," he continued in a voice still lower and softer. "And I—I love my golden-headed goddess. See! Up there on the dais I have her picture and a tress of her golden hair, and I worship them. There, on that dais, she will give up her soul and her beautiful body to me—and you cannot help it, she cannot help it, all the world cannot help it—*and she is coming to me tonight!*"

"*Tonight!*" gasped John Keith.

He, too, leaped to his feet. His face was ghastly. And Kao, in his silken gown, was sweeping his arms about him. "See! The candles are lighted for her. They are waiting. And tonight, when the town is asleep, she will come. *And it is you who will make her come, John Keith!*"

Facing the devils in Kao's eyes, within striking distance of a creature who was no longer a man but a monster, Keith marveled at the coolness that held him back.

"Yes, it is you who will at last give her soul and her beautiful body to me," he repeated. "Come. I will show you how —and why!"

He glided toward the dais. His hand touched a panel. It opened and in the opening he turned about and waited for Keith.

Keith, drawing a deep breath, his soul ready for the shock, his body ready for action, followed him.

The Winning Hand

KAO, bowing, sweeping his flowing raiment with his arms, said, "John Keith, allow me to introduce you to Peter Kirkstone."

For the first time amazement, shock, came to Keith's lips in an audible cry. He advanced a step. Yes, in that pitiable wreck of a man he recognized Peter Kirkstone, the fat creature who had stood under the picture of the Madonna that fateful night, Miriam Kirkstone's brother!

And as he stood, speechless, Kao said: "Peter Kirkstone, you know why I have brought this man to you tonight. You know that he is not Derwent Conniston. You know that he is John Keith, the murderer of your father. Is it not so?"

The thick lips moved. The voice was husky—"Yes."

"He does not believe. So I have brought him that he may listen to you. Peter Kirkstone, is it your desire that your sister, Miriam, give herself to me, Prince Kao, tonight?"

Again the thick lips moved. This time Keith saw the effort. He shuddered. He knew these questions and answers had been prepared. A doomed man was speaking.

And the voice came, choking, "Yes."

"Why?"

The terrible face of Peter Kirkstone seemed to contort. He looked at Kao. And Kao's eyes were shining in that dull room like the eyes of a snake.

"Because—it will save my life."

"And why will it save your life?"

Again that pause, again the sickly, choking effort. "Because—*I have killed a man.*"

Bowing, smiling, rustling, Kao turned to the door. "That is all, Peter Kirkstone. Good night. John Keith, will you follow me?"

Keith, in spite of the horror that had come over him, felt no excitement. The whole situation was clear to him now, and there was nothing to be gained by argument, no possibility of evasion. Kao held the winning hand, the hand that put his back to the wall in the face of impossible alternatives. These alternatives flashed upon him swiftly. There were two and only two—flight, and alone, without Mary Josephine; and betrayal of Miriam Kirkstone. Just how Kao schemed that he should accomplish that betrayal, he could not guess.

"I see. It is a trade, Kao. You are offering me my life in return for Miriam Kirkstone."

"More than that, John Keith. Mine is the small price. And yet it is great to me, for it gives me the golden goddess. But is she more to me than Derwent Conniston's sister may be to you? Yes, I am giving you her, and I am giving you your life, and I am giving Peter Kirkstone his life—all for *one.*"

"And yet, if I should kill you, now—where you sit——"

Kao shrugged his slim shoulders, and Keith heard that soft, gurgling laugh that McDowell had said was like the splutter of oil.

"I have arranged. It is all in writing. If anything should happen to me, there are messengers who would carry it swiftly. To harm me would be to seal your own doom. Besides, you would not leave here alive. I am not afraid."

It was Keith who now smiled into the eyes of the Chinaman, but it was a smile that did not soften that gray and rock-like hardness that had settled in his face. "I had almost made up my mind to kill you. But I won't do that. There's a better way. In half an hour I'll be with McDowell, and I'll beat you out by telling him that I'm John Keith. And I'll tell him this story of Miriam Kirkstone from beginning to end. I'll tell him of that dais you've built for her—your sacrificial altar!—and tomorrow Prince Albert will rise to a man to drag you out of this hole and kill you as they would kill a rat. That is my answer, you slit-eyed, Yale-veneered yellow devil! I may die, and Peter Kirkstone may die, but you'll not get Miriam Kirkstone!"

He was on his feet when he finished, amazed at the calmness of his own voice, amazed that his hands were steady and his brain was cool in this hour of his sacrifice. And Kao was stunned. Before his eyes he saw a white man throwing away his life. Here, in the final play, was a master-stroke he had not foreseen. A moment before the victor, he was now the vanquished. About him he saw his world falling, his power gone, his own life suddenly hanging by a thread. In

Keith's face he read the truth. This white man was not bluffing.

Swift as the strike of a rattler Kao was on his feet, his gown thrown back, one clawing hand jerking a derringer from his silken belt. In the same breath he raised his voice in a sharp call.

Keith sprang back. The snake-like threat in the Chinaman's eyes had prepared him, and his Service automatic leaped from its holster with lightning swiftness. Yet that movement was no swifter than the response to Kao's cry. The panel shot open, the screens moved, tapestries billowed suddenly as if moved by the wind, and Kao's servants sprang forth and were at him like a pack of dogs. Keith had no time to judge their number, for his brain was centered in the race with Kao's derringer. He saw its silver mountings flash in the candle-glow, saw its spurt of smoke and fire. But its report was drowned in the roar of his automatic as it replied with a stream of lead and flame. He saw the derringer fall and Kao crumple up like a jackknife. His brain turned red as he swung his weapon on the others, and as he fired, he backed toward the door. Then something caught him from behind, twisting his head almost from his shoulders, and he went down.

He lost his automatic. Weight of bodies was upon him; yellow hands clutched for his throat; he felt hot breaths and heard throaty cries. A madness of horror possessed him, a horror that was like the blind madness of Laocoön struggling with his sons in the coils of the giant serpent. He struck and broke with a blind fury and a giant strength, until at last, torn and covered with blood, he leaped free and reached the door. As he opened it and sprang through, he had the visual impression that only two of his assailants were rising from the floor.

At the opposite end of the hall was a curtain which he judged must cover a window. With a swift movement he tore down this curtain and found that he was right. In another second he had crashed the window outward with his shoulder, and felt the cool air of the night in his face. He paused long enough to convince himself that his enemies were making no effort to follow him, and as he went down the steps, he caught himself grimly chuckling. He had given them enough. Again the calmness with which he had faced Kao possessed him. The Chinaman was dead. He was sure of that. And for him there was not a minute to lose.

The Last Square Play

AFTER ALL, it was his fate. The game had been played, and he had lost. There was one thing left undone, one play Conniston would still make, if he were there. And he, too, would make it. It was no longer necessary for him to give himself up to McDowell, for Kao was dead, and Miriam Kirkstone was saved. It was still right and just for him to fight for his life. But Mary Josephine must know *from him*. It was the last square play he could make.

He had tried to wipe the blood from his face, but it was still there when he entered and faced Mary Josephine. The wounds made by the razor-like nails of his assailants were bleeding; he was hatless, his hair was disheveled, and his throat and a part of his chest were bare where his clothes had been torn away. As Mary Josephine came toward him, her arms reaching out to him, her face dead white, he stretched out a restraining hand, and said,

"Please wait, Mary Josephine!"

Something stopped her—the strangeness of his voice, the terrible hardness of his face, gray and blood-stained, the something appalling and commanding in the way he had spoken. He passed her quickly on his way to the telephone. Her lips moved; she tried to speak; one of her hands went to her throat. He was calling Miriam Kirkstone's number! And now she saw that his hands, too, were bleeding.

There came the murmur of a voice in the telephone. Someone answered. And then she heard him say,

"*Shan Tung is dead!*"

That was all. He hung up the receiver and turned toward her. With a little cry she moved toward him.

"*Derry—Derry——*"

He evaded her and pointed to the big chair in front of the fireplace. "Sit down, Mary Josephine. I have a great many things to tell you."

She obeyed him. Her face was whiter than he had thought a living face could be. And then, from the beginning to the end, he told her everything. Mary Josephine made no sound, and in the big chair she seemed to crumple smaller and smaller as he confessed the great lie to her, from the hour Conniston and he had traded identities in the little cabin on the Barren.

Until he died he knew she would haunt him as he saw her there for the last time—her dead-white face, her great eyes, her voiceless lips, her two little hands clutched at her breast as she listened to the story of the great lie and his love for her.

Even when he had done, she did not move or speak. He went into his room, closed the door, and turned on the lights. Quickly he put into his pack what he needed. And when he was ready, he drew out a pencil and wrote on a piece of paper:

"*A thousand times I repeat, 'I love you.' Forgive me if you can. If you cannot forgive, you may tell McDowell, and the Law will find me up at the place of our dreams—the river's end.*

           JOHN KEITH."

This last message he left on the table for Mary Josephine.

Then he faced the north. Down the side of the hill and over the valley lay the forests. And through the starlight he strode back to them once more, back to their cloisters and their heritage, the heritage of the hunted and the outcast.

The Solitary Horseman

In the ten days following his flight from Prince Albert he kept utterly out of sight. He avoided trappers' shacks and trails and occasional Indians. He rid himself of his beard and shaved himself every other day. Mary Josephine had never cared much for the beard. It prickled. She had wanted him smooth-faced, and now he was that. He looked better, too. But the most striking resemblance to Derwent Conniston was gone. At the end of the ten days he was at Turtle Lake, fifty miles east of Fort Pitt. He believed that he could show himself openly now, and on the tenth day bartered with some Indians for fresh supplies.

It was six weeks after the night in Kao's place that he struck the Saskatchewan again above the Brazeau. He did not hurry now. Just ahead of him slumbered the mountains; very close was the place of his dreams. But he was no longer impelled by the mighty lure of the years that were gone. Day by day something had worn away that lure, as the ceaseless grind of water wears away rock, and for two weeks he wandered slowly and without purpose in the green valleys that lay under the snow-tipped peaks of the ranges. He was gripped in the agony of an unutterable loneliness, which fell upon and scourged him like a disease. It was a deeper and more bitter thing than a yearning for companionship.

Day and night his body and his soul cried out for Mary Josephine, and in his despair he cursed those who had taken her away from him. It was a crisis which was bound to come, and in his aloneness he fought it out. Day after day he fought it, until his face and his heart bore the scars of it. It was as if a being on whom he had set all his worship had died, only it was worse than death. Dead, Mary Josephine would still have been his inspiration; in a way she would have belonged to him. But living, hating him as she must, his dreams of her were a sacrilege and his love for her like the cut of a sword.

On the second day of this third week he saw advancing toward him a solitary horseman.

Keith unbuttoned the flap of his pistol holster and maneuvered so that he would be partly concealed by his pack when the horseman rode up. The persistence of the stranger suggested to him that Mary Josephine had lost no time in telling McDowell where the law would be most likely to find him.

Then he looked over the neck of his pack at the horseman, who was quite near, and was convinced that he was not an officer. He was still jogging at a canter and riding atrociously. One leg was flapping as if it had lost its stirrup-hold; the rider's arms were pumping, and his hat was sailing behind at the end of a string.

"Whoa!" said Keith.

His heart stopped its action. He was staring at a big red beard and a huge, shaggy head. The horseman reined in, floundered from his saddle, and swayed forward as if seasick.

"Well, I'll be——"

"*Duggan!*"

"*Johnny—Johnny Keith!*"

The Worst About Mary Josephine

Duggan answered with an inarticulate bellow and jumped at Keith as if to bear him to the ground. He hugged him, and Keith hugged, and then for a minute they stood pumping hands until their faces were red, and Duggan was growling over and over:

"An' you passed me there at McCoffin's Bend—an' I didn't know you, I didn't know you, I didn't know you! I thought you was that cussed Conniston! I did. I thought you was Conniston!" He stood back at last. "Johnny—Johnny Keith!"

Keith dug his fingers into Duggan's arm.

"How did you know I was coming *here?*" he demanded. "Who told you?"

"All come out in the wash, Johnny. Pretty mess. Chinaman dead. Johnny Keith, alias Conniston, alive an' living with Conniston's pretty sister. Johnny gone—skipped. No one knew where. I made guesses. Knew the girl would know if anyone did. I went to her, told her how you'n me had been pals, an' she give me the idee you was goin' up to the river's end. I resigned from the Betty M., that night. Told her, though, that she was a ninny if she thought you'd go up there. Made her believe the note was just a blind."

"My God," breathed Keith hopelessly, "I meant it."

"Sure you did, Johnny. I knew it. But I didn't dare let *her* know it. If you could ha' seen that pretty mouth o' hern curlin' up as if she'd liked to have bit open your throat, an' her hands clenched, an' that murder in her eyes—Man, I lied to her then! I told her I was after you, an' that if she wouldn't put the police on you, I'd bring back your head to her, as they used to do in the old times. An' she bit. Yes, sir, she said to me, 'If you'll do that, I won't say a word to the police!' An' here I am, Johnny. An' if I keep my word with that little tiger, I've got to shoot you right now. Haw! Haw!"

K EITH had turned his face away. "Maybe you don't understand, Andy," struggled Keith. "I'm sorry—she feels—like that."

For a moment Duggan was silent. Then he exploded with a sudden curse. "*Sorry!* What the devil you sorry for, Johnny? You treated her square, an' you left her almost all of Conniston's money. She ain't no kick comin', and she ain't no reason for feelin' like she does. Let 'er go to the devil, I say."

The thick-headed old hero, loyal to the bottom of his soul, hadn't guessed. And it came to Keith then that he would never tell him. He would keep that secret. He would bury it in his burned-out soul, and he would be "joyful" if he could.

"God bless you, Andy," he cried. "You're the gamest pal that ever lived!"

"Good thing you come along when you did, Johnny," he said. "I been waitin' in that valley ten days, an' the eats was about gone when you hove in sight. Meant to hike back to the cabin for supplies tomorrow or next day. Gawd, ain't this the life! An' we're goin' to find gold, Johnny, we're goin' to find it!"

"We've got all our lives to—to find it in," said Keith.

Duggan puffed out a huge cloud of smoke and heaved a great sigh of pleasure. Then he grunted and chuckled. "Lord, what a little firebrand that sister of Conniston's is!" he exclaimed. "Johnny, I bet if you'd walk in on her now, she'd kill you with her own hands. Don't see why she hates you so, just because you tried to save your life. Of course you must ha' lied like the devil. Couldn't help it. But a lie ain't nothin'. I've told some whoppers, an' no one ain't never wanted to kill me for it. I ain't afraid of McDowell. Everyone said the Chink was a good riddance. It's the girl. There won't be a minute all her life she ain't thinkin' of you, an' she won't be satisfied until she's got you. That is, she thinks she won't. But we'll fool the little devil, Johnny. We'll keep our eyes open—an' fool her!"

With all its beauty, all its splendor of quiet and peace, the night was a bitter one for Keith, the bitterest of his life. He had not believed the worst of Mary Josephine. He knew he had lost her and that she might despise him, but that she would actually hate him with the desire for a personal vengeance he had not believed. Was Duggan right? Was Mary Josephine unfair? And should he in self-defense fight to poison his own thoughts against her? His face set hard, and a joyless laugh fell from his lips. He knew that he was facing the inevitable.

Home-coming

THE next morning the trail narrowed into a short cañon, and this cañon, to Keith's surprise, opened suddenly into a beautiful valley, a narrow oasis of green hugged in between the two ranges. Scarcely had they entered it, when Duggan raised his voice in a series of wild yells and began firing his rifle into the air.

"Home-coming," he explained to Keith, after he was done. "Cabin's just over that bulge. Be there in ten minutes."

In less than ten minutes Keith saw it, sheltered in the edge of a thick growth of cedar and spruce from which its timbers had been taken. It was a larger cabin than he had expected to see—twice, three times as large.

A dozen rods from the cabin was a creek. Duggan halted here to water his horse and nodded for Keith to go on.

"Take a look, Johnny; go ahead an' take a look! I'm sort of sot up over that cabin."

Keith handed his reins to Duggan and obeyed. The cabin door was open, and he entered. One look assured him that Duggan had good reason to be "sot up." The first big room reminded him of the Shack. Beyond that was another room in which he heard someone moving and the crackle of a fire in a stove. And then he heard the humming of a voice in the kitchen.

And then—and then—

"GREAT GOD IN HEAVEN——"

In the doorway she stood, her arms reaching out to him, love, glory, triumph in her face—*Mary Josephine!*

HOURS later, in a world aglow with the light of stars and a radiant moon, Keith and Mary Josephine were alone out in the heart of their little valley.

"Our valley of dreams," Mary Josephine had named it, an infinite happiness trembling in her voice. "Our beautiful valley of dreams—come true!"

"And you would have come with me—that night?" asked Keith wonderingly. "That night—I ran away?"

"Yes. I didn't hear you go. And at last I went to your door and listened, and then I knocked, and after that I called to you, and when you didn't answer, I entered your room."

"Dear heaven!" breathed Keith. "After all that, you would have come away with me, covered with blood, a—a murderer, they say—a hunted man——"

"John, dear." She took one of his hands in both her own and held it tight. "John, dear, I've got something to tell you."

He was silent.

"You see, John, there was a terrible time after you killed Shan Tung. Only a little while after you had gone, I saw the sky growing red. It was Shan Tung's place—afire. I was terrified, and my heart was broken, and I didn't move. I must have sat at the window a long time, when the door burst open suddenly and Miriam ran in, and behind her came McDowell. Oh, I never heard a man swear as McDowell swore when he found you had gone, and Miriam flung herself on the floor at my feet and buried her head in my lap.

"McDowell tramped up and down, and at last he turned to me as if he was going to eat me, and he fairly shouted, 'Do you know—*that cursed fool didn't kill Judge Kirkstone!*'"

There was a pause in which Keith's brain reeled. And Mary Josephine went on, as quietly as though she were talking about that evening's sunset:

"Of course, I knew all along, from what you had told me about John Keith, that he wasn't what you would call a murderer. You see, John, I had learned to *love* John Keith. It was the other thing that horrified me! In the fight, that night, Judge Kirkstone wasn't badly hurt, just stunned. Peter Kirkstone and his father were always quarreling. Peter wanted money, and his father wouldn't give it to him. It seems impossible,—what happened then. But it's true. After you were gone *Peter Kirkstone killed his father that he might inherit the estate!* And then he laid the crime on you!"

"My God!" breathed Keith. "Mary— Mary Josephine—how do you know?"

"Peter Kirkstone was terribly burned in the fire. He died that night, and before he died he confessed. That was the power Shan Tung held over Miriam. He knew. And Miriam was to pay the price that would save her brother from the hangman."

"And that," whispered Keith, "was why she was so interested in John Keith."

He looked away into the shimmering distance of the night, and for a long time both were silent. A woman had found happiness. A man's soul had come out of darkness into light.

◆

THE LADY'S YES

"YES," I answered you last night;
  "No," this morning, sir, I say.
Colours seen by candle-light
  Will not look the same by day.

When the viols played their best,
  Lamps above, and laughs below,
Love me sounded like a jest,
  Fit for *yes* or fit for *no.*

Call me false or call me free—
  Vow, whatever light may shine,
No man on your face shall see
  Any grief, for change on mine.

Yet the sin is on us both;
  Time to dance is not to woo;
Wooing light makes fickle troth,
  Scorn of *me* recoils on *you.*

Learn to win a lady's faith
  Nobly, as the thing is high,
Bravely, as for life and death—
  With a loyal gravity.

Lead her from the festive boards,
  Point her to the starry skies,
Guard her, by your truthful words,
  Pure from courtship's flatteries.

By your truth she shall be true,
  Ever true, as wives of yore;
And her *yes,* once said to you,
  SHALL be Yes for evermore.
    —*Elizabeth Barrett Browning.*

ANTHONY HOPE

THE PRISONER OF ZENDA

S IR ANTHONY HOPE (Hawkins) was born in London, February 9, 1863. Educated at
Balliol College, Oxford, and the Middle Temple, he opened a law office in the heart
of London. In these mundane surroundings he produced one of the most delightful modern
romances, "The Prisoner of Zenda," forerunner of many similar works by other authors.
Among his other successful novels are "Quisante," "Mrs. Maxon Protests," and "Double
Harness." He died in 1933.

I—I Go to Ruritania

I HAD promised my sis-
ter-in-law, who was
grieved by the useless-
ness of my life, to accept
the post of attaché in
six months' time, if it
were offered to me, and cast about for a
desirable way in which to spend the
interval. Seeing in *The Times* that the
new king of Ruritania, Rudolf V, was
to be crowned in about three weeks'
time, I determined to be present.

There was a remote connection between my family and that of the House
of Elphberg, and I was suddenly eaten
up with curiosity to see the country. I
spoke German as readily as English, was
thoroughly at home in French and had
a smattering of Italian and Spanish. I
was a strong swordsman and a good
shot, and my head was as cool a one as
you could find, for all its flaming colour.

At the Ruritanian frontier I saw by the
paper that, for some unexplained reason,
the date of the coronation had been
changed to the next day but one. The
country seemed all in a stir about it, and
Strelsau was thronged, the hotels overflowing. So I decided to stop at Zenda,
a small town fifty miles short of the
capital, spend the next day in wandering
over the hills, have a look at the famous
castle, and go over by train on the morning of the ceremony.

The inn people at Zenda seemed little
interested in the grand doings; the new
king, they said, was almost a stranger—
he had lived so much abroad. He was
now at the Duke Michael's shooting-
lodge, and, for the landlady's part, she
wished he would stop there, and suffer
the duke to be crowned on Wednesday,
and she added: "There's many to think
as I do."

Next day I climbed the hill to the
castle, an ancient fortress in good preservation, with a deep and broad moat running right round it; while, behind, stood
a handsome modern château, connected
with the old building by a drawbridge.
Soon I entered the forest and walked
for an hour or more, enchanted with its
sombre beauty. I stretched myself on the
ground, and gave myself up to contemplation and went off into the most delightful dreams. I was roused by a rough,
strident voice, exclaiming, "Why, the
devil's in it. Shave him, and he'd be the
king!"

Two men were regarding me with
curiosity. I rose slowly.

"He's the height, too," the elder muttered; then, with a cavalier touch of his
cap, "May I ask your name?"

The younger man stepped forward
with a pleasant smile and said: "This is
Colonel Sapt, and I am called Fritz von
Tarlenheim; we are both in the service
of the King of Ruritania."

I bowed and, baring my head, answered: "I am Rudolf Rassendyll, a
traveller from England."

A RINGING voice sounded behind me: "Fritz, Fritz; where are you, man?"

Then a young man jumped out from behind the trunk of a tree, and I uttered an astonished cry, and he, seeing me, drew back in wonder. Saving the hair on my face, and a manner of conscious dignity his position gave him, the King of Ruritania might have been Rudolf Rassendyll, and I, Rudolf the king.

For an instant we both stood motionless, then I bared my head and bowed.

Old Sapt began to talk in a low growl to his majesty, whose eyes, as he listened, now and again sought mine. Soon he burst into the merriest fit of laughter, and stepped up to me.

"Well met, cousin!" he cried, clapping me on the back. "You must forgive me for being taken aback; a man doesn't expect to see his double at this time of day, eh, Fritz?"

"I must pray pardon, sire, for my presumption," said I. "I trust it will not forfeit your majesty's favour?"

"By Heaven, you'll always enjoy the king's countenance," he laughed, "whether I like it or not. May I enquire where are you travelling to?"

"To Strelsau, sire, for the coronation."

"Fritz, Fritz!" he cried. "A thousand crowns for a sight of brother Michael's face when he sees a pair of us!"

"He mustn't go!" growled old Sapt.

"Come, colonel, you mean I shall be in Mr. Rassendyll's debt, if—"

"Oh, ay, wrap it up in the right way," said Sapt, hauling a great pipe out of his pocket.

"Enough, sire," said I, "I'll leave Ruritania to-day."

"No, by thunder, you shan't; you shall dine with me to-night, happen what will. You don't meet a new relation every day."

He put his arm through mine and walked me off. We soon sat down to a plentiful meal; the king drained a bumper to his cousin Rudolf; the wine that we drank was above all praise, and we did it justice. Fritz at first tried to stay the king's hand, but soon we were all talking at once. At last the king set down his glass. "I have drunk enough," he said, but the servant set before him an old wicker-covered flagon and said the Duke of Strelsau prayed him drink this wine for the love of his brother.

"Well done, Black Michael!" said the king. "I will drink it to the health of that—that sly knave, my brother, Black Michael!"

He drained the bottle, and laid his head on his arms on the table; we drank pleasant dreams to his majesty—and that is all I remember of that particular evening.

II—The King Keeps His Appointment

I AWOKE with a start and a shiver; my face, hair and clothes dripped water, and opposite stood old Sapt, with an empty bucket in his hand.

The king lay full length on the floor. His face was red as his hair, and he breathed heavily.

"We've spent half an hour on him," said Fritz.

"Was it drugged—that last bottle?" I asked, in a whisper.

"I don't know," said Sapt, "but if he's not crowned to-day, I'll lay a crown he's never crowned. As God's alive, man, the throne's lost if the king show himself not in Strelsau to-day. I know Black Michael. Has he no king ready? Has half Strelsau no other candidate?"

For a moment or two we were all silent; then Sapt took his pipe from his mouth, and said to me, "Fate sent you here; fate sends you now to Strelsau."

"Impossible!" I muttered. "I should be known."

"It's a risk—against a certainty," said Sapt. "If you shave, I'll wager you'll not be known. If you don't go, I'll swear Black Michael will sit tonight on the throne, and the king will lie in prison or in his grave. You'll go?"

"Yes, I'll go," said I, and I turned my eyes on the prostrate figure of the king.

I sat down in an armchair, and was clipped and scraped till my moustache and imperial were things of the past and my face was as bare as the king's. And when Fritz saw me thus he drew a long breath, and exclaimed, "By Jove, we shall do it!"

I dressed myself in the uniform of a colonel of the guard, put the king's helmet on my head and took the king's sword in my hand.

Then Fritz carried the king to the wine-cellar, and the plan was that at nightfall the king was to ride to Strelsau and I was to escape to the frontier.

ANTHONY HOPE IN 1898

On the way to the station, old Sapt told me the etiquette of the Ruritanian court and instructed me minutely in the history of the king's past life, family, tastes, friends and servants. We reached Strelsau, and the bells throughout the city broke out into a joyful peal, and the sound of a military band and of men cheering smote upon my ear.

"God save the king!" the people shouted.

King Rudolf the Fifth was in the good city of Strelsau! Presently we formed a procession and were on our way to the cathedral.

Everything was in a mist as I dismounted, and the sudden sense of my audacity almost overcame me.

I knelt before the altar, and the cardinal anointed my head. Then I rose to my feet, and stretched out my hand and took from him the crown of Ruritania and set it on my head, and I swore the old oath of the king. The great organ pealed out, the marshal bade the heralds proclaim me, and Rudolf the Fifth was crowned king!

Then a lady with pale face and glorious hair stepped from her place and came to where I stood. And a herald cried, "Her Royal Highness, the Princess Flavia!"

She curtsied low, and put her hand under mine and raised my hand and kissed it. And for an instant I thought what I had best do. Then I drew her to me and kissed her twice on the cheek, and she blushed red, and—why, then his eminence the Cardinal Archbishop slipped in front of Black Michael, and kissed my hand and presented me with a letter from the Pope —the first and last which I have ever received from that exalted quarter.

And then came Black Michael, the Duke of Strelsau. His step trembled, and he looked to the right and to the left, and his face was patched with red and white. I took my dear Michael by both hands and kissed him on the cheek. I think we were both glad when that was over.

Neither in the face of the princess nor in that of any other did I see the least doubt or questioning. So the likeness served, and for an hour I stood there, feeling as weary as though I had been a king all my life.

Then, back we went through the streets to the palace, and I heard them cheering Black Michael. I was in a carriage now, side by side with the Princess Flavia.

"Do you know, Rudolf," said she, "you look somehow different to-day. You look more sober, more sedate, and, I declare, you're thinner!"

I wondered what the king was doing.

III—I Contend with Black Michael

THAT evening Sapt and I slipped out of the palace, leaving Fritz to give orders that the king was not to be disturbed till next morning. We reached the hunting lodge only to find the door open and the king not there. Black Michael had carried off the king and murdered the man we had left at the lodge.

"Lad," said old Sapt, "if you play the man you may save the king yet. Go back and keep his throne warm for him."

"But the duke knows—the villains he has employed know—"

"Ay, but they can't speak. We've got 'em. How can they denounce you without denouncing themselves? 'This is not the king, because we kidnapped the king, and murdered his servant.' Can they say that? We must have a king in Strelsau, or the city will be Michael's in four-and-twenty hours, and what would the king's life be worth then—or his throne? Lad, you must do it."

"Sapt, suppose they have killed the king?"

"Then, by Heaven, you're as good an Elphberg as Black Michael, and you shall reign in Ruritania! But I don't believe they have; nor will they kill him if you're on the throne."

It was a wild plan; but as I listened to Sapt I saw the strong points in our game; and then I was a young man, and loved action.

"Sapt," I cried, "I'll try it."

So we went back to the palace at Strelsau in the early hours of the morning.

AND now began a duel with Black Michael. I could not expose him without exposing myself, and he could not help exposing himself if he tried to expose me. Six gentlemen whom he maintained in his household were in his secret. Three of them he kept in his castle at Zenda to guard the king whom he had imprisoned, and three of them attended the duke of Strelsau to get rid of the acting king should fortune favour them. Their plan was to kill me and take my body to a low quarter of the town, and let it be found there. Then Michael would proclaim a state of siege in Strelsau, have the king murdered at Zenda; proclaim himself king and marry Flavia.

So much I learnt from a lady in Michael's confidence. But the days went by and I managed to escape the conspirators.

Sapt told me that the people of Strelsau were anxious for the king's marriage, and that I ought to make love to the Princess Flavia.

There was no difficulty about this, for I was already in love with the princess; and on the night of the state ball I found, with mingled joy and shame, that I also was loved. We were alone. I forgot the king in Zenda, I forgot the king in Strelsau. She was a princess—and I an imposter. I said nothing, but pressed kisses on her lips.

She whispered, "How is it that I love you now, Rudolf? I—I never did before."

It was I, then, I—Rudolf Rassendyll —who had won her!

"If I were not the king," I began, "if I were only a private gentleman—"

"If you were a convict in the prison of Strelsau, you would be my king," she said.

Just then Sapt appeared, and we went into the ballroom again.

To uphold the crown and beat Black Michael, that was Sapt's one resolve. Flavia and I were but pawns in his game, and pawns have no business with passions. But Sapt's devices and my own passion had forced me on, and passion still drove me in the same direction as the devices seduced me. I faced all Strelsau that night as the king and accepted suitor of the Princess Flavia.

At three in the morning I was in my dressing-room, and Sapt alone with me.

"Lad, you're bound in honour," he said.

"Look here," I cried, "I could raise all Strelsau on you in an hour, and choke you with your mad lies. I could marry the princess and send Michael and his brother to—"

"I'm not denying it, lad," said he.

"Then, in God's name," I cried, "let us go to Zenda and crush this Michael, and bring the king back to his own again."

The next day it was given out that I was gone on an hunting expedition in the woods of Zenda, and the scene was shifted from Strelsau to the château of Tarlenheim. The task before me was to get the king out of captivity alive. Force was impossible; in some trick lay the chance. Michael would not be blinded by the feint of a boar-hunt; he would understand very well what the real quarry was.

Sure enough, Michael quickly sent the sharpest of his bodyguard, Rupert Hentzau, to seek a private audience with me.

"The duke offers you a safe conduct across the frontier and a million crowns."

I declined the offer, and on his taking his departure Rupert struck at me with a small dagger, and had I not swerved it would have gone to my heart. He leapt upon his horse and was off, pursued in vain by revolver shots.

I fell back bleeding, and lay unconscious; and when I awoke I was in bed with Fritz beside me. He cheered me by saying that my wound would soon heal and, further, that one of the duke's keepers was in the house.

Safeguards and rewards were promised to this keeper, and he, being of opinion that the duke would not want any witnesses left when he had brought off his coup, was not sorry to be with us.

A day or two later the keeper explained the situation at Zenda.

He told us that the king was confined in a room and was always guarded by three of the duke's six. Should any attack be made on the castle the king was to be murdered, and his body dropped down a big pipe till it sank to the bottom of the moat twenty feet deep.

"It's a hard nut!" said I.

"So hard," said old Sapt, "that this time next year is like to find you still king of Ruritania!"

IV—If Love Were All!

According to the official reports I had suffered a grievous hurt from an accidental spear-thrust; and as the result of these bulletins the Princess Flavia herself must needs come to Tarlenheim, while Black Michael was persuaded that I was incapable of action.

In reality I was well and strong, resolved with Sapt that we must risk a decisive blow for the king, who, the keeper told us, grew ill under his rigorous confinement. Moreover, great rumours had arisen in Strelsau as to my continued absence from the city.

We made our plans. I was to get into the castle secretly, to defend the king from murder, and Sapt and his men were to be ready to march boldly in directly the keeper opened the gate. The time fixed was half-past two in the morning.

I had reconnoitred carefully, had learnt the position of the room where the king was confined, and effected my entrance at midnight. I killed two men that night at least, in saving the king, but it was Rupert Hentzau who killed Duke Michael and so made our victory complete. A mortal quarrel between Michael and his henchman, the root of which lay in jealousy for a certain lady, culminated in violence, and Black Michael was slain; Rupert escaped with great difficulty.

It was Fritz who took me into the king's room in the castle two days later. He was lying there in bed, and held out his hand and shook mine.

I took the king's ring from my finger and placed it on his.

"I have tried not to dishonour it, sire," said I.

"I can't talk much," he said in a weak voice, "I wanted to take you to Strelsau and keep you with me. But they tell me I must not, and that the secret must be kept."

"They are right, sire. Let me go."

Then Fritz came in with the doctor. I kissed the king's hand, and let Fritz lead me away. I have never seen the king since.

The secret was kept, though many strange rumours got afloat concerning the prisoner of Zenda. Some said he was dead; others that he had vanished yet alive.

The princess sent for me before I left.

"Does she know everything?" I asked Fritz.

"Yes, everything."

I had meant to humble myself and pray pardon for my presumption, but what I said when I stood before Flavia was: "I love you with all my heart and soul; with all my life and heart." She clung to me closely, and I went on. "Always from the first moment I saw you in the cathedral! There has been but one woman in the world to me—and there will be no other. But God forgive me the wrong I've done you!"

"They made you do it!" she said quickly. "It might have made no difference if I'd know it. It was always you, never the king!" And she kissed me.

"I must go away to-night," I said. "I must go before more people see me."

"If I could come with you!" she whispered very low. "Why not? I love you.

You are as good a gentleman as the king himself!"

Then I was false to all I should have held by, for I prayed her to come with me. And for a while she listened, and then said softly: "Is love the only thing? If love were the only thing I would follow you—in rags, if need be—to the world's end. But if love had been the only thing, you would have let the king die in his cell. Honour binds a woman, too, Rudolf. My Honour lies in being true to my country and my house. I know that I must stay."

THERE struck on our ears the sound of singing. The priests in the chapel were singing masses for the souls of those who lay dead. They seemed to chant a requiem over our buried joy, as we stood there, her hands in mine.

"My queen and my beauty!" said I.

"My lover and true knight!" she said. "Perhaps we shall never see one another again. Kiss me, my dear, and go!"

I kissed her as she bade me; and then I left her.

Sapt and Fritz rode with me to the little wayside station just over the border of Ruritania, and when the train appeared I held out a hand to each of them.

"We have been men, eh, Sapt and Fritz, old friends?" said I. "We have run a good course between us."

I stood with my two friends, and waited till the train came up to us. Then we shook hands again, saying nothing; and both of them bared their heads.

Through the air there echoed from the towers of Zenda into my ears and into my heart the cry of a woman's love—"Rudolf! Rudolf! Rudolf!"

Hark! I hear it now.

Shall I see her face again—the pale face, the glorious hair? Fate has no hint, my heart no presentiment. I do not know. In this world perhaps—nay, it is likely—never.

Violent Love at Length Runs Its Tragic Course

EMILY BRONTË

WUTHERING HEIGHTS

"THAT chainless soul," Emily Jane Brontë, was born at Thornton, Yorkshire, England, on August 30, 1818, and died at Haworth on December 19, 1848. She will always have a place in English literature by reason of her one weird, powerful, strained novel, "Wuthering Heights," and a few poems. Emily Brontë, like her sister Charlotte, was educated at Cowan School and at Brussels. For a time she became a governess, but it seemed impossible for her to live away from the fascination of the Yorkshire moors, and she went home to keep house at the Haworth Parsonage, while her sisters taught. Two months after the publication of "Jane Eyre" by Charlotte, in December, 1847, "Wuthering Heights," by Emily, and "Agnes Grey," by Anne, the third sister in this remarkable trio, were issued in one volume. The critics, who did not discover these books were by women, suggested persistently that "Wuthering Heights" must be an immature work by Currer Bell (Charlotte). A year after the publication of her novel Emily died, unaware of her success in achieving a lasting, if restricted, fame. She was extraordinarily reserved, sensitive, and wayward, and lived in an imagined world of her own, morbidly influenced, no doubt, by the vagaries of her worthless brother Branwell. That she had true genius, allied with fine strength of intellect and character, is the unanimous verdict of competent criticism, while it grieves over unfulfilled possibilities.

A Surly Brood

"MR. HEATHCLIFF?" A nod was the answer.

"Mr. Lockwood, your new tenant at Thrushcross Grange, sir."

"Walk in." But the invitation, uttered with closed teeth, expressed the sentiment "Go to the deuce!" And it was not till my horse's breast fairly pushed the barrier that he put out his hand to unchain it. I felt interested in a man who seemed more exaggeratedly reserved than myself as he preceded me up the causeway, calling, "Joseph, take Mr. Lockwood's horse; and bring up some wine."

Joseph was an old man, very old, though hale and sinewy. "The Lord help us!" he soliloquised in an undertone as he relieved me of my horse.

Wuthering Heights, Mr. Heathcliff's dwelling, is a farmhouse on an exposed and stormy edge, its name being significant of atmospheric tumult. Its owner is a dark-skinned gipsy in aspect, in dress and manners a gentleman, but morose demeanour. One step from the outside brought us into the family living-room, the recesses of which were haunted by a huge liver-coloured bitch pointer, with a swarm of squealing puppies, and other dogs. As the bitch sneaked wolfishly to the back of my legs I attempted to caress her, an action that provoked a long, guttural growl.

"You'd better let the dog alone," growled Mr. Heathcliff in unison, as he checked her with a punch of his foot. "She's not accustomed to be spoiled."

As Joseph was mumbling indistinctly in the depths of the cellar, and gave no sign of ascending, his master dived down to him, leaving me *vis-à-vis* with the ruffianly bitch and half a dozen four-footed fiends that suddenly broke into a fury, while I parried off the attack with a poker and called aloud for assistance.

"What the devil is the matter?" asked Heathcliff, as he returned.

"What the devil, indeed!" I muttered. "You might as well leave a stranger with a brood of tigers!"

"They won't meddle with persons who touch nothing," he remarked. "The dogs are right to be vigilant. Take a glass of wine."

Before I went home I determined to volunteer another visit to my sulky landlord, though evidently he wished for no repetition of my intrusion.

Yesterday I again visited Wuthering Heights, my nearest neighbours to Thrushcross Grange. On that bleak hilltop the earth was hard with a black frost, and the air made me shiver through every limb. As I knocked for admittance, till my knuckles tingled and the dogs howled, vinegar-faced Joseph projected his head from a round window of the barn, and shouted to me.

"What are ye for? T' maister's down i' t' fowld. There's nobbut t' missis. I'll hae no hend wi't," muttered the head.

Then a young man, without coat and shouldering a pitchfork, hailed me to follow him, and showed me into the apartment where I had been formerly received with a gruff "Sit down; he'll be in soon."

In the room sat the "missis," motionless and mute. She was slender, scarcely past girlhood, with the most exquisite little face I have ever had the pleasure of beholding; and her eyes, had they been agreeable in expression, would have been irresistible. But the only sentiment they evinced hovered between scorn and a kind of desperation. As for the young man who had brought me in, he slung on his person a shabby jacket, and, erecting himself before the fire, gazed down on me from the corner of his eyes as if there was some mortal feud unavenged between us. The entrance of Heathcliff relieved me from an uncomfortable state.

I found in the course of the tea which followed that the lady was the widow of Heathcliff's son, and that the rustic youth who sat down to the meal with us was Hareton Earnshaw. Now, before passing the threshold, I had noticed over the principal door, among a wilderness of crumbling griffins and shameless little boys, the name "Hareton Earnshaw" and the date "1500." Evidently the place had a history.

The snow had fallen so deeply since I entered the house that return across the moor in the dusk was impossible.

Spending that night at Wuthering Heights on an old-fashioned couch that filled a recess, or closet, in a disused chamber, I found, scratched on the paint many times, the names "Catherine Earnshaw," "Catherine Heathcliff," and again "Catherine Linton." There were many books in the room in a dilapidated state, and, being unable to sleep, I examined them. Some of them bore the inscription "Catherine Earnshaw, her book"; and on the blank leaves and margins, scrawled in a childish hand, was a regular diary. I read: "Hindley is detestable. Heathcliff and I are going to rebel. . . . How little did I dream Hindley would ever make me cry so! Poor Heathcliff! Hindley calls him a vagabond, and won't let him sit or eat with us any more."

When I slept I was harrowed by nightmare, and next morning I gladly left the house; and, piloted by my landlord across the billowy white ocean of the moor, I reached the Grange benumbed with cold.

When my housekeeper, Mrs. Nelly Dean, brought in my supper that night I asked her why Heathcliff let the Grange and preferred living in a residence so much inferior.

"He's rich enough to live in a finer house than this," said Mrs. Dean; "but he's very close-handed. Young Mrs. Heathcliff is my late master's daughter— Catherine Linton was her maiden name, and I nursed her, poor thing. Hareton Earnshaw is her cousin, and the last of an old family."

"The master, Heathcliff, must have had some ups and downs to make him such a churl. Do you know anything of his history?"

"It's a cuckoo's, sir. I know all about it, except where he was born, and who were his parents, and how he got his money. And Hareton Earnshaw has been cast out like an unfledged dunnock."

I asked Mrs. Dean to bring her sewing, and continue the story.

The Story Runs Backward

BEFORE I came to live here (began Mrs. Dean), I was almost always at Wuthering Heights, because my mother nursed Mr. Hindley Earnshaw, that was Hareton's father, and I used to run errands and play with the children. One day, old Mr. Earnshaw, Hareton's grandfather, went to Liverpool, and promised Hindley and Cathy, his son and daughter, to bring each of them a present. He was absent three days, and at the end of that time brought home, bundled up in his arms under his greatcoat, a dirty, ragged, black-haired child, big enough both to walk and talk, but only able to talk gibberish nobody could understand. He had picked it up, he said, starving and homeless in the streets of Liverpool. Mrs. Earnshaw was ready to fling it out of doors, but Mr. Earnshaw told her to wash it, give it clean things, and let it sleep with the children. The children's presents were forgotten. This was how Heathcliff, as they called him, came to Wuthering Heights.

Miss Cathy and he soon became very thick; but Hindley hated him. He was a patient, sullen child, who would stand blows without winking or shedding a tear. From the beginning he bred bad feeling in the house. Old Earnshaw took to him strangely, and Hindley regarded him as having usurped his father's affections. As for Heathcliff, he was insensible to kindness. Cathy, a wild slip, with the bonniest eye, the sweetest smile, and the lightest foot in the parish, was much too fond of Heathcliff.

Old Mr. Earnshaw died quietly in his chair by the fireside one October evening.

Mr. Hindley, who had been to college, came home to the funeral, and set the neighbours gossiping right and left, for he brought a wife with him. What she was and where she was born he never informed us. She evinced a dislike to Heathcliff, and drove him to the company of the servants, but Cathy clung to him, and the two promised to grow up together as rude as savages. Once Hindley shut them out for the night and they came to Thrushcross Grange, where the Lintons took Cathy in, but would not have anything to do with Heathcliff, the Spanish castaway, as they called him. She stayed five weeks with the Lintons, and became very friendly with the children, Edgar and Isabella, and when she came back was a dignified little person, and quite a beauty.

SOON after, Hindley's son, Hareton, was born, the mother died, and the child fell wholly into my hands, for the father grew desperate in his sorrow, and gave himself up to reckless dissipation. His treatment of Heathcliff now was enough to make a fiend of a saint, and daily the lad became more savagely sullen. I could not half-tell what an infernal house we had, till at last nobody decent came near us, except that Edgar Linton called to see Cathy, who at fifteen was the queen of the country-side—a haughty and headstrong creature.

One day after Edgar Linton had been over from the Grange, Cathy came into the kitchen to me and said, "Nelly, will you keep a secret for me? To-day Edgar Linton has asked me to marry him, and I've given him an answer. I accepted him, Nelly. Be quick and say whether I was wrong."

"First and foremost," I said sententiously, "do you love Mr. Edgar?"

"I love the ground under his feet, and the air over his head, and everything he touches, and every word he says. I love his looks, and all his actions, and him entirely and altogether. There now!"

"Then," said I, "all seems smooth and easy. Where is the obstacle?"

"Here, and here!" replied Catherine, striking one hand on her forehead, and the other on her breast. "In my soul and in my heart I'm convinced I'm wrong! I've no more business to marry Edgar Linton than I have to be in heaven; and if the wicked man in there, my brother, had not brought Heathcliff so low I shouldn't have thought of it. It would degrade me to marry Heathcliff now; so he shall never know how I love him, and that not because he's handsome, Nelly, but because he's more myself than I am. Whatever our souls are made of, his and mine are the same, and Linton's is as different as a moonbeam from lightning, or frost from fire. Nelly, I dreamed I was in heaven, but heaven did not seem to be my home, and I broke my heart with weeping to come back to earth; and the angels were so angry that they flung me out into the middle of the heath on the top of Wuthering Heights, where I woke sobbing for joy."

Ere this speech was ended, Heathcliff, who had been lying out of sight on a bench by the kitchen wall, stole out. He had heard Catherine say it would degrade her to marry him, and he had heard no further.

That night, while a storm rattled over the heights in full fury, Heathcliff disappeared. Catherine suffered uncontrollable grief, and became dangerously ill. When she was convalescent she went to Thrushcross Grange. But Edgar Linton, when he married her, three years subsequent to his father's death, and brought her here to the Grange, was the happiest man alive. I accompanied her, leaving little Hareton, who was now nearly five years old, and had just begun to learn his letters.

On a mellow evening in September, I was coming from the garden with a basket of apples I had been gathering, when, as I approached the kitchen door, I heard a voice say, "Nelly, is that you?"

Something stirred in the porch, and, moving nearer, I saw a tall man, dressed in dark clothes, with dark hair and face.

"What," I cried, "you come back?"

"Yes, Nelly. You needn't be so disturbed. I want one word with your mistress."

I went in, and explained to Mr. Edgar and Catherine who was waiting below.

"Oh, Edgar darling," she panted, flinging her arms round his neck, "Heathcliff's come back—he is!"

"Well, well," he said, "don't strangle me for that. There's no need to be frantic. Try to be glad without being absurd!"

When Heathcliff came in, she seized his hands and laughed like one beside herself.

It seemed that he was staying at Wuthering Heights, invited by Mr. Earnshaw! When I heard this I had a presentiment that he had better have remained away.

Later, we learned from Joseph that Heathcliff had called on Earnshaw, whom he found sitting at cards, had joined in the play, and, seeming plentifully supplied with money, had been asked by his ancient persecutor to come again in the evening. He then offered liberal payment for permission to lodge at the Heights, which Earnshaw's covetousness made him accept.

Heathcliff now commenced visiting Thrushcross Grange, and gradually established his right to be expected. A new source of trouble sprang up in an unexpected form—Isabella Linton evincing a sudden and irresistible attraction towards Heathcliff. At that time she was a charming young lady of eighteen. I tried to persuade her to banish him from her thoughts.

"He's a bird of bad omen, miss," I said, "and no mate for you. How has he been living? How has he got rich? Why is he staying at Wuthering Heights in the house of the man whom he abhors? They say Mr. Earnshaw is worse and worse since he came. They sit up all night together continually, and Hindley has been borrowing money on his land, and does nothing but play and drink."

"You are leagued with the rest," she replied, "and I'll not listen to your slanders." The antipathy of Mr. Linton towards Heathcliff reached a point at last at which he called on his servants one day to turn him out of the Grange, whereupon Heathcliff's revenge took the form of an elopement with Linton's sister. Six weeks later I received a letter of bitter regret from Isabella, asking me distractedly whether I thought her husband was a man or a devil, and how I had preserved the common sympathies of human nature at Wuthering Heights, where they had returned.

On receiving this letter, I obtained permission from Mr. Linton to go to the Heights to see his sister, and Heathcliff, on meeting me, urged me to secure for him an interview with Catherine.

"Nelly," said he, "you know as well as I do that for every thought she spends on Linton she spends a thousand on me. If he loved her with all the powers of his puny being, he couldn't love as much in eighty years as I could in a day. And Catherine has a heart as deep as I have. The sea could be as readily contained in that horse-trough as her whole affection be monopolised by him."

Well, I argued, and refused, but in the long run he forced me to agree to put a missive into Mrs. Linton's hand.

WHEN he met her, I saw that he could hardly bear, for downright agony, to look into her face, for he was stricken with the conviction that she was fated to die.

"Oh, Cathy, how can I bear it?" was the first sentence he uttered.

"You and Edgar have broken my heart, Heathcliff," was her reply. "You have killed me and thriven on it, I think."

"Are you possessed with a devil," he asked, "to talk in that manner to me when you are dying? You know you lie to say I have killed you, and you know that I could as soon forget my existence as forget you. Is it not sufficient that while you are at peace, I shall be in the torments of hell?"

"I shall not be at peace," moaned Catherine.

"Why did you despise me? Why did you betray your own heart? You loved me. What right had you to leave me?"

"Let me alone!" sobbed Catherine.

"I've done wrong, and I'm dying for it! Forgive me!"

That night was born the Catherine you, Mr. Lockwood, saw at the Heights, and her mother's spirit was at home with God.

When in the morning I told Heathcliff, who had been watching near all night, he dashed his head against the knotted trunk of the tree by which he stood and howled, not like a man, but like a savage beast, as he besought her ghost to haunt him. "Be with me always —take any form!" he cried. "Only do not leave me in this abyss, where I cannot find you!"

LIFE with Heathcliff becoming impossible to Isabella, she left the neighbourhood, never to revisit it, and lived near London; and there her son, whom she christened Linton, was born a few months after her escape. He was an ailing, peevish creature. When Linton was twelve, or a little more, and Catherine thirteen, Isabella died, and the boy was brought to Thrushcross Grange. Hindley Earnshaw drank himself to death about the same time, after mortgaging every yard of his land for cash; and Heathcliff was the mortgagee. So Hareton Earnshaw, who should have been the first gentleman in the neighbourhood, was reduced to dependence on his father's enemy, in whose house he lived, ignorant that he had been wronged.

The motives of Heathcliff now became clear. Under the influence of a passionate but calculating revenge, allied with greed, he was planning the destruction of the Earnshaw family, and the union of the Wuthering Heights and Thrushcross Grange estates. To this end, having brought his weakly son home to the Heights and terrorised him into a pitiable slavery, he schemed a marriage between him and young Catherine Linton, who was induced to accept the arrangement through sympathy with her cousin, and the hope of removing him from the paralysing influence of his father. The marriage was almost immediately followed by the death of both Catherine's father and her boyish husband, who, it was afterwards found, had been coaxed or threatened into bequeathing all his property to his father. Thus ended Mrs. Dean's story of how the strangely assorted occupants of Wuthering Heights had come together, my landlord Heath-cliff, the disinherited, poor Hareton Earnshaw, and Catherine Heathcliff, who had been Catherine Linton and the daughter of Catherine Earnshaw. I propose riding over to Wuthering Heights to inform my landlord that I shall spend the next six months in London, and that he may look out for another tenant for the Grange.

The Story Runs Forward

YESTERDAY was bright, calm, and frosty, and I went to the Heights as I proposed. My housekeeper entreated me to bear a little note from her to her young lady, and I did not refuse, for the worthy woman was not conscious of anything odd in her request. Hareton Earnshaw unchained the gate for me. The fellow is as handsome a rustic as need be seen, but he does his best, apparently, to make the least of his advantages. Catherine, who was preparing vegetables for a meal, looked more sulky and less spirited than when I had seen her first. "She does not seem so amiable," I thought, "as Mrs. Dean would persuade me to believe. She's a beauty, it is true, but not an angel."

I approached her, pretending to desire a view of the garden, and dropped Mrs. Dean's note on her knee unnoticed by Hareton. But she asked aloud, "What is that?" and chucked it off.

"A letter from your old acquaintance, the housekeeper at the Grange," I answered. She would gladly have gathered it up at this information, but Hareton beat her. He seized and put it in his waistcoat, saying Mr. Heathcliff should look at it first; but later he pulled out the letter, and flung it on the floor as ungraciously as he could. Catherine perused it eagerly, and then asked, "Does Ellen like you?"

"Yes, very well," I replied hesitatingly.

Whereupon she became more communicative, and told me how dull she was now Heathcliff had taken her books away.

When Heathcliff came in, looking restless and anxious, he sent her to the kitchen to get her dinner with Joseph; and with the master of the house, grim and saturnine, and Hareton absolutely dumb, I made a cheerless meal, and bade adieu early.

NEXT September, when going north for shooting, a sudden impulse seized me to visit Thrushcross Grange and pass a night under my own roof, for the tenancy had not yet expired. When I reached the Grange before sunset I found a girl knitting under the porch, and an old woman reclining on the house-steps, smoking a meditative pipe.

"Is Mrs. Dean within?" I demanded.

"Mistress Dean? Nay!" she answered. "She doesn't bide here; shoo's up at th' Heights."

"Are you housekeeper, then?"

"Eea, aw keep th' house," she replied.

"Well, I'm Mr. Lockwood, the master. Are there any rooms to lodge me in, I wonder? I wish to stay all night."

"T' maister!" she cried in astonishment. "Yah sud ha' sent word. They's nowt norther dry nor mensful abaht t' place!"

Leaving her scurrying about making preparations, I climbed the stony by-road that branches off to Mr. Heathcliff's dwelling. On reaching it I had neither to climb the gate nor to knock—it yielded to my hand. "This is an improvement," I thought. I noticed, too, a fragrance of flowers wafted on the air from among the homely fruit-trees.

"Con-trary!" said a voice as sweet as a silver bell. "That for the third time, you dunce! I'm not going to tell you again."

"Contrary, then," answered another in deep but softened tones. "And now kiss me for minding so well."

The male speaker was a young man, respectably dressed and seated at a table, having a book before him. His handsome features glowed with pleasure, and his eyes kept impatiently wandering from the page to a small white hand over his shoulder. So, not to interrupt Hareton Earnshaw and Catherine Heathcliff, I went round to the kitchen, where my old friend Nelly Dean sat sewing and singing a song.

Mrs. dean jumped to her feet as she recognised me. "Why, bless you, Mr. Lockwood!" she exclaimed. "Pray step in! Have you walked from Gimmerton?"

"No, from the Grange," I replied; "and while they make me a lodging room there I want to finish my business with your master."

"What business, sir?" said Nelly.

"About the rent," I answered.

"Oh, then it is Catherine you must settle with, or rather me, as she has not learned to arrange her affairs yet."

I looked surprised.

"Ah! You have not heard of Heathcliff's death, I see," she continued.

"Heathcliff dead!" I exclaimed. "How long ago?"

"Three months since; but sit down, and I'll tell you all about it."

"I was summoned to Wuthering Heights," she said, "within a fortnight of your leaving us, and I went gladly for Catherine's sake. Mr. Heathcliff, who grew more and more disinclined to society, almost banished Earnshaw from his apartment, and was tired of seeing Catherine—that was the reason why I was sent for—and the two young people were thrown perforce much in each other's company in the house, and presently Catherine began to make it clear to her obstinate cousin that she wished to be friends. The intimacy ripened rapidly, and, Mr. Lockwood, on their wedding day there won't be a happier woman in England than myself. Joseph was the only objector, and he appealed to Heathcliff against 'yon flaysome graceless quean, that's witched our lad wi' her bold een and her forrad ways.' But after a burst of passion at the news, Mr. Heathcliff suddenly calmed down and said to me, 'Nelly, there is a strange change approaching; I'm in its shadow.'

"Soon after that he took to wandering alone, in a state approaching distraction. He could not rest; he could not eat; and he would not see the doctor. One morning as I walked round the house I observed the master's window swinging open and the rain driving straight in. 'He cannot be in bed,' I thought, 'those showers would drench him through.' And so it was, for when I entered the chamber his face and throat were washed with rain, the bed-clothes dripped, and he was perfectly still—dead and stark. I called up Joseph, 'Eh, what a wicked 'un he looks, girning at death,' exclaimed the old man, and then he fell on his knees and returned thanks that the ancient Earnshaw stock were restored to their rights.

"I shall be glad when they leave the Heights for the Grange," concluded Mrs. Dean.

"They are going to the Grange, then?"

"Yes, as soon as they are married; and that will be on New Year's Day."

UNSATISFIED YEARNING

Down in the silent hallway
    Scampers the dog about,
And whines, and barks, and scratches,
    In order to get out.

Once in the glittering starlight,
    He straightway doth begin
To set up a doleful howling
    In order to get in.
                    —*R. K. Munkittrick.*

Fifteen Men on a Dead Man's Chest

Robert Louis Stevenson

TREASURE ISLAND

B REATHES there a boy or man, or for that matter a girl or woman, with pulse so sluggish that it does not beat faster at the mention of that rollicking story, "Treasure Island"? It was written by one of the world's best narrators and rarest souls, Robert Louis Stevenson, who was born in Edinburgh, Scotland, in 1850, and died in 1894 in Samoa on the far Pacific, where he was known and loved by the natives as *Tusitala,* the "teller of tales." What a tale this is!—of "Buccaneers, and buried Gold, and all the old romance, retold exactly in the ancient way." Its period is about 1750 and its events begin in England but occur chiefly in the mysterious island somewhere on the Spanish Main, between the Isthmus of Panama and the mouth of the Amazon, where the golden hoard of redoubtable Captain Flint was buried.

I N THE last few months of my father's life he had as a guest at his inn the Admiral Benbow, a brown old seaman whose face and hands were dreadfully scarred, and whose manners became the terror of the neighborhood. We were ourselves so cowed by his profane blustering that we durst not ask him for a settlement of his account, and so he lived on, eating and drinking as much as he pleased—and it was a great deal in the way of drink—and sleeping in the room above-stairs where he kept his single piece of luggage, a sea-chest, and never paying so much as a farthing into the inn till.

Fearsome though he was, he seemed to be ever oppressed by fear. I learned later that he had good enough cause for it, but at that time I wondered, and was glad to earn the fourpence a month he paid me to "keep my weather eye open for a seafaring man with one leg," and let him know the moment he appeared. The man with one leg never came to the Admiral Benbow; but two other men did, and what resulted from their visits made this story possible.

The first was addressed by our strange guest as Black Dog. They had some private conversation, which ended in a terrible battle that began in our parlor and did much damage to our modest furniture, and then took its roaring way to the road along which our guest pursued Black Dog with drawn cutlass. The visitor was the fleeter, and escaped. When the Captain, as we called our guest, returned, he called for spirits and fell in a fit before I could serve him. Then came Dr. Livesey on a visit to my father, who was then in his last illness. The doctor revived the Captain, helped him to his bed, and solemnly ordered him to forswear rum thenceforth, on pain of speedy death.

My father died soon after this, and hardly had he been laid to rest when the Captain had his second visitor. This was a blind man, and the result of the excitement attending his talk with the Captain, added to the fact that the doctor's orders with regard to rum had been liberally disregarded, was a second fit from which recovery was impossible. So there we were in the inn, my mother and I, with this dead man who had been such a fear and burden to us. The blind man had given him a paper on which was a black spot and words the purport of which was unmistakable. They meant that he was allowed six hours, that is to say until ten o'clock that evening, in which to do something his enemies wanted, or, refusing, to be killed. The inn was in a lonely place, apart from the hamlet, and my mother and I dared not remain there alone. We ran to the hamlet for help, but nobody dared come back with us. Then my mother announced that she meant to be paid for the Captain's board and lodging. She made no doubt that he had money enough in his chest, and she would not be satisfied without getting from it what was our due.

Back to the inn we went, and opened the chest, which we emptied clean of its contents, for what we sought was at the very bottom. There we found a bag filled with gold coins and a packet of what looked like papers done up in oilskin.

My mother insisted on getting her exact due, not a penny less or more; and by the time she had counted out what she wanted we heard the tap-tapping of the blind man's crutch, and knew that the Captain's enemies were at hand. Luckily we had bolted the door, and when there was an imperative knocking we paid no attention to it. Apparently the blind man had come alone, in advance of such party as was in league with him, for presently he went tap-tapping away. Then we hastened, mother carrying the money and I the oilskin packet. Why I took it I hardly know. It was a sudden impulse, and I obeyed it.

We were almost too late. From out the shadows, just after we departed, came a gang of villainous fellows who burst in our door, and we heard them go shouting and cursing through the house. Then my mother fainted and I had to hide her under a bridge, whence I heard all the tow-row in the inn. It appeared that the villains had gone straight to the Captain's chest, and that they were enraged to find that somebody had been there before them. They found the remainder of the buccaneer's gold, but that was not what they wanted. It was clear from their cries that they sought the packet I had taken, and they proceeded to wreck our rooms in their search for it. They were not done when the coast-guard arrived and scattered them. No prisoners were taken, but the blind man was accidentally killed in the confusion.

As soon thereafter as possible I took my packet to Dr. Livesey, finding him at Squire Trelawney's house. We examined the contents of the packet together. There was an accountbook with entries of receipts extending over many years, and this we interpreted as representing the share belonging to the Captain from marauding expeditions.

But of greater interest than this was a map of an island, with a key showing just where the treasure accumulated by the notorious Captain Flint was buried. The latitude and longitude of the island were given precisely; its mountains and rivers were indicated, as well as minor landmarks, like tall trees, and the site of a stockade a little way inland that the pirate had built for defense. It must not be understood that Flint was the Captain who had lived at the Admiral Benbow. Flint was dead. Of that we were certain, and our Captain was Billy Bones, one of Flint's companions. Manifestly he had obtained possession of the chart with a view to seeking the treasure, and others of the piratical crews that had sailed with him had been seeking to wrest it from him.

And now the chart was ours, as well as the treasure to which it was the key. For Squire Trelawney immediately proposed to provide a ship and crew to sail in search of it, and he was for having Dr. Livesey and me accompany the expedition as partners in the enterprise and its prospective profits. We agreed heartily to his proposal, and the Squire proceeded forthwith to Bristol on this business. Dr. Livesey cautioned him earnestly to keep the purpose of the voyage a profound secret, for the Squire was notoriously a gossip, and he promised faithfully to be mum; but when, some weeks later, we were aboard the *Hispaniola,* the beautiful schooner that he had chartered, we discovered that all the crew knew what we were about.

Our Captain, Mr. Smollett, was much disgruntled, for he had been engaged to sail under sealed orders, and he liked it not to discover that we were treasure-hunters, and, worse still, to discover it by overhearing remarks of the crew. He told us bluntly that he distrusted many in the crew—there were twenty altogether —but he could bring no direct accusation against anyone, and after some frank discussion, matters were allowed to rest as they were. Squire Trelawney was as sure of the crew as Mr. Smollett was distrustful. The men had been brought together mainly by the work of the cook, Long John Silver, as he was called, a veteran sailor who had lost a leg, he said, in battle for his country. I could not help thinking of the seafaring man with one leg who had been an unseen terror of Captain Billy Bones; but Silver was so good-humored and industrious that I speedily became fond of him, and as confident of his loyalty as was the Squire himself.

The outward voyage was without incident, save that the mate was lost overboard; but no sooner had we sighted Treasure Island than adventures began in grim earnest. It was the generous Squire's humor to stand a barrel of apples in the waist of the schooner, from which anybody was welcome to help himself. On this evening, when the eagerly sought land was in sight, I went to the barrel, and, as it was all but empty, I crept into it bodily to hunt for an apple. The moment I was inside I heard Silver's voice, and what he said made me sit still and hold my breath. He had brought the youngest man in the crew to the waist as a convenient place for a private conversation, and there they stood while the one-legged cook told that he had sailed with Captain Flint, and painted the glories of buccaneering in the rosiest colors, so as to tempt the sailor to join with the portion of the crew that, it appeared, was ready to mutiny, murder the owners, and get possession of the chart, and so of the gold.

It appeared further that Silver was the leader of the would-be mutineers, and that even now he had to exercise his authority to prevent a premature uprising. Hands, the coxswain, came to the barrel, and grumbled exceedingly that he must continue for as much as one day more to endure the tyrannous discipline of Captain Smollett. Long John showed him that Smollett was necessary to their nefarious enterprise, for he was the only man aboard who could lay a course, and the long and short of it was that the scoundrels were content to abide present conditions and wait until the cook should give the word for action; and it was evident that Silver feared that matters would go amiss because of the unruly haste of his companions.

As soon as they returned to the deck I scrambled from the barrel and contrived a speedy opportunity to lay my information before Squire Trelawney, Dr. Livesey, and Captain Smollett. That they were thunderstruck, and that the Squire manfully apologized to the Captain and agreed thenceforth to follow his lead unhesitatingly may go without saying. So we may pass over the uneasiness of the crew while we were slowly making our way into the anchorage. Now that we knew what was in their minds, it was only too clear that they were impatient to be turned loose on us, and that Silver was having a difficult time of it to hold his hounds in the leash. Meantime we had canvassed the situation to such purpose that we were assured that of the twenty-six men aboard, counting ourselves, there were nineteen who were probably disloyal. As I was a mere boy, this meant that we were six grown men to nineteen as bloodthirsty and reckless pirates as ever sailed the sea.

WE did not come to anchor until noon of the day following the sighting of the island. By that time the atmosphere was so tense with impending mutiny that Captain Smollett resorted to the ruse of giving the men a halfholiday. He announced that as many as chose to do so might spend the afternoon on land, and after a deal of disputing, thirteen were told off to go ashore.

Then I committed the first of several

follies of which I was guilty while at the island, by jumping into one of the small boats just as it was about to leave the schooner's side. My presence was noticed, of course, by Silver, who commanded one of the boats, and by all the others, but nothing unpleasant was said of it while we were making toward the land. Nevertheless, such a terror of them came upon me during this brief trip that, the moment my boat touched the shore, I leaped out and dashed into the forest.

I heard Silver calling to me, but that made me run the faster, and I halted only when I was out of breath, and hid myself under a tree whose branches came close to the ground. Presently I heard voices and, peering forth, beheld Silver and another in earnest conversation. It appeared that this man was, unknown to Captain Smollett, a loyal sailor, and that Silver was trying to persuade him to join the mutineers. The man was not to be persuaded, and while they talked we were all startled by a piercing scream.

"That," said Silver significantly, "was probably Alan," naming another loyal sailor.

Upon that the man whom Silver sought to persuade revolted utterly, not from us, but from the mutineers. "You've killed Alan, have you?" said he. "Kill me, too, if you can!"

He turned away to go back to the

boats. Long John laid hold of a tree, balanced himself thus on his one leg, and hurled his crutch at the sailor. The missile struck him fair in the neck and felled him. The cook hopped after him and buried a knife twice up to the hilt in his defenseless body. Then he whistled as a signal for the other men to come up, and I bolted inland as fast as my legs could take me.

I did not observe which way I went, but when I came to a pause I found myself confronted by a strangely dressed and more strangely acting man. At first he was shy of me, but presently we fell into conversation, and I learned that his name was Ben Gunn, and that he had been marooned on the island three years before. Little else could I learn, save that he knew Flint's treasure was buried on the island, for he was distrustful, not to say crack-brained, and I could not induce him to try to go with me to the *Hispaniola,* although he did tell me of the whereabouts of a boat that he had made.

While we were still talking, a cannon roared, and I made certain that fighting had begun. Ben Gunn told me where to find the stockade, and off I set with no more than a vague idea that it would afford me shelter. There was small difficulty in finding it, for the cannon-balls fired from the long nine on board the schooner were aimed at it; but while they served well as guides, they also deterred me from venturing to climb the fence, for now and again they dropped inside it.

THE British flag was flying from the top of the blockhouse inside the stockade, by which I knew that my friends had come ashore and taken possession, and that the bombardment was conducted by the mutineers, who had now run up the black Jolly Roger on the *Hispaniola.* It proved, when I understood the facts, that my desertion, while interpreted truly as a foolish boy's escapade, had determined Dr. Livesey and the others to go ashore also while there

was opportunity. They had made several trips in the one small boat left with the schooner, carrying arms, ammunition, and provisions, and had made the stockade before Silver's party discovered them, although the long nine had been so well aimed as to sink their boat on the last trip and with it the best part of the food they had taken.

The bombardment ceased about sunset, and then I climbed over the fence and told my friends what had befallen me. One of our men had been killed in the course of the bombardment, but his place was filled by another whom Captain Smollett had won over from those who did not go ashore with Silver.

Next morning came Silver with a flag of truce, by virtue of which he was permitted to climb over the palisade and have parley with us. He offered terms that were fair enough on their face, but Captain Smollett was not one to surrender to a pirate. His reply was to the effect that the only terms he would consider would be the unconditional surrender of the mutineers on his guaranty that they should have a fair trial when we reached England. As that meant hanging for every man-Jack of them, Silver was not inclined to accept, and he hobbled away.

The attack came almost at once, and it was a fierce conflict that narrowly missed making an end of us. We were well armed with muskets, and fired from port-holes in the blockhouse, but they were equally well armed and far outnumbered us. Several of them actually climbed over the palisade in the face of our fire and got as far as the house, but they were driven off; and when we took account of the situation at the end of the battle, we found that five of the mutineers had been killed, and one on our side. But the Captain and one other were severely wounded, so that our effective fighting force was reduced to four. The enemy still counted nine, as we understood, though at a later time we learned that one had been mortally wounded by the Squire, who shot at those left on the schooner while he was in the small boat making the last trip to land.

THERE was no more fighting that day. Early the next morning Dr. Livesey, after a consultation with the Captain and the Squire, quietly left the stockade and disappeared in the forest. I knew not what to make of this strange procedure, and, by the time the hot afternoon was drawing to a close, it led me to commit another act of folly. If the doctor could go away, why should not I? It was inexpressibly foolish, but, boy that I was, I watched my opportunity, and slipped unseen away.

I had no definite purpose at first, but presently thought it would be well to see whether Ben Gunn had really made a boat; and I went by a roundabout way to the spot where he said he had hidden it. There it was, the rudest craft imaginable, but it would float, as I found by trying it, and then it occurred to me that I would paddle to the schooner and cut her adrift. It was after nightfall, but I knew the *Hispaniola's* position by a light in her cabin window, by which I inferred that at least one man was aboard. I was no sooner launched than I discovered that by no manner of skill could I guide the coracle, this being the only name by which I can classify Ben Gunn's strange craft; and had not the tide borne me straight to the schooner I might have floated upon the sea for an indefinite period.

But luck, if I may say so, was with me. I drifted to the schooner and laid hold of her hawser. Two men were aboard, as I knew from their voices, and they were quarreling savagely. One of them was Coxswain Hands. I cut the hawser through, and tried to regain the shore. Despite my most patient and hardest efforts, the coracle persisted in turning around and around, and all the progress I made was such as was caused by the tide, which was on the ebb. At last, despairing and worn out, I lay down in my craft and fell asleep.

When I awoke it was day, and not half a mile distant was the *Hispaniola,* with some of her sails partly up, yawing and dipping in a way that showed she was unguided. We were now on the side of the island opposite to the anchorage, and high hills lay between. I was possessed with the utmost desire to gain the schooner, but I was as powerless as before to propel the coracle. I did find, however, how to guide it a bit, and, as wind and tide again favored me, I succeeded in making the *Hispaniola* after some hours of drifting. I found Hands and his companion lying motionless on deck, silent witnesses of the ferocity of their quarrel; but Hands was not dead, and I revived him with brandy. The other man was cold.

Hands proposed a truce, to the terms of which I felt bound to agree, for I was helpless without him, and he could do nothing without my assistance. I bound up his wounds and brought him refreshments, and he directed me how to sail the schooner. It was agreed that we should beach her in a handy place, and we found one before sunset.

By that time Mr. Hands had recovered remarkably, and I perceived that he meant to break our truce at the first convenient opportunity. So I was on the watch for him, and was in time to leap, just before we grounded, when I saw him making at me with a dirk in his hand. I let go the tiller suddenly. It swung around and knocked him flat, but in a moment he was up and after me. I tried to shoot him, but the priming of my pistols had been dampened during my voyage in the coracle, and, bemoaning my stupidity in not having re-primed them long before this emergency arose, I made for the shrouds and climbed to the cross-trees. Thence I looked down at him where he stood glaring up at me.

But, wounded though he was, Mr. Hands was not yet defeated. He began laboriously to climb after me. I re-primed the pistols then, and warned him of what would happen; but still he came on. The vessel had grounded and now lay heeled over, so that water was directly underneath us. He paused before he had come within reach, and affected to parley, confessing that we had come to an impossible situation with regard to each other; but, of a sudden, he drew his arm back to the shoulder and then thrust it swiftly forward. His dirk flew at me, caught me in the shoulder, and pinned me to the mast. At the same instant, whether it was done consciously I hardly know, my pistols went off, both of them, and both dropped from my hands into the sea. I had not aimed, of that I am sure, but my pistols were not the only things that dropped; for Mr. Hands fell from the rigging, the water splashed and foamed a bit, and when it had quieted I saw his body writhing in death on the sandy bottom.

I LOST no time in freeing my shoulder, descending, leaving the schooner, and setting out overland to find the stockade. It was a long, toilsome tramp, and night was far spent when at last I came to it. All was quiet, and no sentry hailed me as I climbed the fence. Snores from within the blockhouse reassured me, and I made my way in, when I was greeted with a shrill cry, "Pieces of eight! pieces of eight!" and recognized the abominable voice of Silver's parrot, which accompanied him on all his journeyings. The sleepers were instantly aroused, and I was in the hands of the enemy.

There were Silver and five others, all that were left alive of the buccaneers, but they were quite enough for me. And what had become of my friends? For not only was Silver in possession of the stockade, but he had also the chart showing the spot where the treasure was buried. The men were for killing me forthwith, but Silver saved me, as a hostage.

That he did well for himself in sparing me was soon demonstrated. On the following morning, with chart and compass, which he had obtained in return for permitting my friends to leave the stockade unmolested, he directed the party in the search for the treasure. The spot was found about midday, but, behold, it was an empty trench. The buccaneers leaped crazily into it and pawed the dirt, turning up one piece of gold.

Enraged beyond endurance, the five leaped out and made to slay both Silver and me, for they accused him of having played them false; but before they could fire, there were shots from the bushes near that tumbled two of them into the trench, dead. The others fled for their lives. Then came the doctor, Ben Gunn, and one of our men, each with a smoking musket. They had lain in ambush, anticipating just what happened, for the doctor had discovered that I had fallen into Silver's hands.

Dr. Livesey had left the stockade on the morning of my unwise desertion to find Ben Gunn. Succeeding, he had made Gunn an ally, and found that in the course of his three years' solitary residence on the island he had unearthed the treasure and conveyed it all to a cave far up on a mountainside. There it was now, with Squire Trelawney and the wounded Captain guarding it, coins of various realms to the value of seven hundred thousand pounds.

My escapade was forgiven when I told my friends how I had beached the schooner in a safe place, and for many days our little party was busy in transferring the treasure to the vessel's hold. We spared Silver because he had spared me, and, moreover, none of us was for cold-blooded butchery; but we left the three live buccaneers marooned, with an abundance of ammunition, some food, and tobacco.

Silver, however, did not go with us to England. As we were short-handed, we had to sail for the nearest port on the Spanish Main to pick up a crew. While we were there Silver stole a few hundred pounds' worth of our treasure and made off with it, and we made no effort to pursue him. We never heard of him afterward. Having arrived safely home, we divided the gold and disposed of it to our several uses, each in his own way.

ACKNOWLEDGMENTS

INDEX OF AUTHORS

INDEX OF CHARACTERS